Walker's Manual
of
Unlisted Stocks

Walker's Manual of Unlisted Stocks

Published by:

Walker's Manual, LLC
3650 Mt. Diablo Blvd., Suite 240
Lafayette, California 94549-3765

Copyright © 1997 by Walker's Manual, LLC
First Printing 1997
Printed in the United States of America

Publisher's Cataloging-in-Publication
(*Provided by Quality Books, Inc.*)

Walker's manual of unlisted stocks — 2nd ed.
    p. cm.
    Includes index.
    ISBN: 0-9652088-8-5

    1. Corporations — United States — Finance. 2. Over-the-counter
    markets — Directories. 3. Corporations — United States — Directories.
    4. Securities — United States — Directories.

HG4507.W25 1997   332.63'22'0973
                    QBI97-40728

Dedicated to

our public companies.

They build value for their shareholders,

create jobs for our citizens

and act for the betterment

of our communities.

Table of Contents

Indices:

Building America

Our 2nd edition of *Walker's Manual of Unlisted Stocks* includes historical vignettes about fourteen of the companies in our book. We hope you will enjoy reading about these made-in-America success stories.

Acknowledgments

Last year at this time we published our very first book, the 1st edition of the one you now hold in your hands. Many of you know how demanding the task was, particularly if you are aware of how hard it is to obtain this type of information. In spite of the difficulties, this year we decided not only to update the first book, but to add a second title, *Walker's Manual of Community Bank Stocks*. The challenge of producing both of these volumes has been enormous. There are two people in my life that were instrumental in making it possible, although their contributions came in two entirely different ways.

Karen Johnston, president of Walker's Manual LLC, is the guide that leads us through a highly complex world of technology, making achievements possible that otherwise would not be. She is the master of the ship in stormy weather. Always pleasant, personable and fun, Karen will take on any challenge, accomplish it better than imagined, and appropriately manage the rest of us so that we too can outperform our own visions.

Cindy Eisenberg, my loving and caring wife, was enjoying our early retirement with me before I went back to work in 1996. I was wrong in estimating the demands on my time required by the publishing business. Cindy not only participated in the production of the 1st edition but now finds herself consumed with many responsibilities we had shared while I was retired. Rather than having any regrets, however, Cindy accepts my calling as publisher and supports me in every conceivable way.

Walker's is indeed fortunate to have the best of database programmers, Debi Suslow, at our disposal. She has been available to us literally around-the-clock (well, there was that *one* day she had off last year) and has provided us with a thoughtfully designed and dynamic application.

We are indebted to all of the companies that provided us with historical information from which the vignettes included in this book were written. In particular we would like to thank Jean Gilbertson (*Two Men At The Helm - The First 100 Years Of Crowley Maritime Corporation*, by Crowley Maritime Corporation, 1992), Fuller Ripley (*The Fabric Of Troy*, by Troy Mills, Inc., 1986), Fay Ingalls (*The Valley Road*, 1949, by Fay Ingalls), and Martha Sonntag Bradley (*ZCMI - America's First Department Store, by ZCMI*, 1991). Cindy Eisenberg and Deborah Politziner both contributed to the writing of the historical pieces included in this edition.

In our 1st edition I wrote about Ed McLaughlin, a man who was my guiding light in first understanding the world of closely-held, inactive securities. Ed has become a good friend over the last year. I look to him, especially, to explain the unexplainable or to help me acquire that which can not be acquired.

Still, many other people from around the country have helped us to further develop our understanding of this market place and have either encouraged us or made contributions to this manual, including Robert N. Bloch, Mr. Tony Broy (Hill, Thompson Magid & Co.), Walter Carucci (Carr Securities Corp.), Tom Doherty (Robotti & Co.), Steve Fischer, Lisa Gallo (Hoefer & Arnett, Inc.), Martin Glotzer, Lawrence Goldstein (Santa Monica Partners), William Thomas Hardison, Jr., Mark M. Hughes (Lafayette Investments), Jack Ingold (E.E. Powell & Company), Norman Kadehjian (H.C. Wainwright & Co.), Scott Koonce (Koonce Securities), James Mitchell (Mitchell Partners), Jack Norberg (Standard Investment), Daniel Raider, Dennis Reynolds (Ryan, Beck & Co.), Alyn Rumbold, Stephen R. Schuller (Dorsey Investment Securities), Walter R. Sikes, Jerry Stratman (Kirkpatrick, Pettis, Smith, Polian), Bernie Taradash (Advest, Inc.), Sidney R. Unobskey, Wendie Wachtel (Wachtel & Co., Inc.) and Dennis Wood. To all of you and to those I have not mentioned by name, I give my thanks for your assistance and encouragement. Please keep in touch.

Harry Eisenberg
Publisher

Introduction

Hershey Creamery Company was founded in 1894. Please don't confuse it with the more well known Hershey Foods. Hershey Creamery has no long-term debt, has a current ratio of 9.8 to 1, and trades over-the-counter for about $1,800 per share. Hershey Foods, on the other hand, has a lot of long-term debt, has a current ratio of only 1.1 to 1, and trades for about $50 per share on the New York Stock Exchange.

Hershey Creamery simply does not have enough shares outstanding for a more active market, and *that* is why it is traded over-the-counter. We have many fine companies in this manual that are similarly situated — from "A" alone there are A.D. Makepeace Company, AFA Protective Systems, Inc., The Adirondack Trust Company, Adrian Steel Company, Alaska Power and Telephone Company, American River Holdings, Anderson-Tully Company and Ash Grove Cement Company.

The proliferation of information available for companies traded on the major stock exchanges and the constant monitoring of most of these companies by institutional investors as well as the financial press has caused many respected investment experts to recommend that investors try to find companies before they become so well known. According to experts, early discovery may allow for investment before share prices are affected by institutional or individual investing activity. There is validation of this point throughout the pages of this manual.

One of three things will probably happen to stocks of companies that are traded over-the-counter. The Company may wish to keep its shares in the over-the-counter market as it continues to grow, usually because it doesn't have enough shares for an active market. As the Company declares stock splits and stock dividends or issues more shares, this impediment tends to disappear. Does that mean the stock will not appreciate in value beforehand? Absolutely not. Many of the stocks included in our first edition have stayed put on the OTC Bulletin Board and have outperformed the market: Chambersburg Engineering Company — up 148%; Hunter Manufacturing Corp. — up 115% and Stein Industries, Inc. — up 200%, just to name a few.

A second possibility is that the stock could become listed on one of the exchanges, almost always resulting in an increase in the stock price. Below are all of the companies from our 1st edition that are now listed on a major exchange or NASDAQ.

Acacia Research Corporation	Papnet of Ohio, Inc.
Arrow-Magnolia International	Pioneer Railcorp
Artesian Resources	Premier Parks, Inc.
Bentho, Inc.	Prime Capital Corporation
Bolt Technology Corporation	Ramsey Managed Care, Inc.
Brake Headquarters U.S.A., Inc.	Real Goods Trading Corporation
Datamark Holding, Inc.	Riviera Holdings Corporation
Denver and Ephrata Telephone and Telegraph	Stearns & Lehman, Inc.
Emergent Group, Inc.	Summit Bank Corporation
Image Systems Corporation	Tangram Enterprise Solutions, Inc.
Industrial Services of America, Inc.	Tech Electro Industries, Inc.
Inmark Enterprises, Inc.	UCI Medical Affiliates, Inc.
International Speedway Corporation	USANA, Inc.
Labor Ready, Inc.	Woodward Governor Company
Pacific Capital Bancorp	

Lastly, the Company could be acquired, often at a respectable premium to its current trading price. The following companies from our 1st edition were acquired during the last year:

Alaska Northwest Properties

Buffalo Valley Telephone Company

Central Bancorporation

Cochrane Furniture Company, Inc.

Crystal Mountain, Inc.

Farmers National Bancorp, Inc.

Health Insurance Company of Vermont, Inc.

Investors Insurance Holding Corp.

Kansas Bankers Surety Company

Lamcor, Incorporated

Midland Bancorporation, Inc.

Momed Holding Co.

Pioneer Communications, Inc.

Southland National Insurance

United Coasts Corporation

United Screw and Bolt Corp.

Investment Ratings

We have stated that three things might happen to an existing over-the-counter stock. Of course, the Company could simply go out of business as well. Over-the-counter stocks cannot be lumped into a single category. Like all other stock markets, different securities carry varying degrees of risk. It is wrong to assume that only speculative stocks trade over-the-counter, just as it is wrong to assume only Blue Chips trade on the New York Stock Exchange.

To assist our readers, so that there be no misunderstanding about our intentions, we have placed all of the stocks included in the book into one or more of four general categories; *Income*, *Value*, *Growth* and *Speculative*. We did this based on what we see as their main characteristics:

- *Income* stocks generally have a reasonably high dividend yield.

- *Value* usually indicates a stock that is priced at a bargain level relative to its book value or a combination of other factors.

- *Growth* stocks usually have a high growth rate or are in a growth industry.

- *Speculative* indicates that there exists a higher degree of risk with a stock, for any of numerous reasons. The company may be a start-up or an established company with current financial difficulties. An investor may want a speculative stock because these stocks often carry a potential for greater returns. We simply say, "Buyer Beware".

These ratings applied to each stock are found in the Comments section of each individual page. In addition, an index lists all companies having the same designation together so that they may be reviewed as a group.

Listed vs. Unlisted Securities

Those companies whose securities are listed and traded on the major exchanges such as the New York Stock Exchange (NYSE), The American Stock Exchange (AMEX), and the National Association of Securities Dealers Automated Quotation System (NASDAQ) can differ from those that are traded through market makers (firms that facilitate trading in unlisted securities) or through private transactions. Companies listed on the major exchanges are generally, but not always, larger and usually have more shareholders. Listed companies must meet a number of criteria regarding:

- Asset base
- Number of shares publicly traded
- Total market value of the shares traded

Companies trading through market makers or private transactions are less concerned with the above. These companies may not want their shares listed for other reasons, including:

- Substantial listing fees
- Securities and Exchange Commission (SEC) quarterly and annual filing requirements
- Exposure to public review and comment on management's decisions
- Interference by outside investors and related reporting requirements

However, if management's primary responsibility is to maximize shareholder value, then a company should *insure that there is a market for its shares*. Viable markets provide shareholders with the ability to realize an investment's value. Making sure there is a market for desired stock transactions should be an objective of management.

Trading In Unlisted Securities

Most people think of *publicly traded* as referring to companies listed on the NYSE, AMEX or NASDAQ. Trading in these markets is easy. Daily share prices are listed in most papers and up to the minute information on the latest trades and prices is available via online services. An investor simply has to contact a brokerage firm, tell a representative the name, price and quantity of the desired purchase and the transaction can be executed immediately. These markets are very efficient with hundreds of millions of shares being bought and sold each day.

Buying and selling unlisted securities is not always as straightforward. The first step involved is usually the same; the investor communicates with a brokerage firm regarding the security to be purchased. If the security is unlisted, the broker will review the OTC Bulletin Board or the National Quotation Bureau's Stock Summary to determine which market maker handles the company. The broker contacts the company's market maker to determine the shares' offering price. If the price is acceptable to the buyer, the transaction is completed. Market makers use the OTC Bulletin Board (which provides online information) to list information on the companies in which they maintain a market.

What Does Publicly Traded Mean?

When a company's securities are offered for public sale by the company or its shareholders, the securities qualify as being *publicly held*. The number of shares offered, the capital raised, and the offering's geographic dispersion all impact regulatory reporting. Many types of public offerings exist, all with varying filing requirements.

For instance, companies issuing shares with a total market value of less than $5,000,000 to a limited number of investors, all of whom reside within the state where the company does business, may be exempt from annual federal reporting requirements. Companies qualifying for this exemption, however, are generally required to provide potential shareholders with certain information prior to their purchase of shares and, in some cases, annually thereafter. A bank serving a single metropolitan area, as an example, may raise adequate capital without relinquishing its exemption from regulatory filing requirements. American River Holdings, a bank featured in this book, raised $3.3 million in 1983 via such a public stock offering. This allowed it to become a viable competitor in its market. With fifty-two consecutive profitable quarters and performance ratios which rank high according to industry standards, the bank has been a success. On the other hand, a larger bank serving the needs of an entire state might find it difficult to raise enough capital in a stock offering and still stay below the reporting exemption threshold.

Once shares have been issued and trading is taking place, regardless of the type of offering, they are considered *publicly traded* whether there are ten or ten thousand shareholders and irrespective of whether the trading takes place on the NYSE or via the OTC Bulletin Board.

Several other markets exist for securities trading. Among them are the Philadelphia, Chicago, Boston and Pacific Stock Exchanges, all of which are available for listings. Each of these has its own listing requirements.

Investment Considerations

The limited exposure to the investing public of some of the companies profiled in this book has resulted in a limited or *thin* market for their securities. Investments in these companies are typically easy to sell but may not be as easy to buy. We have tried to provide helpful information in this regard. There are also a handful of situations where the market is tightly controlled by a company president or majority shareholder. These are few and are specifically identified in the manual. Some readers may question the value of putting these companies in the book while others have called to thank us for providing an opportunity that was just right for them. In evaluating the companies profiled in this book , some items to be considered include:

Performance — Several performance statistics are included for each of the profiled companies, among them return on average assets, return on average equity, and compound growth rates (earnings per share, net income and total revenues/net interest income). Questions that the investor might ask include:

- Is there earnings growth?
- Are the earnings comparable to similar companies?
- Is there a sufficient return on capital?

Financial Strength — The financial position of the company should be analyzed:

- How does the company's current ratio and debt/equity ratio compare to the industry?
- What is the cash position of the company?
- Have any assets, such as real estate, appreciated above book value?

Products and Markets — Review the nature of the company's business and its future prospects:

- Does the company have a unique product?
- Is there a market niche?
- What is their competitive advantage?

Ownership — Understand the makeup of the profiled company's ownership:

- How many shareholders are there and how many shares are outstanding?
- Is the company buying back its own shares?
- Do employees own an interest in the company either directly or through an employee stock ownership plan?
- Are more shares being generated through stock splits and stock dividends in order to create a more active market or to qualify for a stock exchange listing?

Both the company's financial performance and strength should be reflected in its market price per share. Key ratios to review in this regard are the price/earnings ratio and the price/book value percentage. After answering all of the above questions and comparing the results of these ratios to industry standards, you can make a determination as to the appropriateness of the share's price.

Once you have completed your analysis, you may conclude that more information is necessary before you make an investment decision. The company itself, of course, is the best source of information. Contact information is included in each profile for the company and its market maker.

On pages xviii - xxi you will find a dissection of our company profile page format, including a glossary of terms used in the Per Share Information and Annual Financial Data Section.

Following our presentation of the 502 profiles of companies, we include our indices ranking them by total revenues/net interest income, market capitalization, return on average equity, price/earnings ratio, price/book value %, compound revenue growth % and compound earnings per share growth %. These will give you a quick way to see how the companies compare and to evaluate possible investment opportunities. For your convenience we also include informational indices including those which sort by company name, geographic area, investment classification, SIC Code and World Wide Web address.

Changes From The 1st Edition

We do listen to our readers and take careful notes. Not many of you were interested in either foreign stocks or tax-shelter partnerships. Accordingly, we deleted those entities from this year's manual. Banks, on the other hand, were very popular. Here we did two things: we increased the number of banks covered in this edition to about 100, and we produced a separate book devoted entirely to community banks for real enthusiasts. *Walker's Manual of Community Bank Stocks*, which covers 502 banks, is also available directly through our offices. Lastly, some of our readers identified NASDAQ stocks that behaved more like over-the-counter stocks. We included four of these in this edition because they are interesting companies with very little following.

The information contained in this book has been obtained from company reports and documents. In most cases the financial information has been audited by the company's independent auditors and/or is a part of a required filing with a governmental agency. While we take significant measures to insure that the information which we present is objective and accurate, Walker's Manual, LLC does not take any responsibility for its underlying accuracy or reliability. The inclusion of companies in this book is not an endorsement of their investment desirability.

Certain of the principals of Walker's Manual, LLC in some cases have ownership positions in the profiled companies. In all cases the principals' combined investment represents less than 1 percent of the outstanding shares.

Walker's Manual, LLC, does not accept fees of any kind from the companies that are presented in our books. Our objective is to bring our readers information on companies that is unavailable elsewhere. We will continue our search for new material to include in future editions of our book.

Company Profile
Page Format
&
Glossary

Company Profiles

The company profiles contained in this book follow very similar formats. Banks vary somewhat from other companies and are described on page xx. A descriptive review of a representative profiled company follows:

A.D. Makepeace Company

158 Tihonet Road   Wareham, MA 02571-0151   Telephone (508)295-1000   Fax (508)291-7453

Company Description

A. D. Makepeace owns and operates cranberry bogs at locations in several southeastern Massachusetts towns. The Company is a co-founder and significant member-grower of Ocean Spray Cranberries, Inc., an agricultural cooperative founded in 1930. Ocean Spray produces and markets a wide line of cranberry related products. As a member-grower, the Company delivers all of its cranberry production to the marketing cooperative. During 1995, 2,400 acres of land in Minnesota were acquired. In 1993, the Company issued a tender offer for 770 shares, approximately 10% of outstanding shares, at $5,000 per share. Only a small fraction of the offer was accepted.

At the top of the page are the Company's name, address, phone and fax numbers. Readers interested in contacting the Company for more information should use the address listed here. A brief description of the business is provided. Other information helpful in understanding the Company is also included.

Comments

A cool May and cloudy wet summer months contributed to late fruit set and poor sizing. This coupled with record rainfall were the primary determining factors of the below average crop. Preliminary observations by management indicate the potential for a good crop in 1997. The vine condition is excellent and previously renovated acres should begin to yield substantially. The financial statements are prepared on an income tax basis. The two 12-acre test bogs planted in Minnesota are doing very well. An additional 52 acres will be planted in the spring of 1998. The Company believes that this may result in better economics for future growth and in fulfilling the increasing needs of Ocean Spray. Investment Classification: Value

Comments are located directly below financial data and compound growth %'s. The section is used to discuss transactions or events affecting the balance sheet or operating results that are significant or help the reader to better understand the Company's operations.

◆

Below we list the Company's officers along with the positions that they hold. The next section is ownership information, which covers the Company's stock including number of shares outstanding, market capitalization (year-end stock price times shares outstanding), frequency of dividends paid and number of shareholders.

◆

Officers	Position
Christopher Makepeace	President, CEO
Robert L. Rosbe, Jr.	VP - Finance
George G. Rogers	Vice President
John Otis Drew	Vice President

Ownership Information

Number of Shares Outstanding	7,026
Market Capitalization	$ 64,639,200
Frequency of Dividends	Quarterly
Number of Shareholders	Under 500

In the final section general information is covered such as the stock transfer agent and auditor. Up to two market makers are listed (they post prices for the Bank's stock — see *Trading in Unlisted Securities*). We also advise our readers whether or not a regular stockbroker can be used to acquire shares. If the services of a specialist are required, we have attempted to provide the name of one known to specialize in that stock. On the right-hand side of the page we list where the stock is listed (see *Listed vs. Unlisted Securities*) and the trading symbol. These stocks may be listed in the over-the-counter market, on the electronic bulletin board (OTB-BB), or in the over-the-counter market in the Pink Sheets (OTC-PS). They might also be available by order matching only. This latter could take any of several forms; when it does occur, the particulars are explained in the company description.

Other Information

Transfer Agent	Company Office		Where Listed	OTC-BB
Auditor	Gary R. Oman, P.C.		Symbol	MAKE
Market Maker	H.C. Wainwright & Co.	(800)225-6790	SIC Code	0171
	Sharpe Capital Inc.	(800)355-5781	Employees	160
Broker Dealer	OTC Specialist			
	Standard Investment	(888)783-4688 Ext: Jack		

Per Share Information and Annual Financial Data

Below is a glossary related to financial data line items found in each Company's profile:

Per Share Information	
Stock Price	9,200.00
Earnings Per Share	154.22
Price / Earnings Ratio	59.66
Book Value Per Share	4,018.12
Price / Book Value %	228.96
Dividends Per Share	150.00
Annual Financial Data	
Operating Results (000's)	
Total Revenues	13,608.1
Costs & Expenses	-11,855.1
Income Before Taxes and Other	1,753.0
Other Items	0.0
Income Tax	-669.4
Net Income	1,083.6
Cash Flow From Operations	1,161.9
Balance Sheet (000's)	
Cash & Equivalents	5,866.2
Total Current Assets	8,002.1
Fixed Assets, Net	16,683.6
Total Assets	36,279.5
Total Current Liabilities	1,477.4
Long-Term Debt	4,804.7
Stockholders' Equity	28,231.3
Performance & Financial Condition	
Return on Total Revenues %	7.96
Return on Avg Stockholders' Equity %	3.84
Return on Average Assets %	3.02
Current Ratio	5.42
Debt / Equity %	17.02

Annual Financial Data:

Operating Results

Total Revenues Total sales and revenues.

Costs & Expenses The current period costs and expenses.

Income Before Taxes and Other Total income less all expenses and costs before minority interest, accounting changes and extraordinary items.

Other Items Includes minority shareholders' interest in the earnings of a subsidiary, extraordinary items and the cumulative effect of accounting changes. If considered significant, these items will be discussed in the comments section.

Income Taxes Total income taxes for the period.

Net Income Income net of income taxes, extraordinary items and minority interests. Used to compute earnings per share.

Cash Flow From Operations Cash flow generated from operations during the period. This is obtained from the Company's statements of cash flows, which are not presented.

Balance Sheet

Cash & Equivalents Cash and all items immediately convertible into cash at the end of the year.

Total Current Assets Those assets available for use in operations during the current fiscal year.

Fixed Assets, Net The investment in property, plant and equipment.

Total Assets The sum of all assets at the balance sheet date.

Total Current Liabilities Liabilities at the balance sheet date that must be satisfied during the current fiscal year.

Long-Term Debt Obligations such as bonds, notes and capital lease obligations at the balance sheet date that are due more than one year from the balance sheet date.

Per Share Information

Stock Price Bid price for the stock at the end of the year or period presented unless otherwise noted. Amounts are adjusted for stock splits and stock dividends.

Earnings Per Share Net income after all items divided by average shares outstanding for the period.

Price / Earnings Ratio Year-end stock price divided by earnings per share. The ratio is expressed as a multiple (a p/e of 7.25 means that shares are trading at 7.25 times earnings).

Book Value Per Share Total common stockholders' equity divided by total shares outstanding at the end of the period.

Price / Book Value % The percentage relationship between stock price and book value per share.

Dividends Per Share Dividends paid for the period, expressed on a per share basis.

Stockholders' Equity The amount by which total assets exceed total liabilities.

Performance & Financial Condition

Return on Total Revenues % Net income divided by total revenues; a performance measure based on the year presented.

Return on Avg Stockholders' Equity % Net income divided by average stockholders' equity; a performance measure based on the year presented.

Return on Average Assets % Net income divided by average total assets; a performance measure based on the year presented.

Current Ratio The ratio of current assets to current liabilities.

Debt / Equity % Measures debt as a percentage of equity.

1st Community Bancorp, Inc.

109 East Division Street   Sparta, MI 49345   Telephone (616)887-7366   Fax (616)887-5566

Company Description

Sparta State Bank, the subsidiary of this holding company, is a full service community bank serving portions of rural Kent, Muskegon, Newaygo and Ottawa Counties, Michigan, from three offices. The Cedar Springs office was added in 1996. At the beginning of 1996, the Bank acquired Bradford Insurance Centre, Ltd. which has four locations. This affiliation will enable the Bank to offer insurance products. The Bank is starting to plan its centennial celebration in 1998.

The community bank profiles contained in this book all follow the same format. A descriptive review of a representative profiled bank follows:

◆

At the top of the page are the Company's name, address, phone and fax numbers. Readers interested in contacting the company for more information should use the address listed here. Banks are often owned by a holding company. These generally have broader corporate powers than the Bank itself and allow the Company to engage in non-banking activities or to operate in a greater geographical area, for instance, depending on the laws of a particular state. The Bank's operating name or names will be mentioned in this section as well as a brief description including its service area, subsidiary information and year founded. Other information deemed helpful in understanding the Bank is also included.

Comments are located directly below financial data and compound growth %'s. The section is used to discuss transactions or events affecting the balance sheet or operating results that are significant or help the reader to better understand the Bank's operations.

Comments

The results of Bradford Insurance Centre were first included in the financial statements in 1996. The Company declared 6 for 5 and 5 for 4 splits in 1995 and 1994, respectively. Per shares amounts have been adjusted accordingly to provide consistency. Earnings jumped to an all-time high. Total assets grew 29% as a result of loan expansion in all areas of the portfolio. Management is placing heavy focus on non-bank products and services that are being rolled out at a steady pace. Non-interest income rose 237% during 1996 mostly due to the acquisition referred to above.

Officers	Position
Gerald P. David	Senior VP
Jae M. Maxfield	President, CEO
Denis Crosby	Senior VP
Linda R. Pitsch	Senior VP, Head Cashier
Tom Lampen	Vice President, CFO

Here we list the Company's officers along with the positions that they hold. The next section is ownership information, which covers the Company's stock including number of shares outstanding, market capitalization (year-end stock price times shares outstanding), frequency of dividends paid, number of shareholders, where the stock is listed (see *Listed vs. Unlisted Securities*) and the trading symbol. These stocks may be listed in the over-the-counter market, on the electronic bulletin board (OTB-BB), or in the over-the-counter market in the Pink Sheets (OTC-PS). They might also be available by order matching only. This latter could take any of several forms; when it does occur, the particulars are explained in the company description.

Ownership Information

Number of Shares Outstanding	482,710
Market Capitalization	$ 20,756,530
Frequency Of Dividends	Irregular
Number of Shareholders	572
Where Listed / Symbol	Order Matching Only / n.a.

Other Information

Transfer Agent	Chemical Mellon Shareholder Services	Ridgefield Park, NJ
Auditor	Crowe, Chizek and Company LLP	
Market Maker	D.H. Brush & Associates	(616)285-3700
	Stifel Nicolaus & Company, Inc	(800)676-0477
Broker Dealer	OTC Specialist	
	Kevin Ryan - Ryan, Beck & company	(888)231-7226

In this section general information is covered such as the stock transfer agent and auditor. Up to two market makers are listed (they post prices for the Bank's stock — see *Trading in Unlisted Securities*). We also advise our readers whether or not a regular stockbroker can be used to acquire shares. If the services of a specialist are required, we have attempted to provide the name of one known to specialize in that stock.

◆

Lastly we present loan mix, a breakdown of total loans by category of loan. If the Bank has not provided this detail, we show the loan mix as being Not Allocated.

Loan Mix	%
R/E Mortgages	33.8
Commerical	31.4
Consumer	23.6
Agriculture	9.2
Construction	2.0

Per Share Information and Annual Financial Data - Banks

Below is a glossary related to financial data line items found in each Bank's profile:

Per Share Information	
Stock Price	43.00
Earnings Per Share	3.50
Price / Earnings Ratio	12.29
Book Value Per Share	30.12
Price / Book Value %	142.76
Dividends Per Share	1.37
Annual Financial Data	
Operating Results (000's)	
Net Interest Income	5,754.0
Loan Loss Provision	523.0
Non-Interest Income	1,555.0
Non-Interest Expense	-4,436.0
Income Before Taxes and Other	2,350.0
Other Items	0.0
Income Tax	-655.0
Net Income	1,695.0
Balance Sheet (000's)	
Cash & Securities	27,958.0
Loans, Net	108,592.0
Total Assets	141,731.0
Deposits	191,212.0
Stockholders' Equity	14,537.0
Performance & Financial Condition	
Return on Avg Stockholders' Equity %	11.97
Return on Average Assets %	1.35
Equity to Assets %	10.26
Net Interest Margin	5.16
Reserve as a % of Problem Loans	148.70

Loan Loss Provision The current period addition to loan loss reserve.

Non-Interest Income Income from activities other than loans and investments.

Non-Interest Expense Overhead expenses including salaries, facility costs, insurance expense and other overhead items.

Income Before Taxes and Other Total income less all expenses and costs before minority interest, accounting changes and extraordinary items.

Other Items Includes minority shareholders' interest in the earnings of a subsidiary, extraordinary items and the cumulative effect of accounting changes. If considered significant, these items will be discussed in the comments section.

Income Taxes Total income taxes for the period.

Net Income Income net of income taxes, extraordinary items and minority interests. Used to compute earnings per share.

Balance Sheet

Cash & Securities Represents all cash, items immediately convertible into cash, and marketable securities owned at the end of the year.

Loans, Net Loans outstanding at year-end reduced by reserve for loan losses.

Total Assets The sum of all assets at the balance sheet date.

Deposits The sum of all customer deposit accounts that the bank has in its possession at year end.

Stockholders' Equity The amount by which total assets exceed total liabilities.

Per Share Information

Stock Price Bid price for the stock at the end of the year or period presented unless otherwise noted. Amounts are adjusted for stock splits and stock dividends.

Earnings Per Share Net income after all items divided by average shares outstanding for the period.

Price / Earnings Ratio Year-end stock price divided by earnings per share. The ratio is expressed as a multiple (a p/e of 7.25 means that shares are trading at 7.25 times earnings).

Book Value Per Share Total common stockholders' equity divided by total shares outstanding at the end of the period.

Price / Book Value % The percentage relationship between stock price and book value per share.

Dividends Per Share Dividends paid for the period, expressed on a per share basis.

Annual Financial Data:
Operating Results

Net Interest Income Interest income, principally from loans and investment securities portfolios less interest expense, principally on customer deposits.

Performance & Financial Condition

Return on Avg Stockholders' Equity % Net income divided by average stockholders' equity; a performance measure based on the year presented.

Return on Average Assets % Net income divided by average total assets; a performance measure based on the year presented.

Equity to Assets % Stockholders' equity divided by total assets; a measure of financial condition at the end of the reporting period.

Net Interest Margin Total interest earned on a fully taxable equivalent basis less total interest expense. This difference is expressed as a percentage of average earning assets.

Reserve as a % of Problem Loans Loan loss reserve compared to total identified problem loans. If greater than 100%, then reserve exceeds total problem loans. If less than 100%, then reserve is less than loans identified as potentially uncollectible. Banks have several ways of referring to problem loans: Nonperforming loans are either loans on which accrual of interest has been suspended, loans still accruing interest but 90 days or more past-due, or restructured loans. Loans are considered impaired when it is probable that the bank will be unable to collect all amounts due according to the contractual terms of the loan agreement. Banks may report according to one or both of these criteria. If they report both, we are reporting the largest number of the two as "problem loans".

Walker's Manual
of
Unlisted Stocks

2nd edition

Published by Walker's Manual, LLC
1997

A.D. Makepeace Company

158 Tihonet Road   Wareham, MA 02571-0151   Telephone (508)295-1000   Fax (508)291-7453

Company Description

A. D. Makepeace owns and operates cranberry bogs at locations in several southeastern Massachusetts towns. The Company is a co-founder and significant member-grower of Ocean Spray Cranberries, Inc., an agricultural cooperative founded in 1930. Ocean Spray produces and markets a wide line of cranberry related products. As a member-grower, the Company delivers all of its cranberry production to the marketing cooperative. During 1995, 2,400 acres of land in Minnesota were acquired. In 1993, the Company issued a tender offer for 770 shares, approximately 10% of outstanding shares, at $5,000 per share. Only a small fraction of the offer was accepted.

	12/31/96	12/31/95	12/31/94	12/31/93
Per Share Information				
Stock Price	9,200.00	6,000.00	5,000.00	5,000.00
Earnings Per Share	154.22	431.32	396.31	510.94
Price / Earnings Ratio	59.66	13.91	12.62	9.79
Book Value Per Share	4,018.12	4,012.79	3,739.02	3,485.28
Price / Book Value %	228.96	149.52	133.72	143.46
Dividends Per Share	150.00	150.00	125.00	125.00
Annual Financial Data				
Operating Results (000's)				
Total Revenues	13,608.1	15,992.2	15,322.2	16,347.7
Costs & Expenses	-11,855.1	-10,936.5	-10,641.6	-10,054.6
Income Before Taxes and Other	1,753.0	5,055.7	4,680.6	6,293.1
Other Items	0.0	0.0	0.0	0.0
Income Tax	-669.4	-2,026.5	-1,880.6	-2,641.4
Net Income	1,083.6	3,029.1	2,800.0	3,651.7
Cash Flow From Operations	1,161.9	4,571.2	n.a.	n.a.
Balance Sheet (000's)				
Cash & Equivalents	5,866.2	5,358.1	3,689.9	2,945.5
Total Current Assets	8,002.1	7,873.3	7,077.1	6,448.5
Fixed Assets, Net	16,683.6	15,622.2	14,779.9	14,728.9
Total Assets	36,279.5	35,544.1	33,129.3	32,224.8
Total Current Liabilities	1,477.4	5,265.3	1,616.9	2,005.6
Long-Term Debt	4,804.7	0.0	2,931.4	3,202.6
Stockholders' Equity	28,231.3	28,181.8	26,416.1	24,909.3
Performance & Financial Condition				
Return on Total Revenues %	7.96	18.94	18.27	22.34
Return on Avg Stockholders' Equity %	3.84	11.10	10.91	14.66
Return on Average Assets %	3.02	8.82	8.57	10.77
Current Ratio	5.42	1.50	4.38	3.22
Debt / Equity %	17.02	n.a.	11.10	12.86

Compound Growth %'s	EPS %	-32.92	Net Income %	-33.30	Total Revenues %	-5.93

Comments

A cool May and cloudy wet summer months contributed to late fruit set and poor sizing. This coupled with record rainfall were the primary determining factors of the below average crop in 1996. Preliminary observations by management indicate the potential for a good crop in 1997. The vine condition is excellent and previously renovated acres should begin to yield substantially. The financial statements are prepared on an income tax basis. The two 12-acre test bogs planted in Minnesota are doing very well. An additional 52 acres will be planted in the spring of 1998. The Company believes that this may result in better economics for future growth and in fulfilling the increasing needs of Ocean Spray. Investment Classification: Value

Officers	Position	Ownership Information	
Christopher Makepeace	President, CEO	Number of Shares Outstanding	7,026
Robert L. Rosbe, Jr.	VP - Finance	Market Capitalization	$ 64,639,200
George G. Rogers	Vice President	Frequency of Dividends	Quarterly
John Otis Drew	Vice President	Number of Shareholders	Under 500

Other Information

Transfer Agent	Company Office		Where Listed	OTC-BB
Auditor	Gary R. Oman, P.C.		Symbol	MAKE
Market Maker	H.C. Wainwright & Co., Inc.	(800)225-6790	SIC Code	0171
	Sharpe Capital Inc.	(800)355-5781	Employees	160
Broker Dealer	OTC Specialist			
	Standard Investment	(888)783-4688 Ext: Jack		

AFA Protective Systems, Inc.

155 Michael Drive   Syosset, NY 11791   Telephone (516)496-2322   Fax (516)496-2848

Company Description

Originally founded in 1873, AFA Protective Systems, Inc. has provided 124 years of uninterrupted central station alarm service to its customers. The Company has also proudly paid dividends to its shareholders for 108 consecutive years. The major portion of the Company's revenue consists of the recurring annual service fees paid by 22,000 customers for inspection and maintenance services, primarily in the New York, Massachusetts and New Jersey. The Company also monitors about 9,500 locations for 182 alarm dealers who do not have their own central stations.

	12/31/96	12/31/95	12/31/94	12/31/93
Per Share Information				
Stock Price	116.00	117.50	95.00	92.00
Earnings Per Share	5.43	6.70	7.44	8.14
Price / Earnings Ratio	21.36	17.54	12.77	11.30
Book Value Per Share	70.64	68.28	64.02	58.55
Price / Book Value %	164.21	172.09	148.39	157.13
Dividends Per Share	1.80	1.80	1.60	1.60
Annual Financial Data				
Operating Results (000's)				
Total Revenues	27,416.7	27,817.8	25,913.5	25,262.8
Costs & Expenses	-25,452.1	-25,437.1	-23,197.4	-22,266.0
Income Before Taxes and Other	1,964.6	2,380.7	2,716.1	2,996.8
Other Items	0.0	0.0	0.0	0.0
Income Tax	-905.0	-1,042.0	-1,213.0	-1,343.0
Net Income	1,059.6	1,338.7	1,503.1	1,653.8
Cash Flow From Operations	4,357.4	3,633.6	3,936.6	4,131.5
Balance Sheet (000's)				
Cash & Equivalents	5,293.7	4,564.8	6,446.9	5,466.2
Total Current Assets	10,364.4	10,455.1	10,154.9	9,596.9
Fixed Assets, Net	12,632.6	12,337.7	11,750.8	12,215.1
Total Assets	28,968.2	28,487.3	26,742.4	25,656.0
Total Current Liabilities	4,773.1	3,880.1	3,712.8	4,287.0
Long-Term Debt	1,698.8	2,013.6	754.8	0.0
Stockholders' Equity	13,656.6	13,527.9	12,917.9	11,894.6
Performance & Financial Condition				
Return on Total Revenues %	3.86	4.81	5.80	6.55
Return on Avg Stockholders' Equity %	7.80	10.12	12.12	14.71
Return on Average Assets %	3.69	4.85	5.74	6.70
Current Ratio	2.17	2.69	2.74	2.24
Debt / Equity %	12.44	14.89	5.84	n.a.

Compound Growth %'s	EPS %	-12.62	Net Income %	-13.79	Total Revenues %	2.76

Comments

A restructuring of operations was started in 1995 whereby there will be a consolidation in receiving alarm signals at four separate locations to one location. Management believes that passage of the Telecommunications Act will create opportunities for the Company, particularly in the area of additional acquisitions. 1996 revenues and earnings were adversely affected by a five month strike, expansion of operations into new areas, and consolidation of central station operations. Investment Classification: Value

Officers	Position	Ownership Information	
Philip Kleinman	Chairman	Number of Shares Outstanding	193,319
Richard D. Kleinman	President, COO	Market Capitalization	$ 22,425,004
Robert D. Kleinman	CEO, Secretary	Frequency of Dividends	Quarterly
Raymond S. Greenberger	Treasurer	Number of Shareholders	Under 500
Bruce Thomason	Vice President		

Other Information				
Transfer Agent	ChaseMellon Shareholder Services Ridgefield Park, NJ		Where Listed	OTC-BB
Auditor	Edward Isaacs & Company		Symbol	AFAP
Market Maker	H.C. Wainwright & Co., Inc.	(800)727-7176	SIC Code	7382
	Robotti & Co., Inc.	(212)986-0800	Employees	n.a.
Broker Dealer	Regular Stockbroker			
	Norman Kadehjian - Wainwright	(800)727-7176		

AMCOR Capital Corporation

52300 Enterprise Way   Coachella, CA 92236   Telephone (619)398-9520   Fax (619)398-9530

Company Description

The Company's primary business is agriculture and includes the operations of a wholly-owned subsidiary, ACI Farms, Inc. The Company's principal agribusiness operations involve the production and processing of table grapes and dates. The operations are located in the Coachella Valley of southern California. Land planning and development activities are located in southern California and Texas. Some of the agribusiness and land properties managed by the Company are owned by limited partnerships for which the Company or its affiliates are general partners. The Company was formed in 1988 to acquire AMCOR Capital, Inc., an agricultural holding company.

	08/31/96	08/31/95	08/31/94	11/30/93
Per Share Information				
Stock Price as of 12/31	2.06	0.90	0.69	0.25
Earnings Per Share	0.17	0.10	0.05	n.a.
Price / Earnings Ratio	12.12	9.00	13.80	n.a.
Book Value Per Share	1.03	1.00	0.80	0.31
Price / Book Value %	200.00	90.00	86.25	80.65
Dividends Per Share	0.0	0.0	0.0	n.a.
Annual Financial Data				
Operating Results (000's)				
Total Revenues	11,698.6	11,721.8	7,993.8	8,858.8
Costs & Expenses	-9,483.4	-10,536.2	-7,274.0	-9,409.3
Income Before Taxes and Other	2,215.2	1,185.6	719.8	-740.1
Other Items	0.0	0.0	0.0	697.4
Income Tax	-437.3	-12.3	-81.6	-2.4
Net Income	1,777.9	1,173.3	638.2	-45.1
Cash Flow From Operations	-3,580.2	3,124.9	34.9	-3,337.8
Balance Sheet (000's)				
Cash & Equivalents	1,087.1	1,809.3	384.0	309.6
Total Current Assets	7,740.7	9,510.7	4,622.7	2,399.6
Fixed Assets, Net	9,508.4	10,475.2	9,621.0	3,486.6
Total Assets	32,002.3	21,707.4	21,456.1	17,573.5
Total Current Liabilities	3,144.7	5,455.1	3,257.0	3,197.1
Long-Term Debt	0.0	5,544.9	6,847.4	7,079.7
Stockholders' Equity	12,633.9	10,707.4	9,826.9	3,627.7
Performance & Financial Condition				
Return on Total Revenues %	15.20	10.01	7.98	-0.51
Return on Avg Stockholders' Equity %	15.23	11.43	9.49	-1.21
Return on Average Assets %	6.62	5.44	3.27	-0.19
Current Ratio	2.46	1.74	1.42	0.75
Debt / Equity %	n.a.	51.79	69.68	195.16

Compound Growth %'s	EPS %	84.39	Net Income %	66.91	Total Revenues %	9.71

Comments

The Company changed its fiscal year end from November 30, to August 31, effective in the year beginning September 1, 1994. The 1994 year presented is for a nine month period. The Company's improved performance reflects continued contribution from its core agribusiness operations, augmented by renewed activity in its land development business. The Company also announced a major joint venture contract to develop a 1,354 acre planned community located thirty miles southeast of San Antonio, Texas. Investment Classification: Speculative & Value

Officers	Position	Ownership Information	
Fred H. Behrens	Chairman, CEO	Number of Shares Outstanding	11,596,566
Robert A. Wright	President, COO	Market Capitalization	$ 23,888,926
Barry Goverman	Vice President	Frequency of Dividends	Irregular
Marlene Tapie	Other	Number of Shareholders	1,211

Other Information				
Transfer Agent	American Stock Transfer & Trust Company	New York, NY	Where Listed	OTC-BB
Auditor	Kelly & Company		Symbol	APTO
Market Maker	Acap Financial Inc.	(800)541-3961	SIC Code	0179
	M.H. Meyerson & Co., Inc.	(800)333-3113	Employees	2100
Broker Dealer	Regular Stockbroker			

Acap Corporation

10555 Richmond Avenue   Houston, TX 77042   Telephone (713)974-2242   Fax (713)953-7920

Company Description

Acap Corporation is the parent holding company of American Capitol, a life insurance company that is licensed in thirty-three states and the District of Columbia. Acap primarily engages in the acquisition and servicing of existing life insurance policies, either through direct purchase or the acquisition of insurance companies. American Capitol was founded in 1954. Up until 1996, Fortune National Corporation owned 63.7% of Acap shares. Fortune liquidated in 1996 and shares of Acap were distributed to its shareholders. InsCap Corporation, which was a large shareholder in Fortune, now owns 41% of Acap Corporation.

	12/31/96	12/31/95	12/31/94
Per Share Information			
Stock Price	247.00	180.00	105.00
Earnings Per Share	56.79	9.04	183.04
Price / Earnings Ratio	4.35	19.91	0.57
Book Value Per Share	474.97	518.01	252.22
Price / Book Value %	52.00	34.75	41.63
Dividends Per Share	0.0	0.0	0.0
Annual Financial Data			
Operating Results (000's)			
Total Revenues	6,270.8	5,308.7	5,931.5
Costs & Expenses	-5,609.5	-4,808.3	-3,752.7
Income Before Taxes and Other	661.3	500.4	2,178.7
Other Items	0.0	0.0	0.0
Income Tax	-3.0	-223.3	-460.3
Net Income	658.3	277.0	1,718.4
Cash Flow From Operations	2,647.6	778.0	842.1
Balance Sheet (000's)			
Cash & Equivalents	36.4	123.6	n.a.
Total Current Assets	58,333.4	37,531.4	n.a.
Fixed Assets, Net	156.6	64.3	n.a.
Total Assets	103,807.5	82,881.5	n.a.
Total Current Liabilities	10,912.6	4,451.3	n.a.
Long-Term Debt	1,062.5	1,312.5	n.a.
Stockholders' Equity	5,894.9	6,261.4	n.a.
Performance & Financial Condition			
Return on Total Revenues %	10.50	5.22	28.97
Return on Avg Stockholders' Equity %	10.83	5.40	n.a.
Return on Average Assets %	0.71	n.a.	n.a.
Current Ratio	5.35	8.43	n.a.
Debt / Equity %	18.02	20.96	n.a.

Compound Growth %'s	EPS %	-44.30	Net Income %	-38.11	Total Revenues %	2.82

Comments

The fluctuation of income levels is primarily caused by the varying amount of gains or losses on fixed obligation investments. 1995 results were also diminished by an unusually high mortality rate and a decrease in investment income on a significant asset of the Company. Investment Classification: Value

Officers	Position	Ownership Information	
William F. Guest	President	Number of Shares Outstanding	8,516
John D. Cornett	Exec VP, Treasurer	Market Capitalization	$ 2,103,452
Paul L. Clancy	Secretary	Frequency of Dividends	n.a.
H. Kathleen Musselwhite	Other	Number of Shareholders	806

Other Information

Transfer Agent	Continental Stock Transfer and Trust Co. New York, NY		Where Listed	OTC-BB
Auditor	KPMG Peat Marwick LLP		Symbol	AKAP
Market Maker	Carr Securities Corporation	(800)221-2243	SIC Code	6311
	Hill Thompson Magid & Co., Inc	(800)631-3083	Employees	31
Broker Dealer	Regular Stockbroker			

Adams (R.P.) Company, Inc.

P.O. Bax 963   Buffalo, NY 14240-0963   Telephone (716)877-2608   Fax (716)877-9385

Company Description

R.P. Adams Company, Inc. is engaged in the design and manufacture of gas and liquid filters, automatic water strainers, heat exchangers and cyclone separators for industry. The Company's manufacturing, sales, and administrative operations are located in western New York State. The Company extends credit to customers worldwide.

	12/31/96	12/31/95	12/31/94	12/31/93
Per Share Information				
Stock Price	17.25	22.00	19.00	18.00
Earnings Per Share	-1.30	-4.77	0.51	0.35
Price / Earnings Ratio	n.a.	n.a.	37.25	51.43
Book Value Per Share	38.78	40.42	45.52	45.30
Price / Book Value %	44.48	54.43	41.74	39.74
Dividends Per Share	0.40	0.40	0.40	0.40
Annual Financial Data				
Operating Results (000's)				
Total Revenues	9,925.2	9,817.9	8,987.5	8,543.5
Costs & Expenses	-10,117.5	-9,771.0	-8,911.9	-8,510.3
Income Before Taxes and Other	-192.4	47.0	75.5	33.2
Other Items	0.0	-572.7	0.0	0.0
Income Tax	49.0	1.6	-19.0	5.1
Net Income	-143.3	-524.1	56.5	38.3
Cash Flow From Operations	837.3	-337.3	161.0	-596.9
Balance Sheet (000's)				
Cash & Equivalents	169.3	11.4	64.9	200.0
Total Current Assets	4,307.8	5,082.8	4,361.7	4,382.1
Fixed Assets, Net	1,173.5	1,206.4	1,282.3	1,394.5
Total Assets	5,885.1	6,668.4	5,903.2	6,016.9
Total Current Liabilities	840.5	1,434.0	788.7	995.3
Long-Term Debt	20.1	55.1	90.4	1.6
Stockholders' Equity	4,263.3	4,443.9	5,005.2	4,980.7
Performance & Financial Condition				
Return on Total Revenues %	-1.44	-5.34	0.63	0.45
Return on Avg Stockholders' Equity %	-3.29	-11.09	1.13	n.a.
Return on Average Assets %	-2.28	-8.34	0.95	n.a.
Current Ratio	5.13	3.54	5.53	4.40
Debt / Equity %	0.47	1.24	1.81	0.03

Compound Growth %'s	EPS % n.a.	Net Income % n.a.	Total Revenues % 5.12

Comments

Three events combined to cause a disappointing year: deteriorating performance in manufacturing operations, a decision to declare an unusually large amount of inventory obsolete, and unexpected increases in periodic costs. The manager of manufacturing operations, after consistently missing operations and budgeting targets, has been replaced. Management believes it is addressing the core reasons for operating losses during the past two years. R.J. Adams, president of the Company, has stated his intention to retire by the end of 1998. Investment Classification: Value

Officers	Position	Ownership Information	
R. J. Adams	President	Number of Shares Outstanding	109,947
Richard B. Adams	Secretary	Market Capitalization	$ 1,896,586
		Frequency of Dividends	Quarterly
		Number of Shareholders	Under 500

Other Information

Transfer Agent	Company Office		Where Listed	OTC-BB
Auditor	Lumsden & McCormick, LLP		Symbol	ADRI
Market Maker	Carr Securities Corporation	(800)221-2243	SIC Code	3500
	Hoew Barnes Investments, Inc.	(800)621-2364	Employees	n.a.
Broker Dealer	Regular Stockbroker			

ADDvantage Media Group, Inc.

5100 E. Skelly Dr., Ste. 1080   Tulsa, OK 74135-6552   Telephone (918)665-8414   Fax (918)665-2476

Company Description

ADDvantage Media Group is in the business of marketing solar-powered calculators which attach to the handles of shopping carts. The calculators are marketed under the registered trademark "Shoppers Calculator" and are designed with the three-fold purpose of increasing the retailer's sales, assisting shoppers while they are in the store, and presenting an advertising message targeted to each consumer in space provided on the calculator unit. The Company is currently installing its calculators in all the Supercenter stores operated by Wal-Mart Stores, Inc. ADDvantage Media was formed in 1989.

	12/31/96	12/31/95	12/31/94	12/31/93
Per Share Information				
Stock Price	4.37	2.88	1.00	1.25
Earnings Per Share	0.30	0.31	-0.30	-0.63
Price / Earnings Ratio	14.57	9.29	n.a.	n.a.
Book Value Per Share	0.40	-0.26	-0.85	-0.61
Price / Book Value %	824.53	n.a.	n.a.	n.a.
Dividends Per Share	0.0	0.0	0.0	0.0
Annual Financial Data				
Operating Results (000's)				
Total Revenues	7,044.0	249.6	407.7	389.7
Costs & Expenses	-4,279.7	-2,460.6	-1,419.1	-2,612.7
Income Before Taxes and Other	2,764.3	-2,211.1	-1,011.4	-2,223.1
Other Items	0.0	0.0	0.0	0.0
Income Tax	-940.0	3,910.0	0.0	0.0
Net Income	1,824.3	1,698.9	-1,011.4	-2,223.1
Cash Flow From Operations	2,886.9	-291.6	-84.0	-868.7
Balance Sheet (000's)				
Cash & Equivalents	739.1	20.4	0.2	66.7
Total Current Assets	5,039.9	702.9	26.8	259.7
Fixed Assets, Net	2,233.4	823.7	650.7	668.5
Total Assets	7,723.5	5,244.2	1,254.7	1,598.7
Total Current Liabilities	4,219.4	2,612.8	4,576.5	3,739.5
Long-Term Debt	0.0	3,406.7	0.0	0.0
Stockholders' Equity	3,036.5	-1,290.3	-3,321.7	-2,245.7
Performance & Financial Condition				
Return on Total Revenues %	25.90	680.79	-248.09	-570.53
Return on Avg Stockholders' Equity %	208.95	n.a.	n.a.	n.a.
Return on Average Assets %	28.14	52.28	-70.89	n.a.
Current Ratio	1.19	0.27	0.01	0.07
Debt / Equity %	n.a.	n.a.	n.a.	n.a.

Compound Growth %'s	EPS % -3.23	Net Income % 7.38	Total Revenues % 162.45

Comments

At December 31, 1996, calculators were installed on approximately 266,000 shopping carts in 327 Wal-Mart Supercenters, representing 89% of centers open at that date. Talk about a white knight, Wal-Mart even guaranteed Company debt so it could assemble more units. Virtually all of 1996 revenue is from the placement of advertising. K-mart is not to be left in the cold. They too are under contract with ADDvantage. For the first quarter of 1997, the Company reported revenues of $2.8 million and earnings of $.13 per share. An application to list on NASDAQ is pending. Investment Classification: Speculative

Officers	Position	Ownership Information	
Charles H. Hood	Chairman, President	Number of Shares Outstanding	5,731,089
Gary W. Young	Exec VP, Treasurer	Market Capitalization	$ 25,044,859
Steve C. Oden	VP - Sales	Frequency of Dividends	n.a.
		Number of Shareholders	800

Other Information

Transfer Agent	North American Transfer Co. Freeport, NY		Where Listed	OTC-BB
Auditor	Tullius Taylor Sartain Sartain		Symbol	ADDM
Market Maker	Van Kasper & Company	(800)603-5969	SIC Code	5040
	Troster Singer	(800)526-3160	Employees	n.a.
Broker Dealer	Regular Stockbroker			

Adirondack Trust Company (The)

473 Broadway   Saratoga Springs, NY 12866   Telephone (518)584-5844   Fax (518)584-1107

Company Description

The Adirondack Trust Company has been serving the community of Saratoga Springs in New York since 1900. The City is a vibrant community and winner of the prestigious Great American Main Street Award. Saratoga Springs continues to prosper with a new multi-million dollar brewery, a regional warehouse of a national hardware company, new shopping plazas and new housing projects. The Bank plans on doing most of the financing from its five offices and offers trust services in addition to traditional banking.

	12/31/96	12/31/95	12/31/94	12/31/93
Per Share Information				
Stock Price	495.00	460.00	420.00	390.00
Earnings Per Share	70.83	63.71	54.86	49.70
Price / Earnings Ratio	6.99	7.22	7.66	7.85
Book Value Per Share	557.73	511.84	448.10	420.31
Price / Book Value %	88.75	89.87	93.73	92.79
Dividends Per Share	21.00	20.00	19.50	17.75
Annual Financial Data				
Operating Results (000's)				
Net Interest Income	15,971.0	15,168.5	14,118.5	13,292.8
Loan Loss Provision	-2,464.4	-1,533.3	-744.5	-875.3
Non-Interest Income	3,821.9	2,796.2	1,768.2	1,967.8
Non-Interest Expense	-9,065.4	-8,945.4	-8,774.0	-8,861.7
Income Before Taxes and Other	8,263.1	7,485.9	6,368.2	5,523.6
Other Items	0.0	0.0	0.0	0.0
Income Tax	-2,721.4	-2,501.5	-2,076.2	-1,635.0
Net Income	5,541.6	4,984.5	4,292.0	3,888.6
Balance Sheet (000's)				
Cash & Securities	149,288.3	138,875.2	143,871.8	135,819.2
Loans, Net	189,615.4	175,955.6	167,416.9	153,914.9
Total Assets	350,660.5	326,909.5	323,299.9	300,574.5
Deposits	302,303.2	281,326.9	283,267.8	263,466.1
Stockholders' Equity	43,634.6	40,044.6	35,057.6	32,883.3
Performance & Financial Condition				
Return on Avg Stockholders' Equity %	13.24	13.27	12.63	12.29
Return on Average Assets %	1.64	1.53	1.38	n.a.
Equity to Assets %	12.44	12.25	10.84	10.94
Net Interest Margin	n.a.	n.a.	n.a.	n.a.
Reserve as a % of Problem Loans	3,076.92	n.a.	n.a.	n.a.

Compound Growth %'s	EPS %	12.53	Net Income %	12.53	Net Interest Income %	6.31

Comments

With a sailors theme, the president reports "Basking in a sea of good fortune, it is not wise to bait fate so I will steer away from the shoals of prediction which have foundered many an eager economist. I'll let it suffice to say that our capital and reserves should provide an adequate sea anchor for whatever stormy weather lies ahead." It is hard to find even a cloud in the 1996 report. The Trust department now has $150 million under management and the Bank anticipates opening several new branches over the next few years. Investment Classification: Value & Income

Officers	Position	Ownership Information	
Charles V. Wait	President, CEO	Number of Shares Outstanding	78,236
Vassar H. Curtis	Exec VP, Secretary	Market Capitalization	$ 38,726,820
Clark S. Curtis, Jr.	Senior VP	Frequency of Dividends	Semi-Annual
David W. Brown	Vice President, Treasurer	Number of Shareholders	n.a.
John Boyd	Vice President	Where Listed / Symbol	OTC-BB / ADIR

Other Information		Loan Mix	%
Transfer Agent	Company Office	R/E Mortgages	28.9
Auditor	Not indicated	Other	71.1
Market Maker	First Albany Corporation (800)541-5061		
	Cowen & Co. (800)221-3431		
Broker Dealer	OTC Specialist		
	Frank Procopio - Ryan, Beck (888)231-7226		

Adrian Steel Company

906 James Street   Adrian, MI 49221-3914   Telephone (517)265-6194   Fax (517)263-2877

Company Description

The Company and its subsidiaries, which operate in five different states, are in the business of manufacturing and installing storage components for customized service vehicles, also known as upfitting of service vehicles. Its clientele include many of the Fortune 500 service fleets. A promotion with General Motors has also been very successful in introducing Company products and services to small commercial business owners. Adrian Steel began operations in 1953 and went public in 1961. However, it has been buying back shares as they become available. The Company also has an unusual second class of non-voting stock used in a deferred compensation arrangement for its employees.

	09/30/96	09/30/95	09/30/94	09/30/93
Per Share Information				
Stock Price as of 12/31	160.00	172.52	165.00	165.00
Earnings Per Share	17.01	16.58	14.71	13.08
Price / Earnings Ratio	9.41	10.41	11.22	12.61
Book Value Per Share	126.77	114.59	104.22	100.11
Price / Book Value %	126.21	150.55	158.32	164.82
Dividends Per Share	6.00	8.00	7.00	7.00
Annual Financial Data				
Operating Results (000's)				
Total Revenues	52,979.2	45,947.2	33,394.6	30,673.4
Costs & Expenses	-47,575.9	-40,991.4	-29,036.8	-26,727.1
Income Before Taxes and Other	5,403.3	4,845.0	4,357.8	3,946.4
Other Items	0.0	0.0	0.0	0.0
Income Tax	-1,937.3	-1,502.7	-1,293.0	-1,166.0
Net Income	3,466.1	3,342.3	3,064.8	2,780.4
Cash Flow From Operations	2,788.3	1,815.1	2,178.1	2,973.6
Balance Sheet (000's)				
Cash & Equivalents	2,801.3	2,153.2	2,463.0	2,889.5
Total Current Assets	17,057.2	14,220.0	10,739.5	9,461.9
Fixed Assets, Net	6,281.8	5,625.8	4,473.4	3,672.7
Total Assets	31,273.5	28,366.0	25,535.1	24,992.6
Total Current Liabilities	4,878.0	4,882.3	3,904.9	3,691.4
Long-Term Debt	46.6	92.0	191.2	0.0
Stockholders' Equity	26,016.0	23,081.9	21,324.9	21,269.2
Performance & Financial Condition				
Return on Total Revenues %	6.54	7.27	9.18	9.06
Return on Avg Stockholders' Equity %	14.12	15.05	14.39	13.31
Return on Average Assets %	11.62	12.40	12.13	11.84
Current Ratio	3.50	2.91	2.75	2.56
Debt / Equity %	0.18	0.40	0.90	n.a.

Compound Growth %'s	EPS %	9.15	Net Income %	7.62	Total Revenues %	19.98

Comments

The Company classifies its holdings in marketable securities as non-current assets. These holdings amounted to $5.6 million, $7.2 million, $9.1 million, and $11.5 million for the years 1996, 1995, 1994, and 1993, respectively. The gradual decline is due to substantial investments in property and equipment and the ongoing stock repurchase program. Management attributes the increase in sales to the promotion with General Motors referred to above. For the first half of fiscal 1997, net earnings were $2,572,000 as compared to $1,412,000 for the same period in 1996. Investment Classification: Value & Growth

Officers	Position	Ownership Information	
Harley J. Westfall	President, Treasurer	Number of Shares Outstanding	205,214
Harold E. Stieg	Secretary	Market Capitalization	$ 32,834,240
Lynford R. Baugh	VP - Sales	Frequency of Dividends	Quarterly
Joseph E. Emens	Other	Number of Shareholders	300

Other Information				
Transfer Agent	American Stock Transfer & Trust Company New York, NY		Where Listed	OTC-BB
Auditor	Curtis Bailey Exelby & Sposito		Symbol	ADST
Market Maker	Roney & Co.	(800)321-2038	SIC Code	3312
	H.C. Wainwright & Co., Inc.	(800)727-7176	Employees	130
Broker Dealer	Regular Stockbroker			
	Norman Kadehjian - Wainwright	(800)727-7176		

Advantage Marketing Systems, Inc.

2601 N.W. Expressway, Ste.121W   Oklahoma City, OK 73112   Telephone (405)842-0131   Fax (405)843-4935

Company Description

Advantage Marketing Systems, Inc., as reorganized in 1995, is a marketer of consumer oriented services and products which are packaged together in special programs and sold to independent sales associates who use the products and services themselves and also sell them to others. The programs consist of various services which provide savings on items such as merchandise, groceries and travel, and legal benefits furnished by certain third party providers as well as nutritional supplements, cosmetics and skin care products. The Company was formed in 1988.

	12/31/96	12/31/95	12/31/94	12/31/93
Per Share Information				
Stock Price	5.50	6.00	2.24	0.96
Earnings Per Share	0.29	0.09	0.04	-0.16
Price / Earnings Ratio	18.97	66.67	56.00	n.a.
Book Value Per Share	0.43	-0.01	-0.14	n.a.
Price / Book Value %	1,279.07	n.a.	n.a.	n.a.
Dividends Per Share	0.0	0.0	0.0	0.0
Annual Financial Data				
Operating Results (000's)				
Total Revenues	6,163.7	4,518.2	2,677.9	1,075.4
Costs & Expenses	-5,838.2	-4,268.5	-2,597.9	-1,488.3
Income Before Taxes and Other	325.5	249.7	80.0	-412.9
Other Items	0.0	0.0	0.0	73.0
Income Tax	499.6	0.0	0.0	0.0
Net Income	825.2	249.7	80.0	-340.0
Cash Flow From Operations	426.4	360.8	109.3	-122.8
Balance Sheet (000's)				
Cash & Equivalents	169.6	112.1	0.0	n.a.
Total Current Assets	655.2	283.3	117.8	n.a.
Fixed Assets, Net	377.2	159.8	44.8	n.a.
Total Assets	1,790.3	533.0	177.0	n.a.
Total Current Liabilities	638.9	454.1	456.5	n.a.
Long-Term Debt	19.0	28.5	7.9	n.a.
Stockholders' Equity	921.4	-25.2	-287.4	n.a.
Performance & Financial Condition				
Return on Total Revenues %	13.39	5.53	2.99	-31.61
Return on Avg Stockholders' Equity %	184.15	n.a.	n.a.	n.a.
Return on Average Assets %	71.03	70.34	n.a.	n.a.
Current Ratio	1.03	0.62	0.26	n.a.
Debt / Equity %	2.07	n.a.	n.a.	n.a.

Compound Growth %'s	EPS % n.a.	Net Income % n.a.	Total Revenues % 78.96

Comments

The Company executed a 1 for 8 reverse split in 1996. All per share amounts have been restated accordingly. 1996 results include a nonrecurring benefit from the utilization of tax loss carryforwards of $499,613, or $.18 per share. Compound earnings growth rates were, therefore, omitted. Revenues increased 36.4% during 1996 largely as a result of increased sales volume of dietary and nutritional supplements and the expansion of the Company's network of independent sales representatives. This momentum carried into the first quarter of 1997 as revenue jumped 54%. Income before taxes was marginally higher but income after taxes was lower. Investment Classification: Speculative

Officers	Position	Ownership Information	
John W. Hail	Chairman, CEO	Number of Shares Outstanding	2,143,441
Roger P. Baresel	President, CFO	Market Capitalization	$ 11,788,926
Dennis Huff	Exec VP	Frequency of Dividends	n.a.
Leon Hooter	Exec VP	Number of Shareholders	1,563
Curtis H. Wilson, Sr.	Other		

Other Information

Transfer Agent	U.S. Stock Transfer Corp. Glendale, CA		Where Listed	OTC-BB
Auditor	Deloitte & Touche LLP		Symbol	AMSOD
Market Maker	Olsen Payne & Co.	(800)453-5321	SIC Code	7389
	Wilson-Davis & Co., Inc.	(800)453-5735	Employees	31
Broker Dealer	Regular Stockbroker			

Ainslie Corporation

531 Pond Street   Braintree, MA 02184-9000   Telephone (617)848-0850   Fax (617)843-2584

Company Description

Ainslie Corporation manufactures microwave antennas and related products used primarily in the defense industries. There has been a wide range between bid and ask prices and it is difficult to obtain any information from the Company. Shares were reacquired by the Company for $3.50 per share in 1992 through 1994. In a tender offer expiring March 31, 1997, the Company offered $8 per share. The value of cash and securities alone at year end was $21.44 per share.

	07/31/96	07/31/95	07/31/94	07/31/93
Per Share Information				
Stock Price as of 12/31	8.25	4.50	4.50	3.50
Earnings Per Share	3.53	2.05	1.63	0.33
Price / Earnings Ratio	2.34	2.20	2.76	10.61
Book Value Per Share	30.06	26.53	24.48	22.83
Price / Book Value %	27.45	16.96	18.38	15.33
Dividends Per Share	0.0	0.0	0.0	0.0
Annual Financial Data				
Operating Results (000's)				
Total Revenues	6,908.6	7,987.0	8,940.4	7,782.5
Costs & Expenses	-6,200.7	-7,614.5	-8,662.6	-7,721.8
Income Before Taxes and Other	707.9	372.5	277.8	60.7
Other Items	0.0	0.0	0.0	0.0
Income Tax	-279.1	-123.2	-80.1	-20.6
Net Income	428.8	249.3	197.7	40.1
Cash Flow From Operations	n.a.	n.a.	n.a.	n.a.
Balance Sheet (000's)				
Cash & Equivalents	877.1	604.9	892.0	454.1
Total Current Assets	3,580.5	3,404.1	2,996.5	2,519.7
Fixed Assets, Net	313.3	393.0	359.9	468.9
Total Assets	3,998.0	3,890.0	3,440.2	3,064.8
Total Current Liabilities	333.2	544.1	298.2	291.5
Long-Term Debt	0.0	120.8	170.8	0.0
Stockholders' Equity	3,648.6	3,219.8	2,970.6	2,773.3
Performance & Financial Condition				
Return on Total Revenues %	6.21	3.12	2.21	0.52
Return on Avg Stockholders' Equity %	12.49	8.05	6.88	1.46
Return on Average Assets %	10.87	6.80	6.08	1.23
Current Ratio	10.75	6.26	10.05	8.64
Debt / Equity %	n.a.	3.75	5.75	n.a.

Compound Growth %'s   EPS % 120.34   Net Income % 120.32   Total Revenues % -3.89

Comments

The Company appears to be having an excellent recovery from its 1992 performance and certainly has plenty of cash and T-bills to invest in the right opportunities. Compounded earnings growth rates can be misleading because of the relatively low income in 1993. Property, plant and equipment has been depreciated to less than 10% of its original cost. Investment Classification: Value

Officers	Position	Ownership Information	
Eric G. Sandquist	President, Treasurer	Number of Shares Outstanding	121,361
Janice Mather	Other	Market Capitalization	$ 1,001,228
		Frequency of Dividends	n.a.
		Number of Shareholders	Under 500

Other Information			
Transfer Agent	First National Bank of Boston	Where Listed	OTC-BB
Auditor	Bernard J. McDonald, Jr.	Symbol	ANSE
Market Maker	Hill Thompson Magid & Co., Inc (800)631-3083	SIC Code	3699
	The Seidler Companies Inc. (800)421-0164	Employees	100
Broker Dealer	Regular Stockbroker		

Akron, Bank of

46 Main Street   Akron, NY 14001-0420   Telephone (716)542-5401   Fax (716)542-5510

Company Description

Bank of Akron has been serving the towns of Newstead and Clarence and parts of the surrounding townships of Genesee and Niagara since 1900. The area is a rural part of Erie County in western New York, about thirty miles northeast of Buffalo. The Bank opened a third location during 1996.

	12/31/96	12/31/95	12/31/94	12/31/93
Per Share Information				
Stock Price	30.00	28.00	26.25	20.00
Earnings Per Share	4.40	5.08	4.08	3.58
Price / Earnings Ratio	6.82	5.51	6.43	5.59
Book Value Per Share	44.63	41.41	37.42	33.16
Price / Book Value %	67.22	67.62	70.15	60.31
Dividends Per Share	1.51	1.51	1.31	1.26
Annual Financial Data				
Operating Results (000's)				
Net Interest Income	4,583.2	4,526.7	3,891.4	3,465.0
Loan Loss Provision	-79.7	-192.6	-126.5	-200.0
Non-Interest Income	360.4	328.9	345.3	303.6
Non-Interest Expense	-2,952.1	-2,422.7	-2,348.2	-2,089.4
Income Before Taxes and Other	1,911.9	2,240.3	1,762.1	1,479.1
Other Items	0.0	0.0	0.0	0.0
Income Tax	-591.2	-715.0	-537.4	-406.2
Net Income	1,320.7	1,525.3	1,224.7	1,072.9
Balance Sheet (000's)				
Cash & Securities	43,621.2	44,900.3	42,895.5	34,310.5
Loans, Net	55,892.5	49,719.1	43,773.2	40,303.0
Total Assets	103,658.0	97,560.3	89,289.7	77,250.4
Deposits	89,365.3	84,317.4	77,489.0	67,156.1
Stockholders' Equity	13,390.3	12,424.5	11,225.6	9,948.6
Performance & Financial Condition				
Return on Avg Stockholders' Equity %	10.23	12.90	11.57	11.17
Return on Average Assets %	1.31	1.63	1.47	n.a.
Equity to Assets %	12.92	12.74	12.57	12.88
Net Interest Margin	n.a.	5.07	n.a.	n.a.
Reserve as a % of Problem Loans	n.a.	n.a.	n.a.	n.a.

Compound Growth %'s	EPS %	7.12	Net Income %	7.17	Net Interest Income %	9.77

Comments

Management does not provide any analysis of the Bank's financial results. We note a continuing rise in deposits and loans. The decline in 1996 income is primarily due to large increases in employee costs and depreciation. Investment Classification: Value & Income

Officers	Position	Ownership Information	
E. Peter Forrestel II	President	Number of Shares Outstanding	300,000
Alan Foss	Senior VP	Market Capitalization	$ 9,000,000
Stve Carlson	Vice President	Frequency of Dividends	Quarterly
		Number of Shareholders	65
		Where Listed / Symbol	OTC-BB / BARK

Other Information			Loan Mix	%
Transfer Agent	Company Office		R/E Mortgages	75.1
Auditor	Lucernoni, Schulz, Thrasher		Installment	18.0
Market Maker	Ryan, Beck & Co.	(800)325-7926	Other	6.9
	Hill Thompson Magid & Co., Inc	(800)631-3083		
Broker Dealer	OTC Specialist			
	Frank Procopio - Ryan, Beck	(888)231-7226		

Al-Zar, Ltd.

P.O. Box 1380   Jacksonville, FL 32201-1380   Telephone (904)396-6600   Fax (904)396-4042

Company Description

Al-Zar, Ltd. is a limited partnership which was formed on April 6, 1983, when St. Joe Corporation contributed land that had a fair market value of approximately $14 million for 49,500 partnership units and St. Joseph Land and Development Company contributed $141,000 cash for 500 partnership units. St. Joe Corporation subsequently distributed all of its units of partnership holdings to its shareholders. The purpose of the Partnership is the zoning, development, ownership, maintenance, sale and leasing of certain real property in New Castle County, Delaware.

	12/31/96	12/31/95	12/31/93
Per Unit Information			
Price Per Unit	325.00	325.00	325.00
Earnings Per Unit	0.34	0.23	25.61
Price / Earnings Ratio	955.88	1,413.04	12.69
Book Value Per Unit	13.48	13.14	12.85
Price / Book Value %	2,410.98	2,473.36	2,529.18
Distributions Per Unit	0.0	0.0	30.00
Cash Flow Per Unit	n.a.	n.a.	n.a.
Annual Financial Data			
Operating Results (000's)			
Total Revenues	47.0	14.1	1,408.7
Costs & Expenses	30.1	2.6	-128.4
Operating Income	16.9	11.5	1,280.3
Other Items	0.0	0.0	0.0
Net Income	16.9	11.5	1,280.3
Cash Flow From Operations	n.a.	n.a.	n.a.
Balance Sheet (000's)			
Cash & Equivalents	65.4	48.5	34.3
Total Current Assets	65.4	48.5	34.3
Investments	608.4	608.4	n.a.
Total Assets	673.8	656.9	642.7
Total Current Liabilities	0.0	0.0	0.0
Long-Term Debt	0.0	0.0	0.0
Partners' Capital	673.8	656.9	642.7
Performance & Financial Condition			
Return on Total Revenues %	35.96	81.55	90.88
Return on Average Partners' Capital %	2.54	1.77	n.a.
Return on Average Assets %	2.54	1.77	n.a.
Current Ratio	n.a.	n.a.	n.a.
Debt / Equity %	n.a.	n.a.	n.a.

Compound Growth %'s	EPU % n.a.	Net Income % n.a.	Total Revenues % n.a.

Comments

The Partnership has 254 acres of land, 93% of which are under a land development option contract to a single land developer. The contract would allow the developer to exercise his rights in stages. During 1996, it was discovered that the developer failed to pay certain property taxes and may be in breach of the contract. Management has attempted to seek a non-judicial resolution of claimed breaches, although no outcome of possible settlement can be reasonably estimated at this time. Investment Classification: Value

Officers	Position	Ownership Information	
S. D. Fraser	Vice President	Number of Units Outstanding	50,000
		Market Capitalization	$ 16,250,000
		Frequency of Distributions	n.a.
		Number of Partners	Under 500

Other Information

Transfer Agent	Company Office		Where Listed	OTC-BB
Auditor	KPMG Peat Marwick LLP		Symbol	ALZR
Market Maker	Herzog, Heine, Geduld, Inc.	(800)221-3600	SIC Code	6790
	Ernst & Co.	(800)845-4330	Employees	0
Broker Dealer	OTC Specialist			
	Standard Investment	(888)783-4688 Ext: Jack		

Alaska Power & Telephone Company

P.O. Box 459   Skagway, AK 99840   Telephone (360)385-1733   Fax (360)385-5177

Company Description

Alaska Power & Telephone Company supplies electric and telephone service to communities and serves over 9,000 customers in rural eastern Alaska. Formed in 1957, it has been adding service to a broader territory on an ongoing basis. New communities have been added for eight consecutive years. During 1996, Haines Light and Power Co. was acquired in a stock transaction. The Company is subject to regulation by the state and federal public utility commissions. The Company has an Employee Stock Ownership Plan covering virtually all employees.

	12/31/96	12/31/95	12/31/94	12/31/93
Per Share Information				
Stock Price	22.75	19.00	15.25	13.00
Earnings Per Share	1.82	2.02	1.95	1.72
Price / Earnings Ratio	12.50	9.41	7.82	7.56
Book Value Per Share	14.38	12.68	11.20	9.05
Price / Book Value %	158.21	149.84	136.16	143.65
Dividends Per Share	0.86	0.85	0.48	0.45
Annual Financial Data				
Operating Results (000's)				
Total Revenues	13,796.3	11,895.6	10,641.0	10,031.2
Costs & Expenses	-11,000.0	-8,982.8	-7,862.9	-7,832.2
Income Before Taxes and Other	2,833.5	2,912.8	2,778.0	2,199.0
Other Items	0.0	0.0	0.0	0.0
Income Tax	-926.4	-983.5	-964.3	-660.3
Net Income	1,907.1	1,929.3	1,813.7	1,538.7
Cash Flow From Operations	4,280.6	3,350.8	3,526.4	3,337.0
Balance Sheet (000's)				
Cash & Equivalents	235.4	793.7	443.9	234.6
Total Current Assets	3,421.9	3,603.0	2,670.0	2,626.4
Fixed Assets, Net	36,629.4	28,911.7	21,366.2	13,924.6
Total Assets	42,685.1	34,733.1	25,322.2	18,729.4
Total Current Liabilities	2,361.6	2,199.0	1,930.0	1,863.1
Long-Term Debt	20,965.1	17,613.8	10,676.8	6,609.3
Stockholders' Equity	15,782.8	11,885.5	10,094.8	8,091.1
Performance & Financial Condition				
Return on Total Revenues %	13.82	16.22	17.04	15.34
Return on Avg Stockholders' Equity %	13.79	17.56	19.95	21.55
Return on Average Assets %	4.93	6.43	8.23	8.83
Current Ratio	1.45	1.64	1.38	1.41
Debt / Equity %	132.83	148.20	105.77	81.69

Compound Growth %'s	EPS %	1.90	Net Income %	7.42	Total Revenues %	11.21

Comments

The issuance of shares in connection with the acquisition referred to above has the effect of diluting compound growth in earnings per share. Strong growth, dedicated employees and an increasing dividend make this a particularly interesting company to follow. Management is upbeat about deregulation and is moving rapidly to capitalize on resulting opportunities. Investment Classification: Growth & Income

Officers	Position	Ownership Information	
Robert S. Grimm	President	Number of Shares Outstanding	1,097,881
Vernon Neitzer	Senior VP	Market Capitalization	$ 24,976,793
Howard Garner	Treasurer, VP - Finance	Frequency of Dividends	Quarterly
Michael Garrett	Controller	Number of Shareholders	Under 500

Other Information

Transfer Agent	Marilou R. Sullivan, 800-982-0136 Port Townsend, WA		Where Listed	OTC-BB
Auditor	Ernst & Young LLP		Symbol	APTL
Market Maker	S.J. Wolfe & Co.	(800)262-2244	SIC Code	4910
	Sharpe Capital Inc.	(800)355-5781	Employees	80
Broker Dealer	OTC Specialist			
	Standard Investment	(888)783-4688 Ext: Jack		

Alden Lee Company, Inc.

1215 Chrysler Drive   Menlo Park, CA 94025   Telephone (415)324-5000   Fax (415)324-5001

Company Description

The Company produces and markets a line of fine hardwood furniture for musicians, including wooden music stands, sheet music cabinets, performers' benches and instrument stands. Operations commenced in October, 1996. The Company raised $275,000 in a Reg. D offering followed by a fully subscribed intrastate offering which raised $2,650,000. Another 100,000 shares at $10 per share were being offered in June, 1997. The Company stands available to facilitate trading by introducing buyers to potential sellers. There is only one problem; there are no sellers. The financial information you see below represents a development stage enterprise. Revenues are comprised of interest income. (Contrary to Michael Brush, writer for The New York Times - you do not compute a price-to-sales ratio before a company has sales).

	06/30/96	06/30/95	06/30/94
Per Share Information			
Stock Price as of 12/31	8.00	2.00	0.50
Earnings Per Share	-0.01	-0.01	n.a.
Price / Earnings Ratio	n.a.	n.a.	n.a.
Book Value Per Share	0.18	0.18	0.09
Price / Book Value %	4,444.44	1,111.11	555.56
Dividends Per Share	0.0	0.0	n.a.
Annual Financial Data			
Operating Results (000's)			
Total Revenues	76.7	10.8	0.9
Costs & Expenses	-626.2	-65.5	-14.7
Income Before Taxes and Other	-549.5	-54.7	-13.8
Other Items	0.0	0.0	0.0
Income Tax	-0.8	-0.8	-0.8
Net Income	-550.3	-55.5	-14.6
Cash Flow From Operations	-847.7	-233.3	-14.0
Balance Sheet (000's)			
Cash & Equivalents	1,541.5	306.2	234.5
Total Current Assets	1,541.5	306.2	234.5
Fixed Assets, Net	65.4	19.2	11.8
Total Assets	2,430.1	730.9	334.2
Total Current Liabilities	34.1	28.3	8.8
Long-Term Debt	0.0	0.0	0.0
Stockholders' Equity	2,396.0	702.6	325.4
Performance & Financial Condition			
Return on Total Revenues %	-717.36	-511.69	-1,551.65
Return on Avg Stockholders' Equity %	-35.52	-10.79	n.a.
Return on Average Assets %	-34.82	-10.42	n.a.
Current Ratio	45.24	10.81	26.65
Debt / Equity %	n.a.	n.a.	n.a.

Compound Growth %'s	EPS % n.a.	Net Income % n.a.	Total Revenues % n.a.

Comments

The first catalog is very attractive and was mailed to customers in October, 1996. Response rates are in line with expectations but the average dollar amount per order is twice what was anticipated. The Company recruited some experienced direct mail professionals to join the Company including Dave Smith, formerly associated with Smith & Hawken. Management states that operations are on schedule. Investment Classification: Speculative

Officers	Position	Ownership Information	
Richard J. Lee	President	Number of Shares Outstanding	4,213,125
Nick Keefe	Exec VP	Market Capitalization	$ 33,705,000
Richard A. Denholtz	Other	Frequency of Dividends	n.a.
		Number of Shareholders	Under 500

Other Information

Transfer Agent	Securities Transfer Corp. Dallas, TX	Where Listed	Order Matching Only
Auditor	Frank, Rimerman & Co.	Symbol	n.a.
Market Maker	None - See Note	SIC Code	2490
		Employees	12
Broker Dealer	None		

Allstar Inns, Inc.

200 E. Carrillo St., Ste. 300   Santa Barbara, CA 93101   Telephone (805)730-3354   Fax (805)730-3369

Company Description

The Company was formed in Delaware in 1992, to assume the business and operations of a limited partnership. The Company's primary business is to own and receive rental income from the economy motels it owns and leases. At December 31, 1996, the Company owned or leased 72 motels with a total of 7,641 rooms. In 1992, the Company reached an agreement with a "Motel 6" operator to manage the motels through 2011. The agreement brought unfavorable results and was terminated in 1995. It was replaced with a triple net, 15 year term, master lease agreement with the same operator. The lease agreement has a purchase option through 1998, to purchase the motels for $40 million plus the assumption of their related indebtedness and has certain other provisions. This purchase option was exercised in January, 1997.

	12/31/96	12/31/95	12/31/94	12/31/93
Per Share Information				
Stock Price	27.25	24.50	2.69	7.00
Earnings Per Share	17.82	-0.77	-6.63	-8.17
Price / Earnings Ratio	1.53	n.a.	n.a.	n.a.
Book Value Per Share	-37.71	-55.32	-54.81	-48.19
Price / Book Value %	n.a.	n.a.	n.a.	n.a.
Dividends Per Share	2.00	2.00	0.0	0.0
Annual Financial Data				
Operating Results (000's)				
Total Revenues	24,743.0	52,424.0	56,842.0	52,034.0
Costs & Expenses	-29,031.0	-60,173.0	-63,101.0	-59,755.0
Income Before Taxes and Other	-4,288.0	-7,749.0	-6,259.0	-7,721.0
Other Items	0.0	0.0	0.0	0.0
Income Tax	23,306.0	7,012.0	-2.0	0.0
Net Income	19,018.0	-737.0	-6,261.0	-7,721.0
Cash Flow From Operations	6,003.0	-12,854.0	9,855.0	2,531.0
Balance Sheet (000's)				
Cash & Equivalents	15,131.0	13,518.0	20,320.0	n.a.
Total Current Assets	49,100.0	15,653.0	24,966.0	n.a.
Fixed Assets, Net	127,436.0	136,232.0	145,614.0	n.a.
Total Assets	177,679.0	160,290.0	174,048.0	n.a.
Total Current Liabilities	10,747.0	10,204.0	28,299.0	n.a.
Long-Term Debt	204,105.0	204,556.0	197,533.0	n.a.
Stockholders' Equity	-37,173.0	-54,470.0	-51,784.0	n.a.
Performance & Financial Condition				
Return on Total Revenues %	76.86	-1.41	-11.01	-14.84
Return on Avg Stockholders' Equity %	n.a.	n.a.	n.a.	n.a.
Return on Average Assets %	11.25	-0.44	-3.61	-4.47
Current Ratio	4.57	1.53	0.88	n.a.
Debt / Equity %	n.a.	n.a.	n.a.	n.a.

Compound Growth %'s	EPS % n.a.	Net Income % n.a.	Total Revenues % -21.95

Comments

The exercise of the purchase option, referred to above, will result in the sale of all operating assets, the payment of income taxes, and the probable dissolution of the Company. The net earnings reported in 1996 is attributable to income tax benefits recorded in 1996 resulting from the use of tax loss carryovers to offset a portion of the income realized on the sale of properties in 1997. However, there was also a net cash flow from operations during the year. Investment Classification: Speculative

Officers	Position	Ownership Information	
Daniel R. Shaughnessy	Chairman, CEO	Number of Shares Outstanding	985,710
Edward A. Paul	Vice President, CFO	Market Capitalization	$ 26,860,598
Edward J. Gallagher	Other	Frequency of Dividends	Irregular
		Number of Shareholders	627

Other Information			
Transfer Agent	Chemical Mellon Shareholder Services	Where Listed	OTC-BB
Auditor	Ernst & Young LLP	Symbol	ALST
Market Maker	Carr Securities Corporation (800)221-2243	SIC Code	7011
	Hill Thompson Magid & Co., Inc (800)631-3083	Employees	6
Broker Dealer	Regular Stockbroker		

Alterman Investment Fund, Inc.

1218 W. Paces Ferry Road N.W., Suite 104   Atlanta, GA 30327   Telephone (404)237-9891   Fax (404)233-8076

Company Description

Alterman Investment Fund, Inc. is registered under the Investment Company Act of 1940 as a closed-end regulated investment company. The Company makes distributions to shareholders of at least 90% of its net investment income and all of its taxable net capital gains, thereby avoiding any income tax at the corporate level. The investment portfolio is comprised of municipal bonds.

	04/30/96	04/30/95
Per Share Information		
Stock Price as of 12/31	19.36	19.25
Earnings Per Share	1.48	1.24
Price / Earnings Ratio	13.08	15.52
Book Value Per Share	28.11	28.13
Price / Book Value %	68.87	68.43
Dividends Per Share	1.50	1.60
Annual Financial Data		
Operating Results (000's)		
Total Revenues	1,337.2	1,272.7
Costs & Expenses	-142.4	-136.7
Income Before Taxes and Other	1,163.8	975.6
Other Items	0.0	0.0
Income Tax	0.0	0.0
Net Income	1,163.8	975.6
Cash Flow From Operations	1,163.8	975.6
Balance Sheet (000's)		
Cash & Equivalents	27.8	11.3
Total Current Assets	423.9	413.4
Fixed Assets, Net	0.0	0.0
Total Assets	22,434.8	22,489.7
Total Current Liabilities	289.6	326.6
Long-Term Debt	0.0	0.0
Stockholders' Equity	22,145.2	22,163.1
Performance & Financial Condition		
Return on Total Revenues %	87.03	76.66
Return on Avg Stockholders' Equity %	5.25	n.a.
Return on Average Assets %	5.18	n.a.
Current Ratio	1.46	1.27
Debt / Equity %	n.a.	n.a.

Compound Growth %'s	EPS % n.a.	Net Income % n.a.	Total Revenues % n.a.

Comments

Expenses of administering and managing this portfolio approximate 0.63% of average net assets. The municipal bonds provide a tax-free yield that is very attractive. Compound growth rates are not meaningful because of the nature of the business and have not been displayed. Investment Classification: Income & Value

Officers	Position	Ownership Information	
Max Alterman	President	Number of Shares Outstanding	787,769
C H. Shepherd	Controller, Secretary	Market Capitalization	$ 15,251,208
		Frequency of Dividends	Quarterly
		Number of Shareholders	Under 500

Other Information

Transfer Agent	ChaseMellon Shareholder Services Ridgefield Park, NJ		Where Listed	OTC-BB
Auditor	Birnbrey, Minek & Minek LLC		Symbol	ALIF
Market Maker	Robinson-Humphrey Company Inc.	(800)241-0445	SIC Code	3790
	Howe Barnes Investments, Inc.	(800)621-2364	Employees	1
Broker Dealer	OTC Specialist			

Alydaar Software Corporation

2101 Rexford Road, Ste. 250W   Charlotte, NC 28211   Telephone (704)365-2324   Fax (704)365-5175

Company Description

Alydaar Software Corporation has essentially been a research and development company over the last three years. In 1995, it diverted all efforts to begin work on solving the Year 2000 Problem. Its first major client put the entire project in suspense for internal reasons. In the meantime, the Company positioned itself to bid on major contracts of this nature. In early December, 1996, the Company was awarded a $20 million contract. The Company began work on nine projects or pilots during the first quarter of 1997.

	12/31/96	12/31/95	12/31/94
Per Share Information			
Stock Price	11.42	1.75	1.62
Earnings Per Share	-0.41	-0.05	-0.03
Price / Earnings Ratio	n.a.	n.a.	n.a.
Book Value Per Share	0.0	-0.01	0.01
Price / Book Value %	n.a.	n.a.	n.a.
Dividends Per Share	0.0	0.0	0.0
Annual Financial Data			
Operating Results (000's)			
Total Revenues	69.5	231.0	160.4
Costs & Expenses	-5,202.3	-811.1	-465.4
Income Before Taxes and Other	-5,132.8	-580.1	-305.0
Other Items	0.0	0.0	0.0
Income Tax	0.0	0.0	0.0
Net Income	-5,132.8	-580.1	-305.0
Cash Flow From Operations	-2,635.6	-269.5	n.a.
Balance Sheet (000's)			
Cash & Equivalents	379.4	25.4	21.2
Total Current Assets	1,115.0	70.5	112.8
Fixed Assets, Net	1,694.0	55.0	44.4
Total Assets	2,869.3	133.2	160.0
Total Current Liabilities	2,842.0	253.3	53.4
Long-Term Debt	0.0	0.0	0.0
Stockholders' Equity	27.3	-120.1	106.6
Performance & Financial Condition			
Return on Total Revenues %	-7,388.05	-251.15	-190.13
Return on Avg Stockholders' Equity %	n.a.	n.a.	n.a.
Return on Average Assets %	-341.91	-395.73	n.a.
Current Ratio	0.39	0.28	2.11
Debt / Equity %	n.a.	n.a.	n.a.

Compound Growth %'s	EPS % n.a.	Net Income % n.a.	Total Revenues % -34.19

Comments

Management predicted a loss of $2 to $3 million range for the first quarter of 1997, an operating profit in the second quarter, a strongly profitable third quarter, and an improvement in the fourth quarter profitability as compared to the third quarter profit. As the Company had approximately $1.6 million more in accounts payable and accrued expenses than cash and accounts receivable at December 31, 1996, additional funding was required. The Company had subscriptions for common stock that would fund the Company until the projected cash flow materialized. Investment Classification: Speculative

Officers	Position	Ownership Information	
Robert F. Gruder	President, CEO	Number of Shares Outstanding	13,983,282
Frank G. Milligan	COO	Market Capitalization	$ 159,689,080
Thomas J. Dudchik	Senior VP	Frequency of Dividends	n.a.
V. Hollis Scott	CFO, Secretary	Number of Shareholders	n.a.
J. Alex McMillan	Other		

Other Information				
Transfer Agent	Fidelity Transfer Co. Salt Lake City, UT		Where Listed	OTC-BB
Auditor	Holtz Rubenstein & Co., LLP		Symbol	ALYD
Market Maker	Allen & Company, Inc.	(800)221-2246	SIC Code	7372
	Greenway Capital Corp.	(212)344-2297	Employees	70
Broker Dealer	Regular Stockbroker			

Amboy Bancorporation

3590 U.S. Highway 9 South   Old Bridge, NJ 08857   Telephone (908)591-8700   Fax (908)591-0726

Company Description

Amboy National Bank, the holding company's subsidiary, has been in existence since 1888. The Bank has been producing double digit returns on equity since 1964. It now offers a full range of banking services through its fourteen offices in Middlesex, Somerset and Mercer Counties of heavily populated central New Jersey, including the 1997 opening in Howell Township. Two other offices will be renovated during 1997. In 1996, their web site was added for all of us to take a look: (http://www.amboybank.com).

	12/31/96	12/31/95	12/31/94	12/31/93
Per Share Information				
Stock Price	57.25	50.50	45.00	40.00
Earnings Per Share	6.01	5.45	4.57	4.01
Price / Earnings Ratio	9.53	9.27	9.85	9.98
Book Value Per Share	40.60	35.75	30.56	27.23
Price / Book Value %	141.01	141.26	147.25	146.90
Dividends Per Share	1.06	1.58	0.80	0.74
Annual Financial Data				
Operating Results (000's)				
Net Interest Income	46,720.0	44,600.0	42,364.0	39,542.0
Loan Loss Provision	-2,500.0	-2,750.0	-3,000.0	-3,500.0
Non-Interest Income	1,974.0	2,443.0	3,030.0	3,962.0
Non-Interest Expense	-17,563.0	-18,205.0	-20,974.0	-19,961.0
Income Before Taxes and Other	28,631.0	26,088.0	21,420.0	20,043.0
Other Items	0.0	0.0	0.0	0.0
Income Tax	-9,700.0	-9,119.0	-7,450.0	-7,957.0
Net Income	18,931.0	16,969.0	13,970.0	12,086.0
Balance Sheet (000's)				
Cash & Securities	360,017.0	349,244.0	319,541.0	234,204.0
Loans, Net	670,399.0	650,736.0	647,250.0	632,505.0
Total Assets	1,076,215.0	1,044,373.0	1,013,763.0	915,094.0
Deposits	875,958.0	840,459.0	780,239.0	778,664.0
Stockholders' Equity	124,012.0	108,786.0	90,829.0	80,369.0
Performance & Financial Condition				
Return on Avg Stockholders' Equity %	16.26	17.00	16.32	16.03
Return on Average Assets %	1.79	1.65	1.45	1.35
Equity to Assets %	11.52	10.42	8.96	8.78
Net Interest Margin	n.a.	n.a.	n.a.	n.a.
Reserve as a % of Problem Loans	165.13	227.80	285.50	n.a.

Compound Growth %'s	EPS % 14.44	Net Income % 16.14	Net Interest Income % 5.72

Comments

Returns on assets and equity are some of the best that you will see in the banking sector, particularly with this degree of consistency. The annual report proudly displays a sampling of this data for the last thirty years. Growth in per share earnings is at a slightly lower rate than net income growth due to the exercise of employee stock options. The Bank declared a 3 for 2 split in 1995. All per share amounts have been adjusted for a consistent presentation. Investment Classification: Growth & Value

Officers	Position	Ownership Information	
George E. Scharph	President	Number of Shares Outstanding	3,054,859
Robert D. O'Donnell	Senior VP	Market Capitalization	$ 174,890,678
Peggy Ann Dembowski	Vice President, Head Cashier	Frequency of Dividends	Quarterly
Robert J. Babin	Vice President	Number of Shareholders	n.a.
Shirley M. Croasmun	Vice President	Where Listed / Symbol	OTC-BB / ABYB

Other Information			Loan Mix	%
Transfer Agent	Company Office		R/E Mortgages	95.1
Auditor	KPMG Peat Marwick LLP		Commerical	4.4
Market Maker	Ryan, Beck & Co.	(800)325-7926	Consumer	0.5
	Hill Thompson Magid & Co., Inc	(800)631-3083		
Broker Dealer	OTC Specialist			
	Frank Procopio - Ryan, Beck	(888)231-7226		

Amelco Corporation

19208 S. Vermont Avenue   Gardena, CA 90248   Telephone (310)327-3070   Fax (310)538-3417

Company Description

The Company was organized in 1967, to become the parent of existing operating companies. Through its subsidiaries, the Company engages in specialty construction work, primarily electrical and mechanical construction. Work is generally performed under fixed-price contracts and is undertaken by the Company alone, with subcontractors or in partnership with other contractors. Construction operations are conducted in the western continental U.S., Hawaii and Guam.

	09/30/96	09/30/95	09/30/94	09/30/93
Per Share Information				
Stock Price as of 12/31	4.25	2.50	2.75	3.13
Earnings Per Share	0.49	0.70	0.56	0.63
Price / Earnings Ratio	8.67	3.57	4.91	4.97
Book Value Per Share	10.57	10.23	9.63	9.22
Price / Book Value %	40.21	24.44	28.56	33.95
Dividends Per Share	0.15	0.10	0.15	0.25
Annual Financial Data				
Operating Results (000's)				
Total Revenues	116,220.0	126,611.0	114,504.0	95,882.0
Costs & Expenses	-114,893.0	-124,803.0	-113,021.0	-94,212.0
Income Before Taxes and Other	1,213.0	1,706.0	1,380.0	1,517.0
Other Items	-13.0	0.0	-31.0	20.0
Income Tax	-497.0	-691.0	-545.0	-627.0
Net Income	703.0	1,015.0	804.0	910.0
Cash Flow From Operations	1,250.0	899.0	-125.0	914.0
Balance Sheet (000's)				
Cash & Equivalents	3,841.0	3,863.0	2,690.0	3,406.0
Total Current Assets	34,037.0	38,126.0	35,441.0	24,185.0
Fixed Assets, Net	2,273.0	1,772.0	1,797.0	1,882.0
Total Assets	40,046.0	43,629.0	40,789.0	29,659.0
Total Current Liabilities	22,687.0	26,965.0	24,890.0	14,297.0
Long-Term Debt	2,079.0	1,863.0	1,911.0	1,956.0
Stockholders' Equity	15,252.0	14,767.0	13,896.0	13,309.0
Performance & Financial Condition				
Return on Total Revenues %	0.60	0.80	0.70	0.95
Return on Avg Stockholders' Equity %	4.68	7.08	5.91	6.98
Return on Average Assets %	1.68	2.40	2.28	3.14
Current Ratio	1.50	1.41	1.42	1.69
Debt / Equity %	13.63	12.62	13.75	14.70

Compound Growth %'s	EPS % -8.04	Net Income % -8.24	Total Revenues % 6.62

Comments

Total revenues declined which is attributable to a slow down of new construction activity in Hawaii. However, at September 30, 1996, the Company had a backlog of future construction work of $89.5 million, an amount slightly higher than that of the preceding year. Earnings for the first quarter of fiscal 1997 was $288,000, $.20 per share, as compared to $187,000, $.13 per share reported in 1996. Investment Classification: Value

Officers	Position	Ownership Information	
Samuel M. Angelich	President, CEO	Number of Shares Outstanding	1,443,088
Mark S. Angelich	Exec VP	Market Capitalization	$ 6,133,124
Patrick T. Miike	VP - Finance, Treasurer	Frequency of Dividends	Annual
John M. Carmack	Secretary	Number of Shareholders	294

Other Information

Transfer Agent	U.S. Stock Transfer Corporation Glendale, CA		Where Listed	OTC-BB
Auditor	KPMG Peat Marwick LLP		Symbol	AMLC
Market Maker	The Seidler Companies Inc.	(800)421-0164	SIC Code	1731
	Knight Securities L.P.	(800)232-3684	Employees	440
Broker Dealer	Regular Stockbroker			

American Atlantic Company

900 E. Eighth Avenue, Ste. 107   King of Prussia, PA 19406   Telephone (610)768-8020   Fax (610)768-8941

Company Description

The Company, formerly known as American Dredging Company, is in the process of liquidating. The dredging business constituted virtually all of the Company's revenue and expenses prior to 1993. The preferred stock of the Company was liquidated in 1994. The remaining assets are predominately $4 million in cash and a 617 acre property in an industrial complex in Logan Township, New Jersey.

	12/31/95	12/31/94	12/31/93
Per Share Information			
Stock Price as of 12/31	8.50	7.75	7.50
Earnings Per Share	1.11	2.38	4.12
Price / Earnings Ratio	7.66	3.26	1.82
Book Value Per Share	8.75	7.99	6.32
Price / Book Value %	97.14	97.00	118.67
Dividends Per Share	0.0	0.0	0.0
Annual Financial Data			
Operating Results (000's)			
Total Revenues	1,298.7	420.8	516.0
Costs & Expenses	-464.3	-425.1	-252.2
Income Before Taxes and Other	834.4	-4.4	263.8
Other Items	0.0	1,761.3	3,558.5
Income Tax	0.0	0.0	0.0
Net Income	834.4	1,757.0	3,822.3
Cash Flow From Operations	14.4	4,185.6	1,280.8
Balance Sheet (000's)			
Cash & Equivalents	4,370.9	3,689.2	12,116.9
Total Current Assets	4,490.5	3,969.3	15,951.7
Fixed Assets, Net	0.0	2,852.2	2,852.2
Total Assets	7,169.5	6,821.5	18,804.0
Total Current Liabilities	154.5	641.0	1,767.1
Long-Term Debt	0.0	0.0	0.0
Stockholders' Equity	7,015.0	6,180.6	17,036.9
Performance & Financial Condition			
Return on Total Revenues %	64.25	417.56	740.75
Return on Avg Stockholders' Equity %	12.65	15.13	23.89
Return on Average Assets %	11.93	13.71	22.22
Current Ratio	29.07	6.19	9.03
Debt / Equity %	n.a.	n.a.	n.a.

Compound Growth %'s	EPS % n.a.	Net Income % n.a.	Total Revenues % n.a.

Comments

1994 and 1993 results include income from discontinued operations of $1.8 million and $3.5 million, respectively. The property, which is recorded on the books at $2.7 million, is being offered for sale at an asking price of $8 million. It is part of the largest deep-water-access industrial facility on the East Coast. The 1996 annual report will be available in August, 1997. The stock price at December 31, 1996, was $10.37 per share. Investment Classification: Value & Speculative

Officers	Position	Ownership Information	
Christopher H. Browne	Chairman	Number of Shares Outstanding	801,346
Barry Doney	President	Market Capitalization	$ 6,811,441
		Frequency of Dividends	n.a.
		Number of Shareholders	Under 500

Other Information			
Transfer Agent	Company Office	Where Listed	OTC-BB
Auditor	Price Waterhouse LLP	Symbol	AMRL
Market Maker	Herzog, Heine, Geduld, Inc. (800)221-3600	SIC Code	6790
	Carr Securities Corporation (800)221-2243	Employees	2
Broker Dealer	Regular Stockbroker		

American Bio Medica Corporation

102 Simmons Road   Ancramdale, NY 12503   Telephone (518)329-4485   Fax (518)329-4156

Company Description

American Bio Medica has switched from the business of marketing educational books, software and audiovisual materials to the business of acquiring, developing and marketing biomedical technologies and products. Despite its inception in 1986, it is still considered a developmental stage company. The Company currently owns two technologies for screening drugs of abuse, a workplace screening test and a preliminary test for use by laboratories. During the quarter ended January 31, 1997, the Company started commercial production of its drug test kits and has what management maintains are adequate resources to fund its continuing operations.

	04/30/96	04/30/95
Per Share Information		
Stock Price as of 12/31	3.62	0.62
Earnings Per Share	-0.08	-0.02
Price / Earnings Ratio	n.a.	n.a.
Book Value Per Share	0.03	-0.07
Price / Book Value %	12,066.67	n.a.
Dividends Per Share	0.0	0.0
Annual Financial Data		
Operating Results (000's)		
Total Revenues	158.5	148.0
Costs & Expenses	-1,154.9	-453.4
Income Before Taxes and Other	-996.5	-305.3
Other Items	0.0	0.0
Income Tax	0.0	0.0
Net Income	-996.5	-305.3
Cash Flow From Operations	-460.0	-381.2
Balance Sheet (000's)		
Cash & Equivalents	437.5	82.8
Total Current Assets	494.3	198.1
Fixed Assets, Net	20.6	24.6
Total Assets	646.0	427.3
Total Current Liabilities	165.2	653.3
Long-Term Debt	126.5	126.5
Stockholders' Equity	354.2	-566.5
Performance & Financial Condition		
Return on Total Revenues %	-628.83	-206.25
Return on Avg Stockholders' Equity %	n.a.	n.a.
Return on Average Assets %	-185.69	n.a.
Current Ratio	2.99	0.30
Debt / Equity %	35.71	n.a.

Compound Growth %'s	EPS %	n.a.	Net Income %	n.a.	Total Revenues %	7.04

Comments

Management estimates that total revenues for the twelve month period beginning November 1, 1996, will be $7.6 million. (We will find out who is smoking what real soon.) Additional capitalization has cleansed the balance sheet which, as of January 31, 1997, has $3.3 in cash equivalents and no debts. Investment Classification: Speculative

Officers	Position	Ownership Information	
Stan Cipkowski	President, Treasurer	Number of Shares Outstanding	12,089,561
Edmund Jaskiewicz	Exec VP, Secretary	Market Capitalization	$ 43,764,211
Jay Bendis	Vice President	Frequency of Dividends	n.a.
Henry J. Wells	Vice President	Number of Shareholders	n.a.

Other Information

Transfer Agent	United Stock Transfer, Inc. Englewood, CO		Where Listed	OTC-BB
Auditor	Thomas P. Monahan, C.P.A.		Symbol	ABMI
Market Maker	Kalb, Voorhis & Co.	(800)223-3530	SIC Code	3829
	L.B. Saks Inc.	(800)269-7402	Employees	n.a.
Broker Dealer	Regular Stockbroker			

American Financial Enterprises, Inc.

One East Fourth Street   Cincinnati, OH 45202   Telephone (513)579-2172   Fax (513)579-2580

Company Description

American Financial Enterprises, Inc. is a holding company with interests in three other companies. American Financial Group, Inc. (13% common stock ownership) operates in a variety of financial businesses, including property and casualty insurance and annuities. American Annuity Group, Inc. (10% common stock ownership) is engaged principally in the sale of tax-deferred annuities and certain life and health insurance. Citicaster Inc. (13% common stock ownership) operates 19 radio stations and two network-affiliated television stations in major markets throughout the United States. The Company is 83% owned by American Financial Corporation.

	12/31/95	12/31/94	12/31/93
Per Share Information			
Stock Price as of 12/31	23.12	22.25	25.00
Earnings Per Share	1.57	0.32	3.21
Price / Earnings Ratio	14.73	69.53	7.79
Book Value Per Share	28.89	25.45	26.50
Price / Book Value %	80.03	87.43	94.34
Dividends Per Share	0.55	0.45	0.05
Annual Financial Data			
Operating Results (000's)			
Total Revenues	32,053.0	5,196.0	78,773.0
Costs & Expenses	-3,018.0	-2,745.0	-12,849.0
Income Before Taxes and Other	29,035.0	2,451.0	65,924.0
Other Items	0.0	0.0	0.0
Income Tax	-8,123.0	1,759.0	-23,250.0
Net Income	20,912.0	4,210.0	42,674.0
Cash Flow From Operations	7,539.0	7,088.0	-5,385.0
Balance Sheet (000's)			
Cash & Equivalents	506.0	275.0	n.a.
Total Current Assets	506.0	275.0	n.a.
Fixed Assets, Net	0.0	0.0	n.a.
Total Assets	465,247.0	390,396.0	n.a.
Total Current Liabilities	975.0	1,027.0	n.a.
Long-Term Debt	0.0	16,000.0	n.a.
Stockholders' Equity	384,037.0	338,235.0	n.a.
Performance & Financial Condition			
Return on Total Revenues %	65.24	81.02	54.17
Return on Avg Stockholders' Equity %	5.79	1.22	13.01
Return on Average Assets %	4.89	1.05	9.50
Current Ratio	0.52	0.27	n.a.
Debt / Equity %	n.a.	4.73	n.a.

Compound Growth %'s	EPS % -30.06	Net Income % -30.00	Total Revenues % -36.21

Comments

The Company's results are directly attributable to the financial performance of the companies in which interests are held. American Financial Group, Inc. is the same company that owns 97% of New York and Harlem Railroad Company, also featured in this manual. The price of the Company's shares was $27 at December 31, 1996, but the financial statements were not yet available when we went to press. Investment Classification: Value

Officers	Position	Ownership Information	
Carl H. Linder	Chairman, President	Number of Shares Outstanding	13,291,117
James C. Kennedy	Secretary	Market Capitalization	$ 307,290,625
James E. Evans	Vice President	Frequency of Dividends	Quarterly
Fred J. Runk	Vice President, Treasurer	Number of Shareholders	500
Thomas E. Mischell	Vice President		

Other Information			
Transfer Agent	Securities Transfer Company Cincinnati, OH	Where Listed	PSE
Auditor	Ernst & Young LLP	Symbol	AFEP
Market Maker	None	SIC Code	6700
		Employees	6
Broker Dealer	Regular Stockbroker		

American Industrial Loan Association

3420 Holland Road, Ste. 107   Virginia Beach, VA 23452   Telephone (804)430-1400   Fax (804)430-1978

Company Description

American Industrial Loan Association is primarily engaged in wholesale loan originations and sales of non-conforming residential mortgages, including servicing rights to other investors. Business is conducted primarily in the states of Maryland, Georgia, Virginia, Illinois, Indiana, Wisconsin, Tennessee, Ohio, North Carolina, South Carolina, Florida and the District of Columbia. In 1994, the Company acquired an 11% interest in a joint venture which originates non-conforming residential mortgages at retail locations. American Industrial was founded in 1952.

	12/31/95	12/31/94	12/31/93	12/31/92
Per Share Information				
Stock Price	15.50	8.00	10.50	6.25
Earnings Per Share	1.82	0.79	1.70	1.53
Price / Earnings Ratio	8.52	10.13	6.18	4.08
Book Value Per Share	10.28	8.94	8.46	7.08
Price / Book Value %	150.78	89.49	124.11	88.28
Dividends Per Share	0.32	0.32	0.31	0.30
Annual Financial Data				
Operating Results (000's)				
Total Revenues	11,898.5	5,540.0	6,206.6	6,518.5
Costs & Expenses	-9,515.4	-4,682.3	-4,369.1	-5,052.1
Income Before Taxes and Other	2,109.4	857.7	1,837.4	1,466.4
Other Items	-66.4	3.0	0.0	0.0
Income Tax	-876.3	-360.0	-760.7	-584.0
Net Income	1,166.7	500.7	1,076.7	882.4
Cash Flow From Operations	-7,871.9	-518.6	6,539.2	-1,940.6
Balance Sheet (000's)				
Cash & Equivalents	784.1	405.5	1,398.5	n.a.
Total Current Assets	943.7	405.5	1,398.5	n.a.
Fixed Assets, Net	1,411.1	1,036.3	999.1	n.a.
Total Assets	34,485.4	23,109.4	21,662.9	n.a.
Total Current Liabilities	692.5	278.2	40.9	n.a.
Long-Term Debt	0.0	0.0	0.0	n.a.
Stockholders' Equity	6,235.7	5,644.6	5,371.6	n.a.
Performance & Financial Condition				
Return on Total Revenues %	9.81	9.04	17.35	13.54
Return on Avg Stockholders' Equity %	19.64	9.09	21.83	25.03
Return on Average Assets %	4.05	2.24	n.a.	n.a.
Current Ratio	1.36	1.46	34.18	n.a.
Debt / Equity %	n.a.	n.a.	n.a.	n.a.

Compound Growth %'s	EPS %	5.96	Net Income %	9.76	Total Revenues %	22.21

Comments

With a favorable economic climate and low interest rates, the Company recorded record revenues and income during 1995. The increase in net income came primarily from the increase in loan origination volume and the increased premiums received on the sale of those loans. The joint venture produced $595,818 and $231,027 of income in 1995 and 1994, respectively. The 1996 results were not available when we went to press but are available by calling the Company. Investment Classification: Value

Officers	Position	Ownership Information	
Allen D. Wykle	President, CEO	Number of Shares Outstanding	606,680
Stanley W. Broaddus	Vice President, Secretary	Market Capitalization	$ 9,403,540
		Frequency of Dividends	Quarterly
		Number of Shareholders	Under 500

Other Information				
Transfer Agent	Registrar & Transfer Company Cranford, NJ		Where Listed	OTC-BB
Auditor	Coopers & Lybrand LLP		Symbol	AILY
Market Maker	Anderson & Strudwick, Inc.	(800)827-2515	SIC Code	6090
	Scott & Stringfellow, Inc.	(800)446-7074	Employees	n.a.
Broker Dealer	Regular Stockbroker			

American Mart Corporation

680 N. Lake Shore Dr., 19th FL   Chicago, IL 60611-4402   Telephone (312)943-7000   Fax (312)943-9017

Company Description

American Mart Corporation is primarily involved with wholesale liquor distribution. Through subsidiary entities, the Company is also involved with commercial real estate and the Bismarck Hotel property, also included in this manual. The Wirtz family of Chicago is a majority stockholder.

	06/30/95	06/30/94
Per Share Information		
Stock Price as of 12/31	70.50	46.00
Earnings Per Share	15.48	5.86
Price / Earnings Ratio	4.55	7.85
Book Value Per Share	125.97	110.49
Price / Book Value %	55.97	41.63
Dividends Per Share	0.0	0.0
Annual Financial Data		
Operating Results (000's)		
Total Revenues	71,657.2	65,667.0
Costs & Expenses	-66,356.7	-62,943.6
Income Before Taxes and Other	5,300.5	2,533.1
Other Items	0.0	0.0
Income Tax	-1,118.8	-949.4
Net Income	4,181.7	1,583.7
Cash Flow From Operations	3,948.1	7,463.7
Balance Sheet (000's)		
Cash & Equivalents	4,807.3	5,101.9
Total Current Assets	21,465.0	19,621.1
Fixed Assets, Net	1,839.3	1,705.8
Total Assets	48,797.3	42,974.3
Total Current Liabilities	10,040.8	8,422.4
Long-Term Debt	4,720.4	4,697.6
Stockholders' Equity	34,036.1	29,854.4
Performance & Financial Condition		
Return on Total Revenues %	5.84	2.41
Return on Avg Stockholders' Equity %	13.09	n.a.
Return on Average Assets %	9.11	n.a.
Current Ratio	2.14	2.33
Debt / Equity %	13.87	15.74

Compound Growth %'s	EPS % n.a.	Net Income % n.a.	Total Revenues % 9.12

Comments

On November 19, 1996, the Company announced the sale of the Bismarck Hotel for $20.5 million. This will end years of cash drain to the Company as it never succeeded in making the operation profitable. Although the shareholders of Bismarck won't end up with much, the Company will be repaid $7.5 million in advances. Although there is the possibility that the proceeds will be used by Bismarck in a like-kind exchange, a Company spokesperson thought that was unlikely. In any case, that decision is in the hands of the Wirtz family. We were not able to obtain the 1996 report. Investment Classification: Value

Officers	Position	Ownership Information	
William Wirtz	Chairman, CEO	Number of Shares Outstanding	270,188
		Market Capitalization	$ 19,048,254
		Frequency of Dividends	n.a.
		Number of Shareholders	Under 500

Other Information				
Transfer Agent	Company Office		Where Listed	OTC-BB
Auditor	Kupferberg, Goldberg & Neimark		Symbol	AMRT
Market Maker	Robotti & Co., Inc.	(212)986-0800	SIC Code	5180
	Howe Barnes Investments, Inc.	(800)621-2364	Employees	n.a.
Broker Dealer	OTC Specialist			
	Tom Doherty - Robotti & Co.	(212)986-0800		

American Public Life Insurance Company

P.O. Box 925   Jackson, MS 39205-0925   Telephone (601)936-6600   Fax (601)939-0655

Company Description

American Public Life insurance Company offers a diversified line of insurance products including cancer, general health, disability and dental. The Company is licensed and operates in 21 states. Although the Company executed a 1 for 20 reverse split in 1986, virtually destroying liquidity for its shareholders, it has now formed a holding company with the stated intention of registering with the Securities and Exchange Commission and, eventually, listing its shares on the NASDAQ.

	12/31/96	12/31/95	12/31/94	12/31/93
Per Share Information				
Stock Price	162.25	145.00	101.00	95.00
Earnings Per Share	12.83	8.03	12.70	30.01
Price / Earnings Ratio	12.65	18.06	7.95	3.17
Book Value Per Share	176.79	180.34	170.10	152.59
Price / Book Value %	91.78	80.40	59.38	62.26
Dividends Per Share	4.70	4.70	4.70	5.16
Annual Financial Data				
Operating Results (000's)				
Total Revenues	28,822.6	28,096.3	26,656.0	23,766.3
Costs & Expenses	-27,895.0	-27,533.7	-25,605.0	-21,436.9
Income Before Taxes and Other	927.5	562.6	1,051.0	2,329.5
Other Items	0.0	0.0	0.0	0.0
Income Tax	-249.4	-131.6	-313.2	-585.3
Net Income	678.2	431.1	737.9	1,744.2
Cash Flow From Operations	n.a.	n.a.	n.a.	n.a.
Balance Sheet (000's)				
Cash & Equivalents	596.7	312.6	1,801.7	4,288.6
Total Current Assets	596.7	312.6	1,801.7	4,288.6
Fixed Assets, Net	2,786.4	2,773.5	0.0	0.0
Total Assets	39,411.6	38,273.7	37,489.0	35,845.7
Total Current Liabilities	0.0	0.0	0.0	0.0
Long-Term Debt	0.0	0.0	0.0	0.0
Stockholders' Equity	9,342.1	9,682.7	9,885.3	8,867.7
Performance & Financial Condition				
Return on Total Revenues %	2.35	1.53	2.77	7.34
Return on Avg Stockholders' Equity %	7.13	4.41	7.87	21.20
Return on Average Assets %	1.75	1.14	2.01	5.02
Current Ratio	n.a.	n.a.	n.a.	n.a.
Debt / Equity %	n.a.	n.a.	n.a.	n.a.

Compound Growth %'s	EPS %	-24.67	Net Income %	-27.01	Total Revenues %	6.64

Comments

New management has taken the helm during 1995 and is in the process of re-evaluating all administrative functions as well as market definition, focus and new product development. The Company continues to diversify its product lines and is less dependent on cancer insurance. There is no indication that the financial results have been audited. What is even more confusing is the presentation of the financial statement for American Public Holdings, Inc., which shows a book value of $307.13 per share as compared to $176.79 per share for the Company. Could it be that the new numbers are prepared under generally accepted accounting principles which would be required by the S.E.C.? Will the real financial statements please stand out. Investment Classification: Value

Officers	Position	Ownership Information	
Johnny H. Williamson	President, CEO	Number of Shares Outstanding	52,842
Jerry C. Stovall	Exec VP	Market Capitalization	$ 8,573,615
Frank K. Junkin, Jr.	Senior VP	Frequency of Dividends	Quarterly
Joseph C. Hartley, Jr.	Senior VP, Secretary	Number of Shareholders	Under 500
Alison James, Jr.	Vice President		

Other Information

Transfer Agent	First National Bank of Jackson Jackson, MS		Where Listed	OTC-BB
Auditor	Not indicated		Symbol	APUB
Market Maker	J.C. Bradford & Co.	(800)251-1740	SIC Code	6311
	Hill Thompson Magid & Co., Inc	(800)631-3083	Employees	75
Broker Dealer	OTC Specialist			

American River Holdings

1545 River Park Dr., Suite 107 Sacramento, CA 95815 Telephone (916)565-6100 Fax (916)641-1262

Company Description

American River Holdings is the parent company of American River Bank. The Bank is a regional bank with four branches serving the greater Sacramento, California area. Sacramento, with 1.7 million people, sits at the crossroads of an interstate freeway system, and has a major airport, a deep water port, two rivers, and it is quickly developing into a cargo and transportation hub. The Bank was formed in 1983 and had 52 consecutive quarters of earnings through December 31, 1996.

	12/31/96	12/31/95	12/31/94	12/31/93
Per Share Information				
Stock Price	13.50	11.25	8.35	8.00
Earnings Per Share	1.47	1.51	1.16	0.89
Price / Earnings Ratio	9.18	7.45	7.20	8.99
Book Value Per Share	11.98	10.73	9.20	8.59
Price / Book Value %	112.69	104.85	90.76	93.13
Dividends Per Share	0.27	0.26	0.25	0.25
Annual Financial Data				
Operating Results (000's)				
Net Interest Income	7,351.0	7,195.0	6,234.0	3,537.0
Loan Loss Provision	-490.0	-420.0	-300.0	-241.0
Non-Interest Income	968.0	1,272.0	1,000.0	1,325.0
Non-Interest Expense	-5,134.0	-5,249.0	-4,906.0	-3,202.0
Income Before Taxes and Other	2,695.0	2,798.0	2,028.0	1,419.0
Other Items	0.0	0.0	0.0	52.0
Income Tax	-1,034.0	-1,153.0	-833.0	-571.0
Net Income	1,661.0	1,645.0	1,195.0	900.0
Balance Sheet (000's)				
Cash & Securities	43,215.0	34,085.0	26,704.0	23,253.0
Loans, Net	89,527.0	90,986.0	82,570.0	74,763.0
Total Assets	136,326.0	134,496.0	120,181.0	111,869.0
Deposits	122,065.0	122,233.0	109,528.0	102,468.0
Stockholders' Equity	12,839.0	11,455.0	9,820.0	8,656.0
Performance & Financial Condition				
Return on Avg Stockholders' Equity %	13.67	15.46	12.94	10.80
Return on Average Assets %	1.23	1.29	1.03	0.96
Equity to Assets %	9.42	8.52	8.17	7.74
Net Interest Margin	n.a.	n.a.	n.a.	n.a.
Reserve as a % of Problem Loans	99.24	239.76	370.74	5,254.17

Compound Growth %'s	EPS %	18.21	Net Income %	22.66	Net Interest Income %	27.62

Comments

The Bank seems to benefit from the winning combination of a strong local economy and housing market, good management and satisfied customers. A recent annual survey showed 97% overall client satisfaction. The Bank does an excellent job in keeping investors informed with interesting quarterly reports as well as the detailed annual which, among other items, discloses the overall shareholder return including appreciation and dividends. It was 22% in 1996. Investment Classification: Value & Growth

Officers	Position	Ownership Information	
William L. Young	President, CEO	Number of Shares Outstanding	1,072,053
David T. Taber	Exec VP, COO	Market Capitalization	$ 14,472,716
Bill Badham	Senior VP	Frequency of Dividends	Semi-Annual
Mitchell A. Derenzo	Senior VP, CFO	Number of Shareholders	400
Douglas E. Tow	Senior VP	Where Listed / Symbol	OTC-BB / AMRB

Other Information		Loan Mix	%
Transfer Agent	U.S. Stock Transfer Corporation Glendale, CA	R/E Mortgages	64.8
Auditor	Perry-Smith & Co.	Commerical	29.8
Market Maker	Hoefer & Arnett, Incorporated (800)346-5544	Construction	3.2
	Sutro & Co., Incorporated (800)227-4422	Consumer	2.2
Broker Dealer	Regular Stockbroker		

American Tire Corporation

446 West Lake Street   Ravenna, OH 44266   Telephone (330)296-8778   Fax (330)296-9787

Company Description

American Tire Company was organized in 1995 to take advantage of existing proprietary and non-proprietary technology available for the manufacturing of specialty tires. The Company is currently in a developmental stage and intends to engage in the manufacturing, marketing, distribution, and sales of airless "specialty" tires and tire-wheel assemblies. Initially, the Company will manufacture airless bicycle tires. The Company sold 344,083 common shares in an initial public offering during 1996 at $6 per share.

	12/31/96	06/30/96	06/30/95
Per Share Information			
Stock Price	6.12	6.00	1.00
Earnings Per Share	-0.09	-0.16	-0.06
Price / Earnings Ratio	n.a.	n.a.	n.a.
Book Value Per Share	0.35	0.07	0.16
Price / Book Value %	1,748.57	8,571.43	625.00
Dividends Per Share	0.0	0.0	0.0
Annual Financial Data			
Operating Results (000's)			
Total Revenues	7.5	7.2	3.6
Costs & Expenses	-394.2	-604.3	-252.2
Income Before Taxes and Other	-386.7	-597.1	-248.6
Other Items	0.0	0.0	0.0
Income Tax	0.0	0.0	0.0
Net Income	-386.7	-597.1	-248.6
Cash Flow From Operations	-405.7	n.a.	-300.4
Balance Sheet (000's)			
Cash & Equivalents	634.3	4.5	92.7
Total Current Assets	929.6	278.8	377.1
Fixed Assets, Net	610.6	483.4	380.8
Total Assets	1,542.8	921.1	834.6
Total Current Liabilities	68.9	664.3	232.9
Long-Term Debt	0.0	0.0	0.0
Stockholders' Equity	1,473.9	256.8	601.7
Performance & Financial Condition			
Return on Total Revenues %	-5,170.23	-8,338.08	-6,885.35
Return on Avg Stockholders' Equity %	n.a.	-139.10	n.a.
Return on Average Assets %	n.a.	-68.02	n.a.
Current Ratio	13.49	0.42	1.62
Debt / Equity %	n.a.	n.a.	n.a.

Compound Growth %'s	EPS % n.a.	Net Income % n.a.	Total Revenues % n.a.

Comments

The period ended June 30, 1995 is a partial year that began on January 30, 1995. The period ended December 31, 1996, is for the six months since June 30, 1996. The fact that there are over four million shares of stock outstanding before a product has been introduced makes this the kind of investment to avoid unless you have personal contact with management. Investment Classification: Speculative

Officers	Position	Ownership Information	
Richard Steinke	Chairman, CEO	Number of Shares Outstanding	4,176,748
Dennis S. Chrobak	President	Market Capitalization	$ 25,561,698
Philip J. Chrobak	Secretary	Frequency of Dividends	n.a.
David K. Griffiths	Treasurer, Controller	Number of Shareholders	n.a.
Gary Dalton	VP - Sales		

Other Information				
Transfer Agent	Interwest Transfer Co., Inc. Salt Lake City, UT		Where Listed	OTC-BB
Auditor	Saltz, Shamis & Goldfarb, Inc.		Symbol	ATRY
Market Maker	Alpine Securities Corporation	(800)521-5588	SIC Code	3010
	Neuberger & Berman	(800)543-8481	Employees	n.a.
Broker Dealer	Regular Stockbroker			

Americold Corporation

7007 S.W. Cardinal Lane, Suite 125   Portland, OR 97224-7140   Telephone (503)624-8585   Fax (503)598-8610

Company Description

Americold, the nation's largest supplier of public refrigerated warehouse space, provides integrated logistics services for the frozen food industry consisting of warehousing and transportation management. These services are provided through a nationwide network of 49 owned or leased refrigerated warehouse facilities in 17 states and through a refrigerated transportation management unit. The Company reorganized under Chapter 11 of the Bankruptcy Code in 1995. Net sales to H.J. Heinz, its largest customer, were $45.5 million in 1997 comprising 14.7% of total sales. The Company was founded in 1911.

	02/28/97	02/28/96	02/28/95	02/28/94
Per Share Information				
Stock Price as of 12/31	14.00	14.00	10.00	3.50
Earnings Per Share	-1.46	-2.13	1.00	-16.00
Price / Earnings Ratio	n.a.	n.a.	10.00	n.a.
Book Value Per Share	-21.89	-21.78	-21.10	-20.51
Price / Book Value %	n.a.	n.a.	n.a.	n.a.
Dividends Per Share	0.0	0.0	0.0	0.0
Annual Financial Data				
Operating Results (000's)				
Total Revenues	311,699.0	280,396.0	234,783.0	200,324.0
Costs & Expenses	-319,588.0	-283,594.0	-222,716.0	-211,297.0
Income Before Taxes and Other	-9,144.0	-11,506.0	10,791.0	-12,222.0
Other Items	0.0	-1,794.0	0.0	-66,082.0
Income Tax	2,604.0	3,426.0	-5,227.0	1,183.0
Net Income	-6,540.0	-9,874.0	5,564.0	-77,121.0
Cash Flow From Operations	18,858.0	12,560.0	12,684.0	18,476.0
Balance Sheet (000's)				
Cash & Equivalents	13,702.0	20,857.0	33,163.0	3,892.0
Total Current Assets	51,755.0	58,297.0	61,992.0	34,836.0
Fixed Assets, Net	384,484.0	375,851.0	367,248.0	375,772.0
Total Assets	531,034.0	526,992.0	544,595.0	528,703.0
Total Current Liabilities	64,285.0	55,092.0	76,910.0	42,293.0
Long-Term Debt	465,834.0	461,667.0	442,912.0	467,337.0
Stockholders' Equity	-107,956.0	-101,669.0	-91,958.0	-97,229.0
Performance & Financial Condition				
Return on Total Revenues %	-2.10	-3.52	2.37	-38.50
Return on Avg Stockholders' Equity %	n.a.	n.a.	n.a.	n.a.
Return on Average Assets %	-1.24	-1.84	1.04	-15.14
Current Ratio	0.81	1.06	0.81	0.82
Debt / Equity %	n.a.	n.a.	n.a.	n.a.

Compound Growth %'s	EPS % n.a.	Net Income % n.a.	Total Revenues % 15.88

Comments

After a serious fire in 1992, the Company has been regaining financial strength. Long-term debt was successfully restructured during this last year and the Chapter 11 proceedings allowed the renegotiation of some unfavorable warehouse leases. The business is largely managed by total revenues and cash flows as depreciation expenses typically produce red ink. Investment Classification: Speculative

Officers	Position	Ownership Information	
Ronald H. Dykehouse	President, CEO	Number of Shares Outstanding	4,931,194
John P. Lenevue	Exec VP	Market Capitalization	$ 69,036,716
F. Stanley F. Sena	Exec VP	Frequency of Dividends	n.a.
Joel M. Smith	Senior VP, CFO	Number of Shareholders	82
J. Roy Coxe	Senior VP		

Other Information

Transfer Agent	Company Office		Where Listed	Order Matching Only
Auditor	KPMG Peat Marwick LLP		Symbol	n.a.
Market Maker	Dabney/Resnick Inc.	(310)246-3700	SIC Code	4222
			Employees	1889
Broker Dealer	None			

Ammonia Hold, Inc.

P.O. Box 25403   Little Rock, AR 72221   Telephone (501)676-2994   Fax (501)676-5274

Company Description

Ammonia Hold, Inc. is a manufacturer of odor-eliminating products for consumer and industrial markets. The core product uses a monocalcium phosphate base blended with trace minerals and other inert ingredients to counter the natural formation of ammonia that occurs when animal wastes are exposed to oxygen. On April 30, 1997, the Company announced that it had received regulatory approval to start phase II testing of its products which could cut the cost and speed up the process of composting municipal biosolids. Ammonia Hold was founded in 1990.

	06/30/96	06/30/95	06/30/94
Per Share Information			
Stock Price as of 12/31	5.62	5.50	6.50
Earnings Per Share	0.0	0.01	-0.05
Price / Earnings Ratio	n.a.	550.00	n.a.
Book Value Per Share	0.40	0.15	0.14
Price / Book Value %	1,405.00	3,666.67	4,642.86
Dividends Per Share	n.a.	0.0	0.0
Annual Financial Data			
Operating Results (000's)			
Total Revenues	841.4	704.5	506.7
Costs & Expenses	-830.5	-661.3	-582.4
Income Before Taxes and Other	10.9	43.2	-75.7
Other Items	0.0	0.0	0.0
Income Tax	-2.2	-9.0	0.0
Net Income	8.7	34.2	-75.7
Cash Flow From Operations	n.a.	n.a.	n.a.
Balance Sheet (000's)			
Cash & Equivalents	349.5	28.4	n.a.
Total Current Assets	708.6	234.6	n.a.
Fixed Assets, Net	221.8	28.4	n.a.
Total Assets	1,581.0	553.9	n.a.
Total Current Liabilities	34.2	50.9	n.a.
Long-Term Debt	0.0	0.0	n.a.
Stockholders' Equity	1,546.8	503.1	n.a.
Performance & Financial Condition			
Return on Total Revenues %	1.03	4.85	-14.94
Return on Avg Stockholders' Equity %	0.85	n.a.	n.a.
Return on Average Assets %	0.81	n.a.	n.a.
Current Ratio	20.70	4.61	n.a.
Debt / Equity %	n.a.	n.a.	n.a.

Compound Growth %'s	EPS % n.a.	Net Income % n.a.	Total Revenues % 28.86

Comments

The Company has made it through its development stage in good financial condition except there are a lot of shares outstanding. It remains to be seen if the live-stock pen products can be turned into cash cows. Management did report sales for the six months ended December 31, 1996, of $635,075 which is nearly the same as the whole year of fiscal 1996. We were skeptical of the report that retail distribution currently includes over 1,900 Wal-Mart stores, 200 international outlets, PETCO and Target. The president explained that the Wal-Mart relationship has existed for four years and that the product requires very little shelf space. Investment Classification: Speculative

Officers	Position	Ownership Information	
Michael D. Parnell	President, CEO	Number of Shares Outstanding	3,867,278
Dan N. Thompson	CFO	Market Capitalization	$ 21,734,102
Jeffrey England	Other	Frequency of Dividends	n.a.
Robert Ligon	Other	Number of Shareholders	n.a.
Eugene England	Other		

Other Information

Transfer Agent	Atlas Stock Transfer Corp. Salt Lake City, UT		Where Listed	OTC-BB
Auditor	Crouch, Bierwolf & Chisholm		Symbol	AMHD
Market Maker	Sharpe Capital Inc.	(800)355-5781	SIC Code	2890
	S.W. Ryan & Company Inc.	(610)668-8241	Employees	n.a.
Broker Dealer	Regular Stockbroker			

Anchorage, The First National Bank of

646 West 4th Avenue   Anchorage, AK 99510-0720   Telephone (907)276-6300   Fax (907)265-3528

Company Description

The First National Bank of Anchorage is a full service bank and also provides trust, escrow, contract collection and Bank Card services through its twenty-eight branches throughout the state of Alaska. We received a chilly reception on our first contact with the Bank but then received information from both the Bank and one of its shareholders. An investor who purchased one share of stock for $100 on the Bank's formation in 1922 would today have 400 shares worth $640,000 and would have received $142,895 in dividends through December 31, 1996.

	12/31/96	12/31/95	12/31/94	12/31/93
Per Share Information				
Stock Price	1,605.00	1,530.00	1,500.00	1,865.00
Earnings Per Share	163.02	138.58	137.17	175.23
Price / Earnings Ratio	9.85	11.04	10.94	10.64
Book Value Per Share	1,772.59	1,681.46	1,497.64	1,401.36
Price / Book Value %	90.55	90.99	100.16	133.09
Dividends Per Share	50.00	40.00	40.00	24.00
Annual Financial Data				
Operating Results (000's)				
Net Interest Income	76,237.0	70,467.0	68,095.0	71,389.0
Loan Loss Provision	-1,286.0	-875.0	-773.0	-1,453.0
Non-Interest Income	19,993.0	18,323.0	18,224.0	22,723.0
Non-Interest Expense	-50,534.0	-51,361.0	-50,043.0	-44,658.0
Income Before Taxes and Other	44,410.0	36,554.0	35,503.0	48,001.0
Other Items	0.0	0.0	0.0	0.0
Income Tax	-11,806.0	-8,839.0	-8,069.0	-12,955.0
Net Income	32,604.0	27,715.0	27,434.0	35,046.0
Balance Sheet (000's)				
Cash & Securities	794,197.0	834,811.0	873,169.0	840,796.0
Loans, Net	577,904.0	549,902.0	505,202.0	450,751.0
Total Assets	1,440,421.0	1,437,172.0	1,429,533.0	1,334,655.0
Deposits	902,506.0	946,973.0	970,255.0	920,141.0
Stockholders' Equity	354,517.0	336,292.0	299,528.0	280,271.0
Performance & Financial Condition				
Return on Avg Stockholders' Equity %	9.44	8.72	9.46	13.22
Return on Average Assets %	2.27	1.93	1.98	2.65
Equity to Assets %	24.61	23.40	20.95	21.00
Net Interest Margin	n.a.	n.a.	n.a.	n.a.
Reserve as a % of Problem Loans	166.62	86.90	62.82	68.21

Compound Growth %'s	EPS %	-2.38	Net Income %	-2.38	Net Interest Income %	2.21

Comments

Management attributes improved results to the substantial reinvestment of a maturing loan portfolio into a growing loan portfolio and into higher yielding bonds. Increases are also the result of decisions to aggressively hold down operating expenses. The Bank has still not returned to the level of profits that it demonstrated in 1993 and 1992, which may be the explanation of the drop in price per share. However, investors have good reason to feel secure with this conservative behemoth of the Alaskan landscape. Investment Classification: Value

Officers	Position	Ownership Information	
D.H. Cuddy	Chairman, President	Number of Shares Outstanding	200,000
Betsy Lawer	COO	Market Capitalization	$ 321,000,000
Richard Enberg	Exec VP	Frequency of Dividends	Quarterly
David Lawer	Senior VP	Number of Shareholders	701
Doug Longacre	Senior VP	Where Listed / Symbol	OTC-BB / FNAN

Other Information			Loan Mix	%
Transfer Agent	Company Office		R/E Mortgages	60.0
Auditor	Deloitte & Touche LLP		Commerical	22.3
Market Maker	Ragen MacKenzie Incorporated	(800)426-5964	Construction	8.0
	Hill Thompson Magid & Co., Inc	(800)631-3083	Consumer	7.8
Broker Dealer	Regular Stockbroker		Other	1.9
	Standard Investment	(888)783-4688 Ext: Jack		

Anderson-Tully Company

P.O. Box 28   Memphis, TN 38101   Telephone (901)576-1400   Fax (901)526-8842

Company Description

Anderson-Tully Company, founded in 1889, is a fourth-generation, family-run wood and wood products business and has substantial timberland and timber resources. It also generates miscellaneous revenues from its properties. Prior to 1988, there were 1,200 shares of stock issued to 180 stockholders of record. In 1988 the shareholders approved a reverse split of 1 for 20 thereby decreasing the number of shares outstanding. The purpose of the split was explained as helping to prevent the Company from being required to report to the Securities and Exchange Commission. The Company has since refused to transfer shares from one party to another, making a market almost impossible.

	07/31/96	07/31/95	07/31/94	07/31/93
Per Share Information				
Stock Price as of 12/31	100,000.00	170,000.00	122,100.00	111,111.00
Earnings Per Share	10,503.39	12,935.32	9,913.84	8,312.45
Price / Earnings Ratio	9.52	13.14	12.32	13.37
Book Value Per Share	90,250.39	58,579.83	51,283.33	46,171.43
Price / Book Value %	110.80	290.20	238.09	240.65
Dividends Per Share	6,230.00	5,250.00	4,750.00	4,175.00
Annual Financial Data				
Operating Results (000's)				
Total Revenues	80,837.5	84,224.3	80,423.8	75,636.3
Costs & Expenses	-71,727.4	-72,726.3	-71,888.0	-68,105.4
Income Before Taxes and Other	9,110.1	11,498.0	8,535.9	7,530.8
Other Items	0.0	0.0	0.0	0.0
Income Tax	-3,023.0	-3,969.6	-2,766.0	-2,693.0
Net Income	6,087.1	7,528.4	5,769.9	4,837.8
Cash Flow From Operations	14,072.0	10,033.8	9,429.5	11,985.5
Balance Sheet (000's)				
Cash & Equivalents	287.6	415.2	1,254.4	1,316.1
Total Current Assets	16,007.5	20,081.6	17,460.4	16,548.3
Fixed Assets, Net	59,100.3	32,998.4	20,736.9	17,586.4
Total Assets	110,862.0	68,911.9	52,400.4	47,099.9
Total Current Liabilities	10,490.2	8,115.9	6,584.6	9,740.8
Long-Term Debt	33,330.6	26,702.5	14,179.0	8,207.3
Stockholders' Equity	52,345.2	34,093.5	29,846.9	26,871.8
Performance & Financial Condition				
Return on Total Revenues %	7.53	8.94	7.17	6.40
Return on Avg Stockholders' Equity %	14.08	23.55	20.35	18.80
Return on Average Assets %	6.77	12.41	11.60	10.44
Current Ratio	1.53	2.47	2.65	1.70
Debt / Equity %	63.67	78.32	47.51	30.54

Compound Growth %'s	EPS %	8.11	Net Income %	7.96	Total Revenues %	2.24

Comments

The Company owns over 300,000 acres of ash, oak and other hardwoods along the Mississippi River as well as mills, a fleet of barges, a construction business and commercial real estate. According to Forbes Magazine (July 29, 1996), Toronto investor Frederic Jackman estimates each share to be worth $1 million. It is a widely-held belief that the Tully heirs own 60% of the Company and are more concerned about avoiding estate taxes than maximizing share value. Two shares were reacquired by the Company during 1996. The current price per share was an estimate provided to us by an investment professional. No known trading has occurred this last year. Investment Classification: Value & Speculative

Officers	Position	Ownership Information	
John M. Tully	President	Number of Shares Outstanding	580
Mary Ann Sandidge	Secretary	Market Capitalization	$ 58,000,000
		Frequency of Dividends	Quarterly
		Number of Shareholders	Under 500

Other Information			
Transfer Agent	Company Office	Where Listed	OTC-BB
Auditor	Deloitte & Touche LLP	Symbol	ANTY
Market Maker	Martin Nelson & Co., Inc.	(206)938-5783	SIC Code	2490
	Hill Thompson Magid & Co., Inc	(800)601-9888	Employees	873
Broker Dealer	OTC Specialist		
	Standard Investment	(888)783-4688 Ext: Jack	

Annie's Homegrown, Inc.

200 Gate Five Road, Suite 211   Sausalito, CA 94965   Telephone (415)332-2322   Fax (415)332-4932

Company Description

Annie's Homegrown, Inc. is engaged in the manufacture, marketing and sale of premium natural macaroni and cheese dinners and other pasta products to the natural food and grocery business, mainly in the Northeast and West Coast markets. The Company was formed in 1989 and completed its initial public offering of 600,000 shares at $6 per share in 1996. In the first quarter of 1997, the Company introduced a new line of all natural pasta dinners called Annie's One-Step. The One-Step dinners combine different pasta shapes with five sauce recipes which provide the convenience and simplicity of one-step, one-pot cooking. The Company has not yet taken steps to create a formal market in the Company's shares although there are 2,580 shareholders.

	12/31/96	12/31/95	12/31/94	12/31/93
Per Share Information				
Stock Price	6.00	6.00	0.80	0.80
Earnings Per Share	-0.11	-0.07	0.01	0.03
Price / Earnings Ratio	n.a.	n.a.	80.00	26.67
Book Value Per Share	0.16	-0.02	0.04	-0.01
Price / Book Value %	3,750.00	n.a.	2,000.00	n.a.
Dividends Per Share	0.0	0.0	0.0	0.0
Annual Financial Data				
Operating Results (000's)				
Total Revenues	4,820.0	4,557.1	3,070.6	1,760.6
Costs & Expenses	-5,096.0	-5,005.2	-3,044.4	-1,636.8
Income Before Taxes and Other	-276.1	-448.1	26.2	123.8
Other Items	0.0	0.0	0.0	0.0
Income Tax	-3.3	-2.9	-2.3	-2.0
Net Income	-279.4	-451.0	23.9	121.8
Cash Flow From Operations	-170.4	40.6	-79.9	76.3
Balance Sheet (000's)				
Cash & Equivalents	860.5	35.5	2.4	4.7
Total Current Assets	2,284.3	667.2	808.8	483.2
Fixed Assets, Net	39.2	32.3	23.2	7.9
Total Assets	2,424.2	793.7	833.3	491.1
Total Current Liabilities	1,719.9	860.6	682.2	512.3
Long-Term Debt	0.0	0.0	0.0	0.0
Stockholders' Equity	704.3	-66.9	151.1	-21.1
Performance & Financial Condition				
Return on Total Revenues %	-5.80	-9.90	0.78	6.92
Return on Avg Stockholders' Equity %	-87.66	n.a.	36.74	n.a.
Return on Average Assets %	-17.36	-55.44	3.61	n.a.
Current Ratio	1.33	0.78	1.19	0.94
Debt / Equity %	n.a.	n.a.	n.a.	n.a.

Compound Growth %'s	EPS % n.a.	Net Income % n.a.	Total Revenues % 39.89

Comments

The big news is Annie's Homegrown reported its first profit in the first quarter of 1997, amounting to $20,162. Revenue had increased to $1,948,000, up 38.3%. The Company's strategy is to continue to expand its supermarket distribution nationally in addition to developing new and unique all-natural food products to sell to its existing customer base. Investment Classification: Speculative

Officers	Position	Ownership Information	
Andrew Martin	Chairman, CEO	Number of Shares Outstanding	4,368,801
Paul Nardone	President	Market Capitalization	$ 26,212,806
Neil Raiff	Treasurer, CFO	Frequency of Dividends	n.a.
Deborah Churchill	Secretary	Number of Shareholders	2,580
Ann E. Withey	Other		

Other Information			
Transfer Agent	Company Office	Where Listed	Order Matching Only
Auditor	KPMG Peat Marwick LLP	Symbol	n.a.
Market Maker	None - See Note	SIC Code	2098
		Employees	9
Broker Dealer	None		

Arthur Treacher's, Inc.

7400 Baymeadows Way, Ste. 300   Jacksonville, FL 32256   Telephone (904)739-1200   Fax (904)739-2500

Company Description

The Company operates twenty-five Arthur Treacher's Fish & Chips restaurants, of which all but one are owned by the Company, in Ohio, Florida, Michigan, South Carolina and New York. The Company is also franchisor of 100 restaurants located throughout the United States and Canada. When an individual franchise is sold, the Company assists the franchisee in site selection, training personnel, implementation of an accounting and store management system, and various other services.

	06/30/96	06/30/95
Per Share Information		
Stock Price as of 12/31	3.00	0.39
Earnings Per Share	-0.10	-0.05
Price / Earnings Ratio	n.a.	n.a.
Book Value Per Share	n.a.	-0.05
Price / Book Value %	n.a.	n.a.
Dividends Per Share	0.0	0.0
Annual Financial Data		
Operating Results (000's)		
Total Revenues	7,873.2	7,317.6
Costs & Expenses	-8,624.1	-7,854.2
Income Before Taxes and Other	-750.9	-536.6
Other Items	-403.4	0.0
Income Tax	329.1	146.6
Net Income	-825.2	-390.0
Cash Flow From Operations	734.4	69.3
Balance Sheet (000's)		
Cash & Equivalents	985.6	26.1
Total Current Assets	1,241.3	460.3
Fixed Assets, Net	1,390.5	1,381.9
Total Assets	2,999.4	1,874.5
Total Current Liabilities	2,494.1	1,213.8
Long-Term Debt	458.9	970.8
Stockholders' Equity	0.0	-374.8
Performance & Financial Condition		
Return on Total Revenues %	-10.48	-5.33
Return on Avg Stockholders' Equity %	n.a.	n.a.
Return on Average Assets %	-33.86	n.a.
Current Ratio	0.50	0.38
Debt / Equity %	n.a.	n.a.

Compound Growth %'s	EPS % n.a.	Net Income % n.a.	Total Revenues % 7.59

Comments

During the year ended June 30, 1996, four locations were opened, twenty-three were closed, and one franchise was sold. The company raised needed working capital by selling 679,963 shares of common stock in a private placement. Additional warrants were issued in exchange for services and personal guarantees of corporate debt. There is nothing fishy going on; the Company is simply trying to keep its head above water as it restructures itself into a profitable base of operations. Investment Classification: Speculative

Officers	Position	Ownership Information	
Bruce R. Galloway	Chairman	Number of Shares Outstanding	11,118,620
R. Frank Brown	President, CEO	Market Capitalization	$ 33,355,860
William F. Saculla	Secretary	Frequency of Dividends	n.a.
		Number of Shareholders	Under 500

Other Information				
Transfer Agent	Atlas Stock Transfer Corp. Salt Lake City, UT		Where Listed	OTC-BB
Auditor	Lytkowski & Pease, Inc.		Symbol	ATCH
Market Maker	Brookstreet Securities, Inc.	(800)285-2578	SIC Code	5800
	M.H. Meyerson & Co., Inc.	(800)333-3113	Employees	n.a.
Broker Dealer	Regular Stockbroker			

Ash Grove Cement Company

8900 Indian Creek Parkway, Suite 600   Overland Park, KS 66225   Telephone (913)451-8900   Fax (913)451-8324

Company Description

Ash Grove Cement operates eight cement manufacturing plants throughout the midstates and northwest United States and a lime manufacturing plant in Portland, Oregon. Products include ready-mixed concrete, aggregates and package materials and are sold to customers in over twenty states and parts of Canada. Ash Grove Cement is ranked as the fourth largest cement manufacturer in the United States and is also involved in real estate development. The Company was formed in 1882.

	12/31/96	12/31/95	12/31/94	12/31/93
Per Share Information				
Stock Price	56.75	56.00	34.00	30.50
Earnings Per Share	7.44	6.33	5.17	1.48
Price / Earnings Ratio	7.63	8.85	6.58	20.61
Book Value Per Share	49.09	42.55	36.79	32.05
Price / Book Value %	115.60	131.61	92.42	95.16
Dividends Per Share	0.85	0.70	0.60	0.50
Annual Financial Data				
Operating Results (000's)				
Total Revenues	417,526.6	407,745.3	370,848.1	314,102.1
Costs & Expenses	-322,070.4	-326,131.0	-301,441.5	-270,704.3
Income Before Taxes and Other	90,612.1	79,986.5	66,383.9	42,395.6
Other Items	-361.4	-1,030.6	-1,337.8	-14,802.9
Income Tax	-31,333.9	-28,563.0	-23,937.8	-15,759.0
Net Income	58,916.8	50,392.9	41,108.3	11,833.8
Cash Flow From Operations	80,635.9	64,610.5	65,749.6	56,530.0
Balance Sheet (000's)				
Cash & Equivalents	2,470.0	30,425.5	10,006.3	8,395.2
Total Current Assets	168,319.4	133,240.0	102,586.0	92,411.9
Fixed Assets, Net	325,320.4	312,698.3	310,047.7	320,206.1
Total Assets	584,553.8	532,918.3	499,888.2	448,187.9
Total Current Liabilities	47,055.1	42,043.3	40,495.1	34,355.9
Long-Term Debt	68,371.2	70,750.1	86,626.1	73,542.8
Stockholders' Equity	387,641.3	338,524.4	292,641.1	255,288.1
Performance & Financial Condition				
Return on Total Revenues %	14.11	12.36	11.08	3.77
Return on Avg Stockholders' Equity %	16.23	15.97	15.00	4.70
Return on Average Assets %	10.54	9.76	8.67	n.a.
Current Ratio	3.58	3.17	2.53	2.69
Debt / Equity %	17.64	20.90	29.60	28.81

Compound Growth %'s	EPS %	71.31	Net Income %	70.75	Total Revenues %	9.95

Comments

The Company declared a 2 for 1 stock split in 1996. All per share amounts have been adjusted for consistency. The Company, which had been operating at capacity levels, completed its expansion of the Leamington, Utah facility during 1996 and contracted for a major expansion of the Durkee, Oregon plant. Liquidity is excellent with $57.3 million invested in short-term securities. Sales and earnings were both at record levels. Management believes that future demand for portland cement will be strong into the next century. Investment Classification: Value & Growth

Officers	Position	Ownership Information	
James P. Sunderland	Chairman	Number of Shares Outstanding	7,897,262
George M. Wells	President	Market Capitalization	$ 448,169,619
John H. Ross III	Senior VP	Frequency of Dividends	Quarterly
Charles T. Wiedenhoft	Senior VP	Number of Shareholders	Under 500
Kent W. Sunderland	Vice President, Secretary		

Other Information			
Transfer Agent	Company Office	Where Listed	OTC-BB
Auditor	KPMG Peat Marwick LLP	Symbol	ASHG
Market Maker	George K. Baum & Company (800)821-7570	SIC Code	3240
	Ernst & Co. (800)845-4330	Employees	1800
Broker Dealer	Regular Stockbroker		

Asha Corporation

600 C Ward Drive   Santa Barbara, CA 93111   Telephone (805)683-2331   Fax (805)964-9948

Company Description

Asha Corporation's primary product line is an automatic hydromechanical traction control device which has been named The Asha Gerodisc System. It is a self-activating device that can prevent wheel spin and improve traction and handling on all types of vehicle platforms. Unlike electronic traction control systems which reduce wheel spin by limiting power to a vehicle's driven wheels, Gerodisc transmits power to the wheels in proportion to the traction available at each driven wheel.

	09/30/96	09/30/95	09/30/94	09/30/93
Per Share Information				
Stock Price as of 12/31	3.50	4.75	6.25	n.a.
Earnings Per Share	-0.26	0.22	-0.14	n.a.
Price / Earnings Ratio	n.a.	21.59	n.a.	n.a.
Book Value Per Share	0.24	0.41	0.17	n.a.
Price / Book Value %	1,458.33	1,158.54	3,676.47	n.a.
Dividends Per Share	0.0	0.0	0.0	n.a.
Annual Financial Data				
Operating Results (000's)				
Total Revenues	941.6	4,065.8	1,260.3	1,844.2
Costs & Expenses	-2,753.2	-2,493.0	-2,175.9	-1,382.4
Income Before Taxes and Other	-1,811.5	1,572.8	-915.6	461.8
Other Items	0.0	0.0	0.0	0.0
Income Tax	-0.8	-41.4	0.0	0.0
Net Income	-1,812.3	1,531.3	-915.6	461.8
Cash Flow From Operations	545.5	-22.1	-392.7	n.a.
Balance Sheet (000's)				
Cash & Equivalents	13.6	12.8	625.8	n.a.
Total Current Assets	1,415.9	1,725.1	1,154.5	n.a.
Fixed Assets, Net	203.5	147.4	97.4	n.a.
Total Assets	2,219.9	3,131.5	1,251.9	n.a.
Total Current Liabilities	486.2	332.4	92.5	n.a.
Long-Term Debt	0.0	0.0	0.0	n.a.
Stockholders' Equity	1,733.6	2,799.2	1,159.4	n.a.
Performance & Financial Condition				
Return on Total Revenues %	-192.47	37.66	-72.65	n.a.
Return on Avg Stockholders' Equity %	-79.96	77.37	n.a.	n.a.
Return on Average Assets %	-67.73	69.87	n.a.	n.a.
Current Ratio	2.91	5.19	12.48	n.a.
Debt / Equity %	n.a.	n.a.	n.a.	n.a.

Compound Growth %'s	EPS % n.a.	Net Income % n.a.	Total Revenues % -20.07

Comments

The substantial decrease in revenue was due to a reduction of license and right of first refusal revenue of approximately $2,775,000 as compared to the prior year. The decline continued into the first six months of fiscal 1997 and as of March 31, 1997, a loss of $524,000 was incurred. The Company continues to build prototypes for evaluation by OEM's or first tier suppliers. Investment Classification: Speculative

Officers	Position	Ownership Information	
Alain J-M Clenet	Chairman, CEO	Number of Shares Outstanding	7,076,217
John C. McCormack	President, COO	Market Capitalization	$ 24,766,760
Kenneth R. Black	VP - Sales	Frequency of Dividends	n.a.
		Number of Shareholders	2,602

Other Information			
Transfer Agent	American Securities Transfer, Inc. Denver, CO	Where Listed	OTC-BB
Auditor	McDirmid, Mikkelsen & Secret	Symbol	ASHA
Market Maker	Coastal Securities Ltd. (800)964-4446	SIC Code	3714
	Wm. V. Frankel & Co., Inc. (800)631-3091	Employees	n.a.
Broker Dealer	Regular Stockbroker		

Athanor Group, Inc.

921 East California Avenue   Ontario, CA 91761   Telephone (909)467-1205   Fax (909)467-1208

Company Description

Athanor Group, Inc., since its inception in 1958, has been engaged in the manufacture of screw machine products (nonproprietary metal components) produced in large quantities to customer specifications. In meeting customer orders, the Company manufactures a wide range of products. Before placing an order, a customer provides the Company with detailed drawings and specifications for a specific product. During 1996, the Company continued to expand into the secondary operations that had been contracted to outsiders. The ability to perform these operations in-house will afford the Company better control over inventory and quality standards.

	10/31/96	10/31/95	10/31/94	10/31/93
Per Share Information				
Stock Price as of 12/31	1.87	1.37	1.25	0.62
Earnings Per Share	0.36	0.18	0.37	0.13
Price / Earnings Ratio	5.19	7.61	3.38	4.77
Book Value Per Share	1.70	1.34	1.21	0.84
Price / Book Value %	110.00	102.24	103.31	73.81
Dividends Per Share	0.0	0.0	0.0	0.0
Annual Financial Data				
Operating Results (000's)				
Total Revenues	23,652.7	19,329.5	17,369.1	14,364.6
Costs & Expenses	-22,846.3	-18,844.8	-16,927.1	-14,116.5
Income Before Taxes and Other	806.4	484.7	442.0	248.1
Other Items	0.0	0.0	478.7	77.1
Income Tax	-277.2	-220.9	-344.3	-124.3
Net Income	529.2	263.8	576.4	200.9
Cash Flow From Operations	633.1	219.3	-4.8	771.8
Balance Sheet (000's)				
Cash & Equivalents	115.5	62.4	149.2	n.a.
Total Current Assets	6,097.4	5,532.0	5,352.0	n.a.
Fixed Assets, Net	1,177.5	1,108.5	903.5	n.a.
Total Assets	7,364.9	6,723.2	6,341.9	n.a.
Total Current Liabilities	3,705.7	3,686.1	3,486.0	n.a.
Long-Term Debt	1,095.2	974.1	850.7	n.a.
Stockholders' Equity	2,497.4	1,968.3	1,904.5	n.a.
Performance & Financial Condition				
Return on Total Revenues %	2.24	1.36	3.32	1.40
Return on Avg Stockholders' Equity %	23.70	13.62	35.70	16.75
Return on Average Assets %	7.51	4.04	n.a.	n.a.
Current Ratio	1.65	1.50	1.54	n.a.
Debt / Equity %	43.85	49.49	44.67	n.a.

Compound Growth %'s	EPS %	40.43	Net Income %	38.12	Total Revenues %	18.09

Comments

Should you judge the quality of a stock by its price per share? We admit that we tend to move quickly past penny stocks (stocks priced under $5) and immediately focus on stocks over $200. Athanor Group is a lesson for us to remember to always keep an open mind. Although not right for everyone, this Company makes money, has a relatively simple business for an investor to understand, has a reasonable balance sheet, has shown excellent growth, and has management that is clearly focused on the business. Investment Classification: Growth & Value

Officers	Position	Ownership Information	
Robert W. Miller	Chairman, Secretary	Number of Shares Outstanding	1,471,354
Duane L. Femrite	President, CEO	Market Capitalization	$ 2,751,432
Richard Krause	Vice President	Frequency of Dividends	n.a.
Naomi Applegate	Other	Number of Shareholders	318

Other Information

Transfer Agent	U.S. Stock Transfer Corporation Glendale, CA		Where Listed	OTC-BB
Auditor	KPMG Peat Marwick		Symbol	ATHR
Market Maker	Paragon Capital Corporation	(800)345-0505	SIC Code	3450
	Ronda, Inc.	(201)579-0029	Employees	n.a.
Broker Dealer	Regular Stockbroker			

Audio Communications Network, Inc.

1000 Legion Place, Ste. 1515   Orlando, FL 32801   Telephone (407)649-8877   Fax (407)649-8873

Company Description

The Company owns and operates MUZAK franchises, which provide background music programming and ancillary services to customers located in Baltimore, Maryland and the Delmarva peninsula area encompassing the Maryland Eastern Shore; Kansas City and St. Louis Missouri; Fresno, California; and Jacksonville, Florida and surrounding areas. During the second quarter of 1997, the Company acquired franchises in Hillsborough and Charlotte, North Carolina and Phoenix, Arizona. In addition, other sound, video, and communication system products and services are provided. The Company was founded in 1953.

	12/31/96	12/31/95	12/31/94	12/31/93
Per Share Information				
Stock Price	2.75	1.57	1.19	1.25
Earnings Per Share	0.30	0.27	0.15	0.08
Price / Earnings Ratio	9.17	5.81	7.93	15.63
Book Value Per Share	1.56	1.24	0.97	0.54
Price / Book Value %	176.28	126.61	122.68	231.48
Dividends Per Share	0.0	0.0	0.0	0.0
Annual Financial Data				
Operating Results (000's)				
Total Revenues	11,177.9	7,690.4	7,019.0	5,534.6
Costs & Expenses	-10,383.1	-7,023.8	-6,669.3	-5,380.1
Income Before Taxes and Other	794.8	666.6	349.7	154.5
Other Items	0.0	0.0	0.0	0.0
Income Tax	-95.4	-57.5	-37.7	-12.7
Net Income	699.4	609.1	312.0	141.8
Cash Flow From Operations	1,179.8	624.5	902.2	871.6
Balance Sheet (000's)				
Cash & Equivalents	995.8	590.1	509.1	363.3
Total Current Assets	2,564.3	1,503.2	1,373.8	1,118.4
Fixed Assets, Net	4,961.5	3,358.2	2,896.5	2,032.3
Total Assets	14,593.1	8,411.1	8,241.6	5,604.0
Total Current Liabilities	2,169.4	1,484.9	1,651.1	1,146.4
Long-Term Debt	8,815.0	4,089.0	4,366.8	3,472.1
Stockholders' Equity	3,608.8	2,787.2	2,161.0	907.5
Performance & Financial Condition				
Return on Total Revenues %	6.26	7.92	4.45	2.56
Return on Avg Stockholders' Equity %	21.87	24.62	20.34	17.46
Return on Average Assets %	6.08	7.32	4.51	2.42
Current Ratio	1.18	1.01	0.83	0.98
Debt / Equity %	244.26	146.71	202.07	382.60

Compound Growth %'s	EPS %	55.36	Net Income %	70.23	Total Revenues %	26.40

Comments

The Company has grown profitably by expanding existing business and acquiring other companies with similar operations. The increase in operating profits during 1996 is largely offset by additional interest expense on long-term debt. Compound earnings per share growth is diluted by the exercise and issuance of employee stock options. Investment Classification: Speculative

Officers	Position	Ownership Information	
A.J. Schell	President, CEO	Number of Shares Outstanding	2,309,203
Doris K. Krummenacker	Secretary, Treasurer	Market Capitalization	$ 6,350,308
Mary Flemmings	Vice President	Frequency of Dividends	n.a.
Frank Crooks	Vice President	Number of Shareholders	599
Mike Regan	Vice President		

Other Information

Transfer Agent	Chemical Mellon Shareholder Services		Where Listed	OTC-BB
Auditor	Deloitte & Touche LLP		Symbol	AUCM
Market Maker	Gruntal & Co., Incorporated	(212)943-6418	SIC Code	7389
	Koonce Securities, Inc.	(800)368-2802	Employees	82
Broker Dealer	Regular Stockbroker			

Auric Corporation

470 Frelinghuysen Avenue Newark, NJ 07114 Telephone (201)242-4110 Fax (201)242-5796

Company Description

Auric Corporation manufactures and sells chemical products for the metal finishing industry in general and for electronic manufacturers in particular. In March, 1997, the Company completed construction and began operations of a chemical manufacturing plant in Sarawak, Malaysia. This facility is intended to service the growing sales to Asia in general and South East Asia in particular. An Employee Stock Ownership Plan owns approximately 30% of the Company's shares.

	09/30/96	09/30/95	09/30/94	09/30/93
Per Share Information				
Stock Price as of 12/31	46.00	39.25	24.62	15.00
Earnings Per Share	12.10	6.26	2.73	4.01
Price / Earnings Ratio	3.80	6.27	9.02	3.74
Book Value Per Share	49.57	32.65	26.54	22.38
Price / Book Value %	92.80	120.21	92.77	67.02
Dividends Per Share	0.0	0.0	0.0	0.0
Annual Financial Data				
Operating Results (000's)				
Total Revenues	41,613.6	29,994.7	22,872.7	21,149.9
Costs & Expenses	-33,589.6	-25,385.3	-19,900.0	-18,229.2
Income Before Taxes and Other	7,725.4	4,212.4	1,630.8	2,616.3
Other Items	0.0	0.0	0.0	0.0
Income Tax	-2,962.6	-1,744.3	-603.2	-1,015.3
Net Income	4,762.8	2,468.1	1,027.6	1,601.0
Cash Flow From Operations	3,816.8	4,565.9	1,251.0	1,446.6
Balance Sheet (000's)				
Cash & Equivalents	4,006.1	4,424.3	1,641.3	2,708.1
Total Current Assets	15,703.5	13,519.2	11,423.6	10,086.8
Fixed Assets, Net	9,919.9	5,076.4	3,800.0	2,790.8
Total Assets	26,128.6	19,061.1	15,613.3	13,219.1
Total Current Liabilities	6,791.6	4,887.9	4,076.0	2,618.8
Long-Term Debt	2,755.0	328.7	395.5	326.1
Stockholders' Equity	15,758.1	12,873.7	9,989.9	8,936.3
Performance & Financial Condition				
Return on Total Revenues %	11.45	8.23	4.49	7.57
Return on Avg Stockholders' Equity %	33.27	21.59	10.86	20.09
Return on Average Assets %	21.08	14.24	7.13	12.89
Current Ratio	2.31	2.77	2.80	3.85
Debt / Equity %	17.48	2.55	3.96	3.65

Compound Growth %'s	EPS % 44.50	Net Income % 43.82	Total Revenues % 25.31

Comments

Sales climbed 38% during 1996. Net earnings were 93% higher due to increased sales, slightly higher gross margin percentages, and slightly lower selling, general and administrative expense percentages. Management reports that, although the electronics industry seems relatively weaker, 1997 should still be a reasonably good year for Auric as its customer base is strong and several interesting new products are under development. Investment Classification: Value & Growth

Officers	Position	Ownership Information	
Maurice Bick	President	Number of Shares Outstanding	317,900
Daniel Davitt, Jr.	CFO	Market Capitalization	$ 14,623,400
Alan J. Ruffini	Vice President	Frequency of Dividends	n.a.
		Number of Shareholders	Under 500

Other Information				
Transfer Agent	Midlantic National Bank		Where Listed	OTC-BB
Auditor	J.H. Cohn & Company		Symbol	AURP
Market Maker	S.J. Wolfe & Co.	(800)262-2244	SIC Code	2810
	Sharpe Capital Inc.	(800)355-5781	Employees	n.a.
Broker Dealer	OTC Specialist			

Auto-Graphics, Inc.

3201 Temple Avenue   Pomona, CA 91768-3200   Telephone (909)595-7204   Fax (909)595-3506

Company Description

Auto-Graphics, Inc. provides software products and processing services to information and database publishers. These products and services are used to create, maintain and distribute information databases through printed and/or electronic reference products such as CD-ROM and Internet/Web software systems. The Company was formed in 1960.

	12/31/96	12/31/95	12/31/94	12/31/93
Per Share Information				
Stock Price	2.25	1.88	1.36	2.00
Earnings Per Share	0.21	0.16	0.12	0.10
Price / Earnings Ratio	10.71	11.75	11.33	20.00
Book Value Per Share	2.36	2.16	1.99	1.87
Price / Book Value %	95.34	87.04	68.34	106.95
Dividends Per Share	0.0	0.0	0.0	0.0
Annual Financial Data				
Operating Results (000's)				
Total Revenues	9,251.9	9,612.9	9,219.8	9,759.3
Costs & Expenses	-8,825.0	-9,254.8	-8,925.6	-9,524.8
Income Before Taxes and Other	426.9	358.2	294.2	234.5
Other Items	0.0	0.0	0.0	0.0
Income Tax	-190.0	-164.0	-136.0	-102.0
Net Income	236.9	194.2	158.2	132.5
Cash Flow From Operations	1,359.8	1,622.9	880.9	1,816.0
Balance Sheet (000's)				
Cash & Equivalents	364.1	106.5	80.9	63.1
Total Current Assets	2,557.9	2,547.8	2,603.0	2,279.4
Fixed Assets, Net	4,425.5	3,929.3	3,307.0	3,279.7
Total Assets	7,132.0	6,687.7	6,106.1	5,840.9
Total Current Liabilities	1,747.8	1,746.1	1,372.1	1,392.8
Long-Term Debt	2,100.9	1,905.9	1,695.9	1,591.9
Stockholders' Equity	2,618.4	2,441.8	2,550.7	2,440.9
Performance & Financial Condition				
Return on Total Revenues %	2.56	2.02	1.72	1.36
Return on Avg Stockholders' Equity %	9.36	7.78	6.34	5.57
Return on Average Assets %	3.43	3.04	2.65	2.12
Current Ratio	1.46	1.46	1.90	1.64
Debt / Equity %	80.24	78.05	66.49	65.22

Compound Growth %'s	EPS %	28.06	Net Income %	21.38	Total Revenues %	-1.76

Comments

The Company has reacquired 197,888 of its shares over the last four years, thereby explaining the difference in compound earnings growth rates. Management reports considerable interest in the Internet products that they have developed and has higher gross margins than its traditional business lines. Net income is expected to increase in 1997 based on a more profitable mix of products and services. In addition, the Company believes it is well positioned to capitalize on the exploding potential of the Internet/World Wide Web. Investment Classification: Speculative & Value

Officers	Position	Ownership Information	
Robert S. Cope	President, CEO	Number of Shares Outstanding	1,109,278
William J. Kliss	COO	Market Capitalization	$ 2,495,876
Daniel E. Luebben	Secretary, CFO	Frequency of Dividends	n.a.
		Number of Shareholders	237

Other Information				
Transfer Agent	ChaseMellon Shareholder Services, LLC Los Angeles, CA		Where Listed	OTC-BB
Auditor	Ernst & Young LLP		Symbol	AUGR
Market Maker	Carr Securities Corporation	(800)221-2243	SIC Code	7375
	Robotti & Co., Inc.	(212)986-0800	Employees	115
Broker Dealer	Regular Stockbroker			

Avoca, Incorporated

P.O. Box 61260   New Orleans, LA 70161   Telephone (504)552-4720   Fax (504)586-3613

Company Description

The Company owns and manages approximately 16,000 acres, comprising virtually all of Avoca Island, located about 90 miles west of New Orleans. The island is rural and undeveloped except for the exploration and development of its oil and gas reserves. The Company is largely a passive royalty company which derives most of its income from royalties, bonuses and rentals under oil and gas leases covering the island's acreage. The Company was formed in 1931.

	12/31/96	12/31/95	12/31/94	12/31/93
Per Share Information				
Stock Price	8.25	6.13	6.44	5.75
Earnings Per Share	0.51	0.19	0.21	0.21
Price / Earnings Ratio	16.18	32.26	30.67	27.38
Book Value Per Share	2.61	2.55	2.51	2.46
Price / Book Value %	316.09	240.39	256.57	233.74
Dividends Per Share	0.45	0.15	0.15	0.11
Annual Financial Data				
Operating Results (000's)				
Total Revenues	827.5	289.9	403.5	307.3
Costs & Expenses	-180.1	-174.0	-161.9	-181.9
Income Before Taxes and Other	647.4	115.9	241.6	125.4
Other Items	0.0	69.6	0.0	73.4
Income Tax	-223.7	-28.6	-69.7	-24.6
Net Income	423.7	157.0	171.9	174.2
Cash Flow From Operations	364.0	34.4	147.4	76.5
Balance Sheet (000's)				
Cash & Equivalents	65.1	204.7	15.0	1,090.8
Total Current Assets	1,869.8	1,521.1	2,175.2	2,116.2
Fixed Assets, Net	75.6	78.3	72.7	23.8
Total Assets	2,584.5	2,321.9	2,247.9	2,140.0
Total Current Liabilities	400.1	186.9	137.8	75.2
Long-Term Debt	0.0	0.0	0.0	0.0
Stockholders' Equity	2,170.6	2,120.6	2,088.2	2,040.9
Performance & Financial Condition				
Return on Total Revenues %	51.20	54.15	42.61	56.70
Return on Avg Stockholders' Equity %	19.75	7.46	8.33	8.71
Return on Average Assets %	17.27	6.87	7.84	8.33
Current Ratio	4.67	8.14	15.78	28.14
Debt / Equity %	n.a.	n.a.	n.a.	n.a.

Compound Growth %'s	EPS %	34.42	Net Income %	34.47	Total Revenues %	39.13

Comments

Revenues fluctuate primarily as a result of production related to the oil and gas leases on the Company's property. During 1996, the Intercoastal Shipyard No. 2 well became the Company's largest producing well as a result of a successful workover by its operator, Black Gold Production Company. Royalties from the Intercoastal Shipyard No. 2 well were responsible for 44% of the Company's royalty income. The Company is encouraging its lessees to further develop the property's resources. Investment Classification: Value & Speculative

Officers	Position	Ownership Information	
Edward B. Grimball	President, CFO	Number of Shares Outstanding	830,500
M. Cleland Powell, III	Treasurer, Secretary	Market Capitalization	$ 6,851,625
		Frequency of Dividends	Semi-Annual
		Number of Shareholders	848

Other Information				
Transfer Agent	Company Office		Where Listed	OTC-BB
Auditor	Ernst & Young LLP		Symbol	AVOC
Market Maker	Howard, Weil, et al	(504)582-2612	SIC Code	6792
	Robotti & Co., Inc.	(212)986-0800	Employees	n.a.
Broker Dealer	Regular Stockbroker			

Aztec Land and Cattle Company, Limited

1715 West Northern, Room 104   Phoenix, AZ 85021   Telephone (602)870-4811   Fax (602)870-9636

Company Description

The Company's principal revenue sources are from rentals of land used for grazing purposes and water well sites located in Navajo County, Arizona. Leases of water well sites to Arizona Public Service Co. represents over 50% of the Company's annual lease income. These leases expire in 2007 and 2009. The grazing leases expire at various times, are written for 5 year terms, and are expected to be renewed as they expire.

	12/31/96	12/31/95	12/31/94
Per Share Information			
Stock Price	43.00	51.00	55.00
Earnings Per Share	1.19	0.69	0.01
Price / Earnings Ratio	36.13	73.91	5,500.00
Book Value Per Share	10.30	9.15	9.02
Price / Book Value %	417.48	557.38	609.76
Dividends Per Share	0.05	0.05	0.0
Annual Financial Data			
Operating Results (000's)			
Total Revenues	240.4	387.6	139.3
Costs & Expenses	-132.2	-324.4	-138.0
Income Before Taxes and Other	108.2	63.1	1.3
Other Items	0.0	0.0	0.0
Income Tax	-0.4	-0.4	-0.4
Net Income	107.8	62.7	0.9
Cash Flow From Operations	107.8	62.7	0.9
Balance Sheet (000's)			
Cash & Equivalents	8.8	78.1	17.5
Total Current Assets	173.0	178.1	17.5
Fixed Assets, Net	745.5	735.9	784.2
Total Assets	929.7	925.3	814.7
Total Current Liabilities	0.0	0.0	0.0
Long-Term Debt	0.0	0.0	0.0
Stockholders' Equity	929.7	826.4	814.7
Performance & Financial Condition			
Return on Total Revenues %	44.84	16.17	0.64
Return on Avg Stockholders' Equity %	12.28	7.64	n.a.
Return on Average Assets %	11.62	7.21	n.a.
Current Ratio	n.a.	n.a.	n.a.
Debt / Equity %	n.a.	n.a.	n.a.

Compound Growth %'s	EPS %	n.a.	Net Income %	n.a.	Total Revenues %	n.a.

Comments

The Company's balance sheet is highly unusual. When income taxation was enacted in 1913, Aztec Land was allowed to adjust its cost basis of land to the appraised value in 1913. The adjustment is still reflected on the books. It is hard to know what all this property might be worth. Gains of $98,935 and $247,336 were recognized on property sales in 1996 and 1995, respectively. Compound growth rates were not displayed because of the distortion caused by land sales. Investment Classification: Value

Officers	Position	Ownership Information	
Stephen M. Brophy	President	Number of Shares Outstanding	90,288
George R. Carlock	Secretary	Market Capitalization	$ 3,882,384
		Frequency of Dividends	Annual
		Number of Shareholders	Under 500

Other Information			
Transfer Agent	Service Data Corp. Omaha, NE	Where Listed	OTC-BB
Auditor	DeMarcus & Associates, P.C.	Symbol	AZLC
Market Maker	Hill Thompson Magid & Co., Inc (800)631-3083	SIC Code	6510
	Boenning & Scattergood, Inc. (800)883-8383	Employees	1
Broker Dealer	Regular Stockbroker		
	Standard Investment (888)783-4688 Ext: Jack		

B.B. Walker Company

414 East Dixie Drive   Asheboro, NC 27203-1167   Telephone (910)625-1380   Fax (910)625-8258

Company Description

B.B. Walker Company manufacturers and distributes men's and women's footwear. The Company's products consist of high quality, medium-priced western and work/outdoor boots and shoes. A majority of the Company's sales are under trademarked brands. The Company also operates two retail stores. A substantial portion of the Company's common stock is owned by an Employee Stock Ownership Plan. The Company was founded in 1952.

	11/02/96	10/28/95	10/29/94	10/30/93
Per Share Information				
Stock Price as of 12/31	4.00	2.00	7.00	6.75
Earnings Per Share	-2.34	-0.72	0.26	1.12
Price / Earnings Ratio	n.a.	n.a.	26.92	6.03
Book Value Per Share	2.57	4.91	5.56	5.47
Price / Book Value %	155.64	40.73	125.90	123.40
Dividends Per Share	0.0	0.0	0.07	0.10
Annual Financial Data				
Operating Results (000's)				
Total Revenues	37,549.0	43,453.0	51,148.0	55,777.0
Costs & Expenses	-42,208.0	-45,321.0	-50,336.0	-52,722.0
Income Before Taxes and Other	-4,659.0	-1,868.0	812.0	3,055.0
Other Items	-2.0	-2.0	-2.0	-2.0
Income Tax	620.0	626.0	-336.0	-1,160.0
Net Income	-4,041.0	-1,244.0	474.0	1,893.0
Cash Flow From Operations	3,309.0	-1,918.0	-1,366.0	738.0
Balance Sheet (000's)				
Cash & Equivalents	1.0	1.0	1.0	1.0
Total Current Assets	24,953.0	30,898.0	30,264.0	27,727.0
Fixed Assets, Net	2,208.0	2,968.0	3,593.0	2,148.0
Total Assets	27,375.0	34,377.0	34,016.0	30,028.0
Total Current Liabilities	19,534.0	21,533.0	20,510.0	17,357.0
Long-Term Debt	3,286.0	4,257.0	3,692.0	3,189.0
Stockholders' Equity	4,522.0	8,553.0	9,780.0	9,447.0
Performance & Financial Condition				
Return on Total Revenues %	-10.76	-2.86	0.93	3.39
Return on Avg Stockholders' Equity %	-61.81	-13.57	4.93	22.15
Return on Average Assets %	-13.09	-3.64	1.48	6.61
Current Ratio	1.28	1.43	1.48	1.60
Debt / Equity %	72.67	49.77	37.75	33.76

Compound Growth %'s	EPS % n.a.	Net Income % n.a.	Total Revenues % -12.36

Comments

The Company declared a 3 for 2 stock split in 1994. 1993 per share amounts have been adjusted accordingly. In December, 1995, the Company reorganized its internal structure, moving from a functional organization to two vertically-integrated, separate divisions operating independently and supported by a small corporate staff. However, during fiscal 1996, a soft retail environment persisted and sales and profits did not respond as anticipated. During the fourth quarter, the Company began implementation of another plan to consolidate operations and reduce overhead. During the first quarter of fiscal 1997, the Company reduced its net loss to $136,000 for the quarter as compared to $449,000 for the equivalent period in the preceding year. Investment Classification: Speculative

Officers	Position	Ownership Information	
Kent T. Anderson	President, CEO	Number of Shares Outstanding	1,726,534
French P. Humphries	Exec VP	Market Capitalization	$ 6,906,136
William C. Massie	Exec VP	Frequency of Dividends	Irregular
Dorothy W. Craven	Secretary	Number of Shareholders	1,169
John R. Whitener	Controller		

Other Information

Transfer Agent	Company Office		Where Listed	OTC-PS
Auditor	Price Waterhouse LLP		Symbol	WLKB
Market Maker	Scott & Stringfellow, Inc.	(800)446-7074	SIC Code	3140
	Hill Thompson Magid & Co., Inc	(800)631-3083	Employees	637
Broker Dealer	Regular Stockbroker			

BFC Financial Corporation

1750 E. Sunrise Boulevard   Ft. Lauderdale, FL 33304   Telephone (305)665-8100   Fax (305)665-7770

Company Description

BFC Financial Corporation owns and manages real estate and owns approximately a 40% interest in BankAtlantic, a federal savings bank. The Bank provides a full range of commercial banking products and related financial services from 56 branch offices located primarily in Dade, Broward and Palm Beach Counties in south Florida. The Company's investment in the Bank represents approximately 60% of total assets.

	12/31/96	12/31/95	12/31/94	12/31/93
Per Share Information				
Stock Price	12.25	7.62	3.25	3.00
Earnings Per Share	2.98	3.54	13.45	-1.47
Price / Earnings Ratio	4.11	2.15	0.24	n.a.
Book Value Per Share	17.81	11.15	15.51	-3.03
Price / Book Value %	68.78	68.34	20.95	n.a.
Dividends Per Share	0.0	0.0	0.0	0.0
Annual Financial Data				
Operating Results (000's)				
Total Revenues	21,953.0	11,711.0	27,289.0	15,815.0
Costs & Expenses	-12,971.0	-7,481.0	-24,376.0	-17,118.0
Income Before Taxes and Other	8,982.0	4,230.0	2,913.0	-1,303.0
Other Items	853.0	3,702.0	22,744.0	-501.0
Income Tax	-2,924.0	0.0	2,009.0	0.0
Net Income	6,911.0	7,932.0	27,666.0	-1,804.0
Cash Flow From Operations	-5,485.0	-1,963.0	948.0	-523.0
Balance Sheet (000's)				
Cash & Equivalents	1,796.0	1,152.0	711.0	349.0
Total Current Assets	8,615.0	6,257.0	6,580.0	20,722.0
Fixed Assets, Net	0.0	0.0	0.0	0.0
Total Assets	98,841.0	96,896.0	96,896.0	87,495.0
Total Current Liabilities	0.0	0.0	0.0	0.0
Long-Term Debt	0.0	0.0	0.0	0.0
Stockholders' Equity	41,462.0	35,758.0	35,758.0	-6,988.0
Performance & Financial Condition				
Return on Total Revenues %	31.48	67.73	101.38	-11.41
Return on Avg Stockholders' Equity %	17.90	22.18	192.33	n.a.
Return on Average Assets %	7.06	8.19	30.01	n.a.
Current Ratio	n.a.	n.a.	n.a.	n.a.
Debt / Equity %	n.a.	n.a.	n.a.	n.a.

Compound Growth %'s	EPS % n.a.	Net Income % n.a.	Total Revenues % 11.55

Comments

Equity in the earnings of BankAtlantic are $8.7 million, $8.4 million, $8.0 million and $10.8 million for 1996, 1995, 1994 and 1993, respectively. During these years the percentage ownership of the Bank decreased from about 77% to about 40%. Comparisons of other operations are difficult because of numerous nonrecurring items arising from settlement of litigation, extraordinary items, sales of assets and other items. Compound earnings growth rates are not meaningful and have not been displayed. A thorough analysis of the Company's Form 10-K filing with the Securities and Exchange Commission is appropriate. Investment Classification: Value & Speculative

Officers	Position	Ownership Information	
Alan B. Levan	President, CEO	Number of Shares Outstanding	2,327,682
Glen R. Gilbert	Secretary, CFO	Market Capitalization	$ 28,514,105
		Frequency of Dividends	n.a.
		Number of Shareholders	1,100

Other Information			
Transfer Agent	Chemical Mellon Shareholder Services Ridgefield Park, NJ	Where Listed	OTC-BB
Auditor	KPMG Peat Marwick LLP	Symbol	BFCF
Market Maker	Ryan, Beck & Co.	(800)325-7926	SIC Code	6700
	Bishop Rosen & Co., Inc.	(212)602-0681	Employees	n.a.
Broker Dealer	Regular Stockbroker		

BSM Bancorp

2739 Santa Maria Way   Santa Maria, CA 93456   Telephone (805)937-8551   Fax (805)937-6582

Company Description

Bank of Santa Maria, subsidiary of this recently formed holding company, is a community bank serving the central coast of California with fourteen offices. Management's stated goal is to serve the entire central coast area and they are moving rapidly towards that accomplishment. Citizens Bank of Paso Robles was acquired in 1996 and El Camino National Bank in Lompoc was acquired in the first quarter of 1997. The Lompoc area is expected to have fine potential because of the conversion of Vandenberg AFB to commercial use. A new branch was also opened in Atascadero, in the first quarter, as a natural progression into northern San Luis Obispo County. The Bank was founded in 1978.

	12/31/96	12/31/95	12/31/94	12/31/93
Per Share Information				
Stock Price	15.37	14.00	12.50	11.25
Earnings Per Share	1.33	1.15	0.96	0.81
Price / Earnings Ratio	11.56	12.17	13.02	13.89
Book Value Per Share	10.97	10.01	8.96	8.20
Price / Book Value %	140.11	139.86	139.51	137.20
Dividends Per Share	0.35	0.11	0.08	0.05
Annual Financial Data				
Operating Results (000's)				
Net Interest Income	14,408.2	14,248.0	12,790.0	11,814.9
Loan Loss Provision	0.0	-700.0	-250.0	-601.8
Non-Interest Income	2,985.9	2,592.3	2,357.9	2,460.2
Non-Interest Expense	-11,293.4	-11,112.0	-10,808.2	-10,307.5
Income Before Taxes and Other	6,100.7	5,028.3	4,089.8	3,365.8
Other Items	0.0	0.0	0.0	0.0
Income Tax	-2,382.0	-1,878.9	-1,529.0	-1,245.7
Net Income	3,718.7	3,149.4	2,560.8	2,120.1
Balance Sheet (000's)				
Cash & Securities	117,421.0	99,738.7	82,399.0	65,689.4
Loans, Net	164,607.0	148,690.5	146,533.5	129,189.1
Total Assets	302,421.9	263,577.3	244,135.5	208,087.2
Deposits	269,662.2	234,054.4	218,594.8	188,786.8
Stockholders' Equity	30,415.6	27,503.6	23,973.8	17,928.9
Performance & Financial Condition				
Return on Avg Stockholders' Equity %	12.84	12.24	12.22	12.50
Return on Average Assets %	1.31	1.24	1.13	1.03
Equity to Assets %	10.06	10.43	9.82	8.62
Net Interest Margin	5.91	6.53	6.15	5.97
Reserve as a % of Problem Loans	403.99	752.79	164.77	76.20

Compound Growth %'s	EPS %	17.97	Net Income %	20.60	Net Interest Income %	6.84

Comments

Bank of Santa Maria has recorded eighteen consecutive years of increases in total assets and profits. The 1996 results reflect an 18% increase in profits over the preceding year. Management reports that the Paso Robles branch is fully integrated and has quickly become one of the most active brances. In addition to registering fine returns on assets and equity, they are equally as proud of their "Santa Maria Style," greeting each customer with a smile and a cup of coffee. Investment Classification: Growth & Value

Officers	Position	Ownership Information	
William A. Hares	President, CEO	Number of Shares Outstanding	2,771,661
Susan Forgnone	Exec VP	Market Capitalization	$ 42,600,430
F. Dean Fletcher	Exec VP, CFO	Frequency of Dividends	Annual
Carol Bradfield	Exec VP	Number of Shareholders	2,000
James D. Glines	Exec VP	Where Listed / Symbol	OTC-BB / BSMR

Other Information			Loan Mix	%
Transfer Agent	Chemical Mellon Shareholder Services Ridgefield Park, NJ		Commerical	28.6
Auditor	Dayton & Associates		R/E Mortgages	27.3
Market Maker	Everen Securities Corp.	(800)321-2338	Consumer	25.1
	Sutro & Co., Incorporated	(800)227-4422	Agriculture	19.0
Broker Dealer	Regular Stockbroker			

Bar Harbor Bankshares

P.O. Box 400   Bar Harbor, ME 04609-0400   Telephone (207)288-3314   Fax (207)288-2626

Company Description

Bar Harbor Banking and Trust Company, subsidiary of this holding company, has ten offices serving eastern Maine. The Bank's trust department is one of the largest among independent banks in the State. As a community bank, Bar Harbor cares about improving the quality of life for the people in the communities it serves. In addition to local lending, the Bank supports numerous civic and community organizations. Bar Harbor Banking and Trust Company was founded in 1887.

	12/31/96	12/31/95	12/31/94	12/31/93
Per Share Information				
Stock Price	36.00	26.25	16.00	14.40
Earnings Per Share	3.90	3.43	2.87	1.47
Price / Earnings Ratio	9.23	7.65	5.57	9.80
Book Value Per Share	22.05	19.40	16.82	14.64
Price / Book Value %	163.27	135.31	95.12	98.36
Dividends Per Share	1.18	0.86	0.74	0.62
Annual Financial Data				
Operating Results (000's)				
Net Interest Income	16,241.5	15,527.6	14,119.5	13,079.7
Loan Loss Provision	-720.0	-960.0	-960.0	-1,080.0
Non-Interest Income	5,000.5	4,398.3	4,012.3	4,152.9
Non-Interest Expense	-10,913.8	-10,471.3	-10,161.6	-10,956.9
Income Before Taxes and Other	9,608.1	8,494.6	7,010.2	5,195.7
Other Items	0.0	0.0	0.0	-1,058.2
Income Tax	-2,899.4	-2,616.0	-2,096.0	-1,631.8
Net Income	6,708.7	5,878.6	4,914.2	2,505.7
Balance Sheet (000's)				
Cash & Securities	121,023.3	114,654.4	101,033.7	84,813.6
Loans, Net	208,003.6	197,786.2	182,357.9	160,156.3
Total Assets	345,142.7	326,608.7	296,687.5	257,346.8
Deposits	251,675.2	251,471.4	225,544.6	203,523.1
Stockholders' Equity	37,886.9	33,242.8	28,760.8	24,987.3
Performance & Financial Condition				
Return on Avg Stockholders' Equity %	18.86	18.96	18.29	10.32
Return on Average Assets %	2.00	1.89	1.77	0.99
Equity to Assets %	10.98	10.18	9.69	9.71
Net Interest Margin	n.a.	n.a.	n.a.	n.a.
Reserve as a % of Problem Loans	100.44	96.17	96.54	106.71

Compound Growth %'s	EPS %	38.44	Net Income %	38.86	Net Interest Income %	7.48

Comments

The Company declared a 5 for 1 stock split in 1995. All per share amounts have been adjusted for consistency. Earnings increased 13.7% due to an improvement in net interest margin and non-interest income. Management believes that its 1997 estimates, which target a performance slightly ahead of 1996, are conservative. The Bank is gearing up for an entry into interstate branching as the old regional barriers are disappearing. Considerable effort has been expended to insure that the latest technology is in place and operational. Investment Classification: Growth

Officers	Position	Ownership Information	
Sheldon F. Goldthwait, Jr.	President, CEO	Number of Shares Outstanding	1,718,237
Lewis H. Payne	Exec VP	Market Capitalization	$ 61,856,532
Dwight L. Eaton	Senior VP	Frequency of Dividends	Semi-Annual
Virginia M. Vendrell	Senior VP, CFO	Number of Shareholders	1,040
Marsha C. Sawyer	Vice President, Senior Clerk	Where Listed / Symbol	OTC-BB / BHBS

Other Information			Loan Mix	%
Transfer Agent	American Stock Transfer & Trust Company New York, NY		R/E Mortgages	69.4
Auditor	Berry, Dunn, McNeil & Parker		Commerical	21.5
Market Maker	Hill Thompson Magid & Co., Inc	(800)631-3083	Installment	5.3
	Sharpe Capital Inc.	(800)355-5781	Consumer	2.6
Broker Dealer	Regular Stockbroker		Other	1.2

Barnstable Holding Co., Inc.

47 Old Yarmouth Road   Hyannis, MA 02601-0326   Telephone (508)775-0063   Fax (508)790-1313

Company Description

The Company provides water service to residential and business customers in the Hyannis area of Massachusetts through its subsidiary, Barnstable Water Company, of which it owns 95.5%. There are 20 registered shareholders in the Company, 15 of whom are thought to be members of one family. Although it might appear that a lot of value has accumulated in the Company, there is a problem in terms of doing anything with it. Since the original funding was made in part by a local municipality, Massachusetts law might require that some or all of the assets by paid to the government upon liquidation. Direct contact with the Company or one of the shareholders may be the only way to acquire shares.

	12/31/96	12/31/95	12/31/94	12/31/93
Per Share Information				
Stock Price	100.00	100.00	100.00	100.00
Earnings Per Share	20.93	19.41	13.61	17.68
Price / Earnings Ratio	4.78	5.15	7.35	5.66
Book Value Per Share	175.31	162.98	150.38	140.44
Price / Book Value %	57.04	61.36	66.50	71.20
Dividends Per Share	8.60	6.80	3.67	0.0
Annual Financial Data				
Operating Results (000's)				
Total Revenues	2,099.7	2,185.4	1,900.1	1,876.0
Costs & Expenses	-1,701.1	-1,739.4	-1,449.3	-1,530.0
Income Before Taxes and Other	393.7	438.7	253.3	153.0
Other Items	-16.4	-16.3	-12.2	86.9
Income Tax	-152.5	-214.0	-94.9	-50.0
Net Income	224.8	208.4	146.1	189.9
Cash Flow From Operations	-49.4	751.5	188.8	297.3
Balance Sheet (000's)				
Cash & Equivalents	52.3	194.8	138.0	114.6
Total Current Assets	367.8	968.2	987.4	869.5
Fixed Assets, Net	5,986.2	5,485.6	4,919.0	4,965.6
Total Assets	6,580.0	6,611.1	6,127.2	5,979.8
Total Current Liabilities	360.0	370.0	390.1	336.1
Long-Term Debt	2,000.0	2,000.0	2,000.0	2,000.0
Stockholders' Equity	1,882.9	1,750.4	1,615.0	1,508.3
Performance & Financial Condition				
Return on Total Revenues %	10.71	9.54	7.69	10.12
Return on Avg Stockholders' Equity %	12.37	12.39	9.36	13.44
Return on Average Assets %	3.41	3.27	2.41	3.24
Current Ratio	1.02	2.62	2.53	2.59
Debt / Equity %	106.22	114.26	123.84	132.60

Compound Growth %'s	EPS %	5.79	Net Income %	5.78	Total Revenues %	3.83

Comments

The Company declared a 15 for 1 stock split in 1995. All per share amounts have been adjusted for consistency. 1993 results include a one-time benefit from changing methods of accounting for income taxes in the amount of $103,539, or $9.64 per share. With 1996 income at record levels and no rate adjustments pending, management predicts little or no increase in income with greater potential for a significant decline. Investment Classification: Income & Value

Officers	Position	Ownership Information	
George D. Wadsworth	President	Number of Shares Outstanding	10,740
Mary W. Darby	Senior Clerk	Market Capitalization	$ 1,074,000
		Frequency of Dividends	Quarterly
		Number of Shareholders	Under 500

Other Information

Transfer Agent	Company Office		Where Listed	Order Matching Only
Auditor	Ernst & Young LLP		Symbol	n.a.
Market Maker	None - Company Office		SIC Code	4941
			Employees	9
Broker Dealer	None			

Batterymarch Trust (The)

200 Clarendon Street   Boston, MA 02116-5021   Telephone (617)266-8300   Fax (617)266-0633

Company Description

The Batterymarch Trust is a Massachusetts business trust whose primary activities have been investment in marketable securities, real estate partnerships, and oil and gas operating properties. The Trust was formed as a result of the 1987 liquidation of Federal Power & Light Co. & American Electric Share Co.

	12/31/96	12/31/95	12/31/94	12/31/93
Per Share Information				
Stock Price	225.00	260.00	225.00	260.00
Earnings Per Share	47.52	54.75	47.64	5.78
Price / Earnings Ratio	4.73	4.75	4.72	44.98
Book Value Per Share	365.99	331.47	289.72	255.07
Price / Book Value %	61.48	78.44	77.66	101.93
Dividends Per Share	13.00	13.00	13.00	13.00
Annual Financial Data				
Operating Results (000's)				
Total Revenues	3,869.4	4,573.3	124.6	707.8
Costs & Expenses	-267.4	-243.6	-237.3	-268.6
Income Before Taxes and Other	3,602.0	4,329.6	-112.7	439.2
Other Items	0.0	0.0	2,415.7	0.0
Income Tax	-1,185.0	-1,545.0	120.0	-145.0
Net Income	2,417.0	2,784.6	2,423.1	294.2
Cash Flow From Operations	465.3	n.a.	344.2	226.2
Balance Sheet (000's)				
Cash & Equivalents	3.6	3.5	3.0	2.3
Total Current Assets	112.2	17,894.5	14,544.5	11,436.1
Fixed Assets, Net	0.0	0.0	0.0	0.0
Total Assets	21,547.3	18,944.5	15,691.4	13,125.0
Total Current Liabilities	264.8	186.8	277.2	146.7
Long-Term Debt	0.0	0.0	0.0	0.0
Stockholders' Equity	18,614.5	16,858.7	14,735.2	12,978.3
Performance & Financial Condition				
Return on Total Revenues %	62.46	60.89	1,943.99	41.57
Return on Avg Stockholders' Equity %	13.63	17.63	17.49	2.21
Return on Average Assets %	11.94	16.08	16.82	2.15
Current Ratio	0.42	95.78	52.47	77.94
Debt / Equity %	n.a.	n.a.	n.a.	n.a.

Compound Growth %'s	EPS %	101.83	Net Income %	101.78	Total Revenues %	76.16

Comments

The Trust has benefitted from a third consecutive year of appreciation on the value of its investment holdings. 1994 results include a one-time benefit of $2.4 million, or $47.50 per share, from changing accounting methods to reflect investments at their fair market value. Compound growth rates may be distorted because of low revenue and income in 1993 and a high revenue and income in 1996. Trust expenses totalled 1.63% of average assets during 1996. Investment Classification: Income & Value

Officers	Position	Ownership Information	
Tania Zouikin	CEO	Number of Shares Outstanding	50,860
		Market Capitalization	$ 11,443,500
		Frequency of Dividends	Quarterly
		Number of Shareholders	Under 500

Other Information				
Transfer Agent	Company Office		Where Listed	OTC-BB
Auditor	Michael K. Schaefer		Symbol	BTYM
Market Maker	Gruntal & Co., Incorporated	(800)223-7632	SIC Code	6790
	Hill Thompson Magid & Co., Inc	(800)631-3083	Employees	n.a.
Broker Dealer	OTC Specialist			

Bay Commercial Services

1495 East 14th Street   San Leandro, CA 94577   Telephone (510)357-2265   Fax (510)357-1677

Company Description

Bay Bank of Commerce, subsidiary of this holding company, commenced operations in 1981. Headquartered in downtown San Leandro, with branches in Hayward and San Ramon (opened in 1996), the Bank provides the Alameda County business community high quality banking products and emphasizes exceptional customer service with an experienced, professional staff. The Bank's Construction Lending Division provides construction financing to individuals and builders throughout the fast-growing East Bay portion of the greater San Francisco metropolitan area. Alameda County is also home to the Oakland Zoo where the animals are so happy with their all-natural environment that they are reproducing in record numbers. The Bank is only reproducing money, but, like the animals, the shareholders are smiling.

	12/31/96	12/31/95	12/31/94	12/31/93
Per Share Information				
Stock Price	10.00	8.50	5.25	4.25
Earnings Per Share	0.89	0.78	0.55	0.35
Price / Earnings Ratio	11.24	10.90	9.55	12.14
Book Value Per Share	8.75	8.14	7.36	7.07
Price / Book Value %	114.29	104.42	71.33	60.11
Dividends Per Share	0.30	0.30	0.20	0.0
Annual Financial Data				
Operating Results (000's)				
Net Interest Income	5,369.0	5,146.0	4,320.0	3,968.0
Loan Loss Provision	0.0	155.0	100.0	0.0
Non-Interest Income	1,080.0	716.0	1,076.0	1,178.0
Non-Interest Expense	-4,686.0	-4,472.0	-4,518.0	-4,626.0
Income Before Taxes and Other	1,763.0	1,545.0	978.0	520.0
Other Items	0.0	0.0	0.0	0.0
Income Tax	-680.0	-600.0	-359.0	-146.0
Net Income	1,083.0	945.0	619.0	374.0
Balance Sheet (000's)				
Cash & Securities	22,988.0	32,167.0	33,994.0	29,547.0
Loans, Net	70,391.0	57,170.0	50,810.0	48,777.0
Total Assets	96,769.0	92,819.0	89,193.0	81,895.0
Deposits	83,291.0	80,253.0	79,258.0	72,609.0
Stockholders' Equity	9,418.0	8,767.0	7,946.0	7,632.0
Performance & Financial Condition				
Return on Avg Stockholders' Equity %	11.91	11.31	7.95	5.04
Return on Average Assets %	1.14	1.04	0.72	0.46
Equity to Assets %	9.73	9.45	8.91	9.32
Net Interest Margin	6.32	6.30	5.70	n.a.
Reserve as a % of Problem Loans	223.22	991.92	120.77	n.a.

Compound Growth %'s	EPS %	36.49	Net Income %	42.53	Net Interest Income %	10.60

Comments

The Bank has expanded its marketing and business development efforts as a result of the recent merger of several local community banks into a large, multi-state bank. The San Ramon office is positioned in the fast-growing Tri-Valley area. Bay Bank of Commerce is the only bank to qualify in Alameda County as a Preferred Lender under the Small Business Administration programs. Compound growth rates may be distorted by a lower than normal income during 1993, the base year, as the Bank was recovering from a loss in the 1992 year. Investment Classification: Growth & Value

Officers	Position	Ownership Information	
Richard M. Kahler	President, CEO	Number of Shares Outstanding	1,076,720
Randall Greenfield	Senior VP	Market Capitalization	$ 10,767,200
Robert A. Perantoni	Senior VP, Sr Loan Officer	Frequency of Dividends	Quarterly
Jane C. Christopherson	Vice President, CFO	Number of Shareholders	440
Nancy Bowers	Vice President	Where Listed / Symbol	OTC-BB / BCSV

Other Information			Loan Mix	%
Transfer Agent	First Interstate Bank of California San Francisco, CA		R/E Mortgages	65.9
Auditor	Deloitte & Touche LLP		Commerical	21.8
Market Maker	Sutro & Co., Incorporated	(800)288-2811	Construction	9.5
	F.J. Morrissey & Co., Inc.	(800)842-8928	Installment	2.2
Broker Dealer	Regular Stockbroker		Other	0.6

Beaver Coal Company, Limited

668 Public Ledger Bldg. Philadelphia, PA 19106 Telephone (215)923-3641 Fax (215)923-5535

Company Description

Beaver Coal Company holds fee and mineral rights to approximately 40,000 acres of coal bearing lands and additionally holds approximately 9,800 acres without coal rights in Raleigh County, West Virginia. Timber and surface rental income are generated in addition to coal royalties. Pursuant to the liquidation of Beaver Coal Corporation in 1967, cash and coal lands were contributed in the formation of this limited partnership. This entity will continue until October 31, 2009, unless terminated before then.

	12/31/96	12/31/95	12/31/94	12/31/93
Per Unit Information				
Price Per Unit	470.00	366.00	316.00	275.00
Earnings Per Unit	62.22	42.61	35.42	33.98
Price / Earnings Ratio	7.55	8.59	8.92	8.09
Book Value Per Unit	108.51	108.51	108.31	108.31
Price / Book Value %	433.14	337.30	291.76	253.90
Distributions Per Unit	62.25	43.50	35.00	33.50
Cash Flow Per Unit	63.55	43.56	34.86	32.12
Annual Financial Data				
Operating Results (000's)				
Total Revenues	2,149.8	1,541.1	1,354.7	1,274.0
Costs & Expenses	-602.0	-481.2	-473.4	-428.6
Operating Income	1,547.8	1,060.0	881.2	845.3
Other Items	0.0	0.0	0.0	0.0
Net Income	1,547.8	1,060.0	881.2	845.3
Cash Flow From Operations	1,580.9	1,083.7	867.3	799.2
Balance Sheet (000's)				
Cash & Equivalents	152.2	56.3	184.1	175.1
Total Current Assets	172.4	162.5	184.1	175.1
Investments	n.a.	n.a.	n.a.	n.a.
Total Assets	2,768.5	2,753.7	2,759.1	2,748.7
Total Current Liabilities	11.1	10.7	33.8	0.0
Long-Term Debt	0.0	0.0	0.0	0.0
Partners' Capital	2,699.5	2,699.5	2,725.2	2,716.3
Performance & Financial Condition				
Return on Total Revenues %	72.00	68.78	65.05	66.36
Return on Average Partners' Capital %	57.34	39.08	32.39	31.18
Return on Average Assets %	56.06	38.45	32.00	30.99
Current Ratio	15.49	15.22	5.44	n.a.
Debt / Equity %	n.a.	n.a.	n.a.	n.a.

Compound Growth %'s	EPU %	22.34	Net Income %	22.34	Total Revenues %	19.06

Comments

The earnings distribution in 1996 was the highest in the last twelve years of operations as the Company experienced strong demand for coal, natural gas and timber. Substantial coal production resulted from the Baylor mine activities of lessee Western Pocahontas Corp. Increased natural gas production included results from six new wells. Gas royalties were also affected by stronger pricing. 1997 projections indicate lower levels for coal and natural gas. Investment Classification: Income

Officers	Position	Ownership Information	
Paul M. Ingersoll	President	Number of Units Outstanding	24,878
A.J. Drexel Paul, Jr.	Vice President, Secretary	Market Capitalization	$ 11,692,660
David R. Wilmerding, Jr.	Vice President, Treasurer	Frequency of Distributions	Quarterly
R. Woodrow Duba	General Manager	Number of Partners	Under 500

Other Information

Transfer Agent	Company Office		Where Listed	OTC-BB
Auditor	Price Waterhouse LLP		Symbol	BVERS
Market Maker	Herzog, Heine, Geduld, Inc.	(800)221-3600	SIC Code	1200
	Carr Securities Corporation	(800)221-2243	Employees	10
Broker Dealer	OTC Specialist			

Belle Isle Net Profits Units

P.O. Box 2009   Amarillo, TX 79189-2009   Telephone (806)378-1000   Fax (806)378-8614

Company Description

The Trust is an entity with no existing activities. Arrangements have been made whereby the unit holders receive their share of royalty payments made to the Trust. Under the terms of a 1964 agreement, Pioneer Natural Gas Company purchased certain property interests from Belle Isle Corporation, subject to specified net profits payments. In 1986, Mesa Limited Partnership, now Mesa Inc., acquired Pioneer Natural Gas Company and, accordingly, the obligations under the agreement.

	12/31/96	12/31/95	12/31/94	12/31/93
Per Share Information				
Stock Price	7.75	2.12	3.00	3.00
Earnings Per Share	1.61	0.48	0.82	0.57
Price / Earnings Ratio	4.81	4.42	3.66	5.26
Book Value Per Share	n.a.	n.a.	n.a.	n.a.
Price / Book Value %	n.a.	n.a.	n.a.	n.a.
Dividends Per Share	1.61	0.48	0.82	0.57
Annual Financial Data				
Operating Results (000's)				
Total Revenues	1,488.5	446.9	762.4	525.8
Costs & Expenses	0.0	0.0	0.0	0.0
Income Before Taxes and Other	1,488.5	446.9	762.4	525.8
Other Items	0.0	0.0	0.0	0.0
Income Tax	0.0	0.0	0.0	0.0
Net Income	1,488.5	446.9	762.4	525.8
Cash Flow From Operations	1,488.5	446.9	762.4	525.8
Balance Sheet (000's)				
Cash & Equivalents	n.a.	n.a.	n.a.	n.a.
Total Current Assets	n.a.	n.a.	n.a.	n.a.
Fixed Assets, Net	n.a.	n.a.	n.a.	n.a.
Total Assets	n.a.	n.a.	n.a.	n.a.
Total Current Liabilities	n.a.	n.a.	n.a.	n.a.
Long-Term Debt	n.a.	n.a.	n.a.	n.a.
Stockholders' Equity	n.a.	n.a.	n.a.	n.a.
Performance & Financial Condition				
Return on Total Revenues %	100.00	100.00	100.00	100.00
Return on Avg Stockholders' Equity %	n.a.	n.a.	n.a.	n.a.
Return on Average Assets %	n.a.	n.a.	n.a.	n.a.
Current Ratio	n.a.	n.a.	n.a.	n.a.
Debt / Equity %	n.a.	n.a.	n.a.	n.a.

Compound Growth %'s	EPS %	41.36	Net Income %	41.46	Total Revenues %	41.46

Comments

There is no valuation of the remaining royalty interests. Royalty payments will only cease when less than $250,000 of royalties are earned for two consecutive years. Proved oil and gas reserves are estimated each year and increased substantially during 1996. Higher prices and quantities of natural gas were the key contributors toward the increased cash flow in the latest year. Payments to the unitholders are considered royalties and may be subject to depletion deductions under current income tax regulations. Investment Classification: Income & Value

Officers	Position	Ownership Information	
Not Available		Number of Shares Outstanding	925,000
		Market Capitalization	$ 7,168,750
		Frequency of Dividends	Quarterly
		Number of Shareholders	Under 500

Other Information

Transfer Agent	American Stock Transfer & Trust Company New York, NY		Where Listed	OTC-BB
Auditor	Arthur Andersen LLP		Symbol	BISLU
Market Maker	Robotti & Co., Inc.	(212)986-0800	SIC Code	6733
	Hill Thompson Magid & Co., Inc	(800)631-3083	Employees	0
Broker Dealer	Regular Stockbroker			

BENCHMARK Bankshares, Inc.

100 South Broad Street   Kenbridge, VA 23944   Telephone (804)676-8444   Fax (804)676-2703

Company Description

Benchmark Community Bank is the operating arm of this bank holding company. Originally founded in 1970 as The Lunenburg County Bank, it has grown to six offices serving the greater population and economic bases of Prince Edward, Mecklenburg, Nottoway and Lunenburg Counties, known as Southside, Virginia. The sixth office was added in May, 1996 in the town of Crewe.

	12/31/96	12/31/95	12/31/94	12/31/93
Per Share Information				
Stock Price	17.25	14.00	13.25	12.00
Earnings Per Share	1.69	1.54	1.39	1.23
Price / Earnings Ratio	10.21	9.09	9.53	9.76
Book Value Per Share	9.91	8.72	6.94	6.12
Price / Book Value %	174.07	160.55	190.92	19.61
Dividends Per Share	0.35	0.35	0.28	0.22
Annual Financial Data				
Operating Results (000's)				
Net Interest Income	6,567.6	5,780.6	5,295.7	4,906.6
Loan Loss Provision	-295.2	-188.3	-162.8	-251.9
Non-Interest Income	565.3	602.5	531.4	533.0
Non-Interest Expense	-3,327.5	-3,047.4	-2,856.7	-2,678.5
Income Before Taxes and Other	3,510.2	3,147.5	2,807.6	2,509.3
Other Items	0.0	0.0	0.0	0.0
Income Tax	-1,063.8	-938.3	-832.9	-780.2
Net Income	2,446.5	2,209.2	1,974.6	1,729.1
Balance Sheet (000's)				
Cash & Securities	26,936.2	29,379.0	22,512.5	19,539.8
Loans, Net	118,864.3	102,410.6	89,531.7	80,501.8
Total Assets	150,907.8	135,363.5	115,306.1	102,902.6
Deposits	135,359.8	121,622.6	104,636.5	93,434.0
Stockholders' Equity	14,361.7	12,500.6	9,861.3	8,691.1
Performance & Financial Condition				
Return on Avg Stockholders' Equity %	18.21	19.76	21.29	21.65
Return on Average Assets %	1.71	1.76	1.81	1.81
Equity to Assets %	9.52	9.23	8.55	8.45
Net Interest Margin	n.a.	n.a.	n.a.	n.a.
Reserve as a % of Problem Loans	105.11	1,069.89	n.a.	n.a.

Compound Growth %'s	EPS %	11.17	Net Income %	12.26	Net Interest Income %	10.21

Comments

The Company declared a 2 for 1 stock split in 1994. 1993 per share amounts have been restated for consistency. Management credits the consistency in high earnings to the fortunate position of being able to maximize the utilization of its resources in high-yielding loans while maintaining a reasonable net interest margin between loans and deposits. The Richmond Times-Dispatch provides the lastest stock price on a daily basis. Investment Classification: Growth

Officers	Position	Ownership Information	
Ben L. Watson, III	President, CEO	Number of Shares Outstanding	1,449,896
Michael O. Walker	Senior VP	Market Capitalization	$ 25,010,706
Janice C. Whitlow	Senior VP, Head Cashier	Frequency of Dividends	Semi-Annual
Jay A. Stafford	Vice President	Number of Shareholders	n.a.
R. Marshall Womack, Jr.	Vice President	Where Listed / Symbol	OTC-BB / BMRB

Other Information			Loan Mix	%
Transfer Agent	Company Office		R/E Mortgages	53.7
Auditor	Creedle, Jones, and Alga, P.C.		Installment	18.4
Market Maker	Davenport & Co.	(800)277-0120	Other	27.9
	McKinnon & Company, Inc.	(800)846-4391		
Broker Dealer	Regular Stockbroker			

Benjamin Moore & Co.

51 Chestnut Ridge Road   Montvale, NJ 07645-1862   Telephone (201)573-9600   Fax (201)573-9046

Company Description

Benjamin Moore & Co., founded in 1883, formulates, manufactures and sells a broad line of coatings consisting of paints, stains and clear finishes for use by the general public, painting contractors and industrial and commercial users. The Company operates in both the United States and international markets and also has its own retail stores in certain markets. Benjamin Moore has reacquired more than $10 million of its shares in each of the last five years with a record $23,411,000 purchased in 1996.

	12/31/96	12/31/95	12/31/94	12/31/93
Per Share Information				
Stock Price	56.00	71.50	70.50	64.00
Earnings Per Share	4.67	3.19	4.29	3.66
Price / Earnings Ratio	11.99	22.41	16.43	17.49
Book Value Per Share	25.79	24.05	23.02	21.70
Price / Book Value %	217.14	297.30	306.26	294.93
Dividends Per Share	1.92	1.80	1.78	1.68
Annual Financial Data				
Operating Results (000's)				
Total Revenues	625,190.0	564,211.4	547,063.6	512,700.1
Costs & Expenses	-548,926.0	-509,764.3	-476,344.7	-451,749.1
Income Before Taxes and Other	74,188.0	52,800.0	70,366.2	60,950.9
Other Items	823.0	210.7	-626.0	-543.0
Income Tax	-31,672.0	-22,554.6	-28,417.7	-23,897.1
Net Income	43,339.0	30,456.1	41,322.4	36,510.9
Cash Flow From Operations	52,971.0	19,978.3	48,300.5	32,281.8
Balance Sheet (000's)				
Cash & Equivalents	3,365.0	11,232.3	3,435.1	5,011.5
Total Current Assets	211,601.0	207,284.4	192,185.1	185,197.8
Fixed Assets, Net	80,169.0	78,360.8	74,268.5	60,269.7
Total Assets	330,382.0	330,155.3	304,087.8	276,040.1
Total Current Liabilities	82,080.0	85,487.0	65,479.3	51,996.0
Long-Term Debt	3,239.0	3,968.1	5,005.5	6,477.2
Stockholders' Equity	232,933.0	227,660.8	221,538.4	209,760.3
Performance & Financial Condition				
Return on Total Revenues %	6.93	5.40	7.55	7.12
Return on Avg Stockholders' Equity %	18.82	13.56	19.16	17.86
Return on Average Assets %	13.12	9.60	14.25	13.53
Current Ratio	2.58	2.42	2.94	3.56
Debt / Equity %	1.39	1.74	2.26	3.09

Compound Growth %'s	EPS %	8.46	Net Income %	5.88	Total Revenues %	6.84

Comments

After a disappointing 1995 which was hurt by unanticipated raw material cost increases that could not be recouped through price increases, 1996 results were aided by an overall decrease in such costs. In the latter part of 1996, the Company began the manufacture and sale of the Crayola Paints line under a license agreement. After success in the Boston and New York test markets, it was rolled out nationally in early 1997. Management sees substantial growth opportunities within the independent dealer channel of distribution including a substantial increase in the Company's share of the medium and large contractor segments of the business. Investment Classification: Value

Officers	Position	Ownership Information	
Richard Roob	Chairman, CEO	Number of Shares Outstanding	9,033,585
Yvan Dupuy	President, COO	Market Capitalization	$ 505,880,760
Benjamin M. Belcher, Jr.	Exec VP	Frequency of Dividends	Quarterly
William J. Foote	VP - Finance	Number of Shareholders	1,750
Donald W. Everett	VP - Sales		

Other Information

Transfer Agent	Company Office		Where Listed	OTC-PS
Auditor	Deloitte & Touche LLP		Symbol	MBEN
Market Maker	Ernst & Company	(800)845-4330	SIC Code	2851
	Howe Barnes Investments, Inc.	(800)621-2364	Employees	2000
Broker Dealer	Regular Stockbroker			

Best Lock Corporation

P.O. Box 50444   Indianapolis, IN 46250   Telephone (317)849-2250   Fax (317)595-7626

Company Description

Best Lock Corporation's principal business is the manufacture, distribution and sale of access control products and services, including locks and lock components. The Company specializes in providing locking systems for commercial end-users, including institutional, industrial and government facilities. The Company was formed in 1928 and has two non-operating parent companies. Its immediate parent, Best Universal Lock Co. owns 79% of the Company. Frank E. Best, Inc., in turn, owns 83% of Universal. All three companies are traded on the electronic bulletin board and are presented in this manual. For the quarter ended March 31, 1997, revenues were up 21% and earnings per share were $9.71.

	12/31/96	12/31/95	12/31/94	12/31/93
Per Share Information				
Stock Price	100.00	220.00	325.00	370.00
Earnings Per Share	28.43	-33.88	16.83	13.73
Price / Earnings Ratio	3.52	n.a.	19.31	26.95
Book Value Per Share	225.96	208.38	312.61	370.00
Price / Book Value %	44.26	105.58	103.96	100.00
Dividends Per Share	5.42	5.41	5.40	5.00
Annual Financial Data				
Operating Results (000's)				
Total Revenues	122,630.7	118,546.5	104,669.0	98,731.2
Costs & Expenses	-116,583.1	-124,620.8	-101,891.1	-96,700.0
Income Before Taxes and Other	6,047.5	-6,563.9	2,403.4	2,031.2
Other Items	0.0	0.0	0.0	0.0
Income Tax	-2,592.9	2,359.4	-195.3	-881.7
Net Income	3,454.6	-4,204.5	2,208.2	1,149.5
Cash Flow From Operations	3,324.1	1,376.0	11,053.6	5,391.9
Balance Sheet (000's)				
Cash & Equivalents	2,049.0	1,348.9	4,792.1	1,602.5
Total Current Assets	37,356.0	33,502.8	37,364.7	33,092.5
Fixed Assets, Net	26,895.7	30,871.6	30,137.1	30,789.3
Total Assets	68,882.5	69,016.9	71,003.4	64,217.0
Total Current Liabilities	15,017.3	16,546.2	14,339.7	8,517.0
Long-Term Debt	15,000.0	15,197.1	0.0	0.0
Stockholders' Equity	33,346.5	31,282.3	49,949.4	48,559.7
Performance & Financial Condition				
Return on Total Revenues %	2.82	-3.55	2.11	1.16
Return on Avg Stockholders' Equity %	10.69	-10.35	4.48	2.39
Return on Average Assets %	5.01	-6.01	3.27	1.82
Current Ratio	2.49	2.02	2.61	3.89
Debt / Equity %	44.98	48.58	n.a.	n.a.

Compound Growth %'s	EPS % n.a.	Net Income % n.a.	Total Revenues % n.a.

Comments

The Company experienced record sales in 1995. However, several factors arose during the year resulting in the Company posting a significant loss. But 1996 was a rebound year as gross margin improved to 47.7% of sales, compared to 41.0% in the prior year. Sales were only modestly higher in 1996. However the year end backlog improved to $4.7 million from $4.2 million in 1995. The Company has the value of its shares determined by a third party professional appraiser each year for the purpose of the Best Lock Corporation Stock Bonus Plan. The value at December 31, 1996 was $400 per share. Investment Classification: Value & Income

Officers	Position	Ownership Information	
Walter E. Best	Chairman, President	Number of Shares Outstanding	120,654
Russell C. Best	CEO	Market Capitalization	$ 12,065,400
Roger E. Beaverson	Treasurer, Secretary	Frequency of Dividends	Annual
Gregg A. Dykstra	Vice President	Number of Shareholders	197
Richard E. Best	Vice President		

Other Information				
Transfer Agent	Company Office		Where Listed	OTC-BB
Auditor	Arthur Andersen LLP		Symbol	BLOC
Market Maker	Martin Nelson & Co., Inc.	(206)682-6261	SIC Code	3429
	Howe Barnes Investments, Inc.	(800)621-2364	Employees	1195
Broker Dealer	OTC Specialist			

Best Universal Lock Co.

P.O. Box 50444   Indianapolis, IN 46250   Telephone (317)849-2250   Fax (317)595-7626

Company Description

Best Universal Lock Co. is a nonoperating holding company. It owns a 79% interest in Best Lock Corporation which manufactures, distributes and sells access control products and services, including locks and lock components with a specialization in providing locking systems for commercial end-users, including institutional, industrial and government facilities. Frank E. Best, Inc. owns 83% of Best Universal Lock Co. All three companies are traded on the electronic bulletin board and are presented in this manual.

	12/31/96	12/31/95	12/31/94	12/31/93
Per Share Information				
Stock Price	32.00	38.00	62.50	63.00
Earnings Per Share	8.11	-9.95	3.92	3.30
Price / Earnings Ratio	3.95	n.a.	15.94	19.09
Book Value Per Share	60.66	55.23	93.82	91.29
Price / Book Value %	52.75	68.80	66.62	69.01
Dividends Per Share	1.67	1.66	1.63	1.61
Annual Financial Data				
Operating Results (000's)				
Total Revenues	2,975.5	-3,682.9	1,554.3	1,310.2
Costs & Expenses	-50.1	-55.6	-39.3	-34.4
Income Before Taxes and Other	2,925.3	-3,738.5	1,514.9	1,275.9
Other Items	0.0	0.0	0.0	0.0
Income Tax	0.0	0.0	0.0	0.0
Net Income	2,925.3	-3,738.5	1,514.9	1,275.9
Cash Flow From Operations	-29.7	-18.3	450.8	447.1
Balance Sheet (000's)				
Cash & Equivalents	50.9	41.0	23.8	43.9
Total Current Assets	50.9	41.0	23.8	35,400.2
Fixed Assets, Net	0.0	0.0	0.0	0.0
Total Assets	21,971.0	19,995.0	36,353.2	35,400.2
Total Current Liabilities	138.2	87.4	94.4	120.3
Long-Term Debt	0.0	0.0	0.0	0.0
Stockholders' Equity	21,814.1	19,863.3	36,258.7	35,279.9
Performance & Financial Condition				
Return on Total Revenues %	98.32	101.51	97.47	97.38
Return on Avg Stockholders' Equity %	14.04	-13.32	4.24	3.77
Return on Average Assets %	13.94	-13.27	4.22	3.78
Current Ratio	0.37	0.47	0.25	294.37
Debt / Equity %	n.a.	n.a.	n.a.	n.a.

Compound Growth %'s	EPS %	34.95	Net Income %	31.86	Total Revenues %	31.44

Comments

The only significant asset of the Company is its investment in Best Lock Corporation, which is carried at book value. The only item of income or loss is its share of income of Best Lock Corporation, reported under the equity method of accounting. Please refer to the comments on Best Lock Corporation for information as to recent operations. Based on the independent appraisal of Best Lock Corporation at $400 per share, which is significantly higher than its trading range, Best Universal Lock would be worth about $106 per share, also higher than its trading range. Investment Classification: Value & Income

Officers	Position	Ownership Information	
Russell C. Best	President, CEO	Number of Shares Outstanding	359,637
Mark G. Ahearn	Secretary	Market Capitalization	$ 11,508,384
Stephen J. Cooper	Treasurer	Frequency of Dividends	Quarterly
Paula J. Tinkey	Controller	Number of Shareholders	711

Other Information

Transfer Agent	Company Office		Where Listed	OTC-BB
Auditor	Arthur Andersen LLP		Symbol	BUNIA
Market Maker	Hill Thompson Magid & Co., Inc	(800)631-3083	SIC Code	3420
	Howe Barnes Investments, Inc.	(800)621-2364	Employees	n.a.
Broker Dealer	OTC Specialist			

Best, Inc., Frank E.

P.O. Box 50444   Indianapolis, IN 46250   Telephone (317)849-2250   Fax (317)595-7626

Company Description

Frank E. Best, Inc. is a nonoperating holding company. It owns an 83% interest in Best Universal Lock Co., also a nonoperating holding company, which owns a 79% interest in Best Lock Corporation which manufactures, distributes and sells access control products and services, including locks and lock components with a specialization in providing locking systems for commercial end-users, including institutional, industrial and governmental facilities. All three companies are traded on the electronic bulletin board and are presented in this manual.

	12/31/96	12/31/95	12/31/94	12/31/93
Per Share Information				
Stock Price	17.75	19.50	24.00	28.00
Earnings Per Share	4.89	-6.24	2.53	2.13
Price / Earnings Ratio	3.63	n.a.	9.49	13.15
Book Value Per Share	28.87	25.87	46.86	45.52
Price / Book Value %	61.48	75.38	51.22	61.51
Dividends Per Share	0.54	0.53	0.52	0.51
Annual Financial Data				
Operating Results (000's)				
Total Revenues	2,486.4	-3,212.3	1,175.7	1,059.0
Costs & Expenses	0.0	-42.8	-22.4	0.0
Income Before Taxes and Other	2,486.4	-3,255.1	1,153.3	1,059.0
Other Items	0.0	0.0	0.0	0.0
Income Tax	0.0	0.0	0.0	0.0
Net Income	2,486.4	-3,255.1	1,153.3	1,059.0
Cash Flow From Operations	314.3	313.1	280.5	300.0
Balance Sheet (000's)				
Cash & Equivalents	14.2	23.5	27.7	20.0
Total Current Assets	14.2	23.5	27.7	20.0
Fixed Assets, Net	0.0	0.0	0.0	0.0
Total Assets	17,450.3	15,630.9	28,170.2	27,353.4
Total Current Liabilities	166.0	139.4	113.5	100.0
Long-Term Debt	0.0	0.0	0.0	0.0
Stockholders' Equity	17,284.3	15,491.4	28,056.7	27,253.4
Performance & Financial Condition				
Return on Total Revenues %	100.00	101.33	98.09	100.00
Return on Avg Stockholders' Equity %	15.17	-14.95	4.17	3.92
Return on Average Assets %	15.03	-14.86	4.15	3.92
Current Ratio	0.09	0.17	0.24	0.20
Debt / Equity %	n.a.	n.a.	n.a.	n.a.

Compound Growth %'s	EPS %	31.92	Net Income %	32.91	Total Revenues %	32.91

Comments

The only significant asset of the Company is its investment in Best Universal Lock Co., which is carried at book value. The only item of income or loss is its share of income of Best Universal Lock, reported under the equity method of accounting. Since Best Universal Lock is also a holding company, please refer to the comments on Best Lock Corporation for information as to recent operations. Based on the independent appraisal of Best Lock Corporation at $400 per share, which is significantly higher than its trading range, Best Universal Lock would be worth about $106 per share and Frank E. Best Co. would the be worth about $52 per share, which is also significantly higher than its trading range. Investment Classification: Value

Officers	Position	Ownership Information	
Not Available		Number of Shares Outstanding	598,710
		Market Capitalization	$ 10,627,103
		Frequency of Dividends	Quarterly
		Number of Shareholders	557

Other Information			
Transfer Agent	Company Office	Where Listed	OTC-BB
Auditor	Arthur Andersen LLP	Symbol	BFKR
Market Maker	Southwest Securities, Inc. (800)527-7655	SIC Code	3420
	Howe Barnes Investments, Inc. (800)621-2364	Employees	n.a.
Broker Dealer	Regular Stockbroker		

Biddeford and Saco Water Company

181 Elm Street   Biddeford, ME 04005-2351   Telephone (207)282-1543   Fax (207)282-1544

Company Description

The Company provides water service to individuals, businesses and government agencies in Biddeford, Saco, Old Orchard Beach, Scarborough, Old Orchard Beach, Pine Port, Kennebunk, Kennebunkport and Wells Water District, all in coastal Maine. The Company is also authorized to serve Dayton and Lyman. Rates for water are regulated by the Maine Public Utilities Commission. Biddeford and Saco Water Company was formed in 1880.

	12/31/96	12/31/95	12/31/94	12/31/93
Per Share Information				
Stock Price	48.50	46.50	44.00	42.00
Earnings Per Share	3.18	3.74	3.54	3.63
Price / Earnings Ratio	15.25	12.43	12.43	11.57
Book Value Per Share	46.62	46.44	50.57	50.04
Price / Book Value %	104.03	100.13	87.01	83.93
Dividends Per Share	3.00	3.00	3.00	3.00
Annual Financial Data				
Operating Results (000's)				
Total Revenues	3,193.6	3,201.2	3,100.2	2,943.9
Costs & Expenses	-2,669.5	-2,543.6	-2,734.1	-2,562.9
Income Before Taxes and Other	515.6	657.1	366.1	381.0
Other Items	0.0	0.0	0.0	-17.5
Income Tax	-178.2	-260.8	-25.0	-13.0
Net Income	337.4	396.3	341.1	350.5
Cash Flow From Operations	818.2	894.9	688.6	648.6
Balance Sheet (000's)				
Cash & Equivalents	30.3	79.0	261.8	504.0
Total Current Assets	754.6	872.6	1,162.6	1,312.1
Fixed Assets, Net	12,569.3	12,361.3	11,921.9	11,636.2
Total Assets	13,604.6	13,496.2	13,331.7	13,149.8
Total Current Liabilities	564.2	531.3	435.9	349.1
Long-Term Debt	4,225.0	4,275.0	4,325.0	4,375.0
Stockholders' Equity	4,946.6	4,927.5	4,878.2	4,826.5
Performance & Financial Condition				
Return on Total Revenues %	10.56	12.38	11.00	11.90
Return on Avg Stockholders' Equity %	6.83	8.08	7.03	7.31
Return on Average Assets %	2.49	2.95	2.58	2.75
Current Ratio	1.34	1.64	2.67	3.76
Debt / Equity %	85.41	86.76	88.66	90.65

Compound Growth %'s	EPS %	-4.32	Net Income %	-1.26	Total Revenues %	2.75

Comments

The fortunes of most water companies are loosely tied to the whims of Mother Nature. When weather is good, maintenance expenses tend to go down and sales rise, while bad weather tends to push in the opposite direction. With harsh winter weather, including well over 100 inches of snow, and record rain throughout most of the year, 1996 was a bad weather year. Over 100 new homes were constructed during 1996 in the service area. Management reports that 1997 should be an improved year. Investment Classification: Income & Value

Officers	Position	Ownership Information	
Harry M. Wooster	Chairman	Number of Shares Outstanding	106,104
Clifford S. Mansfield, Jr.	President, Treasurer	Market Capitalization	$ 5,146,044
John W. L. White	Senior Clerk	Frequency of Dividends	Annual
Robert R. Theriault	Other	Number of Shareholders	Under 500

Other Information

			Where Listed	OTC-BB
Transfer Agent	Company Office		Symbol	BIDS
Auditor	Berry, Dunn, McNeil & Parker		SIC Code	4940
Market Maker	Gruntal & Co., Incorporated	(800)225-8520	Employees	28
Broker Dealer	OTC Specialist			
	Norman Kadehjian - Wainwright	(800)727-7176		

Biochem International Inc.

W238 N1650 Rockwood Drive   Waukesha, WI 53188-1199   Telephone (414)542-3100   Fax (414)523-4313

Company Description

Biochem International is a designer and manufacturer of patient monitoring equipment. The Company's products are used to monitor respiration, gases, blood pressure and related cardiovascular/pulmonary functions. The Company was formed in 1976 in order to acquire certain assets, patents and technology associated with its blood gas chemistry business from General Electric. At June 30, 1996, officers and directors owned 79% of the outstanding common shares.

	06/30/96	06/30/95	06/30/94	06/30/93
Per Share Information				
Stock Price as of 12/31	4.87	4.31	3.06	0.31
Earnings Per Share	0.41	0.32	0.56	0.14
Price / Earnings Ratio	11.88	13.47	5.46	2.21
Book Value Per Share	1.18	0.77	0.45	-0.12
Price / Book Value %	412.71	559.74	680.00	n.a.
Dividends Per Share	0.0	0.0	0.0	0.0
Annual Financial Data				
Operating Results (000's)				
Total Revenues	29,377.5	25,207.3	17,972.0	12,895.9
Costs & Expenses	-20,906.0	-18,472.7	-14,468.4	-11,041.3
Income Before Taxes and Other	8,471.5	6,734.6	3,503.6	1,854.6
Other Items	0.0	0.0	5,196.6	0.0
Income Tax	-3,101.8	-2,474.8	-1,308.8	-46.2
Net Income	5,369.7	4,259.8	7,391.4	1,808.4
Cash Flow From Operations	5,906.4	6,230.6	2,853.7	1,068.0
Balance Sheet (000's)				
Cash & Equivalents	6,034.3	2,628.4	1,756.6	40.3
Total Current Assets	14,703.7	10,579.9	10,062.5	4,746.9
Fixed Assets, Net	1,711.9	1,437.7	431.2	345.0
Total Assets	18,428.8	12,304.9	12,767.1	5,093.8
Total Current Liabilities	2,921.8	2,191.5	6,916.1	2,693.8
Long-Term Debt	0.0	0.0	0.0	3,948.4
Stockholders' Equity	15,484.5	10,113.3	5,851.0	-1,548.4
Performance & Financial Condition				
Return on Total Revenues %	18.28	16.90	41.13	14.02
Return on Avg Stockholders' Equity %	41.95	53.37	343.58	n.a.
Return on Average Assets %	34.94	33.98	82.77	42.14
Current Ratio	5.03	4.83	1.45	1.76
Debt / Equity %	n.a.	n.a.	n.a.	n.a.

Compound Growth %'s	EPS % 43.07	Net Income % 43.73	Total Revenues % 31.58

Comments

Revenue growth of 11.7% in fiscal 1996 led to a healthy increase in net earnings. 75% of the additional revenue was attributable to export sales, principally to the Far East, Central and South America and Western Europe. For the first nine months of fiscal 1997, the Company reported earnings of $.25 per share as compared to $.29 for the same period during 1996. Biochem has plenty of cash and no long term debt. Investment Classification: Growth

Officers	Position	Ownership Information	
David H. Sanders	Chairman, CEO	Number of Shares Outstanding	13,086,784
Frank A. Katarow	President, COO	Market Capitalization	$ 63,732,638
Keith R. Harper	Senior VP	Frequency of Dividends	n.a.
Ann M. Johnson	VP - Finance	Number of Shareholders	750
Ken M. Davee	Secretary		

Other Information

Transfer Agent	First Bank Milwaukee,		Where Listed	OTC-BB
Auditor	Coopers & Lybrand L.L.P.		Symbol	BCHM
Market Maker	Robert W. Baird & Co., Inc.	(800)562-2288	SIC Code	3845
	The Seidler Companies Inc.	(800)421-0164	Employees	106
Broker Dealer	Regular Stockbroker			

Birmingham Utilities, Inc.

230 Beaver Street   Ansonia, CT 64010-0426   Telephone (203)735-1888   Fax (203)732-2616

Company Description

Birmingham Utilities, Inc., formerly Ansonia-Derby Water Co., is a public service corporation in the business of collecting and distributing water for domestic, commercial and industrial uses and fire protection in Ansonia and Derby, Connecticut, and in small parts of the contiguous Town of Seymour. With less than a million shares outstanding and largely closely-held, the Company has characteristics of an over-the-counter stock although it technically is listed on NASDAQ. It, as well as three other stocks of this nature, are included in the manual to test reader interest. The others are Farmer Bros. Co., Paradise Inc. and Pennichuck Corporation.

	12/31/96	12/31/95	12/31/94
Per Share Information			
Stock Price	8.50	10.00	10.50
Earnings Per Share	1.02	0.69	0.48
Price / Earnings Ratio	8.33	14.49	21.88
Book Value Per Share	5.07	4.53	4.29
Price / Book Value %	167.65	220.75	244.76
Dividends Per Share	0.50	0.48	0.48
Annual Financial Data			
Operating Results (000's)			
Total Revenues	5,112.7	4,865.2	4,240.8
Costs & Expenses	-4,114.4	-4,204.7	-3,908.5
Income Before Taxes and Other	1,159.3	782.4	458.4
Other Items	0.0	0.0	0.0
Income Tax	-394.6	-264.3	-95.9
Net Income	764.7	518.1	362.5
Cash Flow From Operations	348.8	471.2	333.6
Balance Sheet (000's)			
Cash & Equivalents	185.5	398.9	59.0
Total Current Assets	1,364.6	1,614.9	1,559.0
Fixed Assets, Net	12,294.9	11,222.0	11,687.0
Total Assets	15,568.4	14,623.8	15,246.0
Total Current Liabilities	1,041.3	749.5	165.0
Long-Term Debt	5,981.0	6,000.6	6,329.0
Stockholders' Equity	3,841.0	3,407.6	3,220.0
Performance & Financial Condition			
Return on Total Revenues %	14.96	10.65	8.55
Return on Avg Stockholders' Equity %	21.10	15.63	11.26
Return on Average Assets %	5.07	3.47	2.43
Current Ratio	1.31	2.15	9.45
Debt / Equity %	155.72	176.09	196.55

Compound Growth %'s	EPS % 45.77	Net Income % 45.24	Total Revenues % 9.80

Comments

The Company is regulated by the Connecticut Department of Public Utility Control. 1996 and 1995 earnings include nonrecurring gains on the sale of land of $386,709 and $279,101, respectively. The Company has entered a non-binding agreement to sell 145 acres of land to the City of Derby for $1.8 million and has also received approval to sell six building lots. These transactions, if completed, could add considerable strength to the balance sheet. Investment Classification: Income & Value

Officers	Position	Ownership Information	
Betsy Henley-Cohn	Chairman	Number of Shares Outstanding	757,892
Aldore J. Rivers	President, CEO	Market Capitalization	$ 6,442,082
Anne A. Hobson	Secretary	Frequency of Dividends	Quarterly
John J. Keefe, Jr.	Vice President	Number of Shareholders	n.a.
Diane G. DeBiase	Other		

Other Information			
Transfer Agent	American Stock Transfer & Trust Company New York, NY	Where Listed	NASDAQ
Auditor	Dworken Hillman LaMorte et al	Symbol	BIRM
Market Maker	Legg Mason Wood Walker, Inc. (800)221-9732	SIC Code	4940
	Dorsey Investment Securities (800)375-5431	Employees	18
Broker Dealer	Regular Stockbroker		
	Stephen Schuller - Dorsey (800)375-5431		

Bismarck Hotel Company

171 West Randolph Street   Chicago, IL 60601   Telephone (312)236-0123   Fax (312)236-3177

Company Description

The Company owns and operates a 500 room hotel located on The Loop in downtown Chicago and an adjacent office building. The hotel is 102 years old and, although it had been restored to much of its original grandeur, is reportedly in need of some additional work. American Mart Corporation, a subsidiary of the Wirtz Corporation, owns an 80.7% interest in the Company.

	06/30/96	06/30/95	06/30/94
Per Share Information			
Stock Price as of 12/31	40.00	35.00	45.00
Earnings Per Share	-12.67	-40.34	-27.32
Price / Earnings Ratio	n.a.	n.a.	n.a.
Book Value Per Share	-114.91	-102.24	-61.90
Price / Book Value %	n.a.	n.a.	n.a.
Dividends Per Share	0.0	0.0	0.0
Annual Financial Data			
Operating Results (000's)			
Total Revenues	13,065.2	11,604.0	10,240.0
Costs & Expenses	-13,847.2	-14,323.4	-12,060.5
Income Before Taxes and Other	-782.0	-2,719.4	-1,820.5
Other Items	0.0	0.0	0.0
Income Tax	244.0	1,006.0	660.0
Net Income	-538.0	-1,713.4	-1,160.5
Cash Flow From Operations	270.4	-2,011.2	-671.6
Balance Sheet (000's)			
Cash & Equivalents	320.0	0.0	205.2
Total Current Assets	1,479.9	1,888.2	1,710.7
Fixed Assets, Net	4,310.9	4,012.5	3,587.4
Total Assets	5,790.8	5,900.6	5,298.1
Total Current Liabilities	10,589.5	10,204.0	7,869.4
Long-Term Debt	0.0	0.0	0.0
Stockholders' Equity	-4,880.3	-4,342.3	-2,629.0
Performance & Financial Condition			
Return on Total Revenues %	-4.12	-14.77	-11.33
Return on Avg Stockholders' Equity %	n.a.	n.a.	n.a.
Return on Average Assets %	-9.20	-30.60	n.a.
Current Ratio	0.14	0.19	0.22
Debt / Equity %	n.a.	n.a.	n.a.

Compound Growth %'s	EPS % n.a.	Net Income % n.a.	Total Revenues % 12.96

Comments

Last year we reported that although the Company currently shows an operating loss, one would have to factor in the potential value of this historic property in any analysis. On November 19, 1996, management reported that, subject only to shareholder approval, the property was sold for $20.5 million. If the proceeds are not invested in like-kind property to defer income tax, it is likely that the Company will be liquidated. A spokesperson for Bismarck Hotel Company estimated the liquidation payment, should it occur, at between $100 and $125 per share. Investment Classification: Value & Speculative

Officers	Position	Ownership Information	
William Wirtz	Chairman, CEO	Number of Shares Outstanding	42,472
Linda Boskelly	Controller	Market Capitalization	$ 1,698,880
		Frequency of Dividends	n.a.
		Number of Shareholders	Under 500

Other Information			
Transfer Agent	First Trust of Illinois, N.A. Chicago, IL	Where Listed	OTC-BB
Auditor	Kupferberg, Goldberg & Neimark	Symbol	BSMK
Market Maker	Chicago Corporation, The	(800)621-1674	SIC Code	7000
	Howe Barnes Investments, Inc.	(800)621-2364	Employees	n.a.
Broker Dealer	OTC Specialist		

Bison Instruments, Inc.

5610 Rowland Road   Minneapolis, MN 55343-8956   Telephone (612)931-0051   Fax (612)931-0997

Company Description

Bison Instruments, Inc. develops, markets and sells instrumentation for applied earth sciences. Since its founding in 1964, the Company has developed portable, reliable and rugged seismographs, resistivity meters, ground penetrating radar, magnetometers, seismic accessories, outdoor computers, analysis and application software and 3-D seismic imaging software. 60% of sales are made outside the United States.

	10/31/96	10/31/95	10/31/94	10/31/93
Per Share Information				
Stock Price as of 12/31	3.50	4.00	4.00	2.25
Earnings Per Share	-0.03	-0.39	0.25	-0.19
Price / Earnings Ratio	n.a.	n.a.	16.00	n.a.
Book Value Per Share	1.69	1.71	2.10	1.88
Price / Book Value %	207.10	233.92	190.48	119.68
Dividends Per Share	0.0	0.0	0.04	0.0
Annual Financial Data				
Operating Results (000's)				
Total Revenues	3,091.8	2,497.5	3,351.8	2,088.3
Costs & Expenses	-3,114.6	-2,985.3	-3,052.5	-2,348.6
Income Before Taxes and Other	-22.8	-487.8	299.4	-260.3
Other Items	0.0	0.0	0.0	0.0
Income Tax	0.0	144.9	-73.9	87.0
Net Income	-22.8	-342.9	225.4	-173.3
Cash Flow From Operations	108.0	-127.8	296.8	245.3
Balance Sheet (000's)				
Cash & Equivalents	50.7	18.4	120.7	239.4
Total Current Assets	1,972.4	1,749.8	1,803.1	1,461.0
Fixed Assets, Net	193.7	196.7	237.8	300.4
Total Assets	2,309.2	2,157.3	2,268.9	1,781.2
Total Current Liabilities	807.2	625.3	373.8	96.5
Long-Term Debt	0.0	5.3	21.7	0.0
Stockholders' Equity	1,500.1	1,522.9	1,865.8	1,676.0
Performance & Financial Condition				
Return on Total Revenues %	-0.74	-13.73	6.73	-8.30
Return on Avg Stockholders' Equity %	-1.51	-20.24	12.73	n.a.
Return on Average Assets %	-1.02	-15.49	11.13	n.a.
Current Ratio	2.44	2.80	4.82	15.13
Debt / Equity %	n.a.	0.35	1.16	n.a.

Compound Growth %'s	EPS % n.a.	Net Income % n.a.	Total Revenues % 13.97

Comments

Sales have fluctuated over recent years with only a little momentum to the upside. Although the balance sheet is strong for this relatively small company, there has been no indication that management is concerned about expanding the business and, ultimately, paying a dividend to its shareholders. Investment Classification: Speculative

Officers	Position	Ownership Information	
Nicholas Jermihov	President, COO	Number of Shares Outstanding	889,890
Kenneth J. Abdo	Secretary	Market Capitalization	$ 3,114,615
		Frequency of Dividends	n.a.
		Number of Shareholders	Under 500

Other Information

Transfer Agent	Company Office		Where Listed	OTC-PS
Auditor	KPMG Peat Marwick LLP		Symbol	BSOI
Market Maker	R. J Steichen and Co.	(800)328-8217	SIC Code	3500
			Employees	n.a.
Broker Dealer	Regular Stockbroker			

Blue Diamond Coal Company

P.O. Box 59015   Knoxville, TN 37950-9015   Telephone (423)588-8511   Fax (423)584-5080

Company Description

Blue Diamond Coal Company is in the business of leasing coal properties and the purchasing, processing and selling of bituminous coal. Most of the Company's operations are located in Kentucky. Beginning in 1991, and lasting until April, 1995, the Company was operating under protection of the bankruptcy court. In January and May, 1993, pursuant to a plan of reorganization, 30% of the then outstanding common shares were issued to creditors as partial payment for their claims and 30% to an equity investor for cash. The Company was originally formed in 1922.

	03/31/96	03/31/95	03/31/94	03/31/93
Per Share Information				
Stock Price as of 12/31	23.00	14.25	13.00	7.75
Earnings Per Share	5.61	3.97	-30.38	1.67
Price / Earnings Ratio	4.10	3.59	n.a.	4.64
Book Value Per Share	32.43	26.80	22.80	53.09
Price / Book Value %	70.92	53.17	57.02	14.60
Dividends Per Share	0.0	0.0	0.0	0.0
Annual Financial Data				
Operating Results (000's)				
Total Revenues	89,966.8	77,253.6	69,276.5	65,029.2
Costs & Expenses	-87,566.0	-73,540.5	-63,824.3	-64,094.1
Income Before Taxes and Other	2,400.9	3,713.1	5,452.2	935.1
Other Items	2,674.1	0.0	-31,891.1	571.0
Income Tax	167.0	0.0	-1,970.4	-655.1
Net Income	5,242.0	3,713.1	-28,409.3	851.0
Cash Flow From Operations	2,700.0	4,724.0	9,601.1	7,793.3
Balance Sheet (000's)				
Cash & Equivalents	304.8	694.8	1,453.6	496.5
Total Current Assets	15,600.2	12,002.5	10,121.8	10,536.2
Fixed Assets, Net	68,819.5	72,211.9	74,439.8	75,870.5
Total Assets	86,845.6	86,053.7	86,817.9	89,055.2
Total Current Liabilities	13,898.0	12,011.6	10,648.2	9,789.0
Long-Term Debt	7,200.2	17,204.1	21,100.0	24,383.4
Stockholders' Equity	30,325.0	25,067.3	21,322.4	49,659.2
Performance & Financial Condition				
Return on Total Revenues %	5.83	4.81	-41.01	1.31
Return on Avg Stockholders' Equity %	18.93	16.01	-80.05	1.84
Return on Average Assets %	6.06	4.30	-32.31	0.93
Current Ratio	1.12	1.00	0.95	1.08
Debt / Equity %	23.74	68.63	98.96	49.10

Compound Growth %'s	EPS %	49.77	Net Income %	83.31	Total Revenues %	11.43

Comments

During the year ended March 31, 1994, the Company accrued a liability for coal miners retiree health care of $26.6 million which is included as a charge to income and reflected in Other Items. The combination of the highest average selling price per ton that has been realized in the past five years and higher volume of production are the main reasons for the improved profitability. For the nine months ended December 31, 1996, the Company had total revenues of $65.7 million and net income of $2.7 million ($2.74 per share) as compared to $62 million and $4.2 million ($4.12 per share) for the same period in 1995. Investment Classification: Value

Officers	Position	Ownership Information	
Ted B. Helms	President	Number of Shares Outstanding	935,220
William S. Lyon, III	Treasurer	Market Capitalization	$ 21,510,060
K. Roger Foster	Vice President, Secretary	Frequency of Dividends	n.a.
John E. Way, Jr.	Vice President	Number of Shareholders	442

Other Information

			Where Listed	OTC-BB
Transfer Agent	Company Office - K. Roger Foster		Symbol	BLDC
Auditor	Coulter & Justus PC		SIC Code	1221
Market Maker	Carr Securities Corporation	(800)221-2243	Employees	51
	Robotti & Co., Inc.	(212)986-0800		
Broker Dealer	Regular Stockbroker			

Blue Fish Clothing, Inc.

No. 3 Sixth Street   Frenchtown, NJ 08825   Telephone (908)996-7333   Fax (908)996-7151

Company Description

The Company is a designer, manufacturer, wholesaler and retailer of hand block-printed women's and children's clothing and home accessories sold to upscale department and specialty stores and through three Company-owned stores. The Company has an attractive product brochure which you can obtain by calling (908)996-7333. The Company completed its initial public offering with the issuance of 787,200 shares at $5 per share. The stock began trading on May 14, 1996. The proceeds are being used for store expansion, management information systems and working capital. The Company was founded in 1985.

	12/31/96	12/31/95	12/31/94	12/31/93
Per Share Information				
Stock Price	5.50	n.a.	n.a.	n.a.
Earnings Per Share	-0.04	n.a.	n.a.	n.a.
Price / Earnings Ratio	n.a.	n.a.	n.a.	n.a.
Book Value Per Share	0.82	n.a.	n.a.	n.a.
Price / Book Value %	670.73	n.a.	n.a.	n.a.
Dividends Per Share	0.0	n.a.	n.a.	n.a.
Annual Financial Data				
Operating Results (000's)				
Total Revenues	11,610.9	9,657.8	7,651.7	5,212.1
Costs & Expenses	-11,886.0	-9,018.7	-6,800.2	-4,916.4
Income Before Taxes and Other	-275.1	-234.2	851.5	295.7
Other Items	0.0	0.0	0.0	0.0
Income Tax	238.0	-13.5	-355.1	-123.3
Net Income	-37.1	-247.7	496.4	172.4
Cash Flow From Operations	-1,155.3	347.5	350.6	86.6
Balance Sheet (000's)				
Cash & Equivalents	1,888.0	124.9	348.7	n.a.
Total Current Assets	5,745.3	3,071.6	2,623.8	n.a.
Fixed Assets, Net	1,113.4	743.2	586.9	n.a.
Total Assets	7,129.2	4,438.5	3,345.7	n.a.
Total Current Liabilities	2,878.9	3,150.9	2,205.8	n.a.
Long-Term Debt	483.0	109.6	239.4	n.a.
Stockholders' Equity	3,767.3	991.1	900.6	n.a.
Performance & Financial Condition				
Return on Total Revenues %	-0.32	-2.56	6.49	3.31
Return on Avg Stockholders' Equity %	-1.56	-26.19	n.a.	n.a.
Return on Average Assets %	-0.64	-6.36	n.a.	n.a.
Current Ratio	2.00	0.97	1.19	n.a.
Debt / Equity %	12.82	11.06	26.58	n.a.

Compound Growth %'s	EPS % n.a.	Net Income % n.a.	Total Revenues % 30.60

Comments

Revenue increased 20% during 1996, only a small portion of which was related to one new store location. Same store sales and wholesale sales were both strong. During 1997, the Company will prepare to move into a new leased 60,000 square foot facility for production and administration as well as complete the installation and integration of numerous software systems. Remaining funds from the public offering, together with planned additional working capital financing, are expected to meet the Company's funding needs to achieve its objectives and growth strategy through 1997. Investment Classification: Speculative

Officers	Position	Ownership Information	
Jennifer Barclay	Chairman	Number of Shares Outstanding	4,599,200
Marc Wallach	President, CEO	Market Capitalization	$ 25,295,600
Richard Swartz	VP - Finance, CFO	Frequency of Dividends	n.a.
Lana Schempp	Secretary	Number of Shareholders	2,638
Jolie C. Doyle	VP - Sales		

Other Information			
Transfer Agent	U.S. Stock Transfer Corporation Glendale, CA	Where Listed	CE
Auditor	Arthur Andersen LLP	Symbol	BLF
Market Maker	None	SIC Code	2300
		Employees	n.a.
Broker Dealer	Regular Stockbroker		

Blue Ridge Real Estate Company

P.O. Box 707   Blakeslee, PA 18610-0707   Telephone (717)443-8433   Fax (717)443-8479

Company Description

This entity is represented by two companies with similar ownership: Blue Ridge Real Estate Company and Big Boulder Corporation. Shares of the Companies are combined in unit certificates, each certificate representing concurrent ownership of the same number of shares of each Company. The Companies operate two ski resorts in the Pocono Mountains of northeastern Pennsylvania. Big Boulder Ski Area just concluded celebrating its 50th year of operations. The Companies have large landholdings with future development and sales potential; permits for 800 homesites and a golf course are in place.

	05/31/96	05/31/95	05/31/94	05/31/93
Per Share Information				
Stock Price as of 12/31	6.75	5.38	5.88	6.38
Earnings Per Share	0.02	-0.21	-0.08	0.06
Price / Earnings Ratio	337.50	n.a.	n.a.	106.33
Book Value Per Share	4.80	4.78	5.05	5.14
Price / Book Value %	140.63	112.55	116.44	124.12
Dividends Per Share	0.0	0.0	0.0	0.0
Annual Financial Data				
Operating Results (000's)				
Total Revenues	15,397.0	12,327.4	13,529.8	13,493.8
Costs & Expenses	-15,438.6	-13,036.0	-13,813.2	-13,369.0
Income Before Taxes and Other	-41.6	-708.6	-283.4	124.9
Other Items	0.0	0.0	8.4	0.0
Income Tax	84.8	272.8	111.2	5.4
Net Income	43.3	-435.8	-163.9	130.2
Cash Flow From Operations	1,961.6	1,660.2	2,076.5	1,463.3
Balance Sheet (000's)				
Cash & Equivalents	1,959.0	2,085.3	2,888.6	3,015.1
Total Current Assets	3,487.8	2,879.7	3,599.4	3,542.1
Fixed Assets, Net	19,648.1	20,733.5	21,578.5	22,615.7
Total Assets	23,209.7	23,663.7	25,232.8	26,190.0
Total Current Liabilities	2,248.9	2,090.3	1,863.7	1,925.2
Long-Term Debt	9,189.5	9,578.0	10,051.5	10,571.0
Stockholders' Equity	9,613.5	9,570.2	10,615.8	10,905.1
Performance & Financial Condition				
Return on Total Revenues %	0.28	-3.53	-1.21	0.96
Return on Avg Stockholders' Equity %	0.45	-4.32	-1.52	1.19
Return on Average Assets %	0.18	-1.78	-0.64	0.50
Current Ratio	1.55	1.38	1.93	1.84
Debt / Equity %	95.59	100.08	94.68	96.94

Compound Growth %'s	EPS % -30.66	Net Income % -30.74	Total Revenues % 4.50

Comments

Included in 1996 results is a nonrecurring write-off of $179,000 of costs related to real estate development. Despite the accounting losses, the Companies continue to generate positive cash flow from operations. While management waits for a firmer real estate market before developing homesites, other avenues are increasing income including expansion of the camp ground and operation of the ski shops in-house rather than on a concession basis. For the nine months ended February 28, 1997, net income was $825,952 ($.41 per share) as compared to $244,935 ($.12 per share) for the same period in 1996. Investment Classification: Speculative

Officers	Position	Ownership Information	
Michael J. Flynn	Chairman	Number of Shares Outstanding	2,004,014
Gary A. Smith	President	Market Capitalization	$ 13,527,095
Lois K. McCurdy	Secretary	Frequency of Dividends	n.a.
Melanie A. Murphy	Vice President	Number of Shareholders	759
Russell S. Mollath	Controller		

Other Information

			Where Listed	OTC-BB
Transfer Agent	Summit Bank Hackensack, NJ		Symbol	BLRGZ
Auditor	Coopers & Lybrand L.L.P.		SIC Code	6979
Market Maker	Robotti & Co., Inc.	(212)986-0800	Employees	69
	Carr Securities Corporation	(800)221-2243		
Broker Dealer	Regular Stockbroker			

Borel Bank and Trust Company

160 Bovet Road   San Mateo, CA 94402   Telephone (415)378-3700   Fax (415)378-3774

Company Description

Borel Bank & Trust Company is a one-branch community bank, primarily servicing businesses in the upper-class communities of San Mateo and Hillsborough in the greater San Francisco metropolitan area. The Bank began operations in 1980. In 1995, an independent study by a marketing firm disclosed that 97% of respondents indicated that they were either satisfied or extremely satisfied with the Bank's services. This may be community banking at its best.

	12/31/96	12/31/95	12/31/94	12/31/93
Per Share Information				
Stock Price	23.00	15.00	9.92	7.44
Earnings Per Share	1.93	1.69	1.23	1.01
Price / Earnings Ratio	11.92	8.88	8.07	7.37
Book Value Per Share	13.89	13.50	12.08	11.95
Price / Book Value %	165.59	111.11	82.12	62.26
Dividends Per Share	1.35	0.91	0.49	0.25
Annual Financial Data				
Operating Results (000's)				
Net Interest Income	10,051.2	9,939.6	8,479.4	7,735.4
Loan Loss Provision	-265.0	-425.0	-380.0	-540.0
Non-Interest Income	2,240.2	2,131.1	2,085.3	2,283.7
Non-Interest Expense	-7,573.7	-7,671.0	-7,346.2	-7,194.8
Income Before Taxes and Other	4,452.7	3,974.6	2,838.5	2,284.3
Other Items	0.0	0.0	0.0	0.0
Income Tax	-1,907.1	-1,665.6	-1,180.4	-926.4
Net Income	2,545.6	2,309.0	1,658.0	1,357.9
Balance Sheet (000's)				
Cash & Securities	58,209.2	74,115.9	68,573.3	55,320.9
Loans, Net	142,585.9	94,632.2	90,061.8	96,803.6
Total Assets	208,549.4	177,199.8	169,205.8	159,739.0
Deposits	186,478.8	156,746.4	151,395.0	142,315.8
Stockholders' Equity	19,666.6	18,379.0	16,264.3	16,022.5
Performance & Financial Condition				
Return on Avg Stockholders' Equity %	13.38	13.33	10.27	8.79
Return on Average Assets %	1.32	1.33	1.01	0.83
Equity to Assets %	9.43	10.37	9.61	10.03
Net Interest Margin	5.76	6.40	5.60	5.26
Reserve as a % of Problem Loans	150.43	168.94	149.90	58.51

Compound Growth %'s   EPS %   24.09   Net Income %   23.30   Net Interest Income %   9.12

Comments

The Bank declared 10% stock dividends in 1996 and 1995. All per share amounts have been adjusted for consistency. Aggressive marketing was just one factor in the 50.1% increase in the loan portfolio. Management shares credit with an improved local economy as well as the many mergers of large and small banks in California. Borel Bank has become a safe harbor for those seeking continuity in their banking relationship. The Trust Department experienced its best year ever as income rose to $1.6 million. Investment Classification: Growth

Officers	Position	Ownership Information	
Harold A. Fick	President, CEO	Number of Shares Outstanding	1,415,659
Ronald G. Fick	Exec VP, Secretary	Market Capitalization	$ 32,560,157
William W. Abraham	Senior VP, Senior Loan Officer	Frequency of Dividends	Irregular
Carol J. Olson	Senior VP, COO	Number of Shareholders	681
Emanuela M. Allgood	Senior VP, CFO	Where Listed / Symbol	OTC-BB / BLCA

Other Information			Loan Mix	%
Transfer Agent	First Interstate Bank		Commerical	72.9
Auditor	KPMG Peat Marwick LLP		Consumer	15.8
Market Maker	Hoefer & Arnett, Incorporated	(800)346-5544	Construction	9.7
	Ryan, Beck & Co.	(800)325-7926	Other	1.6
Broker Dealer	OTC Specialist			
	Hoefer & Arnett, Retail	(800)346-5544 Ext: Lisa		

Boston Sand & Gravel Company

169 Portland Street   Boston, MA 02114   Telephone (617)227-9000   Fax (617)523-7947

Company Description

Boston Sand & Gravel Company's principal business activities consist of the production and sale of ready-mixed concrete, sand, gravel and quarry materials throughout the New England region. The Company was founded in 1917 and went public in 1929. During 1996, the Company successfully concluded negotiations with the Commonwealth of Massachusetts that will enable it to continue operations at the main production facility in Boston. The City of Boston is gearing up for the largest construction project in its history. The Central Artery will require a rebuilding of the entire City's infrastructure and continue well into the next century. Needless to say, it will require a lot of concrete.

	12/31/96	12/31/95	12/31/94	12/31/93
Per Share Information				
Stock Price	195.00	155.00	144.00	119.00
Earnings Per Share	78.85	16.47	32.20	21.69
Price / Earnings Ratio	2.47	9.41	4.47	5.49
Book Value Per Share	336.03	259.10	246.49	217.20
Price / Book Value %	58.03	59.82	58.42	54.79
Dividends Per Share	2.00	1.50	2.50	1.00
Annual Financial Data				
Operating Results (000's)				
Total Revenues	57,112.8	50,869.7	67,227.6	60,472.5
Costs & Expenses	-54,500.9	-47,122.0	-59,377.5	-56,294.6
Income Before Taxes and Other	2,173.2	3,329.1	7,393.2	3,888.6
Other Items	9,523.0	0.0	0.0	442.0
Income Tax	-697.0	-1,020.0	-2,879.0	-1,290.0
Net Income	10,999.1	2,309.1	4,514.2	3,040.6
Cash Flow From Operations	3,590.5	7,217.6	8,383.6	3,227.7
Balance Sheet (000's)				
Cash & Equivalents	4,140.3	6,369.6	4,122.0	1,160.5
Total Current Assets	19,246.2	18,514.8	19,300.5	15,876.5
Fixed Assets, Net	19,955.5	15,694.0	15,997.6	17,466.8
Total Assets	61,484.4	44,244.5	45,608.2	43,770.9
Total Current Liabilities	6,547.3	5,142.6	7,272.0	8,469.1
Long-Term Debt	195.6	560.1	681.2	787.3
Stockholders' Equity	46,716.6	36,309.8	34,552.1	30,446.5
Performance & Financial Condition				
Return on Total Revenues %	19.26	4.54	6.71	5.03
Return on Avg Stockholders' Equity %	26.50	6.52	13.89	10.45
Return on Average Assets %	20.81	5.14	10.10	7.16
Current Ratio	2.94	3.60	2.65	1.87
Debt / Equity %	0.42	1.54	1.97	2.59

Compound Growth %'s	EPS % n.a.	Net Income % n.a.	Total Revenues % -1.89

Comments

Earnings included an extraordinary gain of $9,522,957, $68.27 per share, net of income tax of $6,347,000, from the expropriation by the Massachusetts Highway Department of Company property located in Charlestown, Massachusetts. Management believes that the loss of this property will not have a material impact on the Company's future operations. The Company has $12.7 million of marketable securities that are not included in current assets. Capital investment is expected to be heavy over the next several years as management prepares to reap huge rewards from the Central Artery project. Deferred income tax of $6 million may not have to be paid if the Company properly reinvests monies received in the expropriation. Investment Classification: Value

Officers	Position	Ownership Information	
Dean M. Boylan, Jr.	President	Number of Shares Outstanding	139,026
Mary C. Moran	VP - Finance	Market Capitalization	$ 27,110,070
Jeanne-Marie Boylan	Vice President, Treasurer	Frequency of Dividends	Quarterly
David B. McNeil	VP - Sales	Number of Shareholders	Under 500

Other Information				
Transfer Agent	Boston EquiServe Boston, MA		Where Listed	OTC-BB
Auditor	Ernst & Young LLP		Symbol	BSND
Market Maker	Gruntal & Co., Incorporated	(800)225-8520	SIC Code	3273
	H.C. Wainwright & Co., Inc.	(617)973-0550	Employees	150
Broker Dealer	Regular Stockbroker			
	Standard Investment	(888)783-4688 Ext: Jack		

Boswell (J.G.) Company

101 West Walnut Street   Pasadena, CA 91103   Telephone (818)583-3000   Fax (818)583-3090

Company Description

J.G. Boswell Company generates most of its revenue from the production, processing and marketing of cotton, cottonseed products and, to a lesser extent, other farm commodity products. Domestic cotton is grown and processed in California. The Company has a foreign subsidiary which has cotton operations in the state of New South Wales, Australia. The Company also owns and operates two real estate development projects, one in California and the other in Colorado.

	06/30/96	06/30/95	06/30/94	06/30/93
Per Share Information				
Stock Price as of 12/31	1,180.00	1,217.50	1,125.00	1,100.00
Earnings Per Share	53.04	64.99	63.99	9.97
Price / Earnings Ratio	22.25	18.73	17.58	110.33
Book Value Per Share	1,338.84	1,268.34	1,248.83	1,174.55
Price / Book Value %	88.14	95.99	90.08	93.65
Dividends Per Share	35.00	35.00	27.50	25.00
Annual Financial Data				
Operating Results (000's)				
Total Revenues	262,291.0	224,232.0	250,490.0	240,632.0
Costs & Expenses	-256,082.0	-207,351.0	-233,476.0	-239,968.0
Income Before Taxes and Other	6,209.0	16,881.0	17,014.0	1,761.0
Other Items	0.0	0.0	0.0	0.0
Income Tax	4,432.0	-3,730.0	-3,994.0	278.0
Net Income	10,641.0	13,151.0	13,020.0	2,039.0
Cash Flow From Operations	22,160.0	-1,832.0	47,063.0	31,346.0
Balance Sheet (000's)				
Cash & Equivalents	2,608.0	526.0	18,475.0	100,000.0
Total Current Assets	122,231.0	111,231.0	125,942.0	100,000.0
Fixed Assets, Net	265,715.0	256,679.0	211,486.0	200,000.0
Total Assets	548,266.0	524,042.0	460,386.0	458,700.0
Total Current Liabilities	70,272.0	80,849.0	64,714.0	60,217.0
Long-Term Debt	152,939.0	157,121.0	126,467.0	147,839.0
Stockholders' Equity	266,986.0	256,568.0	253,039.0	239,282.0
Performance & Financial Condition				
Return on Total Revenues %	4.06	5.86	5.20	0.85
Return on Avg Stockholders' Equity %	4.06	5.16	5.29	0.83
Return on Average Assets %	1.98	2.67	2.83	0.42
Current Ratio	1.74	1.38	1.95	1.66
Debt / Equity %	57.28	61.24	49.98	61.78

Compound Growth %'s	EPS % n.a.	Net Income % n.a.	Total Revenues %	2.91

Comments

During 1995, the Company acquired an additional 26,000 acres of farmland, significant water rights and related processing facilities. Accessible water has always been a problem for the Company. There is reportedly a large potential for appreciation of the properties held if the water problem can be solved. Subsequent to year end, approximately 60,000 acres of Company land in the Tulare Lake Basin were flooded during the heavy rains and early snowmelt in January, 1997. This flooding prevented the Company from planting 40% of the normal summer acreage. To conserve cash flow, the Board of Directors reduced the dividend by 50%. Compound earnings growth rates were distorted by a lower than normal base year and have not been presented. Investment Classification: Value

Officers	Position	Ownership Information	
James W. Boswell	President, CEO	Number of Shares Outstanding	199,416
Edward C. Giermann	Secretary	Market Capitalization	$ 235,310,880
		Frequency of Dividends	Quarterly
		Number of Shareholders	Under 500

Other Information				
Transfer Agent	Company Office		Where Listed	OTC-PS
Auditor	Ernst & Young LLP		Symbol	BWEL
Market Maker	The Seidler Companies Inc.	(800)421-0164	SIC Code	0720
	Carr Securities Corporation	(800)221-2243	Employees	40
Broker Dealer	Regular Stockbroker			
	Standard Investments	(888)783-4688 Ext: Jack		

Bozzuto's Inc.

275 Schoolhouse Road   Cheshire, CT 06410-0340   Telephone (203)272-3511   Fax (203)250-7955

Company Description

Bozzuto's is engaged in the wholesale distribution of food products and certain non-food, household and personal items to independent retail supermarket and convenience store operators in Long Island, southeastern New York, northern New Jersey and southern New England. The Company also owns and operates retail supermarkets. A new state-of-the-art distribution center was completed in 1995. Buzzuto's began business in 1945.

	09/30/96	09/30/95	09/30/94	09/30/93
Per Share Information				
Stock Price as of 12/31	24.50	28.25	20.75	16.00
Earnings Per Share	1.35	2.73	3.68	3.49
Price / Earnings Ratio	18.15	10.35	0.64	4.58
Book Value Per Share	34.39	27.78	25.83	23.09
Price / Book Value %	71.24	101.69	80.33	69.29
Dividends Per Share	0.40	0.40	0.40	0.40
Annual Financial Data				
Operating Results (000's)				
Total Revenues	379,169.5	372,438.0	346,219.9	319,641.1
Costs & Expenses	-377,714.3	-369,653.2	-342,861.0	-316,467.7
Income Before Taxes and Other	1,455.3	2,784.8	3,358.9	3,173.4
Other Items	-6.1	-57.2	0.5	0.0
Income Tax	-735.7	-1,289.3	-1,417.7	-1,332.9
Net Income	713.4	1,438.3	1,941.7	1,840.5
Cash Flow From Operations	1,020.9	5,168.0	4,609.8	2,503.0
Balance Sheet (000's)				
Cash & Equivalents	1,191.8	773.4	1,544.3	1,304.5
Total Current Assets	36,562.9	32,006.1	32,052.2	29,106.0
Fixed Assets, Net	6,156.0	7,207.0	7,338.8	7,472.8
Total Assets	50,692.4	46,584.4	45,348.2	41,875.7
Total Current Liabilities	29,159.0	20,589.7	17,501.2	14,069.2
Long-Term Debt	2,548.9	7,663.2	10,800.5	12,615.8
Stockholders' Equity	18,131.8	17,523.9	16,296.4	14,565.7
Performance & Financial Condition				
Return on Total Revenues %	0.19	0.39	0.56	0.58
Return on Avg Stockholders' Equity %	4.00	8.51	12.58	13.38
Return on Average Assets %	1.47	3.13	4.45	n.a.
Current Ratio	1.25	1.55	1.83	2.07
Debt / Equity %	14.06	43.73	66.28	86.61

Compound Growth %'s	EPS %	-27.14	Net Income %	-27.09	Total Revenues %	5.86

Comments

Management was disappointed with the 1996 results as little increased volume materialized for the new distribution center. Changes to the sales mix reduced overall gross margins. An additional $431,058 of profit was hidden from view by use of the LIFO method of inventory calculation. Management reports that first quarter sales for fiscal 1997 has shown a very significant improvement. Investment Classification: Value

Officers	Position	Ownership Information	
Adam J. Bozzuto	Chairman	Number of Shares Outstanding	527,251
Michael A. Bozzuto	President, Treasurer	Market Capitalization	$ 12,917,650
Thomas A. Zatina	Exec VP, COO	Frequency of Dividends	Quarterly
Robert H. Wood	VP - Finance	Number of Shareholders	Under 500
Jayne A. Bozzuto	Vice President		

Other Information			
Transfer Agent	First National Bank of Boston Boston, MA	Where Listed	OTC-BB
Auditor	Daniel J. Bartz, C.P.A.	Symbol	BOZZ
Market Maker	Macallaster Pitfield MacKay	(212)422-9250	SIC Code	5140
	Prime Capital Services, Inc.	(800)552-0067	Employees	450
Broker Dealer	Regular Stockbroker		
	Norman Kadehjian - Wainwright	(800)727-7176	

68

Bresler & Reiner, Inc.

401 M Street, S.W. Washington D.C., 20024 Telephone (202)488-8800 Fax (202)488-8084

Company Description

Bresler & Reiner has two principal activities: residential land development and construction and rental property ownership and management. The Company holds for sale or development several partially developed residential tracts of land within the greater Washington, D.C. metropolitan area. The Company also owns and manages apartments, offices, a motel and a hotel.

	12/31/96	12/31/95	12/31/94	12/31/93
Per Share Information				
Stock Price	11.00	10.25	10.50	10.00
Earnings Per Share	2.60	2.18	1.20	-1.81
Price / Earnings Ratio	4.23	4.70	8.75	n.a.
Book Value Per Share	23.36	20.76	18.41	17.21
Price / Book Value %	47.09	49.37	57.03	58.11
Dividends Per Share	0.0	0.0	0.0	0.0
Annual Financial Data				
Operating Results (000's)				
Total Revenues	35,143.0	33,824.0	39,563.0	31,683.0
Costs & Expenses	-24,281.0	-26,302.0	-46,033.0	-45,414.0
Income Before Taxes and Other	10,862.0	7,522.0	-6,470.0	-13,731.0
Other Items	-57.0	1,705.0	7,538.0	3,293.0
Income Tax	-3,532.0	-3,087.0	2,336.0	5,305.0
Net Income	7,273.0	6,140.0	3,404.0	-5,133.0
Cash Flow From Operations	13,210.0	7,214.0	7,575.0	9,547.0
Balance Sheet (000's)				
Cash & Equivalents	6,761.0	10,921.0	7,200.0	6,287.0
Total Current Assets	6,793.0	11,912.0	9,933.0	31,395.0
Fixed Assets, Net	36,488.0	38,018.0	40,337.0	42,948.0
Total Assets	94,926.0	101,395.0	103,401.0	151,681.0
Total Current Liabilities	3,404.0	3,562.0	4,229.0	11,327.0
Long-Term Debt	22,238.0	34,229.0	42,495.0	91,336.0
Stockholders' Equity	65,242.0	57,969.0	52,214.0	48,813.0
Performance & Financial Condition				
Return on Total Revenues %	20.70	18.15	8.60	-16.20
Return on Avg Stockholders' Equity %	11.81	11.15	6.74	-9.99
Return on Average Assets %	7.41	6.00	2.67	-3.24
Current Ratio	2.00	3.34	2.35	2.77
Debt / Equity %	34.09	59.05	81.39	187.11

Compound Growth %'s	EPS %	47.20	Net Income %	46.17	Total Revenues %	3.52

Comments

In an effort to eliminate underperforming properties, the Company has allowed certain properties it owned to be foreclosed and has renegotiated the debt terms on others. As a result of these transactions, the Company expensed substantial amounts in the years 1992 through 1994. All that seems to be behind it now as the Company reported two consecutive strong years and a backlog of 18 home construction contracts as of April 1, 1997. Bresler & Reiner is also in the process of renovating its Holiday Inn while the Doubletree Hotel in Baltimore posted a 20% increase in total revenue. Investment Classification: Value

Officers	Position	Ownership Information	
Charles S. Bresler	Chairman, CEO	Number of Shares Outstanding	2,792,653
Burton J. Reiner	President	Market Capitalization	$ 30,719,183
Edwin Horowitz	Secretary	Frequency of Dividends	n.a.
William L. Oshinsky	Treasurer	Number of Shareholders	156

Other Information

Transfer Agent	Continental Stock Transfer & Trust Co. New York, NY		Where Listed	OTC-BB
Auditor	Arthur Andersen LLP		Symbol	BRER
Market Maker	Herzog, Heine, Geduld, Inc.	(212)962-0300	SIC Code	6513
	Carr Securities Corporation	(800)221-2243	Employees	137
Broker Dealer	Regular Stockbroker			

Broughton Foods Company

P.O. Box 656   Marietta, OH 45750   Telephone (614)373-4121   Fax (614)373-2861

Company Description

Broughton Foods Company is primarily in the business of producing dairy and dairy-related food products for wholesale and retail distribution. The Company was founded in 1933. Up until 1996, members of the Broughton family were in absolute control of the Company. On November 15, 1996, Marshall T. Reynolds, an unrelated individual, completed a tender offer to all shareholders at $75 per share conditioned only upon him obtaining majority control. The tender was successful. Mr. Reynolds now serves as Chairman of the Board of Directors.

	12/31/96	12/31/95	12/31/94	12/31/93
Per Share Information				
Stock Price	37.25	42.00	35.00	33.00
Earnings Per Share	17.70	-2.83	5.13	5.57
Price / Earnings Ratio	2.10	n.a.	6.82	5.92
Book Value Per Share	71.92	56.29	58.61	53.19
Price / Book Value %	51.79	74.61	59.72	62.04
Dividends Per Share	0.80	0.80	0.80	0.80
Annual Financial Data				
Operating Results (000's)				
Total Revenues	87,163.0	72,384.5	73,624.3	68,231.0
Costs & Expenses	-83,401.9	-72,949.1	-72,467.6	-66,860.3
Income Before Taxes and Other	3,761.1	-564.6	1,156.7	1,370.7
Other Items	0.0	0.0	0.0	0.0
Income Tax	-1,431.2	184.8	-432.5	-558.4
Net Income	2,329.9	-379.8	724.2	812.3
Cash Flow From Operations	126.2	-216.2	1,650.1	1,120.3
Balance Sheet (000's)				
Cash & Equivalents	2,307.8	161.2	956.5	596.7
Total Current Assets	12,059.5	10,145.9	10,056.0	9,722.2
Fixed Assets, Net	4,313.2	5,790.8	5,247.9	5,663.0
Total Assets	17,687.3	16,204.0	15,574.7	15,663.2
Total Current Liabilities	5,595.9	6,479.7	5,239.0	5,589.7
Long-Term Debt	1,652.1	1,862.5	1,524.0	1,769.7
Stockholders' Equity	9,907.8	7,359.9	8,243.1	7,757.2
Performance & Financial Condition				
Return on Total Revenues %	2.67	-0.52	0.98	1.19
Return on Avg Stockholders' Equity %	26.99	-4.87	9.05	10.95
Return on Average Assets %	13.75	-2.39	4.64	5.30
Current Ratio	2.16	1.57	1.92	1.74
Debt / Equity %	16.68	25.31	18.49	22.81

Compound Growth %'s	EPS %	n.a.	Net Income %	n.a.	Total Revenues %	8.51

Comments

A gain on the sale of investment in stock accounted for 79% of the pre-tax income in 1996. Accordingly, compound earnings growth rates were not displayed. Yet the Company still had a nice turnaround from the previous year. Management attributes the 1995 loss to unusually competitive markets and the erratic behavior of butterfat costs, which nearly doubled during the year before falling back in December. Food division capacity is at maximum and additional expansion will be required. The food division, according to management, represents the greatest opportunity for future growth. The new majority owner has awarded key employees with stock ownership and praises the younger members of the Broughton family who will be staying in the business. Investment Classification: Value

Officers	Position	Ownership Information	
Rodney M. Collier	President, CEO	Number of Shares Outstanding	137,322
George W. Broughton	Exec VP	Market Capitalization	$ 5,115,245
John R. Broughton	Treasurer	Frequency of Dividends	Quarterly
Samuel R. Lipscomb	Vice President	Number of Shareholders	Under 500
Gary R. Cowell	VP - Manufacturing		

Other Information			
Transfer Agent	BancOhio National Bank Columbus, OH	Where Listed	OTC-BB
Auditor	Coopers & Lybrand LLP	Symbol	BRGHB
Market Maker	Carr Securities Corporation	(800)221-2243	SIC Code	2020
	Robotti & Co., Inc.	(212)986-0800	Employees	200
Broker Dealer	OTC Specialist		
	Tom Doherty - Robotti	(212)986-0800	

Bruno's, Inc.

800 Lakeshore Parkway   Birmingham, AL 35211   Telephone (205)940-9400   Fax (205)912-4534

Company Description

Bruno's, Inc. is a leading supermarket operator in the southeastern United States and is the largest supermarket operator in the State of Alabama. The Company, which was formed in 1959, currently operates 218 supermarkets under the names, Bruno's, Food World, FoodMax, Piggly Wiggly, and Seessel's. The Company also operates 17 "Supercenter" stores which offer an expanded mix of general merchandise products. In 1995, 82.4% of the Company was acquired by Kohlberg Kravis Roberts & Co.(KKR) in a transaction in which the Company obligated itself on additional debt in order to redeem a majority of the former shareholders.

	02/01/97	01/27/96	07/01/95	07/02/94
Per Share Information				
Stock Price as of 12/31	16.75	10.50	10.50	8.12
Earnings Per Share	-2.03	-2.19	0.43	0.48
Price / Earnings Ratio	n.a.	n.a.	24.42	16.92
Book Value Per Share	-13.03	-11.25	5.50	5.40
Price / Book Value %	n.a.	n.a.	190.91	150.37
Dividends Per Share	0.0	0.0	0.26	0.24
Annual Financial Data				
Operating Results (000's)				
Total Revenues	2,899,044.0	1,674,659.0	2,869,569.0	2,834,688.0
Costs & Expenses	-2,890,668.0	-1,773,837.0	-2,816,307.0	-2,765,918.0
Income Before Taxes and Other	-80,212.0	-99,178.0	53,262.0	68,770.0
Other Items	-1,674.0	-4,902.0	0.0	-3,288.0
Income Tax	30,697.0	22,879.0	-19,920.0	-28,189.0
Net Income	-51,189.0	-81,201.0	33,342.0	37,293.0
Cash Flow From Operations	78,649.0	97,932.0	125,663.0	86,866.0
Balance Sheet (000's)				
Cash & Equivalents	4,908.0	57,387.0	25,916.0	30,259.0
Total Current Assets	233,549.0	316,228.0	324,599.0	330,741.0
Fixed Assets, Net	466,997.0	491,664.0	516,374.0	540,139.0
Total Assets	791,431.0	873,146.0	895,641.0	927,208.0
Total Current Liabilities	234,365.0	250,515.0	183,179.0	156,349.0
Long-Term Debt	813,722.0	834,223.0	200,642.0	276,015.0
Stockholders' Equity	-330,149.0	-281,343.0	429,814.0	421,354.0
Performance & Financial Condition				
Return on Total Revenues %	-1.77	-4.85	1.16	1.32
Return on Avg Stockholders' Equity %	n.a.	n.a.	7.83	53.27
Return on Average Assets %	-6.15	n.a.	3.66	4.14
Current Ratio	1.00	1.26	1.77	2.12
Debt / Equity %	n.a.	n.a.	46.68	65.51

Compound Growth %'s	EPS %	n.a.	Net Income %	n.a.	Total Revenues %	0.75

Comments

Operating results for the period ended January 27, 1996 represent a 30 week period. During the 1997 fiscal year, the Company developed and completed a divestiture program under which a distribution center and 47 stores were closed. The Company would have reported a pre-tax profit of $8.4 million had it not been for $88.6 million in costs associated with the divestiture program. KKR is betting that it can somehow reduce the formidable debt. If it can, KKR will be exercising warrants to acquire another 10 million shares at $12 per share, further diluting any other remaining shareholders. Investment Classification: Speculative

Officers	Position	Ownership Information	
William J. Bolton	Chairman, CEO	Number of Shares Outstanding	25,333,607
David B. Clark	Exec VP	Market Capitalization	$ 424,337,917
James J. Hagan	Exec VP, CFO	Frequency of Dividends	n.a.
Laura Hayden	Senior VP	Number of Shareholders	4,150
Walter M. Grant	Senior VP, Secretary		

Other Information			
Transfer Agent	Birmingham Trust National Bank Birmingham, AL	Where Listed	OTC-BB
Auditor	Arthur Andersen LLP	Symbol	BRNO
Market Maker	Mayer & Schweitzer, Inc. (800)631-3094	SIC Code	5410
	Gabelli & Company, Inc. (914)921-5153	Employees	n.a.
Broker Dealer	Regular Stockbroker		

Bryan Steam Corporation

State Road 19 North   Peru, IN 46970   Telephone (317)473-6651   Fax (317)473-3074

Company Description

Bryan Steam Corporation manufactures and sells oil, gas and electrically fired boilers, commercial water heaters and swimming pool heaters. The Company also manufactures and sells a limited number of storage tanks and other equipment for use in connection with boilers. Most boilers are sold directly to contractors for installation in new apartment, commercial, industrial and institutional buildings. The Company also operates a tank manufacturing facility that it acquired during the 1996 fiscal year. Bryan Steam Corporation was founded in 1916.

	06/30/96	06/30/95	06/30/94	06/30/93
Per Share Information				
Stock Price as of 12/31	38.00	46.00	40.50	30.00
Earnings Per Share	6.01	4.85	3.74	5.56
Price / Earnings Ratio	6.32	9.48	10.83	5.40
Book Value Per Share	68.43	63.82	60.28	58.84
Price / Book Value %	55.53	72.08	67.19	50.99
Dividends Per Share	1.40	1.30	1.30	0.95
Annual Financial Data				
Operating Results (000's)				
Total Revenues	22,733.4	17,727.6	17,179.3	16,416.0
Costs & Expenses	-20,890.9	-13,913.9	-13,708.0	-12,503.7
Income Before Taxes and Other	1,842.6	1,475.6	1,125.1	1,578.4
Other Items	0.0	0.0	0.0	0.0
Income Tax	-693.6	-548.5	-409.7	-513.1
Net Income	1,148.9	927.1	715.4	1,065.3
Cash Flow From Operations	-8.3	1,008.1	1,000.0	2,152.6
Balance Sheet (000's)				
Cash & Equivalents	304.7	2,192.9	360.2	751.6
Total Current Assets	11,336.6	11,545.6	9,928.2	9,875.2
Fixed Assets, Net	4,568.2	3,524.4	3,293.4	2,984.9
Total Assets	16,178.0	15,090.7	13,247.4	12,906.3
Total Current Liabilities	2,461.0	1,751.2	1,408.5	1,491.3
Long-Term Debt	238.2	800.0	0.0	0.0
Stockholders' Equity	13,089.1	12,208.0	11,530.8	11,254.5
Performance & Financial Condition				
Return on Total Revenues %	5.05	5.23	4.16	6.49
Return on Avg Stockholders' Equity %	9.08	7.81	6.28	9.76
Return on Average Assets %	7.35	6.54	5.47	8.41
Current Ratio	4.61	6.59	7.05	6.62
Debt / Equity %	1.82	6.55	n.a.	n.a.

Compound Growth %'s	EPS %	2.63	Net Income %	2.55	Total Revenues %	11.46

Comments

The acquisition of the tank operation, referred to above, had a very positive affect on financial results. The Company also acquired assets associated with a discontinued tank operation in Indiana which effectively amounted to a start-up situation. Both of these tank operations exceeded expectations. Sales and net income for the nine months ended March 31, 1997, amounted to $19.4 million and $1,097,000 ($5.74 per share) as compared to $16.9 million and $824,000 ($4.31 per share) for the same period in 1996. Investment Classification: Value & Income

Officers	Position	Ownership Information	
Albert J. Bishop	Chairman	Number of Shares Outstanding	191,284
H. Jesse McVay	President	Market Capitalization	$ 7,268,792
Kurt J. Krauskopf	Secretary	Frequency of Dividends	Annual
Paul D. Donaldson	Treasurer	Number of Shareholders	997

Other Information

Transfer Agent	Company Office		Where Listed	OTC-BB
Auditor	Cassen Company, LLC		Symbol	BSTM
Market Maker	Robotti & Co., Inc.	(212)986-0800	SIC Code	3443
	Howe Barnes Investments, Inc.	(800)621-2364	Employees	180
Broker Dealer	OTC Specialist			
	Tom Doherty - Robotti	(212)986-0800		

Buck Hill Falls Company

P.O. Box 426   Buck Hill Falls, PA 18323   Telephone (717)595-7511   Fax (717)595-9426

Company Description

Buck Hill Falls Company provides a variety of services to the residents of Buck Hill Falls, Pennsylvania. These services include recreational facilities, water and sewage services and miscellaneous maintenance services. In addition, certain of the Company's recreational facilities are made available to the general public. Recreational facilities include a 27 hole golf course, a tennis club, an Olympic-sized swimming pool, two lawn bowling greens, deer hunting and trout fishing areas. The Company was founded in 1901.

	10/31/96	10/31/95	10/31/94	10/31/93
Per Share Information				
Stock Price as of 12/31	22.00	29.50	20.00	12.50
Earnings Per Share	-1.68	-1.21	0.74	1.35
Price / Earnings Ratio	n.a.	n.a.	27.03	9.26
Book Value Per Share	11.32	12.25	13.45	12.70
Price / Book Value %	194.35	240.82	148.70	98.43
Dividends Per Share	0.0	0.0	0.0	0.0
Annual Financial Data				
Operating Results (000's)				
Total Revenues	2,196.9	2,218.1	2,203.5	2,048.5
Costs & Expenses	-2,322.0	-2,306.9	-2,135.1	-1,914.6
Income Before Taxes and Other	-125.1	-88.7	68.4	99.5
Other Items	0.0	0.0	21.6	33.8
Income Tax	0.0	0.0	-35.3	-33.8
Net Income	-125.1	-88.7	54.7	99.5
Cash Flow From Operations	1.8	-106.4	239.5	203.5
Balance Sheet (000's)				
Cash & Equivalents	106.7	31.5	20.2	13.4
Total Current Assets	403.4	307.1	219.0	180.4
Fixed Assets, Net	2,692.7	2,756.4	2,761.8	2,234.0
Total Assets	3,172.6	3,149.9	3,104.0	2,536.5
Total Current Liabilities	981.0	1,079.3	1,192.9	1,002.6
Long-Term Debt	940.0	1,096.2	815.9	498.5
Stockholders' Equity	1,043.0	900.5	989.3	934.6
Performance & Financial Condition				
Return on Total Revenues %	-5.70	-4.00	2.48	4.86
Return on Avg Stockholders' Equity %	-12.88	-9.39	5.68	11.24
Return on Average Assets %	-3.96	-2.84	1.94	4.11
Current Ratio	0.41	0.28	0.18	0.18
Debt / Equity %	90.13	121.73	82.48	53.34

Compound Growth %'s	EPS %	n.a.	Net Income %	n.a.	Total Revenues %	2.36

Comments

Revenues declined during 1996 as annual dues to the 290 residents of Buck Hill Falls were reduced from $2,400 to $2,300. There was also less lumbering activity and unfavorable weather for golf and lawn bowling. The Company has raised additional capital through a stock offering at $20 per share that was made to the residents of Buck Hill Falls and to the existing shareholders. The shares subscribed to by residents is a restricted class of stock that can only be owned by residents. Forbes Magazine reported on July 29, 1996, that a storm is brewing between the locals, who like things as they are, and the nonresident owners who would like some of the valuable lands developed to maximize shareholder value. The posted ask price is $40 per share at December 31, 1996. Investment Classification: Speculative & Value

Officers	Position	Ownership Information	
David B. Ottaway	Chairman, President	Number of Shares Outstanding	92,157
Richard C. Unger, Jr.	Secretary	Market Capitalization	$ 2,027,454
Anthony C. Bowe	Vice President, CFO	Frequency of Dividends	n.a.
Frank J. Dracos	Vice President, COO	Number of Shareholders	493

Other Information

Transfer Agent	Chemical Mellon Shareholder Services New York, NY		Where Listed	OTC-BB
Auditor	Parente Randolph Orlando et al		Symbol	BUHF
Market Maker	Robotti & Co., Inc.	(212)986-4800	SIC Code	6500
	Carr Securities Corporation	(800)221-2243	Employees	17
Broker Dealer	Regular Stockbroker			

Bulova Corporation

One Bulova Avenue   Woodside, NY 11377-7874   Telephone (718)204-3300   Fax (718)204-3546

Company Description

Bulova Corporation, which is 97% owned by Loews Corporation, distributes and sells watches, clocks and timepiece parts for consumer use. The principal watch brands are Bulova, Caravelle, Accutron and Sportstime. Bulova's principal markets are the U.S. and Canada, which account for 90% and 10%, respectively, of sales.

	12/31/96	12/31/95	12/31/94	12/31/93
Per Share Information				
Stock Price	4.75	4.13	3.25	4.00
Earnings Per Share	1.52	0.57	0.18	0.54
Price / Earnings Ratio	3.13	7.25	18.06	7.41
Book Value Per Share	15.74	14.23	13.68	13.94
Price / Book Value %	30.18	29.02	23.76	28.69
Dividends Per Share	0.0	0.0	0.0	0.0
Annual Financial Data				
Operating Results (000's)				
Total Revenues	120,792.0	109,223.0	100,046.0	101,303.0
Costs & Expenses	-109,123.0	-102,309.0	-98,683.0	-98,174.0
Income Before Taxes and Other	11,669.0	6,756.0	783.0	1,708.0
Other Items	0.0	363.0	302.0	603.0
Income Tax	-4,668.0	-4,487.0	-251.0	203.0
Net Income	7,001.0	2,632.0	834.0	2,514.0
Cash Flow From Operations	9,569.0	528.0	-3,931.0	10,272.0
Balance Sheet (000's)				
Cash & Equivalents	10,665.0	5,963.0	3,857.0	5,639.0
Total Current Assets	118,596.0	104,758.0	121,276.0	120,230.0
Fixed Assets, Net	11,582.0	12,260.0	12,750.0	13,072.0
Total Assets	148,454.0	134,127.0	151,035.0	149,865.0
Total Current Liabilities	23,072.0	17,748.0	18,240.0	22,190.0
Long-Term Debt	0.0	0.0	19,200.0	16,600.0
Stockholders' Equity	72,381.0	65,463.0	62,930.0	64,101.0
Performance & Financial Condition				
Return on Total Revenues %	5.80	2.41	0.83	2.48
Return on Avg Stockholders' Equity %	10.16	4.10	1.31	3.99
Return on Average Assets %	4.96	1.85	0.55	1.51
Current Ratio	5.14	5.90	6.65	5.42
Debt / Equity %	n.a.	n.a.	30.51	25.90

Compound Growth %'s	EPS %	41.19	Net Income %	40.69	Total Revenues %	6.04

Comments

In January, 1995, the Company sold its industrial and defense products segment for $20.8 million in cash. The Company applied $18.0 million to repay the entire debt owed to its parent. Also, during 1995, the Company collected $10.6 million from its parent relating to a tax audit adjustment from the examination of the parent's tax returns for 1984 through 1990. Increased sales of 14.5% and an improvement in gross margins led 1996 to record profits. The absence of debt on the balance sheet makes the Company look particularly attractive. The big payoff to shareholders would be if and when Loews decides to sell this gem. Investment Classification: Value & Growth

Officers	Position	Ownership Information	
Herbert C. Hofmann	President, CEO	Number of Shares Outstanding	4,599,000
Paul S. Sayegh	COO	Market Capitalization	$ 21,845,250
Warren J. Neitzel	Secretary	Frequency of Dividends	n.a.
John T. O'Reilly	Controller	Number of Shareholders	1,500

Other Information				
Transfer Agent	Registrar & Transfer Company Cranford, NJ		Where Listed	OTC-BB
Auditor	Deloitte & Touche LLP		Symbol	BULV
Market Maker	Carr Securities Corporation	(800)221-2243	SIC Code	3873
	Howe Barnes Investments, Inc.	(800)621-2364	Employees	440
Broker Dealer	Regular Stockbroker			

Burke & Herbert Bank & Trust Company

P.O. Box 268   Alexandria, VA 22313   Telephone (703)549-6600   Fax (703)836-2092

Company Description

Founded in 1852, Burke & Herbert Bank & Trust Company now serves customers throughout northern Virginia. Although it has grown to twelve banking offices and 240 employees, you can still find many members of the Burke family involved with operations. The stock trades infrequently so we suggest obtaining the help of a specialist.

	12/31/96	12/31/95	12/31/94	12/31/93
Per Share Information				
Stock Price	310.00	290.00	205.00	150.00
Earnings Per Share	50.57	39.45	29.81	25.04
Price / Earnings Ratio	6.13	7.35	6.88	5.99
Book Value Per Share	287.41	254.21	218.38	195.20
Price / Book Value %	107.86	114.08	93.87	76.84
Dividends Per Share	15.00	8.00	5.50	4.50
Annual Financial Data				
Operating Results (000's)				
Net Interest Income	26,104.6	22,850.3	21,344.3	20,389.0
Loan Loss Provision	-1,125.0	-1,500.0	-2,000.0	-3,070.0
Non-Interest Income	2,849.7	2,551.3	2,318.8	2,205.1
Non-Interest Expense	-12,457.3	-12,428.2	-12,998.4	-12,241.3
Income Before Taxes and Other	15,372.0	11,473.4	8,664.7	7,282.8
Other Items	0.0	0.0	0.0	0.0
Income Tax	-5,257.6	-3,583.3	-2,703.2	-2,275.3
Net Income	10,114.4	7,890.1	5,961.5	5,007.5
Balance Sheet (000's)				
Cash & Securities	223,781.3	224,847.8	233,739.2	245,717.1
Loans, Net	361,285.5	337,420.9	308,596.7	273,197.6
Total Assets	610,396.2	587,108.3	563,052.3	539,903.3
Deposits	549,661.7	532,913.8	512,604.2	498,684.1
Stockholders' Equity	57,481.5	50,842.5	43,676.7	39,039.9
Performance & Financial Condition				
Return on Avg Stockholders' Equity %	18.67	16.70	14.41	13.54
Return on Average Assets %	1.69	1.37	1.08	0.95
Equity to Assets %	9.42	8.66	7.76	7.23
Net Interest Margin	n.a.	n.a.	n.a.	n.a.
Reserve as a % of Problem Loans	57.79	117.97	156.34	n.a.

Compound Growth %'s	EPS %	26.40	Net Income %	26.41	Net Interest Income %	8.59

Comments

Return on equity has risen in each of the last three years and the Bank has generously raised the dividend. Management reports that this is the normal level of earnings that should be expected. The annual report to shareholders is typically a one page letter with the audited financial statements. The shareholders are not complaining as they have seen their investment more than double over the last three years in addition to a 5% dividend yield. Investment Classification: Growth & Income & Value

Officers	Position	Ownership Information	
C.S. Taylor Burke, Jr.	Chairman, CEO	Number of Shares Outstanding	200,000
David M. Burke	President	Market Capitalization	$ 62,000,000
Charles K. Collum, Jr.	Exec VP	Frequency of Dividends	Semi-Annual
C.S. Taylor Burke, III	Senior VP	Number of Shareholders	n.a.
E. Hunt Burke	Senior VP	Where Listed / Symbol	OTC-BB / BHRB

Other Information			Loan Mix	%
Transfer Agent	Company Office		R/E Mortgages	58.6
Auditor	Keller Bruner & Company		Commerical	26.8
Market Maker	Koonce Securities, Inc.	(800)368-2802	Consumer	14.6
	Ferris, Baker Watts Inc.	(800)638-7411		
Broker Dealer	OTC Specialist			
	Jack Ingold	(412)391-4594		

Burke-Parsons-Bowlby Corporation

P.O. Box 231   Ripley, WV 25271   Telephone (304)372-2211   Fax (304)372-1211

Company Description

The Company is a producer of wood products of various kinds, primarily pressure-treated heavy timbers for industrial, construction, railroad, mining, highway, farm, and general use. It operates four treatment plants located in West Virginia, Virginia, Kentucky and Pennsylvania. 37% of total outstanding shares are owned by an Employee Stock Ownership Plan. The Company was founded in 1955.

	03/31/96	03/31/95	03/31/94	03/31/93
Per Share Information				
Stock Price as of 12/31	8.25	7.50	6.00	4.75
Earnings Per Share	1.21	1.71	1.19	0.50
Price / Earnings Ratio	6.82	4.39	5.04	9.50
Book Value Per Share	11.79	10.81	9.31	6.30
Price / Book Value %	69.97	69.38	64.45	75.40
Dividends Per Share	0.19	0.14	0.14	0.11
Annual Financial Data				
Operating Results (000's)				
Total Revenues	50,203.0	52,132.9	43,699.8	34,405.1
Costs & Expenses	-48,646.8	-49,916.5	-42,377.4	-33,586.7
Income Before Taxes and Other	1,556.1	2,216.4	1,322.3	818.4
Other Items	0.0	0.0	0.0	0.0
Income Tax	-598.9	-901.4	-437.6	-329.8
Net Income	957.2	1,315.0	884.8	488.6
Cash Flow From Operations	1,464.0	-532.8	-3,826.8	1,212.5
Balance Sheet (000's)				
Cash & Equivalents	77.7	97.2	170.5	124.9
Total Current Assets	21,890.2	22,013.8	18,836.8	13,044.5
Fixed Assets, Net	5,210.1	4,549.9	3,707.4	3,602.5
Total Assets	27,802.7	27,018.7	22,960.1	16,981.6
Total Current Liabilities	11,659.9	14,178.5	10,828.9	8,007.3
Long-Term Debt	6,089.9	3,913.5	4,762.4	2,568.8
Stockholders' Equity	9,652.3	8,586.0	7,169.2	6,213.5
Performance & Financial Condition				
Return on Total Revenues %	1.91	2.52	2.02	1.42
Return on Avg Stockholders' Equity %	10.50	16.69	13.22	8.22
Return on Average Assets %	3.49	5.26	4.43	2.87
Current Ratio	1.88	1.55	1.74	1.63
Debt / Equity %	63.09	45.58	66.43	41.34

Compound Growth %'s	EPS %	34.26	Net Income %	25.13	Total Revenues %	13.42

Comments

Although management was optimistic at the beginning of fiscal 1996, an early winter disrupted nearly all outside construction and delivery schedules. Overall, the Company still salvaged a respectable year. Fiscal 1997 has been severely challenged by lower profit margins and a slowdown due to uncertainty of proposed railroad mergers. For the nine months ended December 31, 1996, earnings were $.35 per share as compared to $1.06 for the same period in fiscal 1996. Management expects much improved sales and profit during the last quarter. Investment Classification: Growth & Value

Officers	Position	Ownership Information	
Richard E. Bowlby	Chairman, President	Number of Shares Outstanding	818,911
R. Floyd Bowlby	Secretary	Market Capitalization	$ 6,756,016
Melvin R. Cobb, Jr.	Treasurer, Controller	Frequency of Dividends	Quarterly
Richard E. Bowlby, Jr.	Vice President	Number of Shareholders	Under 500
Norman C. Hildreth	VP - Manufacturing		

Other Information				
Transfer Agent	The Huntington National Bank VW Charleston, WV		Where Listed	OTC-BB
Auditor	Simpson & Osborne		Symbol	BPAB
Market Maker	Koonce Securities, Inc.	(800)368-2802	SIC Code	2490
	Robotti & Co., Inc.	(212)986-0800	Employees	720
Broker Dealer	Regular Stockbroker			

Burnham Corporation

P.O. Box 3205   Lancaster, PA 17604-3205   Telephone (717)293-5800   Fax (717)293-5816

Company Description

Burnham Corporation is a producer of boilers and related heating equipment for residential, commercial and industrial applications and also a distributor of a broad range of residential boilers, radiators and light commercial boilers to plumbing and heating wholesale distributors. Underlying Burnham's long-term success is its development and engineering capability which ensures the Company's industry leadership with highly efficient, environmentally safe, state-of-the-art products. The Company reacquires its shares as a good use of excess cash and a way to further maximize shareholder value.

	12/31/96	12/31/95	12/31/94	12/31/93
Per Share Information				
Stock Price	29.50	25.12	27.75	23.50
Earnings Per Share	3.95	3.37	3.17	3.30
Price / Earnings Ratio	7.47	7.45	8.75	7.12
Book Value Per Share	28.30	25.76	23.71	21.78
Price / Book Value %	104.24	97.52	117.04	107.90
Dividends Per Share	1.42	1.32	1.20	2.20
Annual Financial Data				
Operating Results (000's)				
Total Revenues	160,233.0	148,730.0	143,837.0	128,494.0
Costs & Expenses	-145,727.0	-136,396.0	-132,386.0	-117,945.0
Income Before Taxes and Other	14,506.0	12,334.0	11,451.0	10,549.0
Other Items	0.0	0.0	0.0	854.0
Income Tax	-5,662.0	-4,706.0	-4,291.0	-3,999.0
Net Income	8,844.0	7,628.0	7,160.0	7,404.0
Cash Flow From Operations	18,545.0	6,984.0	5,698.0	8,040.0
Balance Sheet (000's)				
Cash & Equivalents	19,342.0	2,725.0	8,142.0	12,292.0
Total Current Assets	65,580.0	48,603.0	53,278.0	52,963.0
Fixed Assets, Net	45,945.0	45,057.0	35,480.0	32,304.0
Total Assets	114,285.0	95,759.0	90,524.0	86,759.0
Total Current Liabilities	23,990.0	22,219.0	21,114.0	19,539.0
Long-Term Debt	16,507.0	5,218.0	8,252.0	11,307.0
Stockholders' Equity	63,369.0	58,641.0	53,796.0	49,119.0
Performance & Financial Condition				
Return on Total Revenues %	5.52	5.13	4.98	5.76
Return on Avg Stockholders' Equity %	14.50	13.57	13.91	15.86
Return on Average Assets %	8.42	8.19	8.08	8.83
Current Ratio	2.73	2.19	2.52	2.71
Debt / Equity %	26.05	8.90	15.34	23.02

Compound Growth %'s	EPS %	6.18	Net Income %	6.10	Total Revenues %	7.64

Comments

The Company declared a 2 for 1 stock split in 1995. All per share amounts were adjusted for consistency. 1993 results include a nonrecurring benefit of $854,000, $.76 cents per share, for adopting an accounting change. This reduces the compound growth rates in earnings that would otherwise have been displayed. Management has its eye on the ball by watching cash flow as a leading indicator; it has more than doubled since 1991, averaging a 17% increase per year. Investment Classification: Income & Value

Officers	Position	Ownership Information	
John B. Dodge	Chairman	Number of Shares Outstanding	2,224,732
Albert Morrison, III	President, CEO	Market Capitalization	$ 65,629,594
Ronald L. Griffith	Senior VP, CFO	Frequency of Dividends	Quarterly
Donald E. Sweigart	Senior VP	Number of Shareholders	Under 500
Shaun D. McMeans	Controller		

Other Information

Transfer Agent	First Union National Bank of NC Charlotte, NC		Where Listed	OTC-PS
Auditor	Arthur Andersen LLP		Symbol	BURCA
Market Maker	Robotti & Co., Inc.	(212)986-0800	SIC Code	3430
	Hill Thompson Magid & Co., Inc	(800)631-3083	Employees	400
Broker Dealer	Regular Stockbroker			

Butte Community Bank

672 Pearson Road   Paradise, CA 95969-5133   Telephone (916)877-0857   Fax (916)877-8820

Company Description

Butte Community Bank has four offices serving Butte County, northern California. It was formed in 1991 with the issuance of 350,000 shares of common stock at $10 per share. The Bank now has 76 employees.

	12/31/96	12/31/95	12/31/94	12/31/93
Per Share Information				
Stock Price	14.00	10.50	6.64	5.00
Earnings Per Share	1.18	1.05	0.81	0.74
Price / Earnings Ratio	11.86	10.00	8.20	6.76
Book Value Per Share	8.15	6.87	5.75	4.90
Price / Book Value %	171.78	152.84	115.48	102.04
Dividends Per Share	0.0	0.0	0.0	0.0
Annual Financial Data				
Operating Results (000's)				
Net Interest Income	4,630.0	3,672.0	2,953.8	2,418.7
Loan Loss Provision	-257.0	-160.0	-120.0	-113.0
Non-Interest Income	1,461.7	1,001.6	836.0	568.4
Non-Interest Expense	-3,869.7	-2,854.5	-2,399.3	-1,864.0
Income Before Taxes and Other	1,965.0	1,659.1	1,270.5	1,010.1
Other Items	0.0	0.0	0.0	19.8
Income Tax	-741.0	-642.0	-512.0	-384.6
Net Income	1,224.0	1,017.1	758.5	645.3
Balance Sheet (000's)				
Cash & Securities	20,308.2	15,605.9	16,097.9	n.a.
Loans, Net	63,636.9	53,560.4	38,015.0	n.a.
Total Assets	90,104.6	72,578.1	56,720.6	n.a.
Deposits	81,578.5	65,603.1	51,144.3	n.a.
Stockholders' Equity	7,433.6	6,089.7	4,915.4	n.a.
Performance & Financial Condition				
Return on Avg Stockholders' Equity %	18.10	18.48	16.77	17.13
Return on Average Assets %	1.50	1.57	n.a.	n.a.
Equity to Assets %	8.25	8.39	8.67	n.a.
Net Interest Margin	n.a.	n.a.	n.a.	n.a.
Reserve as a % of Problem Loans	559.14	120.66	n.a.	n.a.

Compound Growth %'s	EPS %	16.83	Net Income %	23.79	Net Interest Income %	24.17

Comments

The Company declared 4 for 3 stock splits in each of the last three years. All per share amounts have been restated for consistency. This young bank didn't waste any time in reaching outstanding performance numbers. Deposit growth was an impressive 24.4% during 1996. The Bank is generating excess loans which are generating income on their sale in the secondary market. Investment Classification: Growth

Officers	Position	Ownership Information	
Keith C. Robbins	President, CEO	Number of Shares Outstanding	911,861
John F. Coger	Senior VP, CFO	Market Capitalization	$ 12,766,054
John A. Stanton	Senior VP	Frequency of Dividends	n.a.
		Number of Shareholders	n.a.
		Where Listed / Symbol	OTC-BB / BTCB

Other Information		Loan Mix	%
Transfer Agent	U.S. Stock Transfer Corp. Glendale, CA	Not Allocated	100
Auditor	Perry-Smith & Co.		
Market Maker	Sutro & Co., Incorporated	(800)227-4422	
	Hill Thompson Magid & Co., Inc	(800)631-3083	
Broker Dealer	Regular Stockbroker		

CBR Brewing Company, Inc.

433 N. Camden Dr, Suite 1200   Beverly Hills, CA 90210   Telephone (310)274-5172   Fax (310)274-6403

Company Description

The Company manages and controls all of the production and sale of Pabst Blue Ribbon beer in the People's Republic of China. The Company was formed in 1988 to operate in a different line of business. In October, 1994, it acquired a 60% interest in the Zhaoqing Brewery located in China. Commencing from April, 1995, Zhaoqing Brewery ceased the production of Zhaoqing beer and started to produce Blue Ribbon beer.

	09/30/96	12/31/95	12/31/94
Per Share Information			
Stock Price as of 12/31	2.00	2.57	2.57
Earnings Per Share	0.19	0.30	0.05
Price / Earnings Ratio	n.a.	8.57	51.40
Book Value Per Share	2.12	1.91	1.59
Price / Book Value %	94.34	134.55	161.64
Dividends Per Share	0.0	0.0	0.0
Annual Financial Data			
Operating Results (000's)			
Total Revenues	114,690.7	72,309.2	1,493.2
Costs & Expenses	-111,890.8	-67,736.1	-1,152.7
Income Before Taxes and Other	2,800.0	4,573.1	-8.2
Other Items	-1,149.8	-2,094.0	447.6
Income Tax	-117.8	-120.2	0.0
Net Income	1,532.3	2,358.9	439.5
Cash Flow From Operations	124.9	15,023.1	-706.4
Balance Sheet (000's)			
Cash & Equivalents	8,708.5	6,904.8	875.5
Total Current Assets	46,916.0	39,278.8	3,143.3
Fixed Assets, Net	29,660.0	23,714.9	13,297.8
Total Assets	100,538.7	89,771.5	42,266.2
Total Current Liabilities	58,373.9	51,004.2	7,991.9
Long-Term Debt	8,930.8	8,869.6	12,167.4
Stockholders' Equity	16,947.6	15,309.7	12,751.6
Performance & Financial Condition			
Return on Total Revenues %	1.34	3.26	29.43
Return on Avg Stockholders' Equity %	n.a.	16.81	n.a.
Return on Average Assets %	n.a.	3.57	n.a.
Current Ratio	0.80	0.77	0.39
Debt / Equity %	52.70	57.93	95.42

Compound Growth %'s	EPS % n.a.	Net Income % n.a.	Total Revenues % n.a.

Comments

Prior to October, 1994, when it acquired a 60% interest in Zhaoqing Brewery, the Company had no operations and there was no trading activity in its stock. The results of operations and balance sheets presented above are for December 31, 1994, and the two months then ended, for the full year ended December 31, 1995, and as of September 30, 1996, and the nine months then ended. The annual report and financial statements for the year ended December 31, 1996, are not yet available. Although the current bid price was $2 per share, the ask price was $6 per share as of December 31, 1996. Investment Classification: Speculative

Officers	Position	Ownership Information	
John Z. Li	President	Number of Shares Outstanding	8,000,013
Gary C. K. Lui	CFO	Market Capitalization	$ 16,000,026
Niu Z. Hang	Vice President, COO	Frequency of Dividends	n.a.
Liu Y. Zhong	General Manager, Chairman	Number of Shareholders	26
Wong L. Tak	Other		

Other Information			
Transfer Agent	Interwest Transfer Co., Inc. Salt Lake City, UT	Where Listed	OTC-BB
Auditor	Ernst & Young LLP	Symbol	BLUE
Market Maker	Paragon Capital Corporation	(800)521-8877	SIC Code	2082
	Wilson-Davis & Co., Inc.	(800)453-5735	Employees	1341
Broker Dealer	Regular Stockbroker		

CMP Industries, Inc.

413 North Pearl Street   Albany, NY 12207   Telephone (518)434-3147   Fax (518)434-1288

Company Description

CMP Industries, Inc. and subsidiaries manufacture alloys, investment powders, and other products used by dental laboratories to fabricate dental prosthetics such as crowns, bridges, and partial dentures.   The Company consists of six divisions which market these products to domestic and international markets.   The six divisions are Ticonium, Nobilium, Vernon-Benshoff,Tecnadent, and International Dental Products.

	05/31/96	05/31/95	05/31/94	05/31/93
Per Share Information				
Stock Price as of 12/31	34.50	37.75	25.00	35.00
Earnings Per Share	3.63	4.43	5.59	4.79
Price / Earnings Ratio	9.50	8.52	4.47	7.31
Book Value Per Share	55.06	50.81	47.71	42.20
Price / Book Value %	62.66	74.30	52.40	82.94
Dividends Per Share	0.0	0.88	0.60	0.60
Annual Financial Data				
Operating Results (000's)				
Total Revenues	8,834.5	8,699.2	8,089.7	8,313.1
Costs & Expenses	-8,127.8	-7,886.9	-7,356.8	-7,460.1
Income Before Taxes and Other	606.5	720.8	715.7	662.2
Other Items	0.0	0.0	128.7	0.0
Income Tax	-217.6	-221.3	-204.3	-112.0
Net Income	388.8	499.6	640.0	550.2
Cash Flow From Operations	947.0	459.5	829.5	457.8
Balance Sheet (000's)				
Cash & Equivalents	1,146.8	811.4	1,247.5	764.6
Total Current Assets	5,773.8	5,511.4	5,106.8	5,011.2
Fixed Assets, Net	1,008.7	889.4	840.2	772.6
Total Assets	7,247.4	7,076.5	6,715.9	6,714.0
Total Current Liabilities	1,103.2	802.2	787.0	955.7
Long-Term Debt	0.0	0.0	0.0	0.0
Stockholders' Equity	5,693.1	5,736.4	5,367.7	4,840.9
Performance & Financial Condition				
Return on Total Revenues %	4.40	5.74	7.91	6.62
Return on Avg Stockholders' Equity %	6.80	9.00	12.54	11.96
Return on Average Assets %	5.43	7.24	9.53	8.59
Current Ratio	5.23	6.87	6.49	5.24
Debt / Equity %	n.a.	n.a.	n.a.	n.a.

Compound Growth %'s	EPS %	-8.83	Net Income %	-10.93	Total Revenues %	2.05

Comments

The Company has not shown much growth due to a decline in the domestic market although management is expecting a rebound in activity. Export sales comprised 33% of total sales during 1996. 1994 results reflect a nonrecurring benefit of $128,722, or $1.12 per share, arising from the change of an accounting method. In September, 1996, the Company made a tender offer for up to 10,000 shares at $40 per share. The stated reason was to enhance shareholder value. Investment Classification: Value

Officers	Position	Ownership Information	
Jeffrey M. Herr	Chairman	Number of Shares Outstanding	103,400
William J. Regan	President, CEO	Market Capitalization	$ 3,567,300
Robert J. Briggs	Secretary	Frequency of Dividends	n.a.
Edward J. Civiok, Jr.	Treasurer, Controller	Number of Shareholders	Under 500
James E. Fortin	Other		

Other Information			
Transfer Agent	Company Office	Where Listed	OTC-BB
Auditor	KPMG Peat Marwick LLP	Symbol	CMPN
Market Maker	Hill Thompson Magid & Co., Inc	(800)631-3083	SIC Code	3843
	Koonce Securities, Inc.	(800)368-2802	Employees	60
Broker Dealer	OTC Specialist		
	Norman Kadehjian - Wainwright	(800)727-7176	

CT Communications, Inc.

68 Cabarrrus Avenue East   Concord, NC 28026-0227   Telephone (704)788-0268   Fax (704)788-6322

Company Description

CT Communications and its subsidiaries operate entirely in the communications industry. The Concord Telephone Company, the principal subsidiary, provides local services as well as telephone and equipment rental to customers who are primarily residents of Cabarrus, Stanly and Rowan Counties in North Carolina. The Company also provides long distance service through CTC LDS. Revenue is generated mostly through local, access and toll service charges. During 1996, the Company invested in Wireless One of North Carolina which participates in the wireless cable television market in North Carolina.

	12/31/96	12/31/95	12/31/94	12/31/93
Per Share Information				
Stock Price	160.00	107.00	95.00	50.00
Earnings Per Share	6.98	8.74	5.59	5.32
Price / Earnings Ratio	22.92	12.24	16.99	9.40
Book Value Per Share	53.83	50.29	43.68	40.38
Price / Book Value %	297.23	212.77	217.49	123.82
Dividends Per Share	2.78	2.70	2.64	2.58
Annual Financial Data				
Operating Results (000's)				
Total Revenues	69,100.2	56,018.8	50,427.4	43,281.3
Costs & Expenses	-52,055.1	-38,802.6	-39,057.8	-31,811.4
Income Before Taxes and Other	17,045.1	19,777.4	13,033.3	12,241.1
Other Items	0.0	-93.1	-93.9	-93.6
Income Tax	-6,583.7	-6,760.6	-4,688.9	-4,282.2
Net Income	10,461.4	12,923.6	8,250.4	7,865.3
Cash Flow From Operations	22,440.8	20,335.7	24,071.4	16,271.8
Balance Sheet (000's)				
Cash & Equivalents	2,162.7	4,751.2	8,346.2	2,661.2
Total Current Assets	13,548.6	18,926.0	21,994.0	14,760.4
Fixed Assets, Net	71,989.6	57,975.7	53,840.4	56,102.1
Total Assets	115,064.0	107,765.5	99,886.6	91,938.4
Total Current Liabilities	16,070.1	12,697.6	13,578.9	7,060.5
Long-Term Debt	2,014.0	4,074.0	4,714.0	6,331.0
Stockholders' Equity	81,656.3	76,272.7	66,150.5	61,294.6
Performance & Financial Condition				
Return on Total Revenues %	15.14	23.07	16.36	18.17
Return on Avg Stockholders' Equity %	13.25	18.15	12.95	13.27
Return on Average Assets %	9.39	12.45	8.60	8.78
Current Ratio	0.84	1.49	1.62	2.09
Debt / Equity %	2.47	5.34	7.13	10.33

Compound Growth %'s	EPS %	9.47	Net Income %	9.97	Total Revenues %	16.88

Comments

The Company declared a 3 for 1 stock split in 1996. All per share amounts were adjusted for consistency. The decline in net earnings was attributable to a substantial investment and startup costs associated with new business ventures as well as a large nonrecurring gain that was included in 1995 results. Although pleased with a rise in operating income of 11%, management is more focused on being positioned correctly during this period of rapid deregulation. They believe that the Company is well prepared. Investment Classification: Growth

Officers	Position	Ownership Information	
L.D. Coltrane, III	Chairman	Number of Shares Outstanding	1,485,376
Michael R. Coltrane	President, CEO	Market Capitalization	$ 237,660,160
Catherine A. Duda	Senior VP, General Manager	Frequency of Dividends	Quarterly
Thomas A. Norman	Senior VP	Number of Shareholders	1,375
Nicholas L. Kottyan	Senior VP		

Other Information

Transfer Agent	Company Office		Where Listed	OTC-BB
Auditor	KPMG Peat Marwick LLP		Symbol	CNOTB
Market Maker	Hill Thompson Magid & Co., Inc	(800)631-3083	SIC Code	4813
	Ryan, Beck & Co.	(800)395-7926	Employees	296
Broker Dealer	Regular Stockbroker			

CVF Corp.

300 International Dr., Ste 100   Williamsville, NY 14221   Telephone (716)626-3044   Fax (716)626-3001

Company Description

CVF Corp., formerly Western Growth Corporation, is engaged in the business of developing and managing early stage and start-up companies engaged in the information and environmental technologies areas. The Company has made seven major investments in private companies located in Canada since 1989.

	12/31/96	12/31/95
Per Share Information		
Stock Price	6.62	2.00
Earnings Per Share	-0.03	-0.22
Price / Earnings Ratio	n.a.	n.a.
Book Value Per Share	2.91	0.64
Price / Book Value %	227.49	312.50
Dividends Per Share	0.0	0.0
Annual Financial Data		
Operating Results (000's)		
Total Revenues	5,611.0	2,060.1
Costs & Expenses	-4,605.3	-3,125.0
Income Before Taxes and Other	709.0	-1,064.8
Other Items	0.0	0.0
Income Tax	-892.8	0.0
Net Income	-183.8	-1,064.8
Cash Flow From Operations	-2,221.5	-1,503.7
Balance Sheet (000's)		
Cash & Equivalents	1,895.3	445.5
Total Current Assets	2,702.9	1,092.0
Fixed Assets, Net	217.6	171.4
Total Assets	29,138.0	6,282.7
Total Current Liabilities	3,067.8	1,552.5
Long-Term Debt	438.3	151.4
Stockholders' Equity	17,431.8	3,830.5
Performance & Financial Condition		
Return on Total Revenues %	-3.28	-51.69
Return on Avg Stockholders' Equity %	-1.73	n.a.
Return on Average Assets %	-1.04	n.a.
Current Ratio	0.88	0.70
Debt / Equity %	2.51	3.95

Compound Growth %'s	EPS %	n.a.	Net Income %	n.a.	Total Revenues %	n.a.

Comments

Subsequent to December 31, 1996, the Company sold substantially all of its remaining stock in Certicom, realizing net proceeds of approximately $19 million. Net earnings for the quarter were $1.73 per share. All of this is already reflected in book value at December 31, 1996. The Company had $19 million of cash at March 31, 1997, some of which is scheduled to be mailed to Uncle Sam. Most other investments are reported at cost. Investment Classification: Speculative

Officers	Position	Ownership Information	
Jeffrey Dreben	President, CEO	Number of Shares Outstanding	5,982,349
Robert Nally	Secretary, Treasurer	Market Capitalization	$ 39,603,150
		Frequency of Dividends	n.a.
		Number of Shareholders	n.a.

Other Information

Transfer Agent	Colonial Stock Transfer Co., Inc. Salt Lake City, UT		Where Listed	OTC-BB
Auditor	Feldman Radin & Co., P.C.		Symbol	CVFJ
Market Maker	Alpine Securities Corporation	(800)521-5588	SIC Code	6799
	Coastal Securities Ltd.	(800)964-4446	Employees	n.a.
Broker Dealer	Regular Stockbroker			

Cable Link, Inc.

280 Cozzins Street   Columbus, OH 43215-2379   Telephone (614)221-3131   Fax (614)222-0581

Company Description

The Company sells new and refurbished cable television equipment in addition to repairing equipment for cable companies within the United States and various international markets. Their single leased facility is located in Columbus, Ohio. The Company began business in 1983 as a sole proprietorship and was incorporated in 1987. In 1992, the Company sold 28,000 shares in a private placement. This was followed by two placements in 1993 totalling 122,000 shares at $7 per share.

	12/31/96	12/31/95	12/31/94	12/31/93
Per Share Information				
Stock Price	1.50	1.62	3.25	4.00
Earnings Per Share	0.02	-0.43	0.12	0.24
Price / Earnings Ratio	75.00	n.a.	27.08	16.67
Book Value Per Share	0.79	0.86	1.29	0.95
Price / Book Value %	189.87	188.37	251.94	421.05
Dividends Per Share	0.0	0.0	0.0	0.0
Annual Financial Data				
Operating Results (000's)				
Total Revenues	8,253.5	7,650.4	8,736.3	6,139.6
Costs & Expenses	-8,252.9	-7,999.3	-8,313.3	-5,999.1
Income Before Taxes and Other	0.6	-360.1	184.8	140.5
Other Items	0.0	0.0	0.0	0.0
Income Tax	17.6	68.9	-103.0	0.0
Net Income	18.2	-291.2	81.7	140.5
Cash Flow From Operations	330.1	-198.1	-309.3	-550.6
Balance Sheet (000's)				
Cash & Equivalents	115.8	149.8	27.0	35.2
Total Current Assets	2,218.7	2,471.6	2,227.1	1,487.1
Fixed Assets, Net	719.1	539.0	393.0	265.9
Total Assets	2,979.8	3,053.6	2,652.4	1,761.5
Total Current Liabilities	2,207.2	2,365.2	1,744.4	1,138.3
Long-Term Debt	106.8	2.0	12.0	15.7
Stockholders' Equity	665.8	586.0	877.2	607.5
Performance & Financial Condition				
Return on Total Revenues %	0.22	-3.81	0.94	2.29
Return on Avg Stockholders' Equity %	2.91	-39.80	11.01	81.61
Return on Average Assets %	0.60	-10.21	3.70	9.81
Current Ratio	1.01	1.04	1.28	1.31
Debt / Equity %	16.03	0.34	1.37	2.59

Compound Growth %'s	EPS % -56.32	Net Income % -49.39	Total Revenues % 10.37

Comments

The Company declared a 2 for 1 stock split in 1994. 1993 per share amounts were adjusted for consistency. The Company replaced and added senior management in 1994 and 1995 but then had a major upheaval in 1996 with several departures of key personnel and their opening of a business in direct competition with Cable Link. A new management team was again in place as the Company began its next fiscal year. First quarter 1997 results were much improved over the prior two quarters with the Company reporting income of $126,052 ($.09 per share). Investment Classification: Speculative

Officers	Position	Ownership Information	
Bob Binsky	Chairman, CEO	Number of Shares Outstanding	839,288
Brenda Thompson	President	Market Capitalization	$ 1,258,932
Richard M. Rozic	Exec VP, COO	Frequency of Dividends	n.a.
E. Charles Hanchett	Vice President	Number of Shareholders	Under 500
Richard L. Baker	VP - Manufacturing		

Other Information			
Transfer Agent	Fifth Third Bank Cincinatti,	Where Listed	OTC-BB
Auditor	Coopers & Lybrand LLP	Symbol	CBLK
Market Maker	Wien Securities Corp.	(800)624-0050	SIC Code	4840
	Paragon Capital Corp.	(800)345-0505	Employees	100
Broker Dealer	Regular Stockbroker		

Cable-Sat Systems, Inc.

2105 Hamilton Avenue, Ste. 140   San Jose, CA 95125   Telephone (408)879-6600   Fax (408)559-8793

Company Description

Cable-Sat Systems, Inc. is developing products to allow the facsimile transmission of color images from computers equipped with the Company's software programs. The Company's first product which is currently in internal testing is called Chromafax. It enables users to send and receive color faxes to and from their personal computer. On September 30, 1996, the Company completed its initial public offering of stock and issued 1,050,000 shares at $6 per share.

	09/30/96	09/30/95
Per Share Information		
Stock Price as of 12/31	6.37	0.92
Earnings Per Share	-0.76	-0.06
Price / Earnings Ratio	n.a.	n.a.
Book Value Per Share	1.04	0.20
Price / Book Value %	612.50	460.00
Dividends Per Share	0.0	0.0
Annual Financial Data		
Operating Results (000's)		
Total Revenues	11.2	1.8
Costs & Expenses	-2,204.2	-256.6
Income Before Taxes and Other	-3,093.0	-254.8
Other Items	0.0	0.0
Income Tax	0.0	0.0
Net Income	-3,093.0	-254.8
Cash Flow From Operations	-1,662.0	-326.6
Balance Sheet (000's)		
Cash & Equivalents	155.5	314.1
Total Current Assets	5,705.1	423.1
Fixed Assets, Net	136.1	56.8
Total Assets	5,959.1	488.4
Total Current Liabilities	764.0	42.9
Long-Term Debt	0.0	0.0
Stockholders' Equity	5,195.1	445.5
Performance & Financial Condition		
Return on Total Revenues %	-27,503.14	-14,240.64
Return on Avg Stockholders' Equity %	-109.67	n.a.
Return on Average Assets %	-95.94	n.a.
Current Ratio	7.47	9.85
Debt / Equity %	n.a.	n.a.

Compound Growth %'s	EPS %	n.a.	Net Income %	n.a.	Total Revenues %	n.a.

Comments

The Company is still in its developmental stage. For the quarter ended December 31, 1996, a net loss was reported of $1.3 million or $.26 per share. In January, 1997, the Company finalized a five-year agreement with an Australian company to manufacture and market the "light" version of Chromafax on a world-wide basis. The Company anticipates the expenditure of significant funds for marketing and commercialization of the initial color fax products. First product sales were shipped in June, 1997. Investment Classification: Speculative

Officers	Position	Ownership Information	
Abraham Ostrovsky	Chairman, CEO	Number of Shares Outstanding	4,972,000
Peter Whealton	President	Market Capitalization	$ 31,671,640
Shelley Harrison	Senior VP	Frequency of Dividends	n.a.
Lisa E. D'Alencon	CFO	Number of Shareholders	855
Rick Lazansky	Vice President		

Other Information				
Transfer Agent	American Stock Transfer & Trust Co. New York, NY		Where Listed	OTC-BB
Auditor	Ernst & Young LLP		Symbol	CSSA
Market Maker	Sharpe Capital Inc.	(800)355-5781	SIC Code	7372
	M.H. Meyerson & Co., Inc.	(800)333-3113	Employees	n.a.
Broker Dealer	Regular Stockbroker			

Calcasieu Real Estate & Oil Co., Inc.

3401 Ryan Street   Lake Charles, LA 70602   Telephone (318)433-2265   Fax (318)494-4351

Company Description

Calcasieu Real Estate & Oil Co., Inc. was spun-off from the Calcasieu National Bank in 1930 to hold certain real estate and royalty interests that had been owned by the Bank. The principal business of the Company has been the ownership and preservation of the assets acquired at the time of its formation. The Company owns interests in approximately 7,244 acres of land most of which is located within 100 miles of the City of Lake Charles, in southwestern and central Louisiana.

	12/31/96	12/31/95	12/31/94	12/31/93
Per Share Information				
Stock Price	2.75	1.75	1.50	1.50
Earnings Per Share	0.40	0.17	0.05	0.13
Price / Earnings Ratio	6.88	10.29	30.00	11.54
Book Value Per Share	1.56	1.31	1.06	0.97
Price / Book Value %	176.28	133.59	141.51	154.64
Dividends Per Share	0.09	0.06	0.04	0.0
Annual Financial Data				
Operating Results (000's)				
Total Revenues	1,479.2	849.6	460.9	574.1
Costs & Expenses	-234.6	-331.5	-340.2	-283.6
Income Before Taxes and Other	1,244.6	518.1	120.8	290.5
Other Items	0.0	0.0	0.0	44.0
Income Tax	-439.5	-169.3	-12.7	-76.2
Net Income	805.1	348.8	108.1	258.3
Cash Flow From Operations	170.5	681.8	-1.9	281.8
Balance Sheet (000's)				
Cash & Equivalents	313.5	289.2	36.5	n.a.
Total Current Assets	895.5	559.3	152.2	n.a.
Fixed Assets, Net	2,028.9	2,039.3	2,138.7	n.a.
Total Assets	3,445.7	3,018.5	2,587.1	n.a.
Total Current Liabilities	339.5	403.5	167.8	n.a.
Long-Term Debt	0.0	0.0	93.1	n.a.
Stockholders' Equity	3,106.3	2,615.0	2,326.2	n.a.
Performance & Financial Condition				
Return on Total Revenues %	54.43	41.05	23.45	44.99
Return on Avg Stockholders' Equity %	28.14	14.12	4.70	11.33
Return on Average Assets %	24.91	12.44	n.a.	n.a.
Current Ratio	2.64	1.39	0.91	n.a.
Debt / Equity %	n.a.	n.a.	4.00	n.a.

Compound Growth %'s	EPS % n.a.	Net Income % n.a.	Total Revenues % n.a.

Comments

The large increase in 1996 earnings was attributable to the sale of the Company's holdings in Calcasieu National Bank which had been purchased by another bank in an all cash transaction. Accordingly, compound growth rates were not displayed. Oil and gas revenues actually decreased during the year although there are rumors that a new well may be successful. The Company owns a large undeveloped tract of land on the boundary of the city of Lake Charles which is being considered as the cite for a new high school. If approved, the Company would give the City enough land for the school and develop the surrounding areas. Stephen Schuller, analyst with Dorsey Investment Securities, praised the Company for clearly operating for the benefit of its shareholders. Investment Classification: Value

Officers	Position	Ownership Information	
Arthur Hollins, III	President	Number of Shares Outstanding	1,997,272
William D. Blake	Vice President, Treasurer	Market Capitalization	$ 5,492,498
Charles D. Viccellio	Vice President, Secretary	Frequency of Dividends	Quarterly
		Number of Shareholders	750

Other Information			
Transfer Agent	ChaseMellon Shareholder Services Ridgefield Park, NJ	Where Listed	OTC-BB
Auditor	McElios, Quirk & Burch	Symbol	CLUO
Market Maker	Dorsey Investment Securities	(800)375-5431	SIC Code	1311
	Carr Securities Corporation	(800)221-2243	Employees	5
Broker Dealer	Regular Stockbroker		
	Stephen R. Schuller - Dorsey	(800)375-5431	

California Orchard Company

P.O. Box O   King City, CA 93930   Telephone (408)385-3858   Fax (408)385-5909

Company Description

California Orchard Company is primarily engaged in leasing farm land to growers for vegetable row crop production in southern Monterey County, California. The Company also owns substantial water rights most of which are used by the tenant farmers. 170 acres of premium varietal wine grapes were planted during the spring, 1997. Drip irrigation was installed to improve the irrigation efficiency and reduce water consumption by 60%. In several years this property will generate additional lease income.

	12/31/96	12/31/95	12/31/94	12/31/93
Per Share Information				
Stock Price	62.00	62.00	62.00	50.00
Earnings Per Share	4.57	4.06	4.18	6.47
Price / Earnings Ratio	13.57	15.27	14.83	7.73
Book Value Per Share	32.26	35.70	35.64	35.46
Price / Book Value %	192.19	173.67	173.96	141.00
Dividends Per Share	8.00	4.00	4.00	6.00
Annual Financial Data				
Operating Results (000's)				
Total Revenues	1,006.2	946.0	923.0	993.7
Costs & Expenses	-867.3	-829.8	-802.3	-790.4
Income Before Taxes and Other	138.9	116.2	120.7	203.3
Other Items	0.0	0.0	0.0	0.0
Income Tax	-47.8	-35.2	-37.3	-74.2
Net Income	91.2	81.0	83.4	129.1
Cash Flow From Operations	97.8	238.8	-4.8	262.8
Balance Sheet (000's)				
Cash & Equivalents	289.2	351.1	194.2	284.1
Total Current Assets	347.7	402.0	356.4	366.9
Fixed Assets, Net	450.1	482.3	515.5	546.2
Total Assets	797.9	884.3	871.9	913.0
Total Current Liabilities	147.0	163.4	151.9	199.8
Long-Term Debt	0.0	0.0	0.0	0.0
Stockholders' Equity	644.0	712.6	711.4	707.9
Performance & Financial Condition				
Return on Total Revenues %	9.06	8.56	9.03	13.00
Return on Avg Stockholders' Equity %	13.44	11.38	11.75	17.76
Return on Average Assets %	10.84	9.23	9.34	14.69
Current Ratio	2.36	2.46	2.35	1.84
Debt / Equity %	n.a.	n.a.	n.a.	n.a.

Compound Growth %'s	EPS % -10.94	Net Income % -10.96	Total Revenues % 0.42

Comments

Shareholders were rewarded with a $8 dividend during 1996. Operations continue to be very stable because no farming risk is assumed by the Company with respect to the properties. Management is aggressively defining and protecting its water rights. Reservoirs were well stocked after the early rains during the 1996/1997 rainy season. Investment Classification: Income & Value

Officers	Position	Ownership Information	
Alan M. Teague	President	Number of Shares Outstanding	19,962
Gregory H. Smith	Secretary	Market Capitalization	$ 1,237,644
Lawrence J. Porter	Treasurer, General Manager	Frequency of Dividends	Annual
C.J. Hurst, Jr.	Vice President	Number of Shareholders	Under 500

Other Information				
Transfer Agent	Company Office		Where Listed	OTC-BB
Auditor	Hayashi & Wayland		Symbol	CAOX
Market Maker	Robotti & Co., Inc.	(212)986-0800	SIC Code	6510
	The Seidler Companies Inc.	(800)421-0164	Employees	14
Broker Dealer	OTC Specialist			
	Standard Investment	(888)783-4688 Ext: Jack		

California-Michigan Land and Water Company

3725 East Mountain View Avenue   Pasadena, CA 91107   Telephone (818)793-6189   Fax (818)793-0503

Company Description

The primary business conducted by it's subsidiary, East Pasadena Water Company, is the sale and distribution of water to residential and commercial consumers. These operations also include water production and storage. The Company is also engaged in real estate investment activities. A reliable source estimated a trading range of $400 to $600 per share. Market makers were posting a $40 bid price at the end of 1996 and the Company reacquired seven shares at $30 per share during the last year. You never know who is going to get lucky.

	12/31/96	12/31/95	12/31/94	12/31/93
Per Share Information				
Stock Price	600.00	600.00	600.00	600.00
Earnings Per Share	119.83	53.33	-5.51	89.10
Price / Earnings Ratio	5.01	11.25	n.a.	6.73
Book Value Per Share	1,067.52	951.99	896.60	920.68
Price / Book Value %	56.21	63.03	66.92	65.17
Dividends Per Share	5.35	5.51	8.91	9.75
Annual Financial Data				
Operating Results (000's)				
Total Revenues	1,637.0	1,356.9	1,381.8	1,278.6
Costs & Expenses	-1,233.9	-1,175.5	-1,197.6	-973.2
Income Before Taxes and Other	403.1	181.4	184.2	305.4
Other Items	0.0	0.0	-131.6	-3.9
Income Tax	-143.8	-65.6	-64.6	-108.0
Net Income	259.3	115.7	-12.0	193.4
Cash Flow From Operations	599.8	244.1	222.0	383.6
Balance Sheet (000's)				
Cash & Equivalents	329.3	249.7	654.5	446.8
Total Current Assets	858.9	583.2	1,015.9	1,199.5
Fixed Assets, Net	2,712.2	2,727.1	2,494.7	2,755.3
Total Assets	4,296.6	4,270.0	4,347.8	4,748.1
Total Current Liabilities	479.2	343.4	406.3	400.4
Long-Term Debt	385.5	526.6	656.9	851.8
Stockholders' Equity	2,310.1	2,066.8	1,946.5	1,998.8
Performance & Financial Condition				
Return on Total Revenues %	15.84	8.53	-0.87	15.13
Return on Avg Stockholders' Equity %	11.85	5.77	-0.61	10.11
Return on Average Assets %	6.05	2.69	-0.26	4.30
Current Ratio	1.79	1.70	2.50	3.00
Debt / Equity %	16.69	25.48	33.75	42.61

Compound Growth %'s	EPS %	10.38	Net Income %	10.26	Total Revenues %	8.59

Comments

Two new reservoirs and a rate increase pushed revenue higher by 21.6%. On May 30, 1997, the Board of Directors declared a dividend equal to 10% of after-tax earnings, a healthy $11.98 per share. 1994 results include a one-time charge of $131,605, or $60.62 per share, due to a change in depreciation methods, causing the net loss for the year. Shirley King retired in March, 1997, after 15 years of dedicated service as general manager. Investment Classification: Value

Officers	Position	Ownership Information	
Anton C. Garnier	President	Number of Shares Outstanding	2,164
Jo Ann Lee	Vice President, COO	Market Capitalization	$ 1,298,400
		Frequency of Dividends	Annual
		Number of Shareholders	Under 500

Other Information			
Transfer Agent	Company Office	Where Listed	OTC-BB
Auditor	Horsfall, Murphy & Pindroh	Symbol	CMLW
Market Maker	Hill Thompson Magid & Co., Inc (800)631-3083	SIC Code	4940
	Howe Barnes Investments, Inc. (800)621-2364	Employees	11
Broker Dealer	OTC Specialist		

Call Now, Inc.

P.O. Box 531399   Miami Shores, FL 33153   Telephone (305)751-5115   Fax (305)751-7761

Company Description

Call Now, Inc. exited the long distance telephone business in 1996 and has redeployed its assets into other ventures including the acquisition of 118 acres of land in Williamson County, Texas, which it intends to develop, and $46 million face amount bonds and notes, currently in default, secured by a lien on the Retama Park Horse Racing facility in suburban San Antonio, Texas. The Company also has investments in certain telecommunication companies.

	12/31/96	12/31/95	12/31/94	12/31/93
Per Share Information				
Stock Price	1.87	1.50	1.13	3.63
Earnings Per Share	0.40	-0.09	0.56	-0.05
Price / Earnings Ratio	4.68	n.a.	2.02	n.a.
Book Value Per Share	1.12	1.00	0.73	0.03
Price / Book Value %	166.96	150.00	154.79	12,100.00
Dividends Per Share	0.0	0.0	0.0	0.0
Annual Financial Data				
Operating Results (000's)				
Total Revenues	6,027.5	1,376.3	1,492.8	54.3
Costs & Expenses	-1,462.1	-2,395.4	-2,830.5	-257.2
Income Before Taxes and Other	4,565.4	-1,019.1	-1,337.7	-202.9
Other Items	85.6	0.0	4,240.8	0.0
Income Tax	-1,716.2	377.8	685.0	-35.4
Net Income	2,934.7	-641.2	3,588.1	-238.2
Cash Flow From Operations	-1,830.7	-553.6	905.2	-93.6
Balance Sheet (000's)				
Cash & Equivalents	1,670.1	241.3	0.0	78.7
Total Current Assets	12,479.4	12,979.5	9,079.6	129.3
Fixed Assets, Net	2,412.8	79.9	108.7	86.7
Total Assets	15,053.1	13,573.7	9,455.2	261.0
Total Current Liabilities	4,893.8	6,352.0	4,162.0	88.8
Long-Term Debt	1,757.6	11.1	28.4	0.0
Stockholders' Equity	8,401.7	7,210.6	5,264.9	172.2
Performance & Financial Condition				
Return on Total Revenues %	48.69	-46.59	240.36	-438.60
Return on Avg Stockholders' Equity %	37.60	-10.28	131.99	-143.77
Return on Average Assets %	20.50	-5.57	73.86	-108.88
Current Ratio	2.55	2.04	2.18	1.46
Debt / Equity %	20.92	0.15	0.54	n.a.

Compound Growth %'s	EPS % n.a.	Net Income % n.a.	Total Revenues % n.a.

Comments

The results for 1993 are for the six months ended December 31, 1993. The Company recognized a gain of $5.7 million on the sale of its investment in Intermedia Communications in 1996. During the first quarter of 1997, the Company realized revenue of $3.8 million on the exchange of industrial revenue bonds of Retama Development pursuant to a Plan of Adjustment approved by the bankruptcy court reviewing Retama's situation. Net earnings for the quarter were $.29 per share and the Company has $6,234,000 in cash at March 31, 1997. Investment Classification: Speculative

Officers	Position	Ownership Information	
William M. Allen	Chairman	Number of Shares Outstanding	7,519,400
Bryan P. Brown	President	Market Capitalization	$ 14,061,278
James D. Grainger	CFO	Frequency of Dividends	n.a.
Susan Lurvey	Secretary	Number of Shareholders	307

Other Information

Transfer Agent	Interwest Transfer Co., Inc. Salt Lake City, UT		Where Listed	OTC-BB
Auditor	BDO Seidman LLP		Symbol	CNOW
Market Maker	Barron Chase Securities, Inc.	(800)937-4466	SIC Code	4813
	Fidelity Capital Markets	(800)679-5748	Employees	4
Broker Dealer	Regular Stockbroker			

Capital Properties, Inc.

One Hospital Trust Plaza, #920   Providence, RI 02903   Telephone (401)331-0100   Fax (401)331-2965

Company Description

The Company's business consists of the leasing of certain of its real estate interests in downtown Providence, Rhode Island, the operation of other downtown Providence properties, and the leasing of its petroleum storage terminal facilities in East Providence. Through its wholly-owned subsidiary, the Company also leases outdoor advertising locations along interstate and primary highways. The Company was formed in 1983.

	12/31/96	12/31/95	12/31/94	12/31/93
Per Share Information				
Stock Price	8.37	8.50	7.31	7.88
Earnings Per Share	0.33	0.08	0.19	-0.63
Price / Earnings Ratio	25.36	106.25	38.47	n.a.
Book Value Per Share	13.13	13.35	13.57	13.77
Price / Book Value %	63.75	63.67	53.87	57.23
Dividends Per Share	0.55	0.30	0.40	0.32
Annual Financial Data				
Operating Results (000's)				
Total Revenues	2,793.0	3,020.0	2,832.0	2,709.0
Costs & Expenses	-2,236.0	-2,859.0	-2,493.0	-2,390.0
Income Before Taxes and Other	557.0	161.0	339.0	319.0
Other Items	0.0	0.0	0.0	-866.0
Income Tax	-225.0	-83.0	-146.0	-89.0
Net Income	332.0	78.0	193.0	-636.0
Cash Flow From Operations	545.0	167.0	436.0	540.0
Balance Sheet (000's)				
Cash & Equivalents	948.0	767.0	757.0	813.0
Total Current Assets	1,969.0	1,175.0	1,175.0	1,330.0
Fixed Assets, Net	9,027.0	9,376.0	9,793.0	10,151.0
Total Assets	15,208.0	15,444.0	17,803.0	18,669.0
Total Current Liabilities	2,081.0	536.0	648.0	610.0
Long-Term Debt	0.0	0.0	2,053.0	2,627.0
Stockholders' Equity	13,127.0	13,345.0	13,567.0	13,774.0
Performance & Financial Condition				
Return on Total Revenues %	11.89	2.58	6.81	-23.48
Return on Avg Stockholders' Equity %	2.51	0.58	1.41	-4.45
Return on Average Assets %	2.17	0.47	1.06	-3.35
Current Ratio	0.95	2.19	1.81	2.18
Debt / Equity %	n.a.	n.a.	15.13	19.07

Compound Growth %'s	EPS %	31.79	Net Income %	31.16	Total Revenues %	1.02

Comments

The Company's primary source of revenue is the leasing and renting of its properties. The Company has development plans for a number of its properties and is exploring development opportunities on others. Capital Properties is classified as a personal holding company for federal income tax purposes and, therefore, must distribute a formula amount of dividends to avoid the excise tax. This is good news for shareholders interested in cash income as the dividend yield is intriguing. Investment Classification: Value & Income

Officers	Position	Ownership Information	
Robert Eder	Chairman	Number of Shares Outstanding	1,000,000
Barbara J. Dreyer	President, Treasurer	Market Capitalization	$ 8,370,000
Edwin G. Torrance	Secretary	Frequency of Dividends	Semi-Annual
		Number of Shareholders	491

Other Information			
Transfer Agent	Fleet National Bank Providence, RI	Where Listed	BE
Auditor	Lefkowitz, Garfinkel et. al.	Symbol	CPI
Market Maker	Herzog, Heine, Geduld, Inc. (800)221-3600	SIC Code	6510
	Carr Securities Corporation (800)221-2243	Employees	4
Broker Dealer	Regular Stockbroker		

Carc, Inc.

500 Downs Loop   Clemson, SC 29631   Telephone (864)654-1155   Fax (864)654-1191

Company Description

CARC operates a retirement community, known as Clemson Downs, which includes apartment buildings, a health care center and recreational and social facilities. The health care center is accredited by the regulatory authority. Apartment revenues consist of rental, meals and miscellaneous other income. Health Care Center revenues consist primarily of room and board fees as well as fees for medical supplies and physical therapy. Dietary revenues consist of fees charged for meals and catered functions.

	03/31/97	03/31/96	03/31/95	03/31/94
Per Share Information				
Stock Price as of 12/31	5.00	5.00	5.00	4.50
Earnings Per Share	0.45	0.47	0.42	0.41
Price / Earnings Ratio	11.67	10.64	11.90	10.98
Book Value Per Share	3.36	2.91	2.44	2.03
Price / Book Value %	156.25	171.82	204.92	221.67
Dividends Per Share	0.0	0.0	0.0	0.0
Annual Financial Data				
Operating Results (000's)				
Total Revenues	3,169.9	3,006.4	3,031.4	2,988.4
Costs & Expenses	-2,928.8	-2,756.6	-2,806.1	-2,764.9
Income Before Taxes and Other	241.1	249.8	223.0	219.2
Other Items	0.0	0.0	0.0	0.0
Income Tax	0.0	0.0	0.0	0.0
Net Income	241.1	249.8	223.0	219.2
Cash Flow From Operations	647.0	506.1	530.5	373.1
Balance Sheet (000's)				
Cash & Equivalents	236.2	225.7	221.6	187.0
Total Current Assets	599.9	498.5	520.7	462.1
Fixed Assets, Net	3,857.8	3,943.8	4,099.6	4,233.4
Total Assets	4,669.0	4,765.8	4,946.3	5,047.9
Total Current Liabilities	475.9	377.1	402.2	330.1
Long-Term Debt	2,287.5	2,731.0	3,145.5	3,527.3
Stockholders' Equity	1,799.7	1,558.7	1,308.9	1,085.9
Performance & Financial Condition				
Return on Total Revenues %	7.61	8.31	7.36	7.33
Return on Avg Stockholders' Equity %	14.36	17.42	18.62	22.45
Return on Average Assets %	5.11	5.14	4.46	4.27
Current Ratio	1.26	1.32	1.29	1.40
Debt / Equity %	127.10	175.21	240.32	324.83

Compound Growth %'s	EPS %	3.15	Net Income %	3.23	Total Revenues %	1.98

Comments

The Company has net operating loss carryforwards of $945,000. The Company has shown five consecutive years of net profit after several years of losses. The Company acts as its own stock transfer agent and order matcher for stock transactions. While no published price quotes were available, the Company indicated that trades, when made, were generally at $5.00 per share. Investment Classification: Speculative

Officers	Position	Ownership Information	
Anita M. Davis	CEO	Number of Shares Outstanding	536,000
Hazel C. Poe	Secretary	Market Capitalization	$ 2,814,000
Debra Turner	Other	Frequency of Dividends	n.a.
		Number of Shareholders	536

Other Information			
Transfer Agent	Company Office	Where Listed	Order Matching Only
Auditor	Crisp Hughes & Co. LLP	Symbol	n.a.
Market Maker	None - Company Office	SIC Code	8052
		Employees	75
Broker Dealer	None		

Carco Electronics

195 Constitution Drive   Menlo Park, CA 94025   Telephone (415)321-8174   Fax (415)321-1890

Company Description

Carco Electronics designs, manufactures, and markets precision, servo-controlled systems including flight motion simulators, precision rotary tables, microwave boresight measuring systems, and target positioners. There are two classes of stock but only A shares trade. Class B shares are held by the founder for voting control purposes. The Company was formed in 1961.

	09/30/96	09/30/95	09/30/94	09/30/93
Per Share Information				
Stock Price as of 12/31	10.75	7.50	5.00	6.25
Earnings Per Share	-0.28	-0.57	0.09	0.32
Price / Earnings Ratio	n.a.	n.a.	55.56	19.53
Book Value Per Share	8.54	9.20	9.78	9.69
Price / Book Value %	125.88	81.52	51.12	64.50
Dividends Per Share	0.0	0.0	0.0	0.06
Annual Financial Data				
Operating Results (000's)				
Total Revenues	9,249.0	5,582.8	6,549.2	9,649.6
Costs & Expenses	-9,427.0	-5,891.2	-6,467.5	-9,434.0
Income Before Taxes and Other	-178.0	-308.3	81.7	215.6
Other Items	0.0	0.0	-22.5	0.0
Income Tax	52.5	77.8	-23.3	-88.0
Net Income	-125.5	-230.6	35.9	127.6
Cash Flow From Operations	-877.6	-1,096.8	2,577.7	-1,289.3
Balance Sheet (000's)				
Cash & Equivalents	358.0	700.9	1,852.8	48.3
Total Current Assets	7,464.8	3,970.9	4,211.5	5,077.3
Fixed Assets, Net	318.1	241.7	282.1	384.6
Total Assets	7,973.8	4,225.2	4,506.2	5,477.2
Total Current Liabilities	4,039.8	490.2	540.6	1,585.5
Long-Term Debt	0.0	0.0	0.0	0.0
Stockholders' Equity	3,901.5	3,697.0	3,927.6	3,891.7
Performance & Financial Condition				
Return on Total Revenues %	-1.36	-4.13	0.55	1.32
Return on Avg Stockholders' Equity %	-3.30	-6.05	0.92	3.32
Return on Average Assets %	-2.06	-5.28	0.72	2.29
Current Ratio	1.85	8.10	7.79	3.20
Debt / Equity %	n.a.	n.a.	n.a.	n.a.

Compound Growth %'s	EPS % n.a.	Net Income % n.a.	Total Revenues % -1.40

Comments

The Company has rebounded from two consecutive drops in sales in 1995 and 1994. The 1996 increase was a whopping 67%. However, a net loss was posted for the year because of cost overruns on several major jobs. The year end backlog was at a record $13.4 million compared to $8.7 in the preceding year. The best news is that most of those orders are for more standard and highly profitable products. The Company continues not to require any long-term debt. Investment Classification: Value & Speculative

Officers	Position	Ownership Information	
John M. Carter	Chairman, CEO	Number of Shares Outstanding	456,710
Hugh D. Carter	President, COO	Market Capitalization	$ 4,909,633
William R. Meckfessel	CFO, Treasurer	Frequency of Dividends	Annual
Helen Carter	Secretary	Number of Shareholders	Under 500
Clay E. Falkner	VP - Manufacturing		

Other Information

Transfer Agent	Company Office			Where Listed	OTC-BB
Auditor	KPMG Peat Marwick LLP			Symbol	CAROA
Market Maker	Seidler Companies, Inc., The	(800)421-0164		SIC Code	3500
	Newby & Co.	(800)456-3992		Employees	110
Broker Dealer	Regular Stockbroker				

Cardinal Bancorp, Inc.

140 East Main Street   Everett, PA 15537-0327   Telephone (814)652-2131   Fax (814)652-9338

Company Description

Cardinal Bancorp, Inc., is the bank holding company of First American National Bank of Pennsylvania. The Bank has five full-service offices in south central Pennsylvania in the communities of Everett, Bedford, Breezewood, Altoona/Hollidaysburg and Woodbury. It has been serving the area since 1902.

	12/31/96	12/31/95	12/31/94	12/31/93
Per Share Information				
Stock Price	19.25	16.66	16.00	14.50
Earnings Per Share	1.54	1.76	1.68	1.06
Price / Earnings Ratio	12.50	9.47	9.52	13.68
Book Value Per Share	15.38	14.98	12.25	12.17
Price / Book Value %	125.16	111.21	130.61	119.15
Dividends Per Share	0.37	0.30	0.55	0.22
Annual Financial Data				
Operating Results (000's)				
Net Interest Income	5,433.6	5,243.4	4,713.9	4,368.4
Loan Loss Provision	0.0	0.0	300.0	-125.0
Non-Interest Income	533.1	475.9	456.8	529.2
Non-Interest Expense	-4,095.8	-3,714.1	-3,487.2	-3,509.5
Income Before Taxes and Other	1,870.9	2,005.2	1,983.4	1,263.1
Other Items	0.0	0.0	0.0	60.0
Income Tax	-347.2	-265.5	-318.3	-273.0
Net Income	1,523.7	1,739.7	1,665.1	1,050.1
Balance Sheet (000's)				
Cash & Securities	57,911.5	59,245.3	48,401.0	53,471.9
Loans, Net	66,216.4	60,267.8	59,351.3	62,918.2
Total Assets	129,556.7	124,472.0	112,606.2	121,221.8
Deposits	105,754.9	108,796.2	99,650.1	108,589.9
Stockholders' Equity	15,223.5	14,829.4	12,123.2	12,052.5
Performance & Financial Condition				
Return on Avg Stockholders' Equity %	10.14	12.91	13.78	9.04
Return on Average Assets %	1.20	1.47	1.42	0.87
Equity to Assets %	11.75	11.91	10.77	9.94
Net Interest Margin	4.83	4.81	4.45	4.06
Reserve as a % of Problem Loans	163.82	72.30	240.61	203.64

Compound Growth %'s	EPS %	13.26	Net Income %	13.21	Net Interest Income %	7.54

Comments

The Company declared a 2 for 1 split in 1996. All per share amounts have been restated for consistency. James Bexley, who led the Bank's turnaround after a big loss in 1992, has retired and was replaced with young and energetic Merle Helsel. This was not without a cost to the Bank, as approximately $300,000 in negotiated benefits to Mr. Bexley were accrued in 1996. Without this accrual, net earnings would have been higher than last year. Investment Classification: Growth & Value

Officers	Position	Ownership Information	
Merle W. Helsel	President, CEO	Number of Shares Outstanding	990,000
Ted J. Chwatek	Senior VP, Senior Loan Officer	Market Capitalization	$ 19,057,500
Richard J. Horton	Vice President	Frequency of Dividends	Quarterly
Robert F. Lafferty	Vice President, CFO	Number of Shareholders	487
Bonnie K. Redinger	Head Cashier	Where Listed / Symbol	OTC-BB / CADL

Other Information				Loan Mix	%
Transfer Agent	Company Office			R/E Mortgages	53.9
Auditor	S.R. Snodgrass, A.C.			Consumer	26.9
Market Maker	Legg Mason Wood Walker, Inc.	(212)428-4949		Commerical	19.2
	Ryan, Beck & Co.	(800)325-7926			
Broker Dealer	OTC Specialist				
	Jack Ingold	(412)391-4594			

Carolina Mills Inc.

618 Carolina Avenue   Maiden, NC 28650   Telephone (704)428-9911   Fax (704)428-2335

Company Description

Carolina Mills has several divisions: weaving, finishing, yarn manufacturing, yarn sales, and furniture manufacture and sales. The Company has been in existence for more than 65 years. Revenue has not shown any growth since 1987 although the Company has had a profit and paid a dividend in each of the twelve years for which we have information (1985 through 1996). New shareholders receive a warm personal letter from the president welcoming them as new shareholders and offering to answer any questions about the Company or phase of operations that may arise from time to time.

	09/28/96	09/30/95	10/01/94	10/02/93
Per Share Information				
Stock Price as of 12/31	21.00	21.25	20.50	20.50
Earnings Per Share	1.75	1.59	1.24	1.61
Price / Earnings Ratio	12.00	13.36	16.53	12.73
Book Value Per Share	23.05	22.34	21.67	21.43
Price / Book Value %	91.11	95.12	94.60	95.66
Dividends Per Share	1.00	1.00	1.00	1.00
Annual Financial Data				
Operating Results (000's)				
Total Revenues	169,937.3	190,996.7	191,707.7	200,452.6
Costs & Expenses	-159,621.3	-180,038.6	-185,072.1	-190,699.1
Income Before Taxes and Other	8,867.6	9,547.3	6,635.6	9,753.5
Other Items	0.0	0.0	0.0	0.0
Income Tax	-2,154.0	-3,407.4	-1,780.3	-3,425.0
Net Income	6,713.6	6,139.9	4,855.3	6,328.5
Cash Flow From Operations	15,163.4	14,430.5	12,900.9	14,138.8
Balance Sheet (000's)				
Cash & Equivalents	400.5	564.6	805.3	1,091.1
Total Current Assets	48,158.4	55,268.1	58,183.6	56,913.8
Fixed Assets, Net	62,580.7	53,020.3	56,303.4	54,697.2
Total Assets	120,003.5	117,706.3	115,955.0	116,305.0
Total Current Liabilities	18,116.2	17,578.6	18,813.7	19,466.4
Long-Term Debt	290.7	459.2	626.2	835.0
Stockholders' Equity	87,814.7	86,189.3	84,217.5	84,153.8
Performance & Financial Condition				
Return on Total Revenues %	3.95	3.21	2.53	3.16
Return on Avg Stockholders' Equity %	7.72	7.21	5.77	7.61
Return on Average Assets %	5.65	5.26	4.18	5.50
Current Ratio	2.66	3.14	3.09	2.92
Debt / Equity %	0.33	0.53	0.74	0.99

Compound Growth %'s	EPS %	2.82	Net Income %	1.99	Total Revenues %	-5.36

Comments

Much is happening behind what appears to be sleepy numbers. Each of the nine yarn plants are monitored for production, safety, and waste recycling improvements. Furthermore, a five-year capital spending plan is repositioning the division. The Knit Finishing group completed streamlining production flow. In 1996, a state-of-the-art center for the production of Canton Flannel was placed in service. Shareholders are starting to see the results. For the half quarter of fiscal 1997, the Company reported earnings of $2,320,000 ($.61 per share) as compared to $4,118,000 ($1.07) in the same period of 1996. The earlier year numbers included a gain on the sale of assets. Investment Classification: Income & Value

Officers	Position	Ownership Information	
Edward P. Schrum	President, CEO	Number of Shares Outstanding	3,809,905
Thomas P. Pruitt, Jr.	Vice President	Market Capitalization	$ 80,008,005
Stephen G. Dobbins, Jr.	Vice President, Secretary	Frequency of Dividends	Quarterly
George A. Moretz	Vice President	Number of Shareholders	Under 500

Other Information

Transfer Agent	Company Office		Where Listed	OTC-BB
Auditor	Not indicated		Symbol	CMLL
Market Maker	Interstate/Johnson Lane Corp.	(800)438-4134	SIC Code	2200
	Hill Thompson Magid & Co., Inc	(800)631-3083	Employees	2220
Broker Dealer	Regular Stockbroker			

Case, Pomeroy & Company, Inc.

529 Fifth Avenue   New York, NY 10017-4608   Telephone (212)867-2211   Fax (212)682-2353

Company Description

The Company operates in the mining, oil and gas, investment and real estate industries. Mining revenues are from the sale of gold ore. Oil and gas revenue is from the sale of crude oil and natural gas within the contiguous U.S. and the Gulf of Mexico. The Company is involved in numerous joint ventures and participations. In 1986, a class B stock was created. Class A has a 25% greater dividend. Class B has 10 times the voting power, a right to convert to class A at any time, and equal liquidation preferences.

	06/30/96	06/30/95	06/30/94	06/30/93
Per Share Information				
Stock Price as of 12/31	1,186.00	1,237.50	1,140.00	1,350.00
Earnings Per Share	84.64	90.69	95.40	58.93
Price / Earnings Ratio	14.01	13.65	11.95	22.91
Book Value Per Share	927.55	862.20	792.83	711.51
Price / Book Value %	127.86	143.53	143.79	189.74
Dividends Per Share	18.75	21.75	13.75	5.50
Annual Financial Data				
Operating Results (000's)				
Total Revenues	70,856.0	62,541.0	68,533.0	53,044.3
Costs & Expenses	-49,080.0	-42,352.0	-43,026.0	-38,979.8
Income Before Taxes and Other	18,508.0	19,465.0	20,457.0	12,371.5
Other Items	0.0	0.0	311.0	0.0
Income Tax	-4,655.0	-4,570.0	-5,018.0	-2,550.0
Net Income	13,853.0	14,895.0	15,750.0	9,821.5
Cash Flow From Operations	5,207.0	14,192.0	19,075.0	12,454.4
Balance Sheet (000's)				
Cash & Equivalents	32,052.0	43,703.0	27,363.0	15,427.4
Total Current Assets	73,643.0	60,183.0	68,374.0	46,364.8
Fixed Assets, Net	77,223.0	73,571.0	57,345.0	62,404.2
Total Assets	191,287.0	182,491.0	155,966.0	141,435.0
Total Current Liabilities	5,503.0	7,330.0	5,982.0	5,041.4
Long-Term Debt	27,315.0	27,607.0	12,977.0	13,060.8
Stockholders' Equity	152,050.0	141,674.0	131,112.0	118,658.9
Performance & Financial Condition				
Return on Total Revenues %	19.55	23.82	22.98	18.52
Return on Avg Stockholders' Equity %	9.43	10.92	12.61	8.40
Return on Average Assets %	7.41	8.80	10.59	7.38
Current Ratio	13.38	8.21	11.43	9.20
Debt / Equity %	17.96	19.49	9.90	11.01

Compound Growth %'s	EPS %	12.83	Net Income %	12.15	Total Revenues %	10.13

Comments

1996 results included a pretax gain of $13.4 million from the sale of securities as compared to $10.5 million in 1995. In March, 1996, regulatory approval was received to build and operate a new mill to process the large quantities of higher grade nonoxidized ore at Round Mountain Mine. The mill is under construction and is expected to be operational in late 1997. The Company has a 25% interest in the mill. Gold reserves increased significantly during 1996, up about 45%. Real estate activities generated profits of $4.8 million during 1996 as compared to a loss of $900,000 in 1995. Investment Classification: Value

Officers	Position	Ownership Information	
Roger H. Clark, Jr.	President, CEO	Number of Shares Outstanding	161,791
Adele R. Wailand	Vice President, Secretary	Market Capitalization	$ 191,884,126
Felix M. Lista	Vice President, Treasurer	Frequency of Dividends	Quarterly
Douglas B. Keith, III	Vice President	Number of Shareholders	Under 500
Paul R. Totilo	Controller		

Other Information			
Transfer Agent	The Bank of New York New York, NY	Where Listed	OTC-BB
Auditor	Arthur Andersen LLP	Symbol	CASP
Market Maker	Ragen MacKenzie Incorporated	(206)343-5000	SIC Code	1041
	Carr Securities Corporation	(800)221-2243	Employees	n.a.
Broker Dealer	Regular Stockbroker		
	Standard Investment	(888)783-4688 Ext: Jack	

Cass County Iron Company

215 East 48th Street   New York, NY 10017   Telephone (212)753-1902   Fax (212)753-1902

Company Description

Cass County Iron Company holds investments and certain mineral properties for lease and exploration and continues to search for new opportunities primarily in the development of natural resources. The Company was incorporated in 1974 as a result of a spin-off of certain assets of East Texas Iron Company.

	09/30/96	09/30/95	09/30/94
Per Share Information			
Stock Price as of 12/31	184.50	175.00	175.00
Earnings Per Share	17.49	21.12	20.29
Price / Earnings Ratio	10.55	8.29	8.62
Book Value Per Share	237.37	222.09	212.51
Price / Book Value %	77.73	78.80	82.35
Dividends Per Share	10.00	5.00	5.00
Annual Financial Data			
Operating Results (000's)			
Total Revenues	170.8	193.3	171.7
Costs & Expenses	-56.1	-61.4	-56.9
Income Before Taxes and Other	114.7	131.9	114.8
Other Items	0.0	0.0	0.0
Income Tax	-28.6	-37.5	-28.0
Net Income	86.0	94.4	86.8
Cash Flow From Operations	-15.8	38.8	-46.3
Balance Sheet (000's)			
Cash & Equivalents	254.0	252.4	138.6
Total Current Assets	1,385.5	1,274.6	1,050.7
Fixed Assets, Net	7.4	7.6	7.8
Total Assets	1,392.9	1,282.1	1,058.5
Total Current Liabilities	3.7	10.1	4.0
Long-Term Debt	0.0	0.0	0.0
Stockholders' Equity	1,167.6	1,092.5	917.8
Performance & Financial Condition			
Return on Total Revenues %	50.38	48.85	50.56
Return on Avg Stockholders' Equity %	7.61	9.39	n.a.
Return on Average Assets %	6.43	8.07	n.a.
Current Ratio	370.75	126.82	263.92
Debt / Equity %	n.a.	n.a.	n.a.

Compound Growth %'s	EPS % -7.16	Net Income % -0.44	Total Revenues % -0.27

Comments

Although income from mineral rights declined by 61% in 1996, it was noted that the year end price of oil was $23 per barrel as compared to $16 at the end of the preceding year. There are also some signs of greater interest in hydrocarbon development in east Texas. A recent emphasis in granting leases is intended to carve out participations for the Company. Investment Classification: Value & Speculative

Officers	Position	Ownership Information	
Beverley B. Wadsworth	President	Number of Shares Outstanding	4,919
Dyer S. Wadsworth	CEO, Treasurer	Market Capitalization	$ 907,556
Lewin B. Barringer	Secretary	Frequency of Dividends	Annual
		Number of Shareholders	Under 500

Other Information			
Transfer Agent	Company Office	Where Listed	OTC-BB
Auditor	James Matthews, CPA	Symbol	CIRN
Market Maker	Legg Mason Wood Walker, Inc.	(212)428-4890	SIC Code	6790
	Carr Securities Corporation	(800)221-2243	Employees	1
Broker Dealer	OTC Specialist		

Central Coal & Coke Corporation

127 W. 10th Street, Ste. 666   Kansas City, MO 64105   Telephone (816)842-2430   Fax (816)471-8676

Company Description

The primary business of the Company is the leasing of its interests in real property to others for the exploration and the extraction of coal, oil and gas and for surface use. The Company's property interests consist of whole or part interests in approximately 64,000 acres of real property located in Arkansas, Louisiana, Texas, Kansas, Oklahoma and Missouri. Through a subsidiary, the Company began a fast food bagel and delicatessen business during 1993. Four locations existed at December 31, 1996. The Company began business in 1936.

	12/31/96	12/31/95	12/31/94	12/31/93
Per Share Information				
Stock Price	30.25	30.00	27.50	26.00
Earnings Per Share	2.13	2.22	1.26	1.22
Price / Earnings Ratio	14.20	13.51	21.83	21.31
Book Value Per Share	29.69	29.16	28.58	28.17
Price / Book Value %	101.89	102.88	96.22	92.30
Dividends Per Share	1.85	1.85	1.00	1.00
Annual Financial Data				
Operating Results (000's)				
Total Revenues	2,871.8	2,560.4	1,558.8	1,316.4
Costs & Expenses	-1,737.6	-1,377.1	-767.8	-474.7
Income Before Taxes and Other	1,134.2	1,183.2	791.0	841.7
Other Items	0.0	0.0	0.0	-20.0
Income Tax	-344.1	-352.6	-321.6	-367.7
Net Income	790.1	830.7	469.4	454.0
Cash Flow From Operations	257.4	542.5	285.5	347.2
Balance Sheet (000's)				
Cash & Equivalents	1,343.0	755.4	1,589.0	1,729.5
Total Current Assets	8,850.6	9,198.4	7,907.8	8,224.6
Fixed Assets, Net	1,387.6	0.0	0.0	1,168.4
Total Assets	11,037.5	11,181.5	10,741.7	10,691.1
Total Current Liabilities	101.1	244.1	57.0	71.3
Long-Term Debt	0.0	0.0	0.0	0.0
Stockholders' Equity	10,847.4	10,899.3	10,684.6	10,609.8
Performance & Financial Condition				
Return on Total Revenues %	27.51	32.44	30.11	34.49
Return on Avg Stockholders' Equity %	7.27	7.70	4.41	4.30
Return on Average Assets %	7.11	7.58	4.38	4.27
Current Ratio	87.55	37.69	138.64	115.34
Debt / Equity %	n.a.	n.a.	n.a.	n.a.

Compound Growth %'s	EPS %	20.41	Net Income %	20.28	Total Revenues %	29.69

Comments

Coal deposits, mineral rights and surface lands were acquired from a trustee in bankruptcy and are recorded at the valuations placed on them by the receivers in bankruptcy in 1931. The Company used some of its capital to reacquire 8,464 common shares during 1996. The foray into the bagel business has met with mixed results. Management predicts either continued expansion or a complete exit from the business. Investment Classification: Income & Value

Officers	Position	Ownership Information	
Beekman Winthrop	President	Number of Shares Outstanding	365,366
S.M. Riddle	Secretary	Market Capitalization	$ 11,052,322
Leonard Noah	Vice President, Treasurer	Frequency of Dividends	Quarterly
Gary J. Pennington	General Manager	Number of Shareholders	530
Ernest N. Yarnevich, Jr.	Other		

Other Information			
Transfer Agent	UMB Bank, n.a. Kansas City, MO	Where Listed	OTC-BB
Auditor	KPMG Peat Marwick LLP	Symbol	CCCK
Market Maker	Carr Securities Corporation (800)221-2243	SIC Code	6792
	George K. Baum & Co. (800)821-7570	Employees	89
Broker Dealer	Regular Stockbroker		

Central Financial Corporation

21 Main Street   Randolph, VT 05060   Telephone (802)728-9611   Fax (802)728-5993

Company Description

Central Financial Corporation is the parent company of Randolph National Bank which operates from five offices in and around Randolph, central Vermont. The economic recession that settled on Vermont in the early 1990's posed a significant challenge to management, but issues concerning loan quality and overhead expenses now appear to have been addressed quite well. The comparative statements reflect this recovery. Randolph National has plenty of experience in weathering hard times as it was founded in 1875.

	12/31/96	12/31/95	12/31/94	12/31/93
Per Share Information				
Stock Price	37.00	31.75	23.50	37.00
Earnings Per Share	5.25	5.03	3.88	2.08
Price / Earnings Ratio	7.05	6.31	6.06	17.79
Book Value Per Share	51.10	47.41	42.20	38.74
Price / Book Value %	72.41	66.97	55.69	95.51
Dividends Per Share	1.50	1.05	0.25	0.0
Annual Financial Data				
Operating Results (000's)				
Net Interest Income	3,884.1	3,798.0	3,689.1	3,694.5
Loan Loss Provision	0.0	0.0	-18.7	16.5
Non-Interest Income	521.7	521.8	531.2	796.9
Non-Interest Expense	-3,158.8	-3,108.6	-3,250.7	-4,122.9
Income Before Taxes and Other	1,247.0	1,211.2	951.0	385.1
Other Items	0.0	0.0	0.0	0.0
Income Tax	-417.9	-410.2	-300.6	-36.5
Net Income	829.0	801.1	650.4	348.5
Balance Sheet (000's)				
Cash & Securities	30,411.7	23,759.1	17,740.2	16,157.2
Loans, Net	49,298.1	52,268.1	51,995.2	52,739.9
Total Assets	82,034.7	78,764.3	72,565.6	71,933.6
Deposits	71,729.8	68,696.5	63,289.0	64,012.2
Stockholders' Equity	8,067.5	7,484.5	7,076.2	6,497.2
Performance & Financial Condition				
Return on Avg Stockholders' Equity %	10.66	11.00	9.58	n.a.
Return on Average Assets %	1.03	1.06	0.90	n.a.
Equity to Assets %	9.83	9.50	9.75	9.03
Net Interest Margin	n.a.	n.a.	n.a.	n.a.
Reserve as a % of Problem Loans	119.13	696.21	86.61	64.32

Compound Growth %'s	EPS %	36.15	Net Income %	33.49	Net Interest Income %	1.68

Comments

An aggressive sales program was launched in 1997 to promote the Bank as "The White River Valley's Hometown Bank." The fifth office, located in Royalton, opened in March, 1997, and should spark more growth as well. Shares trade thinly partly because of the low price posted by market makers. An interested buyer may want to consider other channels. Investment Classification: Growth & Value & Income

Officers	Position	Ownership Information	
Steven H. Dimick	President, CEO	Number of Shares Outstanding	157,867
Scott A. Cooper	Exec VP, CFO	Market Capitalization	$ 5,841,079
Joseph A. Boyd	Senior VP, Sr Loan Officer	Frequency of Dividends	Semi-Annual
Edna D. Burnett	Vice President	Number of Shareholders	n.a.
Susan G. Sherman	Vice President	Where Listed / Symbol	OTC-BB / CEVT

Other Information			Loan Mix	%
Transfer Agent	Company Office		Commerical	49.8
Auditor	A.M. Peisch & Company		R/E Mortgages	33.7
Market Maker	First Albany Corporation	(800)541-5061	Installment	13.4
	Hill Thompson Magid & Co., Inc	(800)631-3083	Consumer	2.9
Broker Dealer	OTC Specialist		Other	0.2
	Norman Kadehjian - Wainwright	(800)727-7176		

Central Investment Corporation

10560 Ashview Place, Ste. 250   Cincinnati, OH 45242-0670   Telephone (513)563-4700   Fax (513)563-5912

Company Description

The Company's principal business consists of the bottling and distribution of soft drinks to supermarkets, mass merchandisers, convenience stores and other customers, either directly or through vending machines in certain northern Ohio and southern Florida franchised territories.

	09/30/95	09/30/94	09/30/93	09/30/92
Per Share Information				
Stock Price as of 12/31	460.00	310.00	300.00	261.88
Earnings Per Share	32.76	32.29	51.42	46.49
Price / Earnings Ratio	14.04	9.60	5.83	5.63
Book Value Per Share	491.98	476.73	459.44	415.20
Price / Book Value %	93.50	65.03	65.30	63.07
Dividends Per Share	17.50	15.00	10.00	35.00
Annual Financial Data				
Operating Results (000's)				
Total Revenues	164,792.3	157,924.7	148,502.3	139,762.7
Costs & Expenses	-158,245.6	-148,431.2	-138,196.4	-129,928.1
Income Before Taxes and Other	6,546.7	7,115.8	10,305.9	9,834.7
Other Items	0.0	0.0	0.0	0.0
Income Tax	-2,464.0	-3,091.2	-3,896.7	-3,931.6
Net Income	4,082.7	4,024.6	6,409.2	5,903.0
Cash Flow From Operations	10,335.7	11,397.3	7,513.4	12,394.8
Balance Sheet (000's)				
Cash & Equivalents	5,089.2	7,588.2	6,269.1	5,035.5
Total Current Assets	36,310.9	36,453.2	34,417.7	35,294.0
Fixed Assets, Net	34,936.6	34,017.2	31,036.1	26,822.9
Total Assets	80,562.5	79,173.8	74,640.7	69,429.4
Total Current Liabilities	8,532.6	8,742.2	7,732.9	7,897.4
Long-Term Debt	5,701.5	6,481.6	5,314.9	3,943.7
Stockholders' Equity	61,321.4	59,419.9	57,264.9	52,718.9
Performance & Financial Condition				
Return on Total Revenues %	2.48	2.55	4.32	4.22
Return on Avg Stockholders' Equity %	6.76	6.90	11.65	11.73
Return on Average Assets %	5.11	5.23	8.90	8.76
Current Ratio	4.26	4.17	4.45	4.47
Debt / Equity %	9.30	10.91	9.28	7.48

Compound Growth %'s   EPS %   n.a.   Net Income %   n.a.   Total Revenues %   n.a.

Comments

The Company did not issue a 1996 financial statement. Instead it executed a cash merger to freeze out all outside shareholders at $460 per share when the trading range was approximately $600 per share. Some of the minority shareholders are seeking appraisal rights under the Ohio courts. An investment professional that follows the company told us that this is what can happen when you are dealing with people that aren't necessarily influenced by the regulators that govern most security transactions. (Central Investment is not required to report to the Securities and Exchange Commission.) We hope that this is the exception and not the rule. Investment Classification: Speculative

Officers	Position	Ownership Information	
Keven E. Shell	Vice President, Treasurer	Number of Shares Outstanding	124,640
		Market Capitalization	$ 57,334,400
		Frequency of Dividends	Quarterly
		Number of Shareholders	Under 500

Other Information				
Transfer Agent	Star Bank, N.A. Cincinnati, OH		Where Listed	OTC-BB
Auditor	J.D. Cloud & Co. PLL		Symbol	COHI
Market Maker	Chicago Corporation, The	(312)855-7664	SIC Code	2086
			Employees	25
Broker Dealer	Regular Stockbroker			

Central Sierra Bank

373 W. St. Charles Street San Andreas, CA 95249 Telephone (209)754-3000 Fax (209)754-3709

Company Description

Central Sierra Bank is a California State chartered bank which commenced operations in 1981 with the opening of two branches. The Bank has grown to seven offices with the Copperopolis branch opening in 1996. A loan center was also opened in 1996. The Bank's operations have been designed to meet the banking needs of individuals and small to medium-size businesses in the central Sierra area of California. The primary counties served are Calaveras, Tuolumne, San Joaquin and Amador.

	12/31/96	12/31/95	12/31/94	12/31/93
Per Share Information				
Stock Price	11.25	9.56	7.55	8.02
Earnings Per Share	1.17	1.33	1.16	1.01
Price / Earnings Ratio	9.62	7.19	6.51	7.94
Book Value Per Share	9.58	9.07	8.39	7.74
Price / Book Value %	117.43	105.40	89.99	103.62
Dividends Per Share	0.60	0.65	0.51	0.51
Annual Financial Data				
Operating Results (000's)				
Net Interest Income	4,802.0	4,565.9	4,695.8	4,383.8
Loan Loss Provision	-265.0	-102.5	-135.0	-204.7
Non-Interest Income	751.3	741.7	731.2	814.1
Non-Interest Expense	-3,697.4	-3,403.8	-3,733.7	-3,649.1
Income Before Taxes and Other	1,590.8	1,801.4	1,558.3	1,344.1
Other Items	0.0	0.0	0.0	0.0
Income Tax	-637.9	-737.2	-631.1	-535.6
Net Income	952.9	1,064.2	927.2	808.5
Balance Sheet (000's)				
Cash & Securities	31,283.3	35,104.7	26,485.5	25,813.9
Loans, Net	57,157.7	47,556.7	46,129.2	49,015.1
Total Assets	92,255.4	86,020.7	75,797.2	77,685.7
Deposits	83,657.4	77,870.1	68,642.1	70,974.2
Stockholders' Equity	7,833.9	7,260.1	6,717.0	6,197.6
Performance & Financial Condition				
Return on Avg Stockholders' Equity %	12.63	15.23	14.36	13.64
Return on Average Assets %	1.07	1.32	1.21	1.02
Equity to Assets %	8.49	8.44	8.86	7.98
Net Interest Margin	n.a.	n.a.	n.a.	n.a.
Reserve as a % of Problem Loans	115.28	77.12	120.85	75.22

Compound Growth %'s	EPS %	5.02	Net Income %	5.63	Net Interest Income %	3.08

Comments

The Bank declared a 6% stock dividend in 1996. All per share amounts were adjusted for consistency. 1996 results suffered from a problem loan to a real estate subdivision that required a large reserve for possible loan loss. Otherwise, the Bank stayed on course in continuing to produce good returns and asset growth. The new branch and loan center should give a boost to earnings once they are established. Investment Classification: Income & Value

Officers	Position	Ownership Information	
Clarence E. Hartley	Chairman, CEO	Number of Shares Outstanding	817,631
Roger H. Wold	Senior VP, Sr Loan Officer	Market Capitalization	$ 9,198,349
David C. Vietmeier	Vice President, Head Cashier	Frequency of Dividends	Quarterly
Carolyn L. Cavalli	Vice President, COO	Number of Shareholders	n.a.
		Where Listed / Symbol	BE / CESR

Other Information			Loan Mix	%
Transfer Agent	Company Office		R/E Mortgages	48.9
Auditor	Arthur Andersen LLP		Construction	27.0
Market Maker	Hoefer & Arnett, Incorporated	(800)346-5544	Consumer	13.7
	Ryan, Beck & Co.	(800)325-7926	Installment	8.9
Broker Dealer	Regular Stockbroker		Agriculture	1.5

Central Steel and Wire Company

3000 W. 51st Street   Chicago, IL 60632-2198   Telephone (312)471-3800   Fax (800)232-9279

Company Description

Central Steel and Wire Company distributes, from its service centers, processed and unprocessed ferrous and non-ferrous metals in many forms purchased from producing mills or specialty mills. The Company carries about 21,000 separate inventory items in plants located in Chicago, Detroit, Cincinnati and Milwaukee. The plants are in excellent condition and equipment is regularly replaced to keep the facilities the most modern in the industry. Shareholders were given a personal tour of the Chicago plant after the official 1997 shareholders meeting. Central Steel and Wire Company was founded in 1908.

	12/31/96	12/31/95	12/31/94	12/31/93
Per Share Information				
Stock Price	575.00	585.00	587.50	600.00
Earnings Per Share	53.69	61.26	49.56	19.58
Price / Earnings Ratio	10.71	9.55	11.85	30.64
Book Value Per Share	509.39	498.59	478.32	468.53
Price / Book Value %	112.88	117.33	122.83	128.06
Dividends Per Share	· 42.00	40.00	40.00	22.00
Annual Financial Data				
Operating Results (000's)				
Total Revenues	594,100.0	628,700.0	596,400.0	504,200.0
Costs & Expenses	-568,800.0	-599,000.0	-572,500.0	-494,800.0
Income Before Taxes and Other	25,300.0	29,700.0	23,900.0	9,400.0
Other Items	0.0	0.0	0.0	0.0
Income Tax	-10,200.0	-12,300.0	-9,700.0	-3,800.0
Net Income	15,100.0	17,400.0	14,200.0	5,600.0
Cash Flow From Operations	12,200.0	39,300.0	10,700.0	18,400.0
Balance Sheet (000's)				
Cash & Equivalents	49,700.0	54,400.0	33,000.0	44,500.0
Total Current Assets	195,800.0	197,100.0	206,600.0	168,200.0
Fixed Assets, Net	33,100.0	34,200.0	34,900.0	29,100.0
Total Assets	236,300.0	238,400.0	248,200.0	203,700.0
Total Current Liabilities	75,500.0	80,400.0	95,300.0	54,500.0
Long-Term Debt	0.0	0.0	0.0	0.0
Stockholders' Equity	142,900.0	141,100.0	136,800.0	134,000.0
Performance & Financial Condition				
Return on Total Revenues %	2.54	2.77	2.38	1.11
Return on Avg Stockholders' Equity %	10.63	12.52	10.49	4.16
Return on Average Assets %	6.36	7.15	6.28	2.86
Current Ratio	2.59	2.45	2.17	3.09
Debt / Equity %	n.a.	n.a.	n.a.	n.a.

Compound Growth %'s	EPS %	39.97	Net Income %	39.19	Total Revenues %	5.62

Comments

On January 4, 1996, president and chief executive officer James R. Lowenstine died. Mr. Lowenstine's shares are retained by a perpetual charitable trust. Management intends for the Company to remain independent which is consistent with Mr. Lowenstine's wishes. There has been no long term debt for the last 17 years. The Company accounts for inventory using the LIFO method which is lower than market. The excess of current cost over LIFO amounted to $108.8 million as of December 31, 1996. If cost were used, the stock would be trading at a substantial discount from book value. Investment Classification: Income & Value

Officers	Position	Ownership Information	
Alfred G. Jensen	President	Number of Shares Outstanding	280,529
Frank A. Troike	CEO, Treasurer	Market Capitalization	$ 161,304,175
John M. Tiernan	Exec VP	Frequency of Dividends	Quarterly
Edward J. Kentra	Senior VP	Number of Shareholders	285
Michael X. Cronin	Vice President, Secretary		

Other Information

Transfer Agent	First Chicago Trust Company of New York Jersey City, NJ		Where Listed	OTC-BB
Auditor	KPMG Peat Marwick LLP		Symbol	CSTW
Market Maker	Herzog, Heine, Geduld, Inc.	(800)523-4936	SIC Code	5051
	Howe Barnes Investments, Inc.	(800)621-2364	Employees	1400
Broker Dealer	Regular Stockbroker			
	Standard Investment	(888)783-4688 Ext: Jack		

Century Realty Trust

320 N. Meridian St., Ste. 823   Indianapolis, MN 46204   Telephone (317)632-5467   Fax (317)685-1588

Company Description

The principal business of the Trust, is the ownership of income producing properties, which consists of nine apartment complexes, two restaurants, two commercial properties, and various parcels of undeveloped land. Four of the apartment properties have been acquired since mid-1993. The trust has elected to be treated as a real estate investment trust and, as such, distributes virtually all of its income and pays only state income tax.

	12/31/96	12/31/95	12/31/94	12/31/93
Per Share Information				
Stock Price	10.62	8.82	8.81	8.00
Earnings Per Share	0.70	0.60	0.52	1.66
Price / Earnings Ratio	15.17	14.70	16.94	4.82
Book Value Per Share	5.73	5.84	5.91	5.95
Price / Book Value %	185.34	151.03	149.07	134.45
Dividends Per Share	0.82	0.78	0.75	0.77
Annual Financial Data				
Operating Results (000's)				
Total Revenues	8,384.7	7,761.5	6,043.7	5,237.4
Costs & Expenses	-7,218.0	-6,798.0	-5,225.0	-3,076.9
Income Before Taxes and Other	1,166.7	963.5	818.7	2,160.5
Other Items	0.0	0.0	0.0	0.0
Income Tax	-144.2	-131.1	-115.7	-74.1
Net Income	1,022.5	832.4	703.0	2,086.4
Cash Flow From Operations	1,976.9	1,887.5	1,440.5	1,407.4
Balance Sheet (000's)				
Cash & Equivalents	315.3	483.9	255.7	557.1
Total Current Assets	1,241.6	793.7	420.7	932.0
Fixed Assets, Net	28,343.4	29,101.4	22,896.2	17,164.9
Total Assets	30,538.5	30,762.1	24,180.7	18,877.1
Total Current Liabilities	1,373.1	2,103.7	1,068.5	907.9
Long-Term Debt	20,437.7	19,748.1	14,606.8	10,014.2
Stockholders' Equity	8,333.2	8,485.5	8,158.8	7,676.8
Performance & Financial Condition				
Return on Total Revenues %	12.19	10.72	11.63	39.84
Return on Avg Stockholders' Equity %	12.16	10.00	8.88	30.04
Return on Average Assets %	3.34	3.03	3.27	15.63
Current Ratio	0.90	0.38	0.39	1.03
Debt / Equity %	245.26	232.73	179.03	130.45

Compound Growth %'s	EPS % n.a.	Net Income % n.a.	Total Revenues % 16.98

Comments

The Trust continues to grow in terms of total assets and total revenues. Included in Total Revenues for 1993, is a gain on the disposal of real estate of $1.3 million. This had the effect of distorting compound growth rates in earnings so we did not display them. As of December 31, 1996, the occupancy rate in apartment properties owned by the Trust was 94%. While no properties were acquired during 1996, two property acquisitions in 1997 were pending as we went to press. Investment Classification: Income & Value

Officers	Position	Ownership Information	
King R. Traub	President	Number of Shares Outstanding	1,453,939
John I. Bradshaw, Jr.	Exec VP, CEO	Market Capitalization	$ 15,440,832
		Frequency of Dividends	Semi-Annual
		Number of Shareholders	3,481

Other Information

Transfer Agent	Company Office		Where Listed	OTC-BB
Auditor	Ernst & Young LLP		Symbol	CRLTS
Market Maker	Traub and Comapny, Inc.	(317)639-5474	SIC Code	6510
	Hill Thompson Magid & Co., Inc	(800)631-3083	Employees	35
Broker Dealer	Regular Stockbroker			

Chamber of Commerce Building Corporation

320 N. Meridian Street   Indianapolis, IN 46204-1719   Telephone (317)634-2515   Fax (317)634-2514

Company Description

Chamber of Commerce Building Corporation owns and operates an office building in downtown Indianapolis, Indiana, known as the Chamber of Commerce Building. Space in the building is held for rental under operating leases which expire at various dates.

	12/31/94	12/31/93
Per Share Information		
Stock Price as of 12/31	60.00	60.00
Earnings Per Share	-5.34	-8.90
Price / Earnings Ratio	n.a.	n.a.
Book Value Per Share	48.73	54.07
Price / Book Value %	123.13	110.97
Dividends Per Share	0.0	0.0
Annual Financial Data		
Operating Results (000's)		
Total Revenues	1,213.8	1,182.8
Costs & Expenses	-1,288.7	-1,344.8
Income Before Taxes and Other	-74.9	-161.9
Other Items	0.0	0.0
Income Tax	-0.2	36.7
Net Income	-75.1	-125.2
Cash Flow From Operations	88.9	72.1
Balance Sheet (000's)		
Cash & Equivalents	13.7	12.7
Total Current Assets	25.4	59.2
Fixed Assets, Net	1,472.4	1,547.3
Total Assets	1,513.0	1,621.5
Total Current Liabilities	127.7	141.1
Long-Term Debt	700.0	720.0
Stockholders' Equity	685.3	760.4
Performance & Financial Condition		
Return on Total Revenues %	-6.19	-10.59
Return on Avg Stockholders' Equity %	-10.39	n.a.
Return on Average Assets %	-4.79	n.a.
Current Ratio	0.20	0.42
Debt / Equity %	102.14	94.68

Compound Growth %'s	EPS % n.a.	Net Income % n.a.	Total Revenues %	2.61

Comments

The years presented reflect an approximate occupancy of 83%. The market was suffering from excessive square footage when we talked with the Company in early 1996. More current information was not available except that the December 31, 1996, bid price was $80 per share. Investment Classification: Speculative & Value

Officers	Position	Ownership Information	
William L. Elder, Jr.	President	Number of Shares Outstanding	14,064
William F. Welch	Secretary	Market Capitalization	$ 843,840
Jane E. Kunz	Treasurer	Frequency of Dividends	n.a.
King R. Traub	Vice President	Number of Shareholders	Under 500
Brian W. Welch	Other		

Other Information				
Transfer Agent	Company Office		Where Listed	OTC-BB
Auditor	Geo. S. Olive & Co. LLC		Symbol	CHBRA
Market Maker	Robotti & Co., Inc.	(212)986-0800	SIC Code	6510
	Hill Thompson Magid & Co., Inc	(800)631-3083	Employees	n.a.
Broker Dealer	OTC Specialist			
	Tom Doherty - Robotti	(212)986-0800		

Chambersburg Engineering Company

150 Derbyshire Street   Chambersburg, PA 17201-0802   Telephone (717)264-7151   Fax (717)267-2201

Company Description

Chambersburg Engineering Company engineers and manufactures a line of heavy capital equipment used to shape or form ferrous and non-ferrous metals by impaction. The Company was formed in 1897 and went public in the 1920's. In 1994, the Company entered into a joint venture with a foreign manufacturer of forging equipment. The venture had its first sales during 1996. The Company is currently celebrating its centennial anniversary.

	12/31/96	12/31/95	12/31/94	12/31/93
Per Share Information				
Stock Price	62.00	25.00	22.00	22.00
Earnings Per Share	17.58	36.83	0.58	-1.83
Price / Earnings Ratio	3.53	0.68	37.93	n.a.
Book Value Per Share	77.06	60.72	24.14	23.56
Price / Book Value %	80.46	41.17	91.14	93.38
Dividends Per Share	1.25	0.25	0.0	0.0
Annual Financial Data				
Operating Results (000's)				
Total Revenues	6,770.6	6,291.8	3,996.0	4,772.5
Costs & Expenses	-5,594.7	-5,054.9	-3,947.6	-4,387.8
Income Before Taxes and Other	1,175.9	1,237.0	31.2	326.4
Other Items	0.0	0.0	0.0	-371.6
Income Tax	-355.0	482.4	-4.1	-40.0
Net Income	820.8	1,719.4	27.1	-85.2
Cash Flow From Operations	686.3	1,142.4	543.5	343.7
Balance Sheet (000's)				
Cash & Equivalents	1,773.7	1,355.2	457.4	82.6
Total Current Assets	3,959.2	4,298.7	2,629.8	1,793.1
Fixed Assets, Net	725.5	281.4	243.8	224.4
Total Assets	4,764.5	4,697.4	2,898.7	2,042.5
Total Current Liabilities	915.5	1,862.6	1,746.2	824.9
Long-Term Debt	251.7	0.0	25.3	117.6
Stockholders' Equity	3,597.3	2,834.8	1,127.1	1,100.0
Performance & Financial Condition				
Return on Total Revenues %	12.12	27.33	0.68	-1.79
Return on Avg Stockholders' Equity %	25.52	86.79	2.43	-7.46
Return on Average Assets %	17.35	45.27	1.10	-3.36
Current Ratio	4.32	2.31	1.51	2.17
Debt / Equity %	7.00	n.a.	2.25	10.69

Compound Growth %'s	EPS % n.a.	Net Income % n.a.	Total Revenues % 12.36

Comments

1995 results included an income tax benefit from a change in accounting method. Earnings before taxes for 1996 were just slightly lower than for 1995. 1993 results include nonrecurring expenses related to discontinued operations of $371,620, or $7.98 per share. The rebound of revenue and earnings is attributable to a revival of activity in the impression die forging industry. Back orders for new state-of-the-art machinery as well as for parts for older machinery were $1.4 million at the last year end. Compound earnings growth rates are misleading because of losses in 1993 and a relatively low income in 1994 and are therefore not presented. Investment Classification: Value

Officers	Position	Ownership Information	
Eugene C. Clarke	Chairman	Number of Shares Outstanding	46,684
Samuel C. Clarke	President	Market Capitalization	$ 2,894,408
Erma M. Fleming	Secretary	Frequency of Dividends	Annual
George A. Davis	Vice President, Treasurer	Number of Shareholders	Under 500

Other Information

Transfer Agent	Company Office		Where Listed	OTC-BB
Auditor	Mathieson Aitken Jemison, LLP		Symbol	CEGR
Market Maker	Carr Securities Corporation	(800)221-2243	SIC Code	3540
	Koonce Securities, Inc.	(800)368-2802	Employees	55
Broker Dealer	Regular Stockbroker			

Charter National Bancorp, Inc.

3058 First Street   Wyandotte, MI 48192   Telephone (313)285-1900   Fax (313)285-1955

Company Description

Charter National Bancorp, Inc. is a bank holding company for its wholly owned subsidiary, Charter National Bank. The Bank offers standard banking services through eight offices in Wayne County, Michigan. A ninth office is scheduled to open in Allen Park in the second half of 1997. The Bank was founded in 1933 with $165,000 of capital and a handful of employees. It has been profitable in every year of its existence. They ask for you to visit them in cyberspace (http://www.charternational.com) or stop by for a cup of coffee.

	12/31/96	12/31/95	12/31/94	12/31/93
Per Share Information				
Stock Price	41.75	40.50	34.06	32.37
Earnings Per Share	7.67	6.92	5.65	4.28
Price / Earnings Ratio	5.44	5.85	6.03	7.56
Book Value Per Share	59.76	56.16	49.06	48.47
Price / Book Value %	69.86	72.12	69.43	66.78
Dividends Per Share	3.45	3.00	2.50	1.75
Annual Financial Data				
Operating Results (000's)				
Net Interest Income	10,024.0	9,343.0	8,627.0	7,533.0
Loan Loss Provision	-240.0	-220.0	-225.0	-100.0
Non-Interest Income	2,432.0	2,359.0	1,939.0	1,682.0
Non-Interest Expense	-8,213.0	-7,706.0	-7,385.0	-6,869.0
Income Before Taxes and Other	4,003.0	3,776.0	2,956.0	2,246.0
Other Items	0.0	0.0	0.0	0.0
Income Tax	-1,271.0	-1,311.0	-936.0	-710.0
Net Income	2,732.0	2,465.0	2,020.0	1,536.0
Balance Sheet (000's)				
Cash & Securities	89,059.0	96,069.0	74,044.0	57,349.0
Loans, Net	129,551.0	115,838.0	106,052.0	108,015.0
Total Assets	226,018.0	219,997.0	186,792.0	170,490.0
Deposits	197,477.0	189,081.0	166,741.0	150,573.0
Stockholders' Equity	21,283.0	20,005.0	17,481.0	17,410.0
Performance & Financial Condition				
Return on Avg Stockholders' Equity %	13.23	13.15	11.58	9.10
Return on Average Assets %	1.23	1.21	1.13	0.90
Equity to Assets %	9.42	9.09	9.36	10.21
Net Interest Margin	n.a.	n.a.	n.a.	n.a.
Reserve as a % of Problem Loans	213.70	736.84	415.00	1,969.33

Compound Growth %'s	EPS %	21.46	Net Income %	21.16	Net Interest Income %	9.99

Comments

Shares of Company stock are thinly-traded because of a small float. But we counted six market makers posting bid prices which is an indication of some trading activity. The bid price is cheap when compared to the outstanding growth and financial performance of the last few years. There is no indication that a slow down is near as the Bank continues with geographic expansion. Investment Classification: Value & Growth & Income

Officers	Position	Ownership Information	
Charles A. Brethen, Jr.	Chairman	Number of Shares Outstanding	356,152
Robert M. Taylor	President, CEO	Market Capitalization	$ 14,869,346
Paul R. Krueger	Exec VP, Secretary	Frequency of Dividends	Quarterly
Richard S. Metzger	Senior VP	Number of Shareholders	n.a.
Alan L. Anderson	Treasurer	Where Listed / Symbol	OTC-BB / CNAT

Other Information			Loan Mix	%
Transfer Agent	Company Office		Commerical	57.7
Auditor	Plante & Moran, LLP		R/E Mortgages	31.4
Market Maker	McDonald & Company Securities	(216)443-2350	Installment	10.9
	Roney & Co.	(800)521-1196		
Broker Dealer	OTC Specialist			
	Kevin Ryan - Ryan, Beck & Co.	(888)231-7226		

Chatham Corporation

350 Barclay Boulevard   Lincolnshire, IL 60069   Telephone (847)634-5506

Company Description

Chatham Corporation is a diversified domestic manufacturer and service provider. The Company's principal lines of business are livestock feed manufacturing (57% of revenue), sterilization services (21% of revenue), and electronic controls manufacturing (17% of revenue). Livestock feeds are sold to wholesale and retail feed distributors nationwide. Sterilization services are provided primarily to domestic medical equipment suppliers. Electronic controls are sold to printing equipment and publishing concerns worldwide.

	12/31/96	12/31/95
Per Share Information		
Stock Price	1,300.00	1,300.00
Earnings Per Share	67.67	-109.37
Price / Earnings Ratio	19.21	n.a.
Book Value Per Share	4,604.81	4,586.90
Price / Book Value %	28.23	28.34
Dividends Per Share	57.00	57.00
Annual Financial Data		
Operating Results (000's)		
Total Revenues	38,539.0	39,001.0
Costs & Expenses	-37,633.0	-39,602.0
Income Before Taxes and Other	906.0	-601.0
Other Items	-355.0	7.0
Income Tax	-357.0	280.0
Net Income	194.0	-314.0
Cash Flow From Operations	1,401.0	175.0
Balance Sheet (000's)		
Cash & Equivalents	8,550.0	7,883.0
Total Current Assets	19,857.0	19,752.0
Fixed Assets, Net	3,718.0	3,680.0
Total Assets	24,448.0	23,818.0
Total Current Liabilities	4,922.0	4,424.0
Long-Term Debt	0.0	0.0
Stockholders' Equity	13,202.0	13,169.0
Performance & Financial Condition		
Return on Total Revenues %	0.50	-0.81
Return on Avg Stockholders' Equity %	1.47	-2.34
Return on Average Assets %	0.80	n.a.
Current Ratio	4.03	4.46
Debt / Equity %	n.a.	n.a.

Compound Growth %'s	EPS % n.a.	Net Income % n.a.	Total Revenues % -1.18

Comments

Both years presented have substantial nonrecurring items including losses from discontinued operations. According to Jack Norberg, analyst with Standard Investment, an investor must approach this with an analysis of cash flow from the distinct businesses of the Company as most of the real estate and some of the equipment are leased from a principal stockholder. Mr. Norberg is quick to point out, however, that the Company has over $8 million in cash and a current ratio of four to one. Investment Classification: Value & Income

Officers	Position	Ownership Information	
Not Available		Number of Shares Outstanding	2,867
		Market Capitalization	$ 3,727,100
		Frequency of Dividends	Quarterly
		Number of Shareholders	Under 500

Other Information

Transfer Agent	Registrar and Transfer Co. Cranford, NJ			Where Listed	OTC-BB
Auditor	Ernst & Young LLP			Symbol	CHTM
Market Maker	S.J. Wolfe & Co.	(800)262-2244		SIC Code	0700
	Howe Barnes Investments, Inc.	(800)621-2364		Employees	n.a.
Broker Dealer	OTC Specialist				
	Standard Investment	(888)783-4688	Ext: Jack		

Chemung Financial Corporation

One Chemung Plaza Elmira, NY 14902 Telephone (607)737-3711 Fax (607)737-3732

Company Description

Chemung Canal Trust Company, founded in 1833 and subsidiary of the Corporation, is a commercial bank operating fourteen locations in Chemung, Schuyler, Steuben and Tioga Counties, central southern New York. In 1994, the Bank acquired three offices of a regional bank and $46 million of deposits from the Resolution Trust Corporation. Effective at the beginning of 1995, Owego National Financial Corporation was merged into the operations of the Bank. 193,368 shares of common stock and $1.2 million were paid in connection with that acquisition.

	12/31/96	12/31/95	12/31/94	12/31/93
Per Share Information				
Stock Price	33.50	26.75	24.50	23.00
Earnings Per Share	2.96	2.68	2.45	2.87
Price / Earnings Ratio	11.32	9.98	10.00	8.01
Book Value Per Share	27.08	25.41	21.85	20.25
Price / Book Value %	123.71	105.27	112.13	113.58
Dividends Per Share	1.06	0.98	0.94	0.88
Annual Financial Data				
Operating Results (000's)				
Net Interest Income	22,468.1	21,849.8	19,303.6	18,671.7
Loan Loss Provision	-741.7	-564.4	-623.8	-906.7
Non-Interest Income	7,105.5	6,735.8	5,685.2	6,118.9
Non-Interest Expense	-19,407.8	-19,559.8	-17,374.7	-15,626.6
Income Before Taxes and Other	9,424.2	8,461.4	6,990.3	8,257.3
Other Items	0.0	0.0	0.0	-933.2
Income Tax	-3,266.7	-2,859.5	-2,342.8	-2,830.0
Net Income	6,157.5	5,601.9	4,647.5	4,494.1
Balance Sheet (000's)				
Cash & Securities	227,472.6	216,847.9	236,377.6	167,203.8
Loans, Net	279,746.0	259,101.3	232,897.5	218,761.1
Total Assets	532,213.0	501,892.8	494,332.3	398,123.7
Deposits	439,649.3	426,878.9	432,270.7	342,851.3
Stockholders' Equity	56,120.2	52,898.9	45,738.7	38,326.4
Performance & Financial Condition				
Return on Avg Stockholders' Equity %	11.30	11.36	11.06	12.17
Return on Average Assets %	1.19	1.12	1.04	1.15
Equity to Assets %	10.54	10.54	9.25	9.63
Net Interest Margin	4.79	4.89	4.89	5.07
Reserve as a % of Problem Loans	233.74	443.41	299.86	218.02

Compound Growth %'s	EPS %	1.03	Net Income %	11.07	Net Interest Income %	6.36

Comments

1993 results include a nonrecurring expense of $933,183, $.50 per share, due to the adoption of new accounting rules in the reporting of postretirement benefits. The Bank's acquisitions in 1994 and 1995, noted above, account for an undetermined amount of the increase in assets and income between 1994 and 1995. The issuance of shares has the effect of reducing the compound increase in earnings per share. Included in 1996 results is the one-time assessment of the Savings Association Insurance Fund in the amount of $191,000 which even makes the 1996 performance more impressive. Investment Classification: Value

Officers	Position	Ownership Information	
John W. Bennett	Chairman, CEO	Number of Shares Outstanding	2,072,214
Jan P. Updergraff	President, COO	Market Capitalization	$ 69,419,169
Daniel F. Agan	Vice President	Frequency of Dividends	Quarterly
James E. Corey, III	Vice President	Number of Shareholders	833
Robert J. Hodgson	Vice President	Where Listed / Symbol	OTC-BB / CHMG

Other Information		Loan Mix	%
Transfer Agent	Company Office	Consumer	39.8
Auditor	KPMG Peat Marwick LLP	Commerical	32.6
Market Maker	Ryan, Beck & Co. (800)395-7926	R/E Mortgages	27.6
	Herzog, Heine, Geduld, Inc. (800)221-3600		
Broker Dealer	Regular Stockbroker		

Chequemate International, Inc.

57 West 200 South, Suite 350   Salt Lake City, UT 84101   Telephone (801)322-1111   Fax (801)322-1165

Company Description

The Company is the result of the November, 1994 merger of Chequemate International (CMI) into Automated Compliance & Training, Inc. (ACT). ACT was a development stage enterprise involved with various computer software applications. CMI was engaged in the process of providing financial record keeping and money management services to the general public. The Company now has two lines of software products. Compliance Software is used to provide training of and compliance with federal safety and health regulations. Families in Focus programs are self-guided activities that enrich and strengthen families in seven key areas.

	03/31/96	03/31/95	03/31/94	03/31/93
Per Share Information				
Stock Price as of 12/31	5.75	7.00	4.50	5.00
Earnings Per Share	-0.15	-0.25	-0.29	-0.16
Price / Earnings Ratio	n.a.	n.a.	n.a.	n.a.
Book Value Per Share	0.01	-0.03	-0.07	0.01
Price / Book Value %	57,500.00	n.a.	n.a.	50,000.00
Dividends Per Share	0.0	0.0	0.0	0.0
Annual Financial Data				
Operating Results (000's)				
Total Revenues	382.1	401.8	302.3	243.3
Costs & Expenses	-2,260.9	-2,151.4	-1,543.5	-803.3
Income Before Taxes and Other	-1,878.7	-1,749.6	-1,241.2	-560.1
Other Items	0.0	0.0	0.0	0.0
Income Tax	-0.3	-0.4	-0.3	-0.3
Net Income	-1,879.0	-1,750.0	-1,241.5	-560.3
Cash Flow From Operations	-1,773.0	-1,519.1	-877.8	-893.5
Balance Sheet (000's)				
Cash & Equivalents	30.4	32.2	15.3	n.a.
Total Current Assets	184.7	203.8	246.0	n.a.
Fixed Assets, Net	93.5	95.6	66.3	n.a.
Total Assets	546.4	646.5	399.1	n.a.
Total Current Liabilities	243.9	360.6	293.9	n.a.
Long-Term Debt	80.6	113.6	0.0	n.a.
Stockholders' Equity	120.2	-388.1	-310.6	n.a.
Performance & Financial Condition				
Return on Total Revenues %	-491.71	-435.50	-410.64	-230.31
Return on Avg Stockholders' Equity %	n.a.	n.a.	n.a.	n.a.
Return on Average Assets %	-315.02	-334.71	n.a.	n.a.
Current Ratio	0.76	0.57	0.84	n.a.
Debt / Equity %	67.05	n.a.	n.a.	n.a.

Compound Growth %'s	EPS % n.a.	Net Income % n.a.	Total Revenues % 16.24

Comments

For the nine month period ended December 31, 1996, the Company reported sales of $551,942 as compared to $240,221 in the same period in the prior year. Most of the increase relates to Family Finance software. Sales of Compliance Software has been stalled because of federal budget cuts in OSHA. Management believes that there will still be strong demand once matters are sorted out in our Capitol. As a development stage company, the bottom line is still red. Investments should be made based on sound evidence of product success or personal knowledge of management. Investment Classification: Speculative

Officers	Position	Ownership Information	
Blaine Harris	CEO	Number of Shares Outstanding	12,666,053
Lavar Butler	President	Market Capitalization	$ 72,829,805
Ken Redding	Exec VP	Frequency of Dividends	n.a.
John Garrett	CFO	Number of Shareholders	740
Greg L. Popp	Secretary, Treasurer		

Other Information			
Transfer Agent	Company Office	Where Listed	OTC-PS
Auditor	Jones, Jensen & Company	Symbol	CQMT
Market Maker	Fahnestock & Co., Inc.	(800)223-3012	SIC Code	7372
	Alpine Securities Corp.	(800)521-5588	Employees	n.a.
Broker Dealer	Regular Stockbroker		

Cherokee Equity Corporation

3022 Vanderbilt Place   Nashville, TN 37212   Telephone (615)327-4089   Fax (615)327-4626

Company Description

The Company has two major lines of business: a marine terminal located in Nashville, Tennessee and real estate operations located in Tennessee, Mississippi and Kentucky. The marine terminal provides loading, unloading, storage and barge towing services. Cherokee Equity also owns interests in a corporation that sells and services telephone equipment and another that sells and services computer equipment. The Company was spun-off to shareholders of Cherokee Insurance Co. in 1968.

	12/31/96	12/31/95	12/31/94	12/31/93
Per Share Information				
Stock Price	21.50	19.50	18.00	18.00
Earnings Per Share	5.70	2.07	2.12	4.05
Price / Earnings Ratio	3.77	9.42	8.49	4.44
Book Value Per Share	62.88	52.19	39.36	41.76
Price / Book Value %	34.19	37.36	45.73	43.10
Dividends Per Share	0.0	0.0	0.0	0.0
Annual Financial Data				
Operating Results (000's)				
Total Revenues	7,788.1	5,707.3	5,584.9	3,816.0
Costs & Expenses	-4,449.2	-4,730.0	-4,501.8	-3,244.2
Income Before Taxes and Other	3,338.9	977.3	1,083.1	571.8
Other Items	9.3	117.1	69.1	1,045.8
Income Tax	-1,318.3	-354.8	-397.1	-168.7
Net Income	2,029.9	739.6	755.2	1,448.9
Cash Flow From Operations	1,577.3	1,093.7	1,450.2	935.6
Balance Sheet (000's)				
Cash & Equivalents	551.3	325.2	1,358.6	813.6
Total Current Assets	19,593.2	15,329.7	10,241.8	11,252.7
Fixed Assets, Net	9,834.8	11,159.1	10,733.7	6,310.5
Total Assets	37,557.1	34,395.8	26,793.2	21,642.0
Total Current Liabilities	6,797.4	6,759.1	2,577.5	2,956.5
Long-Term Debt	7,056.3	7,977.5	9,242.6	2,349.9
Stockholders' Equity	22,553.2	19,243.1	14,687.8	14,924.4
Performance & Financial Condition				
Return on Total Revenues %	26.06	12.96	13.52	37.97
Return on Avg Stockholders' Equity %	9.71	4.36	5.10	12.17
Return on Average Assets %	5.64	2.42	3.12	8.20
Current Ratio	2.88	2.27	3.97	3.81
Debt / Equity %	31.29	41.46	62.93	15.75

Compound Growth %'s	EPS %	12.07	Net Income %	11.90	Total Revenues %	26.85

Comments

1996 results include gains on the sale of marketable securities of $1,759,274. 1993 results include a nonrecurring benefit of $1 million due to a change in accounting method for the reporting of income taxes. Both of these items have the effect of distorting compound earnings growth rates. Marine terminal revenues were 11% higher during 1996. Interests in three partnerships and six corporations are reported under the equity method of accounting. Investment Classification: Value & Growth

Officers	Position	Ownership Information	
David K. Wilson	Chairman	Number of Shares Outstanding	355,912
William M. Wilson	President	Market Capitalization	$ 7,652,108
Wilma T. Ward	Secretary	Frequency of Dividends	n.a.
James R. Sweeney	Treasurer	Number of Shareholders	Under 500
Frank M. Farris, Jr.	Vice President		

Other Information				
Transfer Agent	Company Office		Where Listed	OTC-BB
Auditor	Byrd, Proctor & Mills, P.C.		Symbol	CQTY
Market Maker	Robotti & Co., Inc.	(212)986-0800	SIC Code	4499
	Sharpe Capital Inc.	(800)355-5781	Employees	10
Broker Dealer	OTC Specialist			
	Tom Doherty - Robotti	(212)986-0800		

Chesapeake Investors, Inc.

11785 Beltsville Drive, Suite 1600   Beltsville, MD 20705-3121   Telephone (301)572-7800   Fax (301)572-4797

Company Description

Chesapeake Investors, Inc. is registered under the investment Company Act of 1940 as a diversified, closed-end, management investment company. Its investment portfolio consists of tax exempt municipal bonds. The Company makes distributions to its shareholders of all cash flow, exclusive of reinvesting funds as bonds mature or are called. Distributions received by shareholders are not subject to federal income tax.

	09/30/96	09/30/95	09/30/94	09/30/93
Per Share Information				
Stock Price as of 12/31	3.25	3.12	4.00	4.00
Earnings Per Share	0.22	0.31	-0.06	0.38
Price / Earnings Ratio	14.77	10.06	n.a.	10.53
Book Value Per Share	4.18	4.19	4.16	4.49
Price / Book Value %	77.75	74.46	96.15	89.09
Dividends Per Share	0.23	0.28	0.29	0.30
Annual Financial Data				
Operating Results (000's)				
Total Revenues	1,004.7	1,294.4	1,229.7	1,570.7
Costs & Expenses	-114.8	-117.7	-119.8	-117.1
Income Before Taxes and Other	889.9	1,176.7	-99.7	1,453.7
Other Items	0.0	0.0	0.0	0.0
Income Tax	0.0	0.0	0.0	0.0
Net Income	889.9	1,176.7	-99.7	1,453.7
Cash Flow From Operations	986.1	1,176.7	-99.7	1,453.7
Balance Sheet (000's)				
Cash & Equivalents	0.0	0.0	0.0	0.0
Total Current Assets	1,085.0	0.0	0.0	0.0
Fixed Assets, Net	0.0	0.0	0.0	0.0
Total Assets	16,580.4	15,884.1	15,774.8	17,013.5
Total Current Liabilities	757.4	24.0	22.5	35.8
Long-Term Debt	0.0	0.0	0.0	0.0
Stockholders' Equity	15,823.0	15,860.1	15,752.4	16,977.8
Performance & Financial Condition				
Return on Total Revenues %	88.58	90.91	-8.11	92.55
Return on Avg Stockholders' Equity %	5.62	7.44	-0.61	8.63
Return on Average Assets %	5.48	7.43	-0.61	8.62
Current Ratio	1.43	n.a.	n.a.	n.a.
Debt / Equity %	n.a.	n.a.	n.a.	n.a.

Compound Growth %'s	EPS % -16.65	Net Income % -15.09	Total Revenues % -13.84

Comments

Expenses of administering and managing this portfolio approximate 0.72% of average net assets. The decline in income was due to the fact that $3.25 million of bonds matured or were called during 1996. Replacement bonds have a lower yield. Investment Classification: Income

Officers	Position	Ownership Information	
Albert W. Turner	Chairman	Number of Shares Outstanding	3,783,960
Warren W. Pearce, Jr.	President	Market Capitalization	$ 12,297,870
Herndon G. Kilby	Secretary, Treasurer	Frequency of Dividends	Quarterly
		Number of Shareholders	Under 500

Other Information

Transfer Agent	Registrar & Transfer Company Cranford, NJ		Where Listed	OTC-BB
Auditor	Stoy, Malone & Company, PC		Symbol	CPVI
Market Maker	Mayer & Schweitzer, Inc.	(800)631-3094	SIC Code	6799
	Carr Securities Corporation	(800)221-2243	Employees	2
Broker Dealer	OTC Specialist			

Christian Brothers, Inc.

P.O. Box C   Warroad, MN 56763-1003   Telephone (218)386-1111   Fax (218)386-2067

Company Description

Christian Brothers, Inc. is engaged in the manufacturing and distribution of hockey sticks and related products primarily to the Canadian and U.S. markets. In 1994, the Company introduced a new line of inline sticks, blades and balls and, in 1996, its own line of protective equipment for both inline and ice hockey. The Company has been repurchasing small amounts of its shares every year.

	12/31/96	12/31/95	12/31/94	12/31/93
Per Share Information				
Stock Price	11.00	13.50	15.00	13.00
Earnings Per Share	-0.83	-0.37	-0.76	1.07
Price / Earnings Ratio	n.a.	n.a.	n.a.	12.15
Book Value Per Share	10.87	11.70	12.07	12.92
Price / Book Value %	101.20	115.38	124.28	100.62
Dividends Per Share	0.0	0.0	0.0	0.0
Annual Financial Data				
Operating Results (000's)				
Total Revenues	5,461.5	5,721.6	5,651.9	5,989.5
Costs & Expenses	-5,758.0	-5,853.8	-5,980.0	-5,678.9
Income Before Taxes and Other	-296.5	-140.7	-328.1	310.6
Other Items	0.0	0.0	0.0	0.0
Income Tax	115.2	59.4	160.0	-68.1
Net Income	-181.3	-81.3	-168.1	242.5
Cash Flow From Operations	-110.5	301.2	-400.6	162.1
Balance Sheet (000's)				
Cash & Equivalents	171.5	106.2	165.5	216.2
Total Current Assets	3,133.4	3,276.8	3,639.9	3,589.2
Fixed Assets, Net	463.3	508.0	580.2	585.1
Total Assets	4,005.9	4,106.1	4,550.2	4,359.5
Total Current Liabilities	1,621.6	1,537.3	1,867.6	1,441.4
Long-Term Debt	0.0	0.0	0.0	0.0
Stockholders' Equity	2,384.3	2,568.9	2,682.6	2,908.6
Performance & Financial Condition				
Return on Total Revenues %	-3.32	-1.42	-2.97	4.05
Return on Avg Stockholders' Equity %	-7.32	-3.10	-6.01	8.66
Return on Average Assets %	-4.47	-1.88	-3.77	5.68
Current Ratio	1.93	2.13	1.95	2.49
Debt / Equity %	n.a.	n.a.	n.a.	n.a.

Compound Growth %'s	EPS % n.a.	Net Income % n.a.	Total Revenues %	-3.03

Comments

Declining sales in recent years are in part attributable to the weak Canadian dollar. The Company has taken definitive action by aligning itself with a well respected distributor for the 1997 season. The Company is confident that this relationship will reverse the three year trend and convert Canada into a profitable market. Additional equipment and a totally redesigned stick line in conjunction with a realigned sales staff should also boost sales. Investment Classification: Speculative

Officers	Position	Ownership Information	
Hal Bakke	President	Number of Shares Outstanding	219,315
Roger A. Christian	Secretary, Treasurer	Market Capitalization	$ 2,412,465
William D. Christian	Vice President	Frequency of Dividends	Irregular
		Number of Shareholders	Under 500

Other Information				
Transfer Agent	Mellon Financial Services Chicago, IL		Where Listed	OTC-BB
Auditor	Brady, Martz & Associates, PC		Symbol	CHBI
Market Maker	Hill Thompson Magid & Co., Inc	(800)631-3083	SIC Code	3940
	Carr Securities Corporation	(800)221-2243	Employees	65
Broker Dealer	Regular Stockbroker			

Chromaline Corporation

4832 Grand Avenue   Duluth, MN 55807-2743   Telephone (218)628-2217   Fax (218)628-3245

Company Description

The Chromaline Corporation develops and manufactures high quality photochemical imaging systems for sale primarily to a wide range of printers and decorators of surfaces. Applications include circuit boards, fine china, billboards, glassware and textiles. Although the principal markets are throughout the United States, the Company also sells products to Western Europe, Latin America, Asia, and other parts of the world. The Company was founded in 1952 as a screen printer of precision graphics and went public in 1961.

	12/31/96	12/31/95	12/31/94	12/31/93
Per Share Information				
Stock Price	7.25	6.81	5.50	2.87
Earnings Per Share	0.86	0.65	0.43	0.13
Price / Earnings Ratio	8.43	10.48	12.79	22.08
Book Value Per Share	4.20	3.34	2.70	2.27
Price / Book Value %	172.62	203.89	203.70	126.43
Dividends Per Share	0.0	0.0	0.0	0.0
Annual Financial Data				
Operating Results (000's)				
Total Revenues	8,857.5	7,583.8	6,515.7	4,994.1
Costs & Expenses	-7,879.2	-6,787.7	-5,998.5	-4,902.8
Income Before Taxes and Other	978.3	796.1	517.2	91.2
Other Items	0.0	0.0	0.0	35.0
Income Tax	-313.0	-296.0	-186.0	-23.0
Net Income	665.3	500.1	331.2	103.2
Cash Flow From Operations	651.3	452.6	410.3	99.0
Balance Sheet (000's)				
Cash & Equivalents	70.0	132.4	64.1	113.0
Total Current Assets	2,644.3	2,358.1	1,952.3	1,627.4
Fixed Assets, Net	1,335.5	879.1	768.5	801.9
Total Assets	3,979.9	3,277.2	2,760.8	2,461.4
Total Current Liabilities	729.1	691.7	683.4	688.0
Long-Term Debt	0.0	0.0	0.0	21.4
Stockholders' Equity	3,250.7	2,585.4	2,077.3	1,752.0
Performance & Financial Condition				
Return on Total Revenues %	7.51	6.59	5.08	2.07
Return on Avg Stockholders' Equity %	22.80	21.45	17.30	6.04
Return on Average Assets %	18.34	16.57	12.68	4.57
Current Ratio	3.63	3.41	2.86	2.37
Debt / Equity %	n.a.	n.a.	n.a.	1.22

Compound Growth %'s	EPS %	87.72	Net Income %	86.11	Total Revenues %	21.05

Comments

Sales have grown from $1.5 million in 1986 to $8.8 million in 1996, a compounded growth rate of nearly 20%. 1996 itself was no exception with a 16.8% increase. Foreign sales approximated 32% of total sales in each of the last two years. The Company has no long term debt. Investment Classification: Growth

Officers	Position	Ownership Information	
William C. Ulland	Chairman	Number of Shares Outstanding	773,377
Thomas L. Erickson	President, CEO	Market Capitalization	$ 5,606,983
Richard G. Bourman	VP - Finance	Frequency of Dividends	n.a.
Claude Piquet	VP - Manufacturing	Number of Shareholders	Under 500
Toshifumi Komatsu	VP - Research		

Other Information			
Transfer Agent	Norwest Bank Duluth, N.A. Duluth, MN	Where Listed	OTC-BB
Auditor	Deloitte & Touche LLP	Symbol	CMLH
Market Maker	Adkins Securities, Inc. (800)443-8103	SIC Code	2759
	Koonce Securities, Inc. (800)368-2802	Employees	62
Broker Dealer	Regular Stockbroker		

Cimetrix Incorporated

100 North Tampa Street   Tampa, FL 33602   Telephone (813)277-9199   Fax (813)277-0065

Company Description

Cimetrix is the developer of the world's first open architecture, standards-based, personal computer software for controlling machine tools, robots and electronics industry equipment that operate on the factory floor. Products are targeted for current users of automation devices seeking alternative methods to lower the cost of automation and improve production efficiency. Since its inception in 1989, the Company has incurred operating losses. These losses have been financed by several stock offerings, the latest in 1995, when the Company sold one million common shares at $4 per share.

	12/31/96	12/31/95	12/31/94	12/31/93
Per Share Information				
Stock Price	6.50	7.31	4.13	3.00
Earnings Per Share	-0.19	-0.16	-0.08	-0.07
Price / Earnings Ratio	n.a.	n.a.	n.a.	n.a.
Book Value Per Share	0.41	0.49	0.25	-0.03
Price / Book Value %	1,585.37	1,491.84	1,652.00	n.a.
Dividends Per Share	0.0	0.0	0.0	0.0
Annual Financial Data				
Operating Results (000's)				
Total Revenues	2,874.0	836.9	530.9	1,141.6
Costs & Expenses	-6,329.0	-3,580.0	-1,961.3	-2,212.0
Income Before Taxes and Other	-3,455.0	-2,743.1	-1,433.1	-1,073.9
Other Items	0.0	198.8	288.1	0.0
Income Tax	0.0	0.0	0.0	-0.1
Net Income	-3,455.0	-2,544.2	-1,145.1	-1,074.0
Cash Flow From Operations	-2,002.0	-2,944.4	-1,817.2	-775.6
Balance Sheet (000's)				
Cash & Equivalents	2,785.0	2,345.5	3,365.2	0.8
Total Current Assets	4,220.0	3,267.8	3,835.1	229.9
Fixed Assets, Net	614.0	1,732.2	1,271.0	118.2
Total Assets	9,227.0	9,722.1	5,632.0	351.5
Total Current Liabilities	1,344.0	337.6	1,451.2	853.4
Long-Term Debt	252.0	271.7	0.0	33.4
Stockholders' Equity	7,631.0	9,070.6	3,613.3	-535.3
Performance & Financial Condition				
Return on Total Revenues %	-120.22	-304.00	-215.68	-94.08
Return on Avg Stockholders' Equity %	-41.37	-40.12	-74.40	n.a.
Return on Average Assets %	-36.47	-33.14	-38.27	-373.99
Current Ratio	3.14	9.68	2.64	0.27
Debt / Equity %	3.30	3.00	n.a.	n.a.

Compound Growth %'s	EPS % n.a.	Net Income % n.a.	Total Revenues %	36.04

Comments

Net revenue from product sales and services increased more than three-fold to $2.4 million during 1996. 43% of revenues were from companies based in foreign countries, principally Japan. Is Cimetrix off and running? We suggest paying close attention to its quarterly reports, particularly the revenue line. For the quarter ended March 31, 1997, the Company reported revenues of $512,000 and a loss of $825,000, $.05 per share. Investment Classification: Speculative

Officers	Position	Ownership Information	
Paul A. Bilzerian	President, CEO	Number of Shares Outstanding	18,456,103
David L. Redmond	Exec VP, CFO	Market Capitalization	$ 119,964,670
David P. Faulkner	Exec VP	Frequency of Dividends	n.a.
Robert H. Reback	Exec VP	Number of Shareholders	1,500
Xuguang Wang	Vice President		

Other Information			
Transfer Agent	ChaseMellon Shareholder Services New York, NY	Where Listed	OTC-BB
Auditor	Pritchett, Siler & Hardy PC	Symbol	CMXX
Market Maker	Alpine Securities Corporation	(800)274-5588	SIC Code	7372
	Wilson-Davis & Co., Inc.	(800)453-5735	Employees	52
Broker Dealer	Regular Stockbroker		

Citizens Bancorp, Inc.

10 North Main Street   Coudersport, PA 16915   Telephone (814)274-9150   Fax (814)274-0401

Company Description

Citizens Trust Company, founded in 1905, operates three branches serving Potter, Cameron and McKean Counties in north central Pennsylvania. In addition to banking, Citizens Trust offers a full range of trust services. The Bank has hired the highly regarded Omega Performance Company to undertake a comprehensive training program for all employees. It will focus on developing a true sales culture throughout the organization and reinforce the importance of superior customer service.

	12/31/96	12/31/95	12/31/94	12/31/93
Per Share Information				
Stock Price	44.00	35.64	29.90	26.57
Earnings Per Share	4.38	3.64	3.44	3.41
Price / Earnings Ratio	10.05	9.79	8.69	7.79
Book Value Per Share	33.70	31.82	28.53	26.55
Price / Book Value %	130.56	112.01	104.80	100.08
Dividends Per Share	1.98	1.47	1.18	1.02
Annual Financial Data				
Operating Results (000's)				
Net Interest Income	3,257.6	3,029.6	2,877.8	2,840.7
Loan Loss Provision	-70.0	-70.0	-70.0	-77.0
Non-Interest Income	659.4	526.6	490.5	494.4
Non-Interest Expense	-2,027.2	-2,010.8	-1,939.9	-1,889.0
Income Before Taxes and Other	1,819.8	1,475.4	1,358.4	1,369.1
Other Items	0.0	0.0	0.0	0.0
Income Tax	-419.0	-309.5	-257.0	-276.9
Net Income	1,400.8	1,165.9	1,101.4	1,092.3
Balance Sheet (000's)				
Cash & Securities	50,876.0	39,154.8	38,488.0	42,573.2
Loans, Net	41,088.3	38,759.2	36,596.2	32,817.8
Total Assets	94,103.6	79,875.8	77,179.1	77,496.0
Deposits	72,665.2	68,204.1	65,770.4	68,923.4
Stockholders' Equity	10,784.4	10,087.2	8,958.3	8,257.4
Performance & Financial Condition				
Return on Avg Stockholders' Equity %	13.42	12.24	12.80	13.87
Return on Average Assets %	1.61	1.48	1.42	1.46
Equity to Assets %	11.46	12.63	11.61	10.66
Net Interest Margin	n.a.	n.a.	n.a.	n.a.
Reserve as a % of Problem Loans	1,339.33	4,266.38	3,232.21	1,539.07

Compound Growth %'s	EPS %	8.70	Net Income %	8.65	Net Interest Income %	4.67

Comments

Citizens Trust must be providing excellent service to their customers, even without the training referred to above. Returns on assets and equity place them high as ranked against other banks. Trust assets under management increased 44% to just over $51 million and net income from trust operations jumped 35% to $350,000. The Company declared 1% stock dividends in each of the last four years. All per share amounts were adjusted for consistency. Investment Classification: Value & Income

Officers	Position	Ownership Information	
Charles H. Updegraff, Jr.	President, CEO	Number of Shares Outstanding	320,051
Edwin H. Corey	Vice President, Treasurer	Market Capitalization	$ 14,082,244
George M. Raup	Vice President, Secretary	Frequency of Dividends	Quarterly
Justin F. Krellner	Vice President	Number of Shareholders	n.a.
Stan R. Dunsmore	Vice President, Sr Loan Officer	Where Listed / Symbol	OTC-BB / CZEC

Other Information			Loan Mix	%
Transfer Agent	Company Office		R/E Mortgages	66.0
Auditor	Clyde, Ferraro & Co.		Commerical	24.6
Market Maker	Ryan, Beck & Co.	(800)342-2325	Installment	0.8
	Anthony Misciagna & Co., Inc.	(800)343-5149	Other	8.6
Broker Dealer	OTC Specialist			
	Norman Kadehjian - Wainwright	(800)727-7176		

Citizens Growth Properties

188 East Capitol Street   Jackson, MS 39225-2728   Telephone (601)948-4091   Fax (601)949-4077

Company Description

Citizens Growth Properties holds marketable securities and a 34.55% interest in a resort development in Highlands, North Carolina, known as Golf Properties, Inc. The officers of the Company oversee these investments without the need for active management. The Company is buying back shares as they become available and acquired 8,250, 17,300, and 12,100 shares in 1996, 1995, and 1994, respectively.

	01/31/96	01/31/95	01/31/94	01/31/93
Per Share Information				
Stock Price as of 12/31	6.50	5.75	4.50	2.75
Earnings Per Share	-0.06	0.31	0.36	-0.69
Price / Earnings Ratio	n.a.	18.55	12.50	n.a.
Book Value Per Share	11.25	9.66	7.92	7.98
Price / Book Value %	57.78	59.52	56.82	34.46
Dividends Per Share	0.0	0.0	0.0	1.00
Annual Financial Data				
Operating Results (000's)				
Total Revenues	17.5	129.0	143.0	290.0
Costs & Expenses	-62.7	-56.0	-68.0	-75.0
Income Before Taxes and Other	-45.1	73.0	75.0	215.0
Other Items	0.0	0.0	0.0	0.0
Income Tax	31.1	1.0	15.0	4.0
Net Income	-14.1	74.0	90.0	219.0
Cash Flow From Operations	n.a.	-33.0	-26.0	-32.0
Balance Sheet (000's)				
Cash & Equivalents	49.3	40.0	264.0	142.0
Total Current Assets	49.3	1,844.0	1,346.0	1,123.0
Fixed Assets, Net	0.0	0.0	0.0	0.0
Total Assets	2,500.9	2,232.0	1,973.0	2,090.0
Total Current Liabilities	13.1	16.0	18.0	24.0
Long-Term Debt	0.0	0.0	0.0	0.0
Stockholders' Equity	2,487.8	2,216.0	1,955.0	2,066.0
Performance & Financial Condition				
Return on Total Revenues %	-80.20	57.36	62.94	75.52
Return on Avg Stockholders' Equity %	-0.60	3.55	4.48	10.21
Return on Average Assets %	-0.59	3.52	4.43	10.11
Current Ratio	3.78	115.25	74.78	46.79
Debt / Equity %	n.a.	n.a.	n.a.	n.a.

Compound Growth %'s	EPS % n.a.	Net Income % n.a.	Total Revenues % -60.75

Comments

The joint venture interest is on the balance sheet at $272,000 and produced income of $33,000 and $76,000 in the years ended January, 1996 and 1995, respectively. There is no estimate of current value available. The January, 1997, results were not available when we went to press and it was questionable as to whether any accounting would be prepared. The accounting for the last fiscal year was not audited and was without typical disclosures. It may be difficult to follow the activities of this Company in the future. Investment Classification: Value & Speculative

Officers	Position	Ownership Information	
David R. Bell	Chairman	Number of Shares Outstanding	221,142
Brent D. Baird	President, CEO	Market Capitalization	$ 1,437,423
David Fowler	Vice President	Frequency of Dividends	n.a.
Susan Egger	Vice President, Treasurer	Number of Shareholders	Under 500

Other Information				
Transfer Agent	Keycorp Shareholder Services, Inc. Brooklyn, OH		Where Listed	OTC-BB
Auditor	Ernst & Young LLP		Symbol	CITGS
Market Maker	Carr Securities Corporation	(800)221-2243	SIC Code	6790
	Robotti & Co., Inc.	(212)986-0800	Employees	n.a.
Broker Dealer	Regular Stockbroker			

Citizens National Bancorp, Inc.

182 Main Street Putnam, CT 06260 Telephone (860)928-7921 Fax (860)928-7558

Company Description

The Citizens National Bank, subsidiary of this holding Corporation, was established in 1924. It now operates from five offices in this rural area of Connecticut, about fifty-five miles from Hartford. Several large companies operate within this area of Windham County including two giant companies; International Paper and Staples.

	12/31/96	12/31/95	12/31/94	12/31/93
Per Share Information				
Stock Price	42.25	28.18	24.95	23.21
Earnings Per Share	5.42	4.25	4.17	3.83
Price / Earnings Ratio	7.80	6.63	5.98	6.06
Book Value Per Share	43.12	39.34	36.09	41.59
Price / Book Value %	97.98	71.63	69.13	55.81
Dividends Per Share	1.70	1.00	0.85	0.85
Annual Financial Data				
Operating Results (000's)				
Net Interest Income	5,670.8	5,037.7	4,798.5	4,743.3
Loan Loss Provision	-30.0	-28.0	-65.0	-170.0
Non-Interest Income	1,129.1	777.0	596.1	553.0
Non-Interest Expense	-3,704.2	-3,418.3	-2,997.2	-2,961.9
Income Before Taxes and Other	3,065.7	2,368.4	2,332.3	2,164.4
Other Items	0.0	0.0	0.0	-12.8
Income Tax	-1,082.1	-813.1	-804.6	-749.2
Net Income	1,983.5	1,555.3	1,527.7	1,402.4
Balance Sheet (000's)				
Cash & Securities	50,887.6	45,699.3	49,862.2	49,453.1
Loans, Net	55,932.7	54,797.0	49,126.7	44,650.7
Total Assets	112,732.4	105,555.9	103,222.3	97,196.5
Deposits	96,449.1	90,544.1	88,353.0	84,597.3
Stockholders' Equity	15,787.8	14,402.1	13,211.1	11,992.0
Performance & Financial Condition				
Return on Avg Stockholders' Equity %	13.14	11.26	12.12	12.26
Return on Average Assets %	1.82	1.49	1.52	1.48
Equity to Assets %	14.00	13.64	12.80	12.34
Net Interest Margin	n.a.	n.a.	n.a.	n.a.
Reserve as a % of Problem Loans	330.90	406.74	98.45	92.82

Compound Growth %'s	EPS %	12.27	Net Income %	12.25	Net Interest Income %	6.13

Comments

The Corporation declared a 10% stock dividend in 1996 and 7.5% stock dividends in 1995, 1994 and 1993. All per share amounts have been restated for consistency. Net income and net interest income have increased in each of the last six years (all the years in which we have information). Return on assets and equity have been impressive. The Corporation has been able to maintain a strong growth rate and a strong capital structure at the same time. Investment Classification: Value & Income

Officers	Position	Ownership Information	
Paul B. Grenier	Vice President	Number of Shares Outstanding	366,111
Robert M. Silva	President, CEO	Market Capitalization	$ 15,468,190
Thomas A. Charpentier	Senior VP, Head Cashier	Frequency of Dividends	Annual
Lauren E. Andrews	Vice President, Sr Loan Officer	Number of Shareholders	n.a.
Diane M. Rasicot	Vice President	Where Listed / Symbol	OTC-PS / CTZP

Other Information			Loan Mix	%
Transfer Agent	Company Office		R/E Mortgages	91.0
Auditor	Shatswell, MacLeod & Co, PC		Commerical	5.1
Market Maker	Ryan, Beck & Co.	(800)395-7926	Consumer	3.8
	Advest, Inc.	(800)998-9834	Other	0.1
Broker Dealer	Regular Stockbroker			

Citizens' Electric Company

1775 Industrial Boulevard   Lewisburg, PA 17837   Telephone (717)524-2231   Fax (717)524-5887

Company Description

Citizens' Electric Company provides electrical service in the area in and around Lewisburg, Pennsylvania, through production and redistribution of purchased power. In late 1996, Pennsylvania adopted the "Electricity Generation Customer Choice and Competition Act" which, over a period of years, allows residents of the State to chose their electricity provider. Management is preparing a reorganization plan to comply with the new law that will be filed with the Public Utilities Commission on September 30, 1997. The Company takes pride in having been a private investor utility since 1911.

	12/31/96	12/31/95	12/31/94	12/31/93
Per Share Information				
Stock Price	28.75	26.00	26.00	25.75
Earnings Per Share	3.60	3.45	3.39	3.41
Price / Earnings Ratio	7.99	7.54	7.67	7.55
Book Value Per Share	40.14	38.52	35.80	33.56
Price / Book Value %	71.62	67.50	72.63	76.73
Dividends Per Share	1.72	1.68	1.64	1.60
Annual Financial Data				
Operating Results (000's)				
Total Revenues	8,849.3	9,253.6	9,162.6	9,377.5
Costs & Expenses	-8,048.1	-8,494.8	-8,396.7	-8,616.2
Income Before Taxes and Other	787.3	746.9	753.7	751.4
Other Items	0.0	0.0	0.0	0.0
Income Tax	-290.1	-271.3	-286.2	-280.6
Net Income	497.2	475.6	467.5	470.7
Cash Flow From Operations	n.a.	n.a.	n.a.	n.a.
Balance Sheet (000's)				
Cash & Equivalents	1,295.2	1,173.5	1,216.6	1,196.7
Total Current Assets	2,077.5	1,959.9	1,899.9	1,879.3
Fixed Assets, Net	5,086.3	4,907.2	4,701.3	4,609.7
Total Assets	7,865.3	7,705.3	7,215.1	6,955.5
Total Current Liabilities	1,271.2	1,516.3	1,323.1	1,438.3
Long-Term Debt	111.9	141.5	171.0	200.6
Stockholders' Equity	5,548.8	5,312.6	4,937.7	4,628.0
Performance & Financial Condition				
Return on Total Revenues %	5.62	5.14	5.10	5.02
Return on Avg Stockholders' Equity %	9.15	9.28	9.77	10.45
Return on Average Assets %	6.39	6.38	6.60	6.90
Current Ratio	1.63	1.29	1.44	1.31
Debt / Equity %	2.02	2.66	3.46	4.33

Compound Growth %'s	EPS %	1.82	Net Income %	1.84	Total Revenues %	-1.91

Comments

The Company is a consistent performer and has increased dividends in each of the last eighteen consecutive years. A very severe winter and gains from the sale of investment securities produced record results in 1996. The audit report is available only at the Company's office. The years ahead will clearly test management's ability as deregulation provides opportunities for the Company as well as its competitors. 11,400 shares of Company stock were traded during 1996 at prices ranging from $27 to $33 per share. Investment Classification: Income & Value

Officers	Position	Ownership Information	
Eric L. Brouse	President	Number of Shares Outstanding	138,222
Graham C. Showalter	Secretary	Market Capitalization	$ 3,973,883
Kathy A. Zechman	Treasurer	Frequency of Dividends	Quarterly
Bonnie L. Shadle	Vice President, Treasurer	Number of Shareholders	Under 500
Eric W. Winslow	Vice President		

Other Information

Transfer Agent	Company Office		Where Listed	OTC-BB
Auditor	Not indicated		Symbol	CZEL
Market Maker	Legg Mason Wood Walker, Inc.	(212)428-4949	SIC Code	4910
	Carr Securities Corporation	(800)221-2243	Employees	15
Broker Dealer	OTC Specialist			
	Standard Investment	(888)783-4688 Ext: Jack		

Clinicor, Inc.

307 Camp Craft Road, Ste. 200   Austin, TX 78746   Telephone (512)344-3300   Fax (512)477-9449

Company Description

Clinicor is a full service clinical research organization serving the pharmaceutical, biotechnology and medical device industries. The Company designs, manages and monitors clinical trials in North America and Europe and provides clinical and product development services for its clients. The Company maintains clinical management staffs in four cities: Austin, Denver, Phoenix and San Antonio. An office was established in the United Kingdom in December, 1996. Clinicor was founded in 1992.

	12/31/96	12/31/95
Per Share Information		
Stock Price	4.00	1.62
Earnings Per Share	-0.52	-0.36
Price / Earnings Ratio	n.a.	n.a.
Book Value Per Share	0.51	0.01
Price / Book Value %	784.31	16,200.00
Dividends Per Share	0.0	0.0
Annual Financial Data		
Operating Results (000's)		
Total Revenues	3,631.3	2,005.6
Costs & Expenses	-5,597.4	-3,182.8
Income Before Taxes and Other	-1,966.2	-1,177.2
Other Items	0.0	0.0
Income Tax	0.0	0.0
Net Income	-1,966.2	-1,177.2
Cash Flow From Operations	-2,018.2	-1,536.2
Balance Sheet (000's)		
Cash & Equivalents	1,484.0	267.3
Total Current Assets	3,117.5	908.4
Fixed Assets, Net	1,118.9	192.9
Total Assets	4,276.1	1,107.7
Total Current Liabilities	2,166.2	1,049.3
Long-Term Debt	0.0	0.0
Stockholders' Equity	2,093.9	23.3
Performance & Financial Condition		
Return on Total Revenues %	-54.15	-58.70
Return on Avg Stockholders' Equity %	-185.74	n.a.
Return on Average Assets %	-73.04	n.a.
Current Ratio	1.44	0.87
Debt / Equity %	n.a.	n.a.

Compound Growth %'s   EPS % n.a.   Net Income % n.a.   Total Revenues % 81.06

Comments

Beginning in 1996, the Company is entering into more time and materials contracts and expects that trend to continue. Revenue increased 79% due to both the volume and size of clinical trials. Much of the cash needs have been financed through private placements of common shares. Since the infrastructure is becoming more established, management forecasts a lower use of cash in 1997. The Company has also had to absorb a large increase in accounts receivable as the business has grown. Investment Classification: Speculative

Officers	Position	Ownership Information	
Thomas P. O'Donnell	President, CEO	Number of Shares Outstanding	4,086,400
Robert S. Sammis	Exec VP, COO	Market Capitalization	$ 16,345,600
Amy B. Russell	Controller	Frequency of Dividends	n.a.
		Number of Shareholders	61

Other Information

			Where Listed	OTC-BB
Transfer Agent	Pacific Stock Transfer Co. Las Vegas, NV		Symbol	CLCR
Auditor	Price Waterhouse LLP		SIC Code	8734
Market Maker	Van Kasper & Company	(800)603-5969	Employees	150
	Hill Thompson Magid & Co., Inc	(800)631-3083		
Broker Dealer	Regular Stockbroker			

Cloverleaf Kennel Club

P.O. Box 88   Loveland, CO 80539-0088   Telephone (970)667-6211   Fax (970)667-9106

Company Description

Cloverleaf Kennel Club is the owner and operator of a state licensed greyhound race track located in Loveland, Colorado, at the intersection of Interstate 25 and Highway 34. The timing and extent of the racing programs are determined by the Colorado State Racing Association. The Company has been operating since 1944.

	09/30/96	09/30/95	09/30/94	09/30/93
Per Share Information				
Stock Price as of 12/31	3.12	4.00	2.00	3.00
Earnings Per Share	0.34	0.46	0.36	0.36
Price / Earnings Ratio	9.18	8.70	5.56	8.33
Book Value Per Share	1.44	1.71	1.24	1.22
Price / Book Value %	216.67	233.92	161.29	245.90
Dividends Per Share	0.40	0.0	0.34	0.74
Annual Financial Data				
Operating Results (000's)				
Total Revenues	40,969.0	43,556.6	38,358.8	42,339.3
Costs & Expenses	-40,481.3	-42,980.7	-37,910.2	-41,889.5
Income Before Taxes and Other	487.7	575.9	448.5	449.8
Other Items	0.0	0.0	0.0	0.0
Income Tax	-181.0	-214.2	-166.8	-167.3
Net Income	306.7	361.8	281.8	282.5
Cash Flow From Operations	384.1	481.8	267.7	346.5
Balance Sheet (000's)				
Cash & Equivalents	679.4	951.6	585.8	603.8
Total Current Assets	770.5	1,052.9	639.8	661.6
Fixed Assets, Net	821.5	448.2	408.3	491.4
Total Assets	1,592.0	1,501.1	1,048.1	1,153.0
Total Current Liabilities	150.0	166.5	75.3	195.4
Long-Term Debt	157.7	0.0	0.0	0.0
Stockholders' Equity	1,284.3	1,334.5	972.8	957.6
Performance & Financial Condition				
Return on Total Revenues %	0.75	0.83	0.73	0.67
Return on Avg Stockholders' Equity %	23.42	31.36	29.19	25.53
Return on Average Assets %	19.83	28.38	25.60	21.30
Current Ratio	5.13	6.32	8.50	3.39
Debt / Equity %	12.28	n.a.	n.a.	n.a.

Compound Growth %'s	EPS %	-1.89	Net Income %	2.78	Total Revenues %	-1.09

Comments

Management reports that several large improvements to the facility were made during 1996. Revenue at the track was down slightly but commission income from satellite uplink facilities was higher. The Company is liquid and the underlying property is of an unknown value. Investment Classification: Speculative & Income & Value

Officers	Position	Ownership Information	
David Scherer	President	Number of Shares Outstanding	892,374
Joseph Pardi	Secretary, Treasurer	Market Capitalization	$ 2,784,207
Luther F. Hess	Vice President	Frequency of Dividends	Annual
Madeline Yoho	Other	Number of Shareholders	Under 500
Ruth L. Faith	Other		

Other Information

Transfer Agent	Corporate Stock Transfer, Inc. Denver,		Where Listed	BE
Auditor	Brock, Watkins and Schommer		Symbol	CLVFA
Market Maker	Hanifen, Imhoff, Inc.	(800)525-2136	SIC Code	7948
	Paragon Capital Corp.	(800)345-0505	Employees	150
Broker Dealer	Regular Stockbroker			

Coal Creek Mining and Manufacturing Company

800 S. Gay Street, Ste. 1706   Knoxville, TN 37929-1706   Telephone (423)435-7158   Fax (423)637-5464

Company Description

The Coal Creek Mining and Manufacturing Company receives royalties from coal mined on its properties in Tennessee and has various other revenues from timber sales, gas and oil royalties, and investments. The Company also owns a 50.2% interest in Tennessee Energy Pipe and Storage Company, a transporter of natural gas to distributors. In 1992, the Company sold real property for cash and a $3.8 million promissory note. A portion of the income will be reported in every year through 2002. The Company has been acquiring its shares on the open market and plans to continue this program. Substantially all of the Company's land and related coal reserves were acquired upon its incorporation in 1872.

	12/31/96	12/31/95	12/31/94	12/31/93
Per Share Information				
Stock Price	103.00	99.50	113.50	95.00
Earnings Per Share	5.25	7.67	5.96	8.15
Price / Earnings Ratio	19.62	12.97	19.04	11.66
Book Value Per Share	42.62	46.04	45.04	45.34
Price / Book Value %	241.67	216.12	252.00	209.53
Dividends Per Share	6.00	6.00	6.00	6.00
Annual Financial Data				
Operating Results (000's)				
Total Revenues	2,120.7	2,607.4	2,495.2	2,429.3
Costs & Expenses	-913.1	-931.5	-938.2	-853.4
Income Before Taxes and Other	1,083.9	1,567.0	1,115.7	1,541.9
Other Items	0.0	0.0	0.0	0.0
Income Tax	-446.4	-610.6	-369.6	-521.4
Net Income	637.5	956.5	746.1	1,020.5
Cash Flow From Operations	347.9	720.3	803.7	450.4
Balance Sheet (000's)				
Cash & Equivalents	206.1	1,120.3	364.7	195.6
Total Current Assets	1,775.1	2,082.7	1,634.0	1,710.4
Fixed Assets, Net	2,318.6	2,330.3	2,398.6	2,371.7
Total Assets	7,138.3	7,993.5	8,104.8	8,347.1
Total Current Liabilities	192.2	190.6	125.1	112.1
Long-Term Debt	61.6	0.0	0.0	0.0
Stockholders' Equity	5,028.0	5,699.0	5,643.4	5,680.3
Performance & Financial Condition				
Return on Total Revenues %	30.06	36.68	29.90	42.01
Return on Avg Stockholders' Equity %	11.89	16.87	13.18	18.40
Return on Average Assets %	8.43	11.88	9.07	12.16
Current Ratio	9.24	10.93	13.06	15.26
Debt / Equity %	1.22	n.a.	n.a.	n.a.

Compound Growth %'s	EPS % -13.64	Net Income % -14.51	Total Revenues % -4.43

Comments

Earnings in 1996 were adversely affected by lower than anticipated coal production. Income from timber harvesting and natural gas production increased slightly. Current plans call for an acceleration in timber cutting to take advantage of favorable market conditions. A new surface coal mining venture is expected to begin production in 1997. Investment Classification: Value & Income

Officers	Position	Ownership Information	
Lewis S. Howard	President	Number of Shares Outstanding	117,960
Fred W. Wyatt	Exec VP	Market Capitalization	$ 12,149,880
Laura F. Martin	Secretary, Treasurer	Frequency of Dividends	Quarterly
McGhee T. Gilpin	Vice President	Number of Shareholders	Under 500

Other Information			
Transfer Agent	Company Office	Where Listed	OTC-BB
Auditor	Cherry, Bekaert & Holland, LLP	Symbol	CCRK
Market Maker	Carr Securities Corporation (800)221-2243	SIC Code	1200
	Herzog, Heine, Geduld, Inc. (800)221-3600	Employees	n.a.
Broker Dealer	Regular Stockbroker		
	Standard Investment (888)783-4688 Ext: Jack		

Colony Bankcorp, Inc.

302 South Main Street Fitzgerald, GA 31750 Telephone (912)426-6000 Fax (912)426-6039

Company Description

The Company is a bank holding company owning six subsidiary commercial banks that serve a seven county area in southern Georgia. These are Community Bank of Wilcox (founded in 1906 as Pitts Banking Company), The Bank of Dodge County (founded in 1966 under the name Bank of Chester), The Bank of Worth, Ashburn Bank (founded in 1900), The Bank of Fitzgerald (founded in 1975), and Broxton State Bank (founded in 1966). Broxton was acquired in 1996. The Banks of Colony serve their customers through a network of twelve offices in Ashburn, Broxton, Chester, Eastman, Fitzgerald, Leesburg, Pitts, Rochelle and Sylvester. Two offices were added during 1996, one of which was added in the acquisition.

	12/31/96	12/31/95	12/31/94	12/31/93
Per Share Information				
Stock Price	22.00	19.00	17.00	15.00
Earnings Per Share	2.02	1.75	1.82	0.49
Price / Earnings Ratio	10.89	10.86	9.34	30.61
Book Value Per Share	17.66	16.31	13.77	13.12
Price / Book Value %	124.58	116.49	123.46	114.33
Dividends Per Share	0.28	0.29	0.26	0.26
Annual Financial Data				
Operating Results (000's)				
Net Interest Income	13,366.5	12,647.7	11,998.3	10,915.3
Loan Loss Provision	-2,194.6	-3,216.1	-2,080.5	-4,089.5
Non-Interest Income	2,649.1	2,052.5	1,764.2	1,608.6
Non-Interest Expense	-9,568.8	-8,420.5	-8,440.9	-7,716.7
Income Before Taxes and Other	4,252.2	3,063.6	3,241.1	717.7
Other Items	0.0	0.0	0.0	0.0
Income Tax	-1,318.7	-923.1	-1,022.0	-120.9
Net Income	2,933.5	2,140.5	2,219.1	596.8
Balance Sheet (000's)				
Cash & Securities	99,561.3	79,865.2	64,005.5	60,057.6
Loans, Net	202,428.3	184,500.5	170,330.5	161,979.5
Total Assets	319,540.2	278,568.3	248,815.7	234,933.6
Deposits	285,676.2	253,243.2	227,042.6	214,508.0
Stockholders' Equity	25,591.0	21,055.2	16,749.7	15,956.6
Performance & Financial Condition				
Return on Avg Stockholders' Equity %	12.58	11.32	13.57	3.77
Return on Average Assets %	0.98	0.81	0.92	0.26
Equity to Assets %	8.01	7.56	6.73	6.79
Net Interest Margin	4.80	5.27	5.24	4.82
Reserve as a % of Problem Loans	59.97	74.30	144.74	105.81

Compound Growth %'s	EPS % n.a.	Net Income % n.a.	Net Interest Income % 6.99

Comments

The Company declared a 2 for 1 stock split in 1995. All per share amounts have been restated for consistency. Operating performances of each of the subsidiaries is disclosed in the annual shareholder's report. We did not display compound growth rates in earnings because the base year was not representative due to large reserves for problem loans. The Broxton acquisition was accounted for as a pooling of interests and financials were restated. We did not restate the three earlier years presented above so that the information would be meaningful to the trading range of the stock. Investment Classification: Value

Officers	Position	Ownership Information	
James D. Minix	President, CEO	Number of Shares Outstanding	1,448,842
Terry L. Hester	Exec VP, CFO	Market Capitalization	$ 31,874,524
Edwin W. Hortman, Jr.	Senior VP	Frequency of Dividends	Annual
Patricia M. Owens	Vice President	Number of Shareholders	n.a.
Gerald H. Thompson	Vice President	Where Listed / Symbol	OTC-PS / CBAN

Other Information			Loan Mix	%
Transfer Agent	Company Office		R/E Mortgages	55.4
Auditor	McNair, McLemore, Middlebrooks		Installment	21.6
Market Maker	Sterne, Agee & Leach, Inc.	(800)239-2408	Commerical	18.7
	J.C. Bradford & Co.	(800)251-1740	Construction	0.4
Broker Dealer	OTC Specialist		Other	3.9

Colorado Gaming & Entertainment Co.

12596 West Bayaud, Ste. 450 Lakewood, CO 80228 Telephone (303)716-5600 Fax (303)716-5601

Company Description

Colorado Gaming & Entertainment Co. develops, owns and operates gaming and related entertainment facilities. It currently owns Bullwhackers Central City, Bullwhackers Black Hawk and Silver Hawk Casino, which opened on June 26, 1996, in historic mining towns in Colorado. Colorado law permits limited stakes gaming in three historic mining towns. The Casinos offer slot machines and the table games of blackjack and poker. As a result of the financial difficulties of a river boat gaming project, the predecessor company sought bankruptcy protection in November, 1995. The Company emerged from those proceedings on June 7, 1996.

	12/31/96	12/31/95	12/31/94
Per Share Information			
Stock Price	4.25	n.a.	n.a.
Earnings Per Share	0.04	n.a.	n.a.
Price / Earnings Ratio	106.25	n.a.	n.a.
Book Value Per Share	0.95	n.a.	n.a.
Price / Book Value %	447.37	n.a.	n.a.
Dividends Per Share	0.0	n.a.	n.a.
Annual Financial Data			
Operating Results (000's)			
Total Revenues	50,817.0	47,789.0	45,126.0
Costs & Expenses	-50,576.0	-92,728.0	-77,257.0
Income Before Taxes and Other	241.0	-115,216.0	-32,131.0
Other Items	164,358.0	0.0	0.0
Income Tax	0.0	0.0	0.0
Net Income	164,599.0	-115,216.0	-32,131.0
Cash Flow From Operations	10,549.0	6,002.0	2,714.0
Balance Sheet (000's)			
Cash & Equivalents	5,758.0	3,623.0	n.a.
Total Current Assets	6,487.0	4,572.0	n.a.
Fixed Assets, Net	41,322.0	32,127.0	n.a.
Total Assets	67,048.0	37,680.0	n.a.
Total Current Liabilities	6,788.0	4,357.0	n.a.
Long-Term Debt	55,391.0	0.0	n.a.
Stockholders' Equity	4,869.0	-153,137.0	n.a.
Performance & Financial Condition			
Return on Total Revenues %	323.91	n.a.	-71.20
Return on Avg Stockholders' Equity %	n.a.	n.a.	n.a.
Return on Average Assets %	314.34	n.a.	n.a.
Current Ratio	0.96	1.05	n.a.
Debt / Equity %	1137.63	n.a.	n.a.

Compound Growth %'s	EPS % n.a.	Net Income % n.a.	Total Revenues % 6.12

Comments

1996 results include a gain in connection with the bankruptcy relief of debt of $164 million. Earnings per share are calculated based on the short period beginning June 7, 1996 and ending December 31, 1996. Despite the reorganization, the Company still has a mountain of debt. For the first quarter of 1997, the Company lost $346,000, $.07 per share. Investment Classification: Speculative

Officers	Position	Ownership Information	
Stephen J. Szapor, Jr.	President, CEO	Number of Shares Outstanding	5,138,888
Alan L. Mayer	Senior VP, Secretary	Market Capitalization	$ 21,840,274
Richard J. Rabin	Senior VP	Frequency of Dividends	n.a.
Robert J. Stephens	VP - Finance, Treasurer	Number of Shareholders	50
Jack Breslin	Vice President		

Other Information

Transfer Agent	IBJ Schroder Bank & Trust Co. New York, NY		Where Listed	OTC-BB
Auditor	Arthur Andersen LLP		Symbol	CGME
Market Maker	Oscar Gruss & Son	(212)943-7616	SIC Code	7990
	Credit Research & Trading	(203)629-6436	Employees	n.a.
Broker Dealer	Regular Stockbroker			

Colorocs Information Technologies, Inc.

5600 Oakbrook Pkwy., Ste. 240   Norcross, GA 30093   Telephone (770)447-3570   Fax (770)447-3590

Company Description

The Company was founded in 1982 to capitalize on the trend toward the use of color in business communications. The principal operations, historically, were the design, manufacture and sale of full color copiers and color printers. Beginning in 1994, the Company's focus shifted to product support for color copiers previously sold and the licensing of patented color printing and copier technology. In 1995 and 1996, the Company developed two new technology based lines of businesses: the delivery of the Internet through the television and the provision of network printing and file sharing software products.

	12/31/96	12/31/95
Per Share Information		
Stock Price	5.12	6.40
Earnings Per Share	-3.51	1.07
Price / Earnings Ratio	n.a.	5.98
Book Value Per Share	-0.58	2.90
Price / Book Value %	n.a.	220.69
Dividends Per Share	0.0	0.0
Annual Financial Data		
Operating Results (000's)		
Total Revenues	2,863.4	6,344.9
Costs & Expenses	-10,747.7	-2,849.7
Income Before Taxes and Other	-7,983.0	3,495.2
Other Items	822.5	0.0
Income Tax	0.0	-1,332.0
Net Income	-7,160.5	2,163.2
Cash Flow From Operations	-2,208.4	2,494.2
Balance Sheet (000's)		
Cash & Equivalents	282.6	n.a.
Total Current Assets	1,173.8	n.a.
Fixed Assets, Net	1,165.5	n.a.
Total Assets	3,850.6	n.a.
Total Current Liabilities	4,058.8	n.a.
Long-Term Debt	0.0	n.a.
Stockholders' Equity	-1,200.8	n.a.
Performance & Financial Condition		
Return on Total Revenues %	-250.07	34.09
Return on Avg Stockholders' Equity %	-303.50	52.06
Return on Average Assets %	n.a.	n.a.
Current Ratio	0.29	n.a.
Debt / Equity %	n.a.	n.a.

Compound Growth %'s	EPS % n.a.	Net Income % n.a.	Total Revenues % n.a.

Comments

1995 revenue included certain licensing of patented technology. In 1996, $3.2 million was spent on research and development. In 1997, the Company combined forces with NetChannel, Inc., a privately owned company, to execute the delivery of the Internet through the television. Management believes that the joining of two of the leading companies in this area will increase the likelihood of success as the market is quickly consolidating. The auditors issued a going concern opinion in their 1996 report. Investment Classification: Speculative

Officers	Position	Ownership Information	
Rudolph P. Russo	Chairman, CEO	Number of Shares Outstanding	2,071,544
Alan McKeon	President, COO	Market Capitalization	$ 10,606,305
		Frequency of Dividends	n.a.
		Number of Shareholders	674

Other Information				
Transfer Agent	ChaseMellon Shareholder Services Ridgefiled Park, NJ		Where Listed	OTC-BB
Auditor	Arthur Andersen LLP		Symbol	CLRC
Market Maker	Knight Securities L.P.	(800)222-4910	SIC Code	3861
	Herzog, Heine, Geduld, Inc.	(800)221-3600	Employees	n.a.
Broker Dealer	Regular Stockbroker			

Columbia Financial Corporation

11 West Main Street   Bloomsburg, PA 17815   Telephone (717)784-1660   Fax (717)784-3912

Company Description

First Columbia Bank & Trust Co., the operating subsidiary of the Corporation, is a full service community commercial bank serving a market area in Columbia, Eastern Montour, Northumberland, and Luzerne Counties of Pennsylvania. The Bank offers a full line of personal, business and municipal financial services and a complete line of corporate and personal fiduciary services through its main office facility and a network of satellite units. The Bank was established in 1899 as Bloomsburg National Bank and changed to its present name in 1990.

	12/31/96	12/31/95	12/31/94	12/31/93
Per Share Information				
Stock Price	33.75	28.50	25.00	30.50
Earnings Per Share	3.08	2.33	2.01	2.05
Price / Earnings Ratio	10.96	12.23	12.44	14.88
Book Value Per Share	26.79	24.94	22.98	21.99
Price / Book Value %	125.98	114.27	108.79	138.70
Dividends Per Share	0.88	0.81	0.80	0.80
Annual Financial Data				
Operating Results (000's)				
Net Interest Income	6,936.7	6,585.3	6,131.9	5,837.8
Loan Loss Provision	-416.8	-211.0	-164.4	-150.0
Non-Interest Income	1,299.6	916.7	784.2	742.5
Non-Interest Expense	-4,826.3	-4,833.9	-4,692.5	-4,433.9
Income Before Taxes and Other	2,993.2	2,457.1	2,059.1	1,996.4
Other Items	0.0	0.0	0.0	90.5
Income Tax	-972.1	-806.0	-607.8	-610.0
Net Income	2,021.1	1,651.1	1,451.3	1,476.9
Balance Sheet (000's)				
Cash & Securities	43,936.8	46,249.0	44,220.0	51,295.5
Loans, Net	116,975.7	112,716.4	107,499.6	87,111.8
Total Assets	165,406.6	163,314.8	156,142.8	142,366.5
Deposits	134,220.4	135,495.9	125,297.0	118,794.4
Stockholders' Equity	16,993.9	17,394.1	16,589.4	15,880.0
Performance & Financial Condition				
Return on Avg Stockholders' Equity %	11.75	9.72	8.94	9.57
Return on Average Assets %	1.23	1.03	0.97	n.a.
Equity to Assets %	10.27	10.65	10.62	11.15
Net Interest Margin	4.47	4.42	4.38	4.51
Reserve as a % of Problem Loans	595.97	n.a.	n.a.	n.a.

Compound Growth %'s	EPS %	14.53	Net Income %	11.02	Net Interest Income %	5.92

Comments

The Corporation bought 63,107 and 24,481 shares of its common stock in 1996 and 1995, respectively. The effect of these purchases of treasury shares can be seen in a compound growth rate in earnings per share that is higher than the growth rate in earnings. The Bank experienced a 25% increase in its trust department, now managing $137 million of assets. Management is "optimistically and confidently embracing" 1997 to continue the favorable patterns of the last six years. Investment Classification: Value

Officers	Position	Ownership Information	
R. Robert McCoy	President, CEO	Number of Shares Outstanding	634,422
Thomas C. Blass	Senior VP, Secretary	Market Capitalization	$ 21,411,743
Kevin Sauers	Vice President, Sr Loan Officer	Frequency of Dividends	Quarterly
Shirley K. Alters	Vice President, CFO	Number of Shareholders	n.a.
Michael D. Good	Vice President	Where Listed / Symbol	OTC-BB / CLBF

Other Information			Loan Mix	%
Transfer Agent	Fulton Bank Lancaster, PA		Commerical	44.3
Auditor	KPMG Peat Marwick LLP		R/E Mortgages	43.9
Market Maker	F.J. Morrissey & Co., Inc.	(800)842-8928	Consumer	11.8
	Ryan, Beck & Co.	(800)325-7926		
Broker Dealer	Regular Stockbroker			

Columbia Water Company

220 Locust Street   Columbia, PA 17512   Telephone (717)684-2188   Fax (717)684-4566

Company Description

The Columbia Water Company was incorporated in 1823 and provides water service to residential and business customers in the Borough of Columbia, parts of West Hempfield Township and parts of Manor Township. The Company is regulated by the Pennsylvania Public Utility Commission. There is no formal market for the shares although the Company will try to help sellers by posting a notice with the Board of directors. Buyers are on their own.

	12/31/95	12/31/94	12/31/93	12/31/92
Per Share Information				
Stock Price as of 12/31	90.00	80.00	74.00	70.00
Earnings Per Share	16.06	12.99	8.50	9.45
Price / Earnings Ratio	5.60	6.16	8.71	7.41
Book Value Per Share	143.49	129.83	119.24	113.14
Price / Book Value %	62.72	61.62	62.06	61.87
Dividends Per Share	2.40	2.40	2.40	2.40
Annual Financial Data				
Operating Results (000's)				
Total Revenues	2,305.9	2,258.1	1,944.7	1,809.5
Costs & Expenses	-1,640.1	-1,712.0	-1,648.1	-1,378.2
Income Before Taxes and Other	663.2	543.9	294.2	429.1
Other Items	0.0	0.0	0.0	0.0
Income Tax	-258.6	-216.5	-80.2	-190.9
Net Income	404.6	327.5	214.1	238.2
Cash Flow From Operations	696.6	649.7	538.4	-415.4
Balance Sheet (000's)				
Cash & Equivalents	677.2	560.3	737.1	464.4
Total Current Assets	1,341.5	1,213.5	1,337.0	1,066.2
Fixed Assets, Net	11,966.0	11,525.1	10,746.1	10,788.7
Total Assets	13,421.4	13,045.5	12,557.6	11,894.3
Total Current Liabilities	1,188.9	1,279.7	1,182.3	1,210.3
Long-Term Debt	4,193.7	4,479.2	4,749.3	4,500.2
Stockholders' Equity	3,615.9	3,271.8	3,004.8	2,851.2
Performance & Financial Condition				
Return on Total Revenues %	17.55	14.50	11.01	13.16
Return on Avg Stockholders' Equity %	11.75	10.43	7.31	n.a.
Return on Average Assets %	3.06	2.56	1.75	n.a.
Current Ratio	1.13	0.95	1.13	0.88
Debt / Equity %	115.98	136.90	158.06	157.83

Compound Growth %'s	EPS %	37.46	Net Income %	37.47	Total Revenues %	8.89

Comments

The Company continues to expand its service area and also serves new developments within existing service areas. It has generally had a steady growth in revenue over the last 15 years, averaging 9%. During 1995, the Company expanded and improved its distribution system by installing 11,000 feet of new water mains. The annual report is late by traditional standards and was not available for 1996 when we went to press. Investment Classification: Value

Officers	Position	Ownership Information	
Donald H. Nikolaus	President	Number of Shares Outstanding	25,200
John F. Hinkle, Jr.	Secretary, Treasurer	Market Capitalization	$ 2,268,000
Philip H. Glatfelter II	Vice President	Frequency of Dividends	Annual
Charles E. Gohn	General Manager	Number of Shareholders	Under 500
Cornelius H. Westerman	Other		

Other Information			
Transfer Agent	Company Office	Where Listed	Order Matching Only
Auditor	Sager, Swisher and Company	Symbol	n.a.
Market Maker	None	SIC Code	4940
		Employees	13
Broker Dealer	None - See Note		

Columbian Rope Company

145 Towery Street   Guntown, MS 38849   Telephone (601)348-2241   Fax (601)348-5749

Company Description

Columbian Rope Company manufactures traditional rope and cords as well as a variety of specialty products including technically advanced ropes. PlymKraft, a subsidiary, produces monofilament and film cable fiber. Monorail, another subsidiary, develops and exports new car wash systems. Cordage, cable filler and car wash systems approximated 45%, 42% and 13%, respectively, of consolidated net sales for 1996.

	12/31/96	12/31/95	12/31/94	12/31/93
Per Share Information				
Stock Price	10.50	6.75	2.12	1.25
Earnings Per Share	45.65	28.48	29.42	9.19
Price / Earnings Ratio	0.23	0.24	0.07	0.14
Book Value Per Share	139.80	98.40	71.93	44.50
Price / Book Value %	7.51	6.86	2.95	2.81
Dividends Per Share	4.25	2.00	0.0	0.0
Annual Financial Data				
Operating Results (000's)				
Total Revenues	22,299.2	22,156.8	21,565.4	18,328.3
Costs & Expenses	-21,089.0	-21,168.1	-20,353.8	-17,873.6
Income Before Taxes and Other	1,110.9	880.8	1,114.2	339.6
Other Items	0.0	0.0	-475.1	0.0
Income Tax	576.5	171.7	448.4	0.0
Net Income	1,687.4	1,052.5	1,087.6	339.6
Cash Flow From Operations	251.1	1,207.4	912.5	930.1
Balance Sheet (000's)				
Cash & Equivalents	382.2	813.4	755.1	436.8
Total Current Assets	7,417.7	7,359.0	6,993.2	5,971.1
Fixed Assets, Net	2,651.2	1,789.0	1,523.9	1,371.1
Total Assets	11,697.6	10,353.9	9,522.0	7,809.9
Total Current Liabilities	3,722.0	3,099.9	2,695.9	1,846.3
Long-Term Debt	1,472.5	2,304.6	2,870.0	3,447.5
Stockholders' Equity	5,167.4	3,637.1	2,658.5	1,644.9
Performance & Financial Condition				
Return on Total Revenues %	7.57	4.75	5.04	1.85
Return on Avg Stockholders' Equity %	38.33	33.44	50.54	22.81
Return on Average Assets %	15.30	10.59	12.55	4.47
Current Ratio	1.99	2.37	2.59	3.23
Debt / Equity %	28.50	63.36	107.95	209.59

Compound Growth %'s	EPS %	70.62	Net Income %	70.64	Total Revenues %	6.76

Comments

A funny thing happened as we conducted research for the first edition of Walker's Manual. We bought 5 shares of Columbian Rope for $8 per share. It wasn't until months later that we realized what we had accomplished and wished only that it had been 5,000 shares instead. Management reports knowledge of trades in the $60 range and didn't know of our purchase. The numbers speak for themselves and even that $60 per share price looks awfully good. Investment Classification: Value

Officers	Position	Ownership Information	
Michael M. Chapman	Chairman	Number of Shares Outstanding	36,962
Steve Ludt	CFO	Market Capitalization	$ 388,101
Slade R. Metcalf	Secretary	Frequency of Dividends	n.a.
		Number of Shareholders	Under 500

Other Information

Transfer Agent	Company Office		Where Listed	OTC-BB
Auditor	Nail McKinney Tate & Robinson		Symbol	CRPE
Market Maker	Seidler Companies, Inc., The	(800)421-0164	SIC Code	2298
	Carr Securities Corporation	(800)221-2243	Employees	94
Broker Dealer	OTC Specialist			

Community Independent Bank, Inc.

201 North Main Street   Bernville, PA 19506   Telephone (601)488-1200   Fax (601)488-1198

Company Description

Bernville Bank, subsidiary of the Company, operates four banking offices serving customers in Berks County, Pennsylvania. The Company sold 72,919 shares of its common stock in 1996 for $17 per share. A new loan center was opened in Wyomissing in February, 1997. Management is actively pursuing additional expansion. Bernville Bank was formed in 1907 and celebrates its 90th anniversary this year.

	12/31/96	12/31/95	12/31/94	12/31/93
Per Share Information				
Stock Price	17.00	18.67	18.00	15.67
Earnings Per Share	1.99	1.86	1.74	1.85
Price / Earnings Ratio	8.54	10.04	10.34	8.47
Book Value Per Share	18.48	17.14	15.31	14.18
Price / Book Value %	91.99	108.93	117.57	110.51
Dividends Per Share	0.41	0.37	0.33	0.31
Annual Financial Data				
Operating Results (000's)				
Net Interest Income	2,594.0	2,248.4	2,146.0	2,153.9
Loan Loss Provision	-72.0	-12.0	-7.5	-126.0
Non-Interest Income	385.1	254.4	228.3	214.5
Non-Interest Expense	-2,053.8	-1,780.8	-1,693.8	-1,665.3
Income Before Taxes and Other	853.4	710.0	672.9	577.1
Other Items	0.0	0.0	0.0	0.0
Income Tax	-235.7	-196.7	-192.6	-125.2
Net Income	617.7	513.3	480.3	451.9
Balance Sheet (000's)				
Cash & Securities	12,609.8	9,839.2	10,885.4	11,206.5
Loans, Net	52,217.3	48,871.1	38,906.0	34,793.2
Total Assets	68,100.5	61,764.8	52,909.7	49,039.3
Deposits	61,136.0	55,771.9	46,301.2	44,732.3
Stockholders' Equity	6,435.4	4,722.0	4,216.0	3,906.9
Performance & Financial Condition				
Return on Avg Stockholders' Equity %	11.07	11.49	11.83	13.02
Return on Average Assets %	0.95	0.90	0.94	n.a.
Equity to Assets %	9.45	7.65	7.97	7.97
Net Interest Margin	n.a.	n.a.	n.a.	n.a.
Reserve as a % of Problem Loans	52.35	n.a.	255.93	2,941.88

Compound Growth %'s	EPS %	2.46	Net Income %	10.98	Net Interest Income %	6.39

Comments

The Bank declared a 3 for 2 stock split in 1995. All per share amounts have been adjusted for consistency. Management acknowledges the desired improvement in return on equity and targets the 15% mark by the year 2000. In addition, growth is targeted at an annual 20% over the same period. The lower compound growth rate in earnings per share, as compared to net income, is attributable to the additional stock that was issued, referred to above. Investment Classification: Value

Officers	Position	Ownership Information	
Arlan J. Werst	President, CEO	Number of Shares Outstanding	348,287
Martha Wolfe	Other	Market Capitalization	$ 5,920,879
Linda Strohmenger	Other	Frequency of Dividends	Quarterly
Mary Ann Bossard	Other	Number of Shareholders	n.a.
Shirley Luckenbill	Other	Where Listed / Symbol	OTC-BB / CMYI

Other Information			Loan Mix	%
Transfer Agent	Company Office		R/E Mortgages	69.5
Auditor	Beard & Company, Inc.		Commerical	22.3
Market Maker	Wheat, First Sec / Butcher	(610)376-6171	Consumer	8.2
	Ryan, Beck & Co.	(800)223-8969		
Broker Dealer	Regular Stockbroker			

Community Service Communications, Inc.

33 Main Street   Winthrop, ME 04364-0400   Telephone (207)377-9911   Fax (207)377-9969

Company Description

Community Service Communications, Inc. is a holding company whose subsidiaries are engaged in telecommunications activities in both regulated and deregulated environments. The Company's primary business is its local telephone exchange service through exchanges in Monmouth, Litchfield, Greene, Leeds, Mt. Vernon, Winthrop and East Winthrop, Maine. Additionally, the Company owns a cellular radio telephone holding company with investments in cellular properties. The Company was founded in 1905.

	12/31/96	12/31/95	12/31/94	12/31/93
Per Share Information				
Stock Price	137.00	110.00	95.00	90.00
Earnings Per Share	15.67	14.86	20.79	12.10
Price / Earnings Ratio	8.74	7.40	4.57	7.44
Book Value Per Share	122.03	115.60	109.50	96.42
Price / Book Value %	112.27	95.16	86.76	93.34
Dividends Per Share	9.25	8.76	7.71	7.33
Annual Financial Data				
Operating Results (000's)				
Total Revenues	6,254.6	6,130.6	6,204.2	9,272.0
Costs & Expenses	-4,546.7	-4,725.9	-4,400.3	-8,250.9
Income Before Taxes and Other	1,438.2	1,404.6	1,804.0	1,021.1
Other Items	0.0	-73.8	37.0	0.0
Income Tax	-516.8	-457.5	-618.8	-309.8
Net Income	921.4	873.4	1,222.2	711.3
Cash Flow From Operations	2,246.7	2,062.3	2,549.3	2,152.8
Balance Sheet (000's)				
Cash & Equivalents	866.3	900.2	400.7	65.1
Total Current Assets	3,183.9	3,120.2	2,527.9	2,700.6
Fixed Assets, Net	9,414.8	9,038.7	9,230.1	9,525.9
Total Assets	13,159.2	12,586.4	12,190.7	12,248.4
Total Current Liabilities	1,718.5	1,741.8	1,302.0	3,557.1
Long-Term Debt	2,996.7	2,797.4	3,142.7	1,813.3
Stockholders' Equity	7,172.9	6,795.3	6,436.8	5,667.9
Performance & Financial Condition				
Return on Total Revenues %	14.73	14.25	19.70	7.67
Return on Avg Stockholders' Equity %	13.19	13.20	20.19	12.87
Return on Average Assets %	7.16	7.05	10.00	5.75
Current Ratio	1.85	1.79	1.94	0.76
Debt / Equity %	41.78	41.17	48.82	31.99

Compound Growth %'s	EPS %	9.00	Net Income %	9.01	Total Revenues %	-12.30

Comments

On May 17, 1996, the president announced that the Board of Directors had rejected an offer to purchase the Company. The offer was $200 per share, which was the same price the potential acquiring group paid in a private transaction for 3,533 shares. The Board concluded that the offer very substantially understates the value of the Company. Implementation of the Telecommunication Reform Act remains managements greatest concern. 1997 net operating income is expected to decline as the Company builds for the future. Investment Classification: Income & Value

Officers	Position	Ownership Information	
Mark H. Blake	President, Treasurer	Number of Shares Outstanding	58,782
Leland C. Davis	Vice President	Market Capitalization	$ 8,053,134
Normand J. Savard	Vice President, Secretary	Frequency of Dividends	Quarterly
		Number of Shareholders	Under 500

Other Information

Transfer Agent	Company Office		Where Listed	OTC-BB
Auditor	Berry, Dunn, McNeil & Parker		Symbol	CMYS
Market Maker	Carr Securities Corporation	(800)221-2243	SIC Code	4810
	Sharpe Capital Inc.	(800)355-5781	Employees	45
Broker Dealer	OTC Specialist			
	Norman Kadehjian - Wainwright	(800)727-7176		

Components Specialties, Inc.

1172 Route 109   Lindenhurst, NY 11757-0624   Telephone (516)957-8700   Fax (516)957-9142

Company Description

Components Specialties, Inc. sells and distributes electronic equipment manufactured by other companies, including commercial sound equipment, paging systems, sound accessories, surveillance equipment, intercoms and more. Most of the products are imported from the Far East and sold under recognized tradenames.

	03/31/96	03/31/95	03/31/94	03/31/93
Per Share Information				
Stock Price as of 12/31	4.00	2.62	1.75	1.25
Earnings Per Share	0.84	0.58	0.27	0.09
Price / Earnings Ratio	4.76	4.52	6.48	13.89
Book Value Per Share	4.06	3.37	3.17	2.52
Price / Book Value %	98.52	77.74	55.21	49.60
Dividends Per Share	0.0	0.0	0.0	0.0
Annual Financial Data				
Operating Results (000's)				
Total Revenues	11,261.5	9,443.2	6,806.8	5,503.6
Costs & Expenses	-10,591.5	-9,036.8	-6,618.1	-5,439.3
Income Before Taxes and Other	670.0	406.4	188.7	64.3
Other Items	0.0	0.0	0.0	0.0
Income Tax	-293.2	-184.4	-83.7	-31.0
Net Income	376.8	222.0	105.0	33.3
Cash Flow From Operations	-61.9	-134.4	269.2	-241.4
Balance Sheet (000's)				
Cash & Equivalents	198.6	133.2	143.1	181.5
Total Current Assets	3,769.5	3,086.5	2,938.0	2,583.1
Fixed Assets, Net	200.8	127.9	144.5	135.4
Total Assets	4,006.5	3,244.5	3,108.3	2,744.0
Total Current Liabilities	2,213.2	1,751.2	1,826.2	1,586.2
Long-Term Debt	71.5	0.0	0.0	0.0
Stockholders' Equity	1,677.7	1,293.4	1,071.5	966.5
Performance & Financial Condition				
Return on Total Revenues %	3.35	2.35	1.54	0.60
Return on Avg Stockholders' Equity %	25.37	18.77	10.30	3.50
Return on Average Assets %	10.39	6.99	3.59	1.33
Current Ratio	1.70	1.76	1.61	1.63
Debt / Equity %	4.26	n.a.	n.a.	n.a.

Compound Growth %'s	EPS %	110.55	Net Income %	124.57	Total Revenues %	26.96

Comments

The 1996 year was not to be outdone by three previous years of record earnings. The latest year posted a 70% increase in net income fueled by a 19% increase in sales. The new Pro-Video line (surveillance equipment), has proven to be less subject to economic conditions than other products. 1997 results were not available when we went to press but could be obtained directly from the Company. Management was anticipating equally fine results as last reported. Over the last year it has become increasingly difficult to acquire shares. The year end ask price was $6 per share as compared to the bid of $4 per share. Investment Classification: Growth & Value

Officers	Position	Ownership Information	
Louis W. Keller	President, Treasurer	Number of Shares Outstanding	413,240
Todd I. Keller	Exec VP	Market Capitalization	$ 1,652,960
Rhonda Mutterperl	Secretary	Frequency of Dividends	n.a.
		Number of Shareholders	Under 500

Other Information				
Transfer Agent	American Stock Transfer & Trust Company New York, NY		Where Listed	OTC-BB
Auditor	Marden, Harrison & Kreuter		Symbol	CSPC
Market Maker	M. Rimson & Co., Inc.	(800)207-3195	SIC Code	5060
	Paragon Capital Corp.	(800)345-0505	Employees	25
Broker Dealer	Regular Stockbroker			

Computer Services, Inc.

1301 Broadway   Paducah, KY 42001   Telephone (502)442-7361   Fax (502)442-7361, ext. 145

Company Description

Computer Services Inc. and subsidiary provides data processing services, supplies, equipment, forms and maintenance to financial institutions in the central United States. Computer Services has established itself as the nation's premier community bank processor, delivering service to nearly 300 banks with 2,000 locations covering ten states. A new 75,000 square foot corporate headquarters is expected to be occupied in the fall, 1997. The Company began business in 1965.

	02/28/97	02/29/96	02/28/95	02/28/94
Per Share Information				
Stock Price	24.00	27.00	30.00	35.00
Earnings Per Share	1.89	2.03	1.64	1.62
Price / Earnings Ratio	12.70	13.30	18.29	21.60
Book Value Per Share	13.71	12.26	10.72	9.37
Price / Book Value %	175.05	220.23	279.85	373.53
Dividends Per Share	0.46	0.39	0.35	0.31
Annual Financial Data				
Operating Results (000's)				
Total Revenues	38,027.9	38,207.3	36,222.5	36,104.2
Costs & Expenses	-31,266.9	-31,168.0	-30,286.0	-30,465.8
Income Before Taxes and Other	6,760.9	7,039.3	5,936.5	5,638.3
Other Items	0.0	0.0	0.0	0.0
Income Tax	-2,703.1	-2,738.0	-2,431.0	-2,198.0
Net Income	4,057.8	4,301.3	3,505.5	3,440.3
Cash Flow From Operations	6,734.0	4,270.5	7,871.6	5,708.9
Balance Sheet (000's)				
Cash & Equivalents	5,727.5	8,362.2	7,231.3	5,556.5
Total Current Assets	12,936.0	14,706.5	12,300.3	11,073.6
Fixed Assets, Net	15,693.0	10,367.1	10,436.7	9,933.7
Total Assets	32,165.7	28,332.0	25,784.8	23,334.5
Total Current Liabilities	2,512.4	1,803.5	2,975.3	3,154.1
Long-Term Debt	0.0	0.0	0.0	0.0
Stockholders' Equity	28,927.7	25,803.0	22,117.3	19,333.7
Performance & Financial Condition				
Return on Total Revenues %	10.67	11.26	9.68	9.53
Return on Avg Stockholders' Equity %	14.83	17.95	16.91	19.28
Return on Average Assets %	13.41	15.90	14.27	14.87
Current Ratio	5.15	8.15	4.13	3.51
Debt / Equity %	n.a.	n.a.	n.a.	n.a.

Compound Growth %'s	EPS %	5.27	Net Income %	5.66	Total Revenues %	1.75

Comments

The Company declared a 2 for 1 stock split in 1995. All per share amounts have been adjusted for consistency. A number of nonrecurring items that were positive in 1996 and negative in 1997 resulted in earnings that are slightly lower than in the 1996 record year. With plenty of merger activity in the customer base of community banks, the sales force has more than just replaced clients that are acquired by larger institutions. A score card is maintained by top brass; last year's score was 18 gained vs. 8 lost. The extremely healthy balance sheet should provide plenty of expansion capability. Investment Classification: Value

Officers	Position	Ownership Information	
John A. Williams	Chairman, CEO	Number of Shares Outstanding	2,109,705
Steven A. Powless	President, COO	Market Capitalization	$ 50,632,920
David L. Simon	Treasurer, CFO	Frequency of Dividends	n.a.
Ann T. Carney	Vice President, Secretary	Number of Shareholders	Under 500
R. Michael Adams	Vice President		

Other Information

Transfer Agent	Company Office		Where Listed	Order Matching Only
Auditor	Crowe, Chizek and Company LLP		Symbol	n.a.
Market Maker	JJB Hilliard, WL Lyons, Inc.	(800)627-3557	SIC Code	7370
			Employees	376
Broker Dealer	JJB Hilliard, WL Lyons, Inc.	(800)627-3557		

Conbraco Industries, Inc.

P.O. Box 247   Matthews, NC 28106-0247   Telephone (704)847-9191   Fax (704)841-6025

Company Description

Conbraco Industries is a manufacturer of boiler trimmings, bronze and stainless steel water gauges and pop safety and relief valves. Manufacturing facilities are in North and South Carolina and the Company sells most of its products to wholesale distributors throughout the United States and in many foreign countries. These distributors sell to end-users which include the industrial, chemical, pulp and paper and other processing industries. The Company also invests in real estate.

	12/31/96	12/31/95	12/31/94
Per Share Information			
Stock Price	435.00	625.00	495.00
Earnings Per Share	38.22	35.26	40.66
Price / Earnings Ratio	11.38	17.73	12.17
Book Value Per Share	416.91	385.38	355.13
Price / Book Value %	104.34	162.18	139.39
Dividends Per Share	1.81	1.75	1.50
Annual Financial Data			
Operating Results (000's)			
Total Revenues	171,070.5	162,633.2	152,108.9
Costs & Expenses	-153,401.1	-145,536.1	-131,347.8
Income Before Taxes and Other	17,614.2	17,097.2	20,442.9
Other Items	0.0	0.0	0.0
Income Tax	-6,510.9	-6,412.9	-7,692.6
Net Income	11,103.4	10,684.3	12,750.3
Cash Flow From Operations	23,018.8	4,533.4	19,486.2
Balance Sheet (000's)			
Cash & Equivalents	4,695.1	2,042.2	1,438.7
Total Current Assets	74,012.2	77,949.3	60,199.1
Fixed Assets, Net	56,890.5	56,470.7	53,130.0
Total Assets	146,893.1	149,854.0	127,198.5
Total Current Liabilities	13,029.7	23,241.7	8,632.1
Long-Term Debt	12,619.8	9,862.5	7,400.0
Stockholders' Equity	119,540.5	115,559.8	109,923.3
Performance & Financial Condition			
Return on Total Revenues %	6.49	6.57	8.38
Return on Avg Stockholders' Equity %	9.45	9.48	n.a.
Return on Average Assets %	7.48	7.71	n.a.
Current Ratio	5.68	3.35	6.97
Debt / Equity %	10.56	8.53	6.73

Compound Growth %'s	EPS %	-3.05	Net Income %	-6.68	Total Revenues %	6.05

Comments

The Company acquired 13,130, 9,666 and 6,214 shares of its own stock during 1996, 1995 and 1994, respectively. $9 million in real estate investments are carried at cost with no indication of value. The balance sheet shows a favorable current ratio and little debt. Only shareholders are entitled to the annual financial statements. Investment Classification: Value

Officers	Position	Ownership Information	
Carl Mosack	President	Number of Shares Outstanding	286,730
Everett Lowery	CFO	Market Capitalization	$ 124,727,550
		Frequency of Dividends	Quarterly
		Number of Shareholders	Under 500

Other Information				
Transfer Agent	Company Office		Where Listed	OTC-BB
Auditor	Dixon, Odom & Co., LLP		Symbol	CNIN
Market Maker	Roney & Co.	(800)321-2038	SIC Code	5085
	Howe Barnes Investments, Inc.	(800)621-2364	Employees	400
Broker Dealer	Regular Stockbroker			

Conectisys Corporation

7260 Spigno Place, Ste. 220   Agua Dulce, CA 91350   Telephone (805)268-0305   Fax (805)268-0976

Company Description

Conectisys Corporation, formerly known as BDR Industries, Inc., was formed in 1986. For years it was a corporate shell looking to acquire one or more operating businesses. Prior to its current business it both acquired and divested of Creative Image Products, a company that manufactured organic insecticide. In 1995, the Company acquired 80% interests in two companies. One had developed a product line for the monitoring and controlling of various devices in the petroleum and gas industry. The other has a product line that uses cutting edge communications to assist in the monitoring of meters for utility companies and the petroleum industry.

	11/30/96	11/30/95	11/30/94
Per Share Information			
Stock Price as of 12/31	5.00	7.00	12.00
Earnings Per Share	-0.86	-1.16	0.07
Price / Earnings Ratio	n.a.	n.a.	171.43
Book Value Per Share	0.31	0.65	n.a.
Price / Book Value %	1,612.90	1,076.92	n.a.
Dividends Per Share	0.0	0.0	0.0
Annual Financial Data			
Operating Results (000's)			
Total Revenues	209.5	5.1	0.0
Costs & Expenses	-2,569.0	-2,300.1	-30.1
Income Before Taxes and Other	-2,359.5	-2,295.0	-32.5
Other Items	120.6	1.2	0.0
Income Tax	0.0	0.0	0.0
Net Income	-2,238.9	-2,293.9	-32.5
Cash Flow From Operations	-348.9	-447.7	-8.1
Balance Sheet (000's)			
Cash & Equivalents	24.5	1.9	n.a.
Total Current Assets	60.0	21.9	n.a.
Fixed Assets, Net	150.4	121.7	n.a.
Total Assets	2,396.7	2,801.1	n.a.
Total Current Liabilities	840.4	1,006.4	n.a.
Long-Term Debt	527.8	0.0	n.a.
Stockholders' Equity	864.8	1,674.2	n.a.
Performance & Financial Condition			
Return on Total Revenues %	-1,068.61	-45,039.60	n.a.
Return on Avg Stockholders' Equity %	-176.37	n.a.	n.a.
Return on Average Assets %	-86.15	n.a.	n.a.
Current Ratio	0.07	0.02	n.a.
Debt / Equity %	61.04	n.a.	n.a.

Compound Growth %'s	EPS % n.a.	Net Income % n.a.	Total Revenues % n.a.

Comments

The Company is clearly too undercapitalized to execute successful product development and marketing. The value will likely depend on the current state of the technology and the raising of additional equity capital. The auditor issued a going concern opinion in the 1996 report. For the first quarter ended February 28, 1997, revenue increased to $66,092 but a net loss of $310,344 was reported. The stock price had fallen to about $1 per share as we went to press. Investment Classification: Speculative

Officers	Position	Ownership Information	
Robert A. Spigno	President, CEO	Number of Shares Outstanding	2,775,729
Richard Dowler	CFO	Market Capitalization	$ 13,878,645
Patricia A. Spigno	Secretary, Treasurer	Frequency of Dividends	n.a.
		Number of Shareholders	551

Other Information

Transfer Agent	American Securities Transfer Inc. Denver, CO			Where Listed	OTC-BB
Auditor	BDO Seidman, LLP			Symbol	CNES
Market Maker	Smith Benton & Hughes, Inc.	(800)228-6699		SIC Code	3599
	Key West Securities Inc.	(817)428-5020		Employees	n.a.
Broker Dealer	Regular Stockbroker				

Connecticut River Bancorp, Inc.

245 Main Street   Charlestown, NH 03603   Telephone (603)826-7764   Fax (603)826-4034

Company Description

The Company has two banking subsidiaries: wholly-owned Connecticut River Bank, N.A. and 99% owned Peoples Bank of Littleton. In total, ten branch locations serve individual and corporate customers in northwestern and southwestern New Hampshire and southeastern Vermont. Venturing into Vermont became possible once Connecticut River Bank changed from a state to a federal charter. The Bank can also enter the insurance business. Connecticut River Bank was founded in 1864.

	12/31/96	12/31/95	12/31/94	12/31/93
Per Share Information				
Stock Price	7.00	5.75	5.50	5.00
Earnings Per Share	1.01	0.87	0.63	0.43
Price / Earnings Ratio	6.93	6.61	8.73	11.63
Book Value Per Share	6.99	6.43	5.89	5.36
Price / Book Value %	100.14	89.42	93.38	93.28
Dividends Per Share	0.44	0.35	0.10	0.02
Annual Financial Data				
Operating Results (000's)				
Net Interest Income	6,796.6	6,739.7	6,448.0	6,312.0
Loan Loss Provision	-319.0	-249.0	-507.0	-960.0
Non-Interest Income	1,365.5	1,178.3	1,176.4	1,400.4
Non-Interest Expense	-5,392.2	-5,520.2	-5,572.5	-5,754.1
Income Before Taxes and Other	2,450.8	2,148.8	1,544.9	998.4
Other Items	-5.2	-20.2	-15.9	-12.9
Income Tax	-880.4	-775.5	-542.0	-313.2
Net Income	1,565.3	1,353.2	986.9	672.3
Balance Sheet (000's)				
Cash & Securities	31,599.2	31,083.3	24,592.6	27,072.7
Loans, Net	100,716.6	98,909.3	96,069.7	99,523.6
Total Assets	138,402.1	135,481.0	126,559.7	133,594.0
Deposits	126,932.7	124,706.9	116,875.0	124,831.2
Stockholders' Equity	10,885.2	10,009.7	9,173.4	8,339.3
Performance & Financial Condition				
Return on Avg Stockholders' Equity %	14.98	14.11	11.27	7.68
Return on Average Assets %	1.14	1.03	0.76	0.52
Equity to Assets %	7.86	7.39	7.25	6.24
Net Interest Margin	n.a.	n.a.	n.a.	n.a.
Reserve as a % of Problem Loans	237.86	293.30	333.91	80.26

Compound Growth %'s	EPS %	32.93	Net Income %	32.54	Net Interest Income %	2.50

Comments

1996 results continued a positive upward trend with respectable returns on equity and assets. Management is optimistic that the change to a federal charter will have further positive impact as branches can now be opened anywhere in Vermont or New Hampshire. The first Vermont full service office was opened in Springfield, Vermont in 1996. The Company also updated its technology during 1996 which is expected to enhance customer service and provide better information to the employees and management. Investment Classification: Growth & Value & Income

Officers	Position	Ownership Information	
John E. Bentley	President, CEO	Number of Shares Outstanding	1,556,329
Gary W. Gray	Exec VP, Secretary	Market Capitalization	$ 10,894,303
Stephen J. Bentley	Vice President, Head Cashier	Frequency of Dividends	Quarterly
Paul D. Slade	Vice President	Number of Shareholders	n.a.
Thomas D. Bentley	Vice President	Where Listed / Symbol	OTC-PS / CORB

Other Information			Loan Mix	%
Transfer Agent	Company Office		Commerical	53.0
Auditor	A.M. Peisch & Company		R/E Mortgages	38.0
Market Maker	Tucker Anthony Incororated	(800)225-6713	Consumer	9.0
	A.G. Edwards & Sons, Inc.	(800)325-8197		
Broker Dealer	Regular Stockbroker			
	Standard Investment	(888)783-4688 Ext: Jack		

Connectivity Technologies Inc.

667 Madison Avenue, 25th Floor New York, NY 10021 Telephone (212)644-8880 Fax (810)853-0285

Company Description

Connectivity Technologies, formerly Tigera Group, Inc., is engaged in the manufacture, distribution and assembly of wire and cable products primarily for the computer networking market and the security, signal and sound markets through its subsidiary, Connectivity Product Incorporated (CPI). The Company owns 85% of the capital stock of CPI which it acquired on May 31, 1996. Prior to this acquisition, the Company was principally engaged in evaluating candidates for acquisition. In March 1997, the Company announced that CPI is planning an initial public offering which is intended to raise equity capital to fund acquisitions.

	12/31/96	12/31/95	12/31/94
Per Share Information			
Stock Price	6.68	1.09	0.50
Earnings Per Share	0.06	-0.03	-0.02
Price / Earnings Ratio	111.33	n.a.	n.a.
Book Value Per Share	2.34	2.27	2.37
Price / Book Value %	285.47	48.02	21.10
Dividends Per Share	0.0	0.0	0.0
Annual Financial Data			
Operating Results (000's)			
Total Revenues	57,099.7	700.2	715.0
Costs & Expenses	-55,952.6	-853.7	-1,147.0
Income Before Taxes and Other	1,147.2	-153.5	-432.0
Other Items	-153.8	0.0	0.0
Income Tax	-634.3	0.0	0.0
Net Income	359.2	-153.5	-432.0
Cash Flow From Operations	39.9	-192.0	-125.0
Balance Sheet (000's)			
Cash & Equivalents	230.1	176.0	n.a.
Total Current Assets	31,637.8	11,036.0	n.a.
Fixed Assets, Net	7,176.0	0.0	n.a.
Total Assets	63,945.0	12,159.0	n.a.
Total Current Liabilities	17,097.4	104.0	n.a.
Long-Term Debt	34,295.0	0.0	n.a.
Stockholders' Equity	13,019.0	12,055.0	n.a.
Performance & Financial Condition			
Return on Total Revenues %	0.63	-21.91	-60.42
Return on Avg Stockholders' Equity %	2.86	n.a.	n.a.
Return on Average Assets %	0.94	n.a.	n.a.
Current Ratio	1.85	106.12	n.a.
Debt / Equity %	263.42	n.a.	n.a.

Compound Growth %'s	EPS % n.a.	Net Income % n.a.	Total Revenues % n.a.

Comments

The Company declared a 1 for 4 reverse stock split in 1996. All per share amounts were adjusted for consistency. 1996 results reflect operations of CPI starting with the date of acquisition. On a full year basis, CPI had revenues of $97.3 million and net income of $2,034,000 for 1996 as compared to $88.9 million and $1,471,000 for 1995. The price paid for the 85% interest in CPI was $8 million. Investment Classification: Speculative

Officers	Position	Ownership Information	
James S. Harrington	President, CEO	Number of Shares Outstanding	5,565,325
Duane A. Gawron	Senior VP	Market Capitalization	$ 37,176,371
Kurt Cieszkowski	Senior VP	Frequency of Dividends	n.a.
Gregory C. Kowert	Secretary, CFO	Number of Shareholders	1,966
Charles J. Di Bona II	Vice President		

Other Information			
Transfer Agent	ChaseMellon Shareholder Services Ridgefield Park, NJ	Where Listed	OTC-PS
Auditor	Coopers & Lybrand L.L.P.	Symbol	CVTK
Market Maker	Furman Selz Inc.	(800)448-3223	SIC Code	3496
	Nash, Weiss & Co.	(800)526-3041	Employees	n.a.
Broker Dealer	Regular Stockbroker		

Connohio, Inc.

1031 Ellicott Square   Buffalo, NY 14203   Telephone (716)852-6858   Fax (716)852-0694

Company Description

Connohio is involved in a variety of energy providing activities for residents and businesses in the states of Connecticut and New York. It also is involved in a joint exploration and development program for oil and gas reserves. In addition, the Company owns 11.9% of Medina Power Company, a cogeneration plant in western New York.

	12/31/96	12/31/95	12/31/94	12/31/93
Per Share Information				
Stock Price	7.00	6.00	6.00	7.50
Earnings Per Share	2.14	-0.81	-0.77	-1.25
Price / Earnings Ratio	3.27	n.a.	n.a.	n.a.
Book Value Per Share	14.84	6.19	7.20	7.98
Price / Book Value %	47.17	96.93	83.33	93.98
Dividends Per Share	0.20	0.20	0.25	0.30
Annual Financial Data				
Operating Results (000's)				
Total Revenues	3,980.8	3,411.7	3,172.1	3,668.0
Costs & Expenses	-3,460.0	-3,403.4	-3,591.5	-3,745.2
Income Before Taxes and Other	520.8	-260.3	-880.8	-270.4
Other Items	0.0	0.0	538.8	0.0
Income Tax	-47.8	84.4	174.5	-3.6
Net Income	473.0	-175.9	-167.5	-274.0
Cash Flow From Operations	-296.4	-97.9	-199.3	-215.8
Balance Sheet (000's)				
Cash & Equivalents	98.8	92.2	98.8	100.5
Total Current Assets	475.2	484.5	486.3	558.7
Fixed Assets, Net	831.4	951.6	968.2	1,027.1
Total Assets	4,234.7	2,846.7	3,153.4	3,022.6
Total Current Liabilities	912.0	1,423.6	1,506.5	1,150.6
Long-Term Debt	0.0	0.0	0.0	0.0
Stockholders' Equity	3,322.7	1,423.1	1,646.9	1,872.0
Performance & Financial Condition				
Return on Total Revenues %	11.88	-5.15	-5.28	-7.47
Return on Avg Stockholders' Equity %	19.93	-11.46	-9.52	-13.41
Return on Average Assets %	13.36	-5.86	-5.42	-8.29
Current Ratio	0.52	0.34	0.32	0.49
Debt / Equity %	n.a.	n.a.	n.a.	n.a.

Compound Growth %'s	EPS %	n.a.	Net Income %	n.a.	Total Revenues %	2.77

Comments

For years prior to 1996, marketable securities are recorded at cost but are valued at more than $2 million above cost, or approximately $10 per share. The change to fair market value accounting was made through the equity accounts and explains the increase to book value. The Medina Power Company had its power contract cancelled and will be compensated with a cancellation fee over a five year period. 1996 results include $281,424 of these payments. That combined with gains on the sale of securities lifted the Company into profitable territory for the first time this decade. Investment Classification: Value

Officers	Position	Ownership Information	
Jack A. Keenan	President, CEO	Number of Shares Outstanding	219,490
Majorie E. Hutz	Secretary	Market Capitalization	$ 1,536,430
Richard M. Hilliker	Treasurer	Frequency of Dividends	Quarterly
John A. Macey	Vice President	Number of Shareholders	Under 500
William G. Griffin	Vice President		

Other Information				
Transfer Agent	National City Bank Cleveland, OH		Where Listed	OTC-BB
Auditor	Courtney, Fink & Forbes		Symbol	CNNO
Market Maker	Robotti & Co., Inc.	(212)986-0800	SIC Code	4930
	The Seidler Companies Inc.	(800)421-0164	Employees	n.a.
Broker Dealer	Regular Stockbroker			

Continental Health Affiliates, Inc.

910 Sylvan Avenue   Englewood Cliffs, NJ 07632   Telephone (201)567-4600   Fax (201)567-1072

Company Description

Continental Health Affiliates, Inc. provides a variety of non-hospital based health care services to patients. At June 30, 1996, the Company was operating or managing seven nursing homes with approximately 1,100 beds. The Company also provides infusion therapy(i.e., administration of nutrients, antibiotics and other medications either intravenously or through feeding tubes) and other medical products to patients in their homes, in ambulatory suites and in nursing homes. The Company was founded in 1981.

	06/30/96
Per Share Information	
Stock Price as of 12/31	3.00
Earnings Per Share	0.09
Price / Earnings Ratio	33.33
Book Value Per Share	0.24
Price / Book Value %	1,250.00
Dividends Per Share	0.0
Annual Financial Data	
Operating Results (000's)	
Total Revenues	70,651.0
Costs & Expenses	-69,808.0
Income Before Taxes and Other	843.0
Other Items	283.0
Income Tax	-270.0
Net Income	856.0
Cash Flow From Operations	-6,025.0
Balance Sheet (000's)	
Cash & Equivalents	2,900.0
Total Current Assets	17,230.0
Fixed Assets, Net	54,453.0
Total Assets	75,572.0
Total Current Liabilities	17,185.0
Long-Term Debt	50,574.0
Stockholders' Equity	2,196.0
Performance & Financial Condition	
Return on Total Revenues %	1.21
Return on Avg Stockholders' Equity %	76.84
Return on Average Assets %	1.63
Current Ratio	1.00
Debt / Equity %	2303.01

Compound Growth %'s	EPS % n.a.	Net Income % n.a.	Total Revenues % n.a.

Comments

The Company changed its year end from December 31, to June 30, during 1995. The statement of operations for June 30, 1995, is for six months, and is not comparable to those of prior years. It has not been presented. For the nine months ended March 31, 1997, the Company had revenues of $53.6 million and net income of $500,000 (including over $1 million from an extraordinary item) as compared to $51.3 million and net income of $435,000 for the same period in 1996. The main challenge ahead for the Company lies in reducing a very substantial amount of long-term debt. Investment Classification: Speculative

Officers	Position	Ownership Information	
Jack Rosen	Chairman, President	Number of Shares Outstanding	9,286,216
Richard S. Gordon	Exec VP	Market Capitalization	$ 27,858,648
Israel Ingberman	Treasurer, Secretary	Frequency of Dividends	n.a.
Benjamin Geizhals	Vice President	Number of Shareholders	385
Joseph Rosen	Vice President		

Other Information			
Transfer Agent	American Stock Transfer & Trust Company New York, NY	Where Listed	OTC-BB
Auditor	KPMG Peat Marwick LLP	Symbol	CTHL
Market Maker	Ross Securities Corp.	(561)362-1234	SIC Code	8082
	M.H. Meyerson & Co., Inc.	(800)333-3113	Employees	1129
Broker Dealer	Regular Stockbroker		

Continental Investment Corporation

10254 Miller Road   Dallas, TX 75238   Telephone (214)691-1100   Fax (214)691-1173

Company Description

Continental Investment Corporation operates in two principal segments: property development consists primarily of its potential landfill site in Atlanta, Georgia, and its Fiber-Seal fabric care and service protection business. The landfill site, comprised of 133 acres, was acquired in 1965 and is located approximately 10 miles southwest of downtown Atlanta, Georgia. On September 30, 1996, the Company acquired all of the operating assets of Fiber-Seal of Dallas and Fiber-Seal Services International, Inc. Additional common shares were issued during 1996 to raise working capital and to acquire more land.

	09/30/96	09/30/95
Per Share Information		
Stock Price as of 12/31	21.25	5.00
Earnings Per Share	-0.10	-0.08
Price / Earnings Ratio	n.a.	n.a.
Book Value Per Share	0.90	0.08
Price / Book Value %	2,361.11	6,250.00
Dividends Per Share	0.0	0.0
Annual Financial Data		
Operating Results (000's)		
Total Revenues	827.9	903.0
Costs & Expenses	-1,826.7	-1,557.6
Income Before Taxes and Other	-998.8	-655.9
Other Items	0.0	39.2
Income Tax	0.0	0.0
Net Income	-998.8	-616.7
Cash Flow From Operations	-1,181.2	-349.0
Balance Sheet (000's)		
Cash & Equivalents	2,763.1	n.a.
Total Current Assets	3,698.5	n.a.
Fixed Assets, Net	8,564.6	n.a.
Total Assets	12,323.1	n.a.
Total Current Liabilities	474.2	n.a.
Long-Term Debt	920.0	n.a.
Stockholders' Equity	10,181.9	n.a.
Performance & Financial Condition		
Return on Total Revenues %	-120.64	-68.29
Return on Avg Stockholders' Equity %	n.a.	n.a.
Return on Average Assets %	n.a.	n.a.
Current Ratio	7.80	n.a.
Debt / Equity %	9.04	n.a.

Compound Growth %'s   EPS %   n.a.   Net Income %   n.a.   Total Revenues %   -8.32

Comments

An additional 96 acres of land was acquired adjacent to the 133-acre parcel as the Company moves closer to having a fully operational landfill. The property is effectively at the center of the nine-county region that includes Atlanta. The potential resumption of granite mining on the property represents a possible double benefit to the Company. The stock price increase of 400% during the year may be attributable to interest shown by some wealthy investors. Results for the three-month period ended December 31, 1996, look similar to the prior year. Investment Classification: Speculative

Officers	Position	Ownership Information	
R. Dale Sterritt, Jr.	Chairman, CEO	Number of Shares Outstanding	11,310,058
Thomas F. Snodgrass	President, Treasurer	Market Capitalization	$ 240,338,733
Robert D. Luna	Secretary	Frequency of Dividends	n.a.
		Number of Shareholders	1,222

Other Information				
Transfer Agent	Securities Transfer Corp. Dallas, TX		Where Listed	OTC-BB
Auditor	Grant Thornton LLP		Symbol	CICG
Market Maker	J. Alexander Securities, Inc.	(800)421-0258	SIC Code	6512
	Weber Investment Corp.	(800)442-7146	Employees	14
Broker Dealer	Regular Stockbroker			

Continental Resources, Inc.

175 Middlesex Turnpike   Bedford, MA 01730-9137   Telephone (617)275-0850   Fax (617)275-6563

Company Description

The Company's principal business activities are the sale, rental and servicing of electronic instruments and computer equipment. It also produces, configures, tests, maintains and services complete lines of high quality computer and test equipment products. The Company also owns a 49% interest in Wall Industries, Inc., a manufacturer of power supplies and converters. The Company was formed in 1962 and went public in 1970. Shares are hard to come by so be patient.

	12/31/96	12/31/95	12/31/94
Per Share Information			
Stock Price	213.33	65.00	60.00
Earnings Per Share	40.90	22.67	1.38
Price / Earnings Ratio	5.22	2.87	43.48
Book Value Per Share	227.23	186.62	163.95
Price / Book Value %	93.88	34.83	36.60
Dividends Per Share	0.0	0.0	0.0
Annual Financial Data			
Operating Results (000's)			
Total Revenues	126,946.4	107,740.7	58,441.2
Costs & Expenses	-122,226.7	-105,203.5	-58,326.3
Income Before Taxes and Other	4,719.7	2,537.2	114.9
Other Items	0.0	0.0	0.0
Income Tax	-2,020.1	-1,040.8	-23.5
Net Income	2,699.6	1,496.4	91.4
Cash Flow From Operations	10,498.7	14,294.6	4,688.9
Balance Sheet (000's)			
Cash & Equivalents	926.4	940.5	736.2
Total Current Assets	19,539.7	18,129.9	18,143.1
Fixed Assets, Net	5,100.6	18,506.6	17,794.9
Total Assets	42,203.5	37,939.5	37,288.4
Total Current Liabilities	19,645.1	15,452.0	20,077.5
Long-Term Debt	7,378.8	9,352.0	5,416.0
Stockholders' Equity	15,003.6	12,320.0	10,823.6
Performance & Financial Condition			
Return on Total Revenues %	2.13	1.39	0.16
Return on Avg Stockholders' Equity %	19.76	12.93	n.a.
Return on Average Assets %	6.74	3.98	n.a.
Current Ratio	0.99	1.17	0.90
Debt / Equity %	49.18	75.91	50.04

Compound Growth %'s	EPS %	444.41	Net Income %	443.47	Total Revenues %	47.38

Comments

Per share price information for 1996 was derived from treasury stock transactions. Compound growth rates represent the change between 1994 and 1996. Last year we reported that management expected strong growth in all divisions to continue. Wall Industries had just been ranked by World Trade Magazine to be in the top 100 fastest growing, high-tech global manufacturers. Shareholders cannot be disappointed with an 80.4% increase in earnings per share. The annual report is a good one that provides an overview, the highlights, and plans for each operating division. Investment Classification: Growth & Value

Officers	Position	Ownership Information	
James F. McCann, Sr.	Chairman	Number of Shares Outstanding	66,029
James F. McCann, Jr.	President	Market Capitalization	$ 14,085,967
James M. Bunt	VP - Finance	Frequency of Dividends	n.a.
Joseph P. Tyrell	CFO	Number of Shareholders	Under 500
Kevin McCann	Vice President		

Other Information			
Transfer Agent	Boston EquiServe Canton, MA	Where Listed	OTC-PS
Auditor	G.T. Reilly & Company	Symbol	CTLR
Market Maker	The Chicago Corporation (800)621-1674	SIC Code	3600
	Howe Barnes Investments, Inc. (800)621-2364	Employees	n.a.
Broker Dealer	OTC Specialist		

Corning Natural Gas Corporation

330 West William Street   Corning, NY 14830   Telephone (607)936-3755   Fax (607)962-2844

Company Description

Corning Natural Gas Corporation is a gas distribution company providing natural gas to its customers in the southern part of New York State. The Company's service area encompasses about 415 square miles with a population of over 56,000. A subsidiary, Corning Natural Gas Appliance Company sells, rents and services residential and commercial appliances. During 1996, the Company purchased the Hammondsport distribution system from the Finger Lakes Gas Company.

	12/31/96	12/31/95	12/31/94	12/31/93
Per Share Information				
Stock Price	21.50	23.50	24.50	24.50
Earnings Per Share	1.66	1.35	1.43	1.26
Price / Earnings Ratio	12.95	17.41	17.13	19.44
Book Value Per Share	11.16	11.08	10.98	10.78
Price / Book Value %	192.65	212.09	223.13	227.27
Dividends Per Share	1.59	1.25	1.23	1.21
Annual Financial Data				
Operating Results (000's)				
Total Revenues	21,581.7	18,697.4	18,727.5	20,061.6
Costs & Expenses	-19,242.8	-17,834.5	-17,858.1	-19,232.3
Income Before Taxes and Other	948.7	862.9	869.4	829.3
Other Items	0.0	0.0	0.0	0.0
Income Tax	-185.6	-242.1	-212.9	-250.5
Net Income	763.1	620.7	656.5	578.8
Cash Flow From Operations	2,771.2	1,817.4	601.4	1,169.7
Balance Sheet (000's)				
Cash & Equivalents	886.1	142.9	183.1	203.8
Total Current Assets	5,004.4	3,891.3	4,064.5	4,828.7
Fixed Assets, Net	14,270.0	14,157.0	13,499.0	13,223.9
Total Assets	21,423.2	21,812.7	22,439.4	22,428.1
Total Current Liabilities	6,549.5	7,039.6	7,033.7	6,747.8
Long-Term Debt	6,200.0	6,300.0	6,400.0	6,500.0
Stockholders' Equity	5,133.1	5,099.0	5,051.0	4,958.0
Performance & Financial Condition				
Return on Total Revenues %	3.54	3.32	3.51	2.88
Return on Avg Stockholders' Equity %	14.92	12.23	13.12	11.70
Return on Average Assets %	3.53	2.81	2.93	2.77
Current Ratio	0.76	0.55	0.58	0.72
Debt / Equity %	120.78	123.55	126.71	131.10

Compound Growth %'s	EPS %	9.63	Net Income %	9.66	Total Revenues %	2.46

Comments

The Company changed to a fiscal year ending September 30. For purposes of comparison, we added first quarter 1997 unaudited results (the three months ended December 31, 1996) to the nine-month short year ended September 30, 1996. The change was made to conform to a more natural business cycle. 1996 was a record year fueled by exceptionally cold weather. All operating divisions produced improved results and the acquisition, referred to above, exceeded expectations. Investment Classification: Income

Officers	Position	Ownership Information	
Thomas K. Barry	President, CEO	Number of Shares Outstanding	460,000
Kenneth J. Robinson	Exec VP	Market Capitalization	$ 9,890,000
Edgar F. Lewis	Senior VP	Frequency of Dividends	Quarterly
Gary K. Earley	Treasurer	Number of Shareholders	406
Thomas S. Roye	Vice President		

Other Information				
Transfer Agent	Company Office		Where Listed	OTC-BB
Auditor	KPMG Peat Marwick LLP		Symbol	CNNG
Market Maker	First Albany Corporation	(800)541-5061	SIC Code	4923
	Advest, Inc.	(800)998-9834	Employees	72
Broker Dealer	Regular Stockbroker			
	Bernard Taradash - Advest	(800)227-1207		

County Bank Corp

83 W. Nepessing Street Lapeer, MI 48446 Telephone (810)664-2977 Fax (810)667-1742

Company Description

The Company's subsidiary, Lapeer County Bank & Trust Co., operates in rural and suburban communities in Lapeer County, Michigan, out of nine separate offices. The County, which lies sixty miles north of metropolitan Detroit, is home to 75,000 people. The Bank's primary source of revenue results from providing a variety of loans to small and medium sized businesses and, to a lesser extent, individuals. Lapeer County Bank & Trust was chartered in 1902.

	12/31/96	12/31/95	12/31/94	12/31/93
Per Share Information				
Stock Price	40.00	29.75	22.50	17.50
Earnings Per Share	5.02	4.34	3.57	2.96
Price / Earnings Ratio	7.97	6.85	6.30	5.91
Book Value Per Share	33.48	29.87	25.71	23.74
Price / Book Value %	119.47	99.60	87.51	73.72
Dividends Per Share	1.53	1.27	1.04	0.87
Annual Financial Data				
Operating Results (000's)				
Net Interest Income	7,843.0	7,460.0	6,910.0	6,469.0
Loan Loss Provision	-120.0	-240.0	-120.0	-275.0
Non-Interest Income	2,216.0	1,971.0	1,800.0	1,666.0
Non-Interest Expense	-5,739.0	-5,669.0	-5,624.0	-5,507.0
Income Before Taxes and Other	4,200.0	3,522.0	2,966.0	2,353.0
Other Items	0.0	0.0	0.0	0.0
Income Tax	-1,220.0	-948.0	-848.0	-596.0
Net Income	2,980.0	2,574.0	2,118.0	1,757.0
Balance Sheet (000's)				
Cash & Securities	57,235.0	61,241.0	66,049.0	59,800.0
Loans, Net	115,669.0	103,662.0	96,053.0	92,808.0
Total Assets	177,786.0	169,877.0	166,666.0	157,664.0
Deposits	156,518.0	150,888.0	150,511.0	142,523.0
Stockholders' Equity	19,862.0	17,720.0	15,254.0	14,085.0
Performance & Financial Condition				
Return on Avg Stockholders' Equity %	15.86	15.61	14.44	13.05
Return on Average Assets %	1.71	1.53	1.31	1.13
Equity to Assets %	11.17	10.43	9.15	8.93
Net Interest Margin	4.80	4.80	4.60	4.50
Reserve as a % of Problem Loans	n.a.	373.23	162.08	103.37

Compound Growth %'s	EPS %	19.25	Net Income %	19.26	Net Interest Income %	6.63

Comments

The Company declared a 100% stock dividend (effectively a 2 for 1 split) in 1995. All earlier per share amounts have been restated for consistency. Management reports that the 1996 record performance was the result of a solid interest margin and continuing healthy economy. It is believed that 1997 will have more of the same. Investment Classification: Growth & Value & Income

Officers	Position	Ownership Information	
Curt Carter	President	Number of Shares Outstanding	593,236
Patrick F. Brown	Senior VP	Market Capitalization	$ 23,729,440
Joseph Black	CFO	Frequency of Dividends	Quarterly
Laird A. Kellie	Vice President, Head Cashier	Number of Shareholders	419
V. Kenneth Ewing	Vice President	Where Listed / Symbol	OTC-BB / CYBK

Other Information			Loan Mix	%
Transfer Agent	Company Office		Commerical	43.4
Auditor	Plante & Moran, LLP		R/E Mortgages	27.8
Market Maker	Wm. C. Roney & Co.	(800)521-1196	Installment	26.4
	McDonald & Company Securities	(800)321-2190	Construction	2.4
Broker Dealer	Regular Stockbroker			

Covol Technologies, Inc.

3280 North Frontage Road   Lehi, UT 84043   Telephone (801)768-4481   Fax (801)768-4483

Company Description

The primary business of Covol Technologies, Inc. is to commercialize patented and proprietary technologies used to recycle waste by-products from the coal and steel industries into a marketable source of fuel and revert materials in the form of briquettes. The Company has two commercial briquetting plants and one prototype plant. Although the Geneva plant is operational, the primary contract for the sale of briquettes expired on December 31, 1996.

	09/30/96	09/30/95	09/30/94	12/31/93
Per Share Information				
Stock Price as of 12/31	12.25	20.62	n.a.	n.a.
Earnings Per Share	-1.99	-1.25	n.a.	n.a.
Price / Earnings Ratio	n.a.	n.a.	n.a.	n.a.
Book Value Per Share	-0.03	0.22	n.a.	n.a.
Price / Book Value %	n.a.	9,372.73	n.a.	n.a.
Dividends Per Share	0.0	0.0	n.a.	n.a.
Annual Financial Data				
Operating Results (000's)				
Total Revenues	597.7	174.1	n.a.	158.7
Costs & Expenses	-13,363.5	-4,210.5	n.a.	-873.7
Income Before Taxes and Other	-12,931.8	-4,036.4	n.a.	-715.0
Other Items	-881.5	-1,129.2	n.a.	0.0
Income Tax	-23.0	-488.0	n.a.	0.0
Net Income	-13,836.3	-5,653.6	n.a.	-715.0
Cash Flow From Operations	-2,574.7	-237.0	n.a.	n.a.
Balance Sheet (000's)				
Cash & Equivalents	490.1	583.8	155.9	21.6
Total Current Assets	779.1	618.3	199.2	21.6
Fixed Assets, Net	7,125.2	1,330.3	748.0	341.5
Total Assets	8,772.1	2,660.0	4,852.6	2,129.9
Total Current Liabilities	4,261.3	1,098.7	819.1	0.0
Long-Term Debt	151.0	176.6	852.1	511.2
Stockholders' Equity	-233.4	1,182.8	2,989.5	1,107.9
Performance & Financial Condition				
Return on Total Revenues %	-2,314.81	-3,246.52	n.a.	-450.67
Return on Avg Stockholders' Equity %	-2,914.70	-271.00	n.a.	n.a.
Return on Average Assets %	-242.06	-150.51	n.a.	n.a.
Current Ratio	0.18	0.56	0.24	n.a.
Debt / Equity %	n.a.	14.93	28.50	46.14

Compound Growth %'s	EPS % n.a.	Net Income % n.a.	Total Revenues % n.a.

Comments

The Company declared a 2 for 1 stock split in 1996 and a 1 for 20 reverse stock split in 1995. The Company is dependent on raising sufficient capital to finance its expansion plans and working capital requirements. Management intends to finance its capital needs through the receipt of down payments on the sale of future plants, license fees and royalties from the sale of its first full scale briquetting facility and from equity placements. No assurances can be made that the Company will be able to raise sufficient capital. This is reflected in a declining stock price, about $5 per share in June, 1997. Investment Classification: Speculative

Officers	Position	Ownership Information	
Brent M. Cook	President, CEO	Number of Shares Outstanding	7,610,373
Alan D. Ayers	COO	Market Capitalization	$ 93,227,069
Asael T. Sorensen, Jr.	Secretary	Frequency of Dividends	n.a.
Stanley M. Kimball	Treasurer, CFO	Number of Shareholders	2,103
Russ Madsen	Vice President		

Other Information			
Transfer Agent	Atlas Stock Transfer Salt Lake City, UT	Where Listed	OTC-BB
Auditor	Coopers & Lybrand, L.L.P.	Symbol	CVOL
Market Maker	Alpine Securities Corporation	(800)521-5588	SIC Code	1220
	Allen & Company, Inc.	(800)221-2246	Employees	n.a.
Broker Dealer	Regular Stockbroker		

This page intentionally left blank.

Cowles Media Company

329 Portland Avenue   Minneapolis, MN 55415-1112   Telephone (612)673-7100   Fax (612)673-7020

Company Description

Cowles Media Company is a newspaper, magazine, and information services company headquartered in Minneapolis. Publications include the Star Tribune, the Scottsdale Progress, Cowles Magazines, Cowles Enthusiast Media and Cowles Business Media. Business began in 1935 when John Cowles acquired and began to build The Minneapolis Star.

	03/30/96	04/01/95	04/02/94	04/03/93
Per Share Information				
Stock Price as of 12/31	24.50	23.50	23.50	23.00
Earnings Per Share	1.76	1.61	1.40	1.09
Price / Earnings Ratio	13.92	14.60	16.79	21.10
Book Value Per Share	4.56	3.49	2.21	1.06
Price / Book Value %	537.28	673.35	1,063.35	2,169.81
Dividends Per Share	0.60	0.56	0.52	0.49
Annual Financial Data				
Operating Results (000's)				
Total Revenues	497,889.0	455,657.0	360,079.0	337,647.0
Costs & Expenses	-448,023.0	-415,994.0	-326,907.0	-308,928.0
Income Before Taxes and Other	41,565.0	39,663.0	33,172.0	28,719.0
Other Items	0.0	0.0	0.0	-1,336.0
Income Tax	-17,138.0	-17,164.0	-13,744.0	-12,344.0
Net Income	24,427.0	22,499.0	19,428.0	15,039.0
Cash Flow From Operations	31,995.0	32,926.0	38,945.0	37,873.0
Balance Sheet (000's)				
Cash & Equivalents	674.0	2,759.0	34,711.0	30,506.0
Total Current Assets	88,383.0	78,808.0	87,855.0	68,899.0
Fixed Assets, Net	114,235.0	114,710.0	104,546.0	110,518.0
Total Assets	316,166.0	314,221.0	279,169.0	246,365.0
Total Current Liabilities	136,404.0	142,281.0	113,525.0	108,507.0
Long-Term Debt	85,979.0	90,031.0	91,034.0	83,840.0
Stockholders' Equity	63,055.0	48,510.0	30,483.0	14,652.0
Performance & Financial Condition				
Return on Total Revenues %	4.91	4.94	5.40	4.45
Return on Avg Stockholders' Equity %	43.79	56.96	86.09	152.49
Return on Average Assets %	7.75	7.58	7.39	6.21
Current Ratio	0.65	0.55	0.77	0.63
Debt / Equity %	136.36	185.59	298.64	572.21

Compound Growth %'s	EPS %	17.32	Net Income %	17.55	Total Revenues %	13.82

Comments

Ballooning paper costs and sharp increases in postal rates presented a real challenge to the Company in 1996. The end result was a respectable 9% increase in net earnings. Although below the 15% target in annual growth, management appeared relieved that the year was over. Cowles Media is one of the few companies that use Economic Value Added, (EVA), as a tool with which to measure long term performance. EVA measures the amount by which the cash return on invested capital exceeds the cost of capital. In 1996, EVA was $17.1 million as compared to $16.9 million in the preceding year. Investment Classification: Growth

Officers	Position	Ownership Information	
David C. Cox	President, CEO	Number of Shares Outstanding	13,826,455
Pamela R. Busch, Jr.	Secretary	Market Capitalization	$ 338,748,148
Georgina Y. Stephens	Treasurer	Frequency of Dividends	Quarterly
James A. Alcott	Vice President	Number of Shareholders	Under 500
James J. Viera	Vice President, CFO		

Other Information			
Transfer Agent	Sherburne & Coughlin, Ltd. Minneapolis, MN	Where Listed	OTC-PS
Auditor	KPMG Peat Marwick LLP	Symbol	n.a.
Market Maker	Piper Jaffray Inc. (800)328-7488	SIC Code	2700
	Sharpe Capital Inc. (800)355-5781	Employees	n.a.
Broker Dealer	OTC Specialist		

Crowley Maritime Corporation

155 Grand Avenue   Oakland, CA 94612   Telephone (510)251-7500   Fax (510)251-7788

Company Description

Crowley Maritime Corporation was founded in the San Francisco Bay Area in 1892. Today, it is the third largest American shipping company. Crowley provides scheduled liner services, worldwide contract transportation, tug and harbor services, petroleum transportation and distribution services, passenger services, environmental protection and emergency response. It is the leading container carrier to Latin America and the Caribbean Basin and the world's largest tugboat operator.

	12/31/96	12/31/95	12/31/94	12/31/93
Per Share Information				
Stock Price	815.00	1,000.00	825.00	900.00
Earnings Per Share	130.94	142.27	48.45	80.48
Price / Earnings Ratio	6.22	7.03	17.03	11.18
Book Value Per Share	1,468.00	1,314.00	1,173.00	1,123.72
Price / Book Value %	55.52	76.10	70.33	80.09
Dividends Per Share	0.0	0.0	0.0	0.0
Annual Financial Data				
Operating Results (000's)				
Total Revenues	1,093,343.0	1,111,158.0	1,100,004.0	1,074,777.0
Costs & Expenses	-1,046,540.0	-1,067,811.0	-1,072,438.0	-1,041,793.0
Income Before Taxes and Other	46,803.0	42,904.0	27,103.0	31,848.0
Other Items	0.0	0.0	0.0	0.0
Income Tax	-26,723.0	-21,100.0	-16,900.0	-16,800.0
Net Income	20,080.0	21,804.0	10,203.0	15,048.0
Cash Flow From Operations	85,640.0	53,172.0	51,275.0	39,484.0
Balance Sheet (000's)				
Cash & Equivalents	n.a.	54,356.0	44,648.0	27,974.0
Total Current Assets	n.a.	263,981.0	253,465.0	217,321.0
Fixed Assets, Net	n.a.	306,799.0	317,469.0	341,477.0
Total Assets	691,850.0	607,980.0	607,397.0	602,934.0
Total Current Liabilities	264,517.0	214,797.0	219,586.0	213,225.0
Long-Term Debt	202,217.0	132,786.0	143,660.0	160,629.0
Stockholders' Equity	225,116.0	221,075.0	217,184.0	211,611.0
Performance & Financial Condition				
Return on Total Revenues %	1.84	1.96	0.93	1.40
Return on Avg Stockholders' Equity %	9.00	9.95	4.76	7.19
Return on Average Assets %	3.09	3.59	1.69	2.45
Current Ratio	n.a.	1.23	1.15	1.02
Debt / Equity %	89.83	60.06	66.15	75.91

Compound Growth %'s	EPS % 17.61	Net Income % 10.09	Total Revenues % 0.57

Comments

Thomas B. Crowley, Sr. ran the Company until the day he died in July of 1994. Although he had three sisters, Mr. Crowley disenfranchised his siblings by refusing to pay a dividend. Young Tom Crowley, now president, was believed to be less hostile until the 1997 shareholders meeting. When ask by one of the branches if they could ever hope for a dividend, Tom replied, "Cousin, you may hope all you like." The big news at the annual meeting is that the Company will receive $10.5 million per year for the next ten years in a special subsidy from the United States government. This relates to five of its ships qualifying for military usefulness in event of a national emergency. Investment Classification: Value

Officers	Position	Ownership Information	
Thomas B. Crowley, Jr.	Chairman, CEO	Number of Shares Outstanding	133,025
William A. Pennella	Exec VP	Market Capitalization	$ 108,415,375
Richard M. Oster	Senior VP, CFO	Frequency of Dividends	n.a.
Scott G. Skillman	Senior VP	Number of Shareholders	Under 500
Tana G. Shipman	Secretary		

Other Information

Transfer Agent	Company Office		Where Listed	OTC-BB
Auditor	Deloitte & Touche LLP		Symbol	CWLM
Market Maker	The Seidler Companies Inc.	(800)421-0164	SIC Code	4492
	T.R. Winston & Co., Inc.	(800)443-9943	Employees	5000
Broker Dealer	Regular Stockbroker			
	Standard Investment	(888)783-4688 Ext: Jack		

On Water

Thomas Crowley quit school in 1890 to take a job rowing boats on the San Francisco Bay. Merely 15 years of age, he had good reason to believe that he could make his living there. The Bay was awash in traffic, and for the enterprising sort there was opportunity in abundance. San Francisco had become a port of call for ships with every imaginable errand. No matter - they all needed boatmen with Whitehall boats when they came into port. These tiny workhorses ferried captains to shore, delivered groceries back to ships, and basically rowed back and forth doing whatever needed to be done while ships remained at port. It was certainly not child's play, but then Thomas Crowley was no child. He went to work making $5 a week and he never looked back.

By 1892 he managed to buy his own Whitehall, a secondhand one, for $80. Crowley had learned well how to race his boat *and* how to maneuver. He'd hitch his Whitehall to an outgoing ship or tugboat till it hit the Golden Gate or even the Farallon Islands some twenty-five miles offshore. Then he'd drop off and simply wait for ships to come by. When they did, Crowley would be there, bargaining with newcomers for the right to provide services before other boatmen had even so much as left the dock.

The man never seemed to miss a beat. When it was time to expand his fledgling business, he knew his next purchase had to be a gasoline-powered launch. But how was he going to come up with the money for such a thing? By trading in winter coats, of course! Crowley divined opportunity that others missed in the droves of would-be prospectors headed for the Yukon in 1896: they all needed warm fur clothing. San Francisco retailers of this specialty item got their inventory right from the source - men fresh in from Alaska. But Tom saw these men first when they came in on their whaling ships, and he made a perfect middleman. New arrivals, only too delighted to get quick cash out of their now burdensome winter wardrobe, happily sold it to Tom. He then sold in bulk to the retailers, and in no time at all had enough cash to put $900 down on his first launch, the Jenny C.

There was nothing he wouldn't try. No task was too workaday (he ferried the *San Francisco Examiner* to Oakland everyday before the Bay Bridge went up), or out of the ordinary (he safeguarded the assets of San Francisco's banks in a ship's hold after the 1906 earthquake) or unlikely (he assisted in the delivery of Al Capone to Alcatraz Federal Penitentiary in 1934) for him to consider. Crowley Launch and Tugboat Company adopted the slogan "anything, anytime, anywhere, on water", and stretched itself to meet this ideal on every occasion.

Driving over the five-mile span of the Bay Bridge today, you won't see any Whitehalls or even launches like the Jenny C. What you will see all around you are enormous barges and liners, many of them owned and operated by Crowley Maritime Corporation. Their fleet has become huge and impressive, engaging worldwide in such high-tech operations as cleaning up after the Exxon Valdez spill or pushing heavily laden barges through the ice in Prudhoe Bay. But Crowley still calls the San Francisco Bay home and still employs at least part of the fleet in much lower tech work: their Red & White passenger service, for example, still retraces the route to Alcatraz everyday, loaded now with tourists eager to see Al Capone's old haunt in the middle of The Bay for themselves.

Crown City Plating Co.

4350 Temple City Boulevard   El Monte, CA 91731-1010   Telephone (818)444-9291   Fax (818)448-6915

Company Description

Crown City Plating Co., founded in 1911, provides metal-finishing and plastics-finishing to component parts used by companies such as Apple Computer, General Motors, Ford, General Electric and Gillette. Production is at a state-of-the-art facility in California. The original family still manages the business, now in the fourth generation with Robert L. Coombes, Jr. as president. The Company has an Employee Stock Ownership Plan (ESOP) for the benefit of all full-time employees.

	03/31/96	03/31/95	03/31/94	03/31/93
Per Share Information				
Stock Price as of 12/31	9.00	5.25	5.25	4.50
Earnings Per Share	-2.35	1.47	1.63	1.11
Price / Earnings Ratio	n.a.	3.57	3.22	4.05
Book Value Per Share	14.75	17.04	15.70	14.75
Price / Book Value %	61.02	30.81	33.44	30.51
Dividends Per Share	0.0	0.40	0.15	0.0
Annual Financial Data				
Operating Results (000's)				
Total Revenues	15,565.8	23,927.3	22,792.7	22,176.7
Costs & Expenses	-16,786.6	-23,124.5	-21,795.2	-21,953.4
Income Before Taxes and Other	-1,220.8	712.9	897.5	223.4
Other Items	0.0	0.0	0.0	0.0
Income Tax	385.8	-185.0	-312.0	177.2
Net Income	-835.0	527.9	585.5	400.6
Cash Flow From Operations	n.a.	n.a.	n.a.	n.a.
Balance Sheet (000's)				
Cash & Equivalents	0.0	0.0	0.0	0.0
Total Current Assets	6,558.2	5,979.9	7,760.7	7,235.0
Fixed Assets, Net	3,221.4	3,466.6	3,591.1	3,888.4
Total Assets	9,913.5	9,597.4	11,622.2	11,405.5
Total Current Liabilities	4,514.6	2,802.4	4,179.7	4,605.4
Long-Term Debt	0.0	0.0	0.0	0.0
Stockholders' Equity	5,240.6	6,120.6	5,639.1	5,324.4
Performance & Financial Condition				
Return on Total Revenues %	-5.36	2.21	2.57	1.81
Return on Avg Stockholders' Equity %	-14.70	8.98	10.68	7.83
Return on Average Assets %	-8.56	4.98	5.09	3.51
Current Ratio	1.45	2.13	1.86	1.57
Debt / Equity %	n.a.	n.a.	n.a.	n.a.

Compound Growth %'s	EPS % n.a.	Net Income % n.a.	Total Revenues % -11.13

Comments

Management projected fiscal year 1996 to be a difficult year because of the loss of volume associated with the Ford Ranger wheel ornament job. However, problems at Apple Computer made matters far worse. Management was reasonably quick to react and was able to slash operating expenses. The environmental update is favorable as the Company had a number of its plans approved by the Environmental Protection Agency. Investment Classification: Value & Speculative

Officers	Position	Ownership Information	
Robert L. Coombes	Chairman, CEO	Number of Shares Outstanding	355,315
Robert L. Coombes, Jr.	President	Market Capitalization	$ 3,197,835
Thomas A. Gardner	CFO	Frequency of Dividends	Annual
John A. Dom	VP - Sales	Number of Shareholders	Under 500
Brooke Fix	VP - Sales		

Other Information

Transfer Agent	ChaseMellon Shareholder Services Ridgefield Park, NJ		Where Listed	OTC-BB
Auditor	Deloitte & Touche LLP		Symbol	CCPG
Market Maker	The Seidler Companies, Inc.	(800)421-0164	SIC Code	3471
	Carr Securities Corporation	(800)221-2243	Employees	260
Broker Dealer	Regular Stockbroker			

Cuban Electric Company

1111 West Jefferson Street   Boise, ID 83728-0001   Telephone (208)384-7260   Fax (208)384-4913

Company Description

The Cuban Electric Company continues to conserve its assets as it has done since the 1960 confiscation by the Cuban government of all of its properties located in Cuba. Over the years, all other assets were converted to cash equivalents. In 1967, the Company filed its claim under the Cuban Claims Act for compensation from the Cuban government for the properties seized and other connected losses. In 1970, the Commission rendered a Final Decision certifying that the net loss suffered by the Company amounted to $267,568,414. The Commission's decision also calls for interest on the net loss at 6% per annum from August 6, 1960, to the date of eventual settlement.

	06/30/96	06/30/95	06/30/94
Per Share Information			
Stock Price as of 12/31	7.00	3.50	3.00
Earnings Per Share	0.23	0.21	0.11
Price / Earnings Ratio	30.43	16.67	27.27
Book Value Per Share	7.08	6.74	6.43
Price / Book Value %	145.83	51.93	46.66
Dividends Per Share	0.0	0.0	0.0
Annual Financial Data			
Operating Results (000's)			
Total Revenues	955.2	898.3	456.1
Costs & Expenses	-111.1	-132.2	-47.3
Income Before Taxes and Other	844.1	766.1	408.7
Other Items	0.0	0.0	0.0
Income Tax	0.0	0.0	0.0
Net Income	844.1	766.1	408.7
Cash Flow From Operations	844.1	766.1	408.7
Balance Sheet (000's)			
Cash & Equivalents	9.5	20.6	2.8
Total Current Assets	17,291.6	16,478.2	15,748.9
Fixed Assets, Net	0.0	0.0	0.0
Total Assets	25,480.6	24,256.2	23,132.1
Total Current Liabilities	0.0	0.0	0.0
Long-Term Debt	0.0	0.0	0.0
Stockholders' Equity	25,480.6	24,256.2	23,132.1
Performance & Financial Condition			
Return on Total Revenues %	88.37	85.29	89.62
Return on Avg Stockholders' Equity %	3.39	3.23	n.a.
Return on Average Assets %	3.39	3.23	n.a.
Current Ratio	n.a.	n.a.	n.a.
Debt / Equity %	n.a.	n.a.	n.a.

Compound Growth %'s	EPS % n.a.	Net Income % n.a.	Total Revenues % n.a.

Comments

On March 12, 1996, the United States government enacted the Cuban Liberty and Democratic Solidarity Act of 1996. Among other things, the Act provides to U.S. Nationals, such as the Company, a right to sue and obtain damages against a person trafficking in property confiscated by the Cuban government. This right has been suspended by the President and it is not known if the suspension will be lifted. In the meantime, the Company is reviewing developments relative to its possible right to sue. Our only observation is that $267 million plus interest at 6% for 37 years is one heck of a lot of cigars, about 278 cigars per share. Investment Classification: Speculative & Value

Officers	Position	Ownership Information	
Irving Littman	President	Number of Shares Outstanding	3,600,011
		Market Capitalization	$ 25,200,077
		Frequency of Dividends	n.a.
		Number of Shareholders	1,678

Other Information				
Transfer Agent	Registrar and Transfer Co. Cranford, NJ		Where Listed	OTC-BB
Auditor	Not indicated		Symbol	CGAR
Market Maker	Herzog, Heine, Geduld, Inc.	(800)221-3600	SIC Code	6790
	Carr Securities Corporation	(800)221-2243	Employees	1
Broker Dealer	Regular Stockbroker			

D.H. Marketing & Consulting, Inc.

HC 77 Box 394 B, Routes 6 & 209   Milford, PA 18337-9444   Telephone (717)296-8515   Fax (717)296-9687

Company Description

The Company is segmented into four distinct operations, consisting of the Network Marketing Division, the Collectible Division, Acquisitions and Consulting Division and the Burn Cleansing Solution Division. The Company had an initial public offering in 1995. The Collectible Division is involved with the purchase and sale of valuable rare stamps, coins, fine art and other tangible asset collectibles and has been the fastest growing business segment. Its revenues were $1.2 million in 1996.

	12/31/96	12/31/95	12/31/94
Per Share Information			
Stock Price	27.50	6.00	1.00
Earnings Per Share	0.60	-0.18	-0.22
Price / Earnings Ratio	45.83	n.a.	n.a.
Book Value Per Share	1.62	0.33	0.01
Price / Book Value %	1,697.53	1,818.18	10,000.00
Dividends Per Share	0.0	0.0	0.0
Annual Financial Data			
Operating Results (000's)			
Total Revenues	2,033.4	265.7	44.2
Costs & Expenses	-1,115.4	-451.8	-227.9
Income Before Taxes and Other	918.0	-186.1	-183.6
Other Items	0.0	0.0	0.0
Income Tax	-233.0	0.0	0.0
Net Income	685.0	-186.1	-183.6
Cash Flow From Operations	609.0	-358.8	-253.3
Balance Sheet (000's)			
Cash & Equivalents	147.6	171.1	0.0
Total Current Assets	1,512.3	382.9	18.8
Fixed Assets, Net	22.3	2.9	3.1
Total Assets	2,051.8	449.5	88.1
Total Current Liabilities	162.0	9.7	7.7
Long-Term Debt	0.0	74.4	67.0
Stockholders' Equity	1,884.5	365.5	13.5
Performance & Financial Condition			
Return on Total Revenues %	33.69	-70.03	-415.34
Return on Avg Stockholders' Equity %	60.89	-98.21	n.a.
Return on Average Assets %	54.77	-69.22	n.a.
Current Ratio	9.34	39.51	2.46
Debt / Equity %	n.a.	20.35	497.85

Compound Growth %'s	EPS % n.a.	Net Income % n.a.	Total Revenues % n.a.

Comments

This young company has turned a nice profit in its third year of operations. The Acquisitions and Consulting Division commenced activities in the third quarter of 1996 and it acquired a 42% interest in a contract manufacturer of electromechanical and electronic devices. Management is looking for this division to expand significantly in 1997. For the quarter ended March 31, 1997, the Company had revenues of $1,864,142 and net earnings of $683,695, $.18 per share. Investment Classification: Growth

Officers	Position	Ownership Information	
David D. Hagen	President, CEO	Number of Shares Outstanding	1,166,447
T. Christopher Ciesielka	Vice President, Secretary	Market Capitalization	$ 32,077,293
Michael J. Daily	Vice President	Frequency of Dividends	n.a.
Steve Krakonchuk	VP - Sales	Number of Shareholders	185
Becky Anke	Other		

Other Information

Transfer Agent	Interwest Tansfer Co., Inc. Salt Lake City, UT		Where Listed	OTC-PS
Auditor	Niessen, Dunlap & Pritchard		Symbol	DHMKIN
Market Maker	South Beach Securities Inc.	(908)226-1441	SIC Code	2833
	Key West Securities Inc.	(817)428-5020	Employees	n.a.
Broker Dealer	Regular Stockbroker			

DHB Capital Group Inc.

11 Old Westbury Road   Old Westbury, NY 11568   Telephone (516)997-1155   Fax (516)997-1144

Company Description

DHB Capital Group, through several subsidiaries acquired since 1992, manufactures and distributes ballistic-resistant equipment, apparel and related products used by police and other law-enforcement and security personnel and protective athletic apparel and equipment. Other businesses include a majority interest in a development stage telecommunications company and a 100% interest in an orthopedic products company. On March 4, 1997, DHB announced the acquisition of Zunblindage S.A., a Belgian company. DHB was formed in 1992 and has raised money via private placements. The Company's stock was first traded in 1993.

	12/31/96	12/31/95	12/31/94	12/31/93
Per Share Information				
Stock Price	2.62	4.00	3.51	5.00
Earnings Per Share	-0.20	0.02	-0.01	0.02
Price / Earnings Ratio	n.a.	200.00	n.a.	250.00
Book Value Per Share	0.56	0.86	0.62	0.47
Price / Book Value %	467.86	465.12	566.13	1,063.83
Dividends Per Share	0.0	0.0	0.0	0.0
Annual Financial Data				
Operating Results (000's)				
Total Revenues	23,853.6	15,519.0	9,103.5	7,292.7
Costs & Expenses	-28,024.0	-14,442.0	-8,937.2	-7,054.3
Income Before Taxes and Other	-5,700.1	827.1	-546.3	238.4
Other Items	0.0	0.0	91.7	0.0
Income Tax	834.2	-517.3	379.4	-7.6
Net Income	-4,865.9	309.8	-75.2	230.8
Cash Flow From Operations	-2,159.0	-742.4	-1,039.3	-758.4
Balance Sheet (000's)				
Cash & Equivalents	1,249.7	475.1	407.4	1,880.3
Total Current Assets	13,636.6	14,189.2	8,743.8	5,940.3
Fixed Assets, Net	1,834.8	1,077.1	659.0	479.8
Total Assets	19,160.4	19,555.9	11,675.5	6,871.2
Total Current Liabilities	4,736.2	7,688.6	3,355.6	1,924.4
Long-Term Debt	1,444.1	0.0	0.0	0.0
Stockholders' Equity	12,980.1	11,867.3	7,180.0	4,946.8
Performance & Financial Condition				
Return on Total Revenues %	-20.40	2.00	-0.83	3.16
Return on Avg Stockholders' Equity %	-39.17	3.25	-1.24	9.91
Return on Average Assets %	-25.14	1.98	-0.81	4.51
Current Ratio	2.88	1.85	2.61	3.09
Debt / Equity %	11.13	n.a.	n.a.	n.a.

Compound Growth %'s	EPS % n.a.	Net Income % n.a.	Total Revenues % 48.44

Comments

The Company continued to demonstrate spectacular growth through the end of 1996, while maintaining a conservative balance sheet. For the three months ended March 31, 1997, the Company reported sales of $7.1 million and income before taxes of $377,000, as compared to $7.0 million and $711,000 (including $548,000 of gains on marketable securities) for the same period in 1996. The increase in revenue was entirely attributable to the acquisition referred to above. Investment Classification: Growth

Officers	Position	Ownership Information	
David H. Brooks	Chairman, CEO	Number of Shares Outstanding	23,146,008
Mary Kreidell	Secretary, Treasurer	Market Capitalization	$ 60,642,541
		Frequency of Dividends	n.a.
		Number of Shareholders	1,000

Other Information			
Transfer Agent	American Stock Transfer & Trust Company New York, NY	Where Listed	OTC-BB
Auditor	Capraro, Centofranchi, et al	Symbol	DHB
Market Maker	Wm. V. Frankel & Co., Inc. (800)631-3091	SIC Code	3842
	Herzog, Heine, Geduld, Inc. (800)221-3600	Employees	271
Broker Dealer	Regular Stockbroker		

DK Investors, Inc.

333 Seventh Avenue, Third Fl. New York, NY 10001-4509 Telephone (212)239-7979 Fax (212)239-7978

Company Description

DK Investors Inc. is registered under the Investment Company Act of 1940 as a diversified, closed-end, management investment company. Its investment portfolio consists of municipal bonds. The Company makes distributions to its shareholders of all cash flow, exclusive of reinvesting funds as bonds mature or are called. Distributions received by shareholders are not subject to federal income tax.

	12/31/96	12/31/95	12/31/94
Per Share Information			
Stock Price	8.62	10.37	11.75
Earnings Per Share	0.47	1.04	0.08
Price / Earnings Ratio	18.34	9.97	146.88
Book Value Per Share	13.17	13.35	13.04
Price / Book Value %	65.45	77.68	90.11
Dividends Per Share	0.65	0.78	0.73
Annual Financial Data			
Operating Results (000's)			
Total Revenues	721.0	1,389.7	261.4
Costs & Expenses	-169.1	-167.0	-167.7
Income Before Taxes and Other	551.9	1,222.7	93.6
Other Items	0.0	0.0	0.0
Income Tax	0.0	0.0	0.0
Net Income	551.9	1,222.7	93.6
Cash Flow From Operations	786.3	842.6	915.1
Balance Sheet (000's)			
Cash & Equivalents	23.5	28.9	42.4
Total Current Assets	344.7	16,516.6	16,035.9
Fixed Assets, Net	0.0	0.0	0.0
Total Assets	16,242.6	16,516.6	16,035.9
Total Current Liabilities	757.8	819.4	703.1
Long-Term Debt	0.0	0.0	0.0
Stockholders' Equity	15,484.9	15,697.2	15,332.8
Performance & Financial Condition			
Return on Total Revenues %	76.54	87.99	35.82
Return on Avg Stockholders' Equity %	3.54	7.88	n.a.
Return on Average Assets %	3.37	7.51	n.a.
Current Ratio	0.45	20.16	22.81
Debt / Equity %	n.a.	n.a.	n.a.

Compound Growth %'s	EPS % n.a.	Net Income % n.a.	Total Revenues % n.a.

Comments

Expenses of administering and managing this portfolio approximate 1.03% of average net assets. Noteworthy is that the tax-free yield is quite favorable since the stock sells below book value. Compound net income and earnings per share growth are not meaningful because of the nature of the business and have not been presented. Investment Classification: Income & Value

Officers	Position	Ownership Information	
Gene Nadler	Chairman, President	Number of Shares Outstanding	1,175,664
Andrew Brucker, Esq.	Secretary	Market Capitalization	$ 10,134,224
Harry Nadler	Vice President	Frequency of Dividends	Quarterly
		Number of Shareholders	Under 500

Other Information

Transfer Agent	American Stock Transfer & Trust Company New York, NY		Where Listed	OTC-BB
Auditor	Cummings & Carroll, PC		Symbol	DKII
Market Maker	The Chicago Corporation	(800)621-1674	SIC Code	6790
	Carr Securities Corporation	(800)221-2243	Employees	1
Broker Dealer	Regular Stockbroker			

DNB Financial Corporation

4 Brandywine Avenue   Downington, PA 19335   Telephone (610)269-1040   Fax (610)873-5298

Company Description

Downingtown National Bank, subsidiary of this holding corporation, was founded in 1861 and is the oldest, locally-owned, independent bank in Chester County, southeast Pennsylvania. It has grown to six offices serving highly desirable communities within a twenty mile commute to Philadelphia. Trust and investment services have been growing in recent years. Old banks can be more dynamic than young ones. Check out their web page (http://www.dnb4you.com) as well as some of the numbers below.

	12/31/96	12/31/95	12/31/94	12/31/93
Per Share Information				
Stock Price	31.00	24.05	20.12	15.37
Earnings Per Share	3.35	2.71	1.91	1.01
Price / Earnings Ratio	9.25	8.87	10.53	15.22
Book Value Per Share	23.45	20.76	18.16	16.35
Price / Book Value %	132.20	115.85	110.79	94.01
Dividends Per Share	0.52	0.18	0.09	0.0
Annual Financial Data				
Operating Results (000's)				
Net Interest Income	8,702.8	8,208.3	7,489.8	6,669.7
Loan Loss Provision	0.0	-0.1	-0.5	-63.3
Non-Interest Income	895.8	814.2	900.4	1,060.5
Non-Interest Expense	-6,623.1	-6,983.1	-7,070.3	-6,731.5
Income Before Taxes and Other	2,975.6	2,039.3	1,319.5	935.4
Other Items	0.0	0.0	0.0	0.0
Income Tax	-658.0	-169.0	0.0	-234.0
Net Income	2,317.6	1,870.3	1,319.5	701.4
Balance Sheet (000's)				
Cash & Securities	82,019.5	67,584.6	51,787.5	62,742.7
Loans, Net	116,460.1	112,370.8	107,279.6	98,868.0
Total Assets	207,128.1	188,781.0	166,267.7	168,560.9
Deposits	178,423.6	165,008.9	150,926.4	156,411.9
Stockholders' Equity	16,216.0	14,355.0	12,556.1	11,302.3
Performance & Financial Condition				
Return on Avg Stockholders' Equity %	15.16	13.90	11.06	6.40
Return on Average Assets %	1.17	1.05	0.79	0.40
Equity to Assets %	7.83	7.60	7.55	6.71
Net Interest Margin	4.66	4.81	4.71	4.17
Reserve as a % of Problem Loans	365.18	134.50	104.54	71.43

Compound Growth %'s	EPS %	49.13	Net Income %	48.94	Net Interest Income %	9.27

Comments

The Corporation declared 5% and 10% stock dividends in 1996 and 1995, respectively. All per share amounts have been adjusted for consistency. Growth rates reflect the Bank's recovery from back-to-back losses in 1992 and 1991. 1993, the base year for the compound calculations, was a year of transition back to profitability. Management reports an improvement in asset quality and success in obtaining a 69% efficiency ratio in 1996. A Visa debit card was introduced in the second quarter, 1997. Further expansion of the branch network is being considered as a response to rapid growth in Chester County. Investment Classification: Growth & Value

Officers	Position	Ownership Information	
Henry F. Thorne	President, CEO	Number of Shares Outstanding	691,422
Ronald K. Dankanich	Senior VP, Secretary	Market Capitalization	$ 21,434,082
Bruce E. Moroney	Senior VP, CFO	Frequency of Dividends	Quarterly
Richard L. Bergey	Senior VP, Sr Loan Officer	Number of Shareholders	900
Eileen M. Knott	Senior VP	Where Listed / Symbol	OTC-BB / DNBF

Other Information			Loan Mix	%
Transfer Agent	Company Office		R/E Mortgages	52.3
Auditor	KPMG Peat Marwick LLP		Commerical	24.7
Market Maker	Hopper Soliday & Co., Inc.	(800)456-9234	Consumer	20.8
	F.J. Morrissey & Co., Inc.	(800)842-8928	Other	2.2
Broker Dealer	Regular Stockbroker			

Danbury Industrial Corporation

57 North Street, Ste. 407   Danbury, CT 06810   Telephone (203)743-0306   Fax (203)744-0915

Company Description

Danbury Industrial Corporation owns, in whole or in part, five commercial buildings in Commerce Park, in Danbury, Connecticut. The Company was organized in 1918 as a community development corporation to attract industry to the greater Danbury area through commercial development. Management now performs community service through a nonprofit affiliate which assists companies in obtaining financing for the purchase, construction and/or renovation of facilities.

	07/31/96	07/31/95	07/31/94	07/31/93
Per Share Information				
Stock Price as of 12/31	101.00	101.00	100.00	65.00
Earnings Per Share	5.32	1.57	-0.78	14.30
Price / Earnings Ratio	18.98	64.33	n.a.	4.55
Book Value Per Share	202.46	200.07	201.50	203.50
Price / Book Value %	n.a.	50.48	49.63	31.94
Dividends Per Share	3.00	3.00	3.00	3.00
Annual Financial Data				
Operating Results (000's)				
Total Revenues	1,003.0	895.1	795.2	980.0
Costs & Expenses	-875.0	-808.7	-796.9	-645.3
Income Before Taxes and Other	128.0	27.6	-9.3	334.7
Other Items	0.0	0.0	0.0	0.0
Income Tax	-55.8	-6.3	-1.3	-139.3
Net Income	72.2	21.3	-10.6	195.4
Cash Flow From Operations	294.5	350.3	-11.1	380.7
Balance Sheet (000's)				
Cash & Equivalents	96.3	146.7	139.7	351.8
Total Current Assets	130.3	189.4	261.5	409.4
Fixed Assets, Net	5,284.3	4,831.6	4,538.4	3,935.5
Total Assets	5,620.9	5,151.2	4,953.2	4,519.3
Total Current Liabilities	369.2	330.4	413.0	268.4
Long-Term Debt	2,431.6	2,072.3	1,804.8	1,462.8
Stockholders' Equity	2,746.4	2,716.0	2,735.4	2,775.6
Performance & Financial Condition				
Return on Total Revenues %	7.20	2.38	-1.33	19.94
Return on Avg Stockholders' Equity %	2.64	0.78	-0.38	7.25
Return on Average Assets %	1.34	0.42	-0.22	4.38
Current Ratio	0.35	0.57	0.63	1.53
Debt / Equity %	88.54	76.30	65.98	52.70

Compound Growth %'s	EPS %	-28.08	Net Income %	-28.25	Total Revenues %	0.77

Comments

All properties were fully leased at the end of fiscal 1996. A new lease for 30,000 square feet with Demetron Research Corporation required the Company to make extensive renovations at a cost of $600,000. Shareholders wishing to sell their stock are reminded that the Company is a buyer. Only 10 shares were tendered during 1996 at $100 each. Investment Classification: Value & Speculative

Officers	Position	Ownership Information	
Ricard F. Gretsch, Sr.	Chairman	Number of Shares Outstanding	13,565
Charles E. Wrinn	President	Market Capitalization	$ 1,370,065
James C. Driscoll, III	Secretary	Frequency of Dividends	Annual
Anthony M. Rizzo	Treasurer	Number of Shareholders	Under 500
John D. Dolan	Vice President		

Other Information			
Transfer Agent	Registrar & Transfer Company Cranford, NJ	Where Listed	OTC-BB
Auditor	Seward and Monde	Symbol	DBRI
Market Maker	Legg Mason Wood Walker, Inc.	(212)428-4949	SIC Code	6510
	Ernst & Co.	(800)845-4330	Employees	2
Broker Dealer	OTC Specialist		
	Norman Kadehjian - Wainwright	(800)727-7176	

Davey Tree Expert Company (The)

Company Description

The Davey Tree Expert Company is in the business of providing horticultural services to a variety of residential, corporate, institutional and government customers. Services include care for trees, shrubs and other plant life as well as landscaping. The Company was formed in 1909. Since 1979, it has offered to buy stock from any selling shareholder. In 1991, the Company adopted a plan restricting transfer of Company shares without the selling shareholder first giving the Employee Stock Ownership Plan the right to buy the shares.

	12/31/96	12/31/95	12/31/94	12/31/93
Per Share Information				
Stock Price	15.08	13.56	12.19	14.82
Earnings Per Share	1.86	1.27	0.84	1.17
Price / Earnings Ratio	8.11	10.68	14.51	12.67
Book Value Per Share	11.61	10.06	9.11	8.47
Price / Book Value %	129.89	134.79	133.81	174.97
Dividends Per Share	0.30	0.24	0.26	0.27
Annual Financial Data				
Operating Results (000's)				
Total Revenues	267,206.0	230,101.0	209,961.0	218,645.0
Costs & Expenses	-252,365.0	-219,754.0	-202,946.0	-208,537.0
Income Before Taxes and Other	14,841.0	10,347.0	6,865.0	10,057.0
Other Items	0.0	0.0	0.0	0.0
Income Tax	-6,082.0	-3,974.0	-2,826.0	-4,001.0
Net Income	8,759.0	6,373.0	4,039.0	6,056.0
Cash Flow From Operations	17,104.0	21,192.0	16,205.0	18,102.0
Balance Sheet (000's)				
Cash & Equivalents	627.0	1,470.0	973.0	1,022.0
Total Current Assets	46,718.0	43,007.0	37,885.0	35,320.0
Fixed Assets, Net	57,084.0	54,136.0	54,424.0	59,464.0
Total Assets	111,386.0	104,452.0	99,779.0	99,780.0
Total Current Liabilities	27,435.0	30,514.0	25,302.0	21,861.0
Long-Term Debt	19,640.0	17,049.0	21,124.0	26,778.0
Stockholders' Equity	52,470.0	46,530.0	44,531.0	44,058.0
Performance & Financial Condition				
Return on Total Revenues %	3.28	2.77	1.92	2.77
Return on Avg Stockholders' Equity %	17.69	14.00	9.12	14.35
Return on Average Assets %	8.12	6.24	4.05	6.29
Current Ratio	1.70	1.41	1.50	1.62
Debt / Equity %	37.43	36.64	47.44	60.78

Compound Growth %'s	EPS %	16.71	Net Income %	13.09	Total Revenues %	6.91

Comments

The Company declared a 2 for 1 stock split during 1996. All per share amounts were adjusted accordingly. The restrictions placed on the trading of the stock will dampen most investor interest even though the stock appears to be undervalued. An investment, if one can clear the hurdles, must be based on the belief that over the long term the zebra, in this case management, will change its stripes. We have seen such a change this last year with J.C. Nichols which, for many years, was investor unfriendly. In any case, the Company reported record earnings, up 37% from the preceding year. Investment Classification: Value & Speculative

Officers	Position	Ownership Information	
R. Douglas Cowan	President, CEO	Number of Shares Outstanding	4,518,817
David E. Adante	Exec VP, CFO	Market Capitalization	$ 68,143,760
Karl J. Warnke	Exec VP	Frequency of Dividends	Quarterly
Howard D. Bowles	Vice President	Number of Shareholders	1,668
Bradley L. Comport	Controller		

Other Information				
Transfer Agent	Company Office		Where Listed	OTC-PS
Auditor	Deloitte & Touche LLP		Symbol	n.a.
Market Maker	Hill Thompson Magid & Co., Inc	(800)631-3083	SIC Code	0783
			Employees	5800
Broker Dealer	OTC Specialist			

Dayton and Michigan Railroad Company

500 Water Street   Jacksonville, FL 32202   Telephone (904)359-3100   Fax (904)359-1899

Company Description

Dayton and Michigan Railroad, incorporated in 1851, owns a line of railroad 141 miles long which lies between Dayton and Toledo, Ohio. Under the terms of a perpetual lease, dated in 1863, CSX Transportation, Inc., (CSXT) as successor by merger, operates the property and pays a rental charge measured principally by the dividend requirements of the two classes of the Company's stock. CSXT owns 66.75% of the preferred and 80.39% of the common.

	12/31/95	12/31/94	12/31/93	12/31/92
Per Share Information				
Stock Price	20.50	19.00	18.00	18.00
Earnings Per Share	8.88	6.42	8.06	5.51
Price / Earnings Ratio	2.31	2.96	2.23	3.27
Book Value Per Share	67.83	60.03	182.53	n.a.
Price / Book Value %	30.22	31.65	n.a.	n.a.
Dividends Per Share	1.75	1.75	1.75	1.75
Annual Financial Data				
Operating Results (000's)				
Total Revenues	156.3	126.7	147.8	114.0
Costs & Expenses	0.0	0.0	0.0	0.0
Income Before Taxes and Other	156.3	126.7	109.5	114.0
Other Items	0.0	0.0	0.0	0.0
Income Tax	-40.5	-32.9	0.0	-28.9
Net Income	115.8	93.9	109.5	85.1
Cash Flow From Operations	115.8	93.9	109.5	85.1
Balance Sheet (000's)				
Cash & Equivalents	0.0	0.0	0.0	n.a.
Total Current Assets	0.0	0.0	0.0	n.a.
Fixed Assets, Net	681.0	685.0	688.8	n.a.
Total Assets	1,850.2	1,783.1	1,738.6	n.a.
Total Current Liabilities	0.0	0.0	0.0	n.a.
Long-Term Debt	0.0	0.0	0.0	n.a.
Stockholders' Equity	1,850.2	1,783.1	1,738.6	n.a.
Performance & Financial Condition				
Return on Total Revenues %	74.07	74.07	74.07	74.63
Return on Avg Stockholders' Equity %	6.37	5.33	n.a.	n.a.
Return on Average Assets %	6.37	5.33	n.a.	n.a.
Current Ratio	n.a.	n.a.	n.a.	n.a.
Debt / Equity %	n.a.	n.a.	n.a.	n.a.

Compound Growth %'s	EPS %	4.96	Net Income %	2.84	Total Revenues %	2.84

Comments

CSXT is no longer making financial reports available to anyone except shareholders. Acquiring shares, if available, should be viewed as for income only. The question looms as to whether a lease of this nature can ever be broken. The only problem is that we might have to wait another 100 years to find out. The bid price on December 31, 1996, was $21.12 per share which would compute to a 8.28% dividend yield. Investment Classification: Income

Officers	Position	Ownership Information	
Gerald L. Nichols	President	Number of Shares Outstanding	9,420
P. Michael Giftos	Senior VP	Market Capitalization	$ 193,110
Carl N. Taylor	Senior VP	Frequency of Dividends	Quarterly
Michael J. Ward	Senior VP	Number of Shareholders	75
Patricia J. Aftoora	Vice President, Secretary		

Other Information

Transfer Agent	Harris Trust Co. of New York New York, NY		Where Listed	OTC-BB
Auditor	Ernst & Young LLP		Symbol	DMRR
Market Maker	Legg Mason Wood Walker, Inc.	(800)221-9732	SIC Code	4011
	Baird, Patrick & Co., Inc.	(800)221-5853	Employees	n.a.
Broker Dealer	OTC Specialist			

Decker Manufacturing Corporation

703 North Clark Street   Albion, MI 49224-1455   Telephone (517)629-3955   Fax (517)629-3535

Company Description

Decker Manufacturing Company is in the business of manufacturing cold headed industrial fasteners and pipe plugs. Approximately two-thirds of its product are sold to a customer base which is either directly or indirectly engaged in the manufacture of automobiles. The Company was formed in 1927 and, unlike the automobile industry, notes 58 consecutive years of profitability.

	12/31/96	12/31/95	12/31/94	12/31/93
Per Share Information				
Stock Price	41.00	39.75	40.25	28.75
Earnings Per Share	4.19	4.28	3.56	3.54
Price / Earnings Ratio	9.79	9.29	11.31	8.12
Book Value Per Share	28.76	27.75	26.37	25.51
Price / Book Value %	142.56	143.24	152.64	112.70
Dividends Per Share	3.15	2.90	2.70	2.45
Annual Financial Data				
Operating Results (000's)				
Total Revenues	22,073.7	22,199.9	21,456.7	19,967.8
Costs & Expenses	-18,182.0	-18,223.2	-18,147.5	-16,253.7
Income Before Taxes and Other	3,861.2	3,976.8	3,309.2	3,714.1
Other Items	0.0	0.0	0.0	0.0
Income Tax	-1,208.1	-1,262.1	-1,052.3	-1,468.9
Net Income	2,653.1	2,714.6	2,256.9	2,245.1
Cash Flow From Operations	3,625.7	1,935.4	3,116.9	3,016.9
Balance Sheet (000's)				
Cash & Equivalents	1,043.5	2,286.7	2,229.1	0.0
Total Current Assets	17,087.4	16,161.1	15,445.3	14,232.6
Fixed Assets, Net	3,263.9	3,401.2	3,517.0	3,838.2
Total Assets	20,504.5	19,731.1	19,172.0	18,270.8
Total Current Liabilities	1,878.6	1,737.1	2,046.7	1,752.9
Long-Term Debt	3.2	0.0	0.0	0.0
Stockholders' Equity	18,231.8	17,591.1	16,715.0	16,169.8
Performance & Financial Condition				
Return on Total Revenues %	12.02	12.23	10.52	11.24
Return on Avg Stockholders' Equity %	14.81	15.83	13.73	14.23
Return on Average Assets %	13.19	13.96	12.06	12.68
Current Ratio	9.10	9.30	7.55	8.12
Debt / Equity %	0.02	n.a.	n.a.	n.a.

Compound Growth %'s	EPS %	5.78	Net Income %	5.72	Total Revenues %	3.40

Comments

Two labor strikes at General Motors facilities caused a trickle down effect to many of Decker's customers, the end result affecting the Company as well. But even bad years look good as the Company has in excess of $9.6 million in cash and marketable securities as part of a 9.1 to 1 current ratio. Management is preparing for years of growth ahead both internally and through possible acquisitions. Investment Classification: Income & Value

Officers	Position	Ownership Information	
Henry R. Konkle	Chairman, CEO	Number of Shares Outstanding	633,958
Bernard L. Konkle I	President, General Manager	Market Capitalization	$ 25,992,278
Terrence B. DeWeerd	Secretary, Treasurer	Frequency of Dividends	Quarterly
Steven M. Konkle	Vice President	Number of Shareholders	Under 500
Bernard L. Konkle II	Vice President		

Other Information			
Transfer Agent	Manufacturers Bank, NA Detroit, MI	Where Listed	OTC-BB
Auditor	Foote and Lloyd	Symbol	DMCO
Market Maker	The Seidler Companies Inc. (800)421-0164	SIC Code	3499
	Howe Barnes Investments, Inc. (800)621-2364	Employees	140
Broker Dealer	Regular Stockbroker		

Delhi Bank Corp

124 Main Street   Delhi, NY 13753   Telephone (607)746-2356   Fax (607)746-7711

Company Description

The Company is the parent holding company of The Delaware National Bank of Delhi, originally chartered in 1839, which serves the community of Delhi, New York. Delhi is a community of 4,000 people in the Catskill Mountains in southeastern New York. Management calls themselves "The Old Bank...With New Ideas". It is hard to argue with either of these points.

	12/31/96	12/31/95	12/31/94	12/31/93
Per Share Information				
Stock Price	52.00	36.50	34.83	27.00
Earnings Per Share	5.63	4.81	3.76	4.23
Price / Earnings Ratio	9.24	7.59	9.26	6.38
Book Value Per Share	41.85	38.42	31.88	31.53
Price / Book Value %	124.25	95.00	109.25	85.63
Dividends Per Share	1.67	1.55	1.26	1.08
Annual Financial Data				
Operating Results (000's)				
Net Interest Income	4,019.3	3,899.5	3,370.2	3,259.7
Loan Loss Provision	-102.6	-210.6	-20.7	0.0
Non-Interest Income	833.9	513.3	289.6	433.3
Non-Interest Expense	-2,779.8	-2,572.9	-2,359.2	-2,429.3
Income Before Taxes and Other	1,970.8	1,629.3	1,279.9	1,263.7
Other Items	0.0	0.0	0.0	0.0
Income Tax	-670.2	-518.9	-410.5	-287.1
Net Income	1,300.5	1,110.4	869.4	976.6
Balance Sheet (000's)				
Cash & Securities	30,780.8	29,618.4	33,813.3	40,491.3
Loans, Net	59,082.8	55,853.7	50,541.6	46,629.0
Total Assets	92,736.7	88,068.7	87,546.4	89,711.4
Deposits	82,709.5	78,176.3	80,321.3	81,773.2
Stockholders' Equity	9,362.9	8,792.7	7,093.4	7,283.7
Performance & Financial Condition				
Return on Avg Stockholders' Equity %	14.33	13.98	12.09	14.11
Return on Average Assets %	1.44	1.26	0.98	1.10
Equity to Assets %	10.10	9.98	8.10	8.12
Net Interest Margin	n.a.	n.a.	n.a.	n.a.
Reserve as a % of Problem Loans	n.a.	n.a.	n.a.	n.a.

Compound Growth %'s	EPS %	10.00	Net Income %	10.02	Net Interest Income %	7.23

Comments

The Company issued three shares for each one share of The Delaware Bank of Delhi at the time the holding company was formed in 1994, although there remains a thin market in this security. 1993 per share amounts have been restated for consistency. Management reports the last known stock trading price in its annual report. These amounts are considerably higher than the bid prices posted by market makers but can be expected to be a truer reflection of the market. Management has many plans for 1997 including a "NY Yankee repeat." Only a great bank can tell something like that to their shareholders. Investment Classification: Value

Officers	Position	Ownership Information	
Timothy C. Townsend	President, CEO	Number of Shares Outstanding	223,704
Robert W. Armstrong	Vice President, Head Cashier	Market Capitalization	$ 11,632,608
Donald G. Stevenson	Vice President	Frequency of Dividends	Quarterly
David A. Avery	Vice President, Sr Loan Officer	Number of Shareholders	n.a.
Martha B. Burczak	Vice President	Where Listed / Symbol	OTC-BB / DWNB

Other Information		Loan Mix	%
Transfer Agent	Company Office	Not Allocated	100
Auditor	Not indicated		
Market Maker	Cowen & Co. (212)495-6263		
	Ryan, Beck & Co. (800)325-7926		
Broker Dealer	OTC Specialist		
	Frank Procopio - Ryan, Beck (888)231-7226		

DeltaPoint, Inc.

22 Lower Ragsdale Drive   Monterey, CA 93940   Telephone (408)648-4000   Fax (408)648-4020

Company Description

DeltaPoint, Inc. develops and markets Internet software tools designed to allow users to effectively and easily create, manage and enhance sites on the Internet's World Wide Web. A key element of the Company's objective of becoming a leading Internet software tools provider is to increase its strategic alliances with key partners. The Company entered into various agreements with IBM, Borland International, Sony, McGraw-Hill, Earthlink, Compaq and Netcom Interactive for the distribution of its products. The Company was founded in 1989.

	12/31/96	12/31/95
Per Share Information		
Stock Price	6.25	8.00
Earnings Per Share	-2.17	-2.42
Price / Earnings Ratio	n.a.	n.a.
Book Value Per Share	0.42	1.70
Price / Book Value %	1,488.10	470.59
Dividends Per Share	0.0	0.0
Annual Financial Data		
Operating Results (000's)		
Total Revenues	5,024.0	4,043.0
Costs & Expenses	-9,872.0	-6,675.0
Income Before Taxes and Other	-4,848.0	-2,632.0
Other Items	0.0	0.0
Income Tax	0.0	0.0
Net Income	-4,848.0	-2,632.0
Cash Flow From Operations	-4,618.0	-1,646.0
Balance Sheet (000's)		
Cash & Equivalents	3,142.0	4,629.0
Total Current Assets	5,736.0	6,230.0
Fixed Assets, Net	277.0	49.0
Total Assets	6,346.0	6,764.0
Total Current Liabilities	5,305.0	3,315.0
Long-Term Debt	0.0	0.0
Stockholders' Equity	1,041.0	3,449.0
Performance & Financial Condition		
Return on Total Revenues %	-96.50	-65.10
Return on Avg Stockholders' Equity %	-215.95	n.a.
Return on Average Assets %	-73.96	n.a.
Current Ratio	1.08	1.88
Debt / Equity %	n.a.	n.a.

Compound Growth %'s	EPS % n.a.	Net Income % n.a.	Total Revenues %	24.26

Comments

Mounting losses slammed the stock price to the $1.50 range at May 31, 1997. Although revenue was higher by 34% for the first quarter of 1997, an overall loss was reported of $2.5 million, $1.01 per share. The Company's overall financial condition has also slipped as working capital was negative by $1.5 million. The auditors last report contained a "going concern" qualification. Investment Classification: Speculative

Officers	Position	Ownership Information	
John J. Ambrose	CEO	Number of Shares Outstanding	2,485,540
Donald B. Witmer	COO, CFO	Market Capitalization	$ 15,534,625
		Frequency of Dividends	n.a.
		Number of Shareholders	n.a.

Other Information

Transfer Agent	U.S. Stock Transfer Corp. Glendale, CA		Where Listed	OTC-BB
Auditor	Price Waterhouse LLP		Symbol	DTPT
Market Maker	Sharpe Capital Inc.	(800)355-5781	SIC Code	7372
	Wien Securities Corp.	(800)624-0050	Employees	n.a.
Broker Dealer	Regular Stockbroker			

Detroit Legal News Company

2001 W. Lafayette Boulevard   Detroit, MI 48216   Telephone (313)961-3949   Fax (313)961-7817

Company Description

The Detroit Legal News Company's primary business is producing and selling sheetfeed commercial printing (d.b.a. Inland Press). In addition, the Company publishes The Detroit Legal News, a daily legal newspaper. During 1996 and 1994, the Company redeemed 300 and 578 of its shares for $96 and $80 per share, respectively. The Company also prints in cyberspace: (http://www.legalnews.com).

	12/31/96	12/31/95	12/31/94	12/31/93
Per Share Information				
Stock Price	92.50	80.00	80.00	61.00
Earnings Per Share	19.53	10.04	12.89	4.00
Price / Earnings Ratio	4.74	7.97	6.21	15.25
Book Value Per Share	148.03	126.18	118.29	107.35
Price / Book Value %	62.49	63.40	67.63	56.82
Dividends Per Share	3.00	2.15	2.40	1.73
Annual Financial Data				
Operating Results (000's)				
Total Revenues	14,100.9	13,060.4	12,678.3	11,723.3
Costs & Expenses	-12,882.2	-12,459.5	-11,921.9	-11,491.8
Income Before Taxes and Other	1,218.8	600.9	756.5	231.6
Other Items	1.8	0.0	0.0	0.0
Income Tax	-473.0	-216.0	-261.0	-76.0
Net Income	747.6	384.9	495.5	155.6
Cash Flow From Operations	1,511.4	525.4	1,173.2	661.2
Balance Sheet (000's)				
Cash & Equivalents	2,464.3	1,349.7	1,403.5	679.2
Total Current Assets	5,406.8	3,989.6	4,006.4	3,355.7
Fixed Assets, Net	2,257.2	2,513.2	2,581.9	2,648.5
Total Assets	8,124.9	6,607.9	6,716.9	6,243.3
Total Current Liabilities	1,862.5	1,107.7	1,454.1	1,216.8
Long-Term Debt	300.0	400.0	500.0	600.0
Stockholders' Equity	5,637.3	4,836.3	4,533.8	4,176.5
Performance & Financial Condition				
Return on Total Revenues %	5.30	2.95	3.91	1.33
Return on Avg Stockholders' Equity %	14.28	8.22	11.38	3.76
Return on Average Assets %	10.15	5.78	7.65	2.48
Current Ratio	2.90	3.60	2.76	2.76
Debt / Equity %	5.32	8.27	11.03	14.37

Compound Growth %'s	EPS %	69.65	Net Income %	68.74	Total Revenues %	6.35

Comments

Compound earnings growth rates are distorted because of a lower than normal performance in 1993, the base year for the calculation. The Company is strong financially and produces excellent earnings and cash flow per share. Balance sheet assets may be undervalued. During 1996, the Company acquired the remaining 15% interest it did not own in The Pontiac-Oakland County Legal News Publishing Company and made a commitment to purchase an additional printing press at a cost of $2.5 million. Investment Classification: Value

Officers	Position	Ownership Information	
Bradley L. Thompson II	President	Number of Shares Outstanding	38,083
Laurence M. Scoville, Jr.	Secretary	Market Capitalization	$ 3,522,678
		Frequency of Dividends	Quarterly
		Number of Shareholders	Under 500

Other Information			
Transfer Agent	Company Office	Where Listed	OTC-BB
Auditor	KPMG Peat Marwick LLP	Symbol	DTRL
Market Maker	Roney & Co.	(800)521-1196	SIC Code	2750
	Sharpe Capital Inc.	(800)355-5781	Employees	100
Broker Dealer	OTC Specialist		

Dover Investments Corporation

350 California St., Ste. 1650   San Francisco, CA 94104   Telephone (415)951-0200   Fax (415)951-8905

Company Description

The Company, formerly known as Homestead Financial Corporation, is in the business of developing and building single family homes in Northern California. The Company previously owned all of the stock of Homestead Savings, a federal savings and loan association. In 1992, the Resolution Trust Company took over Homestead. A quasi-reorganization in 1993 resulted in the elimination of $16 million in accumulated deficits, primarily from the prior ownership of Homestead. Class A and B shares have similar rights and trade at the same price.

	12/31/96	12/31/95	12/31/94	12/31/93
Per Share Information				
Stock Price	5.50	6.63	2.38	0.50
Earnings Per Share	-0.18	0.42	0.22	0.32
Price / Earnings Ratio	n.a.	15.79	10.82	1.56
Book Value Per Share	19.71	19.72	13.71	10.51
Price / Book Value %	27.90	33.62	17.36	4.76
Dividends Per Share	0.0	0.0	0.0	0.0
Annual Financial Data				
Operating Results (000's)				
Total Revenues	10,160.0	5,312.0	9,344.0	9,872.0
Costs & Expenses	-10,387.0	-4,609.0	-8,728.0	-8,947.0
Income Before Taxes and Other	-227.0	700.0	616.0	850.0
Other Items	0.0	0.0	0.0	-3.0
Income Tax	53.0	-248.0	-368.0	-489.0
Net Income	-174.0	452.0	248.0	358.0
Cash Flow From Operations	2,081.0	-3,449.0	-796.0	1,813.0
Balance Sheet (000's)				
Cash & Equivalents	1,438.0	639.0	381.0	1,667.0
Total Current Assets	4,292.0	4,202.0	4,072.0	4,167.0
Fixed Assets, Net	21,682.0	22,745.0	22,231.0	21,280.0
Total Assets	26,725.0	28,120.0	29,818.0	27,558.0
Total Current Liabilities	6,696.0	466.0	3,806.0	4,369.0
Long-Term Debt	802.0	8,020.0	10,400.0	11,342.0
Stockholders' Equity	19,096.0	19,583.0	15,315.0	11,847.0
Performance & Financial Condition				
Return on Total Revenues %	-1.71	8.51	2.65	3.63
Return on Avg Stockholders' Equity %	-0.90	2.59	1.83	3.12
Return on Average Assets %	-0.63	1.56	0.86	1.41
Current Ratio	0.64	9.02	1.07	0.95
Debt / Equity %	4.20	40.95	67.91	95.74

Compound Growth %'s	EPS % n.a.	Net Income % n.a.	Total Revenues %	0.96

Comments

A stronger real estate market is improving the Company's ability to build and sell homes. At 1996 year end, lot improvements were completed on 150 lots and partially complete on 99 additional lots. 101 homes have been built, sold and closed on the completed lots. Management also reports that a joint venture to develop 180 acres of land in the town of Tracy is proceeding well. During 1995, the Company received $4.0 million from the Internal Revenue Service as a result of examinations of its consolidated tax returns for the years 1985 through 1990. This included a substantial amount of nonrecurring interest income. Earnings during 1996 were depressed by reduced margins in a real estate development in San Leandro and by expenses associated with holding joint venture real property. Investment Classification: Value & Speculative

Officers	Position	Ownership Information	
Lawrence Weissberg	President, CEO	Number of Shares Outstanding	968,796
Michael Raddie	CFO	Market Capitalization	$ 5,328,378
		Frequency of Dividends	n.a.
		Number of Shareholders	738

Other Information

Transfer Agent	ChaseMellon Shareholder Services New York, NY		Where Listed	OTC-BB
Auditor	Grant Thornton LLP		Symbol	DOVR
Market Maker	Koonce Securities, Inc.	(800)368-2802	SIC Code	1531
	Wm. V. Frankel & Co., Inc.	(800)631-3091	Employees	4
Broker Dealer	Regular Stockbroker			

Drovers Bancshares Corporation

30 South George Street   York, PA 17401   Telephone (717)843-1586   Fax (717)846-5132

Company Description

The Drovers & Mechanics Bank, subsidiary of this one-bank holding company, has been in business since 1883. Headquartered in a five-story complex in downtown York, south central Pennsylvania, it has eight branches and one in-store facility located in the surrounding suburbs of York and four offices further away in Emigsville, York Haven, Windsor and Red Lion. The Bank also offers a variety of Trust services and has about 200 employees.

	12/31/96	12/31/95	12/31/94	12/31/93
Per Share Information				
Stock Price	20.75	19.20	16.07	15.70
Earnings Per Share	1.73	1.53	1.36	1.40
Price / Earnings Ratio	11.99	12.55	11.82	11.21
Book Value Per Share	13.56	12.47	10.63	10.58
Price / Book Value %	153.02	153.97	151.18	148.39
Dividends Per Share	0.57	0.50	0.42	0.39
Annual Financial Data				
Operating Results (000's)				
Net Interest Income	15,264.0	14,524.0	12,894.0	12,199.0
Loan Loss Provision	-645.0	-501.0	-382.0	-447.0
Non-Interest Income	3,364.0	2,837.0	2,457.0	2,651.0
Non-Interest Expense	-12,050.0	-11,058.0	-10,355.0	-9,866.0
Income Before Taxes and Other	5,933.0	5,802.0	4,614.0	4,537.0
Other Items	0.0	0.0	0.0	352.0
Income Tax	-1,084.0	-1,521.0	-845.0	-1,026.0
Net Income	4,849.0	4,281.0	3,769.0	3,863.0
Balance Sheet (000's)				
Cash & Securities	145,865.0	110,594.0	106,867.0	98,098.0
Loans, Net	279,987.0	252,468.0	226,737.0	206,614.0
Total Assets	446,713.0	382,791.0	352,287.0	320,851.0
Deposits	360,204.0	306,653.0	283,173.0	265,917.0
Stockholders' Equity	38,092.0	34,921.0	29,724.0	29,249.0
Performance & Financial Condition				
Return on Avg Stockholders' Equity %	13.28	13.24	12.78	14.87
Return on Average Assets %	1.17	1.16	1.12	1.23
Equity to Assets %	8.53	9.12	8.44	9.12
Net Interest Margin	4.09	4.26	4.13	4.11
Reserve as a % of Problem Loans	116.70	311.45	625.12	605.71

Compound Growth %'s	EPS %	7.31	Net Income %	7.87	Net Interest Income %	7.76

Comments

The Company has declared stock dividends of 25%, 7%, 25% and 5% in 1996, 1995, 1994 and 1993, respectively. All per share amounts have been adjusted for consistency. Drovers has produced higher total earnings for eight consecutive years. Strong deposit growth of 17.5% fueled an increase in net interest income. There were also gains in all categories on non-interest income except for a loss in a real estate joint venture. The first opening of an in-store location in 1996 will likely lead to more of the same through an affiliation with Tom's Convenience Stores. The Company displays a complete summary of ten year's financial data in their annual report. Investment Classification: Value

Officers	Position	Ownership Information	
A. Richard Pugh	President, CEO	Number of Shares Outstanding	2,809,180
Michael J. Groft	Exec VP, Sr Loan Officer	Market Capitalization	$ 58,290,485
Debra A. Goodling	Exec VP, CFO	Frequency of Dividends	Quarterly
George L.F. Guyer, Jr.	Senior VP, Secretary	Number of Shareholders	n.a.
Lorie Y. Runion	Senior VP	Where Listed / Symbol	OTC-BB / DROV

Other Information			Loan Mix	%
Transfer Agent	Chemical Mellon Shareholder Services Ridgefield Park, NJ		R/E Mortgages	59.1
Auditor	Harry Ness & Company		Commerical	25.7
Market Maker	F.J. Morrissey & Co., Inc.	(800)842-8928	Installment	12.1
	Hopper Soliday & Co., Inc.	(800)456-9234	Construction	3.1
Broker Dealer	Regular Stockbroker			

Du Art Film Laboratories, Inc.

245 West 55th Street   New York, NY 10019-5202   Telephone (212)757-4580   Fax (212)333-7647

Company Description

Du Art Film Laboratories, Inc. is engaged in the business of motion picture, sound and video processing and the operation of a majority-owned television property in Puerto Rico. Television broadcasting in Puerto Rico accounts for approximately 13% of total revenue and 32% of total assets. The Company was formed in 1922.

	12/28/96	12/31/95	12/25/94	12/31/93
Per Share Information				
Stock Price as of 12/31	88.00	66.00	61.00	55.12
Earnings Per Share	11.25	8.83	4.98	6.24
Price / Earnings Ratio	7.82	7.47	12.25	8.83
Book Value Per Share	76.38	80.75	60.02	56.04
Price / Book Value %	115.21	81.73	101.63	98.36
Dividends Per Share	0.0	0.0	0.0	0.0
Annual Financial Data				
Operating Results (000's)				
Total Revenues	24,637.6	22,592.4	20,050.7	18,504.6
Costs & Expenses	-20,213.1	-18,962.5	-17,501.3	-16,670.2
Income Before Taxes and Other	4,424.6	3,188.0	1,934.0	1,593.5
Other Items	-403.8	-346.9	0.0	58.5
Income Tax	-2,301.7	-1,500.0	-1,178.8	-709.3
Net Income	1,719.1	1,341.2	755.2	942.7
Cash Flow From Operations	3,585.6	2,704.5	3,488.0	1,454.4
Balance Sheet (000's)				
Cash & Equivalents	1,628.6	1,429.3	2,011.7	535.6
Total Current Assets	11,167.2	9,663.1	8,417.6	7,283.9
Fixed Assets, Net	8,957.4	7,587.6	6,887.4	7,081.8
Total Assets	20,817.3	17,851.9	16,247.0	15,188.0
Total Current Liabilities	2,479.8	1,887.8	2,125.4	1,645.8
Long-Term Debt	145.8	0.0	0.0	187.5
Stockholders' Equity	14,043.5	12,303.3	10,932.8	10,165.2
Performance & Financial Condition				
Return on Total Revenues %	6.98	5.94	3.77	5.09
Return on Avg Stockholders' Equity %	13.05	11.54	7.16	9.72
Return on Average Assets %	8.89	7.87	4.80	6.33
Current Ratio	4.50	5.12	3.96	4.43
Debt / Equity %	1.04	n.a.	n.a.	1.84

Compound Growth %'s	EPS %	21.71	Net Income %	22.17	Total Revenues %	10.01

Comments

Substantial equipment and facility expenditures were incurred in 1996. Management reports that all divisions of the Company had record sales and profits for the year. 1994 results were negatively impacted by a loss of $545,383 resulting from the sale of long term government bonds. The Company has since adopted a policy of investing excess funds in instruments with maturities of two years or less. There is virtually no long term debt and the Company maintains an excellent current ratio. Investment Classification: Value

Officers	Position	Ownership Information	
Irwin W. Young	Chairman	Number of Shares Outstanding	183,853
Robert M. Smith	President	Market Capitalization	$ 16,179,064
Linda Young	Exec VP	Frequency of Dividends	n.a.
Carmine J. Donigi	Senior VP	Number of Shareholders	Under 500
Stewart Deitch	CFO, Treasurer		

Other Information			
Transfer Agent	Registrar & Transfer Company Cranford, NJ	Where Listed	OTC-BB
Auditor	Ernst & Young LLP	Symbol	DAFL
Market Maker	Carr Securities Corporation	(800)221-2243	SIC Code	7810
	Koonce Securities, Inc.	(800)368-2802	Employees	40
Broker Dealer	OTC Specialist		

Dynamic Associates, Inc.

7373 N. Scottsdale Road, Suite B-150   Scottsdale, AZ 85253   Telephone (602)483-8700   Fax (602)443-1235

Company Description

Dynamic Associates, Inc. was formed in 1989 and was in the development stage through 1995. The Company is now engaged in the acquisition of microwave technologies for medical purposes, in the business of managing the operation of geriatric/psychiatric units for various hospitals, and manufacturing highly technologically advanced components and subsystems for the communications and aerospace industries. The Company has issued stock in connection with various acquisitions.

	12/31/96	12/31/95
Per Share Information		
Stock Price	3.25	1.50
Earnings Per Share	-0.11	-0.29
Price / Earnings Ratio	n.a.	n.a.
Book Value Per Share	1.09	0.10
Price / Book Value %	298.17	1,500.00
Dividends Per Share	0.0	0.0
Annual Financial Data		
Operating Results (000's)		
Total Revenues	4,582.3	4.2
Costs & Expenses	-6,159.9	-622.1
Income Before Taxes and Other	-1,577.7	-617.9
Other Items	-64.2	0.0
Income Tax	685.1	-1.6
Net Income	-956.8	-619.5
Cash Flow From Operations	-450.4	-420.8
Balance Sheet (000's)		
Cash & Equivalents	3,342.5	781.0
Total Current Assets	7,462.8	1,027.2
Fixed Assets, Net	425.2	7.1
Total Assets	33,954.8	1,035.3
Total Current Liabilities	5,195.8	338.8
Long-Term Debt	158.4	0.0
Stockholders' Equity	13,200.1	696.5
Performance & Financial Condition		
Return on Total Revenues %	-20.88	-14,634.23
Return on Avg Stockholders' Equity %	-13.77	n.a.
Return on Average Assets %	-5.47	n.a.
Current Ratio	1.44	3.03
Debt / Equity %	1.20	n.a.

Compound Growth %'s	EPS % n.a.	Net Income % n.a.	Total Revenues % n.a.

Comments

At December 31, 1996, the Company had nineteen active contracts to manage various hospitals that will generate monthly billings of $1,122,500. An additional contract was signed in January, 1997. Management estimates that this unit alone will contribute $8 million in pretax profits during 1997. Management's goal is to become a premier Microwave Medical and Senior Care company over the next several years. Investment Classification: Speculative

Officers	Position	Ownership Information	
Jan Wallace	President	Number of Shares Outstanding	12,158,900
Logan Anderson	Secretary, Treasurer	Market Capitalization	$ 39,516,425
Craig Hurst	Vice President	Frequency of Dividends	n.a.
		Number of Shareholders	419

Other Information			
Transfer Agent	National Stock Transfer, Inc. Salt Lake City, UT	Where Listed	OTC-BB
Auditor	Smith & Company	Symbol	DYAS
Market Maker	Rickel & Associates Inc.	(201)379-0374	SIC Code	8000
	Wm. V. Frankel & Co., Inc.	(800)631-3091	Employees	n.a.
Broker Dealer	Regular Stockbroker		

E*Capital Corporation

P.O. Box 71029   Los Angeles, CA 90071-0029   Telephone (213)688-8042   Fax (213)688-6655

Company Description

E*Capital Corporation has a wholly-owned subsidiary, Wedbush Morgan Securities, which is a full-service security brokerage firm with fifteen offices in major metropolitan areas in the United States. Approximately half of all revenues are derived from brokerage commissions. Wedbush Morgan also acts as market maker for a number of securities. Passive income is generated on investment holdings. Common shares must be held in street name at Wedbush Morgan. The Company was formed in 1925.

	06/30/96	06/30/95
Per Share Information		
Stock Price as of 12/31	22.00	16.50
Earnings Per Share	4.26	1.87
Price / Earnings Ratio	5.16	8.82
Book Value Per Share	26.10	21.69
Price / Book Value %	84.29	76.07
Dividends Per Share	0.16	0.16
Annual Financial Data		
Operating Results (000's)		
Total Revenues	105,103.0	78,066.0
Costs & Expenses	-86,280.0	-69,707.0
Income Before Taxes and Other	18,823.0	8,359.0
Other Items	0.0	0.0
Income Tax	-7,631.0	-3,446.0
Net Income	11,192.0	4,913.0
Cash Flow From Operations	-17,078.0	13,905.0
Balance Sheet (000's)		
Cash & Equivalents	12,636.0	27,035.0
Total Current Assets	599,710.0	509,442.0
Fixed Assets, Net	653.0	731.0
Total Assets	640,498.0	542,409.0
Total Current Liabilities	571,573.0	485,679.0
Long-Term Debt	0.0	0.0
Stockholders' Equity	68,925.0	56,730.0
Performance & Financial Condition		
Return on Total Revenues %	10.65	6.29
Return on Avg Stockholders' Equity %	17.81	n.a.
Return on Average Assets %	1.89	n.a.
Current Ratio	1.05	1.05
Debt / Equity %	n.a.	n.a.

Compound Growth %'s	EPS % n.a.	Net Income % n.a.	Total Revenues % 34.63

Comments

Operating results reflect a broad increase in retail sales activity and profitability. During 1996, the Company announced that it would price the Company's shares on monthly brokerage statements at the last known trade. Prior to that time shares were identified without any pricing. The strong results of the last fiscal year are likely to continue as management stays focused on its business in times that are extremely favorable for the industry. For the nine months ended March 31, 1997, the Company reported earnings of $4.09 per share as compared to $3.26 in the same portion of the 1996 fiscal year. Investment Classification: Growth & Value

Officers	Position	Ownership Information	
Thomas L. Ringer	Chairman	Number of Shares Outstanding	2,640,865
Edward W. Wedbush	President, CEO	Market Capitalization	$ 58,099,030
A. Peter Allman-Ward	CFO	Frequency of Dividends	n.a.
Jill A. Lance	Secretary	Number of Shareholders	Under 500

Other Information					
Transfer Agent	Company Office			Where Listed	Order Matching Only
Auditor	KPMG Peat Marwick LLP			Symbol	n.a.
Market Maker	Company Office			SIC Code	6210
				Employees	n.a.
Broker Dealer	Standard Investment	(888)783-4688	Ext: Jack		

EMC Corporation

875 Montreal Way   Saint Paul, MN 55102-4245   Telephone (612)290-2800   Fax (612)290-2828

Company Description

EMC Corporation develops, manufactures and distributes educational materials and provides media manufacturing, recording, packaging and fulfillment services to a broad range of customers nationwide. In December 1996, the Company completed construction of a 125,000 square foot facility which includes 35,000 square feet of offices and conference rooms and a 90,000 square foot distribution center. The new facility greatly enhances the Company's ability to execute its long term strategies.

	12/31/96	12/31/95	12/31/94	12/31/93
Per Share Information				
Stock Price	18.50	16.50	10.00	6.00
Earnings Per Share	0.81	1.05	0.97	0.73
Price / Earnings Ratio	22.84	15.71	10.31	8.22
Book Value Per Share	6.09	5.41	4.55	3.76
Price / Book Value %	303.78	304.99	219.78	159.57
Dividends Per Share	0.19	0.18	0.17	0.15
Annual Financial Data				
Operating Results (000's)				
Total Revenues	32,579.5	29,574.6	27,549.6	22,842.4
Costs & Expenses	-29,526.0	-26,075.9	-24,229.8	-20,145.2
Income Before Taxes and Other	3,053.4	3,498.8	3,319.8	2,133.6
Other Items	0.0	0.0	0.0	220.0
Income Tax	-1,241.9	-1,236.5	-1,224.0	-774.0
Net Income	1,811.6	2,262.3	2,095.8	1,579.6
Cash Flow From Operations	4,631.1	3,101.1	3,942.1	4,039.8
Balance Sheet (000's)				
Cash & Equivalents	314.9	627.7	2,189.6	934.1
Total Current Assets	11,363.6	10,789.8	11,375.7	8,626.7
Fixed Assets, Net	7,052.5	3,026.9	3,047.9	3,074.9
Total Assets	24,419.2	18,867.3	17,962.7	15,800.7
Total Current Liabilities	6,172.0	4,876.8	5,138.2	4,122.4
Long-Term Debt	4,695.6	1,972.9	2,636.3	3,224.7
Stockholders' Equity	13,238.5	11,702.5	9,840.2	8,134.7
Performance & Financial Condition				
Return on Total Revenues %	5.56	7.65	7.61	6.92
Return on Avg Stockholders' Equity %	14.53	21.00	23.32	20.96
Return on Average Assets %	8.37	12.29	12.41	9.99
Current Ratio	1.84	2.21	2.21	2.09
Debt / Equity %	35.47	16.86	26.79	39.64

Compound Growth %'s	EPS %	3.53	Net Income %	4.67	Total Revenues %	12.56

Comments

The Company declared a 20 for 1 stock split in 1994. 1993 per share amounts have been restated accordingly. Sales increased 10% during 1996. Management reported that operating results were impacted by planned substantial increases in expenses for promotion, advertising, and sampling costs for new product introductions both in traditional and new curriculum areas. Investment Classification: Growth & Speculative

Officers	Position	Ownership Information	
David E. Feinberg	Chairman, CEO	Number of Shares Outstanding	2,172,740
Paul Winter	President, Treasurer	Market Capitalization	$ 40,195,690
Wolfgang S. Kraft	Vice President	Frequency of Dividends	Annual
Robert F. O'Reilly	Vice President	Number of Shareholders	109
Richard T. Stevens	Vice President		

Other Information				
Transfer Agent	First Trust, N.A. St. Paul, MN		Where Listed	OTC-BB
Auditor	Coopers & Lybrand L.L.P.		Symbol	EMCM
Market Maker	Dain Bosworth Incorporated	(800)285-4964	SIC Code	2740
	Hill Thompson Magid & Co., Inc	(800)631-3083	Employees	211
Broker Dealer	Regular Stockbroker			

ENDOcare, Inc.

7 Studebaker Road   Irvine, CA 92618   Telephone (714)595-4770   Fax (745)595-4766

Company Description

ENDOcare, Inc. develops, manufactures and markets minimally invasive medical devices to treat a variety of urological conditions. The Company has focused its efforts on the development of surgical devices for the treatment of the two most common diseases of the prostate: Benign Prostate Hyperplasia and prostate cancer. To date, the Company has received marketing clearance by the Food and Drug Administration for six of its products. On January 27, 1997, ENDOcare completed a private placement of 2,218,714 shares of common at $3.50 per share. The Company was formed in 1990.

	12/31/96	12/31/95	12/31/94	12/31/93
Per Share Information				
Stock Price	3.25	1.50	n.a.	n.a.
Earnings Per Share	-0.27	-0.10	n.a.	n.a.
Price / Earnings Ratio	n.a.	n.a.	n.a.	n.a.
Book Value Per Share	-0.03	0.14	n.a.	n.a.
Price / Book Value %	n.a.	1,071.43	n.a.	n.a.
Dividends Per Share	0.0	0.0	n.a.	n.a.
Annual Financial Data				
Operating Results (000's)				
Total Revenues	2,259.3	1,327.8	2,662.1	3,177.1
Costs & Expenses	-3,785.7	-1,904.8	-2,925.1	-3,691.5
Income Before Taxes and Other	-1,526.4	-576.9	-262.9	-514.3
Other Items	0.0	0.0	0.0	0.0
Income Tax	-5.0	0.0	0.0	0.0
Net Income	-1,531.4	-576.9	-262.9	-514.3
Cash Flow From Operations	-691.9	-512.1	-166.0	-595.2
Balance Sheet (000's)				
Cash & Equivalents	476.9	1.9	0.0	0.0
Total Current Assets	1,527.4	331.0	403.4	409.7
Fixed Assets, Net	178.8	398.0	559.1	621.3
Total Assets	1,775.3	805.7	972.4	1,041.0
Total Current Liabilities	1,008.1	0.0	108.5	174.0
Long-Term Debt	0.0	0.0	0.0	0.0
Stockholders' Equity	-149.4	803.1	863.9	867.0
Performance & Financial Condition				
Return on Total Revenues %	-67.78	-43.45	-9.88	-16.19
Return on Avg Stockholders' Equity %	-468.56	-69.21	-30.38	n.a.
Return on Average Assets %	-118.67	-64.89	-26.12	n.a.
Current Ratio	1.52	n.a.	3.72	2.36
Debt / Equity %	n.a.	n.a.	n.a.	n.a.

Compound Growth %'s	EPS % n.a.	Net Income % n.a.	Total Revenues % -10.74

Comments

The private placement referred to above raised $7,050,000 for working capital. The increase in revenue is primarily attributable to the introduction of new products. For the first quarter of 1997, revenue climbed to $680,000, another 83% over the same period in 1996. The loss for the quarter was $739,000 which included $290,000 in research and development expenses. At March 31, 1997, the Company had $7.7 million in current assets, largely cash, and liabilities of $872,000. Investment Classification: Speculative

Officers	Position	Ownership Information	
Paul W. Mikus	President, CEO	Number of Shares Outstanding	5,645,139
Ralph L. Quigley	Vice President	Market Capitalization	$ 18,346,702
David J. Battles	VP - Sales	Frequency of Dividends	n.a.
		Number of Shareholders	372

Other Information

Transfer Agent	U.S. Stock Transfer Corp. Glendale, CA		Where Listed	OTC-BB
Auditor	KPMG Peat Marwick LLP		Symbol	ENDO
Market Maker	Fahnestock & Co., Inc.	(800)223-3012	SIC Code	3845
	Sherwood Securities Corp.	(800)435-1235	Employees	n.a.
Broker Dealer	Regular Stockbroker			

East Carolina Bank (The)

P.O. Box 337   Engelhard, NC 27824   Telephone (919)925-9411   Fax (919)925-3131

Company Description

The East Carolina Bank was opened in 1920. Today it ranks 31st among North Carolina's sixty-one commercial banks. The Bank operates thirteen offices in the eastern part of the State. Eight of those are mainland offices in Hyde, Pitt, Tyrrell and Washington Counties, and five offices are on North Carolina's famed "Outer Banks" from Ocracoke Island to Southern Shores. The most recent office opened in the second quarter, 1996, in the Wal-Mart Supercenter in Greenville. The Bank will facilitate buying and selling of their shares by maintaining lists of interested parties and putting them in contact with one another.

	12/31/96	12/31/95	12/31/94	12/31/93
Per Share Information				
Stock Price	31.00	27.00	26.00	25.00
Earnings Per Share	2.25	1.54	2.10	1.52
Price / Earnings Ratio	13.78	17.53	12.38	16.45
Book Value Per Share	24.01	22.63	20.06	19.76
Price / Book Value %	129.11	119.31	129.61	126.52
Dividends Per Share	0.64	0.60	0.56	0.53
Annual Financial Data				
Operating Results (000's)				
Net Interest Income	7,372.7	6,587.6	6,350.2	5,812.9
Loan Loss Provision	-496.9	-515.1	-396.9	-549.4
Non-Interest Income	1,718.1	1,669.5	1,581.0	1,474.3
Non-Interest Expense	-6,785.1	-6,167.9	-5,786.9	-5,562.9
Income Before Taxes and Other	1,808.8	1,574.2	1,747.4	1,174.9
Other Items	0.0	-278.6	0.0	0.0
Income Tax	-475.0	-384.0	-500.0	-270.0
Net Income	1,333.8	911.6	1,247.4	904.9
Balance Sheet (000's)				
Cash & Securities	49,000.1	64,886.8	61,473.6	67,824.6
Loans, Net	110,456.0	92,538.9	84,097.2	78,137.0
Total Assets	167,217.6	165,407.8	153,552.8	153,447.8
Deposits	151,335.6	150,435.8	141,044.4	141,137.4
Stockholders' Equity	14,249.5	13,426.6	11,904.2	11,724.1
Performance & Financial Condition				
Return on Avg Stockholders' Equity %	9.64	7.20	10.56	7.92
Return on Average Assets %	0.80	0.57	0.81	0.60
Equity to Assets %	8.52	8.12	7.75	7.64
Net Interest Margin	4.37	4.00	4.30	4.03
Reserve as a % of Problem Loans	171.18	107.14	121.41	58.14

Compound Growth %'s	EPS %	13.97	Net Income %	13.80	Net Interest Income %	8.25

Comments

Per share price information was provided by the Bank. 1995 results include a nonrecurring expense of $278,555, $.47 per share, related to a change in accounting for postretirement benefits. Management classified 1996 as a transition year in which a thorough review was conducted on how the Bank runs its various businesses. Despite this activity, a higher income was achieved by placing an increased emphasis on quality loans. Loans grew 19.2% from a year earlier and replaced lower yield investments. Investment Classification: Value

Officers	Position	Ownership Information	
Arthur H. Keeney, III	President, CEO	Number of Shares Outstanding	593,418
J. Dorson White, Jr.	Exec VP	Market Capitalization	$ 18,395,958
Gary M. Adams	Senior VP, CFO	Frequency of Dividends	Quarterly
William I. Plyler, II	Senior VP, Sr Loan Officer	Number of Shareholders	663
Sarah M. Stephens	Vice President	Where Listed / Symbol	Order Matching Only / n.a.

Other Information		Loan Mix	%
Transfer Agent	First Citizens Bank & Trust Company Raleigh, NC	R/E Mortgages	59.6
Auditor	KPMG Peat Marwick LLP	Commerical	20.3
Market Maker	None - See Note	Installment	19.2
		Construction	0.9
Broker Dealer	None - See Note		

Elk Associates Funding Corporation

747 Third Avenue, Fourth Floor   New York, NY 10017   Telephone (212)355-2449   Fax (212)759-3338

Company Description

Elk Associates Funding Corporation is licensed by the Small Business Administration (SBA) to operate a Specialized Small Business Investment Company. The Company makes loans to persons that are socially or economically disadvantaged and own 50% or more of a business. The loan portfolio is predominately to taxi drivers and the loans are secured by the taxi medallion that is required for the driver to operate a taxi service. Most of the taxi drivers operate in New York City.

	06/30/96	06/30/95	06/30/94	06/30/93
Per Share Information				
Stock Price as of 12/31	4.75	4.00	3.12	n.a.
Earnings Per Share	0.73	0.66	0.13	n.a.
Price / Earnings Ratio	6.51	6.06	24.00	n.a.
Book Value Per Share	8.49	11.24	11.22	n.a.
Price / Book Value %	55.95	35.59	27.81	n.a.
Dividends Per Share	0.73	0.0	0.0	n.a.
Annual Financial Data				
Operating Results (000's)				
Total Revenues	3,128.7	2,629.9	2,824.9	2,874.7
Costs & Expenses	-2,220.4	-1,976.9	-2,536.6	-2,814.8
Income Before Taxes and Other	908.3	653.0	288.3	59.9
Other Items	0.0	0.0	0.0	0.0
Income Tax	0.0	0.0	0.0	0.0
Net Income	908.3	653.0	288.3	59.9
Cash Flow From Operations	855.3	727.7	391.8	875.3
Balance Sheet (000's)				
Cash & Equivalents	1,072.8	1,139.5	1,624.1	n.a.
Total Current Assets	1,892.2	1,769.1	2,129.6	n.a.
Fixed Assets, Net	101.9	111.2	104.6	n.a.
Total Assets	26,721.2	25,702.6	25,368.0	n.a.
Total Current Liabilities	6,962.4	5,281.7	6,053.1	n.a.
Long-Term Debt	0.0	0.0	0.0	n.a.
Stockholders' Equity	10,900.8	11,616.9	10,590.4	n.a.
Performance & Financial Condition				
Return on Total Revenues %	29.03	24.83	10.21	2.08
Return on Avg Stockholders' Equity %	8.07	5.88	2.76	n.a.
Return on Average Assets %	3.47	2.56	n.a.	n.a.
Current Ratio	0.27	0.33	0.35	n.a.
Debt / Equity %	n.a.	n.a.	n.a.	n.a.

Compound Growth %'s	EPS % 136.97	Net Income % 147.47	Total Revenues % 2.86

Comments

During 1996, the Company retired its preferred stock at a substantial discount. The transaction with the SBA, holder of the preferred, calls for a restriction on $2,391,000 of capital. The restriction will be released on a pro-rata basis over a period of 60 months as long as the Company remains in compliance with the agreement. In the last half of 1996 and the first two quarters of fiscal 1997, the Company increased its loan portfolio to over $30 million and obtained additional lines of credit from its banks. Investment Classification: Value

Officers	Position	Ownership Information	
Gary C. Granoff	President	Number of Shares Outstanding	1,283,600
Margaret Chance	Secretary	Market Capitalization	$ 6,097,100
Ellen M. Walker	Vice President	Frequency of Dividends	Quarterly
Lee A. Forlenza	Vice President	Number of Shareholders	n.a.
Silvia DiGirolamo	Vice President		

Other Information				
Transfer Agent	Harris Trust Company of New York New York, NY		Where Listed	OTC-BB
Auditor	Marcum & Kliegman LLP		Symbol	EKFG
Market Maker	Carr Securities Corporation	(800)221-2243	SIC Code	6090
	M.H. Meyerson & Co., Inc.	(800)333-3113	Employees	n.a.
Broker Dealer	Regular Stockbroker			

Ellensburg Telephone Company

305 North Ruby   Ellensburg, WA 98926-0308   Telephone (509)925-1425   Fax (509)962-8540

Company Description

Ellensburg Telephone Company provides local and long distance telephone services to the communities that surround and include Ellensburg and Yakima in the state of Washington. Elltel Wireless, Inc., a subsidiary formed in 1995, provides personal communication services to the wireless field. The signing of the 1996 Telecommunications Act began a process which is changing the entire structure of the industry. The management team at Ellensburg is moving rapidly towards capturing every possible advantage.

	12/31/96	12/31/95	12/31/94	12/31/93
Per Share Information				
Stock Price	63.00	56.00	51.50	49.25
Earnings Per Share	5.74	5.27	4.52	4.31
Price / Earnings Ratio	10.98	10.63	11.39	11.43
Book Value Per Share	46.54	43.50	40.83	38.91
Price / Book Value %	135.37	128.74	126.13	126.57
Dividends Per Share	2.70	2.60	2.60	2.60
Annual Financial Data				
Operating Results (000's)				
Total Revenues	14,809.6	13,742.6	12,513.3	11,533.6
Costs & Expenses	-9,115.5	-8,605.7	-8,023.6	-7,289.8
Income Before Taxes and Other	5,694.1	5,136.9	4,489.7	4,243.8
Other Items	0.0	0.0	0.0	0.0
Income Tax	-1,760.0	-1,523.1	-1,395.0	-1,289.0
Net Income	3,934.1	3,613.8	3,094.7	2,954.8
Cash Flow From Operations	7,661.6	6,544.5	6,358.2	5,996.9
Balance Sheet (000's)				
Cash & Equivalents	793.8	1,048.8	743.7	29.4
Total Current Assets	6,942.2	5,079.5	5,086.4	6,092.4
Fixed Assets, Net	30,105.6	28,474.6	28,369.6	27,383.6
Total Assets	40,311.5	37,619.4	35,813.3	35,646.2
Total Current Liabilities	2,271.2	1,858.9	1,854.1	2,985.2
Long-Term Debt	0.0	133.3	266.5	369.3
Stockholders' Equity	31,888.9	29,804.7	27,972.3	26,659.1
Performance & Financial Condition				
Return on Total Revenues %	26.56	26.30	24.73	25.62
Return on Avg Stockholders' Equity %	12.75	12.51	11.33	11.33
Return on Average Assets %	10.10	9.84	8.66	8.57
Current Ratio	3.06	2.73	2.74	2.04
Debt / Equity %	n.a.	0.45	0.95	1.39

Compound Growth %'s	EPS %	10.02	Net Income %	10.01	Total Revenues %	8.69

Comments

The Company's balance sheet shows available capital and no debt which should enable it to pursue a number of growth opportunities and technological advancements. Many projects were undertaken in 1996 including the placement of Digital Loop Carrier systems throughout the service area, the creation of an alternate fiber route from Selah to Yakima, and the development of a strong wireless team. In January, 1997, new technology was made available that allows customers to communicate by voice and data simultaneously over one telephone line. Investment Classification: Value

Officers	Position	Ownership Information	
G F. Kachlein III	President, Chairman of the Board	Number of Shares Outstanding	685,158
		Market Capitalization	$ 43,164,954
		Frequency of Dividends	Quarterly
		Number of Shareholders	Under 500

Other Information				
Transfer Agent	Company Office		Where Listed	OTC-BB
Auditor	Moss Adams LLP		Symbol	ELEN
Market Maker	Ragen MacKenzie Incorporated	(800)426-5964	SIC Code	4810
	Martin Nelson & Co., Inc.	(800)543-3332	Employees	n.a.
Broker Dealer	OTC Specialist			
	Stephen Schuller - Dorsey	(800)375-5431		

Erie Family Life Insurance Company

100 Erie Insurance Place   Erie, PA 16530   Telephone (814)870-2000   Fax (800)533-5144

Company Description

The Company is engaged in the business of underwriting and selling nonparticipating individual and group life insurance policies, including universal life and annuity products. Erie Life markets its products through independent agents in eight states and the District of Columbia. A majority of the Company's business is written in Pennsylvania, Ohio, Maryland and Virginia. The Company also sells a significant amount of annuities to its affiliated companies of the Erie Insurance Group. Approximately 32% of annuity reserves at December 31, 1996 relates to business of affiliates. The Company was founded in 1967.

	12/31/96	12/31/95	12/31/94	12/31/93
Per Share Information				
Stock Price	27.75	19.33	17.50	17.67
Earnings Per Share	1.87	1.89	1.78	1.86
Price / Earnings Ratio	14.84	10.23	9.83	9.50
Book Value Per Share	14.03	13.64	9.61	9.50
Price / Book Value %	197.79	141.72	182.10	186.00
Dividends Per Share	0.50	0.45	0.40	0.37
Annual Financial Data				
Operating Results (000's)				
Total Revenues	82,720.2	78,350.0	66,768.8	64,787.1
Costs & Expenses	-56,077.6	-51,946.1	-40,289.3	-36,910.8
Income Before Taxes and Other	26,642.7	26,403.9	26,479.5	27,876.3
Other Items	0.0	0.0	0.0	-567.6
Income Tax	-8,976.4	-8,522.3	-9,649.8	-9,772.0
Net Income	17,666.3	17,881.6	16,829.7	17,536.6
Cash Flow From Operations	14,480.5	8,297.4	12,805.7	5,270.7
Balance Sheet (000's)				
Cash & Equivalents	6,284.1	34,847.3	6,559.2	14,800.8
Total Current Assets	86,733.8	47,113.2	17,822.1	24,341.5
Fixed Assets, Net	0.0	0.0	0.0	0.0
Total Assets	740,650.7	673,794.2	528,632.1	455,135.6
Total Current Liabilities	10,831.7	4,421.1	4,324.8	4,318.3
Long-Term Debt	0.0	0.0	0.0	0.0
Stockholders' Equity	132,630.5	128,905.4	90,855.6	89,744.9
Performance & Financial Condition				
Return on Total Revenues %	21.36	22.82	25.21	27.07
Return on Avg Stockholders' Equity %	13.51	16.27	18.64	21.23
Return on Average Assets %	2.50	2.97	3.42	4.22
Current Ratio	8.01	10.66	4.12	5.64
Debt / Equity %	n.a.	n.a.	n.a.	n.a.

Compound Growth %'s	EPS %	0.18	Net Income %	0.25	Total Revenues %	8.49

Comments

The Company declared a 3 for 1 stock split in 1996. All per share amounts have been adjusted for consistency. Total life insurance in force topped $10 billion for the first time in 1996 resulting from 197,000 policies. Net earnings took a small dip due to a lower amount of gain realized on the sale of securities. Management is quick to point out that revenue and income from operations, excluding capital gains, were both 11% higher. It was a good year. Investment Classification: Value

Officers	Position	Ownership Information	
Stephen A. Milne	President, CEO	Number of Shares Outstanding	9,450,000
Thomas M. Sider	Exec VP, CFO	Market Capitalization	$ 262,237,500
Jan R. Van Gorder	Exec VP, Secretary	Frequency of Dividends	Annual
John J. Brinling	Exec VP	Number of Shareholders	1,146
Douglas F. Ziegler	Senior VP, Treasurer		

Other Information				
Transfer Agent	Company Office		Where Listed	OTC-BB
Auditor	Brown Schwab Berqquist & Co.		Symbol	ERIF
Market Maker	Advest, Inc.	(800)998-9834	SIC Code	6311
	Legg Mason Wood & Walker, Inc.	(800)221-9732	Employees	79
Broker Dealer	Regular Stockbroker			
	Bernard Taradash - Advest	(800)227-1207		

EvergreenBank

301 Eastlake Avenue East   Seattle, WA 98111-1722   Telephone (206)628-4250   Fax (206)628-8736

Company Description

EvergreenBank, founded in 1971 as Teachers State Bank, has two banking offices serving King, Snohomish and Pierce Counties, Washington. At the time it was founded, Evergreen was only the second bank to have been chartered in downtown Seattle since 1928 and it had to overcome considerable opposition from the banking establishment. The competition maintained that the bank violated state rules because it was to serve a special interest group rather than the general public. Its founder, Robert J. Handy, had already established a teacher's credit union, an insurance company, and a data processing company. All of these eventually became known as PEMCO Financial Services which the Bank is also affiliated with today. And yes, many of the customers are not teachers. You can avoid the notorious Seattle rain by using the Internet: (http:www.evbank.com).

	12/31/96	12/31/95	12/31/94	12/31/93
Per Share Information				
Stock Price	12.00	10.50	9.75	8.50
Earnings Per Share	1.24	1.28	1.18	1.24
Price / Earnings Ratio	9.68	8.20	8.26	6.85
Book Value Per Share	16.86	15.83	14.73	13.72
Price / Book Value %	71.17	66.33	66.19	61.95
Dividends Per Share	0.19	0.18	0.17	0.16
Annual Financial Data				
Operating Results (000's)				
Net Interest Income	5,252.0	5,160.0	4,847.0	4,657.0
Loan Loss Provision	-229.0	-255.0	-210.0	-270.0
Non-Interest Income	1,843.0	1,515.0	3,262.0	3,355.0
Non-Interest Expense	-5,600.0	-5,109.0	-6,711.0	-6,480.0
Income Before Taxes and Other	1,266.0	1,311.0	1,188.0	1,262.0
Other Items	0.0	0.0	0.0	0.0
Income Tax	-398.0	-416.0	-365.0	-399.0
Net Income	868.0	895.0	823.0	863.0
Balance Sheet (000's)				
Cash & Securities	75,350.0	60,175.0	56,427.0	61,882.0
Loans, Net	64,104.0	60,831.0	58,541.0	54,006.0
Total Assets	141,647.0	123,565.0	116,528.0	117,029.0
Deposits	94,892.0	82,163.0	81,907.0	71,773.0
Stockholders' Equity	11,758.0	11,037.0	10,268.0	9,563.0
Performance & Financial Condition				
Return on Avg Stockholders' Equity %	7.62	8.40	8.30	9.39
Return on Average Assets %	0.65	0.75	0.70	0.75
Equity to Assets %	8.30	8.93	8.81	8.17
Net Interest Margin	n.a.	n.a.	n.a.	n.a.
Reserve as a % of Problem Loans	67.24	108.29	97.62	465.48

Compound Growth %'s	EPS %	0.0	Net Income %	0.19	Net Interest Income %	4.09

Comments

The Bank declared a 2 for 1 stock split in 1994. 1993 per share amounts were restated for consistency. Considerable investment in new technology was cited as the reason for the 3% decline in earnings. Asset and loan growth was strong at 14.6% and 15.5%, respectively. The market remains thin as many market makers have expressed interest in the shares on behalf of their clients. Investment Classification: Value

Officers	Position	Ownership Information	
Roy T. Throndson	President, CEO	Number of Shares Outstanding	697,264
Rex M. Wallace	Senior VP	Market Capitalization	$ 8,367,168
William G. Filer II	CFO	Frequency of Dividends	Quarterly
Dan W. Curtis	Vice President	Number of Shareholders	n.a.
Valerie K. Blake	Vice President	Where Listed / Symbol	OTC-PS / n.a.

Other Information			Loan Mix	%
Transfer Agent	Company Office		R/E Mortgages	65.7
Auditor	John L. O'Brien & Company		Commerical	22.0
Market Maker	Ragen MacKinzie Incorporated	(800)426-5964	Consumer	8.8
	First Washington Corp.	(800)543-3332	Other	3.5
Broker Dealer	OTC Specialist			
	John Ballantyne - Black & Co.	(503)248-9600		

Exchange Bank

P.O. Box 403   Santa Rosa, CA 95402   Telephone (707)524-3000   Fax (707)524-3319

Company Description

For over 100 years, Exchange Bank has been providing full banking services to the businesses and population of Sonoma County, California. This region is on the heels of the Napa Valley as the country's finest producer of premium table wines. The growth of businesses to the north of San Francisco has caused a boom in recent years in Santa Rosa and other communities that comprise the Bank's service area. The Bank opened its seventeenth office in Cloverdale in 1996.

	12/31/96	12/31/95	12/31/94	12/31/93
Per Share Information				
Stock Price	64.62	67.50	61.00	58.54
Earnings Per Share	5.58	5.31	5.64	5.33
Price / Earnings Ratio	11.58	12.71	10.82	10.98
Book Value Per Share	46.67	45.69	43.33	41.34
Price / Book Value %	138.46	147.73	140.78	141.61
Dividends Per Share	4.50	4.00	3.50	3.41
Annual Financial Data				
Operating Results (000's)				
Net Interest Income	35,935.0	34,770.0	35,116.0	34,007.0
Loan Loss Provision	-1,215.0	-760.0	-1,620.0	-1,520.0
Non-Interest Income	9,704.0	6,556.0	8,761.0	7,035.0
Non-Interest Expense	-30,900.0	-27,952.0	-28,703.0	-27,127.0
Income Before Taxes and Other	13,524.0	12,614.0	13,554.0	12,395.0
Other Items	0.0	0.0	0.0	0.0
Income Tax	-3,963.0	-3,510.0	-3,877.0	-3,258.0
Net Income	9,561.0	9,104.0	9,677.0	9,137.0
Balance Sheet (000's)				
Cash & Securities	308,412.0	321,779.0	342,478.0	306,231.0
Loans, Net	344,015.0	296,933.0	264,054.0	279,187.0
Total Assets	680,187.0	646,664.0	632,273.0	634,829.0
Deposits	593,984.0	563,046.0	551,442.0	553,712.0
Stockholders' Equity	79,984.0	78,314.0	74,263.0	70,852.0
Performance & Financial Condition				
Return on Avg Stockholders' Equity %	12.08	11.93	13.34	13.33
Return on Average Assets %	1.44	1.42	1.53	1.48
Equity to Assets %	11.76	12.11	11.75	11.16
Net Interest Margin	6.09	5.95	6.40	6.35
Reserve as a % of Problem Loans	1,464.36	5,214.44	2,010.96	n.a.

Compound Growth %'s	EPS %	1.54	Net Income %	1.52	Net Interest Income %	1.86

Comments

The Bank declared a 2 1/2 % stock dividend in 1994. 1993 per share amounts were adjusted for consistency. Management attributes record 1996 earnings to steady loan growth and stable interest rates, controlled cost, increased fee income and a tripling of income from Financial Network Investment Corporation, the Bank's subsidiary that offers mutual funds and other investments. The substantial ownership interest of the Doyle Trust prevents the Bank from being acquired by another institution. This guarantee of remaining a community bank has proven to be an asset in the marketplace. Investment Classification: Income

Officers	Position	Ownership Information	
C. William Reinking	President, CEO	Number of Shares Outstanding	1,714,000
Richard B. McConkie	Exec VP	Market Capitalization	$ 110,758,680
William R. Schrader	Senior VP, Sr Loan Officer	Frequency of Dividends	Quarterly
Sharon E. Stockham	Senior VP, Secretary	Number of Shareholders	n.a.
David J. Voss	Senior VP	Where Listed / Symbol	OTC-BB / EXSR

Other Information			Loan Mix	%
Transfer Agent	U.S. Stock Transfer Corp. Glendale, CA		R/E Mortgages	44.4
Auditor	KPMG Peat Marwick LLP		Commerical	29.0
Market Maker	A.G. Edwards & Sons, Inc.	(707)528-2332	Consumer	26.6
	First Affiliated Securities	(707)545-4810		
Broker Dealer	Regular Stockbroker			
	Standard Investment	(888)783-4688 Ext: Jack		

Exolon-ESK Company

1000 East Niagara Street Tonawanda, NY 14150 Telephone (716)693-4550 Fax (716)693-6607

Company Description

The Company is in the business of manufacturing and selling products which are used principally for abrasive, refractory and metallurgical applications. The primary products are fused aluminum oxide and silicon carbide. The Company's production facilities are located in Illinois, New York and Canada. The Company also has operations in Norway conducted through a 50% owned joint venture. The Exolon Company was founded in 1914. It merged with the ESK Corporation in 1984 and assumed its current name.

	12/31/96	12/31/95	12/31/94	12/31/93
Per Share Information				
Stock Price	26.00	20.32	17.25	20.50
Earnings Per Share	6.05	3.44	1.42	0.03
Price / Earnings Ratio	4.30	5.91	12.15	683.33
Book Value Per Share	26.23	20.70	17.29	15.57
Price / Book Value %	91.55	90.67	99.77	121.59
Dividends Per Share	0.0	0.0	0.0	0.0
Annual Financial Data				
Operating Results (000's)				
Total Revenues	78,462.0	68,592.0	59,494.0	58,225.0
Costs & Expenses	-69,237.0	-62,512.0	-56,142.0	-55,989.0
Income Before Taxes and Other	9,225.0	6,857.0	1,942.0	1,918.0
Other Items	0.0	0.0	0.0	-1,173.0
Income Tax	-3,145.0	-2,893.0	-426.0	-712.0
Net Income	6,080.0	3,964.0	1,516.0	33.0
Cash Flow From Operations	8,986.0	3,539.0	4,176.0	2,197.0
Balance Sheet (000's)				
Cash & Equivalents	275.0	440.0	467.0	113.0
Total Current Assets	28,301.0	29,395.0	25,441.0	25,434.0
Fixed Assets, Net	18,385.0	15,193.0	15,395.0	16,591.0
Total Assets	61,483.0	50,215.0	45,309.0	45,834.0
Total Current Liabilities	8,818.0	7,981.0	7,387.0	8,660.0
Long-Term Debt	20,433.0	15,350.0	14,900.0	16,900.0
Stockholders' Equity	28,258.0	22,298.0	18,628.0	16,770.0
Performance & Financial Condition				
Return on Total Revenues %	7.75	5.78	2.55	0.06
Return on Avg Stockholders' Equity %	24.05	19.37	8.57	0.20
Return on Average Assets %	10.89	8.30	3.33	0.07
Current Ratio	3.21	3.68	3.44	2.94
Debt / Equity %	72.31	68.84	79.99	100.78

Compound Growth %'s	EPS %	486.42	Net Income %	469.02	Total Revenues %	10.45

Comments

The Company has two classes of common stock and two series of convertible preferred stock. We assumed that the preferred shares were converted to common for the book value calculation. Management reports that the 13% increase in sales was due to a strong demand for abrasive products during 1996 as compared to 1995. An improvement in gross margins and lower average debt also contributed to improving the bottom line by a whopping 75.6%. For the quarter ended March 31, 1997, the Company reported earnings per share of $1.38 as compared to $1.45 for the same period of 1996. Investment Classification: Value

Officers	Position	Ownership Information	
Theodore E. Dann, Jr.	Chairman	Number of Shares Outstanding	1,077,189
J. Fred Silver	President, CEO	Market Capitalization	$ 25,867,192
Michael H. Bieger	VP - Finance, CFO	Frequency of Dividends	n.a.
Nancy E. Gates	Secretary	Number of Shareholders	182
John L. Redshaw	VP - Sales		

Other Information			
Transfer Agent	State Street Bank & Trust North Quincy, MA	Where Listed	BE
Auditor	Ernst & Young LLP	Symbol	EXOL
Market Maker	Hill Thompson Magid & Co., Inc (800)631-3083	SIC Code	3290
	Koonce Securities, Inc. (800)368-2802	Employees	285
Broker Dealer	Regular Stockbroker		

ExperTelligence, Inc.

203 Chapala Street, Ste. B   Santa Barbara, CA 93101   Telephone (805)962-2558   Fax (805)962-5788

Company Description

The objective of ExperTelligence is to help companies make their information needs or their information-driven products interactive on the World Wide Web. It does this by providing them with software tools and applications based on advanced, object-oriented, Internet-aware software technologies which are designed, developed, integrated, and sold by the Company and its partners.

	09/30/96	09/30/95
Per Share Information		
Stock Price as of 12/31	3.25	0.75
Earnings Per Share	0.31	0.05
Price / Earnings Ratio	10.48	15.00
Book Value Per Share	1.20	0.91
Price / Book Value %	270.83	82.42
Dividends Per Share	0.0	0.0
Annual Financial Data		
Operating Results (000's)		
Total Revenues	1,283.3	628.5
Costs & Expenses	-1,092.8	-504.2
Income Before Taxes and Other	190.5	124.3
Other Items	0.0	0.0
Income Tax	237.2	-55.8
Net Income	427.7	68.5
Cash Flow From Operations	320.4	25.2
Balance Sheet (000's)		
Cash & Equivalents	523.4	37.7
Total Current Assets	903.7	337.8
Fixed Assets, Net	59.8	32.6
Total Assets	1,720.7	952.8
Total Current Liabilities	124.2	87.5
Long-Term Debt	0.0	0.0
Stockholders' Equity	1,596.5	865.3
Performance & Financial Condition		
Return on Total Revenues %	33.33	10.89
Return on Avg Stockholders' Equity %	34.75	n.a.
Return on Average Assets %	32.00	n.a.
Current Ratio	7.28	3.86
Debt / Equity %	n.a.	n.a.

Compound Growth %'s   EPS % n.a.   Net Income % n.a.   Total Revenues % n.a.

Comments

Compound growth rates were not displayed because of a lack of a meaningful period of comparison. The increase in net income is largely attributable to the sales of licenses to the Company's proprietary software products. For the six months ended March 31, 1997, the Company reported slightly higher revenues and a loss of $10,528, $.01 per share. The loss reflects a substantial investment in research and development as the Company prepares new products for the marketplace. Management intends to increase marketing efforts, as well as research and development costs for the balance of the year in an effort to continue the growth of the business. Investment Classification: Speculative

Officers	Position	Ownership Information	
Denison Bollay	President, CFO	Number of Shares Outstanding	1,331,321
Karl Marlantes	COO	Market Capitalization	$ 4,326,793
Robert Reali	Vice President	Frequency of Dividends	n.a.
		Number of Shareholders	1,110

Other Information				
Transfer Agent	American Securities Transfer, Inc. Denver, CO		Where Listed	OTC-BB
Auditor	McGowan Guntermann		Symbol	EXGP
Market Maker	Newby & Company	(800)456-3992	SIC Code	7372
	Sherwood Securities Corp.	(800)435-1235	Employees	n.a.
Broker Dealer	Regular Stockbroker			

Eyemakers, Inc.

4100 McEwen, Ste. 160   Dallas, TX 75244   Telephone (972)386-8977   Fax (972)386-8979

Company Description

Eyemakers, Inc., formerly 21st Century Vision, Inc., was formed in 1995 for the purpose of acquiring modern technology and marketing concepts related to the eye-care industry, and to develop training, management services and business opportunities for the independent optometrist market. Business activities are primarily with customers in the Dallas-Fort Worth metroplex area. The Company went public in January, 1996, through its issuance of shares with a Regulation D offering.

	12/31/96	12/31/95
Per Share Information		
Stock Price	1.25	1.00
Earnings Per Share	0.08	0.94
Price / Earnings Ratio	15.63	1.06
Book Value Per Share	0.42	0.99
Price / Book Value %	297.62	101.01
Dividends Per Share	0.0	0.0
Annual Financial Data		
Operating Results (000's)		
Total Revenues	2,794.8	2,773.3
Costs & Expenses	-2,186.6	-1,280.0
Income Before Taxes and Other	608.2	1,493.3
Other Items	0.0	0.0
Income Tax	-232.5	-551.9
Net Income	375.7	941.5
Cash Flow From Operations	-855.2	-48.5
Balance Sheet (000's)		
Cash & Equivalents	8.2	7.9
Total Current Assets	1,131.1	334.1
Fixed Assets, Net	140.5	164.9
Total Assets	3,742.4	1,922.8
Total Current Liabilities	942.6	285.1
Long-Term Debt	0.0	0.0
Stockholders' Equity	2,206.8	989.4
Performance & Financial Condition		
Return on Total Revenues %	13.44	33.95
Return on Avg Stockholders' Equity %	23.51	n.a.
Return on Average Assets %	13.26	n.a.
Current Ratio	1.20	1.17
Debt / Equity %	n.a.	n.a.

Compound Growth %'s	EPS % -91.49	Net Income % -60.10	Total Revenues % 0.78

Comments

4.2 million shares of common were issued during 1996, thereby diluting the shares outstanding at the prior year end. On May 15, 1997, the Company announced the acquisition of Budget Opticals of America, a 30-store Texas-based chain of corporate and associate retail optical stores. As of May 31, 1997, the shares were trading in the range of bid $3, ask $4 per share. Investment Classification: Speculative

Officers	Position	Ownership Information	
George Orm	Chairman	Number of Shares Outstanding	5,235,044
Wayne Allison	President, CEO	Market Capitalization	$ 6,543,805
Mike McCauley	COO	Frequency of Dividends	n.a.
Darrell Jolley	CFO	Number of Shareholders	Under 500

Other Information				
Transfer Agent	Silver State Transfer & Registrar Salt Lake City, UT		Where Listed	OTC-BB
Auditor	King Griffin & Adamson P.C.		Symbol	EYEM
Market Maker	Acap Financial Inc.	(800)541-3961	SIC Code	8042
	Paragon Capital Corp.	(800)345-0505	Employees	n.a.
Broker Dealer	Regular Stockbroker			

FCFT, Inc.

1001 Mercer Street   Princeton, WV 24740-5909   Telephone (304)487-9000   Fax (304)487-1269

Company Description

The Company is a multi-bank holding company headquartered in Princeton, West Virginia. Its full service commercial bank subsidiary, First Community Bank, operates from twenty-three branch locations in West Virginia and Virginia. During 1996, Citizens National Bank of Tazewell was acquired in exchange for 263,159 shares of Company stock. Two branches were also acquired from Huntington National Bank in September, 1996. At the end of 1996, a definitive agreement was signed with Blue Ridge Bank of Sparta to merge them into the organization. You can check out this dynamic organization that was founded in 1884 on the Internet: (http://www.fcbinc.com).

	12/31/96	12/31/95	12/31/94	12/31/93
Per Share Information				
Stock Price	34.00	32.50	29.25	24.00
Earnings Per Share	3.09	2.93	2.60	2.15
Price / Earnings Ratio	11.00	11.09	11.25	11.16
Book Value Per Share	19.76	18.19	15.74	15.18
Price / Book Value %	172.06	178.67	185.83	158.10
Dividends Per Share	1.43	1.30	1.10	0.64
Annual Financial Data				
Operating Results (000's)				
Net Interest Income	38,008.0	33,726.0	32,193.0	30,941.0
Loan Loss Provision	-2,273.0	-2,093.0	-1,668.0	-1,841.0
Non-Interest Income	9,070.0	7,056.0	6,865.0	5,851.0
Non-Interest Expense	-24,358.0	-21,526.0	-22,055.0	-21,552.0
Income Before Taxes and Other	20,447.0	17,163.0	15,335.0	13,399.0
Other Items	0.0	0.0	0.0	0.0
Income Tax	-6,530.0	-4,791.0	-4,281.0	-4,228.0
Net Income	13,917.0	12,372.0	11,054.0	9,171.0
Balance Sheet (000's)				
Cash & Securities	263,810.0	253,468.0	278,964.0	293,162.0
Loans, Net	538,716.0	448,750.0	386,292.0	362,427.0
Total Assets	837,664.0	731,398.0	698,870.0	686,465.0
Deposits	643,497.0	577,847.0	573,955.0	570,931.0
Stockholders' Equity	89,325.0	76,606.0	66,740.0	64,650.0
Performance & Financial Condition				
Return on Avg Stockholders' Equity %	16.77	17.26	16.83	14.85
Return on Average Assets %	1.77	1.73	1.60	1.38
Equity to Assets %	10.66	10.47	9.55	9.42
Net Interest Margin	5.39	5.47	5.35	5.25
Reserve as a % of Problem Loans	143.65	165.00	108.00	74.29

Compound Growth %'s	EPS %	12.85	Net Income %	14.91	Net Interest Income %	7.10

Comments

The acquisition referred to above was accounted for as a pooling of interests. Therefore, past financial statements were restated. We did not change information from numbers as originally reported from 1993 through 1995 so as to provide a meaningful relationship to stock price performance. Neither did we restate returns on assets and equity which are outstanding either way. Included in 1996 results is a $3.3 million loss from customer fraud. This hopefully nonrecurring item is partially offset by a $1.5 gain from the termination of the defined benefit pension plan. Investment Classification: Growth & Income

Officers	Position	Ownership Information	
James L. Harrison, Sr.	President, CEO	Number of Shares Outstanding	4,519,996
John M. Mendez	Vice President, CFO	Market Capitalization	$ 153,679,864
Robert L. Buzzo	Vice President, Secretary	Frequency of Dividends	Quarterly
		Number of Shareholders	n.a.
		Where Listed / Symbol	OTC-BB / FCFT

Other Information			Loan Mix	%
Transfer Agent	First Community Bank Bluefield, WV		R/E Mortgages	61.8
Auditor	Deloitte & Touche LLP		Consumer	21.8
Market Maker	Koonce Securities, Inc.	(800)368-2802	Commerical	14.5
	Ferris, Baker Watts Inc.	(800)638-7411	Construction	1.9
Broker Dealer	Regular Stockbroker			

Factory Point Bancorp, Inc.

Route 7A   Manchester Center, VT 05255   Telephone (802)362-2424   Fax (802)362-4101

Company Description

Factory Point National Bank, subsidiary of the Company, has six banking locations in the beautiful Green Mountains region of Vermont, serving communities like Arlington, Manchester, Rutland and Springfield. The Bank has a Trust and Investment Group which managed $200 million in assets at year end 1996, up from $175 million in 1995. Factory Point National Bank was chartered in 1883.

	12/31/96	12/31/95	12/31/94	12/31/93
Per Share Information				
Stock Price	28.50	20.00	16.36	14.65
Earnings Per Share	2.42	2.25	2.13	1.37
Price / Earnings Ratio	11.78	8.89	7.68	10.69
Book Value Per Share	20.74	19.31	17.69	16.23
Price / Book Value %	137.42	103.57	92.48	90.26
Dividends Per Share	0.91	0.69	0.60	0.36
Annual Financial Data				
Operating Results (000's)				
Net Interest Income	6,627.2	6,302.8	5,841.1	5,319.9
Loan Loss Provision	-595.0	-290.0	-40.0	-86.3
Non-Interest Income	1,737.2	1,495.4	1,856.0	1,234.4
Non-Interest Expense	-5,424.3	-5,338.7	-5,549.9	-5,134.0
Income Before Taxes and Other	2,345.0	2,169.4	2,107.2	1,334.0
Other Items	0.0	0.0	0.0	0.0
Income Tax	-786.2	-711.8	-730.1	-441.0
Net Income	1,558.8	1,457.6	1,377.1	893.0
Balance Sheet (000's)				
Cash & Securities	36,316.5	30,619.8	25,022.4	31,596.7
Loans, Net	99,904.2	98,607.8	93,882.2	86,949.5
Total Assets	143,051.8	138,089.6	123,355.4	126,662.9
Deposits	126,307.4	121,874.2	108,972.0	113,035.6
Stockholders' Equity	13,315.8	12,485.5	11,440.3	10,493.3
Performance & Financial Condition				
Return on Avg Stockholders' Equity %	12.08	12.18	12.56	8.79
Return on Average Assets %	1.11	1.12	1.10	0.71
Equity to Assets %	9.31	9.04	9.27	8.28
Net Interest Margin	n.a.	n.a.	n.a.	n.a.
Reserve as a % of Problem Loans	120.36	123.47	98.38	87.76

Compound Growth %'s	EPS %	20.88	Net Income %	20.41	Net Interest Income %	7.60

Comments

The Company declared a 2 for 1 stock split in 1995 and a 10% stock dividend in 1996. All per share amounts were adjusted accordingly for consistency. Noninterest income climbed 16% during 1996 with a strong performance noted in the Trust Department. These excellent results were partially offset by a large provision for loan losses. Management is installing new computer technology to speed the loan application process and intends to generate excess loans, including ones through the Small Business Administration, that can be sold in the secondary market. Investment Classification: Growth & Value

Officers	Position	Ownership Information	
Paul J. Beaulieu	President, CEO	Number of Shares Outstanding	642,050
Dale W. Good	Senior VP	Market Capitalization	$ 18,298,425
David E. Bardin	Vice President	Frequency of Dividends	Quarterly
Linda M. Gordon	Vice President	Number of Shareholders	n.a.
John F. McGrath, III	Vice President, CFO	Where Listed / Symbol	OTC-BB / FAPB

Other Information			Loan Mix	%
Transfer Agent	Company Office		R/E Mortgages	87.3
Auditor	KPMG Peat Marwick LLP		Consumer	10.0
Market Maker	Cowen & Co.	(212)495-6263	Construction	2.7
	Ryan, Beck & Co.	(800)325-7926		
Broker Dealer	Regular Stockbroker			

Fair Grounds Corporation

1751 Gentilly Boulevard   New Orleans, LA 70119   Telephone (504)944-5515   Fax (504)944-2511

Company Description

The Company, founded in 1941, is the owner and operator of the Fair Grounds Race Course in New Orleans, Louisiana, at which thoroughbred horse racing, off-track betting and video poker gaming are conducted. The Fair Grounds Race Course is in its 125th racing season, making it the third oldest thoroughbred racing track in the United States. The Company also operates five off-track betting facilities at other locations in Louisiana. An additional five facilities are operated through an affiliate. Food and beverages are also sold at each of these locations.

	10/31/96	10/31/95	10/31/94	10/31/93
Per Share Information				
Stock Price as of 12/31	12.50	16.00	11.00	11.00
Earnings Per Share	1.87	-1.09	16.48	-6.83
Price / Earnings Ratio	6.68	n.a.	0.67	n.a.
Book Value Per Share	25.38	23.43	24.64	n.a.
Price / Book Value %	49.25	68.29	44.64	n.a.
Dividends Per Share	0.0	0.0	0.0	0.0
Annual Financial Data				
Operating Results (000's)				
Total Revenues	34,505.7	27,796.7	25,402.4	35,441.4
Costs & Expenses	-33,171.4	-28,611.5	-28,804.8	-37,981.8
Income Before Taxes and Other	1,174.6	-916.6	-3,402.4	-2,540.5
Other Items	0.0	104.0	9,237.7	-1,042.7
Income Tax	-294.9	300.5	1,878.6	383.8
Net Income	879.7	-512.1	7,713.9	-3,199.3
Cash Flow From Operations	4,218.9	5,084.8	-1,043.8	2,305.2
Balance Sheet (000's)				
Cash & Equivalents	6,398.9	1,273.5	8,039.3	n.a.
Total Current Assets	8,357.5	3,455.6	11,616.2	n.a.
Fixed Assets, Net	26,332.4	27,427.8	14,819.6	n.a.
Total Assets	34,791.6	30,954.7	26,470.3	n.a.
Total Current Liabilities	18,375.3	15,966.3	9,735.1	n.a.
Long-Term Debt	0.0	0.0	1,000.0	n.a.
Stockholders' Equity	11,890.6	10,968.3	11,535.3	n.a.
Performance & Financial Condition				
Return on Total Revenues %	2.55	-1.84	30.37	-9.03
Return on Avg Stockholders' Equity %	7.70	-4.55	n.a.	n.a.
Return on Average Assets %	2.68	-1.78	n.a.	n.a.
Current Ratio	0.45	0.22	1.19	n.a.
Debt / Equity %	n.a.	n.a.	8.67	n.a.

Compound Growth %'s	EPS % n.a.	Net Income % n.a.	Total Revenues % -0.89

Comments

A fire in December, 1993, destroyed the club house and grandstand building at the race track. Temporary facilities have been used as a temporary solution. Disputes as to insurance coverage are slowly being resolved and contribute to some of the large swings in annual profits. One of the impediments to the Company's ability to obtain long-term financing for the construction of a new facility has been the uncertainty in Louisiana concerning the future of the gaming industry, although partial financing has been arranged. Revenues were 11% higher in the first quarter of 1997 and earnings per share climbed to $2.23 from $1.41 a year earlier. Management believes the new facility will be operational in late 1997, hopefully in time for opening day. And here they come around the last turn. Investment Classification: Value & Speculative

Officers	Position	Ownership Information	
Marie G. Krantz	Chairman, Treasurer	Number of Shares Outstanding	468,580
Bryan G. Krantz	President, General Manager	Market Capitalization	$ 5,857,250
Joan B. Stewart	Secretary	Frequency of Dividends	n.a.
Mervin Muniz, Jr.	Vice President	Number of Shareholders	430
Gordon M. Robertson	Vice President, CFO		

Other Information

Transfer Agent	National Bank of North America New York, NY		Where Listed	OTC-BB
Auditor	Not indicated		Symbol	FGNO
Market Maker	Dorsey Investment Securities	(800)375-5431	SIC Code	7948
	Carr Securities Corporation	(800)221-2243	Employees	n.a.
Broker Dealer	Regular Stockbroker			
	Stephen R. Schuller - Dorsey	(800)375-5431		

Fall River Gas Company

155 North Main Street   Fall River, MA 02722-0911   Telephone (508)675-7811   Fax (508)677-3242

Company Description

The Company sells, distributes, and transports natural gas (mixed with propane and liquefied natural gas during winter months) at retail through a pipeline system in the city of Fall River and the towns of Somerset, Swansea and Westport, Massachusetts. Customers that use gas for heating, cooking and or water heating include over 45,000 residences, federal and state housing projects and commercial entities. The Company was organized in 1880.

	09/30/96	09/30/95	09/30/94	09/30/93
Per Share Information				
Stock Price as of 12/31	16.25	24.50	25.00	18.25
Earnings Per Share	0.80	0.91	1.40	1.32
Price / Earnings Ratio	20.31	26.92	17.86	13.83
Book Value Per Share	7.10	7.26	7.31	6.89
Price / Book Value %	228.87	337.47	342.00	264.88
Dividends Per Share	0.96	0.96	0.98	0.97
Annual Financial Data				
Operating Results (000's)				
Total Revenues	49,756.3	45,190.5	49,145.8	45,509.3
Costs & Expenses	-47,989.2	-43,102.9	-45,666.2	-42,175.0
Income Before Taxes and Other	1,767.1	2,087.6	3,479.6	3,334.3
Other Items	0.0	0.0	0.0	0.0
Income Tax	-341.4	-471.4	-988.5	-981.9
Net Income	1,425.7	1,616.2	2,491.1	2,352.4
Cash Flow From Operations	1,214.5	5,507.2	6,783.6	-1,908.8
Balance Sheet (000's)				
Cash & Equivalents	393.9	315.3	360.8	356.3
Total Current Assets	9,088.2	9,934.3	12,150.2	12,292.1
Fixed Assets, Net	41,415.3	38,821.2	35,539.7	32,748.0
Total Assets	53,191.2	50,956.5	49,625.8	46,501.4
Total Current Liabilities	20,014.2	24,692.3	22,762.3	20,497.9
Long-Term Debt	13,500.0	6,500.0	7,380.0	7,560.0
Stockholders' Equity	12,637.4	12,921.0	13,014.1	12,268.0
Performance & Financial Condition				
Return on Total Revenues %	2.87	3.58	5.07	5.17
Return on Avg Stockholders' Equity %	11.16	12.46	19.71	19.68
Return on Average Assets %	2.74	3.21	5.18	5.55
Current Ratio	0.45	0.40	0.53	0.60
Debt / Equity %	106.83	50.31	56.71	61.62

Compound Growth %'s	EPS %	-15.37	Net Income %	-15.37	Total Revenues %	3.02

Comments

Higher gas sales during 1996 were due in large part to colder weather, approximately 9.8% colder than the prior year. Other operating expenses increased 14.1% over fiscal 1995. Wage increases, escalating health care costs, and inflation were the primary factors causing this increase. Over the last several years, management has had to deal with new regulations concerning the distribution of natural gas. The Company has had to incur certain transition costs in connection with restructuring contracts, etc. to comply with the regulations. For the six months ended March 31, 1997, revenues were off slightly and net earnings were higher, $.97 per share as compared to $.96 per share for the same period of 1996. Investment Classification: Income

Officers	Position	Ownership Information	
Bradford J. Faxon	President, CEO	Number of Shares Outstanding	1,780,542
Peter H. Thanas	Senior VP, Treasurer	Market Capitalization	$ 28,933,808
John F. Fanning	Vice President	Frequency of Dividends	Quarterly
Wallace E. Fletcher	Controller	Number of Shareholders	832

Other Information

Transfer Agent	State Street Bank & Trust Company Boston, MA		Where Listed	OTC-BB
Auditor	Arthur Andersen LLP		Symbol	FALL
Market Maker	Gruntal & Co., Incorporated	(212)344-2297	SIC Code	4924
	Advest, Inc.	(800)998-9834	Employees	175
Broker Dealer	Regular Stockbroker			
	Bernard Taradash - Advest	(800)227-1207		

Farmer Bros. Co.

20333 South Normandie Avenue Torrance, CA 90502 Telephone (310)787-5200 Fax (310)320-2436

Company Description

Farmer Bros. Co., founded in 1923, roasts and packages coffee, processes spices and other restaurant supplies, and manufactures a complete line of coffee-brewing equipment. The Company consists of four divisions: Restaurant and Institutional Sales, Brewmatic (equipment), Spice Products, and Custom Coffee Plan. The Company owns approximately 23 patents and has 97 selling divisions, located in most urban centers in the western states, which market over 300 Company products. This is one of only four NASDAQ listed stocks that we included in this manual for special reasons noted below.

	06/30/96	06/30/95	06/30/94	06/30/93
Per Share Information				
Stock Price as of 12/31	147.00	132.00	120.00	134.00
Earnings Per Share	12.13	10.13	5.36	9.84
Price / Earnings Ratio	12.12	13.03	22.39	13.62
Book Value Per Share	121.30	111.14	102.47	99.65
Price / Book Value %	121.19	118.77	117.11	134.47
Dividends Per Share	2.15	2.00	2.00	1.80
Annual Financial Data				
Operating Results (000's)				
Total Revenues	233,766.0	240,711.0	201,062.0	200,288.0
Costs & Expenses	-194,877.0	-209,427.0	-184,373.0	-160,750.0
Income Before Taxes and Other	38,889.0	31,284.0	16,689.0	39,538.0
Other Items	0.0	0.0	0.0	-5,294.0
Income Tax	-15,526.0	-11,767.0	-6,359.0	-15,294.0
Net Income	23,363.0	19,517.0	10,330.0	18,950.0
Cash Flow From Operations	18,938.0	30,472.0	5,012.0	8,337.0
Balance Sheet (000's)				
Cash & Equivalents	28,165.0	8,321.0	8,681.0	64,742.0
Total Current Assets	167,059.0	149,806.0	103,375.0	155,147.0
Fixed Assets, Net	33,343.0	33,213.0	28,943.0	27,701.0
Total Assets	260,890.0	244,340.0	219,903.0	216,265.0
Total Current Liabilities	14,330.0	18,724.0	12,488.0	15,268.0
Long-Term Debt	0.0	0.0	0.0	0.0
Stockholders' Equity	233,668.0	214,111.0	197,405.0	191,972.0
Performance & Financial Condition				
Return on Total Revenues %	9.99	8.11	5.14	9.46
Return on Avg Stockholders' Equity %	10.44	9.49	5.31	10.26
Return on Average Assets %	9.25	8.41	4.74	9.31
Current Ratio	11.66	8.00	8.28	10.16
Debt / Equity %	n.a.	n.a.	n.a.	n.a.

Compound Growth %'s	EPS %	7.22	Net Income %	7.23	Total Revenues %	5.29

Comments

We began our investigation of the Company when it refused our request for a copy of its financial statement. After we obtained the information from other sources, we first noticed that the number of shareholders was steadily declining; 732, 688, 654 and 628 in 1993, 1994, 1995 and 1996, respectively. We speculate that the Company hopes to become exempt from SEC reporting and/or is trying to suppress the trading value of the stock. Why? One reason might be estate tax planning for Roy F. Farmer, now age 80, who owns 834,000 shares with a value of over $122 million. A redemption may also be in the cards as the Company has accumulated over $100 million excess liquidity. For the nine months ended March 31, 1997, the Company had slightly lower revenues and income of $6.79 per share as compared to $9.22 in the 1996 fiscal year. Investment Classification: Value

Officers	Position	Ownership Information	
Roy F. Farmer	Chairman, CEO	Number of Shares Outstanding	1,926,414
David W. Uhley	Secretary	Market Capitalization	$ 283,182,858
John E. Simmons	Treasurer	Frequency of Dividends	Quarterly
Kenneth R. Carson	VP - Sales	Number of Shareholders	628

Other Information			
Transfer Agent	Chase Melon Shareholder Services Encino, CA	Where Listed	NASDAQ
Auditor	Coopers & Lybrand L.L.P.	Symbol	FARM
Market Maker	See Note	SIC Code	2095
		Employees	1192
Broker Dealer	Regular Stockbroker		

Farmers & Merchants Bank of Long Beach

302 Pine Avenue   Long Beach, CA 90802   Telephone (310)437-0011   Fax (310)437-8672

Company Description

The Bank is engaged primarily in commercial lending and operates primarily in southern Los Angeles County and Orange County, California, from seventeen offices. Farmers & Merchants Bank of Long Beach, founded in 1907, is still largely owned by the Walker family (no relation). Farmers & Merchants emphasis on personalized customer service and conservative lending practices has made them the envy of California's banking community. A proposed management stock option plan awarding options on 4,700 shares was recently approved by the shareholders.

	12/31/96	12/31/95	12/31/94	12/31/93
Per Share Information				
Stock Price	1,855.00	1,830.00	1,700.00	1,825.00
Earnings Per Share	195.39	188.83	198.43	204.99
Price / Earnings Ratio	9.49	9.69	8.57	8.90
Book Value Per Share	2,218.32	2,094.54	1,921.61	1,795.22
Price / Book Value %	83.62	87.37	88.47	101.66
Dividends Per Share	60.00	58.00	50.00	50.00
Annual Financial Data				
Operating Results (000's)				
Net Interest Income	72,356.3	76,871.0	80,524.1	85,517.7
Loan Loss Provision	-2,000.0	-4,000.0	-9,000.0	-14,000.0
Non-Interest Income	8,969.8	6,899.8	9,152.6	6,247.9
Non-Interest Expense	-25,889.4	-27,679.5	-26,208.4	-26,669.7
Income Before Taxes and Other	53,436.7	52,091.3	54,468.3	51,095.9
Other Items	0.0	0.0	0.0	6,851.8
Income Tax	-21,529.5	-21,255.8	-22,065.1	-24,485.3
Net Income	31,907.2	30,835.5	32,403.2	33,462.4
Balance Sheet (000's)				
Cash & Securities	1,084,513.9	1,049,315.9	1,018,460.4	1,047,911.0
Loans, Net	435,506.3	416,775.3	474,061.6	512,364.6
Total Assets	1,573,044.3	1,522,034.2	1,538,951.2	1,600,082.3
Deposits	1,047,324.9	1,036,531.1	1,060,694.3	1,108,150.8
Stockholders' Equity	362,251.9	342,038.6	313,799.3	293,051.0
Performance & Financial Condition				
Return on Avg Stockholders' Equity %	9.06	9.40	10.68	11.93
Return on Average Assets %	2.06	2.01	2.06	2.12
Equity to Assets %	23.03	22.47	20.39	18.31
Net Interest Margin	n.a.	n.a.	n.a.	n.a.
Reserve as a % of Problem Loans	45.69	38.76	35.06	127.93

Compound Growth %'s	EPS % -1.59	Net Income % -1.57	Net Interest Income % -5.42

Comments

The Bank only releases its financial statements to shareholders but without a management letter. The annual meeting is typically a well-attended event. Jack Norberg, financial analyst with Standard Investment, reports "performance ratios for Farmer's & Merchants Bank have been spectacular, despite a severity of government defense cuts, state budgetary problems, difficult real estate markets, and an anemic southern California economy." 1993 results include a nonrecurring benefit of $6,851,800, $41.97 per share, from a change in accounting method. This causes the compound growth rates in earnings to be negative rather than positive. Investment Classification: Value

Officers	Position	Ownership Information	
Kenneth G. Walker	Chairman	Number of Shares Outstanding	163,300
John W. H. Hinrichs	Senior VP	Market Capitalization	$ 302,921,500
James A. Robison	Senior VP	Frequency of Dividends	Quarterly
Daniel K. Walker	Senior VP	Number of Shareholders	n.a.
W. Henry Walker	Secretary	Where Listed / Symbol	OTC-BB / FMBL

Other Information		Loan Mix	%
Transfer Agent	Company Office	Commerical	52.8
Auditor	KPMG Peat Marwick LLP	R/E Mortgages	37.1
Market Maker	Carr Securities Corporation (800)221-2243	Construction	5.7
	Ragen Mackenzie Inc. (800)426-5964	Consumer	4.4
Broker Dealer	Regular Stockbroker		
	Standard Investment (888)783-4688 Ext: Jack		

Fiduciary Trust Company International

Two World Trade Center   New York, NY 10048-0772   Telephone (212)466-4100   Fax (212)313-2677

Company Description

Fiduciary Trust Company International was founded in 1931 to specialize in investment management and administration of assets for individuals and families. The Company extended its investment management services to institutions during the 1930's and began investing globally in the 1960's. Today they have over 600 employees and offices in New York, Los Angeles, Washington, D.C., Miami, London, Geneva and Hong Kong.

	12/31/96	12/31/95	12/31/94	12/31/93
Per Share Information				
Stock Price	25.75	25.00	21.50	17.67
Earnings Per Share	1.75	1.67	1.58	1.45
Price / Earnings Ratio	14.71	14.97	13.61	12.19
Book Value Per Share	11.32	10.47	9.23	8.22
Price / Book Value %	227.47	238.78	232.94	214.96
Dividends Per Share	0.78	0.72	0.70	0.64
Annual Financial Data				
Operating Results (000's)				
Net Interest Income	6,161.8	4,978.5	6,311.7	6,813.2
Loan Loss Provision	0.0	0.0	0.0	0.0
Non-Interest Income	123,329.2	113,454.4	104,111.3	93,364.9
Non-Interest Expense	-109,730.4	-99,098.3	-92,815.5	-83,541.8
Income Before Taxes and Other	19,760.6	19,334.5	17,607.5	16,636.3
Other Items	0.0	0.0	0.0	0.0
Income Tax	-7,606.7	-7,791.4	-6,663.4	-6,563.7
Net Income	12,153.9	11,543.1	10,944.1	10,072.6
Balance Sheet (000's)				
Cash & Securities	290,418.6	247,699.4	227,294.3	202,868.6
Loans, Net	94,843.6	77,303.8	90,361.8	89,574.7
Total Assets	456,475.9	388,688.1	373,846.5	341,590.7
Deposits	325,110.7	264,282.2	248,044.7	241,757.6
Stockholders' Equity	78,424.0	72,528.3	63,989.0	56,937.6
Performance & Financial Condition				
Return on Avg Stockholders' Equity %	16.10	16.91	18.10	18.77
Return on Average Assets %	2.88	3.03	3.06	3.00
Equity to Assets %	17.18	18.66	17.12	16.67
Net Interest Margin	n.a.	n.a.	n.a.	n.a.
Reserve as a % of Problem Loans	n.a.	n.a.	n.a.	n.a.

Compound Growth %'s	EPS %	6.47	Net Income %	6.46	Net Interest Income %	-3.29

Comments

The Company declared a 3 for 1 stock split in 1996. All per share amounts have been adjusted for consistency. Loans are generally due on demand and are fully secured. No loan losses are anticipated. Although the Company reports in the same format as typical bank reporting, a predominant portion of its income is from fiduciary services. The Company should not be evaluated solely by traditional bank criteria. Investment Classification: Value

Officers	Position	Ownership Information	
Lawrence S. Huntington	Chairman, CEO	Number of Shares Outstanding	6,929,805
Anne M. Tatlock	President	Market Capitalization	$ 178,442,479
Stuart C. Hochberger	Exec VP	Frequency of Dividends	Quarterly
Michael O. Magdol	CFO	Number of Shareholders	n.a.
Jeremy H. Biggs	Other	Where Listed / Symbol	OTC-BB / FYNC

Other Information			Loan Mix	%
Transfer Agent	Company Office		Not Allocated	100
Auditor	Ernst & Young LLP			
Market Maker	Furman Selz Inc.	(800)448-3223		
	Hill Thompson Magid & Co., Inc	(800)631-3083		
Broker Dealer	Regular Stockbroker			

Fifty Associates

50 Congress Street, Ste. 543   Boston, MA 02109-4002   Telephone (617)523-4220   Fax (617)523-1388

Company Description

Fifty Associates is a real estate investment trust (REIT) which owns and operates primarily retail real estate properties in Massachusetts, California and Hawaii. Shopping centers are the largest holdings with three centers in California, owned 50% by the Company, and one in Hawaii. A REIT is a special form of business entity that, for tax purposes, allows income to be distributed and taxed to shareholders without a tax at the corporate level.

	12/31/96	12/31/95	12/31/94	12/31/93
Per Share Information				
Stock Price	30.00	23.75	20.50	15.12
Earnings Per Share	2.83	2.66	5.63	1.69
Price / Earnings Ratio	10.60	8.93	3.64	8.95
Book Value Per Share	7.17	7.76	7.92	9.28
Price / Book Value %	418.41	306.06	258.84	162.93
Dividends Per Share	3.45	2.84	6.55	2.00
Annual Financial Data				
Operating Results (000's)				
Total Revenues	5,545.2	5,112.5	7,978.5	5,307.2
Costs & Expenses	-2,808.2	-2,572.2	-3,005.0	-2,693.2
Income Before Taxes and Other	2,737.0	2,540.3	4,973.5	2,261.5
Other Items	0.0	0.0	0.0	0.0
Income Tax	0.0	31.3	473.8	-624.0
Net Income	2,737.0	2,571.6	5,447.3	1,637.5
Cash Flow From Operations	2,657.6	2,845.6	5,208.4	3,100.4
Balance Sheet (000's)				
Cash & Equivalents	4,022.1	2,757.4	2,573.0	3,772.3
Total Current Assets	5,461.8	2,787.4	2,736.0	3,773.4
Fixed Assets, Net	3,803.6	4,494.0	4,740.7	4,995.5
Total Assets	10,345.5	8,333.5	8,471.3	9,439.6
Total Current Liabilities	509.2	357.7	356.7	268.6
Long-Term Debt	2,424.6	0.0	0.0	0.0
Stockholders' Equity	6,950.8	7,514.8	7,660.6	8,547.0
Performance & Financial Condition				
Return on Total Revenues %	49.36	50.30	68.27	30.85
Return on Avg Stockholders' Equity %	37.84	33.89	67.22	18.84
Return on Average Assets %	29.31	30.61	60.83	17.24
Current Ratio	10.73	7.79	7.67	14.05
Debt / Equity %	34.88	n.a.	n.a.	n.a.

Compound Growth %'s	EPS %	18.75	Net Income %	18.68	Total Revenues %	1.47

Comments

Management reports that 1996 was a year during which Massachusetts real estate markets strengthened considerably and California markets began their recovery. The Hawaii real estate market continued to be flat. Planning for the expansion and modernization of the Linda Mar Shopping Center in Pacifica, California, is complete and municipal approvals have been obtained. Construction is expected to be complete by November, 1997. The repositioning of the center is attracting quality tenants. Additional expansion of the Kaneohe Bay Shopping Center in Hawaii is also in process. Investment Classification: Income & Value

Officers	Position	Ownership Information	
Weston Howland, Jr.	Chairman	Number of Shares Outstanding	969,938
George M. Lovejoy, Jr.	President	Market Capitalization	$ 29,098,140
Paul S. Goodof	Treasurer	Frequency of Dividends	Quarterly
Frederick S. Moseley, III	Vice President, Senior Clerk	Number of Shareholders	Under 500

Other Information				
Transfer Agent	Company Office		Where Listed	OTC-BB
Auditor	Arthur Andersen LLP		Symbol	FFTY
Market Maker	Gruntal & Co., Incorporated	(800)223-7632	SIC Code	6510
	Hill Thompson Magid & Co., Inc	(800)631-3083	Employees	2
Broker Dealer	OTC Specialist			
	Norman Kadehjian - Wainwright	(800)727-7176		

Finance Company of Pennsylvania

226 Walnut Street   Philadelphia, PA 19106   Telephone (215)351-4778   Fax (215)351-9012

Company Description

Finance Company of Pennsylvania is a regulated open-end investment company under the Investment Company Act of 1940. Most of the assets are invested in common stocks and common stock mutual funds, approximately 80% of total assets at December 31, 1996. The largest single holding is 484,000 shares of PNC Bank Corp., now worth $18.2 million. To avoid all federal taxation on interest and dividends at the corporate level, the Company is required to pay its shareholders at least 98% of its ordinary income. The Company was founded in 1871.

	12/31/96	12/31/95	12/31/94	12/31/93
Per Share Information				
Stock Price	750.00	665.00	637.50	650.00
Earnings Per Share	116.71	194.89	-54.67	35.33
Price / Earnings Ratio	6.43	3.41	n.a.	18.40
Book Value Per Share	827.81	736.90	568.74	646.40
Price / Book Value %	90.60	90.24	112.09	100.56
Dividends Per Share	25.67	26.73	22.99	22.09
Annual Financial Data				
Operating Results (000's)				
Total Revenues	7,749.0	12,304.5	1,659.8	7,482.8
Costs & Expenses	-382.9	-347.3	-324.0	-311.8
Income Before Taxes and Other	7,366.0	11,957.2	-3,168.4	7,171.0
Other Items	0.0	0.0	0.0	0.0
Income Tax	-631.2	-499.4	0.0	0.0
Net Income	6,734.8	11,457.9	-3,168.4	7,171.0
Cash Flow From Operations	6,734.8	11,457.9	-3,168.4	7,171.0
Balance Sheet (000's)				
Cash & Equivalents	17.2	12.6	0.0	0.0
Total Current Assets	49,424.4	44,506.2	34,761.3	39,262.1
Fixed Assets, Net	0.0	0.0	0.0	0.0
Total Assets	49,443.9	44,509.3	34,761.3	39,262.1
Total Current Liabilities	1,010.4	1,802.4	1,800.0	1,800.0
Long-Term Debt	0.0	0.0	0.0	0.0
Stockholders' Equity	47,770.3	42,706.9	32,961.3	37,462.1
Performance & Financial Condition				
Return on Total Revenues %	86.91	93.12	-190.89	95.83
Return on Avg Stockholders' Equity %	14.89	30.28	-9.00	19.34
Return on Average Assets %	14.34	28.91	-8.56	18.44
Current Ratio	48.92	24.69	19.31	21.81
Debt / Equity %	n.a.	n.a.	n.a.	n.a.

Compound Growth %'s	EPS % n.a.	Net Income % n.a.	Total Revenues % 1.17

Comments

Annual portfolio turnover is usually between 5% and 10%. The ratio of expenses to average net assets was 0.86% in 1996. Because this is an investment trust, compounded earnings growth rates are not particularly valuable and were not displayed. Investment Classification: Value

Officers	Position	Ownership Information	
Charles E. Mather III	President	Number of Shares Outstanding	57,707
Frank A. Wood, Jr.	Secretary, Treasurer	Market Capitalization	$ 43,280,250
Doranne H. Case	Other	Frequency of Dividends	Quarterly
Mary Ellen Christ	Other	Number of Shareholders	Under 500

Other Information

Transfer Agent	Company Office		Where Listed	OTC-BB
Auditor	Deloitte & Touche LLP		Symbol	FCPA
Market Maker	F.J. Morrissey & Co., Inc.	(800)842-8928	SIC Code	6790
	Monroe Securities, Inc.	(800)766-5560	Employees	2
Broker Dealer	OTC Specialist			
	Standard Investment	(888)783-4688 Ext: Jack		

Finch, Pruyn & Company, Incorporated

1 Glen Street   Glens Falls, NY 12801-2167   Telephone (518)793-2541   Fax (518)793-7364

Company Description

Finch, Pruyn & Company is a manufacturer of high quality uncoated free-sheet printing paper sold throughout the United States. The paper is used in the finest text books and printed materials because of its excellent publishing characteristics and texture. The Company has an interesting history that dates all the way back to 1865. Please join us on the next page for a brief look at the last 132 years.

	12/29/96	12/31/95	12/31/94	12/31/93
Per Share Information				
Stock Price as of 12/31	2,506.00	1,730.00	1,600.00	1,250.00
Earnings Per Share	404.27	599.26	263.72	344.99
Price / Earnings Ratio	6.20	2.89	6.07	3.62
Book Value Per Share	4,429.82	4,152.55	4,271.59	1,914.87
Price / Book Value %	56.57	41.66	37.46	65.28
Dividends Per Share	130.40	148.20	107.76	107.76
Annual Financial Data				
Operating Results (000's)				
Total Revenues	227,309.0	268,965.0	208,208.0	193,587.0
Costs & Expenses	-198,765.0	-224,606.0	-191,108.0	-170,444.0
Income Before Taxes and Other	28,544.0	44,359.0	17,100.0	23,143.0
Other Items	0.0	-1,136.0	0.0	0.0
Income Tax	-10,872.0	-16,850.0	-5,229.0	-7,683.0
Net Income	17,672.0	26,373.0	11,871.0	15,460.0
Cash Flow From Operations	36,335.0	51,911.0	25,010.0	28,694.0
Balance Sheet (000's)				
Cash & Equivalents	524.0	459.0	486.0	174.0
Total Current Assets	48,121.0	50,427.0	46,562.0	46,210.0
Fixed Assets, Net	256,609.0	228,734.0	202,740.0	194,722.0
Total Assets	322,328.0	295,380.0	265,392.0	254,938.0
Total Current Liabilities	34,162.0	38,981.0	26,552.0	26,988.0
Long-Term Debt	46,050.0	29,560.0	32,570.0	30,078.0
Stockholders' Equity	190,779.0	179,498.0	162,722.0	156,001.0
Performance & Financial Condition				
Return on Total Revenues %	7.77	9.81	5.70	7.99
Return on Avg Stockholders' Equity %	9.55	15.41	7.45	10.25
Return on Average Assets %	5.72	9.41	4.56	6.26
Current Ratio	1.41	1.29	1.75	1.71
Debt / Equity %	24.14	16.47	20.02	19.28

Compound Growth %'s	EPS %	5.43	Net Income %	4.56	Total Revenues %	5.50

Comments

A sharp drop in the demand for paper had an impact on the Company as 1996 revenues dropped 15.3%. Despite this reversal, the Company still had good earnings and maintained an excellent balance sheet. Annual results are impacted by fluctuations of paper prices, which is the reason earnings bounce around a bit. This stock doesn't have many sellers, but shares do trade. The way to acquire shares is to contact existing shareholders. Investment Classification: Value

Officers	Position	Ownership Information	
Richard J. Carota	President, CEO	Number of Shares Outstanding	43,067
David P. Manny	Exec VP, Secretary	Market Capitalization	$ 107,925,902
		Frequency of Dividends	Quarterly
		Number of Shareholders	Under 500

Other Information

Transfer Agent	Company Office		Where Listed	OTC-BB
Auditor	Coopers & Lybrand LLP		Symbol	FPCNB
Market Maker	The Seidler Companies Inc.	(800)421-0164	SIC Code	2600
			Employees	1100
Broker Dealer	OTC Specialist			
	Standard Investment	(888)783-4688 Ext: Jack		

Paper

The mid-nineteenth century was a time of tremendous growth and expansion in the United States. In 1865, with the end of the Civil War, Americans looked once more towards building their futures. It was an ideal time for Jeremiah Finch, Daniel Finch and Samuel Pruyn to launch their business in building materials with the acquisition of a sawmill, a lumber business and lime and black marble quarries, all located on the Hudson River in Glens Falls, New York.

Cities along the Eastern seaboard initially provided a booming market for the Finch, Pruyn Company. Canal boats carried their products from Glens Falls as far south as New York City and returned with supplies for their logging camps back in the Adirondack Mountains. As the century drew to a close business was brisk, but the market for building materials was already moving westward, so Finch, Pruyn decided to refocus the company. Paper seemed a logical progression, and they acquired their first machine for processing it in 1905. By 1911 they were producing newsprint, which would become their main product until after World War II.

When the time was right, Finch, Pruyn once again resolved to change direction and discontinued newsprint production just as it had ceased the lumber operation years before. The Company decided to concentrate on groundwood printing papers for magazines, books and business paper use. As their success continued, their product line evolved to include uncoated free sheet papers. All of these papers are used by the graphic arts as well as the commercial printing industries for a wide variety of printed products including college and professional textbooks, high-technology manuals and financial reports.

Worth noting is that the company always has been and remains deeply committed to preservation of the environment. They believe in working with nature to encourage new growth and natural reforestation. Their slow growing Adirondack forests are never clear-cut, but are selectively harvested leaving young trees to mature and plant life to feed the forest animals. The Company encourages recreational use of its forests as well and grants leases to various groups for this purpose.

Finch, Pruyn has made a point of changing with the times and continues to stay on top of trends. They are currently focusing on the high-quality segment of the paper market and are working towards becoming a self-sufficient company as well. These developments should contribute to a continuing success as they make their way into the twenty-first century.

First Citizens Bancorporation of South Carolina, Inc.

1230 Main Street Columbia, SC 29202-0029 Telephone (803)771-8700 Fax (803)733-2031

Company Description

First-Citizens Bank and Trust Company of South Carolina, subsidiary of this holding company, was founded in 1964. Its predecessor, Anderson Brothers Bank, was organized in 1936. Today, the Bank is the fifth largest commercial bank in South Carolina and has 123 offices throughout the State. During 1996, First-Citizens opened an additional twelve locations, four of which were acquired from other financial institutions. The Company also has insurance company subsidiaries. Management also claimed a part of cyberspace during 1996: (http://www.fcbsc.com).

	12/31/96	12/31/95	12/31/94	12/31/93
Per Share Information				
Stock Price	180.00	115.00	95.12	83.00
Earnings Per Share	20.02	13.13	10.24	13.57
Price / Earnings Ratio	8.99	8.76	9.29	6.12
Book Value Per Share	139.21	115.32	100.41	85.62
Price / Book Value %	129.30	99.72	94.73	96.94
Dividends Per Share	0.0	0.0	0.0	0.0
Annual Financial Data				
Operating Results (000's)				
Net Interest Income	76,665.0	64,488.0	58,952.0	61,713.0
Loan Loss Provision	-4,574.0	-2,686.0	-2,558.0	-3,927.0
Non-Interest Income	22,257.0	19,704.0	18,676.0	18,724.0
Non-Interest Expense	-65,073.0	-62,171.0	-60,252.0	-57,441.0
Income Before Taxes and Other	29,275.0	19,335.0	14,818.0	19,069.0
Other Items	0.0	0.0	0.0	221.0
Income Tax	-10,321.0	-6,777.0	-4,969.0	-6,286.0
Net Income	18,954.0	12,558.0	9,849.0	13,004.0
Balance Sheet (000's)				
Cash & Securities	600,595.0	566,548.0	590,445.0	579,369.0
Loans, Net	1,246,296.0	1,093,106.0	917,776.0	862,942.0
Total Assets	1,947,699.0	1,751,674.0	1,589,181.0	1,518,978.0
Deposits	1,661,072.0	1,495,939.0	1,386,518.0	1,336,366.0
Stockholders' Equity	132,641.0	112,086.0	98,025.0	84,237.0
Performance & Financial Condition				
Return on Avg Stockholders' Equity %	15.49	11.95	10.81	18.12
Return on Average Assets %	1.02	0.75	0.63	0.91
Equity to Assets %	6.81	6.40	6.17	5.55
Net Interest Margin	4.62	4.38	4.27	4.75
Reserve as a % of Problem Loans	442.32	375.12	383.83	332.43

Compound Growth %'s	EPS %	13.84	Net Income %	13.38	Net Interest Income %	7.50

Comments

Net income increased 50.93% during 1996. This improvement was due primarily to increases in interest margins and noninterest income, as well as to an ongoing emphasis on controlling expenses. Management reported the implementation of a bankwide program to improve the sales culture and cross-selling techniques of all bank employees. Positive results from this program are expected to be realized during 1997. Investment Classification: Growth & Value

Officers	Position	Ownership Information	
Jim B. Apple	President	Number of Shares Outstanding	892,813
Jay C. Case	Exec VP, Controller	Market Capitalization	$ 160,706,340
Charles S. McLaurin, III	Exec VP	Frequency of Dividends	Irregular
William K. Brumbach, Jr.	Senior VP	Number of Shareholders	1,268
E W. Wells	Senior VP, Secretary	Where Listed / Symbol	OTC-BB / FCBN

Other Information			Loan Mix	%
Transfer Agent	Company Office		R/E Mortgages	62.4
Auditor	Price Waterhouse LLP		Installment	26.6
Market Maker	Interstate/Johnson Lane Corp.	(800)438-4134	Commerical	9.6
	Monroe Securities, Inc.	(800)766-5560	Construction	1.4
Broker Dealer	Regular Stockbroker			

First Guaranty Bank

400 East Thomas Street   Hammond, LA 70404-0520   Telephone (504)345-7685   Fax (504)542-8949

Company Description

First Guaranty Bank operates six full service banking centers in Tangipahoa Parish, Louisiana. This is a largely rural area with a concentration in agricultural enterprises. It is sandwiched between two of the fastest growing parishes in Louisiana, St. Tammany and Livingston. Management was quick to recognize a void left by bank consolidations in Livingston Parish and has begun construction of its first new branch since the 1970's. It will open in the fourth quarter, 1997. The Bank began business in 1933. First Guaranty is proving that they are "More Than Just Another Bank" with much community involvement. In fact, the Bank offers in-school banking programs in elementary and secondary schools to introduce the community's youth to the world of finance.

	12/31/96	12/31/95	12/31/94	12/31/93
Per Share Information				
Stock Price	8.67	8.33	5.33	3.33
Earnings Per Share	1.01	0.62	0.57	0.77
Price / Earnings Ratio	8.58	13.44	9.35	4.32
Book Value Per Share	4.41	3.75	3.35	3.00
Price / Book Value %	196.60	222.13	159.10	111.00
Dividends Per Share	0.34	0.28	0.20	0.06
Annual Financial Data				
Operating Results (000's)				
Net Interest Income	9,827.0	9,355.0	8,284.0	8,072.0
Loan Loss Provision	-325.0	-185.0	-235.0	-1,260.0
Non-Interest Income	2,493.0	2,381.0	2,268.0	3,010.0
Non-Interest Expense	-7,366.0	-8,474.0	-7,983.0	-8,048.0
Income Before Taxes and Other	4,629.0	3,077.0	2,334.0	1,774.0
Other Items	0.0	0.0	0.0	895.0
Income Tax	-1,328.0	-1,026.0	-605.0	-588.0
Net Income	3,301.0	2,051.0	1,729.0	2,081.0
Balance Sheet (000's)				
Cash & Securities	65,488.0	60,977.0	46,741.0	45,596.0
Loans, Net	124,456.0	116,206.0	112,111.0	103,494.0
Total Assets	198,064.0	184,311.0	167,990.0	158,780.0
Deposits	179,276.0	167,869.0	153,727.0	148,522.0
Stockholders' Equity	15,485.0	13,477.0	11,071.0	9,005.0
Performance & Financial Condition				
Return on Avg Stockholders' Equity %	22.80	16.71	17.22	33.15
Return on Average Assets %	1.73	1.16	1.06	1.34
Equity to Assets %	7.82	7.31	6.59	5.67
Net Interest Margin	5.50	5.70	5.50	5.90
Reserve as a % of Problem Loans	109.13	59.12	66.70	60.49

Compound Growth %'s	EPS %	9.47	Net Income %	16.62	Net Interest Income %	6.78

Comments

The Bank declared a 3 for 2 stock split during 1996. All per share amounts have been restated for consistency. 1993 results include a nonrecurring benefit of $895,000, $.49 per share, from a change in accounting for the reporting of income taxes. We have trouble believing that management is not satisfied with their stellar performance with returns on assets and equity at 1.73% and 22.8%, respectively. It is hard to find a cloud in the annual report. Investment Classification: Growth & Income

Officers	Position	Ownership Information	
Don W. Ayres	President, CEO	Number of Shares Outstanding	3,056,641
Stanley M. Dameron	Senior VP, Sr Loan Officer	Market Capitalization	$ 26,501,077
Michael D. Landry	Senior VP, CFO	Frequency of Dividends	Quarterly
Ray H. McElveen, Jr.	Senior VP	Number of Shareholders	900
Charles A. Morse	Senior VP	Where Listed / Symbol	OTC-PS / FGYH

Other Information			Loan Mix	%
Transfer Agent	Company Office		R/E Mortgages	64.6
Auditor	Coopers & Lybrand LLP		Commerical	20.8
Market Maker	E.E. Powell & Company, Inc.	(800)282-1940	Consumer	11.0
			Agriculture	3.1
Broker Dealer	OTC Specialist		Other	0.5
	Stephen R. Schuller	(504)524-5431		

First Miami Bancorp, Inc.

5750 Sunset Drive   South Miami, FL 33143-5396   Telephone (305)667-5511   Fax (305)662-5454

Company Description

The Company, through its wholly-owned subsidiary, First National Bank of South Miami, founded in 1952, provides a full range of services to customers primarily in South Miami, Florida, and surrounding communities. There is no formal market for the Company's stock. This has caused some shareholders to sell back their shares to the Company at ridiculously low prices. This may be a great opportunity to run an advertisement in the local newspaper, a technique we know has worked in other situations. Management is targeting the loan department, the trust department and computer banking for future growth.

	12/31/96	12/31/95	12/31/94	12/31/93
Per Share Information				
Stock Price	50.00	50.00	50.00	50.00
Earnings Per Share	22.00	18.12	27.93	52.83
Price / Earnings Ratio	2.27	2.76	1.79	0.95
Book Value Per Share	505.45	451.14	364.11	411.06
Price / Book Value %	9.89	11.08	13.73	12.16
Dividends Per Share	7.50	7.50	7.50	7.50
Annual Financial Data				
Operating Results (000's)				
Net Interest Income	6,989.8	6,841.6	8,411.8	9,944.3
Loan Loss Provision	0.0	10.4	-9.9	-65.0
Non-Interest Income	2,468.6	2,384.0	2,370.9	2,463.8
Non-Interest Expense	-6,563.7	-6,935.4	-7,144.6	-7,238.2
Income Before Taxes and Other	2,894.6	2,300.6	3,628.2	5,104.9
Other Items	0.0	0.0	0.0	1,505.7
Income Tax	-722.4	-506.9	-859.2	-1,372.0
Net Income	2,172.3	1,793.7	2,768.9	5,238.6
Balance Sheet (000's)				
Cash & Securities	255,910.9	253,442.3	234,903.0	253,810.9
Loans, Net	23,378.1	23,304.8	25,221.2	22,856.1
Total Assets	284,326.8	281,571.4	269,159.1	281,601.2
Deposits	189,677.5	196,502.1	193,326.0	207,118.0
Stockholders' Equity	49,898.4	44,653.8	36,091.2	40,761.7
Performance & Financial Condition				
Return on Avg Stockholders' Equity %	4.59	4.44	7.21	14.26
Return on Average Assets %	0.77	0.65	1.01	1.74
Equity to Assets %	17.55	15.86	13.41	14.47
Net Interest Margin	n.a.	n.a.	n.a.	n.a.
Reserve as a % of Problem Loans	n.a.	1,607.14	n.a.	n.a.

Compound Growth %'s	EPS %	-25.32	Net Income %	-25.43	Net Interest Income %	-11.09

Comments

1993 results include a nonrecurring benefit of $1.5 million, $15.18 per share, related to a change of accounting methods for reporting income taxes. This causes an overstatement of the negative compound growth rate in earnings. Per share price information was stated at the prices the Company has acquired treasury shares in each of the last three years. A substantial increase in book value during 1995 was attributable to a $7.4 million swing (to the plus side) in unrealized gains on securities. Investment Classification: Value & Income

Officers	Position	Ownership Information	
Bruce W. MacArthur	Chairman, CEO	Number of Shares Outstanding	98,720
Curtiss F. Sibley	President	Market Capitalization	$ 4,936,000
Edward B. Kitchen	Senior VP, Head Cashier	Frequency of Dividends	Semi-Annual
Robert J. Luss	Senior VP	Number of Shareholders	n.a.
Lillian A. Carpenter	Vice President	Where Listed / Symbol	Order Matching Only / n.a.

Other Information		Loan Mix	%
Transfer Agent	Company Office	Installment	38.0
Auditor	Morrison,Brown,Argiz & Company	Commerical	32.2
Market Maker	None - See Note	R/E Mortgages	29.8
Broker Dealer	None - See Note		

First Morris Bank

250 Madison Avenue   Morristown, NJ 07962-1920   Telephone (201)267-0900   Fax (201)377-6472

Company Description

First Morris Bank has a main office and five branches serving the population and businesses of Morris County, New Jersey, with its population of nearly one-half million people. The Morris Plains office was added in 1996. Management is carefully advancing on its plan of controlled expansion. A new branch in Dover/Rockaway will be opened in July, 1997, and both the Madison and Denville offices will be substantially expanded. Applications have been submitted for an eighth branch in the Mt. Freedom area. An Employee Stock Ownership Plan has an interest in the Bank.

	12/31/96	12/31/95	12/31/94	12/31/93
Per Share Information				
Stock Price	31.00	20.50	16.67	12.58
Earnings Per Share	2.23	1.81	1.88	0.81
Price / Earnings Ratio	13.90	11.33	8.87	15.53
Book Value Per Share	17.16	15.69	14.45	12.80
Price / Book Value %	180.65	130.66	115.36	98.28
Dividends Per Share	0.75	0.60	0.24	0.0
Annual Financial Data				
Operating Results (000's)				
Net Interest Income	7,183.0	6,703.0	7,070.0	6,814.0
Loan Loss Provision	0.0	0.0	558.0	-855.0
Non-Interest Income	623.0	531.0	494.0	693.0
Non-Interest Expense	-4,815.0	-4,821.0	-5,555.0	-5,545.0
Income Before Taxes and Other	2,991.0	2,413.0	2,567.0	1,107.0
Other Items	0.0	0.0	0.0	0.0
Income Tax	-980.0	-786.0	-873.0	-376.0
Net Income	2,011.0	1,627.0	1,694.0	731.0
Balance Sheet (000's)				
Cash & Securities	78,998.0	57,621.0	54,106.0	61,781.0
Loans, Net	114,965.0	108,231.0	106,520.0	104,401.0
Total Assets	201,720.0	171,411.0	165,584.0	167,905.0
Deposits	184,288.0	155,820.0	151,024.0	155,714.0
Stockholders' Equity	15,498.0	14,133.0	12,992.0	11,505.0
Performance & Financial Condition				
Return on Avg Stockholders' Equity %	13.57	12.00	13.83	6.56
Return on Average Assets %	1.08	0.97	1.02	0.46
Equity to Assets %	7.68	8.25	7.85	6.85
Net Interest Margin	n.a.	n.a.	n.a.	n.a.
Reserve as a % of Problem Loans	236.50	206.60	146.83	75.91

Compound Growth %'s	EPS %	40.15	Net Income %	40.12	Net Interest Income %	1.77

Comments

The Bank declared 5% stock dividends in both 1995 and 1994. All per share amounts have been adjusted for consistency. It is unusual to see such large increases in compound net earnings growth with a relatively low increase in net interest income. It appears that tight control over overhead is providing the major boost. With new offices and larger facilities, we would expect net interest income growth rates to accelerate. Investment Classification: Growth

Officers	Position	Ownership Information	
Ralph J. Riccioni	President, CEO	Number of Shares Outstanding	903,000
Brian Giovinazzi	Exec VP, CFO	Market Capitalization	$ 27,993,000
John B. Bonner	Senior VP, Sr Loan Officer	Frequency of Dividends	Quarterly
Christopher M. Gorey	Vice President	Number of Shareholders	n.a.
Georgia L. Price	Vice President	Where Listed / Symbol	OTC-BB / FMJE

Other Information			Loan Mix	%
Transfer Agent	Company Office		R/E Mortgages	76.4
Auditor	KPMG Peat Marwick LLP		Installment	15.1
Market Maker	Ryan, Beck & Co.	(800)325-7926	Commerical	8.5
	Hill Thompson Magid & Co., Inc	(800)631-3083		
Broker Dealer	Regular Stockbroker			

First Real Estate Investment Trust of New Jersey

505 Main Street   Hackensack, NJ 07602   Telephone (201)488-6400   Fax (201)487-7881

Company Description

The Trust is an equity real estate investment trust (REIT), whose purpose is to acquire real estate for long-term investment. Its properties include nine apartment buildings, five shopping centers and four parcels of vacant land. A number of the properties were acquired between 1961 and 1969. The Trust conducts its business in accordance with the requirements of the Internal Revenue Tax Code regarding REIT's. Accordingly, the Trust distributes substantially all of its earnings to its shareholders and does not pay income tax. The Trust was formed in 1961. There was an additional stock offering in 1988.

	10/31/96	10/31/95	10/31/94	10/31/93
Per Share Information				
Stock Price as of 12/31	21.50	22.25	23.00	23.88
Earnings Per Share	1.71	1.79	1.53	1.47
Price / Earnings Ratio	12.57	12.43	15.03	16.24
Book Value Per Share	12.81	12.82	13.56	13.65
Price / Book Value %	167.84	173.56	169.62	174.95
Dividends Per Share	1.71	2.53	1.62	1.56
Annual Financial Data				
Operating Results (000's)				
Total Revenues	13,678.0	13,250.0	11,162.0	9,948.0
Costs & Expenses	-10,218.0	-9,592.0	-8,235.0	-7,268.0
Income Before Taxes and Other	2,812.0	2,915.0	2,468.0	2,303.0
Other Items	-138.0	-123.0	-76.0	0.0
Income Tax	-12.0	-6.0	-9.0	-8.0
Net Income	2,662.0	2,786.0	2,383.0	2,295.0
Cash Flow From Operations	3,872.0	4,120.0	3,740.0	3,448.0
Balance Sheet (000's)				
Cash & Equivalents	243.0	533.0	238.0	928.0
Total Current Assets	2,007.0	1,692.0	1,164.0	1,625.0
Fixed Assets, Net	61,950.0	62,548.0	63,390.0	48,857.0
Total Assets	65,222.0	65,535.0	65,613.0	51,356.0
Total Current Liabilities	1,376.0	1,515.0	344.0	243.0
Long-Term Debt	39,617.0	39,767.0	39,447.0	28,883.0
Stockholders' Equity	19,984.0	19,989.0	21,148.0	21,292.0
Performance & Financial Condition				
Return on Total Revenues %	19.46	21.03	21.35	23.07
Return on Avg Stockholders' Equity %	13.32	13.54	11.23	10.74
Return on Average Assets %	4.07	4.25	4.07	4.53
Current Ratio	1.46	1.12	3.38	6.69
Debt / Equity %	198.24	198.94	186.53	135.65

Compound Growth %'s	EPS %	5.17	Net Income %	5.07	Total Revenues %	11.20

Comments

Earnings were affected by the phased-in shutdown of the Franklin Lakes Shopping Center in anticipation of demolition and reconstruction. The new center, scheduled to open in the fall of 1997, will be 87,832 square feet compared to the 33,322 square feet that is no longer. The Center will be anchored by a modern Grand Union Supermarket. A Pathmark Super Store in Patchgue, New York was acquired in May, 1997. Management expects these properties to have a positive impact on cash flow. Investment Classification: Income & Value

Officers	Position	Ownership Information	
Robert S. Hekemian	Chairman	Number of Shares Outstanding	1,559,788
Donald W. Barney	President	Market Capitalization	$ 33,535,442
John B. Voskian, M.D.	Secretary	Frequency of Dividends	Quarterly
William R. DeLorenzo, Jr.	Secretary, Treasurer	Number of Shareholders	406

Other Information

Transfer Agent	Registrar & Transfer Company Cranford, NJ	Where Listed	OTC-BB
Auditor	J.H. Cohn LLP	Symbol	FREVS
Market Maker	Janney Montgomery Scott, Inc. (212)425-5673	SIC Code	6510
		Employees	n.a.
Broker Dealer	OTC Specialist		

First Republic Corporation of America (The)

302 Fifth Avenue   New York, NY 10001   Telephone (212)279-6100   Fax (212)629-6848

Company Description

The Company has several business segments including ownership and operation of yarn spinning plants and a yarn dyeing plant, an 80.2% interest in Bluepoints Company, Inc., a producer of hard-shell clams which are sold nationally, a 50% interest in Lambert Seafood Company which harvests and markets scallops, a 49.9% interest in three nursing homes and a senior citizen residence, and numerous commercial properties. Bluepoints Company also owns a shrimp farm, has a 38% interest in another shrimp farm and a 62.5% interest in a shrimp hatchery, all of which are located in Ecuador.

	06/30/96	06/30/95	06/30/94	06/30/93
Per Share Information				
Stock Price as of 12/31	30.00	30.50	34.00	40.00
Earnings Per Share	-4.11	1.50	2.31	-2.00
Price / Earnings Ratio	n.a.	20.33	14.72	n.a.
Book Value Per Share	60.16	64.22	62.70	60.30
Price / Book Value %	49.87	47.49	54.23	66.33
Dividends Per Share	0.0	0.0	0.0	0.0
Annual Financial Data				
Operating Results (000's)				
Total Revenues	43,545.9	48,097.3	46,702.4	46,807.6
Costs & Expenses	-46,883.0	-47,388.1	-46,182.1	-48,451.3
Income Before Taxes and Other	-3,337.1	709.2	520.3	-1,643.7
Other Items	1,133.1	748.2	2,095.4	147.7
Income Tax	-563.0	-447.0	-1,055.0	127.0
Net Income	-2,766.9	1,010.4	1,560.7	-1,368.9
Cash Flow From Operations	3,466.2	3,452.8	6,189.8	42.2
Balance Sheet (000's)				
Cash & Equivalents	1,009.1	1,294.5	1,316.1	1,504.8
Total Current Assets	13,659.7	14,524.9	13,975.4	15,671.8
Fixed Assets, Net	39,927.2	41,049.0	40,154.6	39,881.7
Total Assets	79,239.0	82,739.7	80,163.6	79,105.6
Total Current Liabilities	10,659.7	9,534.4	9,412.3	9,939.7
Long-Term Debt	23,809.8	25,539.8	23,870.3	22,233.9
Stockholders' Equity	40,445.7	43,254.1	42,263.7	40,872.2
Performance & Financial Condition				
Return on Total Revenues %	-6.35	2.10	3.34	-2.92
Return on Avg Stockholders' Equity %	-6.61	2.36	3.75	-3.27
Return on Average Assets %	-3.42	1.24	1.96	-1.72
Current Ratio	1.28	1.52	1.48	1.58
Debt / Equity %	58.87	59.05	56.48	54.40

Compound Growth %'s	EPS %	n.a.	Net Income %	n.a.	Total Revenues %	-2.38

Comments

A combination of factors produced a large loss in 1996. Losses in the seafood division were caused by scarcity of product and low prices. The market for textile products was weaker than in the preceding year. A decrease in occupancy at one of the nursing homes reduced income in that division. Real estate holdings are generally doing well. Management reported a number of encouraging signs in its annual report and, sure enough, the nine months ended March 31, 1997, showed a return to profitability of $486,066 ($.72 per share) as compared to a loss of $1,429,526 (-$2.12) in the same period of the preceding year. Investment Classification: Value & Speculative

Officers	Position	Ownership Information	
Norman A. Halper	President	Number of Shares Outstanding	672,269
Harry Bergman	Secretary, Treasurer	Market Capitalization	$ 20,168,070
Louis H. Nimkoff	Vice President	Frequency of Dividends	n.a.
Robert Nimkoff	Vice President	Number of Shareholders	834
Miles J. Berman	Vice President		

Other Information			
Transfer Agent	Chase Mellon Shareholder Services New York, NY	Where Listed	OTC-BB
Auditor	Ernst & Young LLP	Symbol	FRPC
Market Maker	Robotti & Co., Inc. (212)986-0800	SIC Code	2200
	Sharpe Capital Inc. (800)355-5781	Employees	n.a.
Broker Dealer	Regular Stockbroker		

First Star Bancorp, Inc.

418 West Broad Street Bethlehem, PA 18018 Telephone (610)691-2233 Fax (610)691-5658

Company Description

First Star Savings Bank, formerly Greater Bethlehem Savings and Loan Association, is the subsidiary of this one-bank holding company. With the addition of an office in Allentown, Pennsylvania in 1995, the Bank now has five offices serving North Hampton and Lehigh Counties, approximately forty-five miles northwest of Philadelphia. The capital structure of the Company is complicated by the existence of a convertible subordinated debenture that converts at $15.625 per share. This causes a dilution to the equity section of the balance sheet. There is also a convertible preferred stock which can be converted to common on a one-for-one basis. The Bank started business in 1895.

	06/30/96	06/30/95	06/30/94	06/30/93
Per Share Information				
Stock Price as of 12/31	30.87	23.50	22.00	20.00
Earnings Per Share	3.38	3.43	3.65	3.13
Price / Earnings Ratio	9.13	6.85	6.03	6.39
Book Value Per Share	40.91	32.05	27.77	23.08
Price / Book Value %	75.46	73.32	79.22	86.66
Dividends Per Share	0.16	0.20	0.12	0.08
Annual Financial Data				
Operating Results (000's)				
Net Interest Income	4,472.7	4,302.0	4,150.4	3,575.6
Loan Loss Provision	-244.6	-104.1	-329.8	-129.9
Non-Interest Income	548.0	581.4	806.6	793.3
Non-Interest Expense	-2,848.1	-2,694.2	-2,413.6	-2,308.8
Income Before Taxes and Other	1,928.0	2,085.1	2,213.6	1,930.2
Other Items	0.0	-44.3	-35.2	-34.6
Income Tax	-657.5	-766.0	-799.4	-727.7
Net Income	1,270.5	1,274.8	1,379.0	1,167.9
Balance Sheet (000's)				
Cash & Securities	28,376.1	21,637.2	21,562.8	n.a.
Loans, Net	145,953.1	156,426.9	130,034.9	n.a.
Total Assets	181,582.0	186,021.3	157,720.0	n.a.
Deposits	114,266.2	121,746.7	97,436.9	n.a.
Stockholders' Equity	10,570.5	9,112.2	7,897.2	n.a.
Performance & Financial Condition				
Return on Avg Stockholders' Equity %	12.91	14.99	19.07	n.a.
Return on Average Assets %	0.69	0.74	0.98	n.a.
Equity to Assets %	5.82	4.90	5.01	n.a.
Net Interest Margin	n.a.	n.a.	n.a.	n.a.
Reserve as a % of Problem Loans	24.96	33.06	44.13	n.a.

Compound Growth %'s	EPS %	2.59	Net Income %	2.85	Net Interest Income %	7.75

Comments

Earnings per share are on a full dilution basis giving effect to the preferred stock and convertible subordinated debenture. Book value numbers have not been adjusted for the effects of conversion of the debenture. The one-time assessment of $750,000 to recapitalize the Savings Association Insurance Fund is an expense in the year ended June 30, 1997. Investment Classification: Value

Officers	Position	Ownership Information	
Joseph T. Svetik	President, CEO	Number of Shares Outstanding	258,393
Paul J. Sebastian	Senior VP	Market Capitalization	$ 7,976,592
Ruth A. Doncsecz	Secretary	Frequency of Dividends	Quarterly
Michael H. Styer	Vice President, CFO	Number of Shareholders	295
Michael F. Corso	Sr Loan Officer	Where Listed / Symbol	OTC-BB / FSRS

Other Information		Loan Mix	%
Transfer Agent	Company Office	R/E Mortgages	95.0
Auditor	Deloitte & Touche LLP	Commerical	3.5
Market Maker	Ryan, Beck & Co. (800)325-7926	Consumer	0.8
	F.J. Morrissey & Co., Inc. (800)842-8928	Construction	0.6
Broker Dealer	OTC Specialist	Other	0.1
	Dennis Reynolds - Ryan, Beck (888)231-7226		

First of Michigan Capital Corporation

100 Renaissance Center, 26th Floor   Detroit, MI 48243   Telephone (313)259-2600   Fax (313)259-7853

Company Description

The Company's principal subsidiary is First of Michigan Corporation (FoM), founded in 1933. FoM is a securities broker-dealer registered in all fifty states with a total of 35 offices. The Bloomfield Hills and Hillsdale offices were opened in 1996. FoM also acts as an investment banker involved in the underwriting and distribution of securities. FoM has approximately 175,000 active accounts.

	09/27/96	09/29/95	09/30/94	09/24/93
Per Share Information				
Stock Price as of 12/31	8.00	9.50	13.63	13.63
Earnings Per Share	0.66	0.04	0.35	1.16
Price / Earnings Ratio	12.12	237.50	38.94	11.75
Book Value Per Share	11.34	10.59	10.80	11.70
Price / Book Value %	70.55	89.71	126.20	116.50
Dividends Per Share	0.0	0.18	0.16	0.36
Annual Financial Data				
Operating Results (000's)				
Total Revenues	71,707.4	62,864.9	61,196.5	63,029.6
Costs & Expenses	-68,968.7	-62,471.8	-59,728.6	-57,809.1
Income Before Taxes and Other	2,738.7	393.1	1,467.9	5,220.5
Other Items	0.0	0.0	0.0	0.0
Income Tax	-975.0	-285.0	-425.0	-1,820.0
Net Income	1,763.7	108.1	1,042.9	3,400.5
Cash Flow From Operations	14,754.1	-830.4	-12,764.2	-6,231.7
Balance Sheet (000's)				
Cash & Equivalents	4,414.0	2,995.5	2,612.5	2,276.9
Total Current Assets	94,322.1	99,285.2	87,514.2	73,232.0
Fixed Assets, Net	3,063.7	2,828.9	2,597.2	897.0
Total Assets	101,553.4	110,457.5	103,768.0	86,506.3
Total Current Liabilities	52,261.0	49,946.1	44,891.0	43,753.9
Long-Term Debt	18,500.0	30,726.6	27,750.0	12,000.0
Stockholders' Equity	29,851.8	29,784.8	31,127.0	30,752.4
Performance & Financial Condition				
Return on Total Revenues %	2.46	0.17	1.70	5.40
Return on Avg Stockholders' Equity %	5.91	0.35	3.37	11.60
Return on Average Assets %	1.66	0.10	1.10	4.40
Current Ratio	1.80	1.99	1.95	1.67
Debt / Equity %	61.97	103.16	89.15	39.02

Compound Growth %'s	EPS %	-17.14	Net Income %	-19.65	Total Revenues %	4.39

Comments

As stock market indices climbed to record highs with extremely heavy volume, the brokerage industry couldn't help but have a banner year. Company results were driven principally by excellent commission growth on the part of the Investment Executives. The Company reacquired 177,909 shares of its stock during 1996 at an average price of $8.50. Management stated that the Company will be challenged to equal or surpass the 1996 performance. Investment Classification: Value

Officers	Position	Ownership Information	
Edward Soule	Chairman	Number of Shares Outstanding	2,633,533
Conrad W. Koski	President, CEO	Market Capitalization	$ 21,068,264
Lenore P. Denys	Senior VP, Secretary	Frequency of Dividends	Quarterly
Charles M. Grimley	Senior VP, CFO	Number of Shareholders	305
Charles R. Roberts	Senior VP		

Other Information			
Transfer Agent	Boston EquiServe Canton, MA	Where Listed	CE
Auditor	Ernst & Young LLP	Symbol	FMG
Market Maker	None	SIC Code	6211
		Employees	236
Broker Dealer	Regular Stockbroker		

Fisher Companies Inc.

600 University Street   Seattle, WA 98101-3185   Telephone (206)624-2752   Fax (206)224-6769

Company Description

The Company, through its operating subsidiaries, is engaged in television and radio broadcasting, flour milling for the bakery, mix and food service industries, proprietary real estate development and the management and licensing of grain handling and tempering technology. The Company also maintains long-term investments in marketable securities. Broadcasting and milling are the largest two business segments, responsible for 42.2% and 51.2% of 1996 revenues, respectively. The Company began business in 1910.

	12/31/96	12/31/95	12/31/94	12/31/93
Per Share Information				
Stock Price	97.62	76.25	61.50	40.00
Earnings Per Share	6.12	5.32	3.95	2.89
Price / Earnings Ratio	15.95	14.33	15.57	13.84
Book Value Per Share	54.42	47.75	40.03	25.32
Price / Book Value %	179.38	159.69	153.63	157.98
Dividends Per Share	1.72	1.52	1.34	1.26
Annual Financial Data				
Operating Results (000's)				
Total Revenues	265,220.0	220,365.9	184,112.1	169,996.8
Costs & Expenses	-225,759.0	-185,801.5	-156,537.8	-151,823.9
Income Before Taxes and Other	39,461.0	34,564.4	27,574.3	18,172.9
Other Items	0.0	0.0	-1,305.1	0.0
Income Tax	-13,375.0	-11,881.0	-9,422.0	-5,830.0
Net Income	26,086.0	22,683.4	16,847.1	12,342.9
Cash Flow From Operations	36,044.0	29,232.1	19,555.1	18,969.0
Balance Sheet (000's)				
Cash & Equivalents	5,116.0	19,489.1	2,161.6	1,356.0
Total Current Assets	76,316.0	84,946.8	74,918.6	75,820.6
Fixed Assets, Net	134,594.0	134,033.7	131,200.8	121,783.6
Total Assets	394,149.0	353,035.1	308,072.2	211,000.2
Total Current Liabilities	33,895.0	35,202.8	27,691.3	26,831.3
Long-Term Debt	65,713.0	58,109.9	64,314.9	59,573.0
Stockholders' Equity	232,129.0	203,681.3	170,751.1	107,996.1
Performance & Financial Condition				
Return on Total Revenues %	9.84	10.29	9.15	7.26
Return on Avg Stockholders' Equity %	11.97	12.12	12.09	11.81
Return on Average Assets %	6.98	6.86	6.49	6.32
Current Ratio	2.25	2.41	2.71	2.83
Debt / Equity %	28.31	28.53	37.67	55.16

Compound Growth %'s	EPS %	28.42	Net Income %	28.33	Total Revenues %	15.98

Comments

The Company declared a 4 for 1 stock split in 1995. All per share amounts were adjusted for consistency. 1996 was another good year with revenues up 16% and net earnings rising 15%. Included in income is a nonrecurring gain of $2.3 million from the sale of real estate. Management is carefully executing additional expansion but feels a need to balance current earnings with investment in long-term infrastructure. 1997 earnings are expected to approximate those of 1996. Now with over 500 shareholders, the Company is preparing its first S.E.C. filing and believes that this will provide even greater liquidity for shareholders. We agree and hope that the inclusion of this great company in our first edition of Walker's Manual has something to do with it. Investment Classification: Growth

Officers	Position	Ownership Information	
W W. Krippaehne, Jr.	President, CEO	Number of Shares Outstanding	4,265,172
David D. Hillard	Senior VP, CFO	Market Capitalization	$ 416,366,091
Glen P. Christofferson	Vice President, Controller	Frequency of Dividends	Quarterly
		Number of Shareholders	510

Other Information

Transfer Agent	Company Office		Where Listed	OTC-BB
Auditor	Price Waterhouse LLP		Symbol	FSCI
Market Maker	Martin Nelson & Co., Inc.	(206)682-6261	SIC Code	4830
	Robotti & Co., Inc.	(212)986-0800	Employees	970
Broker Dealer	Regular Stockbroker			
	Leigh Pelzel	(206)344-5160		

Florafax International, Inc.

8075 20th Street   Vero Beach, FL 32966   Telephone (561)563-0263   Fax (561)563-9958

Company Description

Florafax International, Inc. is principally in the business of generating floral orders and providing floral order placement services to retail florists. The Company also produces membership directories which are distributed to the members. In addition, the Company is a third party processor of credit cards. The Company was founded in 1970.

	08/31/96	08/31/95	08/31/94	08/31/93
Per Share Information				
Stock Price as of 12/31	2.37	0.50	0.19	0.22
Earnings Per Share	0.35	0.12	-0.06	-0.08
Price / Earnings Ratio	6.77	4.17	n.a.	n.a.
Book Value Per Share	0.39	-0.30	-0.46	-0.40
Price / Book Value %	607.69	n.a.	n.a.	n.a.
Dividends Per Share	0.0	0.0	0.0	0.0
Annual Financial Data				
Operating Results (000's)				
Total Revenues	10,415.0	7,046.0	7,093.0	7,164.0
Costs & Expenses	-9,098.0	-6,094.0	-7,073.0	-7,412.0
Income Before Taxes and Other	1,317.0	707.0	-311.0	-248.0
Other Items	128.0	0.0	0.0	-153.0
Income Tax	817.0	0.0	0.0	0.0
Net Income	2,262.0	707.0	-311.0	-401.0
Cash Flow From Operations	1,836.0	2,406.0	595.0	849.0
Balance Sheet (000's)				
Cash & Equivalents	3,770.0	1,972.0	558.0	186.0
Total Current Assets	5,686.0	4,117.0	2,847.0	2,610.0
Fixed Assets, Net	278.0	369.0	626.0	622.0
Total Assets	8,822.0	6,852.0	5,946.0	5,257.0
Total Current Liabilities	5,198.0	5,515.0	5,259.0	4,270.0
Long-Term Debt	334.0	3,034.0	3,142.0	3,007.0
Stockholders' Equity	3,237.0	-1,756.0	-2,515.0	-2,209.0
Performance & Financial Condition				
Return on Total Revenues %	21.72	10.03	-4.38	-5.60
Return on Avg Stockholders' Equity %	305.47	n.a.	n.a.	n.a.
Return on Average Assets %	28.86	11.05	-5.55	-6.97
Current Ratio	1.09	0.75	0.54	0.61
Debt / Equity %	10.32	n.a.	n.a.	n.a.

Compound Growth %'s	EPS % n.a.	Net Income % n.a.	Total Revenues % 13.28

Comments

The Company continued its recent surge in 1996 with another healthy increase in revenues (22%) and a strong bottom line. The current ratio is also vastly improved. For the six months ended February 28, 1997, the Company had revenues of $5.5 million and net income of $1,785,000 ($.20 per share), as compared to $5.0 million and $743,000 ($.11 per share) for the same period in the prior fiscal year. When we first reported Florafax in our 1996 edition, the stock could be acquired for under $1 per share. Investment Classification: Speculative & Growth

Officers	Position	Ownership Information	
James H. West	President, CFO	Number of Shares Outstanding	8,209,727
Andrew W. Williams	CEO, Chairman	Market Capitalization	$ 19,457,053
Kelly S. McMakin	Treasurer, Secretary	Frequency of Dividends	n.a.
		Number of Shareholders	2,014

Other Information			
Transfer Agent	Mellon Securities Trust Company New York, NY	Where Listed	OTC-BB
Auditor	Ernst & Young LLP	Symbol	FIIF
Market Maker	Carr Securities Corporation	(800)221-2243	SIC Code	7389
	Herzog, Heine, Geduld, Inc.	(800)221-3600	Employees	124
Broker Dealer	Regular Stockbroker		

Food Extrusion, Inc.

1241 Hawk's Flight Court   El Dorado Hills, CA 95762   Telephone (916)933-3000   Fax (916)933-3232

Company Description

Food Extrusion, Inc., founded in 1989, is a food ingredient and nutraceutical company that has developed a stabilization process which converts rice bran, the world's largest wasted food resource, into a highly nutritious food. Rice bran is the outer portion of the rice kernel which is removed during the milling process that converts brown rice to white rice. It is estimated that over 40 million metric tons of rice bran are wasted or underutilized every year. The Company is in commercial production of its products at two large rice mills and expects to install two additional facilities within the next 12 months.

	12/31/96	12/31/95
Per Share Information		
Stock Price	5.00	4.75
Earnings Per Share	-0.13	-0.04
Price / Earnings Ratio	n.a.	n.a.
Book Value Per Share	0.0	-0.02
Price / Book Value %	n.a.	n.a.
Dividends Per Share	0.0	0.0
Annual Financial Data		
Operating Results (000's)		
Total Revenues	907.8	99.6
Costs & Expenses	-3,097.8	-576.9
Income Before Taxes and Other	-2,337.3	-480.6
Other Items	0.0	0.0
Income Tax	0.0	0.0
Net Income	-2,337.3	-480.6
Cash Flow From Operations	n.a.	n.a.
Balance Sheet (000's)		
Cash & Equivalents	1,988.0	144.0
Total Current Assets	2,465.0	157.0
Fixed Assets, Net	-275.0	0.0
Total Assets	4,625.0	834.0
Total Current Liabilities	630.0	1,198.0
Long-Term Debt	3,943.0	0.0
Stockholders' Equity	52.0	-364.0
Performance & Financial Condition		
Return on Total Revenues %	-257.47	-482.41
Return on Avg Stockholders' Equity %	n.a.	n.a.
Return on Average Assets %	-85.63	n.a.
Current Ratio	3.91	0.13
Debt / Equity %	7582.69	n.a.

Compound Growth %'s	EPS % n.a.	Net Income % n.a.	Total Revenues % 811.26

Comments

On February 6, 1997, the Company announced it had entered an agreement with Monsanto Company wherein Monsanto will provide a $5 million, interest-free, 36-month loan that is convertible into common shares at $5 per share. The proceeds will be used by the Company to provide working capital and to fund expansion plans. Monsanto also has been granted certain short-term refusal rights on future financings. This quality partner obviously enhances the respect that Food Extrusion already has in the market place. Investment Classification: Speculative

Officers	Position	Ownership Information	
Daniel L. McPeak	Chairman	Number of Shares Outstanding	18,000,751
Patricia Mayhew	President	Market Capitalization	$ 90,003,755
Allen J. Simon	CEO	Frequency of Dividends	n.a.
Todd C. Crow	CFO	Number of Shareholders	Under 500
Robert H. Hesse	Other		

Other Information

Transfer Agent	American Stock Transfer & Trust Co. New York, NY		Where Listed	OTC-BB
Auditor	Coopers & Lybrand LLP		Symbol	FODX
Market Maker	Sharpe Capital Inc.	(800)355-5781	SIC Code	2000
	J. Alexander Securities Inc.	(800)421-0258	Employees	n.a.
Broker Dealer	Regular Stockbroker			

Four Oaks Bank & Trust Company

6144 US 301 South   Four Oaks, NC 27524-0309   Telephone (919)963-2177   Fax (919)963-2768

Company Description

Four Oaks Bank & Trust Company is a full service financial institution operating from six locations in Four Oaks, Clayton, Smithfield and Gardner, all part of Johnson County in eastern and central North Carolina. The Gardner office was opened in 1996. Johnson County celebrated its 250th anniversary in 1995 and Four Oaks Bank & Trust has been part of Johnson County for the last 85 years.

	12/31/96	12/31/95	12/31/94	12/31/93
Per Share Information				
Stock Price	24.00	20.00	12.37	11.40
Earnings Per Share	2.19	1.85	1.53	1.32
Price / Earnings Ratio	10.96	10.81	8.08	8.64
Book Value Per Share	17.14	15.60	13.52	12.85
Price / Book Value %	140.02	128.21	91.49	88.72
Dividends Per Share	0.51	0.47	0.45	0.42
Annual Financial Data				
Operating Results (000's)				
Net Interest Income	6,554.7	5,679.4	4,938.0	4,171.8
Loan Loss Provision	-396.8	-385.2	-223.7	-239.0
Non-Interest Income	881.2	729.1	390.3	696.6
Non-Interest Expense	-4,375.4	-3,818.5	-3,310.8	-3,050.1
Income Before Taxes and Other	2,663.9	2,204.9	1,793.8	1,579.4
Other Items	0.0	0.0	0.0	0.0
Income Tax	-843.0	-680.5	-537.0	-491.1
Net Income	1,820.9	1,524.4	1,256.8	1,088.3
Balance Sheet (000's)				
Cash & Securities	43,700.5	38,784.4	37,662.8	32,648.2
Loans, Net	108,036.0	88,668.0	73,813.6	66,370.1
Total Assets	159,112.6	133,420.9	116,673.9	103,609.2
Deposits	142,843.0	118,965.4	101,978.3	90,265.2
Stockholders' Equity	14,362.7	12,919.2	11,122.2	10,558.9
Performance & Financial Condition				
Return on Avg Stockholders' Equity %	13.35	12.68	11.59	10.69
Return on Average Assets %	1.24	1.22	1.14	1.11
Equity to Assets %	9.03	9.68	9.53	10.19
Net Interest Margin	4.79	4.87	4.27	3.99
Reserve as a % of Problem Loans	307.69	266.96	216.55	172.10

Compound Growth %'s	EPS %	18.38	Net Income %	18.72	Net Interest Income %	16.25

Comments

The Company declared 4 for 3 and 5 for 4 stock splits in 1995 and 1994, respectively. All per share amounts have been adjusted for consistency. The Bank has continued an impressive record of expansion as assets, loans and deposits grew 19%, 22% and 20%, respectively. Market expansion and technological advancements were credited with the 1996 growth. The Bank continues to maintain a high capital ratio and consistently has respectable returns on assets and equity. Investment Classification: Growth

Officers	Position	Ownership Information	
Ayden R. Lee, Jr.	President, CEO	Number of Shares Outstanding	837,949
Clifton L. Painter	Exec VP, COO	Market Capitalization	$ 20,110,776
J. Horace Keene	Exec VP	Frequency of Dividends	Quarterly
Nancy S. Wise	Senior VP, CFO	Number of Shareholders	900
James F. Langley	Senior VP	Where Listed / Symbol	OTC-BB / FOBT

Other Information			Loan Mix	%
Transfer Agent	United Carolina Bank Whiteville, NC		R/E Mortgages	58.5
Auditor	Daniel G. Matthews & Assoc.		Commerical	18.2
Market Maker	Morgan Keegan & Company, Inc.	(800)688-2137	Consumer	17.1
	Hill Thompson Magid & Co., Inc	(800)631-3083	Agriculture	5.5
Broker Dealer	OTC Specialist		Other	0.7
	Norman Kadehjian - Wainwright	(800)727-7176		

Franklin Credit Management Corp

Six Harrison Street   New York, NY 10013   Telephone (212)925-8745   Fax (212)225-8760

Company Description

The Company, incorporated in Delaware in 1990, is a consumer finance company, and was formed to acquire loans and notes from mortgage and finance companies, the RTC and the FDIC at discounted prices. It then proceeds to collect the amounts due.

	12/31/95	12/31/94	12/31/93	12/31/92
Per Share Information				
Stock Price	2.25	1.00	0.19	n.a.
Earnings Per Share	0.02	0.05	0.80	n.a.
Price / Earnings Ratio	112.50	20.00	0.24	n.a.
Book Value Per Share	0.59	0.48	0.30	0.11
Price / Book Value %	381.36	208.33	63.33	n.a.
Dividends Per Share	0.0	0.0	0.0	n.a.
Annual Financial Data				
Operating Results (000's)				
Net Interest Income	6,176.3	4,655.4	3,207.2	1,822.3
Loan Loss Provision	-1,090.5	-701.1	-329.4	-222.3
Non-Interest Income	320.4	554.1	443.2	611.0
Non-Interest Expense	-5,049.8	-3,718.0	-2,789.0	-969.3
Income Before Taxes and Other	356.4	790.4	532.0	1,241.7
Other Items	-54.8	694.5	3,017.1	-820.6
Income Tax	-176.9	-1,242.6	0.0	0.0
Net Income	124.7	242.3	3,549.1	421.0
Balance Sheet (000's)				
Cash & Securities	1,952.9	1,063.6	953.9	698.8
Loans, Net	66,996.1	42,734.0	16,032.8	5,666.6
Total Assets	77,931.1	48,546.3	19,456.9	7,296.5
Deposits	0.0	0.0	0.0	0.0
Stockholders' Equity	3,254.7	2,495.4	1,414.1	480.7
Performance & Financial Condition				
Return on Avg Stockholders' Equity %	4.34	12.40	374.61	n.a.
Return on Average Assets %	0.20	0.71	26.53	n.a.
Equity to Assets %	4.18	5.14	7.27	6.59
Net Interest Margin	n.a.	n.a.	n.a.	n.a.
Reserve as a % of Problem Loans	n.a.	n.a.	n.a.	n.a.

Compound Growth %'s	EPS % n.a.	Net Income % n.a.	Net Interest Income % n.a.

Comments

The 1993 financial statements have been restated to reflect the pooling-of-interests merger, in 1994, of the Company and Miramar Resources, Inc. The 1992 results are for the former Franklin only. Comparable earnings per share and stock price are not determinable for 1992. Income for 1994 includes $760,000 of litigation proceeds. As of December 31, 1995, officers and directors and directors, as a group, controlled 74% of the outstanding common stock of the Company.

Officers	Position	Ownership Information	
Thomas J. Axon	President	Number of Shares Outstanding	5,503,896
Frank B. Evans	Vice President, CFO	Market Capitalization	$ 12,383,766
Harvey R. Hirschfeld	Vice President	Frequency of Dividends	n.a.
		Number of Shareholders	2,382
		Where Listed / Symbol	OTC-BB / FCMC

Other Information		Loan Mix	%
Transfer Agent	American Securities Transfer, Inc.	R/E Mortgages	100
Auditor	McGladrey & Pullen LLP		
Market Maker	Herzog, Heine, Geduld, Inc. (800)966-7002		
Broker Dealer	Regular Stockbroker		

Frederick Trading Company

7901 Trading Lane   Frederick, MD 21705-0400   Telephone (301)662-2161   Fax (301)662-7243

Company Description

Frederick Trading Company and its wholly-owned subsidiary operate principally as wholesale distributors of hardware, plumbing, heating and other merchandise. The majority of business activity is with customers located in the Mid-Atlantic region of the United States. The Company has been reacquiring shares at prices close to book value. The LIFO inventory reserve was $2,425,000, $7.55 per share, at December 31, 1996.

	12/31/96	12/31/95	12/31/94
Per Share Information			
Stock Price	24.00	22.00	20.00
Earnings Per Share	1.00	1.57	-1.11
Price / Earnings Ratio	24.00	14.01	n.a.
Book Value Per Share	45.88	45.06	43.69
Price / Book Value %	52.31	48.82	45.78
Dividends Per Share	0.20	0.21	0.51
Annual Financial Data			
Operating Results (000's)			
Total Revenues	87,564.7	73,329.3	75,889.3
Costs & Expenses	-87,308.9	-72,594.6	-76,356.8
Income Before Taxes and Other	255.8	734.7	-467.5
Other Items	0.0	0.0	0.0
Income Tax	65.0	-226.0	106.0
Net Income	320.8	508.7	-361.5
Cash Flow From Operations	-3,456.3	969.0	-257.9
Balance Sheet (000's)			
Cash & Equivalents	226.5	104.1	267.7
Total Current Assets	32,284.6	26,649.1	27,327.5
Fixed Assets, Net	5,556.3	5,818.6	6,367.8
Total Assets	37,942.3	32,660.1	33,848.4
Total Current Liabilities	19,560.6	14,671.2	14,297.3
Long-Term Debt	2,400.0	1,600.0	3,478.8
Stockholders' Equity	14,739.7	14,604.0	14,287.4
Performance & Financial Condition			
Return on Total Revenues %	0.37	0.69	-0.48
Return on Avg Stockholders' Equity %	2.19	3.52	-2.45
Return on Average Assets %	0.91	1.53	n.a.
Current Ratio	1.65	1.82	1.91
Debt / Equity %	16.28	10.96	24.35

Compound Growth %'s	EPS % n.a.	Net Income % n.a.	Total Revenues % 7.42

Comments

Compound earnings growth rates were not displayed because of insufficient years of data. There has been a major upswing in business activity and revenues increased 19.8% in 1996. This has resulted from new business obtained from Moor's Lumber and Building Supply, new lines and products added to 84 Lumber, the growth of its large independent hardware dealers, and the closure of a significant competitor. The last year was also plagued with warehouse space constraints and abnormal warehouse employee turnover. Management is swiftly restructuring to better capture the benefits of increased volume. A five year strategic plan is currently being implemented. Investment Classification: Value

Officers	Position	Ownership Information	
Nickolas M. Felsh	President, CEO	Number of Shares Outstanding	321,247
Gary E. Duckworth	Secretary	Market Capitalization	$ 7,709,928
		Frequency of Dividends	Semi-Annual
		Number of Shareholders	Under 500

Other Information

Transfer Agent	Company Office			Where Listed	Order Matching Only
Auditor	McLean,Koehler,Sparks,Hammond			Symbol	n.a.
Market Maker	None			SIC Code	5070
				Employees	n.a.
Broker Dealer	Standard Investment	(888)783-4688	Ext: Jack		

Fremont Corporation

9454 Wilshire Blvd., 6th Floor   Beverly Hills, CA 90212   Telephone (310)358-1006   Fax (310)271-3540

Company Description

Fremont Corporation is engaged in the design, manufacture and marketing of bicycles, bicycle parts and components, steel tubes and exercise equipment. The Company's manufacturing operations, which represent substantially all of the Company's assets, are located in the City of Zhaoqing, which is located in Guangdong Province in The Peoples Republic of China. The market for the Company's products are both within and outside of China and include brand names like Schwinn and Randor. Although the Company was founded in 1955, it was not until 1995 that it entered its current business.

	12/31/96	12/31/95
Per Share Information		
Stock Price	5.75	1.00
Earnings Per Share	0.23	0.16
Price / Earnings Ratio	25.00	6.25
Book Value Per Share	3.01	2.77
Price / Book Value %	191.03	36.10
Dividends Per Share	0.0	0.0
Annual Financial Data		
Operating Results (000's)		
Total Revenues	25,184.0	16,635.0
Costs & Expenses	-24,756.0	-15,768.0
Income Before Taxes and Other	1,510.0	867.0
Other Items	-25.0	-27.0
Income Tax	-164.0	0.0
Net Income	1,321.0	840.0
Cash Flow From Operations	-3,184.0	-4,999.0
Balance Sheet (000's)		
Cash & Equivalents	579.0	781.0
Total Current Assets	28,986.0	22,964.0
Fixed Assets, Net	13,164.0	29,219.0
Total Assets	55,248.0	61,195.0
Total Current Liabilities	31,102.0	31,547.0
Long-Term Debt	4,010.0	5,275.0
Stockholders' Equity	17,506.0	15,514.0
Performance & Financial Condition		
Return on Total Revenues %	5.25	5.05
Return on Avg Stockholders' Equity %	8.00	n.a.
Return on Average Assets %	2.27	n.a.
Current Ratio	0.93	0.73
Debt / Equity %	22.91	34.00

Compound Growth %'s	EPS %	43.75	Net Income %	57.26	Total Revenues %	51.39

Comments

Sales increased dramatically in 1996, up 51.6%, due to the completion of a new production facility at the end of 1995 which substantially increased the production capacity of the Company. Also a 61.7% anti-dumping tariff had been imposed on the Company's export sales of finished bicycles to the United States during the fourth quarter of 1995. As a result of the revocation of the anti-dumping tariff during the second quarter of 1996, the Company renewed exporting finished bicycles to the United States. For the three months ended March 31, 1997, revenue increased 10.1% over the same period of 1996 and earnings were $.09 per share. Investment Classification: Speculative

Officers	Position	Ownership Information	
Winston Wu	President	Number of Shares Outstanding	5,821,639
Rong Shao Jia	CEO	Market Capitalization	$ 33,474,424
Zhao Ya Wen	COO	Frequency of Dividends	n.a.
Robert N. Weingarten	CFO	Number of Shareholders	2,229

Other Information

Transfer Agent	American Securities Transfer, Inc. Lakewood, CO		Where Listed	OTC-BB
Auditor	Arthur Andersen LLP		Symbol	BYCL
Market Maker	Global Financial Group	(800)321-1761	SIC Code	3751
	Wilson-Davis & Co., Inc.	(800)453-5735	Employees	1822
Broker Dealer	Regular Stockbroker			

Gaming Venture Corp., U.S.A.

177 Main Street, Ste. 312   Fort Lee, NJ 07024   Telephone (201)947-4642   Fax (201)585-5217

Company Description

Gaming Venture Corp., U.S.A. is in the business of providing a daily 900 telephone number hotline information service and weekly newsletter regarding all aspects of the gaming industry. The Company also provides consulting services on matters related to the gaming industry. Approximately 72% of 1996 revenue was from consulting activities. The Company was formed in 1995.

	10/31/96	10/31/95
Per Share Information		
Stock Price as of 12/31	4.56	1.50
Earnings Per Share	0.15	-0.34
Price / Earnings Ratio	30.40	n.a.
Book Value Per Share	0.64	0.50
Price / Book Value %	712.50	300.00
Dividends Per Share	0.0	0.0
Annual Financial Data		
Operating Results (000's)		
Total Revenues	423.3	43.6
Costs & Expenses	-186.4	-531.7
Income Before Taxes and Other	236.9	-488.1
Other Items	0.0	0.0
Income Tax	0.0	0.0
Net Income	236.9	-488.1
Cash Flow From Operations	81.7	-77.8
Balance Sheet (000's)		
Cash & Equivalents	812.4	759.8
Total Current Assets	914.3	797.1
Fixed Assets, Net	14.2	8.6
Total Assets	1,260.7	808.6
Total Current Liabilities	247.9	19.1
Long-Term Debt	0.0	0.0
Stockholders' Equity	1,012.8	789.5
Performance & Financial Condition		
Return on Total Revenues %	55.97	-1,119.76
Return on Avg Stockholders' Equity %	26.29	n.a.
Return on Average Assets %	22.90	n.a.
Current Ratio	3.69	41.63
Debt / Equity %	n.a.	n.a.

Compound Growth %'s	EPS %	n.a.	Net Income %	n.a.	Total Revenues %	n.a.

Comments

The Company is holding shares of common stock in two privately held companies that it received in exchange for consulting services. The total value of these investments as of year end was $330,000 of which $202,500 is reflected in deferred income because the services have not yet been provided. During the first quarter of 1997, the Company recorded total revenues of $134,922 and net earnings of $80,978 ($.05 per share). Investment Classification: Speculative

Officers	**Position**	**Ownership Information**	
Alan Woinski	President	Number of Shares Outstanding	1,591,834
Kim Santangelo-Woinski	Vice President, Secretary	Market Capitalization	$ 7,258,763
		Frequency of Dividends	n.a.
		Number of Shareholders	905

Other Information			
Transfer Agent	Florida Atlantic Stock Transfer, Inc. Tamarac, FL	Where Listed	OTC-BB
Auditor	Winter, Scheifley & Associates	Symbol	GVCU
Market Maker	Barron Chase Securities, Inc.	(800)377-8723	SIC Code	7900
	Wien Securities Corp.	(800)624-0050	Employees	n.a.
Broker Dealer	Regular Stockbroker		

Garden City Company

10 Lake Circle   Colorado Springs, CO 80906-0064   Telephone (719)633-7733   Fax (719)471-6181

Company Description

The Garden City Company owns 27,500 acres of farm land in southwest Kansas which it rents to tenant farmers on a crop share basis. Wheat, milo, corn and soybeans are the primary crops. In addition, the Company receives oil and gas royalties from approximately 100 wells maintained by third parties on their property. 22,000 acres are under irrigation and were appraised in 1990 by the Federal Land Bank at $850 per acre. 80% of the Company is owned by the El Pomar Foundation which was established by Spencer Penrose.

	02/28/97	02/28/96	02/28/95	02/28/94
Per Share Information				
Stock Price as of 12/31	301.00	323.00	264.00	260.25
Earnings Per Share	41.69	38.04	42.34	40.50
Price / Earnings Ratio	7.22	8.49	6.24	6.43
Book Value Per Share	316.75	311.62	294.21	260.88
Price / Book Value %	95.03	103.65	89.73	99.76
Dividends Per Share	45.00	35.00	40.00	34.00
Annual Financial Data				
Operating Results (000's)				
Total Revenues	3,936.3	3,685.8	3,831.8	3,618.6
Costs & Expenses	-2,070.9	-1,963.0	-1,956.3	-1,743.2
Income Before Taxes and Other	1,865.4	1,722.9	1,875.5	1,875.5
Other Items	0.0	0.0	0.0	0.0
Income Tax	-587.9	-562.9	-590.8	-646.6
Net Income	1,277.5	1,159.9	1,284.7	1,228.8
Cash Flow From Operations	1,316.7	1,555.0	1,375.1	874.0
Balance Sheet (000's)				
Cash & Equivalents	282.5	236.4	214.7	282.4
Total Current Assets	6,334.7	5,741.4	4,802.6	3,146.1
Fixed Assets, Net	3,820.6	3,927.4	4,047.2	4,221.6
Total Assets	11,301.6	10,957.8	10,019.1	8,429.7
Total Current Liabilities	1,409.5	1,192.8	871.9	251.1
Long-Term Debt	0.0	0.0	0.0	0.0
Stockholders' Equity	9,706.1	9,549.0	8,927.3	7,915.8
Performance & Financial Condition				
Return on Total Revenues %	32.45	31.47	33.53	33.96
Return on Avg Stockholders' Equity %	13.27	12.56	15.25	15.72
Return on Average Assets %	11.48	11.06	13.93	14.74
Current Ratio	4.49	4.81	5.51	12.53
Debt / Equity %	n.a.	n.a.	n.a.	n.a.

Compound Growth %'s	EPS %	0.97	Net Income %	1.30	Total Revenues %	2.84

Comments

1996 was another difficult farming year because of weather related events. In the oil and gas division, there was a net gain of six new wells during the fiscal year. Oil and gas royalty income increased 22% due to higher prices. The Company continues to accumulate cash and marketable securities. The dividend yield is exceptional. Investment Classification: Income & Value

Officers	Position	Ownership Information	
William J. Hybl	President	Number of Shares Outstanding	30,643
R. Thayer Tutt, Jr.	Exec VP	Market Capitalization	$ 9,223,543
Robert J. Hilbert	Secretary, Treasurer	Frequency of Dividends	Quarterly
David A. Brenn	General Manager, Vice President	Number of Shareholders	71
Ronald Conway	Other		

Other Information				
Transfer Agent	Company Office		Where Listed	OTC-BB
Auditor	Lewis, Hooper & Dick, LLC		Symbol	GCTY
Market Maker	Sharpe Capital Inc.	(800)355-5781	SIC Code	6500
	PaineWebber Inc.	(800)221-5532	Employees	12
Broker Dealer	OTC Specialist			

Genetic Vectors, Inc.

2000 S. Dixie Highway, Suite 100   Miami, FL 33133   Telephone (305)859-7800   Fax (305)859-9006

Company Description

Genetic Vectors, Inc. is a biotechnology company which intends to specialize in the development of diagnostic and quality control tools for the biopharmaceutical, food and fermented beverage industries. The Company was founded in 1991 by Dr. Mead McCabe who invented a new nucleic acid labeling and detection technology. The Company will seek sub-licensing and distribution partners on new and existing patented products.

	12/31/96	12/31/95
Per Share Information		
Stock Price	13.50	n.a.
Earnings Per Share	-0.23	n.a.
Price / Earnings Ratio	n.a.	n.a.
Book Value Per Share	2.03	n.a.
Price / Book Value %	665.02	n.a.
Dividends Per Share	0.0	n.a.
Annual Financial Data		
Operating Results (000's)		
Total Revenues	0.0	0.0
Costs & Expenses	-393.4	-226.7
Income Before Taxes and Other	-393.4	-226.7
Other Items	0.0	0.0
Income Tax	0.0	0.0
Net Income	-393.4	-226.7
Cash Flow From Operations	-313.5	-94.0
Balance Sheet (000's)		
Cash & Equivalents	4,745.2	n.a.
Total Current Assets	4,745.2	n.a.
Fixed Assets, Net	17.2	n.a.
Total Assets	4,917.8	n.a.
Total Current Liabilities	135.5	n.a.
Long-Term Debt	35.0	n.a.
Stockholders' Equity	4,747.3	n.a.
Performance & Financial Condition		
Return on Total Revenues %	n.a.	n.a.
Return on Avg Stockholders' Equity %	n.a.	n.a.
Return on Average Assets %	n.a.	n.a.
Current Ratio	35.01	n.a.
Debt / Equity %	0.74	n.a.

Compound Growth %'s	EPS % n.a.	Net Income % n.a.	Total Revenues % n.a.

Comments

In June, 1996, the Company sold 110,000 shares of common stock for $5.00 per share in a private placement. Additional shares were issued as stock options and for the extinguishment of debt. Management believes that the operating capital will last about 18 months. Limited initial revenue is expected in 1997. On January 30, 1997, it was announced that a patent was granted for the Company's EpiDNA Picogram Assay product. Investment Classification: Speculative

Officers	Position	Ownership Information	
Mead M. McCabe, Sr.	Chairman	Number of Shares Outstanding	2,339,634
Mead M. McCabe, Jr.	President	Market Capitalization	$ 31,585,059
Richard H. Tullis	CEO	Frequency of Dividends	n.a.
		Number of Shareholders	95

Other Information

Transfer Agent	Continental Stock & Transfer Co. New York, NY		Where Listed	OTC-BB
Auditor	BDO Seidman, LLP		Symbol	GVEC
Market Maker	Coburn & Meredith, Inc.	(800)825-2244	SIC Code	2834
	Shamrock Partners Ltd.	(800)326-4900	Employees	n.a.
Broker Dealer	Regular Stockbroker			

Geo Petroleum, Inc.

25660 Crenshaw Boulevard, #201   Torrance, CA 90505   Telephone (310)539-8191   Fax (310)539-0101

Company Description

Geo Petroleum, Inc. has been limited in activities to the acquisition of producing oil properties which Geo deems are under-exploited and have additional potential, and to the subsequent enhancement of the production from those properties. Geo has acquired acreage which it believes is prospective for exploratory drilling, but financial limitations have prevented Geo from exploring such properties to date. The Company was founded in 1986.

	12/31/96	12/31/95
Per Share Information		
Stock Price	4.00	1.00
Earnings Per Share	-0.11	0.03
Price / Earnings Ratio	n.a.	33.33
Book Value Per Share	0.63	0.21
Price / Book Value %	634.92	476.19
Dividends Per Share	0.0	0.0
Annual Financial Data		
Operating Results (000's)		
Total Revenues	1,005.9	2,118.9
Costs & Expenses	-1,436.5	-1,965.5
Income Before Taxes and Other	-430.6	153.4
Other Items	0.0	0.0
Income Tax	0.0	0.0
Net Income	-430.6	153.4
Cash Flow From Operations	-325.6	201.8
Balance Sheet (000's)		
Cash & Equivalents	2,228.8	100.6
Total Current Assets	2,852.6	514.3
Fixed Assets, Net	3,880.4	3,727.4
Total Assets	6,733.0	4,241.7
Total Current Liabilities	1,286.3	2,817.7
Long-Term Debt	530.0	0.0
Stockholders' Equity	4,815.5	918.9
Performance & Financial Condition		
Return on Total Revenues %	-42.80	7.24
Return on Avg Stockholders' Equity %	-15.02	n.a.
Return on Average Assets %	-7.85	n.a.
Current Ratio	2.22	0.18
Debt / Equity %	11.01	n.a.

Compound Growth %'s	EPS %	n.a.	Net Income %	n.a.	Total Revenues %	-52.52

Comments

Geo has entered into a joint venture agreement with Saba Petroleum, Inc. pursuant to which development drilling on the Vaca Oil Sand project in the Oxnard Field, Ventura County, California, started in mid-1997. Saba must spend $10 million on the project prior to the end of calendar 1998 to earn a two-thirds interest in the project. In anticipation of a revenue stream, the stock was trading at over $6 per share at the end of May, 1997. Investment Classification: Speculative

Officers	Position	Ownership Information	
Gerald T. Raydon	Chairman, President	Number of Shares Outstanding	7,603,324
Alyda L. Raydon	Secretary, Treasurer	Market Capitalization	$ 30,413,296
		Frequency of Dividends	n.a.
		Number of Shareholders	98

Other Information				
Transfer Agent	U.S. Stock Transfer Corp. Glendale, CA		Where Listed	OTC-BB
Auditor	Ernst & Young LLP		Symbol	GOPL
Market Maker	Drake Capital Securities, Inc.	(800)421-8504	SIC Code	1311
	J. Alexander Securities Inc.	(800)421-0258	Employees	n.a.
Broker Dealer	Regular Stockbroker			

Gloucester Bank & Trust Company

2 Harbor Loop   Gloucester, MA 01930   Telephone (508)281-6270   Fax (508)283-5072

Company Description

Gloucester Bank and Trust Company is a state chartered bank which was incorporated in 1987 and is headquartered in Gloucester, Massachusetts. The Bank is engaged principally in making real estate, consumer and small business loans in the Cape May area of the Commonwealth. This young bank is very friendly to investors and analysts and is receptive to inquiries about quarterly results.

	12/31/96	12/31/95	12/31/94	12/31/93
Per Share Information				
Stock Price	69.00	56.50	35.00	27.50
Earnings Per Share	8.43	8.67	6.06	2.64
Price / Earnings Ratio	8.19	6.52	5.78	10.42
Book Value Per Share	66.66	63.47	56.70	53.63
Price / Book Value %	103.51	89.02	61.73	51.28
Dividends Per Share	4.00	4.00	2.00	0.0
Annual Financial Data				
Operating Results (000's)				
Net Interest Income	4,261.0	4,203.0	3,574.0	3,266.0
Loan Loss Provision	0.0	0.0	190.0	-525.0
Non-Interest Income	803.0	670.0	626.0	706.0
Non-Interest Expense	-3,353.0	-3,115.0	-3,164.0	-2,962.0
Income Before Taxes and Other	1,711.0	1,758.0	1,226.0	485.0
Other Items	0.0	0.0	0.0	20.0
Income Tax	-714.0	-733.0	-510.0	-193.0
Net Income	997.0	1,025.0	716.0	312.0
Balance Sheet (000's)				
Cash & Securities	43,877.0	38,718.0	30,940.0	28,011.0
Loans, Net	61,654.0	55,033.0	50,789.0	49,442.0
Total Assets	111,079.0	99,242.0	87,246.0	82,023.0
Deposits	92,048.0	85,163.0	74,201.0	69,343.0
Stockholders' Equity	7,878.0	7,501.0	6,701.0	6,339.0
Performance & Financial Condition				
Return on Avg Stockholders' Equity %	12.97	14.43	10.98	5.05
Return on Average Assets %	0.95	1.10	0.85	0.38
Equity to Assets %	7.09	7.56	7.68	7.73
Net Interest Margin	n.a.	n.a.	n.a.	n.a.
Reserve as a % of Problem Loans	130.24	106.54	129.53	125.85

Compound Growth %'s	EPS % 47.26	Net Income % 47.29	Net Interest Income % 9.27

Comments

Compound earnings and earnings per share growth are distorted because of lower than average performance in the base year. The Bank experienced difficult times because of the local economy and appears to have completely recovered. In late 1995, the Bank began performing data processing services for another bank and sees this service as becoming an important source of non-interest income in the years ahead. Non-interest income did increase 20% in 1996. Management was pleased that assets and loans grew by more than 11% even though the earnings level of 1995 was not reached. Investment Classification: Growth & Income & Value

Officers	Position	Ownership Information	
David L. Marsh	President, CEO	Number of Shares Outstanding	118,189
Stephen R. Parkhurst	Exec VP	Market Capitalization	$ 8,155,041
Richard J. Edelstein	Senior VP	Frequency of Dividends	Quarterly
Kevin W. Nunes	Senior VP, CFO	Number of Shareholders	340
David B. Sidon	Senior VP	Where Listed / Symbol	OTC-BB / GBTR

Other Information			Loan Mix	%
Transfer Agent	Boston EquiServe		R/E Mortgages	76.7
Auditor	Shatswell, MacLeod & Co, PC		Commerical	14.4
Market Maker	Moors & Cabot Inc.	(800)426-0501	Consumer	5.8
	Ryan, Beck & Co.	(800)395-7926	Construction	2.4
Broker Dealer	Regular Stockbroker		Other	0.7

Golden Cycle Gold Corporation

2340 Robinson Street, Ste. 209   Colorado Springs, CO 80904   Telephone (719)471-9013   Fax (719)520-1442

Company Description

The Company, founded in 1972, was formed for the purpose of acquiring and developing mining properties located in the Cripple Creek Mining District of Colorado. The primary business of the Company is its participation, as a 33% interest holder, in the Cripple Creek & Victor Gold Mining Company, a joint venture with Pikes Peak Mining Company. The Company is also seeking to participate in gold and copper mining activities in the Republic of the Philippines and, in late 1996, entered into a joint participation agreement with a Philippine mining company.

	12/31/96	12/31/95	12/31/94	12/31/93
Per Share Information				
Stock Price	10.50	8.38	7.68	8.20
Earnings Per Share	0.08	0.01	-0.12	-0.06
Price / Earnings Ratio	131.25	838.00	n.a.	n.a.
Book Value Per Share	1.46	0.33	0.32	0.43
Price / Book Value %	719.18	2,539.39	2,400.00	1,906.98
Dividends Per Share	0.0	0.0	0.0	0.0
Annual Financial Data				
Operating Results (000's)				
Total Revenues	596.0	273.1	274.2	272.1
Costs & Expenses	-451.6	-270.8	-456.6	-361.9
Income Before Taxes and Other	144.4	2.3	-182.4	-89.7
Other Items	0.0	0.0	0.0	0.0
Income Tax	0.0	0.0	0.0	0.0
Net Income	144.4	2.3	-182.4	-89.7
Cash Flow From Operations	-125.0	5.0	-151.7	-83.6
Balance Sheet (000's)				
Cash & Equivalents	36.3	9.8	517.4	5.9
Total Current Assets	2,352.0	364.5	844.9	476.0
Fixed Assets, Net	15.9	7.0	11.1	24.7
Total Assets	2,743.1	548.4	1,032.9	693.5
Total Current Liabilities	18.7	14.1	515.0	13.2
Long-Term Debt	0.0	0.0	0.0	0.0
Stockholders' Equity	2,724.4	514.3	497.9	680.3
Performance & Financial Condition				
Return on Total Revenues %	24.23	0.84	-66.52	-32.98
Return on Avg Stockholders' Equity %	8.92	0.45	-30.96	-13.10
Return on Average Assets %	8.78	0.29	-21.13	-12.86
Current Ratio	125.71	25.93	1.64	36.00
Debt / Equity %	n.a.	n.a.	n.a.	n.a.

Compound Growth %'s	EPS % n.a.	Net Income % n.a.	Total Revenues % n.a.

Comments

The joint venture, in which the Company has a 33% interest, had losses during 1995, 1994, and 1993, of $3.7 million, $9.4 million and $8.5 million, respectively. A profit was recorded in 1996 of $1.93 million but the Company is not entitled to any portion of it because of the prior losses. Revenues presented represent minimum distributions from the joint venture. There is no assurance that the joint venture will be able to sustain profitability for an extended period. During 1996, the Company privately placed 270,000 shares of common at $7.50 per share for the purpose of increasing working capital. Investment Classification: Speculative

Officers	**Position**	**Ownership Information**	
Alan P. Ploesser	Chairman	Number of Shares Outstanding	1,870,050
Birl W. Worley, Jr.	President, CEO	Market Capitalization	$ 19,635,525
R. Herbert Hampton	VP - Finance, Secretary	Frequency of Dividends	n.a.
		Number of Shareholders	2,000

Other Information

Transfer Agent	American Stock Transfer & Trust Company New York, NY		Where Listed	PSE
Auditor	KPMG Peat Marwick LLP		Symbol	GCC
Market Maker	Bishop Rosen & Co., Inc.	(212)602-0692	SIC Code	1041
			Employees	9
Broker Dealer	OTC Specialist			

Goodheart-Willcox Company, Inc. (The)

18604 West Creek Drive   Tinley Park, IL 60477   Telephone (708)687-5000   Fax (708)687-5068

Company Description

The Goodheart-Willcox Company publishes textbooks on trade, family and consumer sciences, technology and vocational subjects. Activities include the search for authors, acquisition of manuscripts, and the design and marketing of the books. Printing and binding of the Company's books are done by outside contractors. The customer base includes state schools and community colleges. The terms of an agreement with a principal officer/shareholder requires that the Company repurchase approximately 163,000 shares upon his death. The Company began business in 1949.

	04/30/96	04/30/95	04/30/94	04/30/93
Per Share Information				
Stock Price as of 12/31	31.25	20.50	18.50	17.00
Earnings Per Share	2.13	2.70	1.81	1.63
Price / Earnings Ratio	14.67	7.59	10.22	10.43
Book Value Per Share	14.95	12.26	11.45	10.11
Price / Book Value %	209.03	167.21	161.57	168.15
Dividends Per Share	0.80	0.80	0.70	0.60
Annual Financial Data				
Operating Results (000's)				
Total Revenues	14,872.0	14,968.0	12,742.0	11,983.0
Costs & Expenses	-12,405.0	-11,644.0	-10,260.0	-10,061.0
Income Before Taxes and Other	2,467.0	3,324.0	2,307.0	1,920.0
Other Items	0.0	0.0	0.0	0.0
Income Tax	-871.0	-1,307.0	-950.0	-700.0
Net Income	1,596.0	2,017.0	1,357.0	1,220.0
Cash Flow From Operations	1,427.0	3,505.0	2,091.0	2,227.0
Balance Sheet (000's)				
Cash & Equivalents	5,118.0	7,460.0	5,570.0	4,481.0
Total Current Assets	9,228.0	10,859.0	9,142.0	8,233.0
Fixed Assets, Net	2,253.0	683.0	702.0	671.0
Total Assets	13,705.0	13,192.0	11,136.0	10,385.0
Total Current Liabilities	1,777.0	2,272.0	1,638.0	1,741.0
Long-Term Debt	0.0	0.0	0.0	0.0
Stockholders' Equity	8,739.0	7,169.0	6,697.0	5,914.0
Performance & Financial Condition				
Return on Total Revenues %	10.73	13.48	10.65	10.18
Return on Avg Stockholders' Equity %	20.07	29.09	21.52	20.42
Return on Average Assets %	11.87	16.58	12.61	12.42
Current Ratio	5.19	4.78	5.58	4.73
Debt / Equity %	n.a.	n.a.	n.a.	n.a.

Compound Growth %'s	EPS %	9.33	Net Income %	9.37	Total Revenues %	7.47

Comments

Management reports a good year in light of a soft market. Revenue was assisted by the reintroduction of backlist titles. LIFO inventory accounting has the effect of reducing the inventory amount by $2,645,000 below actual cost. A new warehouse and office facility was occupied in early fiscal 1997. Sales for the nine months ended January 31, 1997, totaled $14.3 million with Net Income of $2.3 million ($3.14 per share) as compared to $12.4 million and $1.6 million ($2.20 per share) for the same period in 1996. Investment Classification: Value

Officers	Position	Ownership Information	
George A. Fischer	Chairman	Number of Shares Outstanding	584,700
John F. Flanagan	President, CEO	Market Capitalization	$ 18,271,875
Donald A. Massucci	Vice President, Treasurer	Frequency of Dividends	Semi-Annual
Dick G. Snyder	VP - Sales, Secretary	Number of Shareholders	150

Other Information

Transfer Agent	First National Bank of Chicago Chicago, IL		Where Listed	OTC-BB
Auditor	Grant Thornton LLP		Symbol	GWOX
Market Maker	Chicago Corporation, The	(312)855-7664	SIC Code	2731
	Koonce Securities, Inc.	(800)368-2802	Employees	60
Broker Dealer	Regular Stockbroker			

Guaranty Corporation

P.O. Box 2231   Baton Rouge, LA 70821-2231   Telephone (504)383-0355   Fax (504)343-0047

Company Description

Guaranty Corporation, through its subsidiaries, operates in the following businesses: life insurance, mortgage banking, radio broadcast, and real estate development. During 1995, the Company discontinued its consumer finance operations. Nine shares of stock were reacquired by the Company at $8,500 per share. The largest single block of shares recently offered was 181 shares by the Balfour family in late 1995. Offers in the $8,000 to $10,000 per share range were received.

	12/31/95	12/31/94	12/31/93	12/31/92
Per Share Information				
Stock Price as of 12/31	8,500.00	8,000.00	5,000.00	4,000.00
Earnings Per Share	2,032.72	1,917.60	1,499.21	48.69
Price / Earnings Ratio	4.18	4.17	3.34	82.15
Book Value Per Share	21,834.00	11,942.16	13,669.57	12,176.56
Price / Book Value %	38.93	66.99	36.58	32.85
Dividends Per Share	75.00	0.0	0.0	0.0
Annual Financial Data				
Operating Results (000's)				
Total Revenues	26,134.0	24,659.0	24,506.0	21,171.0
Costs & Expenses	-23,364.0	-21,760.0	-21,956.0	-21,140.0
Income Before Taxes and Other	2,770.0	2,899.0	2,550.0	31.0
Other Items	0.0	0.0	0.0	0.0
Income Tax	-223.0	-477.0	-658.0	32.0
Net Income	2,547.0	2,422.0	1,892.0	63.0
Cash Flow From Operations	1,940.0	-638.0	1,055.0	39,760.0
Balance Sheet (000's)				
Cash & Equivalents	6,703.0	3,648.0	1,831.0	8,775.0
Total Current Assets	162,714.0	145,366.0	1,831.0	9,028.0
Fixed Assets, Net	3,520.0	2,966.0	2,801.0	2,809.0
Total Assets	207,881.0	201,068.0	208,616.0	206,508.0
Total Current Liabilities	1,905.0	1,731.0	2,100.0	2,803.0
Long-Term Debt	1,050.0	1,898.0	1,100.0	112.0
Stockholders' Equity	27,358.0	15,071.0	17,251.0	15,379.0
Performance & Financial Condition				
Return on Total Revenues %	9.75	9.82	7.72	0.30
Return on Avg Stockholders' Equity %	12.01	14.99	11.60	0.41
Return on Average Assets %	1.25	1.18	0.91	0.03
Current Ratio	85.41	83.98	0.87	3.22
Debt / Equity %	3.84	12.59	6.38	0.73

Compound Growth %'s	EPS %	246.91	Net Income %	243.21	Total Revenues %	7.27

Comments

Most of the increased profits over the last couple of years have been generated from investment transactions in the life insurance company. However, the broadcasting group has begun to contribute and is expected to be a more pronounced contributor in future years. Gains on security sales are not reported on the income statement until the security is sold. Mark-to-market adjustments are, however, reflected in the equity section which accounts for some of the large swings in book value. 1996 results were not available when we went to press. Investment Classification: Value

Officers	Position	Ownership Information	
George A. Foster, Jr.	Chairman, CEO	Number of Shares Outstanding	1,253
Janet D. Baldwin	Secretary	Market Capitalization	$ 10,650,500
		Frequency of Dividends	Irregular
		Number of Shareholders	Under 500

Other Information

Transfer Agent	Company Office		Where Listed	OTC-PS
Auditor	Postlethwaite & Netterville		Symbol	GRTYA
Market Maker	PaineWebber Incorporated	(212)713-3766	SIC Code	6300
	Hill Thompson Magid& Co., Inc.	(800)631-3083	Employees	n.a.
Broker Dealer	OTC Specialist			
	Standard Investment	(888)783-4688 Ext: Jack		

Hamburg Industries, Inc.

218 Pine Street   Hamburg, PA 19526-0027   Telephone (610)562-3031   Fax (610)562-0209

Company Description

The Company is a manufacturer and reseller of brooms, brushes, mops and handles in the mid-Atlantic region of the United States. In 1995, equipment was added for the manufacture of a full line of institutional mops and dust mop handles, metal threaded handles, and wet mop handles. This both allows for greater sales opportunities and makes the Company a more viable supplier. On January 1, 1996, the name was changed from Hamburg Broom Works, which had been the name of the Company since it was founded in 1894.

	12/31/96	12/31/95	12/31/94	12/31/93
Per Share Information				
Stock Price	4.50	4.50	4.25	5.06
Earnings Per Share	0.32	0.04	0.18	0.25
Price / Earnings Ratio	14.06	112.50	23.61	20.24
Book Value Per Share	4.24	3.92	3.88	3.92
Price / Book Value %	106.13	114.80	109.54	129.08
Dividends Per Share	0.0	0.0	0.21	0.19
Annual Financial Data				
Operating Results (000's)				
Total Revenues	2,883.3	2,659.4	2,780.7	2,590.0
Costs & Expenses	-2,800.5	-2,650.0	-2,739.4	-2,517.7
Income Before Taxes and Other	82.8	9.4	41.3	72.3
Other Items	0.0	0.0	0.0	0.0
Income Tax	-18.0	-1.6	-4.7	-22.0
Net Income	64.8	7.7	36.5	50.3
Cash Flow From Operations	161.0	-52.8	156.5	41.9
Balance Sheet (000's)				
Cash & Equivalents	49.3	77.0	55.8	59.1
Total Current Assets	760.3	834.6	658.2	808.7
Fixed Assets, Net	449.5	482.4	320.1	292.3
Total Assets	1,231.1	1,338.2	998.9	1,103.8
Total Current Liabilities	357.0	529.3	201.2	302.2
Long-Term Debt	0.0	0.0	0.0	0.0
Stockholders' Equity	867.7	802.9	791.1	798.4
Performance & Financial Condition				
Return on Total Revenues %	2.25	0.29	1.31	1.94
Return on Avg Stockholders' Equity %	7.76	0.97	4.59	6.34
Return on Average Assets %	5.04	0.66	3.47	4.90
Current Ratio	2.13	1.58	3.27	2.68
Debt / Equity %	n.a.	n.a.	n.a.	n.a.

Compound Growth %'s	EPS %	8.58	Net Income %	8.84	Total Revenues %	3.64

Comments

The Company was having a terrific year until the Company was notified that it was losing a major customer. The negative effect of this loss was not felt until October and will continue throughout 1997 and beyond. An aggressive sales and marketing program is in place and will continue. Management is also cutting expenses for added protection. During 1996, it discontinued the pension plan and changed health care to a lower cost program. We compliment management for not trying to sweep this situation under the rug. Investment Classification: Speculative

Officers	Position	Ownership Information	
William Bierlin, Jr.	Chairman	Number of Shares Outstanding	204,845
Richard E. Stiller	President, CEO	Market Capitalization	$ 921,803
William L. Bast	Secretary, Treasurer	Frequency of Dividends	Irregular
June A. Kline	Other	Number of Shareholders	Under 500
Grace A. Vinglinsky	Other		

Other Information				
Transfer Agent	Midatlantic Bank, N.A. Edison, NJ		Where Listed	OTC-BB
Auditor	Beard & Company, Inc.		Symbol	HBBWB
Market Maker	Carr Securities Corporation	(800)221-2243	SIC Code	3991
	Hill Thompson Magid & Co., Inc	(800)631-3083	Employees	24
Broker Dealer	OTC Specialist			
	Norman Kadehjian - Wainwright	(800)727-7176		

Hamlin Bank and Trust Company

333 W. Main Street   Smethport, PA 16749   Telephone (814)887-5555   Fax (814)887-2478

Company Description

Hamlin Bank and Trust Company is considered the "Pioneer Bank of McKean County" which it has served since 1863. Over the years, it has grown to five branches and nearly 100 employees. The fifth branch was opened in July, 1996 in Bradford. McKean County is a rural area located in upper Pennsylvania and only ten miles east of the beautiful Allegheny National Forest.

	12/31/96	12/31/95	12/31/94
Per Share Information			
Stock Price	83.00	63.00	52.12
Earnings Per Share	8.83	8.20	7.91
Price / Earnings Ratio	9.40	7.68	6.59
Book Value Per Share	94.88	80.31	62.54
Price / Book Value %	87.48	78.45	83.34
Dividends Per Share	3.25	2.75	2.25
Annual Financial Data			
Operating Results (000's)			
Net Interest Income	8,475.9	8,067.0	8,543.1
Loan Loss Provision	-370.0	-200.0	-180.0
Non-Interest Income	1,694.3	1,366.9	631.6
Non-Interest Expense	-4,560.1	-4,380.2	-4,174.6
Income Before Taxes and Other	5,240.1	4,853.7	4,820.1
Other Items	0.0	0.0	-106.6
Income Tax	-1,382.6	-1,260.1	-1,269.3
Net Income	3,857.5	3,593.6	3,444.2
Balance Sheet (000's)			
Cash & Securities	77,146.6	71,782.4	74,013.2
Loans, Net	123,159.7	109,306.8	103,469.0
Total Assets	204,821.3	190,396.7	182,101.9
Deposits	153,706.3	148,914.5	144,681.6
Stockholders' Equity	39,550.7	35,208.2	27,419.4
Performance & Financial Condition			
Return on Avg Stockholders' Equity %	10.32	11.48	14.21
Return on Average Assets %	1.95	1.93	n.a.
Equity to Assets %	19.31	18.49	15.06
Net Interest Margin	n.a.	n.a.	n.a.
Reserve as a % of Problem Loans	n.a.	n.a.	n.a.

Compound Growth %'s	EPS %	5.66	Net Income %	5.83	Net Interest Income %	-0.39

Comments

Hamlin Bank continues to rank among the most well-capitalized banks in Pennsylvania. Over two-thirds of the active employees have ownership through stock purchases made available to them. Shareholders in general have benefited from an ever-increasing dividend; it was $3.25 in 1996 as compared to $1.10 in 1990. As might be expected, existing shareholders are not regularly selling, causing a thin market for trading. Investment Classification: Value & Income

Officers	Position	Ownership Information	
Robert A. Digel, Jr.	Chairman	Number of Shares Outstanding	416,868
Richard G. Brown	President, CEO	Market Capitalization	$ 34,600,044
Doris R. Gustafson	Secretary	Frequency of Dividends	Quarterly
David J. Malone	Vice President, Treasurer	Number of Shareholders	n.a.
Jeffrey A. Wilson	Controller	Where Listed / Symbol	OTC-BB / HMLN

Other Information			Loan Mix	%
Transfer Agent	Company Office		R/E Mortgages	72.3
Auditor	S.R. Snodgrass, A.C.		Consumer	21.7
Market Maker	Ferris, Baker Watts Inc.	(800)638-7411	Commerical	5.1
	Ryan, Beck & Co.	(800)325-7926	Construction	0.9
Broker Dealer	OTC Specialist			
	Dennis Reynolds - Ryan, Beck	(888)231-7226		

Hammett (J.L.) Co.

P.O. Box 859057   Braintree, MA 02185-9057   Telephone (617)848-1000   Fax (617)848-0273

Company Description

J.L. Hammett Co. is a direct mail retailer of educational products that include virtually every item and accessory used by children in classrooms or at home. The Company also operates a retail business with 52 stores in 18 states. Approximately 80% of Company sales are derived from sales to municipalities and school districts. The Holden family continues to own most of the 95,388 shares outstanding and a number of family members are active in the business. There is also an Employee Stock Ownership Plan for all nonunion employees. The Company's products can be reviewed on its Web Page: (http://www.hammett.com).

	12/31/96	12/31/95	12/31/94	12/31/93
Per Share Information				
Stock Price	67.00	66.50	65.00	50.00
Earnings Per Share	-8.10	11.30	4.96	7.09
Price / Earnings Ratio	n.a.	5.88	13.10	7.05
Book Value Per Share	143.81	155.13	117.58	114.82
Price / Book Value %	46.59	42.87	55.28	43.55
Dividends Per Share	3.20	2.20	2.20	1.50
Annual Financial Data				
Operating Results (000's)				
Total Revenues	134,448.7	125,994.0	76,354.9	77,126.2
Costs & Expenses	-135,675.1	-123,485.0	-75,357.7	-76,067.0
Income Before Taxes and Other	-1,226.4	1,968.0	997.2	1,059.2
Other Items	0.0	0.0	0.0	135.7
Income Tax	463.4	-763.6	-416.7	-369.4
Net Income	-763.0	1,204.4	580.5	825.5
Cash Flow From Operations	-4,766.5	3,351.3	4,459.4	825.5
Balance Sheet (000's)				
Cash & Equivalents	200.5	1,000.5	153.3	481.8
Total Current Assets	35,801.3	31,239.6	14,926.5	19,248.8
Fixed Assets, Net	10,371.5	8,164.0	7,526.2	7,924.8
Total Assets	52,910.9	44,703.4	26,907.8	30,337.6
Total Current Liabilities	33,854.8	18,973.7	8,577.7	11,869.1
Long-Term Debt	2,725.4	8,029.7	3,441.4	4,078.8
Stockholders' Equity	13,718.2	14,797.2	13,410.5	13,095.7
Performance & Financial Condition				
Return on Total Revenues %	-0.57	0.96	0.76	1.07
Return on Avg Stockholders' Equity %	-5.35	8.54	4.38	6.45
Return on Average Assets %	-1.56	3.36	2.03	2.81
Current Ratio	1.06	1.65	1.74	1.62
Debt / Equity %	19.87	54.27	25.66	31.15

Compound Growth %'s	EPS % n.a.	Net Income % n.a.	Total Revenues % 20.35

Comments

1993 results include a nonrecurring benefit of $135,700, or $1.19 per share, because of an accounting change. Five new retail stores were opened in 1996. Management reports that the expansion into new markets has gone well. The industry overall, however, is facing increasing competition from large retailers and others that want to be in the school business. The 1996 loss appears to be attributable to a 13.3% increase in overhead expenses without offsetting new revenues. Results for the first quarter of 1997 were positive and revenue was up 28% over the preceding year. Investment Classification: Value

Officers	Position	Ownership Information	
Richmond Y. Holden, Jr.	President, CEO	Number of Shares Outstanding	95,388
Eugene R. Grant	Treasurer	Market Capitalization	$ 6,390,996
Dick Krause	Vice President	Frequency of Dividends	Quarterly
Jeff Holden	VP - Sales	Number of Shareholders	Under 500
Dave Shepard	Other		

Other Information				
Transfer Agent	Company Office		Where Listed	OTC-BB
Auditor	Deloitte & Touche LLP		Symbol	HAMT
Market Maker	Sharpe Capital Inc.	(800)355-5781	SIC Code	5961
	Hill Thompson Magid & Co., Inc	(800)631-3083	Employees	n.a.
Broker Dealer	OTC Specialist			
	Standard Investment	(888)783-4688		

Hanover Foods Corporation

1486 York Street   Hanover, PA 17331-0334   Telephone (717)632-6000   Fax (717)632-6681

Company Description

Hanover Foods is a vertically integrated processor of vegetable products in one industry segment. It is involved in the growing, processing, canning, freezing, freeze-drying, packaging, marketing and distribution of its products under its own trademarks, as well as other branded, customer and private labels. The corporation operates five plants in Pennsylvania, one in Delaware and two plants in Guatemala. The mid-Atlantic states and Florida are the geographic areas with the strongest retail sales. Hanover Foods was founded in 1924.

	03/31/96	04/02/95	04/03/94	03/31/93
Per Share Information				
Stock Price as of 12/31	33.00	57.00	54.00	52.00
Earnings Per Share	0.53	2.53	8.29	7.48
Price / Earnings Ratio	62.26	22.53	6.51	6.95
Book Value Per Share	58.27	59.32	57.89	50.59
Price / Book Value %	56.63	96.09	93.28	102.79
Dividends Per Share	1.10	1.08	1.00	1.00
Annual Financial Data				
Operating Results (000's)				
Total Revenues	263,560.0	257,590.0	235,532.0	216,759.0
Costs & Expenses	-262,927.0	-254,904.0	-225,304.0	-207,491.0
Income Before Taxes and Other	633.0	2,686.0	10,228.0	9,268.0
Other Items	0.0	0.0	0.0	0.0
Income Tax	-213.0	-798.0	-4,067.0	-3,672.0
Net Income	420.0	1,888.0	6,161.0	5,596.0
Cash Flow From Operations	1,422.0	10.0	7,471.0	n.a.
Balance Sheet (000's)				
Cash & Equivalents	914.0	649.0	2,257.0	2,256.0
Total Current Assets	76,025.0	80,735.0	73,013.0	64,597.0
Fixed Assets, Net	49,205.0	49,251.0	49,000.0	46,000.0
Total Assets	128,368.0	132,144.0	124,646.0	117,544.0
Total Current Liabilities	60,981.0	61,166.0	50,734.0	42,015.0
Long-Term Debt	18,453.0	20,658.0	24,436.0	31,056.0
Stockholders' Equity	42,509.0	43,920.0	42,990.0	37,920.0
Performance & Financial Condition				
Return on Total Revenues %	0.16	0.73	2.62	2.58
Return on Avg Stockholders' Equity %	0.97	4.34	15.23	15.66
Return on Average Assets %	0.32	1.47	5.09	4.96
Current Ratio	1.25	1.32	1.44	1.54
Debt / Equity %	43.41	47.04	56.84	81.90

Compound Growth %'s	EPS %	-58.62	Net Income %	-57.82	Total Revenues %	6.73

Comments

Management reported that the industry produced enormous excesses and the competition was fierce. Prices fell and promotions exploded. Despite these circumstances, Hanover Foods produced a profit. Cost reduction programs were initiated which will make the firm a lower cost processor. For the nine months ended March 2, 1997, net earnings had sharply rebounded to $5,039,000, $6.96 per share, from $1,467,000, $1.72 per share, for the same period in 1996. The Company has been reacquiring its shares in recent years. Investment Classification: Value

Officers	Position	Ownership Information	
John A. Warehime	Chairman, CEO	Number of Shares Outstanding	715,995
Gary T. Knisely	Exec VP, Secretary	Market Capitalization	$ 23,627,835
Pietro D. Giraffa, Jr.	Vice President, Controller	Frequency of Dividends	n.a.
Jack A. Brown	Vice President, Treasurer	Number of Shareholders	503

Other Information

Transfer Agent	ChaseMellon Shareholder Services New York, NY		Where Listed	OTC-BB
Auditor	KPMG Peat Marwick LLP		Symbol	HNFS
Market Maker	Fahnestock & Co., Inc.	(800)223-3012	SIC Code	2033
	Sharpe Capital Inc.	(800)355-5781	Employees	1547
Broker Dealer	Regular Stockbroker			

Harford National Bank

8 West Bel Air Avenue   Aberdeen, MD 21001   Telephone (410)272-5000   Fax (410)272-0533

Company Description

In 1964, a determined group of local businessmen opened Aberdeen National Bank. From a modest beginning, the Bank prospered and grew. As more offices opened, it changed its name to Harford National Bank, after the name of the County, in 1980. Today it has offices in Aberdeen, Bel Air, Box Hill, Havre de Grace and Joppatowne, Maryland. Art enthusiasts should obtain the annual report just to look at magnificent photographs taken in Harford County.

	12/31/96	12/31/95	12/31/94	12/31/93
Per Share Information				
Stock Price	46.00	41.74	34.78	34.63
Earnings Per Share	4.72	4.19	4.08	3.64
Price / Earnings Ratio	9.75	9.96	8.52	9.51
Book Value Per Share	34.18	30.49	27.17	23.86
Price / Book Value %	134.58	136.90	128.01	145.14
Dividends Per Share	1.19	1.00	0.85	0.73
Annual Financial Data				
Operating Results (000's)				
Net Interest Income	5,125.3	4,717.5	4,500.0	4,189.7
Loan Loss Provision	-50.0	-112.5	-75.0	-150.0
Non-Interest Income	788.3	807.6	820.0	715.9
Non-Interest Expense	-3,615.3	-3,428.7	-3,373.4	-3,150.8
Income Before Taxes and Other	2,248.3	1,983.8	1,871.6	1,604.8
Other Items	0.0	0.0	0.0	4.2
Income Tax	-736.6	-660.2	-606.0	-496.5
Net Income	1,511.7	1,323.6	1,265.6	1,112.5
Balance Sheet (000's)				
Cash & Securities	29,097.2	26,228.0	22,714.1	26,567.7
Loans, Net	72,787.0	73,790.6	69,087.6	64,526.8
Total Assets	105,072.1	103,397.1	95,159.6	94,482.1
Deposits	93,538.6	93,071.6	86,264.9	86,591.9
Stockholders' Equity	10,981.0	9,652.8	8,469.1	7,308.5
Performance & Financial Condition				
Return on Avg Stockholders' Equity %	14.65	14.61	16.04	16.37
Return on Average Assets %	1.45	1.33	1.33	1.19
Equity to Assets %	10.45	9.34	8.90	7.74
Net Interest Margin	n.a.	n.a.	n.a.	n.a.
Reserve as a % of Problem Loans	92.43	170.66	624.28	205.13

Compound Growth %'s	EPS %	9.05	Net Income %	10.76	Net Interest Income %	6.95

Comments

Harford National Bank has declared 15%, 10%, 5% and 20% stock dividends in 1996, 1995, 1994 and 1993, respectively. All per share amounts have been adjusted for consistency. The Bank has demonstrated excellent returns on assets and equity and reasonable growth. Despite the stock dividends and additional shares issued under a dividend reinvestment plan, trading can still be thin. Investment Classification: Value

Officers	**Position**	**Ownership Information**	
Richard W. Wilkinson	President	Number of Shares Outstanding	321,259
Charles H. Jacobs, Jr.	Exec VP, Head Cashier	Market Capitalization	$ 14,777,914
Charlotte A. Mock	Senior VP, Controller	Frequency of Dividends	Quarterly
Jean C. Royster	Vice President	Number of Shareholders	n.a.
Donald H. Young	Vice President	Where Listed / Symbol	OTC-BB / HRFD

Other Information				**Loan Mix**	**%**
Transfer Agent	Company Office			R/E Mortgages	68.0
Auditor	Rowles & Company			Commerical	17.8
Market Maker	Ferris, Baker Watts Inc.	(800)638-7411		Installment	12.1
	Koonce Securities, Inc.	(800)368-2802		Consumer	2.1
Broker Dealer	OTC Specialist				
	Dennis Reynolds - Ryan, Beck	(888)231-7226			

Harriet & Henderson Yarns, Inc.

1724 Graham Avenue   Henderson, NC 27536-0789   Telephone (919)430-5000   Fax (919)430-5101

Company Description

Harriet & Henderson Yarns operates principally as a manufacturer of cotton, blended and synthetic yarns sold primarily to apparel and hosiery manufacturers located in the southeastern United States. The Company was founded in 1895. Ring-spun yarns have been produced using old technology. This is being phased out as state-of-the-art linked ring-spinning equipment is placed into operation.

	02/02/97	01/28/96	01/29/95	01/30/94
Per Share Information				
Stock Price as of 12/31	95.00	300.00	300.00	145.00
Earnings Per Share	-71.76	-65.71	-56.31	40.43
Price / Earnings Ratio	n.a.	n.a.	n.a.	3.59
Book Value Per Share	419.19	490.96	557.32	607.66
Price / Book Value %	22.66	61.10	53.83	23.86
Dividends Per Share	0.0	1.00	3.75	14.50
Annual Financial Data				
Operating Results (000's)				
Total Revenues	232,942.8	203,669.3	195,829.9	190,552.0
Costs & Expenses	-247,215.3	-216,698.4	-207,617.1	-181,654.2
Income Before Taxes and Other	-14,272.5	-13,541.3	-11,787.2	8,980.4
Other Items	0.0	0.0	0.0	0.0
Income Tax	4,949.9	5,000.3	4,425.9	-3,547.3
Net Income	-9,322.6	-8,541.0	-7,361.2	5,433.1
Cash Flow From Operations	4,688.9	4,745.8	2,496.9	18,297.5
Balance Sheet (000's)				
Cash & Equivalents	981.3	1,234.0	2,837.4	20,121.1
Total Current Assets	48,567.0	43,923.4	44,751.3	57,170.9
Fixed Assets, Net	87,873.4	98,733.6	74,613.7	66,010.5
Total Assets	143,584.0	150,840.7	131,739.9	134,336.7
Total Current Liabilities	16,290.9	8,760.8	28,296.3	14,701.3
Long-Term Debt	62,000.0	65,000.0	14,890.0	23,638.4
Stockholders' Equity	54,456.5	63,779.1	72,508.7	81,637.9
Performance & Financial Condition				
Return on Total Revenues %	-4.00	-4.19	-3.76	2.85
Return on Avg Stockholders' Equity %	-15.77	-12.53	-9.55	6.80
Return on Average Assets %	-6.33	-6.05	-5.53	4.04
Current Ratio	2.98	5.01	1.58	3.89
Debt / Equity %	113.85	101.91	20.54	28.96

Compound Growth %'s	EPS % n.a.	Net Income % n.a.	Total Revenues % 6.92

Comments

$37 million was invested in a new plant and equipment in 1995. The large loss is attributable to a lack of sales volume, continued high costs for raw materials, and lower yarn prices. Despite the losses of the last three years, each year still resulted in positive cash flow from operations. Management is predicting a small profit for the next year and believes it is positioned to take advantage as the industry changes over the next several years. Investment Classification: Value & Speculative

Officers	Position	Ownership Information	
Marshall Y. Cooper, Jr.	Chairman, President	Number of Shares Outstanding	129,908
Thomas R. Allen	VP - Finance, Treasurer	Market Capitalization	$ 12,341,260
Virginia L. Cook	Secretary	Frequency of Dividends	n.a.
Samuel W. Brummitt	VP - Manufacturing	Number of Shareholders	Under 500
C. Gary Walker	VP - Sales		

Other Information				
Transfer Agent	Company Office		Where Listed	OTC-BB
Auditor	McGladrey & Pullen LLP		Symbol	HHYN
Market Maker	Hill Thompson Magid & Co., Inc	(800)631-3083	SIC Code	2280
	The Chicago Corporation	(800)323-1225	Employees	1300
Broker Dealer	OTC Specialist			
	Standard Investment	(888)783-4688 Ext: Jack		

Hawaii National Bancshares, Inc.

45 North King Street   Honolulu, HI 96812   Telephone (808)528-7755   Fax (808)528-7773

Company Description

Hawaii National Bank, subsidiary of this holding company, operates thirteen offices on the beautiful Hawaiian Islands. The last location to open was in Pearl City in May, 1997. As the mainland of the United States embarked upon its sixth year of economic expansion, Hawaii's economy continued to struggle. The State continued to lose jobs in 1996 for the fourth consecutive year and Honolulu ranked last out of 100 metropolitan areas in terms of job growth according to a national survey. The Bank was founded in 1961.

	12/31/96	12/31/95	12/31/94	12/31/93
Per Share Information				
Stock Price	34.00	32.00	27.62	22.12
Earnings Per Share	1.00	1.47	1.23	1.79
Price / Earnings Ratio	34.00	21.77	22.46	12.36
Book Value Per Share	39.10	38.25	36.91	35.83
Price / Book Value %	86.96	83.66	74.83	61.74
Dividends Per Share	0.15	0.15	0.15	0.15
Annual Financial Data				
Operating Results (000's)				
Net Interest Income	15,372.4	15,534.7	14,879.7	14,870.4
Loan Loss Provision	-810.0	-700.0	-765.0	-480.0
Non-Interest Income	2,445.5	2,336.5	2,348.1	2,478.4
Non-Interest Expense	-15,865.6	-15,507.3	-15,085.4	-15,272.7
Income Before Taxes and Other	1,142.2	1,663.9	1,377.3	1,596.1
Other Items	0.0	0.0	0.0	350.0
Income Tax	-431.0	-620.0	-505.0	-670.0
Net Income	711.2	1,043.9	872.3	1,276.1
Balance Sheet (000's)				
Cash & Securities	82,693.6	80,148.8	67,029.9	87,013.9
Loans, Net	204,195.3	209,997.6	213,992.6	210,542.1
Total Assets	296,025.3	299,590.5	290,256.3	306,407.2
Deposits	264,594.4	268,905.8	260,973.1	278,167.7
Stockholders' Equity	27,797.3	27,192.7	26,243.4	25,477.7
Performance & Financial Condition				
Return on Avg Stockholders' Equity %	2.59	3.91	3.37	5.13
Return on Average Assets %	0.24	0.35	0.29	0.41
Equity to Assets %	9.39	9.08	9.04	8.31
Net Interest Margin	5.63	5.74	5.48	5.23
Reserve as a % of Problem Loans	90.43	46.77	95.92	194.38

Compound Growth %'s	EPS %	-17.64	Net Income %	-17.70	Net Interest Income %	1.11

Comments

1993 results include a nonrecurring benefit of $350,000, $.49 per share, from a change in accounting method. This has the effect of increasing the negative compound growth rates in earnings. Lower results in 1996 were attributable to a slow economic recovery, a decline in interest rates, and the increased costs of doing business. Loan quality is reportedly improved from earlier years. The current price per share, at less than book value, is reflective of a depressed economy and disregards historical levels of earnings and a valuable franchise. Investment Classification: Value

Officers	Position	Ownership Information	
K. J. Luke	Chairman	Number of Shares Outstanding	711,000
Warren K.K. Luke	President, CEO	Market Capitalization	$ 24,174,000
Ernest T. Murata	Exec VP, CFO	Frequency of Dividends	Semi-Annual
Lloyd J. Nakao	Senior VP	Number of Shareholders	1,299
Roy S. Nishimoto	Senior VP	Where Listed / Symbol	OTC-BB / HWNB

Other Information			Loan Mix	%
Transfer Agent	Company Office		R/E Mortgages	94.3
Auditor	Coopers & Lybrand LLP		Consumer	3.7
Market Maker	The Chicago Corporation	(800)621-1674	Construction	1.2
	Ryan, Beck & Co.	(800)325-7926	Other	0.8
Broker Dealer	Regular Stockbroker			
	Standard Investment	(888)783-4688 Ext: Jack		

Hayward Industries, Inc.

900 Fairmount Avenue   Elizabeth, NJ 07207   Telephone (908)351-5400   Fax (908)351-2189

Company Description

Hayward Industries is a leading manufacturer of residential swimming pool and spa products, and industrial flow control products. Manufacturing operations are primarily conducted at a manufacturing facility located on a fifty-four acre site in Clemmons, North Carolina. For all years presented, swimming pool and spa products account for approximately 80% of total Company sales.

	12/31/95	12/30/94	12/31/93	12/31/92
Per Share Information				
Stock Price	88.00	84.40	70.00	70.00
Earnings Per Share	9.20	14.17	11.60	11.22
Price / Earnings Ratio	9.57	5.96	6.03	6.24
Book Value Per Share	101.68	95.28	83.60	76.79
Price / Book Value %	86.55	88.58	83.73	91.16
Dividends Per Share	3.00	3.00	3.00	3.00
Annual Financial Data				
Operating Results (000's)				
Total Revenues	205,574.0	203,740.0	178,073.0	179,617.0
Costs & Expenses	-188,881.0	-173,682.0	-152,133.0	-153,329.0
Income Before Taxes and Other	16,693.0	25,054.0	20,678.0	20,123.0
Other Items	0.0	0.0	0.0	0.0
Income Tax	-6,749.0	-9,712.0	-8,201.0	-8,197.0
Net Income	9,944.0	15,342.0	12,477.0	11,926.0
Cash Flow From Operations	4,699.0	16,687.0	13,101.0	22,160.0
Balance Sheet (000's)				
Cash & Equivalents	6,109.0	3,553.0	10,266.0	15,836.0
Total Current Assets	86,653.0	75,707.0	65,206.0	65,146.0
Fixed Assets, Net	76,184.0	63,094.0	58,179.0	60,014.0
Total Assets	193,388.0	168,554.0	153,981.0	156,148.0
Total Current Liabilities	43,852.0	33,812.0	24,608.0	26,395.0
Long-Term Debt	17,030.0	26,222.0	34,724.0	43,373.0
Stockholders' Equity	110,218.0	103,281.0	90,367.0	81,654.0
Performance & Financial Condition				
Return on Total Revenues %	4.84	7.53	7.01	6.64
Return on Avg Stockholders' Equity %	9.32	15.85	14.51	15.37
Return on Average Assets %	5.49	9.51	8.05	76.69
Current Ratio	1.98	2.24	2.65	2.47
Debt / Equity %	15.45	25.39	38.43	53.12

Compound Growth %'s	EPS %	-6.40	Net Income %	-5.88	Total Revenues %	4.60

Comments

The Company doesn't release 1996 results until June. Therefore the results are not possible to include. The bid price as of December 31, 1996, was $103 per share. The Company has demonstrated good growth and has expanded in foreign markets as well. Inventories are valued on a Last-in, First-out basis which is a lower valuation than current cost. Historically, there has been about a $10 million difference between these numbers. This means that the stock trades at a larger discount to book value than what appears because book value as recorded is artificially low by the after-tax impact of an additional $10 million in earnings or value. Investment Classification: Value

Officers	Position	Ownership Information	
Oscar Davis	Chairman	Number of Shares Outstanding	1,083,961
Anthony T. Castor III	President, CEO	Market Capitalization	$ 95,388,568
Edward C. Teter	Vice President	Frequency of Dividends	Quarterly
		Number of Shareholders	Under 500

Other Information

Transfer Agent	ChaseMellon Shareholder Services Ridgefield Park, NJ		Where Listed	OTC-BB
Auditor	Grant Thornton LLP		Symbol	HWRI
Market Maker	Herzog, Heine, Geduld, Inc.	(800)221-3600	SIC Code	3949
	Hill Thompson Magid & Co., Inc	(800)631-3083	Employees	500
Broker Dealer	OTC Specialist			

Health International, Inc.

1840 Century Park East, Suite 670   Los Angeles, CA 90067   Telephone (800)333-3760   Fax (602)948-2523

Company Description

Health International, Inc. is a national health advisory service organization which provides utilization review services, including a second surgical opinion program and a hospital case management program to employers throughout the United States. Utilization review is comprised of several areas, including second surgical opinion plans, hospital review and prolonged rehabilitation review. The Company was founded in 1986.

	09/30/96	09/30/95	09/30/94	09/30/93
Per Share Information				
Stock Price as of 12/31	2.75	4.75	1.75	2.75
Earnings Per Share	0.35	0.08	0.22	0.04
Price / Earnings Ratio	7.86	59.38	7.95	68.75
Book Value Per Share	0.99	0.62	0.54	0.31
Price / Book Value %	277.78	766.13	324.07	887.10
Dividends Per Share	0.0	0.0	0.0	0.0
Annual Financial Data				
Operating Results (000's)				
Total Revenues	11,766.7	7,639.9	7,006.5	4,509.1
Costs & Expenses	-10,533.3	-7,383.0	-6,287.3	-4,387.5
Income Before Taxes and Other	1,233.4	256.9	719.2	121.6
Other Items	0.0	0.0	0.0	36.3
Income Tax	-212.4	-29.8	-68.0	-52.6
Net Income	1,021.0	227.1	651.2	105.3
Cash Flow From Operations	1,308.6	1,252.9	736.2	313.2
Balance Sheet (000's)				
Cash & Equivalents	2,474.1	1,585.6	878.5	106.0
Total Current Assets	2,853.3	1,819.7	1,470.4	714.8
Fixed Assets, Net	1,502.9	1,594.5	935.5	951.2
Total Assets	4,411.7	3,466.8	2,444.9	1,691.3
Total Current Liabilities	1,099.7	1,148.9	664.8	515.7
Long-Term Debt	0.0	0.0	0.0	0.0
Stockholders' Equity	2,723.9	1,701.7	1,468.6	814.9
Performance & Financial Condition				
Return on Total Revenues %	8.68	2.97	9.29	2.33
Return on Avg Stockholders' Equity %	46.14	14.33	57.03	14.12
Return on Average Assets %	25.92	7.68	31.49	7.26
Current Ratio	2.59	1.58	2.21	1.39
Debt / Equity %	n.a.	n.a.	n.a.	n.a.

Compound Growth %'s	EPS %	106.06	Net Income %	113.25	Total Revenues %	37.67

Comments

Management was quite pleased with a 51% increase in revenue as well as a solid bottom line. The balance sheet is also very strong with plenty of cash for a rainy day. For the six months ended March 31, 1997, the Company had slightly higher revenue but lower earnings. Income before taxes was $641,000 as compared to $708,000 in the prior year. The Company now has to pay income taxes because it has used up all of its tax loss carryforwards. After tax earnings were $.13 per share as compared to $.21 in the first six months of fiscal 1996. Investment Classification: Speculative & Growth

Officers	Position	Ownership Information	
Donald K. Kelly, M.D.	Chairman, CEO	Number of Shares Outstanding	2,756,867
		Market Capitalization	$ 7,581,384
		Frequency of Dividends	n.a.
		Number of Shareholders	Under 500

Other Information			
Transfer Agent	ChaseMellon Shareholder Services Ridgefield Park, NJ	Where Listed	OTC-BB
Auditor	Arthur Andersen LLP	Symbol	HTHN
Market Maker	Wilson-Davis & Co., Inc.	(800)453-5735	SIC Code	8090
	Paragon Capital Corp.	(800)345-0505	Employees	130
Broker Dealer	Regular Stockbroker		

Hendrick Ranch Royalties, Inc.

1836 W. Virginia St., Ste. 104   McKinney, TX 75070-1270   Telephone (972)562-3248   Fax (972)548-1500

Company Description

Hendrick Ranch Royalties, Inc. is an investment holding company with a combination of land and marketable securities. The land produces oil and gas royalties as well as lease income. Shareholders receive a one-page annual summary that has not been audited but has been prepared by a certified public accountant. The Company intends to locate and invest in other profitable activities. Although much emphasis has been placed on acquiring an existing business, the right opportunities have not been found. Management now reports an interest in real estate development.

	12/31/96	12/31/95	12/31/94	12/31/93
Per Share Information				
Stock Price	21.75	21.50	21.00	20.00
Earnings Per Share	2.00	6.03	0.82	2.22
Price / Earnings Ratio	10.88	3.57	25.61	9.01
Book Value Per Share	41.86	39.89	33.91	35.43
Price / Book Value %	51.96	53.90	61.93	56.45
Dividends Per Share	0.05	1.00	1.22	1.02
Annual Financial Data				
Operating Results (000's)				
Total Revenues	305.6	659.6	241.0	315.0
Costs & Expenses	-176.9	-166.4	-191.0	-167.8
Income Before Taxes and Other	128.7	493.2	50.0	147.2
Other Items	0.0	0.0	0.0	0.0
Income Tax	-10.2	-135.4	-1.0	-15.5
Net Income	118.4	357.8	49.0	131.7
Cash Flow From Operations	n.a.	n.a.	n.a.	n.a.
Balance Sheet (000's)				
Cash & Equivalents	1,061.6	929.2	301.0	420.0
Total Current Assets	2,322.6	2,140.6	1,801.0	1,924.0
Fixed Assets, Net	155.8	302.5	213.0	180.0
Total Assets	2,478.3	2,443.1	2,014.0	2,104.0
Total Current Liabilities	0.0	77.4	0.0	0.0
Long-Term Debt	0.0	0.0	0.0	0.0
Stockholders' Equity	2,478.3	2,365.6	2,014.0	2,104.0
Performance & Financial Condition				
Return on Total Revenues %	38.75	54.24	20.31	41.81
Return on Avg Stockholders' Equity %	4.89	16.34	2.38	n.a.
Return on Average Assets %	4.81	16.05	2.38	n.a.
Current Ratio	n.a.	27.64	n.a.	n.a.
Debt / Equity %	n.a.	n.a.	n.a.	n.a.

Compound Growth %'s	EPS %	-3.42	Net Income %	-3.48	Total Revenues %	-1.00

Comments

Investments in securities have not been adjusted to their current fair market value although that amount is disclosed on the report. The difference is an additional $3 million before tax at December 31, 1996. This equates to $50 per share. The location targeted for a possible real estate development is McKinney, Texas, which is a rapidly expanding, active real estate market with rising prices. Investment Classification: Value

Officers	Position	Ownership Information	
Bruce G. Duncan	President, Treasurer	Number of Shares Outstanding	59,209
S. E. Roberds	Secretary	Market Capitalization	$ 1,287,796
		Frequency of Dividends	Irregular
		Number of Shareholders	Under 500

Other Information

Transfer Agent	Company Office		Where Listed	OTC-BB
Auditor	Not indicated		Symbol	HDRR
Market Maker	Carr Securities Corporation	(800)221-2243	SIC Code	6790
	Hill Thompson Magid & Co., Inc	(800)631-3083	Employees	2
Broker Dealer	OTC Specialist			

Henry County Plywood Corporation

P.O. Box 406   Ridgeway, VA 24148-0406   Telephone (540)956-3121   Fax (540)956-4742

Company Description

Henry County Plywood Corporation manufactures hardwood plywood, principally for furniture, marine and architectural applications, and completed furniture as a contractor to established furniture manufacturers. Established in 1948, the Company has earned a reputation for high quality and a high level of customer service. It has two major customers in the furniture industry whose combined purchases represent 40% of total sales volume.

	05/31/96	06/02/95	05/27/94	05/28/93
Per Share Information				
Stock Price as of 12/31	3.12	2.50	2.50	2.50
Earnings Per Share	0.04	-0.23	0.22	-0.07
Price / Earnings Ratio	78.00	n.a.	11.36	n.a.
Book Value Per Share	6.39	6.15	6.43	6.20
Price / Book Value %	48.83	40.65	38.88	40.32
Dividends Per Share	0.03	0.12	0.04	0.03
Annual Financial Data				
Operating Results (000's)				
Total Revenues	7,274.1	8,171.3	8,533.5	6,858.2
Costs & Expenses	-7,237.7	-8,307.2	-8,248.1	-6,879.6
Income Before Taxes and Other	4.0	-147.9	237.7	-38.1
Other Items	0.0	0.0	-66.4	0.0
Income Tax	9.0	62.9	-84.7	9.7
Net Income	13.0	-85.0	86.5	-28.4
Cash Flow From Operations	461.2	-7.2	501.7	-69.8
Balance Sheet (000's)				
Cash & Equivalents	43.9	136.6	68.1	22.8
Total Current Assets	1,346.3	1,914.4	1,662.3	1,610.3
Fixed Assets, Net	1,485.5	1,555.5	1,666.8	1,630.7
Total Assets	2,988.8	3,609.7	3,454.2	3,355.7
Total Current Liabilities	724.0	1,151.9	742.2	783.3
Long-Term Debt	57.1	128.2	197.8	107.7
Stockholders' Equity	2,189.2	2,294.4	2,457.2	2,396.8
Performance & Financial Condition				
Return on Total Revenues %	0.18	-1.04	1.01	-0.41
Return on Avg Stockholders' Equity %	0.58	-3.58	3.57	-1.17
Return on Average Assets %	0.39	-2.41	2.54	-0.86
Current Ratio	1.86	1.66	2.24	2.06
Debt / Equity %	2.61	5.59	8.05	4.50

Compound Growth %'s	EPS % n.a.	Net Income % n.a.	Total Revenues %	1.98

Comments

The furniture business environment continues to be very difficult. Belt tightening and improved efficiency pushed the Company into the black. Management reports a very lean and efficient operation that should result in a good payoff when market conditions are more robust. The employee count was reduced to 121 from 146 during 1996. The Company reacquired 30,312 of its shares during the last year at an average price of $3.56. Investment Classification: Speculative & Value

Officers	Position	Ownership Information	
Edward M. Gravely	President, Treasurer	Number of Shares Outstanding	342,629
G. W. Whitmore	Vice President, Secretary	Market Capitalization	$ 1,069,002
J. M. Cassady	VP - Sales	Frequency of Dividends	Quarterly
		Number of Shareholders	171

Other Information

Transfer Agent	Company Office		Where Listed	OTC-BB
Auditor	Fulp and Associates		Symbol	HRYC
Market Maker	Carr Securities Corporation	(800)221-2243	SIC Code	2439
	Hill Thompson Magid & Co., Inc	(800)631-3083	Employees	121
Broker Dealer	Regular Stockbroker			

Heritage Bank of Commerce

150 Almaden Boulevard   San Jose, CA 95113   Telephone (408)947-6900   Fax (408)947-6910

Company Description

If you know the way to San Jose, stop by the new Heritage Bank of Commerce which serves Santa Clara County, California, also known as Silicon Valley. The Bank started business in June, 1994 after a successful stock offering of 1.4 million shares at $10 each. A secondary offering of 525,000 shares at $12.50 per share was oversubscribed in 1996. Only in California would a bank have a picture of their CEO on a motorcycle on the second page of their annual report. In defense of the Company, the cycle is part of a rare collection owned by one of the Bank's founders. The only question we ask is "where's your helmet, John?"

	12/31/96	12/31/95	12/31/94
Per Share Information			
Stock Price	12.75	10.00	9.09
Earnings Per Share	0.77	0.14	-1.30
Price / Earnings Ratio	16.56	71.43	n.a.
Book Value Per Share	9.83	8.23	7.58
Price / Book Value %	129.70	121.51	119.92
Dividends Per Share	0.0	0.0	0.0
Annual Financial Data			
Operating Results (000's)			
Net Interest Income	7,879.0	4,725.0	1,027.0
Loan Loss Provision	-830.0	-496.0	-76.0
Non-Interest Income	296.0	71.0	18.0
Non-Interest Expense	-5,724.0	-4,098.0	-2,976.0
Income Before Taxes and Other	1,621.0	202.0	-2,007.0
Other Items	0.0	0.0	0.0
Income Tax	-220.0	-1.0	-1.0
Net Income	1,401.0	201.0	-2,008.0
Balance Sheet (000's)			
Cash & Securities	87,883.0	87,789.0	46,754.0
Loans, Net	81,513.0	41,950.0	10,455.0
Total Assets	173,303.0	132,160.0	59,037.0
Deposits	146,379.0	118,746.0	47,082.0
Stockholders' Equity	20,524.0	12,829.0	11,741.0
Performance & Financial Condition			
Return on Avg Stockholders' Equity %	8.40	1.64	n.a.
Return on Average Assets %	0.92	0.21	n.a.
Equity to Assets %	11.84	9.71	19.89
Net Interest Margin	n.a.	n.a.	n.a.
Reserve as a % of Problem Loans	n.a.	n.a.	n.a.

Compound Growth %'s	EPS % n.a.	Net Income % n.a.	Net Interest Income % n.a.

Comments

1994 is a short period and the results include $1 million in preopening expenses. Compound growth rates were omitted because the base year was the beginning of operations. All tax loss carryovers from the start-up phase have been utilized in 1996. The Bank was awarded Preferred SBA Lender status in May, 1996. We spoke with one of the market makers to gain a sense of the demand and trading activity and were told that the stock is just not available. We would suggest checking with several of them. Investment Classification: Growth & Value

Officers	Position	Ownership Information	
John E. Rossell III	President, CEO	Number of Shares Outstanding	2,087,131
Robert P. Gionfriddo	Exec VP	Market Capitalization	$ 26,610,920
Kenneth A. Corsello	Exec VP	Frequency of Dividends	n.a.
Daniel P. Myers	Senior VP, Sr Loan Officer	Number of Shareholders	n.a.
Kenneth B. Silveira	Senior VP	Where Listed / Symbol	OTC-PS / n.a.

Other Information			Loan Mix	%
Transfer Agent	Trust Company of America Englewood, CO		Commerical	35.5
Auditor	KPMG Peat Marwick LLP		R/E Mortgages	31.4
Market Maker	Ronald Lohbeck - Sutro & Co.	(800)421-2746	Construction	14.4
	Smith Barney Shearson, Inc.	(800)444-4752	Consumer	0.7
Broker Dealer	OTC Specialist		Other	18.0
	Steve Sherer - Paine Webber	(800)862-4433		

Herkimer Trust Corporation, Inc.

501 East Main Street   Little Falls, NY 13365-1403   Telephone (315)823-0300   Fax (315)823-1606

Company Description

The Herkimer County Trust Company, subsidiary of the Corporation, is in its 165th year of continuous operation as an independent community bank and ranks as the sixth oldest bank in New York State. It operates throughout the county from nine bank offices as well as a trust office. In 1994, the Company acquired two branches of United Northern Federal Savings Bank and raised $4 million through a private placement of redeemable preferred stock. An office was opened in New Hartford during 1995 and an office is scheduled for the Town of Marcy in the second half of 1997. You can also visit this legendary bank on the Internet: (http://www..ntcnet.com).

	12/31/96	12/31/95	12/31/94	12/31/93
Per Share Information				
Stock Price	4,500.00	3,900.00	3,100.00	3,200.00
Earnings Per Share	184.33	416.84	419.93	473.36
Price / Earnings Ratio	24.41	9.36	7.38	6.76
Book Value Per Share	7,747.43	7,600.57	6,538.00	5,582.86
Price / Book Value %	58.08	51.31	47.42	57.32
Dividends Per Share	26.00	26.00	26.00	26.00
Annual Financial Data				
Operating Results (000's)				
Net Interest Income	12,019.0	12,129.0	12,594.0	11,411.0
Loan Loss Provision	-1,315.0	-388.0	-1,255.0	-1,521.0
Non-Interest Income	1,667.0	1,128.0	1,282.0	1,482.0
Non-Interest Expense	-11,188.0	-10,141.0	-10,014.0	-9,056.0
Income Before Taxes and Other	1,183.0	2,728.0	2,607.0	2,316.0
Other Items	0.0	0.0	0.0	0.0
Income Tax	-178.0	-909.0	-825.0	-690.0
Net Income	1,005.0	1,819.0	1,782.0	1,626.0
Balance Sheet (000's)				
Cash & Securities	112,132.0	120,181.0	99,754.0	80,567.0
Loans, Net	158,919.0	153,599.0	160,307.0	157,352.0
Total Assets	283,861.0	286,312.0	273,422.0	247,509.0
Deposits	256,029.0	258,156.0	249,235.0	226,747.0
Stockholders' Equity	27,116.0	26,602.0	22,883.0	19,540.0
Performance & Financial Condition				
Return on Avg Stockholders' Equity %	3.74	7.35	8.40	8.71
Return on Average Assets %	0.35	0.65	0.68	0.68
Equity to Assets %	9.55	9.29	8.37	7.89
Net Interest Margin	n.a.	n.a.	n.a.	n.a.
Reserve as a % of Problem Loans	110.99	134.29	144.00	135.41

Compound Growth %'s	EPS %	-26.98	Net Income %	-14.82	Net Interest Income %	1.75

Comments

A number of nonrecurring events hurt 1996 earnings. Management aggressively provided for loans to the Bank's dairy customers as the industry continues into the dumps. Depressed real estate values also caused a write-down of Bank owned real estate which is currently held for sale. To top it off, a robbery inflicted more emotional harm than dollar loss. We are glad to report that no one was hurt. The introduction of new locations, new products and new technology may mean exciting times ahead for this 165 year old institution. Investment Classification: Value

Officers	Position	Ownership Information	
R. W. Burrows, Jr.	Chairman, CEO	Number of Shares Outstanding	3,500
Stanley K. Dickson	President	Market Capitalization	$ 15,750,000
Laura B. Marcantonio	Exec VP	Frequency of Dividends	Quarterly
Lucille D. Shepardson	Secretary	Number of Shareholders	96
Anne T. Petkovsek	Vice President, Treasurer	Where Listed / Symbol	OTC-BB / HRKM

Other Information			Loan Mix	%
Transfer Agent	Company Office		R/E Mortgages	55.9
Auditor	KPMG Peat Marwick LLP		Installment	19.3
Market Maker	Cowen & Co.	(212)495-6263	Commerical	15.3
	Ryan, Beck & Co.	(800)325-7926	Agriculture	6.6
Broker Dealer	OTC Specialist		Other	2.9
	Frank Procopio - Ryan, Beck	(888)231-7226		

Hershey Creamery Company

301 South Cameron Street   Harrisburg, PA 17105   Telephone (717)238-8134   Fax (717)233-7195

Company Description

Hershey Creamery Company manufactures, distributes, and sells ice cream products from its facilities in Pennsylvania. Distribution is throughout the northeastern sector of the United States. A new plant site in Lower Swatara Township will be operational in the fourth quarter of 1997. Over the next few years, all operations at the Camerson Street facility will be transferred to the new plant. The Company was founded in 1894. Please enjoy the brief history displayed on the opposite page.

	12/31/96	12/31/95	12/31/94	12/31/93
Per Share Information				
Stock Price	1,695.00	1,772.50	1,825.00	1,475.00
Earnings Per Share	130.92	148.91	112.59	154.92
Price / Earnings Ratio	12.95	11.90	16.21	9.52
Book Value Per Share	1,639.52	1,519.12	1,375.59	1,276.25
Price / Book Value %	103.38	116.68	132.67	115.57
Dividends Per Share	10.40	9.90	9.40	8.90
Annual Financial Data				
Operating Results (000's)				
Total Revenues	77,427.0	74,166.1	69,219.1	68,865.5
Costs & Expenses	-69,756.3	-65,778.8	-62,474.5	-59,286.7
Income Before Taxes and Other	7,670.7	8,387.3	6,744.6	9,578.7
Other Items	0.0	0.0	0.0	0.0
Income Tax	-2,882.7	-2,941.5	-2,627.0	-3,913.0
Net Income	4,788.1	5,445.8	4,117.6	5,665.8
Cash Flow From Operations	10,932.3	9,301.4	7,607.1	9,901.7
Balance Sheet (000's)				
Cash & Equivalents	2,224.4	1,717.9	2,255.6	2,053.1
Total Current Assets	30,361.7	31,222.1	29,914.5	13,634.3
Fixed Assets, Net	36,666.9	29,975.3	25,725.4	24,166.2
Total Assets	67,087.3	61,242.4	55,660.2	53,197.9
Total Current Liabilities	3,088.8	2,157.0	1,932.4	3,269.4
Long-Term Debt	0.0	0.0	0.0	0.0
Stockholders' Equity	59,958.8	55,555.8	50,306.8	46,673.9
Performance & Financial Condition				
Return on Total Revenues %	6.18	7.34	5.95	8.23
Return on Avg Stockholders' Equity %	8.29	10.29	8.49	12.88
Return on Average Assets %	7.46	9.32	7.57	11.35
Current Ratio	9.83	14.47	15.48	4.17
Debt / Equity %	n.a.	n.a.	n.a.	n.a.

Compound Growth %'s	EPS %	-5.46	Net Income %	-5.46	Total Revenues %	3.98

Comments

Poor weather conditions were not conducive to ice cream sales and higher dairy costs were not yet passed through with price adjustments. Accordingly, net earnings were off from the previous year. Not many companies have a stronger financial position. This is the reason we found an article by journalist Michael Brush of The New York Times to be so offensive in using Hershey Creamery as an example of a small company that carries larger risks and has a misleading name. Our response to the newspaper was "Hershey Creamery has no long term debt, has a current ratio of over 14 to 1, and trades at $1,800 per share. Hershey Foods, on the other hand, has a .82 to 1.00 debt-equity ratio, a 1.1 to 1 current ratio and trades at $48 per share." Investment Classification: Value

Officers	Position	Ownership Information	
George H. Holder	Chairman	Number of Shares Outstanding	36,571
George Hugh Holder	President	Market Capitalization	$ 61,987,845
Thomas M. Holder	Treasurer	Frequency of Dividends	Quarterly
Walter S. Holder	Vice President, Secretary	Number of Shareholders	Under 500
Thomas J. Ryan, III	Vice President		

Other Information

Transfer Agent	Company Office		Where Listed	OTC-BB
Auditor	KPMG Peat Marwick LLP		Symbol	HRCR
Market Maker	Hopper Soliday & Co., Inc.	(800)646-8647	SIC Code	2024
	Hill Thompson Magid & Co., Inc	(800)631-3083	Employees	450
Broker Dealer	Regular Stockbroker			

Ice Cream

For any of you who grew up in the Harrisburg, Pennsylvania area within the last century, reference to Hershey's Ice Cream must bring back fond memories. Perhaps you savored a Hershey's Ice Cream cone at the local ice cream parlor after a hot walk home from school, or enjoyed some on your birthday. While your childhood memories go back perhaps a few decades, Hershey Creamery Company's long and prosperous history begins way back in 1894.

That was when four Hershey brothers, who owned and operated a small dairy, began making ice cream. Hershey's Ice Cream was born. Decades later, a merger with the Meyer Dairy Company of Bethlehem, Pennsylvania brought the Holder family into the picture, and ever since, either a Holder or a Hershey has been at the helm of the company.

In the beginning and to this day their primary concern has been to manufacture and distribute quality ice cream with the best possible methods. Especially in the early days, the distribution (i.e. refrigeration) part was tough to handle. In those days brine was used to freeze ice cream into three and five gallon metal cans. More brine than ice cream was carried on the original wagons and deliverymen spent more time keeping the brine box than actually delivering ice cream. All of this changed, however, with the advent of the refrigeration truck. Hershey takes great pride in its current fleet of trucks which includes state-of-the-art refrigeration systems and is the envy of the of the ice cream industry.

Of course, they have a lot more to deliver these days. Unlike the early years, when the company was smaller and the demand for various ice cream forms and flavors ran to vanilla, chocolate or strawberry only, today's menu has expanded to include fifty-eight flavors, ice cream bars, premium, super-premium, no-fat, reduced-fat and no-sugar-added ice creams, fat-free ices, sherbet and even low-fat yogurt. Hershey markets them all with flourish, and has a history of making their product affordable without sacrificing quality. Back in the 1930's, their "15 cents a pint" campaign shocked the industry (how could they make any money?) but was undoubtedly a big hit with kids of all ages.

After 103 years, Hershey has expanded well beyond the Harrisburg area. It now operates in seventeen states throughout the northeastern United States and is moving into the South and the Midwest. They have plans to add a new production facility before the end of the decade and it is their hope at that time to expand across the country. The Holder family considers it to be "a reasonable dream" to shoot for the next one hundred years with even greater profitability than the first. With their sound business practices not to mention their experience, undoubtedly they will realize that dream.

Hilliard Corporation (The)

100 West Fourth Street   Elmira, NY 14902-1504   Telephone (607)733-7121   Fax (607)733-3009

Company Description

The Hilliard Corporation is a specialty applications engineering company that manufactures a broad line of motion control products, oil filtration and reclamation equipment, gas turbine starters and plate and frame filter presses, with manufacturing facilities in New York and South Carolina. The Company was founded in 1905.

	12/31/96	12/31/95	12/31/94	12/31/93
Per Share Information				
Stock Price	158.00	118.00	116.00	70.00
Earnings Per Share	39.26	44.92	-31.25	31.14
Price / Earnings Ratio	4.02	2.63	n.a.	2.25
Book Value Per Share	254.70	222.84	183.62	220.76
Price / Book Value %	62.03	52.95	63.17	31.71
Dividends Per Share	7.40	5.70	5.00	4.25
Annual Financial Data				
Operating Results (000's)				
Total Revenues	29,869.5	28,861.5	23,427.8	22,956.6
Costs & Expenses	-26,405.8	-24,911.9	-20,904.1	-20,358.7
Income Before Taxes and Other	2,946.9	3,544.6	2,198.8	2,345.8
Other Items	0.0	0.0	-2,896.0	50.0
Income Tax	-990.0	-1,306.0	-859.4	-850.0
Net Income	1,956.9	2,238.6	-1,556.6	1,545.8
Cash Flow From Operations	2,646.3	2,381.0	952.1	2,490.4
Balance Sheet (000's)				
Cash & Equivalents	1,272.3	699.4	970.8	1,656.3
Total Current Assets	12,666.7	10,571.1	9,706.0	8,426.9
Fixed Assets, Net	7,115.5	6,427.0	5,017.2	4,451.1
Total Assets	22,423.0	19,179.8	16,849.5	13,227.2
Total Current Liabilities	3,961.1	2,653.6	2,623.1	2,133.0
Long-Term Debt	0.0	0.0	0.0	0.0
Stockholders' Equity	12,693.9	11,105.9	9,151.4	10,957.2
Performance & Financial Condition				
Return on Total Revenues %	6.55	7.76	-6.64	6.73
Return on Avg Stockholders' Equity %	16.44	22.10	-15.48	15.03
Return on Average Assets %	9.41	12.43	-10.35	12.10
Current Ratio	3.20	3.98	3.70	3.95
Debt / Equity %	n.a.	n.a.	n.a.	n.a.

Compound Growth %'s	EPS %	8.03	Net Income %	8.18	Total Revenues %	9.17

Comments

1994 results reflect a $2.9 million charge to record postretirement benefits under new accounting guidelines. Earnings per share without this charge would have been $26.88. The Company reports inventory on a LIFO basis which is $3.3 million lower than FIFO numbers at the end of 1996. This, of course, has the effect of reducing book value from what it would be had inventories been stated at their current cost. These numbers do look great; don't expect this stock to be easy to buy. Investment Classification: Value & Income

Officers	Position	Ownership Information	
Nelson Mooers van den Blink	Chairman, CEO	Number of Shares Outstanding	49,838
Gerald F. Schichtel	President, COO	Market Capitalization	$ 7,874,404
John R. Alexander	Secretary	Frequency of Dividends	n.a.
		Number of Shareholders	Under 500

Other Information			
Transfer Agent	Company Office	Where Listed	OTC-BB
Auditor	Mengel, Metzger, Barr & Co.LLP	Symbol	HLRD
Market Maker	Koonce Securities, Inc.	(800)368-2802	SIC Code	3599
	Hill Thompson Magid & Co., Inc	(800)631-3083	Employees	250
Broker Dealer	OTC Specialist		

Hollywood, The Bank of

6930 Hollywood Boulevard   Hollywood, CA 90028   Telephone (213)464-0452   Fax (213)464-0975

Company Description

The Bank has its main office in Hollywood and a branch office in Toluca Lake, southern California. It was formed fifteen years ago and experienced its only loss in 1994 when a combination of riots, earthquake and a devastated real estate market plagued the Los Angeles area. When the famous Hollywood Boulevard found itself in serious decay, the merchants and businesses responded with a plan to rebuild. Property owners completed the first funding for a Business Improvement District that will improve a substantial portion of the Boulevard and attract new merchants into the area.

	12/31/96	12/31/95	12/31/94	12/31/93
Per Share Information				
Stock Price	7.50	5.45	5.45	4.55
Earnings Per Share	0.70	0.29	-0.69	0.45
Price / Earnings Ratio	10.71	18.79	n.a.	10.11
Book Value Per Share	8.39	7.79	7.42	8.25
Price / Book Value %	89.39	69.96	73.45	55.15
Dividends Per Share	0.0	0.0	0.14	0.14
Annual Financial Data				
Operating Results (000's)				
Net Interest Income	5,456.0	4,848.7	4,162.5	4,360.0
Loan Loss Provision	-745.0	-1,090.0	-2,317.0	-332.0
Non-Interest Income	402.0	361.7	318.8	342.7
Non-Interest Expense	-3,686.3	-3,498.6	-3,453.1	-3,419.9
Income Before Taxes and Other	1,426.7	621.7	-1,288.9	950.8
Other Items	0.0	0.0	0.0	0.0
Income Tax	-547.4	-259.0	425.0	-389.9
Net Income	879.4	362.7	-863.9	560.8
Balance Sheet (000's)				
Cash & Securities	66,008.9	53,224.3	54,085.1	37,982.4
Loans, Net	54,605.6	54,784.2	59,689.6	57,864.7
Total Assets	123,107.5	110,655.1	117,914.9	99,113.9
Deposits	112,366.3	100,730.7	108,354.6	88,686.1
Stockholders' Equity	10,528.2	9,770.1	9,309.8	10,344.8
Performance & Financial Condition				
Return on Avg Stockholders' Equity %	8.66	3.80	-8.79	5.53
Return on Average Assets %	0.75	0.32	-0.80	0.58
Equity to Assets %	8.55	8.83	7.90	10.44
Net Interest Margin	n.a.	n.a.	n.a.	n.a.
Reserve as a % of Problem Loans	30.93	43.94	54.83	116.37

Compound Growth %'s	EPS %	15.87	Net Income %	16.18	Net Interest Income %	7.76

Comments

The Bank declared a 10% stock dividend in 1996. All per share amounts have been restated for consistency. The dividend was declared due to continued growth and profitability, according to management. But Walter Sikes, specialist in bank stocks, agrees with us that this does not add to shareholder value as small stock dividends simply increase the number of shares with an offsetting dilution in value. Management anticipates excellent growth opportunities to result from the downtown improvement. Investment Classification: Growth & Value

Officers	Position	Ownership Information	
Terry C. Jorgensen	President, CEO	Number of Shares Outstanding	1,254,390
Henry K. Nadler	Senior VP, COO	Market Capitalization	$ 9,407,925
Jerry D. Smith	Senior VP, CFO	Frequency of Dividends	Irregular
John B. Anderson	Vice President, Sr Loan Officer	Number of Shareholders	n.a.
Debra R. Bordeaux	Vice President	Where Listed / Symbol	OTC-BB / BHOW

Other Information			Loan Mix	%
Transfer Agent	U.S. Stock Transfer Corp. Glendale, CA		R/E Mortgages	70.2
Auditor	Hutchinson and Bloodgood LLP		Commerical	25.1
Market Maker	Hoefer & Arnett, Incorporated	(800)346-5544	Installment	3.3
	J. Alexander Securities Inc.	(800)421-0258	Construction	1.4
Broker Dealer	OTC Specialist			
	Hoefer & Arnett, Retail	(800)346-5544 Ext: Lisa		

Holobeam, Inc.

540 Ravine Court   Wyckoff, NJ 07481   Telephone (201)445-2420   Fax (201)670-1225

Company Description

Holobeam, Inc. is engaged in the rental and development of real estate and in developing methods for applying surgical staples. Four patents have been received on a novel staple. Animal tests are being conducted in the 1997 fiscal year. If the tests are positive, the Company may decide to make a significant investment to pursue this business. The Company presently has two buildings in Paramus, New Jersey, which are leased. The Company has been reacquiring its shares and cumulatively has taken 70% of issued shares out of circulation.

	09/30/96	09/30/95	09/30/94
Per Share Information			
Stock Price as of 12/31	10.00	9.00	6.50
Earnings Per Share	0.97	1.03	1.66
Price / Earnings Ratio	10.31	8.74	3.92
Book Value Per Share	1.78	1.15	0.21
Price / Book Value %	561.80	782.61	3,095.24
Dividends Per Share	0.0	0.0	0.0
Annual Financial Data			
Operating Results (000's)			
Total Revenues	1,856.2	1,895.4	1,239.3
Costs & Expenses	-1,340.8	-1,331.8	-1,205.1
Income Before Taxes and Other	515.4	563.6	32.3
Other Items	0.0	0.0	524.6
Income Tax	-209.0	-229.0	-0.1
Net Income	306.4	334.6	556.8
Cash Flow From Operations	732.7	702.2	153.8
Balance Sheet (000's)			
Cash & Equivalents	598.8	1,347.5	n.a.
Total Current Assets	696.9	1,357.0	n.a.
Fixed Assets, Net	6,317.1	6,523.7	n.a.
Total Assets	7,743.6	8,932.0	n.a.
Total Current Liabilities	517.9	1,614.0	n.a.
Long-Term Debt	6,667.3	6,946.6	n.a.
Stockholders' Equity	558.5	371.4	n.a.
Performance & Financial Condition			
Return on Total Revenues %	16.51	17.65	44.93
Return on Avg Stockholders' Equity %	65.91	152.26	n.a.
Return on Average Assets %	3.68	4.08	7.57
Current Ratio	1.35	0.84	n.a.
Debt / Equity %	1193.87	1870.26	n.a.

Compound Growth %'s	EPS % n.a.	Net Income % n.a.	Total Revenues % 22.38

Comments

There are clearly two businesses that should be separated for analytical purposes. The rental properties produce a substantial amount of rental income and appear to be worth far more than the market capitalization of the entire company. The patented technology continues to be developed and is funded by rental income. Irrespective of these costs, there is still cash left over which has been used, in part, to retire stock. 1994 results include a nonrecurring benefit of $524,586, $1.56 per share, due to a change in accounting method. Therefore, compound earnings growth numbers were not displayed. Investment Classification: Value & Speculative

Officers	**Position**	**Ownership Information**	
Melvin S. Cook	Chairman, President	Number of Shares Outstanding	313,519
Martin R. Infante	Secretary	Market Capitalization	$ 3,135,190
William M. Hackett	Treasurer	Frequency of Dividends	n.a.
Beverly Cook	Other	Number of Shareholders	758

Other Information

Transfer Agent	Trust Co. of New Jersey Jersey City, NJ		Where Listed	OTC-BB
Auditor	Fredericks and Company		Symbol	HOOB
Market Maker	Carr Securities Corporation	(800)221-2243	SIC Code	6512
	Knight Securities L.P.	(800)222-4910	Employees	n.a.
Broker Dealer	Regular Stockbroker			

Homasote Company

P.O. Box 7240   West Trenton, NJ 08628-0240   Telephone (609)883-3300   Fax (609)530-1584

Company Description

Homasote Company manufactures and sells insulated wood fibre board and polyisocyanurate foam products for industrial customers. The Company's primary basic raw material is wastepaper. 75% of the Company's products are sold to building material wholesalers and contractors and 25% to industrial manufacturers. The wastepaper is supplied under contracts from two suppliers. The Company was formed in 1909.

	12/31/96	12/31/95	12/31/94	12/31/93
Per Share Information				
Stock Price	14.25	20.50	15.32	15.44
Earnings Per Share	1.88	2.05	3.06	-4.28
Price / Earnings Ratio	7.58	10.00	5.01	n.a.
Book Value Per Share	23.77	22.32	20.72	17.94
Price / Book Value %	59.95	91.85	73.94	86.06
Dividends Per Share	0.44	0.58	0.50	0.50
Annual Financial Data				
Operating Results (000's)				
Total Revenues	27,147.8	25,733.5	25,792.1	23,903.7
Costs & Expenses	-25,954.1	-24,421.6	-23,801.7	-23,099.3
Income Before Taxes and Other	1,193.7	1,311.9	1,990.5	804.4
Other Items	0.0	0.0	0.0	-2,299.7
Income Tax	-485.2	-525.8	-763.3	-328.7
Net Income	708.5	786.1	1,227.2	-1,824.0
Cash Flow From Operations	2,808.0	440.2	2,222.4	1,812.3
Balance Sheet (000's)				
Cash & Equivalents	2,680.1	2,329.0	3,385.6	2,061.8
Total Current Assets	7,983.3	8,425.6	9,045.6	7,368.5
Fixed Assets, Net	7,539.5	5,695.1	5,341.8	5,631.7
Total Assets	20,067.2	15,303.0	15,501.0	14,253.6
Total Current Liabilities	2,051.3	1,921.9	1,942.7	1,113.7
Long-Term Debt	3,987.5	0.0	775.0	932.2
Stockholders' Equity	8,943.9	8,424.8	8,100.0	7,389.9
Performance & Financial Condition				
Return on Total Revenues %	2.61	3.05	4.76	-7.63
Return on Avg Stockholders' Equity %	8.16	9.51	15.85	-21.18
Return on Average Assets %	4.01	5.10	8.25	-13.00
Current Ratio	3.89	4.38	4.66	6.62
Debt / Equity %	44.58	n.a.	9.57	12.61

Compound Growth %'s	EPS %	-21.62	Net Income %	-24.02	Total Revenues %	4.33

Comments

The net loss in 1993, includes the cumulative effect of changes in accounting principles in the amount of $2.3 million relating to the accrual of employee postretirement benefits. The Company has repurchased 71,590 shares of its stock over the last five years. The Board of Directors has authorized the Company to retain a financial advisor to assist in the investigation of alternatives to enhance the value of the Company's stock. They appear open to any of a number of possibilities including a third party tender offer. Investment Classification: Value

Officers	Position	Ownership Information	
Irving Flicker	Chairman, CEO	Number of Shares Outstanding	376,251
Warren L. Flicker	President, COO	Market Capitalization	$ 5,361,577
Joseph A. Bronsard	Exec VP	Frequency of Dividends	Quarterly
Cindy Adler	Secretary	Number of Shareholders	280
Neil F. Bacon	Treasurer, CFO		

Other Information				
Transfer Agent	Registrar & Transfer Company Cranford, NJ		Where Listed	PHL
Auditor	KPMG Peat Marwick LLP		Symbol	HMST
Market Maker	Carr Securities Corporation	(800)221-2243	SIC Code	2400
	The Chicago Corporation	(800)323-1225	Employees	212
Broker Dealer	OTC Specialist			

Home-Stake Oil & Gas Company (The)

15 East 5th Street, Ste. 2800   Tulsa, OK 74103   Telephone (918)583-0178   Fax (918)583-0237

Company Description

The Company is actively engaged in the acquisition, exploration, development and production of oil and gas properties. Its principal geographic operating areas lie within the states of Oklahoma, Montana, Wyoming, Louisiana and Texas. The Company was formed in 1917. Since the 1950's the Company has participated jointly with The Home-Stake Royalty Corporation, also featured in this manual on the next page. Both companies have been under common management since 1929. The Companies currently operate 63 producing wells.

	12/31/96	12/31/95
Per Share Information		
Stock Price	96.00	90.00
Earnings Per Share	16.06	4.78
Price / Earnings Ratio	5.98	18.83
Book Value Per Share	83.86	70.30
Price / Book Value %	114.48	128.02
Dividends Per Share	2.50	3.50
Annual Financial Data		
Operating Results (000's)		
Total Revenues	7,742.1	5,777.4
Costs & Expenses	-5,859.3	-5,317.4
Income Before Taxes and Other	1,882.8	460.0
Other Items	0.0	0.0
Income Tax	-445.1	-31.9
Net Income	1,437.7	428.2
Cash Flow From Operations	2,320.3	1,936.7
Balance Sheet (000's)		
Cash & Equivalents	350.8	227.1
Total Current Assets	1,573.0	860.7
Fixed Assets, Net	8,602.4	9,743.0
Total Assets	12,932.3	13,031.8
Total Current Liabilities	2,294.7	2,103.6
Long-Term Debt	2,738.6	4,564.4
Stockholders' Equity	7,506.4	6,292.5
Performance & Financial Condition		
Return on Total Revenues %	18.57	7.41
Return on Avg Stockholders' Equity %	20.84	n.a.
Return on Average Assets %	11.07	n.a.
Current Ratio	0.69	0.41
Debt / Equity %	36.48	72.54

Compound Growth %'s	EPS % n.a.	Net Income % n.a.	Total Revenues %	34.01

Comments

Net income for 1996 increased 236%. Oil sales increased 29% primarily as a result of an increase in the average sales price per barrel coupled with an increase in production of 7,447 barrels. Producing properties the Company acquired in 1995 and 1996, along with new drilling in 1996 contributed towards the increase in production. Gas sales increased 36% as a result of an increase in the average sales price. At December 31, 1996, the Company had estimated proved reserves of 8,501,078 Mcf of natural gas and 2,383,955 barrels of oil. Investment Classification: Value

Officers	Position	Ownership Information	
Robert C. Simpson	President, CEO	Number of Shares Outstanding	89,509
Chris K. Corcoran	Exec VP, CFO	Market Capitalization	$ 8,592,864
Gary W. Fisher	Vice President	Frequency of Dividends	Quarterly
Howard E. Gray	Vice President	Number of Shareholders	175

Other Information				
Transfer Agent	Company Office		Where Listed	OTC-PS
Auditor	Ernst & Young LLP		Symbol	HOGC
Market Maker	Pennsylvania Merchant Group	(800)762-8624	SIC Code	1382
	Herzog, Heine, Geduld, Inc.	(800)221-3600	Employees	16
Broker Dealer	Regular Stockbroker			

Home-Stake Royalty Corporation (The)

15 East 5th Street, Suite 2800   Tulsa, OK 74103-4311   Telephone (918)583-0178   Fax (918)583-0237

Company Description

The Home-Stake Royalty Corporation is actively engaged in the acquisition, exploration, development and production of oil and gas properties. Its principal geographic operating areas lie within the states of Oklahoma, Montana, Wyoming, Louisiana and Texas. Since its formation in 1929, the Company has been under common management with the Home-Stake Oil & Gas Company (HSOG). The Company participates with HSOG in the acquisition and development of properties and is currently operating 63 producing wells.

	12/31/96	12/31/95	12/31/94	12/31/93
Per Share Information				
Stock Price	96.00	130.00	120.00	100.00
Earnings Per Share	16.06	8.89	11.10	3.17
Price / Earnings Ratio	5.98	14.62	10.81	31.55
Book Value Per Share	123.14	135.97	132.77	127.66
Price / Book Value %	114.48	95.61	90.38	78.33
Dividends Per Share	2.50	5.70	6.00	9.00
Annual Financial Data				
Operating Results (000's)				
Total Revenues	8,213.5	6,008.6	5,341.9	5,640.0
Costs & Expenses	-5,756.6	-5,239.9	-4,438.5	-5,423.0
Income Before Taxes and Other	2,456.9	768.7	903.3	217.0
Other Items	0.0	0.0	0.0	4.0
Income Tax	-612.7	-147.9	-128.5	0.0
Net Income	1,844.2	620.8	774.9	221.0
Cash Flow From Operations	2,711.3	2,488.1	2,413.8	2,139.0
Balance Sheet (000's)				
Cash & Equivalents	626.9	564.9	289.2	474.0
Total Current Assets	2,418.9	1,929.1	1,928.7	1,697.0
Fixed Assets, Net	8,798.0	9,791.6	7,628.9	7,628.0
Total Assets	14,833.5	14,965.8	13,226.6	12,870.0
Total Current Liabilities	2,636.8	2,575.3	2,144.0	1,882.0
Long-Term Debt	401.8	2,410.7	1,400.5	1,777.0
Stockholders' Equity	11,021.7	9,491.7	9,268.7	8,912.0
Performance & Financial Condition				
Return on Total Revenues %	22.45	10.33	14.51	3.92
Return on Avg Stockholders' Equity %	17.98	6.62	8.52	2.54
Return on Average Assets %	12.38	4.40	5.94	1.78
Current Ratio	0.92	0.75	0.90	0.90
Debt / Equity %	3.65	25.40	15.11	19.94

Compound Growth %'s	EPS %	71.75	Net Income %	102.83	Total Revenues %	13.35

Comments

Net income increased 197% during 1996. Oil sales increased 30% due to an increase in the average sales price per barrel from $16.15 in 1995 to $20.16 in 1996, coupled with an increase in production of 9,799 barrels. The increase in production was contributed by producing properties the Company acquired in 1995 and 1996, along with new drilling in 1996. Gas sales climbed 37% which was entirely related to the price increase. At December 31, 1996 the Company had estimated proven reserves of 8,835,929 Mcf of natural gas and 2,432,711 barrels of oil. Investment Classification: Value

Officers	Position	Ownership Information	
Robert C. Simpson	President, CEO	Number of Shares Outstanding	89,509
Chris K. Corcoran	Exec VP, CFO	Market Capitalization	$ 8,592,864
Gary W. Fisher	Vice President	Frequency of Dividends	Quarterly
Howard E. Gray	Vice President	Number of Shareholders	175

Other Information			
Transfer Agent	Company Office	Where Listed	OTC-BB
Auditor	Ernst & Young LLP	Symbol	HSTK
Market Maker	Pennsylvania Merchant Group	(800)762-8624	SIC Code	1382
	Herzog, Heine, Geduld, Inc.	(800)221-3600	Employees	16
Broker Dealer	Regular Stockbroker		

HomeCapital Investment Corporation

6836 Austin Center Blvd., #280   Austin, TX 78731   Telephone (512)343-8911   Fax (512)343-1837

Company Description

HomeCapital Investment Corporation is a specialized consumer finance company organized in 1993 to originate, purchase, sell and service home improvement and other second mortgage loans secured by residential property. Loans generated or purchased are financed through bank warehouse credit lines and then sold to Fannie Mae, secondary mortgage market investors and other financial institutions. Home originates loans through pre-qualified contractors principally in the southwestern and western regions of the United States.

	09/30/96	09/30/95	09/30/94	09/30/93
Per Share Information				
Stock Price as of 12/31	7.25	1.12	1.00	n.a.
Earnings Per Share	0.30	-0.01	-0.22	n.a.
Price / Earnings Ratio	24.17	n.a.	n.a.	n.a.
Book Value Per Share	0.67	0.01	-0.06	n.a.
Price / Book Value %	1,082.09	11,200.00	n.a.	n.a.
Dividends Per Share	0.0	0.0	0.0	n.a.
Annual Financial Data				
Operating Results (000's)				
Total Revenues	8,913.6	3,695.8	1,403.3	3.4
Costs & Expenses	-5,433.3	-3,767.8	-2,455.8	-141.5
Income Before Taxes and Other	3,480.3	-72.0	-1,052.5	-138.1
Other Items	0.0	0.0	0.0	0.0
Income Tax	-914.0	0.0	0.0	0.0
Net Income	2,566.2	-72.0	-1,052.5	-138.1
Cash Flow From Operations	-3,910.5	81.7	-2,748.6	-149.9
Balance Sheet (000's)				
Cash & Equivalents	343.5	25.7	0.0	n.a.
Total Current Assets	10,848.1	1,779.7	1,923.2	n.a.
Fixed Assets, Net	646.1	373.9	165.0	n.a.
Total Assets	11,684.6	2,153.6	2,145.8	n.a.
Total Current Liabilities	6,766.8	2,083.5	2,419.0	n.a.
Long-Term Debt	0.0	0.0	0.0	n.a.
Stockholders' Equity	4,903.5	28.3	-315.6	n.a.
Performance & Financial Condition				
Return on Total Revenues %	28.79	-1.95	-75.00	-4,093.01
Return on Avg Stockholders' Equity %	104.07	n.a.	n.a.	n.a.
Return on Average Assets %	37.09	-3.35	n.a.	n.a.
Current Ratio	1.60	0.85	0.80	n.a.
Debt / Equity %	n.a.	n.a.	n.a.	n.a.

Compound Growth %'s	EPS % n.a.	Net Income % n.a.	Total Revenues % n.a.

Comments

During 1996, the Company generated over $100 million in loans, an increase of 62% over the preceding year. The Company experienced negative cash flow from operations principally due to the retainage of servicing rights on the sale of loans. These servicing rights will generate income in future periods. Management expects to fund its increased loan production and operational needs by obtaining additional financing through placement of subordinated debt and increased warehouse lines of credit. For the six months ended March 31, 1997, revenue was four times as great as the previous year at $10.8 million. Earnings were $3,788,856, $.38 per share, at the half-way mark. Investment Classification: Growth

Officers	Position	Ownership Information	
John W. Ballard	President, CEO	Number of Shares Outstanding	7,292,711
Tommy M. Parker	Exec VP, CFO	Market Capitalization	$ 52,872,155
Glenn R. Theriac	Senior VP	Frequency of Dividends	n.a.
E. Jeff Bomer	Secretary	Number of Shareholders	969
Michael Vint	Controller		

Other Information

Transfer Agent	OTR California Stock Transfer Portland, OR		Where Listed	OTC-BB
Auditor	Coopers & Lybrand L.L.P.		Symbol	HCAP
Market Maker	H.J. Meyers & Co., Inc.	(212)412-8350	SIC Code	6163
	Wine Investments Inc.	(800)327-5477	Employees	n.a.
Broker Dealer	Regular Stockbroker			

Honat Bancorp, Inc.

733 Main Street   Honesdale, PA 18431-0509   Telephone (717)253-3355   Fax (717)253-5263

Company Description

The Company's wholly-owned subsidiary, The Honesdale National Bank, provides full banking services and trust services principally to customers in Wayne, Luzerne, Lackawanna and Susquehanna Counties, Pennsylvania. The Bank's offices have been increased to five in 1996 with the purchase of two facilities from PCN Bank of Pittsburgh. The Company has been buying its common stock in recent years. The Honesdale National Bank was founded in 1836.

	12/31/96	12/31/95	12/31/94	12/31/93
Per Share Information				
Stock Price	67.00	61.75	53.00	48.50
Earnings Per Share	7.61	7.34	6.17	5.66
Price / Earnings Ratio	8.80	8.41	8.59	8.57
Book Value Per Share	71.67	64.01	49.48	44.89
Price / Book Value %	93.48	96.47	107.11	108.04
Dividends Per Share	2.00	0.95	0.84	0.73
Annual Financial Data				
Operating Results (000's)				
Net Interest Income	5,663.0	5,433.9	5,220.2	4,932.7
Loan Loss Provision	0.0	0.0	0.0	-85.0
Non-Interest Income	1,426.3	964.0	447.4	578.7
Non-Interest Expense	-4,410.1	-3,732.4	-3,376.8	-3,293.3
Income Before Taxes and Other	2,679.2	2,665.4	2,290.9	2,133.1
Other Items	0.0	0.0	0.0	0.0
Income Tax	-622.0	-682.0	-580.6	-524.0
Net Income	2,057.2	1,983.4	1,710.3	1,609.1
Balance Sheet (000's)				
Cash & Securities	52,236.4	47,461.8	44,411.6	53,118.4
Loans, Net	101,344.6	84,579.7	82,159.9	73,846.9
Total Assets	161,978.3	140,185.9	132,525.6	133,130.4
Deposits	139,401.8	121,750.4	116,517.5	116,947.4
Stockholders' Equity	17,237.8	15,394.1	13,717.0	12,760.3
Performance & Financial Condition				
Return on Avg Stockholders' Equity %	12.61	13.63	12.92	12.96
Return on Average Assets %	1.36	1.45	1.29	1.23
Equity to Assets %	10.64	10.98	10.35	9.58
Net Interest Margin	n.a.	n.a.	n.a.	n.a.
Reserve as a % of Problem Loans	385.41	280.67	238.12	184.25

Compound Growth %'s	EPS %	10.37	Net Income %	8.53	Net Interest Income %	4.71

Comments

Record numbers were tallied in every category during 1996 as the Bank broadened into new markets. Management reports that loan demand and customer acceptance in the new offices has been wonderful. In just over six months, $15 million of deposits were generated. We also note a 48% increase in non-interest income led by a 51% increase in mortgage banking activity. Investment Classification: Value

Officers	Position	Ownership Information	
William Schweighofer	President, CEO	Number of Shares Outstanding	240,500
Luke W. Woodmansee	Vice President, Sr Loan Officer	Market Capitalization	$ 16,113,500
Mary T. McElroy	Vice President	Frequency of Dividends	Quarterly
Stanley Yackoski, Jr.	Vice President	Number of Shareholders	n.a.
James V. Musto	Vice President	Where Listed / Symbol	OTC-BB / HONT

Other Information			Loan Mix	%
Transfer Agent	Company Office		R/E Mortgages	41.6
Auditor	Beard & Company, Inc.		Commerical	40.2
Market Maker	Hopper Soliday & Co., Inc.	(800)456-9234	Consumer	18.2
	Ryan, Beck & Co.	(800)325-7926		
Broker Dealer	OTC Specialist			
	Jack Ingold	(412)391-4594		

Horizon Telcom, Inc.

68 E. Main Street   Chillicothe, OH 45601-2503   Telephone (614)772-8244   Fax (614)775-5151

Company Description

Horizon Telcom, formerly Chillicothe Telephone Company, provides basic local service, network access and various other telephone company services to customers in seven states. It celebrated 100 years in business in 1995. Alltel Corporation (NYSE) acquired a 20% interest in 1990. The Company was the successful bidder for Personal Communications Service licenses in a radio spectrum auction conducted by the Federal Communications Commission. These licenses will enable the Company to serve most of southeastern Ohio and portions of West Virginia and Kentucky.

	12/31/96	12/31/95	12/31/94	12/31/93
Per Share Information				
Stock Price	306.00	277.00	250.00	232.00
Earnings Per Share	93.82	33.24	30.18	33.88
Price / Earnings Ratio	3.26	8.33	8.28	6.85
Book Value Per Share	574.44	295.10	279.27	266.49
Price / Book Value %	53.27	93.87	89.52	87.06
Dividends Per Share	18.20	17.40	17.40	17.00
Annual Financial Data				
Operating Results (000's)				
Total Revenues	44,618.1	34,700.8	30,675.2	25,811.8
Costs & Expenses	-32,080.3	-27,698.3	-24,079.7	-17,415.5
Income Before Taxes and Other	12,537.8	6,953.0	6,311.0	7,113.9
Other Items	0.0	0.0	0.0	0.0
Income Tax	-3,181.0	-3,638.6	-3,301.8	-3,735.2
Net Income	9,356.8	3,314.4	3,009.3	3,378.7
Cash Flow From Operations	8,138.5	7,976.8	4,835.8	6,562.0
Balance Sheet (000's)				
Cash & Equivalents	12,763.9	1,213.3	802.4	2,184.2
Total Current Assets	20,949.4	9,326.8	9,850.5	8,540.3
Fixed Assets, Net	44,587.3	40,628.6	38,381.9	36,495.6
Total Assets	79,244.3	54,161.0	51,985.8	48,509.8
Total Current Liabilities	14,967.0	7,714.2	7,757.7	5,649.6
Long-Term Debt	0.0	10,300.0	10,400.0	10,100.0
Stockholders' Equity	57,286.7	29,429.4	27,850.2	26,576.1
Performance & Financial Condition				
Return on Total Revenues %	20.97	9.55	9.81	13.09
Return on Avg Stockholders' Equity %	21.58	11.57	11.06	13.13
Return on Average Assets %	14.03	6.24	5.99	7.25
Current Ratio	1.40	1.21	1.27	1.51
Debt / Equity %	n.a.	35.00	37.34	38.00

Compound Growth %'s	EPS % n.a.	Net Income % n.a.	Total Revenues % 20.01

Comments

To help finance the acquisition of licenses referred to above, the Company sold SmarTView, a direct-to-home satellite television service, for an after-tax gain of $6.6 million, or $66.21 per share. Because this distorted earnings, we did not display compound earnings growth rates. Recurring net earnings actually declined by $5.63 per share, largely reflective of higher depreciation costs. The Company continues to be recognized as a good neighbor by the citizens of Chillicothe. Investment Classification: Growth & Value & Income

Officers	Position	Ownership Information	
Robert McKell	Chairman	Number of Shares Outstanding	99,726
Thomas McKell	President	Market Capitalization	$ 30,516,156
Jack E. Thompson	Secretary, Treasurer	Frequency of Dividends	Quarterly
Phoebe H. McKell	Other	Number of Shareholders	305

Other Information				
Transfer Agent	Company Office		Where Listed	OTC-BB
Auditor	Arthur Andersen LLP		Symbol	CHIL
Market Maker	Hill Thompson Magid & Co., Inc	(800)631-3083	SIC Code	4810
	S.J. Wolfe & Co.	(800)262-2244	Employees	275
Broker Dealer	OTC Specialist			
	Stephen Schuller - Dorsey	(800)375-5431		

Hosoi Garden Mortuary, Inc.

30 North Kukui Street   Honolulu, HI 96817   Telephone (808)538-3877   Fax (808)533-4981

Company Description

The Company is engaged in the funeral and mortuary business in Honolulu, Hawaii. The Company also owns 50% of Garden Life Plan, Ltd. which sells pre-need funeral service contracts. The Company principally serves persons of Japanese ancestry who follow a particular and special order of worship in accordance with their religious beliefs. Hosoi Garden Mortuary, Inc. was incorporated in 1957 as the successor to a business founded in 1900.

	05/31/96	05/31/95	05/31/94	05/31/93
Per Share Information				
Stock Price as of 12/31	3.50	5.00	4.38	4.75
Earnings Per Share	0.22	0.21	0.26	0.14
Price / Earnings Ratio	15.91	23.81	16.85	33.93
Book Value Per Share	2.66	2.50	2.32	2.14
Price / Book Value %	131.58	200.00	188.79	221.96
Dividends Per Share	0.05	0.05	0.04	0.04
Annual Financial Data				
Operating Results (000's)				
Total Revenues	3,140.3	2,959.9	3,194.9	2,582.5
Costs & Expenses	-2,598.9	-2,503.0	-2,547.7	-2,323.0
Income Before Taxes and Other	541.5	456.9	647.1	259.4
Other Items	0.0	0.0	0.0	0.0
Income Tax	-139.0	-65.9	-155.4	11.9
Net Income	402.5	391.0	491.7	271.4
Cash Flow From Operations	233.0	589.9	175.0	238.8
Balance Sheet (000's)				
Cash & Equivalents	711.0	938.7	606.1	572.2
Total Current Assets	2,252.3	2,267.7	2,366.5	1,655.6
Fixed Assets, Net	1,587.0	1,554.5	1,621.8	1,616.2
Total Assets	5,341.8	5,080.9	4,844.3	4,475.4
Total Current Liabilities	402.0	432.5	480.3	314.2
Long-Term Debt	0.0	0.0	0.0	0.0
Stockholders' Equity	4,847.5	4,603.6	4,304.2	4,071.9
Performance & Financial Condition				
Return on Total Revenues %	12.82	13.21	15.39	10.51
Return on Avg Stockholders' Equity %	8.52	8.78	11.74	6.80
Return on Average Assets %	7.72	7.88	10.55	6.13
Current Ratio	5.60	5.24	4.93	5.27
Debt / Equity %	n.a.	n.a.	n.a.	n.a.

Compound Growth %'s	EPS % n.a.	Net Income % n.a.	Total Revenues % n.a.

Comments

The Company has been reacquiring its stock regularly over recent years. After a decline in revenues in 1995, the Company appears back on track. Although there is not much life in the 1996 numbers, the nine months ended February 28, 1997, are strong. Revenues were $2.2 million and Net Income was $469,000 ($.26 per share), as compared to $2.0 million and $368,000 ($.20 per share), for the same period in the prior fiscal year. Investment Classification: Value

Officers	Position	Ownership Information	
Clifford Hosoi	President, CEO	Number of Shares Outstanding	1,819,430
Elaine Nakamura	Secretary	Market Capitalization	$ 6,368,005
Keith Numazu	Treasurer	Frequency of Dividends	Annual
Anne T. Tamori	Vice President	Number of Shareholders	1,737
David Fujishige	Vice President		

Other Information			
Transfer Agent	Hawaiian Trust Company Ltd. Honolulu, HI	Where Listed	OTC-BB
Auditor	Endo & Company	Symbol	HGMI
Market Maker	Abel-Behnke Corp.	(808)536-2341	SIC Code	7261
	Hill Thompson Magid & Co., Inc	(800)631-3083	Employees	29
Broker Dealer	Regular Stockbroker		

Houlihan's Restaurant Group, Inc.

Two Brush Creek Boulevard   Kansas City, MO 64112   Telephone (816)756-2200   Fax (816)561-2842

Company Description

The Company and its subsidiaries operate full service casual restaurants in 23 states. At December 25, 1995, it operated 101 restaurants including 62 Houlihan's, 28 Darryl's, and 11 others. At 1996 year end, the Company also franchised 29 Houlihan's in eleven states and the Commonwealth of Puerto Rico. Houlihan's offers customers a casual dining concept catering to adult guests principally in the 25 to 49 age group. The Company, which was formed in 1968, is the successor to a business founded in Kansas City, Missouri, in 1962. Houlihan's was reorganized in 1992 through a bankruptcy proceeding.

	12/30/96	12/25/95	12/26/94	12/27/93
Per Share Information				
Stock Price as of 12/31	5.37	5.82	8.34	7.82
Earnings Per Share	0.52	0.43	0.30	0.30
Price / Earnings Ratio	10.33	13.53	27.80	26.07
Book Value Per Share	7.54	7.02	6.59	6.30
Price / Book Value %	71.22	82.91	126.56	124.13
Dividends Per Share	0.0	0.0	0.0	0.0
Annual Financial Data				
Operating Results (000's)				
Total Revenues	279,214.0	267,622.0	259,367.0	257,225.0
Costs & Expenses	-269,925.0	-254,178.0	-248,983.0	-245,878.0
Income Before Taxes and Other	9,289.0	8,181.0	5,858.0	6,995.0
Other Items	0.0	0.0	0.0	0.0
Income Tax	-4,092.0	-3,916.0	-2,900.0	-4,026.0
Net Income	5,197.0	4,265.0	2,958.0	2,969.0
Cash Flow From Operations	22,995.0	19,370.0	14,097.0	29,337.0
Balance Sheet (000's)				
Cash & Equivalents	15,620.0	10,314.0	10,310.0	24,380.0
Total Current Assets	25,309.0	18,570.0	18,135.0	31,611.0
Fixed Assets, Net	105,481.0	104,521.0	102,843.0	98,444.0
Total Assets	195,675.0	191,016.0	192,508.0	204,235.0
Total Current Liabilities	31,491.0	34,064.0	30,405.0	39,241.0
Long-Term Debt	71,594.0	72,779.0	83,376.0	89,997.0
Stockholders' Equity	75,389.0	70,192.0	65,927.0	62,969.0
Performance & Financial Condition				
Return on Total Revenues %	1.86	1.59	1.14	1.15
Return on Avg Stockholders' Equity %	7.14	6.27	4.59	4.83
Return on Average Assets %	2.69	2.22	1.49	1.48
Current Ratio	0.80	0.55	0.60	0.81
Debt / Equity %	94.97	103.69	126.47	142.92

Compound Growth %'s	EPS %	20.12	Net Income %	20.52	Total Revenues %	2.77

Comments

Although operations improved over the preceding year, we can't seem to take our eye off the cash flow generated by operations of nearly $23 million. This is allowing the Company to improve its balance sheet. Note the gradual improvement in the debt/equity % over the last four years. The Company reports having fewer than 50 registered owners. This does not count shares held in street name which we believe are substantial. The Glazer family owns 73% of outstanding shares. Investment Classification: Value & Speculative

Officers	Position	Ownership Information	
Malcolm I. Glazer	Chairman	Number of Shares Outstanding	9,998,012
Frederick R. Hipp	President, CEO	Market Capitalization	$ 53,689,324
Henry C. Miller	Senior VP	Frequency of Dividends	n.a.
Andrew C. Gunkler	Senior VP	Number of Shareholders	50
Paul R. Geist	Vice President, Controller		

Other Information

Transfer Agent	UMB Bank, N.A. Kansas City, MO		Where Listed	BE
Auditor	Deloitte & Touche LLP		Symbol	HOUL
Market Maker	Cantor, fitzgerald & Co., Inc.	(800)995-9975	SIC Code	5812
	Knight Securities L.P.	(800)222-4910	Employees	8061
Broker Dealer	Regular Stockbroker			

Humboldt Bancorp

701 Fifth Street   Eureka, CA 95501   Telephone (707)445-3233   Fax (707)441-0124

Company Description

Humboldt Bank is the operating subsidiary of the Company and began business in 1989. It is primarily locally owned and has eight locations in communities of northern California. The Garberville branch opened in May, 1997. The Bank offers a broad range of services to individuals and businesses with an emphasis upon efficiency and personalized attention. In 1996, the Bank added a Non-deposit Investment Products and Services Department. In February, 1997, a leasing company partnership with another bank was started.

	12/31/96	12/31/95	12/31/94	12/31/93
Per Share Information				
Stock Price	21.00	14.55	11.36	9.95
Earnings Per Share	1.93	1.47	1.04	0.89
Price / Earnings Ratio	10.88	9.90	10.92	11.18
Book Value Per Share	13.89	12.15	9.77	8.62
Price / Book Value %	151.19	119.75	116.27	115.43
Dividends Per Share	0.0	0.0	0.0	0.0
Annual Financial Data				
Operating Results (000's)				
Net Interest Income	11,013.0	9,996.9	7,622.7	5,190.0
Loan Loss Provision	-533.0	-792.6	-783.0	-594.0
Non-Interest Income	5,747.0	3,508.9	1,463.4	1,225.1
Non-Interest Expense	-11,325.0	-9,148.6	-6,240.5	-4,466.4
Income Before Taxes and Other	4,902.0	3,564.6	2,062.7	1,354.7
Other Items	0.0	0.0	0.0	0.0
Income Tax	-1,926.0	-1,362.7	-762.0	-453.0
Net Income	2,976.0	2,201.9	1,300.7	901.7
Balance Sheet (000's)				
Cash & Securities	56,770.0	67,746.0	51,201.3	41,519.3
Loans, Net	142,824.0	113,236.9	92,139.8	85,130.3
Total Assets	214,738.0	193,911.9	152,863.1	134,605.8
Deposits	192,576.0	174,526.1	137,624.5	123,830.9
Stockholders' Equity	19,600.0	16,933.5	13,569.2	10,013.4
Performance & Financial Condition				
Return on Avg Stockholders' Equity %	16.29	14.44	11.03	10.78
Return on Average Assets %	1.46	1.27	0.90	0.90
Equity to Assets %	9.13	8.73	8.88	7.44
Net Interest Margin	n.a.	n.a.	n.a.	n.a.
Reserve as a % of Problem Loans	894.17	302.03	1,798.54	474.03

Compound Growth %'s	EPS %	29.44	Net Income %	48.88	Net Interest Income %	28.50

Comments

The Company has declared 10% stock dividends in each of the last four years. All per share amounts have been adjusted for consistency. 1996 was the seventh consecutive year that Humboldt Bank exceeded prior year performance in all major areas. Common shares were issued in both 1993 and 1994 which accounts for a lower growth rate in compound earnings per share as compared to net earnings. Investment Classification: Growth

Officers	Position	Ownership Information	
Theodore S. Mason	President, CEO	Number of Shares Outstanding	1,410,767
Ronald V. Barkley	Senior VP, Sr Loan Officer	Market Capitalization	$ 29,626,107
Alan J. Smyth	Senior VP, CFO	Frequency of Dividends	Irregular
Paul A. Ziegler	Vice President	Number of Shareholders	600
Bill Brobst	Vice President	Where Listed / Symbol	OTC-BB / HBEK

Other Information		Loan Mix	%
Transfer Agent	First Interstate Bank of California San Francisco, CA	R/E Mortgages	63.8
Auditor	Richardson & Company	Construction	14.6
Market Maker	Monroe Securities, Inc. (800)766-5560	Commerical	14.2
	Everen Securities (800)292-1960	Consumer	3.1
Broker Dealer	Regular Stockbroker	Other	4.3
	Hoefer & Arnett, Retail (800)346-5544 Ext: Lisa		

This page intentionally left blank.

Hunter Manufacturing Corp.

P.O. Box 529   Gurnee, IL 60031   Telephone (847)855-9000   Fax (800)323-8320

Company Description

Hunter Manufacturing Corp. conducts its primary business through its wholly owned subsidiary, Tablecraft Products Co., Inc. Tablecraft is a national distributor of kitchen and tabletop supplies for restaurants. The Company went public in 1961, but has been regularly repurchasing shares in recent years.

	12/31/96	12/31/95	12/31/94	12/31/93
Per Share Information				
Stock Price	5.37	2.50	2.25	2.50
Earnings Per Share	1.04	1.75	2.21	0.78
Price / Earnings Ratio	5.16	1.43	1.02	3.21
Book Value Per Share	17.11	16.07	14.27	12.06
Price / Book Value %	31.39	15.56	15.77	20.73
Dividends Per Share	0.0	0.0	0.0	0.0
Annual Financial Data				
Operating Results (000's)				
Total Revenues	12,696.5	12,187.5	11,487.0	10,830.5
Costs & Expenses	-12,175.3	-11,310.0	-10,439.4	-10,387.8
Income Before Taxes and Other	521.3	876.3	1,047.5	441.8
Other Items	0.0	0.0	0.0	-38.0
Income Tax	-216.9	-365.6	-402.3	-175.6
Net Income	304.4	510.8	645.3	228.3
Cash Flow From Operations	267.1	615.0	891.5	381.6
Balance Sheet (000's)				
Cash & Equivalents	364.7	0.0	543.4	699.1
Total Current Assets	5,067.2	5,033.1	4,594.7	4,534.3
Fixed Assets, Net	925.7	810.6	811.7	876.3
Total Assets	6,020.5	5,888.1	5,444.8	5,410.6
Total Current Liabilities	1,006.0	1,183.0	1,286.7	1,897.8
Long-Term Debt	0.0	0.0	0.0	0.0
Stockholders' Equity	4,984.4	4,680.0	4,158.0	3,512.8
Performance & Financial Condition				
Return on Total Revenues %	2.40	4.19	5.62	2.11
Return on Avg Stockholders' Equity %	6.30	11.56	16.82	6.72
Return on Average Assets %	5.11	9.01	11.89	4.57
Current Ratio	5.04	4.25	3.57	2.39
Debt / Equity %	n.a.	n.a.	n.a.	n.a.

Compound Growth %'s	EPS %	10.06	Net Income %	10.06	Total Revenues %	n.a.

Comments

1994 and 1993 results do not reflect positive prior period adjustments of $193,630 and $162,870, respectively. These are shown as increases to retained earnings without being reported on the income statement. It was reported to us that the Company has little competition in its marketplace. There is no long-term debt and a very favorable current ratio is maintained. There is a buy-sell agreement among certain stockholders whereby the Company must purchase all of a deceased stockholder's stock at an agreed price. The Company has life insurance to fund such purchases. Investment Classification: Value

Officers	Position	Ownership Information	
Dalton Davis	President, CEO	Number of Shares Outstanding	291,281
		Market Capitalization	$ 1,564,179
		Frequency of Dividends	Quarterly
		Number of Shareholders	Under 500

Other Information

Transfer Agent	ChaseMellon Shareholder Services Ridgefield Park, NJ		Where Listed	OTC-BB
Auditor	Klayman & Korman		Symbol	HUNM
Market Maker	Wachtel & Co., Inc.	(202)898-1144	SIC Code	3089
			Employees	50
Broker Dealer	Regular Stockbroker			

Hydraulic Press Brick Company

705 Olive Street   St. Louis, MO 63101-2234   Telephone (314)621-9306   Fax (314)621-2795

Company Description

The Company is a producer and supplier of Haydite (a light weight aggregate produced from shale) which is used principally in the construction industry in components of walls, floors and structural elements. A significant portion is delivered to construction companies in the midwest United States. Last year, 11% of sales were attributable to one customer. The Company was founded in 1928 and built its Cleveland plant the same year. In 1958, the Company purchased the Brooklyn, Indiana plant. St. Louis Steel Castings, also presented in this manual, owns 56% of the Company. Please enjoy a glimpse into the Company's past on the next page.

	09/30/96	09/30/95	09/30/94	09/30/93
Per Share Information				
Stock Price as of 12/31	18.50	15.87	8.25	6.37
Earnings Per Share	5.24	3.84	2.57	0.80
Price / Earnings Ratio	3.53	4.13	3.21	7.96
Book Value Per Share	24.66	20.06	16.78	14.53
Price / Book Value %	75.02	79.11	49.17	43.84
Dividends Per Share	0.65	0.55	0.32	0.20
Annual Financial Data				
Operating Results (000's)				
Total Revenues	11,690.0	9,993.0	8,674.0	7,262.0
Costs & Expenses	-9,329.0	-8,147.0	-7,514.0	-6,871.0
Income Before Taxes and Other	2,361.0	1,756.0	1,160.0	391.0
Other Items	0.0	0.0	0.0	0.0
Income Tax	-800.0	-612.0	-394.0	-151.0
Net Income	1,561.0	1,144.0	766.0	240.0
Cash Flow From Operations	2,067.0	1,107.0	1,429.0	712.0
Balance Sheet (000's)				
Cash & Equivalents	1,951.0	537.0	1,760.0	839.0
Total Current Assets	4,516.0	4,093.0	3,570.0	2,858.0
Fixed Assets, Net	4,330.0	3,188.0	2,475.0	2,429.0
Total Assets	8,865.0	7,293.0	6,047.0	5,323.0
Total Current Liabilities	1,139.0	1,045.0	844.0	761.0
Long-Term Debt	0.0	0.0	6.0	58.0
Stockholders' Equity	7,346.0	5,978.0	4,998.0	4,331.0
Performance & Financial Condition				
Return on Total Revenues %	13.35	11.45	8.83	3.30
Return on Avg Stockholders' Equity %	23.43	20.85	16.42	5.66
Return on Average Assets %	19.32	17.15	13.47	4.64
Current Ratio	3.96	3.92	4.23	3.76
Debt / Equity %	n.a.	n.a.	0.12	1.34

Compound Growth %'s	EPS %	87.10	Net Income %	86.67	Total Revenues %	17.20

Comments

Sales increased 20% during 1996 setting the pace for another record year. Results look so good that stockholders are selling very infrequently. Another way to grab a piece of the pie is through ownership of St. Louis Steel Castings which, more often than not, has a posted ask price. Management reports that fiscal 1997 is off to a good start with sales at a higher level than those at the beginning of 1996. Investment Classification: Value & Growth

Officers	Position	Ownership Information	
Christian B. Peper, Jr.	Chairman	Number of Shares Outstanding	297,926
W W. Allen, Jr.	President	Market Capitalization	$ 5,511,631
Donna Stewart	Secretary	Frequency of Dividends	Quarterly
David Charlton	Treasurer	Number of Shareholders	235
R N. Stewart	Vice President, Controller		

Other Information			
Transfer Agent	KeyCorp Shareholder Services, Inc. Cleveland, OH	Where Listed	OTC-BB
Auditor	Kerber, Eck & Braeckel LLP	Symbol	HPRS
Market Maker	Robotti & Co., Inc.	(212)986-0800	SIC Code	3251
	Carr Securities Corporation	(800)221-2243	Employees	100
Broker Dealer	OTC Specialist		

Building Blocks

In 1868, The Hydraulic Press Brick Company of St. Louis had something that none of its competitors had - a hydraulic brick press. This innovative technology used hydraulic energy to mold red clay into harder, smoother, cleaner-edged bricks than those produced by the competition. Widely known as St. Louis Red Stock, these bricks were a nationwide success, the first of many for Hydraulic and for its founder and president, E.C. Sterling.

The company flourished during Sterling's presidency. Over time, Hydraulic was producing an assortment of brick types including sand-mould, salt-glaze, stiff-mud, coated, and Hy-namel varieties. With their high quality finish and durability, Hy-namel bricks in particular proved to be heavy competition for the English imports then so widely used. Hydraulic expanded nationally to keep up with increased demand for its products. By 1904, the company was operating brickyards throughout the Midwest in Ohio, Illinois, Wisconsin, Minnesota, Nebraska and Kansas, with expansion reaching eastward as well into New York, New Jersey and Washington DC.

Having grown outward, it was time now to grow up. So, in 1904 Hydraulic built a giant sized, 400-ton brick building as its showpiece for the St. Louis World's Fair. This was the largest of all the clayworking exhibits, so tall that it could be seen from much of the fairgrounds. The building incorporated Hydraulic's various lines of molded bricks into English and Italian architectural styles to stunning effect. With its walls of transparent glazed brick and enameled frieze and its stairs of mottled-grey fire brick, the exhibit was an impressive advertisement for modern uses of Hydraulic's products.

The company a great success, E.C. Sterling retired the following year in 1905. Despite his absence, Hydraulic continued to prosper as a brick manufacturer, even being noted for its successes in 1960 by the Missouri Historical Society.

But the demand for bricks waned over time as new building materials became available. Hydraulic responded by cutting back on brick making and boosting production of its newer line of concrete aggregate called Haydite. Not merely your typical concrete, Haydite weighs less, offers greater fire resistance, and provides better thermal insulation. Its many and varied applications range from use in masonry and bridge building to landscaping and drinking water treatment. With so many features, Haydite has become popular in the market and enjoys wide distribution.

Today, The Hydraulic Press Brick Company may no longer manufacture bricks, but with its history of innovative product development leading to its current success with Haydite, Hydraulic has clearly laid a strong foundation for future triumphs.

Hytek Microsystems, Inc.

400 Hot Springs Road   Carson City, NV 89703   Telephone (702)883-0820   Fax (702)883-0827

Company Description

Hytek Microsystems, Inc. designs, manufactures and sells custom and standard thick film hybrid microcircuits. Products manufactured by the Company are sold primarily to original equipment manufacturers serving the computer, telecommunications, military, medical, industrial electronics, and automatic test equipment markets. Approximately 94% of the Company's revenues are derived from products designed to meet a particular customers need. Chesapeake Sciences and TRW accounted for 62% and 12%, respectively, of net revenues. The products sold to Chesapeake Sciences are used in the eventual production of off-shore geophysical oil exploration equipment. The Company was formed in 1974.

	12/28/96	12/30/95	12/31/94	12/31/93
Per Share Information				
Stock Price	2.50	2.38	0.13	0.22
Earnings Per Share	0.62	0.18	0.01	-0.09
Price / Earnings Ratio	4.03	13.22	13.00	n.a.
Book Value Per Share	1.15	0.50	0.31	0.31
Price / Book Value %	217.39	476.00	41.94	70.97
Dividends Per Share	0.0	0.0	0.0	0.0
Annual Financial Data				
Operating Results (000's)				
Total Revenues	8,651.0	5,412.3	4,163.4	3,526.7
Costs & Expenses	-6,924.3	-4,891.2	-4,161.4	-3,765.6
Income Before Taxes and Other	1,726.6	521.0	2.0	-238.9
Other Items	0.0	0.0	0.0	0.0
Income Tax	200.0	0.0	0.0	0.0
Net Income	1,926.6	521.0	2.0	-238.9
Cash Flow From Operations	1,510.1	-250.9	181.1	-336.2
Balance Sheet (000's)				
Cash & Equivalents	1,426.7	93.0	383.6	215.4
Total Current Assets	3,863.9	2,544.2	1,380.9	1,522.2
Fixed Assets, Net	370.4	101.4	70.2	124.1
Total Assets	4,434.3	2,645.6	1,457.1	1,664.0
Total Current Liabilities	993.4	1,248.2	608.3	817.2
Long-Term Debt	68.0	0.0	0.0	0.0
Stockholders' Equity	3,372.9	1,397.4	848.8	846.8
Performance & Financial Condition				
Return on Total Revenues %	22.27	9.63	0.05	-6.78
Return on Avg Stockholders' Equity %	80.78	46.39	0.23	-24.73
Return on Average Assets %	54.43	25.40	0.13	-14.80
Current Ratio	3.89	2.04	2.27	1.86
Debt / Equity %	2.02	n.a.	n.a.	n.a.

Compound Growth %'s	EPS % n.a.	Net Income % n.a.	Total Revenues % 34.87

Comments

As the result of a very strong beginning backlog, 1996 was an exceptional year for the Company. However, actual orders received during 1996 were $7 million, off 30% from the 1995 level. Management had forecasted 1997 revenues to be 20% to 25% lower than in 1996. The forecast was correct for the first quarter ended March 31, 1997, as revenue was $1.6 million as compared to $2 million in 1996. However, the backlog was catching up again and was only 8.3% lower at March 31, 1997. Management reports that new customer inquiries and quoting activity remain strong. Investment Classification: Speculative & Growth

Officers	Position	Ownership Information	
Charles S. Byrne	President, CEO	Number of Shares Outstanding	2,933,091
Jonathan B. Presnell	Vice President, General Manager	Market Capitalization	$ 7,332,728
		Frequency of Dividends	n.a.
		Number of Shareholders	220

Other Information

Transfer Agent	U.S. Stock Transfer Corporation Glendale, CA		Where Listed	OTC-BB
Auditor	Ernst & Young LLP		Symbol	HTEK
Market Maker	Paragon Capital Corporation	(800)521-8877	SIC Code	3674
	Allen & Company, Inc.	(800)221-2246	Employees	63
Broker Dealer	Regular Stockbroker			

IBT Bancorp, Inc.

309 Main Street   Irwin, PA 15642   Telephone (412)863-3100   Fax (412)863-3069

Company Description

Irwin Bank and Trust Company, founded in 1922, is the operating subsidiary of this one-bank holding company. The Bank is a full service commercial banking institution serving customers through its six branches, a loan center and main office located in southwestern Pennsylvania. In November, 1996, a full-service branch was opened in the Haymaker Village Shop 'n Save. The new loan center was also opened in 1996. It accepts applications and gives approvals by telephone and maintains longer hours that may be more convenient for customers.

	12/31/96	12/31/95	12/31/94	12/31/93
Per Share Information				
Stock Price	39.25	34.00	33.00	23.50
Earnings Per Share	4.64	3.91	3.21	2.79
Price / Earnings Ratio	8.46	8.70	10.28	8.42
Book Value Per Share	31.34	27.94	24.08	22.53
Price / Book Value %	125.24	121.69	137.04	104.31
Dividends Per Share	1.32	1.10	0.90	0.73
Annual Financial Data				
Operating Results (000's)				
Net Interest Income	12,505.4	11,482.0	9,969.7	8,575.2
Loan Loss Provision	-410.0	-380.0	-240.0	-400.0
Non-Interest Income	1,470.9	1,275.7	1,324.8	1,373.6
Non-Interest Expense	-7,076.3	-6,925.2	-6,659.2	-6,130.4
Income Before Taxes and Other	6,490.0	5,452.5	4,395.3	3,418.4
Other Items	0.0	0.0	0.0	0.0
Income Tax	-2,031.6	-1,702.0	-1,314.2	-743.7
Net Income	4,458.4	3,750.6	3,081.1	2,674.7
Balance Sheet (000's)				
Cash & Securities	127,129.2	113,427.5	112,421.6	109,812.0
Loans, Net	194,676.7	176,998.3	150,871.6	137,736.7
Total Assets	331,415.6	299,434.9	272,817.9	255,261.2
Deposits	293,699.5	268,654.4	238,128.0	228,325.4
Stockholders' Equity	30,089.8	26,827.0	23,115.9	21,631.8
Performance & Financial Condition				
Return on Avg Stockholders' Equity %	15.67	15.02	13.77	12.96
Return on Average Assets %	1.41	1.31	1.17	1.07
Equity to Assets %	9.08	8.96	8.47	8.47
Net Interest Margin	n.a.	n.a.	n.a.	n.a.
Reserve as a % of Problem Loans	1,882.02	10,365.29	8,869.63	3,472.69

Compound Growth %'s	EPS %	18.48	Net Income %	18.57	Net Interest Income %	13.40

Comments

The Company declared a 2 for 1 stock split in 1994. 1993 per share amounts have been adjusted for consistency. This followed the 4 for 1 split in 1993, which may be an indication that the Company is trying to alleviate the problems of a thin market in its stock. Management is very pleased with early results at the new location and loan center. Earnings seem unaffected by the costs associated with expansion. 1997 should be a record year. Investment Classification: Growth

Officers	Position	Ownership Information	
J. Curt Gardner	President, CEO	Number of Shares Outstanding	960,000
Charles G. Urtin	Exec VP, COO	Market Capitalization	$ 37,680,000
Robert A. Bowell	Senior VP, Sr Loan Officer	Frequency of Dividends	Quarterly
Wayne J. Brentzel	Vice President	Number of Shareholders	n.a.
Russell L. McCullough	Vice President	Where Listed / Symbol	OTC-BB / IBTB

Other Information			Loan Mix	%
Transfer Agent	Company Office		R/E Mortgages	54.8
Auditor	Edwards Leap & Sauer		Installment	20.7
Market Maker	Ryan, Beck & Co.	(800)395-7926	Commerical	19.6
	Hopper Soliday & Co., Inc.	(800)456-9234	Other	4.9
Broker Dealer	OTC Specialist			
	Jack Ingold	(412)391-4594		

Indiana Natural Gas Corporation

1080 West Hospital Road   Paoli, IN 47454-0450   Telephone (812)723-2151   Fax (812)723-2188

Company Description

Indiana Natural Gas distributes natural gas to residential, commercial and industrial customers in and around Paoli and Nashville, Indiana. The Company is regulated by the Indiana Utility Regulatory Commission and must receive the Commissions approval on rate adjustments. In August, 1995, the Company offered to buy back up to 5,000 of its shares at $55 per share. Only 1,490 shares were tendered at August 31, 1996.

	08/31/96	08/31/95	08/31/94	08/31/93
Per Share Information				
Stock Price as of 12/31	30.00	55.00	27.00	27.00
Earnings Per Share	6.57	4.77	4.98	5.49
Price / Earnings Ratio	4.57	11.53	5.42	4.92
Book Value Per Share	54.60	61.38	57.06	42.24
Price / Book Value %	54.95	89.61	47.32	63.92
Dividends Per Share	1.30	1.60	1.60	1.25
Annual Financial Data				
Operating Results (000's)				
Total Revenues	5,141.3	4,930.6	6,346.8	5,258.4
Costs & Expenses	-4,085.9	-4,219.0	-5,455.4	-4,420.4
Income Before Taxes and Other	944.1	708.1	850.7	831.8
Other Items	0.0	0.0	0.0	0.0
Income Tax	-396.1	-303.6	-428.1	-356.2
Net Income	548.0	404.5	422.6	475.6
Cash Flow From Operations	19.4	1,024.0	1,335.5	977.0
Balance Sheet (000's)				
Cash & Equivalents	42.2	318.8	373.7	51.4
Total Current Assets	545.9	643.5	704.0	300.5
Fixed Assets, Net	5,292.9	5,189.4	4,534.2	4,220.4
Total Assets	5,931.1	5,854.3	5,279.2	4,601.2
Total Current Liabilities	982.0	1,316.1	1,078.1	734.7
Long-Term Debt	0.0	0.0	0.0	0.0
Stockholders' Equity	4,548.7	4,182.5	3,888.3	3,662.3
Performance & Financial Condition				
Return on Total Revenues %	10.66	8.20	6.66	9.04
Return on Avg Stockholders' Equity %	12.55	10.02	11.19	13.67
Return on Average Assets %	9.30	7.27	8.55	10.92
Current Ratio	0.56	0.49	0.65	0.41
Debt / Equity %	n.a.	n.a.	n.a.	n.a.

Compound Growth %'s	EPS %	6.17	Net Income %	4.84	Total Revenues %	-0.75

Comments

The Company grew from 4,498 customers in 1986 to 6,788 customers in 1996. This is partly attributable to expansion into new territories. Colder weather was held happily responsible for increased revenues. Cash flow was down due mainly to the underrecovery of gas costs from customers, which will be recovered in subsequent gas cost adjustment filings. The Company has no long-term debt. Investment Classification: Income & Value

Officers	Position	Ownership Information	
David K. Ross	President	Number of Shares Outstanding	83,304
James C. Clark	Secretary	Market Capitalization	$ 2,499,120
David A. Osmon	Treasurer	Frequency of Dividends	Quarterly
Michael V. Crouch	Vice President	Number of Shareholders	Under 500

Other Information

Transfer Agent	American Fletcher Nat'l Bank & Trust Co. Indianapolis, IN		Where Listed	OTC-BB
Auditor	London Witte Group LLP		Symbol	INNG
Market Maker	Hill Thompson Magid & Co., Inc	(800)631-3083	SIC Code	1320
	Sharpe Capital Inc.	(800)355-5781	Employees	18
Broker Dealer	OTC Specialist			

Indians, Inc.

501 W. Maryland Street   Indianapolis, IN 46225   Telephone (317)269-3545   Fax (317)269-3541

Company Description

When the first home run was hit at the Indians' new downtown ballpark in 1996, the announcer said "he took that one downtown." He wasn't kidding as the new facility is in the heart of Indianapolis. The Indians, Inc. is a minor league ball club that has been operating since 1902. But unlike the major leagues, this club makes money through ticket sales and a host of related sources. Player salaries are not an issue as they are paid by the sponsoring major league team. The new stadium is owned by the City and leased to the Company.

	09/30/96	09/30/95	09/30/94	09/30/93
Per Share Information				
Stock Price as of 12/31	2,000.00	1,500.00	1,120.00	1,300.00
Earnings Per Share	600.27	271.63	221.75	109.37
Price / Earnings Ratio	3.33	5.52	5.05	11.89
Book Value Per Share	1,381.56	821.83	753.40	557.17
Price / Book Value %	144.76	182.52	148.66	233.32
Dividends Per Share	300.00	220.00	40.00	20.00
Annual Financial Data				
Operating Results (000's)				
Total Revenues	5,085.9	2,895.0	2,530.3	1,911.5
Costs & Expenses	-3,047.3	-1,970.5	-1,765.3	-1,551.3
Income Before Taxes and Other	2,038.6	924.5	765.0	360.2
Other Items	0.0	0.0	0.0	0.0
Income Tax	-766.0	-348.7	-294.9	-128.8
Net Income	1,272.6	575.8	470.1	231.4
Cash Flow From Operations	n.a.	n.a.	n.a.	n.a.
Balance Sheet (000's)				
Cash & Equivalents	25.0	268.8	235.1	216.6
Total Current Assets	2,751.5	1,953.4	1,668.2	1,060.8
Fixed Assets, Net	770.0	63.9	47.8	33.7
Total Assets	5,341.0	2,631.9	2,238.1	1,511.4
Total Current Liabilities	1,537.1	823.9	604.9	330.2
Long-Term Debt	0.0	0.0	0.0	0.0
Stockholders' Equity	2,928.9	1,742.3	1,597.2	1,181.2
Performance & Financial Condition				
Return on Total Revenues %	25.02	19.89	18.58	12.11
Return on Avg Stockholders' Equity %	54.49	34.49	33.84	n.a.
Return on Average Assets %	31.92	23.65	25.08	n.a.
Current Ratio	1.79	2.37	2.76	3.21
Debt / Equity %	n.a.	n.a.	n.a.	n.a.

Compound Growth %'s	EPS %	76.39	Net Income %	76.50	Total Revenues %	38.57

Comments

The nostalgia of the three final months at Bush Stadium, in service since 1931, combined with the excitement of the first two months in the new stadium resulted in a record-breaking season. Regular season attendance was 544,592. 1997 will even be better as the Company benefits from a full season of the new skyboxes and many other facility enhancements. Now for what you have been waiting for: the Indians won the Eastern Division championship by upsetting Buffalo. Unfortunately, the Tribe lost the League Championship series to Oklahoma City. But remember, the final score card in this book is earnings per share. Investment Classification: Income & Value

Officers	Position	Ownership Information	
Henry R. Warren, Jr.	Chairman	Number of Shares Outstanding	2,120
Max B. Schumacher	President	Market Capitalization	$ 4,240,000
		Frequency of Dividends	Annual
		Number of Shareholders	Under 500

Other Information			
Transfer Agent	Company Office	Where Listed	Order Matching Only
Auditor	Not indicated	Symbol	n.a.
Market Maker	None	SIC Code	7940
		Employees	n.a.
Broker Dealer	Jeffrey J. Winters	(800)800-2489	
	City Securities Corporation	(800)800-2489	

Information Analysis Incorporated

11240 Waples Hill Road, #400   Fairfax, VA 22030   Telephone (703)383-3000   Fax (703)293-7979

Company Description

The activities of the Company are primarily related to software applications development, hardware and software consulting services, software sales and support services. Software sales are limited to a few products for which the Company has a particular market niche. One relatively new product that the Company has acquired is Computer Aided Software Translator (CAST). This software program has the ability to remedy, primarily on an automated basis, the Year 2000 problem which many computer systems now confront. The Company has been engaged in various facets of the computer and information field since it was founded in 1979.

	12/31/96	12/31/95	12/31/94	12/31/93
Per Share Information				
Stock Price	20.33	1.33	1.33	1.58
Earnings Per Share	-0.09	-0.05	-0.04	0.04
Price / Earnings Ratio	n.a.	n.a.	n.a.	39.50
Book Value Per Share	1.36	1.38	1.43	1.47
Price / Book Value %	1,494.85	96.38	93.01	107.48
Dividends Per Share	0.0	0.0	0.0	0.0
Annual Financial Data				
Operating Results (000's)				
Total Revenues	11,231.6	15,704.5	16,704.9	15,621.0
Costs & Expenses	-11,467.9	-15,805.1	-16,789.9	-15,584.2
Income Before Taxes and Other	-236.3	-100.6	-85.0	36.8
Other Items	0.0	0.0	0.0	48.8
Income Tax	76.6	26.0	26.3	-16.5
Net Income	-159.7	-74.6	-58.7	69.1
Cash Flow From Operations	1,029.7	990.5	-144.0	n.a.
Balance Sheet (000's)				
Cash & Equivalents	323.9	57.0	35.2	24.0
Total Current Assets	2,310.9	3,661.3	4,382.8	4,378.6
Fixed Assets, Net	291.1	344.1	462.3	496.6
Total Assets	3,121.2	4,173.1	4,899.6	4,885.2
Total Current Liabilities	875.0	2,162.4	2,712.1	2,553.4
Long-Term Debt	90.4	58.9	78.8	55.7
Stockholders' Equity	2,087.5	1,932.9	2,088.1	2,235.1
Performance & Financial Condition				
Return on Total Revenues %	-1.42	-0.48	-0.35	0.44
Return on Avg Stockholders' Equity %	-7.94	-3.71	-2.72	3.09
Return on Average Assets %	-4.38	-1.65	-1.20	1.43
Current Ratio	2.64	1.69	1.62	1.71
Debt / Equity %	4.33	3.05	3.77	2.49

Compound Growth %'s	EPS % n.a.	Net Income % n.a.	Total Revenues % -10.41

Comments

The Company declared a 3 for 1 stock split in early 1997. All per share amounts have been adjusted. Because of the prospects associated with CAST, in 1996, the Company commenced its transition from primarily a professional services orientation to that of a product provider for the Year 2000 remediation market. This is requiring a significant investment in marketing and technical resources that will continue through 1997. The anticipated returns will not be realized until companies commence their Year 2000 remediation efforts, assuming CAST becomes an effective tool. However, on May 12, 1997, the Company announced that it completed two successful projects using the technology. Market speculation has had an impact on share pricing. Investment Classification: Speculative

Officers	Position	Ownership Information	
Sandor Rosenberg	President, Secretary	Number of Shares Outstanding	1,529,997
Richard S. DeRose	Exec VP, Treasurer	Market Capitalization	$ 31,104,839
		Frequency of Dividends	n.a.
		Number of Shareholders	575

Other Information

Transfer Agent	American Stock Transfer & Trust Company New York, NY		Where Listed	OTC-BB
Auditor	Rubino & McGeehin		Symbol	IAIC
Market Maker	Wachtel & Co., Inc.	(202)898-1018	SIC Code	7379
	Carr Securities Corporation	(800)221-2243	Employees	74
Broker Dealer	Regular Stockbroker			

InterCounty Bancshares, Inc.

48 North South Street   Wilmington, OH 45177   Telephone (513)382-1441   Fax (800)837-3012

Company Description

National Bank and Trust Company, subsidiary of this holding company, was founded in 1859. Today it operates thirteen full-service branches and four limited-service locations in Clinton, Brown, Clermont and Warren Counties, Ohio. These Counties are located within an hour's drive of the larger metropolitan areas of Cincinnati, Dayton and Columbus. The last branch to open was in Batavia in March, 1996. The Bank acquired Williamsburg Building & Loan Company in 1993, in a transaction in which Williamsburg converted from a mutual to a stock form of ownership. 229,475 shares of common at $19.25 per share were issued at that time. The Bank also acquired Kentucky National Bank of Ohio in 1992.

	12/31/96	12/31/95	12/31/94	12/31/93
Per Share Information				
Stock Price	27.00	20.00	20.00	19.25
Earnings Per Share	3.18	2.63	1.44	2.08
Price / Earnings Ratio	8.49	7.60	13.89	9.25
Book Value Per Share	23.86	21.84	18.56	17.50
Price / Book Value %	113.16	91.58	107.76	110.00
Dividends Per Share	0.56	0.37	0.0	0.16
Annual Financial Data				
Operating Results (000's)				
Net Interest Income	15,009.0	13,740.0	12,140.0	11,451.0
Loan Loss Provision	-600.0	-360.0	-275.0	-660.0
Non-Interest Income	3,138.0	2,339.0	828.0	3,303.0
Non-Interest Expense	-10,827.0	-10,103.0	-9,881.0	-9,472.0
Income Before Taxes and Other	6,720.0	5,616.0	2,812.0	4,622.0
Other Items	0.0	0.0	0.0	0.0
Income Tax	-1,858.0	-1,591.0	-617.0	-1,513.0
Net Income	4,862.0	4,025.0	2,195.0	3,109.0
Balance Sheet (000's)				
Cash & Securities	100,978.0	109,100.0	73,424.0	79,742.0
Loans, Net	266,596.0	239,863.0	205,593.0	190,727.0
Total Assets	380,607.0	360,271.0	289,267.0	280,029.0
Deposits	309,128.0	291,503.0	248,941.0	243,484.0
Stockholders' Equity	36,748.0	33,834.0	28,714.0	27,051.0
Performance & Financial Condition				
Return on Avg Stockholders' Equity %	13.78	12.87	7.87	15.26
Return on Average Assets %	1.31	1.24	0.77	1.27
Equity to Assets %	9.66	9.39	9.93	9.66
Net Interest Margin	4.33	4.61	4.58	4.58
Reserve as a % of Problem Loans	502.06	842.04	1,071.55	3,212.99

Compound Growth %'s	EPS %	15.20	Net Income %	16.07	Net Interest Income %	9.44

Comments

All acquisitions were accounted for as a pooling of interests and financial statements have been restated to show the companies on a combined basis. Record earnings were reported as net interest income and non-interest income scored big gains. The new branch is exceeding all projections. The Trust department, now in its 75th year, established an Investment Services Department to enable the offering of annuities, mutual funds and brokerage services. Investment Classification: Growth & Value

Officers	Position	Ownership Information	
Timothy L. Smith	President, CEO	Number of Shares Outstanding	1,540,039
Charles L. Dehner	Exec VP	Market Capitalization	$ 41,581,053
R. James Parker	Exec VP	Frequency of Dividends	Quarterly
Andrew J. McCreanor	Senior VP	Number of Shareholders	375
Walter H. Rowsey	Senior VP	Where Listed / Symbol	OTC-PS / ICYB

Other Information			Loan Mix	%
Transfer Agent	Company Office		R/E Mortgages	41.2
Auditor	J.D. Cloud & Co. PLL		Installment	30.1
Market Maker	Trident Securities Inc.	(800)340-6321	Commerical	21.5
	Hill Thompson Magid & Co., Inc	(800)631-3083	Agriculture	6.1
Broker Dealer	OTC Specialist		Other	1.1
	Harry Jaffe-The Chicago Corp.	(800)621-1674		

InterUnion Financial Corporation

249 Royal Palm Way, Ste. 301H   Palm Beach, FL 33480   Telephone (561)820-0084   Fax (416)955-0777

Company Description

InterUnion Financial Corporation, formerly AU 'N AG, Inc., was formed to acquire a majority interest in existing securities firms, banks, insurance companies, and other financial and brokerage companies located in the United States and Canada. The Company intends to actively engage in the business of the companies in which it invests by serving as an "information link" between these companies. The Company's goal in providing this information link is to improve access to new markets and business opportunities for these companies.

	03/31/96	03/31/95
Per Share Information		
Stock Price as of 12/31	4.50	0.53
Earnings Per Share	0.60	-0.02
Price / Earnings Ratio	7.50	n.a.
Book Value Per Share	5.98	1.38
Price / Book Value %	75.25	38.41
Dividends Per Share	0.0	0.0
Annual Financial Data		
Operating Results (000's)		
Total Revenues	5,915.4	4,965.0
Costs & Expenses	-5,900.8	-5,108.9
Income Before Taxes and Other	14.6	-143.9
Other Items	315.2	0.0
Income Tax	-28.2	9.4
Net Income	301.6	-134.4
Cash Flow From Operations	431.8	404.2
Balance Sheet (000's)		
Cash & Equivalents	722.8	490.8
Total Current Assets	6,896.8	38,546.2
Fixed Assets, Net	948.9	150.1
Total Assets	10,469.7	47,578.4
Total Current Liabilities	6,210.6	37,089.4
Long-Term Debt	119.5	0.0
Stockholders' Equity	4,139.6	10,170.3
Performance & Financial Condition		
Return on Total Revenues %	5.10	-2.71
Return on Avg Stockholders' Equity %	4.21	n.a.
Return on Average Assets %	1.04	n.a.
Current Ratio	1.11	1.04
Debt / Equity %	2.89	n.a.

Compound Growth %'s	EPS % n.a.	Net Income % n.a.	Total Revenues % 19.14

Comments

Over the last two years the Company has acquired Bearhill, Limited, Inc., Guardian Timing Services, Inc., and Credifinance Capital, Inc. The Company acquired and disposed of Rosedale Realty Corporation. The Company also formed an auction subsidiary, Reeve, Mackay & Associates Limited. Fiscal 1996 results include a gain on the sale of Rosedale Realty of $409,000. For the nine months ended December 31, 1996, the Company reported revenues of $5.9 million, as compared to $4.2 million in the same period of the preceding year, and a net loss of $346,681, $.43 per share. The Reeve, Mackay operation is not expected to reach break-even until 1998. Its share of the loss for the nine month period was over $300,000. Investment Classification: Speculative

Officers	Position	Ownership Information	
George Benarroch	President, CEO	Number of Shares Outstanding	692,558
T. Jack Gary, III	Secretary	Market Capitalization	$ 3,116,511
John Illidge	Vice President	Frequency of Dividends	n.a.
Michel Woodtli	Other	Number of Shareholders	383

Other Information			
Transfer Agent	OTC Stock Transfer Inc. Salt Lake City, UT	Where Listed	OTC-BB
Auditor	Mintz & Partners	Symbol	IUFC
Market Maker	Wm. V. Frankel & Co., Inc. (800)631-3091	SIC Code	6159
	Hill Thompson Magid & Co., Inc (800)631-2083	Employees	n.a.
Broker Dealer	Regular Stockbroker		

International Automated Systems, Inc.

512 South 860 East   American Fork, UT 84003   Telephone (801)763-9965   Fax (801)763-8839

Company Description

International Automated Systems, a development stage company, designs, produces and markets technology based products. One set of products includes an automated self-service check-out system which allows retail customers to ring up their purchases without a cashier or clerk. The Company also is developing an automated fingerprint identification machine and other technology for transmitting information and data using transmission waves in the electromagnetic spectrum. The first anticipated product of the latter technology is the commercialization of a high speed modem.

	06/30/96	06/30/95
Per Share Information		
Stock Price as of 12/31	6.75	17.00
Earnings Per Share	-0.04	-0.20
Price / Earnings Ratio	n.a.	n.a.
Book Value Per Share	0.03	-0.01
Price / Book Value %	22,500.00	n.a.
Dividends Per Share	0.0	0.0
Annual Financial Data		
Operating Results (000's)		
Total Revenues	106.1	6.0
Costs & Expenses	-793.3	-207.2
Income Before Taxes and Other	-687.2	-201.2
Other Items	0.0	0.0
Income Tax	0.0	0.0
Net Income	-687.2	-201.2
Cash Flow From Operations	-904.4	-97.4
Balance Sheet (000's)		
Cash & Equivalents	545.8	10.0
Total Current Assets	815.3	10.0
Fixed Assets, Net	131.6	58.2
Total Assets	1,099.2	86.5
Total Current Liabilities	695.5	11.9
Long-Term Debt	10.3	14.0
Stockholders' Equity	393.4	-73.5
Performance & Financial Condition		
Return on Total Revenues %	-647.63	-3,353.70
Return on Avg Stockholders' Equity %	-429.68	n.a.
Return on Average Assets %	-115.92	n.a.
Current Ratio	1.17	0.84
Debt / Equity %	2.61	n.a.

Compound Growth %'s	EPS % n.a.	Net Income % n.a.	Total Revenues % n.a.

Comments

The first product sales occurred in 1996 and are reasons to celebrate for this ten year old company. But the auditor added a going concern exception in their report. During the six months ended December 31, 1996, revenue increased only slightly to $25,928. The loss for the six-month period was $670,007 which was financed by additional advances from the majority shareholder. Investment Classification: Speculative

Officers	Position	Ownership Information	
Neldon Johnson	Chairman, President	Number of Shares Outstanding	15,186,100
Ina Johnson	Secretary	Market Capitalization	$ 102,506,175
Donnel Johnson	Vice President	Frequency of Dividends	n.a.
Douglas H. Lloyd	Vice President	Number of Shareholders	980
Randale Johnson	Vice President		

Other Information			
Transfer Agent	Colonial Stock Transfer Co., Inc. Salt Lake City, UT	Where Listed	OTC-BB
Auditor	Hansen, Barnett & Maxwell	Symbol	IAUS
Market Maker	Wilson-Davis & Co., Inc. (800)453-5735	SIC Code	7372
	Olsen Payne & Co. (800)453-5321	Employees	n.a.
Broker Dealer	Regular Stockbroker		

Investment Properties Associates

60 East 42nd Street   New York, NY 10165   Telephone (212)687-6400   Fax (212)687-6437

Company Description

The Partnership owns fourteen office buildings, one loft building and two unimproved real properties in metropolitan areas of Illinois, New York, New Jersey and Texas. One of the office buildings is vacant. The properties have a total rentable area of approximately 5,423,000 square feet. Leasing the properties to tenants is the only activity of the partnership. Harry Helmsley, who died on January 7, 1997, was one of the Partnership's general partners. Mr. Helmsley was New York's preeminent real estate investor, broker and dealmaker who amassed billions of dollars worth of properties; not a bad partner to have. The Partnership was formed in 1969.

	12/31/96	12/31/95	12/31/94	12/31/93
Per Unit Information				
Price Per Unit	38.00	35.88	49.50	47.50
Earnings Per Unit	5.86	5.84	5.43	6.61
Price / Earnings Ratio	6.48	6.14	9.12	7.19
Book Value Per Unit	19.07	19.60	20.54	21.08
Price / Book Value %	199.27	183.06	240.99	225.33
Distributions Per Unit	6.39	6.35	6.40	6.69
Cash Flow Per Unit	15.59	13.65	14.13	19.30
Annual Financial Data				
Operating Results (000's)				
Total Revenues	52,290.7	53,988.4	52,807.9	55,719.3
Costs & Expenses	-42,694.7	-44,272.6	-43,722.1	-45,954.5
Operating Income	9,218.0	9,331.3	8,702.5	9,369.9
Other Items	-766.0	0.0	0.0	0.0
Net Income	8,452.1	9,331.3	8,702.5	9,369.9
Cash Flow From Operations	12,787.5	11,190.6	11,590.6	15,826.7
Balance Sheet (000's)				
Cash & Equivalents	5,187.6	3,090.4	4,138.9	2,403.1
Total Current Assets	13,017.1	10,782.3	11,585.3	9,754.9
Investments	42,504.3	44,279.0	43,939.2	44,807.6
Total Assets	55,521.4	55,061.3	55,524.6	54,562.4
Total Current Liabilities	32,110.1	28,517.4	24,860.2	26,174.6
Long-Term Debt	60,261.2	61,363.3	64,408.7	60,330.8
Partners' Capital	-36,849.9	-34,819.4	-33,744.3	-31,943.0
Performance & Financial Condition				
Return on Total Revenues %	16.16	17.28	16.48	16.82
Return on Average Partners' Capital %	n.a.	n.a.	n.a.	n.a.
Return on Average Assets %	15.29	16.88	15.81	16.66
Current Ratio	0.41	0.38	0.47	0.37
Debt / Equity %	n.a.	n.a.	n.a.	n.a.

Compound Growth %'s	EPU %	-3.93	Net Income %	-3.38	Total Revenues %	-2.09

Comments

The Partnership has three types of partners: general partners, special limited partners and limited partners, who share in the distributable net income of the Partnership at 1.5%, 48.5%, and 50%, respectively. The general partners and special limited partners owned directly or beneficially approximately 45% of the limited partnership participation units at December 31, 1996. Under the terms of the partnership agreement the general partners are obligated to create a new limited partnership because of Mr. Helmsley passing. On February 5, 1997, the Partnership announced that all of the properties included in the portfolio are available for sale. Investment Classification: Income & Value

Officers	Position	Ownership Information	
Irving Schneider	CFO	Number of Units Outstanding	820,000
		Market Capitalization	$ 31,160,000
		Frequency of Distributions	Annual
		Number of Partners	651

Other Information

Transfer Agent	American Stock Transfer & Trust Company New York, NY		Where Listed	OTC-BB
Auditor	Ernst & Young LLP		Symbol	IVPA
Market Maker	Robotti & Co., Inc.	(212)986-0800	SIC Code	6530
	Carr Securities Corporation	(800)221-2243	Employees	175
Broker Dealer	Regular Stockbroker			

Investors Financial Corporation

P.O. Box 797   Bainbridge, GA 31718   Telephone (912)248-3800   Fax (912)248-3826

Company Description

Bainbridge National Bank, founded in 1991, is the operating subsidiary of this holding company. It serves the 26,000 residents of Decatur County, Georgia, from a single location. This is a beautiful area of the state where, as explained by the Bank, "everyone knows everyone." The Bank facilitates trading in its stock by maintaining lists of people interested in buying and selling shares.

	12/31/96	12/31/95	12/31/94	12/31/93
Per Share Information				
Stock Price	15.00	16.50	12.00	11.50
Earnings Per Share	1.87	1.61	1.30	1.20
Price / Earnings Ratio	8.02	10.25	9.23	9.58
Book Value Per Share	16.07	14.69	11.89	12.15
Price / Book Value %	93.34	112.32	100.93	94.65
Dividends Per Share	0.44	0.35	0.30	0.30
Annual Financial Data				
Operating Results (000's)				
Net Interest Income	3,084.9	2,885.3	2,731.7	2,559.3
Loan Loss Provision	-120.0	-132.0	-120.0	-120.0
Non-Interest Income	601.7	567.7	527.9	602.2
Non-Interest Expense	-2,049.9	-2,088.3	-2,161.7	-2,152.1
Income Before Taxes and Other	1,516.7	1,232.8	977.9	889.3
Other Items	0.0	0.0	0.0	0.0
Income Tax	-548.5	-407.0	-320.5	-278.0
Net Income	968.2	825.9	657.5	611.3
Balance Sheet (000's)				
Cash & Securities	25,987.6	28,114.9	24,823.7	27,005.6
Loans, Net	44,630.5	40,688.2	39,829.6	36,562.0
Total Assets	75,468.9	73,681.4	70,102.1	68,746.5
Deposits	65,390.1	62,815.9	60,457.1	58,690.0
Stockholders' Equity	7,550.5	6,906.3	5,588.2	5,711.8
Performance & Financial Condition				
Return on Avg Stockholders' Equity %	13.39	13.22	11.64	11.31
Return on Average Assets %	1.30	1.15	0.95	0.88
Equity to Assets %	10.00	9.37	7.97	8.31
Net Interest Margin	n.a.	n.a.	n.a.	n.a.
Reserve as a % of Problem Loans	543.43	1,201.68	1,335.41	857.24

Compound Growth %'s	EPS %	15.94	Net Income %	16.57	Net Interest Income %	6.42

Comments

Another record year was reported in 1996 by this young bank as earnings increased 17.2%. The Bank continues to be heavily capitalized and manages growth with a tight control on overhead expenses. Management predicts another successful year for 1997. There is no apparent reason for the drop in stock price. As not much trading occurs, it may have been a function of timing. Investment Classification: Value & Growth

Officers	Position	Ownership Information	
Bill J. Jones	Chairman	Number of Shares Outstanding	470,000
Tracy A. Dixon	President, CEO	Market Capitalization	$ 7,050,000
M.H. (Hal) Brannen	Senior VP	Frequency of Dividends	Semi-Annual
Judy M. Powell	Vice President, Head Cashier	Number of Shareholders	n.a.
Karon Elwell	Other	Where Listed / Symbol	Order Matching Only / n.a.

Other Information		Loan Mix	%
Transfer Agent	Company Office	R/E Mortgages	59.5
Auditor	Mauldin & Jenkins, LLC	Installment	25.9
Market Maker	None - See Note	Commerical	9.9
		Agriculture	2.7
Broker Dealer	None - See Note	Construction	1.9
		Other	0.1

Investors Heritage Life Insurance Company

200 Capital Avenue   Frankfort, KY 40602   Telephone (502)223-2361   Fax (502)227-7205

Company Description

Investors Heritage Life Insurance Company sells and administers various insurance and annuity products including participating, non-participating, whole life, preneed and final expense life insurance, limited pay, universal life, annuity contracts, credit life, credit accident and health and group insurance policies. The principal markets are in Kentucky, Virginia, North Carolina, South Carolina, Ohio, Indiana, Florida, Tennessee, Illinois, Kansas, West Virginia and Texas. Kentucky Investors, Inc., an investment holding company, owns 74% of Investors Heritage's outstanding shares. The Company was formed in 1960.

	12/31/96	12/31/95	12/31/94	12/31/93
Per Share Information				
Stock Price	26.50	26.75	27.00	26.00
Earnings Per Share	1.78	1.02	2.66	2.54
Price / Earnings Ratio	14.89	26.23	10.15	10.24
Book Value Per Share	41.83	42.93	34.13	37.05
Price / Book Value %	63.35	62.31	79.11	70.18
Dividends Per Share	0.76	0.76	0.74	0.72
Annual Financial Data				
Operating Results (000's)				
Total Revenues	47,779.6	44,076.4	46,804.2	45,426.0
Costs & Expenses	-14,501.7	-14,742.5	-18,162.3	-20,208.7
Income Before Taxes and Other	1,555.6	884.6	2,792.0	2,448.0
Other Items	0.0	0.0	0.0	182.0
Income Tax	46.0	32.0	-391.0	-328.0
Net Income	1,601.6	916.6	2,401.0	2,302.0
Cash Flow From Operations	15,632.5	11,999.4	10,313.0	5,772.6
Balance Sheet (000's)				
Cash & Equivalents	2,647.6	2,377.0	2,309.8	3,042.1
Total Current Assets	18,759.5	10,894.2	17,245.8	27,786.4
Fixed Assets, Net	1,942.8	1,823.8	1,921.7	2,130.9
Total Assets	227,139.6	210,489.9	194,262.0	201,196.6
Total Current Liabilities	5,547.8	6,369.1	3,243.0	7,760.5
Long-Term Debt	0.0	0.0	0.0	0.0
Stockholders' Equity	37,672.0	38,660.0	30,768.4	33,539.0
Performance & Financial Condition				
Return on Total Revenues %	3.35	2.08	5.13	5.07
Return on Avg Stockholders' Equity %	4.20	2.64	7.47	7.04
Return on Average Assets %	0.73	0.45	1.21	1.23
Current Ratio	3.38	1.71	5.32	3.58
Debt / Equity %	n.a.	n.a.	n.a.	n.a.

Compound Growth %'s	EPS % -11.18	Net Income % -11.39	Total Revenues % 1.70

Comments

Earnings rebounded with a 74.5% increase over the preceding year. Considering earnings, asset growth, continued asset quality, sales and strategic execution of the business plan, management categorizes 1996 as one of the best years in its thirty-six year history. Some assets have been shifted to a higher yield mortgage portfolio all loans of which are performing as of year end. Record sales during five of the last six years is evidence that the sales effort is on target. The floods in March, 1997, did affect Frankfort but no damage was suffered by the Company. Investment Classification: Value

Officers	Position	Ownership Information	
Harry Lee Waterfield II	President, CEO	Number of Shares Outstanding	900,574
Wilma Yeary	Secretary	Market Capitalization	$ 23,865,211
Jane S. Jackson	Secretary	Frequency of Dividends	Annual
Jimmy R. McIver	Treasurer	Number of Shareholders	2,834
Robert M. Hardy, Jr.	Vice President		

Other Information

Transfer Agent	Company Office		Where Listed	OTC-BB
Auditor	Ernst & Young LLP		Symbol	INLF
Market Maker	Hilliard, Lyons, Inc.	(800)627-3557	SIC Code	6311
	Wiley Brothers & Co., Inc.	(800)827-9276	Employees	119
Broker Dealer	Regular Stockbroker			

Irex Corporation

120 North Lime Street Lancaster, PA 17608 Telephone (717)397-3633 Fax (717)399-5325

Company Description

Irex Corporation is primarily in the business of thermal insulation contracting and the direct sale of insulation and acoustical materials throughout the U.S. and Canada, the fabrication of insulation materials, and interior contracting. ACandS, a major division, is a horizontally-integrated national provider of specialty contracting services. Irex Corporation has, over the years, reacquired 643,175 shares of common stock, 62.5% of total shares. The Company was formed in 1969.

	12/31/96	12/31/95	12/31/94	12/31/93
Per Share Information				
Stock Price	20.75	18.63	14.00	17.50
Earnings Per Share	4.80	2.01	3.11	-3.36
Price / Earnings Ratio	4.32	9.27	4.50	n.a.
Book Value Per Share	30.58	25.59	23.14	19.94
Price / Book Value %	67.85	72.80	60.50	87.76
Dividends Per Share	0.0	0.0	0.0	0.0
Annual Financial Data				
Operating Results (000's)				
Total Revenues	271,232.0	244,532.0	240,704.0	237,708.0
Costs & Expenses	-266,309.0	-243,700.0	-236,763.0	-238,088.0
Income Before Taxes and Other	4,923.0	832.0	3,941.0	-380.0
Other Items	0.0	1,377.0	0.0	0.0
Income Tax	-2,050.0	-431.0	-1,714.0	-9.0
Net Income	2,873.0	1,778.0	2,227.0	-389.0
Cash Flow From Operations	1,799.0	-454.0	2,770.0	-2,937.0
Balance Sheet (000's)				
Cash & Equivalents	193.0	411.0	1,564.0	1,068.0
Total Current Assets	78,749.0	78,317.0	78,695.0	76,484.0
Fixed Assets, Net	3,082.0	3,199.0	3,481.0	4,107.0
Total Assets	85,325.0	81,635.0	82,560.0	81,483.0
Total Current Liabilities	44,636.0	48,518.0	47,043.0	45,544.0
Long-Term Debt	9,286.0	12,543.0	15,800.0	17,414.0
Stockholders' Equity	11,786.0	10,078.0	9,221.0	8,029.0
Performance & Financial Condition				
Return on Total Revenues %	1.06	0.73	0.93	-0.16
Return on Avg Stockholders' Equity %	26.28	18.43	25.82	-4.42
Return on Average Assets %	3.44	2.17	2.72	-0.49
Current Ratio	1.76	1.61	1.67	1.68
Debt / Equity %	78.79	124.46	171.35	216.89

Compound Growth %'s	EPS %	24.23	Net Income %	13.58	Total Revenues %	4.50

Comments

What is especially good about the 1996 results is that they were achieved notwithstanding approximately $2 million in losses from discontinued operations, $500,000 in expenses from the restructuring of ACandS, and the startup costs of several new operations. Since 1984, Irex's return on common stockholders' equity has averaged 15.8%. Management believes that the materials distribution and non-union specialty contracting businesses have been developed to the point where they are now able to provide both a significant portion of company earnings and a lower overall company risk profile by means of a greater diversification of markets and services provided. Investment Classification: Value

Officers	Position	Ownership Information	
W. Kirk Liddell	President, CEO	Number of Shares Outstanding	385,458
L. A. Pickell	Treasurer	Market Capitalization	$ 7,998,254
James E. Hipolit	Vice President, Secretary	Frequency of Dividends	Irregular
Jane E. Pinkerton	Vice President	Number of Shareholders	340

Other Information			
Transfer Agent	Company Office	Where Listed	OTC-BB
Auditor	Arthur Andersen LLP	Symbol	IREX
Market Maker	F.J. Morrissey & Co., Inc.	(800)842-8928	SIC Code	1742
	Robotti & Co., Inc.	(212)986-0800	Employees	67
Broker Dealer	Regular Stockbroker		

Iron and Glass Bancorp, Inc.

1114 E. Carson Street   Pittsburgh, PA 15203   Telephone (412)488-5200   Fax (412)488-5224

Company Description

The Company's subsidiary, Iron and Glass Bank, is a full service commercial bank established in 1871, and now operates six banking offices in the South Hills area of Allegheny County, Pennsylvania. The last office to open was on January 13, 1997, in the rapidly growing suburban corridor of Chartiers Valley. The Bank boasts twenty-six years of increasing dividends.

	12/31/96	12/31/95	12/31/94	12/31/93
Per Share Information				
Stock Price	45.12	36.50	27.00	31.00
Earnings Per Share	3.01	2.33	0.96	2.87
Price / Earnings Ratio	14.99	15.67	28.13	10.80
Book Value Per Share	28.80	27.17	24.60	26.04
Price / Book Value %	156.67	134.34	109.76	119.05
Dividends Per Share	0.92	0.86	0.81	0.77
Annual Financial Data				
Operating Results (000's)				
Net Interest Income	7,284.5	6,305.4	6,017.0	6,177.3
Loan Loss Provision	-436.0	-478.0	-1,421.2	-347.4
Non-Interest Income	446.0	342.1	468.1	574.8
Non-Interest Expense	-4,814.0	-4,513.1	-4,552.6	-4,251.3
Income Before Taxes and Other	2,480.5	1,656.3	511.3	2,153.4
Other Items	0.0	0.0	0.0	91.6
Income Tax	-675.0	-255.4	66.8	-521.4
Net Income	1,805.5	1,400.9	578.1	1,723.6
Balance Sheet (000's)				
Cash & Securities	75,640.0	74,897.8	70,631.8	72,343.8
Loans, Net	100,790.4	87,801.1	68,253.0	69,502.2
Total Assets	181,768.6	166,298.2	143,876.4	146,249.3
Deposits	159,911.4	145,618.1	123,113.6	126,203.5
Stockholders' Equity	17,278.9	16,302.1	14,760.4	15,622.8
Performance & Financial Condition				
Return on Avg Stockholders' Equity %	10.75	9.02	3.81	11.63
Return on Average Assets %	1.04	0.90	0.40	1.15
Equity to Assets %	9.51	9.80	10.26	10.68
Net Interest Margin	n.a.	n.a.	n.a.	n.a.
Reserve as a % of Problem Loans	171.15	54.86	60.52	102.43

Compound Growth %'s	EPS %	1.60	Net Income %	1.56	Net Interest Income %	5.65

Comments

1994 results reflect an income tax credit which slightly improved a poor bottom line. The decline was largely attributable to a substantial increase in the allowance for loan losses. Management attributes this problem, in part, to changes in the regulatory environment and would rather focus on 1996 results. The big increase in earnings was driven by the continued expansion of the loan portfolio and tight controls on overhead expenses. The main thrust of the loan growth has been lending to small businesses in the community. Investment Classification: Value

Officers	Position	Ownership Information	
Michael Hagan	President, CEO	Number of Shares Outstanding	600,000
Karen Joyce	Exec VP, Sr Loan Officer	Market Capitalization	$ 27,072,000
James R. Rendulic	Senior VP, CFO	Frequency of Dividends	Quarterly
Donald Lajevic	Vice President	Number of Shareholders	n.a.
Mary Catherine Rossi	Vice President	Where Listed / Symbol	OTC-BB / IRGB

Other Information			Loan Mix	%
Transfer Agent	Company Office		R/E Mortgages	54.0
Auditor	S.R. Snodgrass, A.C.		Commerical	30.0
Market Maker	Legg Mason Wood Walker, Inc.	(800)346-5075	Consumer	6.5
	E.E. Powell & Company	(800)282-1940	Construction	1.9
Broker Dealer	Regular Stockbroker		Other	7.6

Justiss Oil Co., Inc.

1810 E. Oak Street   Jena, LA 71342-1385   Telephone (318)992-4111   Fax (318)992-7201

Company Description

Justiss Oil Co., Inc. explores for and extracts oil and gas from its own properties and in conjunction with certain working interests. There is also a tank manufacturing division, farming division and warehousing operations division. In 1995, the Company began operations in Venezuela. The same family has operated the company since its formation in 1946.

	11/30/95	11/30/94	11/30/93
Per Share Information			
Stock Price as of 12/31	43.00	41.00	37.00
Earnings Per Share	-0.28	3.48	8.14
Price / Earnings Ratio	n.a.	11.78	4.55
Book Value Per Share	63.67	64.95	55.33
Price / Book Value %	67.54	63.13	66.87
Dividends Per Share	1.00	1.00	1.00
Annual Financial Data			
Operating Results (000's)			
Total Revenues	42,495.3	51,621.2	62,633.5
Costs & Expenses	-42,567.5	-48,524.7	-54,833.6
Income Before Taxes and Other	-72.2	3,096.5	7,799.9
Other Items	0.0	0.0	0.0
Income Tax	-117.1	-745.8	-2,296.0
Net Income	-189.3	2,350.7	5,503.8
Cash Flow From Operations	n.a.	n.a.	n.a.
Balance Sheet (000's)			
Cash & Equivalents	2,757.4	2,051.2	n.a.
Total Current Assets	16,148.2	22,328.4	n.a.
Fixed Assets, Net	24,281.2	23,705.7	n.a.
Total Assets	49,095.9	58,666.5	n.a.
Total Current Liabilities	5,893.2	14,214.4	n.a.
Long-Term Debt	16.5	0.0	n.a.
Stockholders' Equity	43,044.1	43,909.5	n.a.
Performance & Financial Condition			
Return on Total Revenues %	-0.45	4.55	8.79
Return on Avg Stockholders' Equity %	-0.44	n.a.	n.a.
Return on Average Assets %	-0.35	n.a.	n.a.
Current Ratio	2.74	1.57	n.a.
Debt / Equity %	0.04	n.a.	n.a.

Compound Growth %'s	EPS %	n.a.	Net Income %	n.a.	Total Revenues %	n.a.

Comments

The decline in revenue and profits in 1995 was mostly attributable to the low price received by the industry for natural gas in 1995 and the Company's decision to reduce U.S. production. On March 31, 1997, shareholders received word that the annual report would be delayed for what is hoped to be good news. Although the Venezuela operation was commenced on a small scale, unanticipated demand for equipment and personnel has resulted in growth far beyond managements expectations. We just have to wait for the numbers. The price per share at December 31, 1996 was $39 bid/$45 ask. Investment Classification: Value

Officers	Position	Ownership Information	
J F. Justiss, Jr.	Chairman, Exec VP	Number of Shares Outstanding	676,044
J F. Justiss, III	COO	Market Capitalization	$ 29,069,892
W B. McCartney, Jr.	Exec VP	Frequency of Dividends	n.a.
R L. Wood	Secretary, Treasurer	Number of Shareholders	Under 500
R L. Reiner	VP - Manufacturing		

Other Information			
Transfer Agent	Company Office	Where Listed	OTC-BB
Auditor	Not indicated	Symbol	JSTS
Market Maker	Robotti & Co., Inc.	(212)986-0800	SIC Code	1300
	Carr Securities Corporation	(800)220-2743	Employees	350
Broker Dealer	Regular Stockbroker		

This page intentionally left blank.

Kahiki Foods, Inc.

3583 East Broad Street   Columbus, OH 43213   Telephone (614)237-5425   Fax (614)237-3122

Company Description

Kahiki Foods, Inc., formerly Kahiki Supper Club, was organized in 1982 to acquire a full service restaurant in Columbus, Ohio. The Company completed a public offering of 120,310 shares at $8 per share in 1994, and acquired the land and building where the restaurant was situated in 1995. We asked Tyler Abrams, a food critic of local notoriety, to investigate the operation. His report was excellent overall. Staff were friendly and accommodating. The bar offers a world-class drink menu with free refills of the Polynesian specials. The appetizers and entrees are very large portions of well prepared dishes and are reasonably priced (entrees from $12 to $15). All reputable food critics always check the bathrooms. Mr. Abrams gave the mens room a five-star rating. Overall, Kahiki is highly recommended for an enjoyable and entertaining evening.

	03/31/96	03/31/95	03/31/94	03/31/93
Per Share Information				
Stock Price as of 12/31	6.50	5.00	8.00	n.a.
Earnings Per Share	-0.22	-0.13	0.02	0.19
Price / Earnings Ratio	n.a.	n.a.	400.00	n.a.
Book Value Per Share	2.05	2.27	2.06	0.09
Price / Book Value %	317.07	220.26	388.35	n.a.
Dividends Per Share	0.0	0.0	0.0	0.0
Annual Financial Data				
Operating Results (000's)				
Total Revenues	3,326.0	2,999.8	2,583.4	2,705.6
Costs & Expenses	-3,341.0	-3,071.3	-2,569.7	-2,605.0
Income Before Taxes and Other	-96.9	-85.7	10.4	95.5
Other Items	0.0	0.0	0.0	0.0
Income Tax	0.0	30.0	-2.1	-16.8
Net Income	-96.9	-55.8	8.3	78.7
Cash Flow From Operations	-31.3	-10.6	5.4	52.4
Balance Sheet (000's)				
Cash & Equivalents	61.8	44.9	62.6	20.2
Total Current Assets	407.2	352.6	865.0	131.7
Fixed Assets, Net	2,016.2	2,076.3	207.5	176.8
Total Assets	2,445.6	2,432.5	1,081.4	319.1
Total Current Liabilities	371.4	300.8	206.9	269.4
Long-Term Debt	1,160.2	1,120.7	8.5	12.6
Stockholders' Equity	914.0	1,010.9	865.9	37.0
Performance & Financial Condition				
Return on Total Revenues %	-2.91	-1.86	0.32	n.a.
Return on Avg Stockholders' Equity %	-10.07	-5.94	1.83	19.10
Return on Average Assets %	-3.97	-3.17	1.18	n.a.
Current Ratio	1.10	1.17	4.18	0.49
Debt / Equity %	126.94	110.86	0.99	34.02

Compound Growth %'s	EPS % n.a.	Net Income % n.a.	Total Revenues % 7.12

Comments

The Company also manufactures and processes frozen foods for wholesale distribution. This is the only business segment that has shown revenue growth (44% in 1996) but is operating at a loss. The restaurant shows a small profit. Investment Classification: Speculative

Officers	Position	Ownership Information	
Michael C. Tsao	President, CEO	Number of Shares Outstanding	444,785
Kenneth H. Kisner	Treasurer	Market Capitalization	$ 2,891,103
Alice W. Tsao	Vice President, Secretary	Frequency of Dividends	n.a.
Ngan Chan	Other	Number of Shareholders	Under 500

Other Information			
Transfer Agent	Fifth Third Bank Cincinnati, OH	Where Listed	OTC-BB
Auditor	Cavanaugh, Moore & Co.	Symbol	KSCI
Market Maker	Paragon Capital Corporation (800)345-0505	SIC Code	5800
		Employees	n.a.
Broker Dealer	Regular Stockbroker		

Keller Manufacturing Company, Inc.

P.O. Box 8   Corydon, IN 47112   Telephone (812)738-2222   Fax (812)738-7382

Company Description

Keller Manufacturing Company manufactures and sells quality solid wood furniture and is Harrison County's largest private employer. It has a 7,000 square foot showroom in Corydon, Indiana, and is visited by retailers around the world. We have had more calls from our subscribers regarding Keller than any other company in last year's manual. Many who chose to invest have doubled the value of their investment in one year and have thanked us. Others have called just to confirm what a neat company this is and that all contact with management has been truly pleasurable. Please enjoy our historical vignette on the opposite page.

	12/31/96	12/31/95	12/31/94	12/31/93
Per Share Information				
Stock Price	9.50	6.87	6.37	6.00
Earnings Per Share	1.19	1.04	0.75	0.45
Price / Earnings Ratio	7.98	6.61	8.49	13.33
Book Value Per Share	6.15	5.26	4.37	3.66
Price / Book Value %	154.47	130.61	145.77	163.93
Dividends Per Share	0.18	0.12	0.12	0.10
Annual Financial Data				
Operating Results (000's)				
Total Revenues	54,168.3	50,329.6	45,964.4	35,232.9
Costs & Expenses	-46,509.7	-43,470.1	-40,945.7	-32,385.4
Income Before Taxes and Other	7,658.6	6,859.6	5,018.7	2,847.5
Other Items	0.0	0.0	0.0	0.0
Income Tax	-2,988.9	-2,794.8	-2,080.4	-1,108.1
Net Income	4,669.7	4,064.8	2,938.3	1,739.4
Cash Flow From Operations	3,908.8	n.a.	n.a.	n.a.
Balance Sheet (000's)				
Cash & Equivalents	2,270.2	1,900.6	620.0	125.6
Total Current Assets	21,952.6	19,710.8	16,387.7	15,082.9
Fixed Assets, Net	7,844.1	6,847.8	5,722.9	4,872.8
Total Assets	31,137.0	27,429.8	22,895.0	20,809.3
Total Current Liabilities	5,989.2	6,180.3	5,167.8	4,412.3
Long-Term Debt	0.0	0.0	0.0	848.1
Stockholders' Equity	24,118.2	20,625.1	17,222.5	14,341.1
Performance & Financial Condition				
Return on Total Revenues %	8.62	8.08	6.39	4.94
Return on Avg Stockholders' Equity %	20.87	21.48	18.62	12.55
Return on Average Assets %	15.95	16.15	13.45	8.77
Current Ratio	3.67	3.19	3.17	3.42
Debt / Equity %	n.a.	n.a.	n.a.	5.91

Compound Growth %'s	EPS %	38.29	Net Income %	38.98	Total Revenues %	15.42

Comments

The Company declared a 2 for 1 stock split effective on Valentine's Day, 1997. All per share amounts have been adjusted to be consistent with current pricing. Company has shown excellent growth over the last several years and has the financial strength to accommodate more. Keller shares have outperformed all leading indices and in the last eleven years the stock has been accumulatively split 120 for 1. So what else do you want to know about this stock that trades at less than ten times earnings? Investment Classification: Growth

Officers	Position	Ownership Information	
William H. Keller	Chairman	Number of Shares Outstanding	3,922,402
Robert Byrd	President, CEO	Market Capitalization	$ 37,262,819
Danny Utz	VP - Finance, CFO	Frequency of Dividends	Quarterly
		Number of Shareholders	Under 500

Other Information			
Transfer Agent	Company Office	Where Listed	OTC-BB
Auditor	Deloitte & Touche LLP	Symbol	KMFC
Market Maker	JJB Hilliard, WL Lyons, Inc. (800)627-3557	SIC Code	2510
		Employees	680
Broker Dealer	Regular Stockbroker		
	Jim Stuckert (800)444-1854		

Farm Wagons

The Keller Manufacturing Company has a long history that includes many successes and well as financial challenges. Their story begins with John L. Keller's immigration to the United States from Germany in 1846. Penniless upon arrival, he made his way from New York to his sister's home in Indiana, traveling in the company of a freed slave and working for food and lodging en route. Keller decided to remain in Harrison County and began to sell housewares as a country pack peddler. His business eventually developed into a store and in 1866, the business moved to its present location in Corydon, Indiana.

The manufacturing company started up in 1900 with the production of wagon spokes. By 1901 *Corydon and Keller* farm wagons were the company's main products. The high quality of these wagons was recognized by International Harvester Company, who negotiated an agreement for Keller to produce wagons for them as well. With this and other successes, Keller's domestic and international markets grew during the 1920's. By 1929, sales of 12,615 wagons and farm truck parts produced record profits of $622,245.

But the prosperity of these years was fleeting indeed. Merely three years later, now mired in the Great Depression, Keller's customer base became virtually nonexistent and cash was depleted. Fortunately, International Harvester was able to come to the rescue with a $15,000 loan. Keller hung on.

By 1936 it was producing all of the wagons sold worldwide by International Harvester, but even as matters improved Keller was thinking ahead, anticipating the bleak prospects of the wagon business. With this in mind the company launched its business in the manufacture of dining room furniture in 1943. Roller-coaster-like operating results were reported over the ensuing decade, but by 1953 profits were at record levels. In the ten years ending in 1955, Keller's sales had doubled to $2,000,000.

Plants were built in Virginia and Indiana so that manufacture could keep pace with customer demand. Eventually, Keller expanded production to include bedroom furniture, and a product line made of cheaper lumber which is aimed at the price sensitive but quality conscious consumer was added as well. Sales have continued to grow and reached $54,000,000 in 1996, capping records set in each of the four preceding years.

The company had plenty to celebrate in 1995, not the least of which was C.E.O. William H. Keller's fiftieth anniversary with the firm. A special edition rocking chair was created to honor Mr. Keller, and it has proven to have broad appeal with the company's customer base. Such a symbol of rest and relaxation commemorating years of hard work seems an interesting study in contrasts, but we bet that the people at Keller aren't the ones relaxing. Clearly they keep their corporate ear to the ground and are undoubtedly strategizing even now for their next hundred years.

Kentucky Investors, Inc.

200 Capital Avenue Frankfort, KY 40602 Telephone (502)223-2361 Fax (502)227-7205

Company Description

The Company is the holding company of a 74% interest in Investors Heritage Life Insurance Company (Investors Heritage), Investors Heritage Printing Company, and Investors Heritage Financial Services Group, Inc. Investors Heritage, which is featured elsewhere in this book, comprises most of the Company's operations. Investors Heritage sells and administers various insurance and annuity products including various types of life insurance, preneed and final expense life insurance, annuity contracts, credit accident and health group insurance policies. The Company was founded in 1963.

	12/31/96	12/31/95	12/31/94	12/31/93
Per Share Information				
Stock Price	13.00	13.25	13.00	13.00
Earnings Per Share	1.41	0.71	1.97	1.55
Price / Earnings Ratio	9.22	18.66	6.60	8.39
Book Value Per Share	29.70	30.38	23.54	26.31
Price / Book Value %	43.77	43.61	55.23	49.41
Dividends Per Share	0.38	0.38	0.37	0.36
Annual Financial Data				
Operating Results (000's)				
Total Revenues	47,961.7	44,004.6	46,655.7	45,387.6
Costs & Expenses	-46,319.6	-43,190.9	-44,039.4	-43,091.2
Income Before Taxes and Other	1,642.0	813.8	2,616.3	2,296.4
Other Items	-418.4	-239.8	-632.6	-681.6
Income Tax	-77.0	-19.0	-461.0	-422.0
Net Income	1,146.6	554.9	1,522.7	1,192.8
Cash Flow From Operations	15,583.4	11,744.0	9,953.1	13,187.7
Balance Sheet (000's)				
Cash & Equivalents	2,684.5	2,417.4	2,336.7	3,067.7
Total Current Assets	10,275.0	12,935.1	17,273.3	27,812.2
Fixed Assets, Net	1,990.9	1,881.0	1,955.2	2,163.0
Total Assets	224,997.4	208,045.1	191,367.0	198,230.0
Total Current Liabilities	3,528.3	7,827.4	4,651.9	9,086.5
Long-Term Debt	0.0	0.0	0.0	0.0
Stockholders' Equity	24,157.8	24,641.5	18,357.4	20,306.2
Performance & Financial Condition				
Return on Total Revenues %	2.39	1.26	3.26	2.63
Return on Avg Stockholders' Equity %	4.70	2.58	7.88	6.00
Return on Average Assets %	0.53	0.28	0.78	0.65
Current Ratio	2.91	1.65	3.71	3.06
Debt / Equity %	n.a.	n.a.	n.a.	n.a.

Compound Growth %'s	EPS %	-3.11	Net Income %	-1.31	Total Revenues %	1.86

Comments

As insurance premium sales set a record for the third consecutive year and for the fifth out of six years. It is no wonder that 1996 was one of the best years ever for the Company. Please refer to Investors Heritage for comments on its operations. Interesting is the pricing of these two stocks as compared to one another. This Company trades at a substantial discount from the pricing of Investors Heritage when looking at the price/earnings ratio and price/book value %. We cannot find a good reason for these stocks not to trade close to parity with one another. Investment Classification: Value

Officers	Position	Ownership Information	
Harry Lee Waterfield II	President, CEO	Number of Shares Outstanding	813,401
Wilma Yeary	Secretary	Market Capitalization	$ 10,574,213
Jimmy R. McIver	Treasurer	Frequency of Dividends	Annual
Howard L. Graham	Vice President	Number of Shareholders	2,515
Nancy W. Walton	Vice President		

Other Information				
Transfer Agent	Company Office		Where Listed	OTC-BB
Auditor	Ernst & Young LLP		Symbol	KINV
Market Maker	Hilliard, Lyons, Inc.	(800)627-3557	SIC Code	6311
	Howe Barnes Investments, Inc.	(800)621-2364	Employees	119
Broker Dealer	Regular Stockbroker			

Kentucky River Coal Corporation

200 West Vine Street, Ste. 8-K   Lexington, KY 40507   Telephone (606)254-8498   Fax (606)255-9362

Company Description

Kentucky River Coal Company is primarily engaged in leasing mineral reserves and, to a lesser degree, participating in partnerships and joint ventures which explore for and develop oil and gas properties. The majority of the Company's revenue-producing properties are located in eastern Kentucky. Management states that "the main objective of the Company over the years has been to provide a stable and growing source of dividend income for the shareholders while utilizing retained earnings to build value for the future."

	12/31/96	12/31/95	12/31/94	12/31/93
Per Share Information				
Stock Price	2,780.00	2,700.00	3,175.00	3,125.00
Earnings Per Share	296.31	322.51	259.01	236.22
Price / Earnings Ratio	9.38	8.37	12.26	13.23
Book Value Per Share	1,300.35	1,208.54	1,056.55	1,037.57
Price / Book Value %	213.79	223.41	300.51	301.18
Dividends Per Share	215.00	200.00	195.00	170.00
Annual Financial Data				
Operating Results (000's)				
Total Revenues	42,662.0	46,428.0	36,848.0	36,981.0
Costs & Expenses	-6,784.0	-6,812.0	-6,841.0	-7,987.0
Income Before Taxes and Other	35,878.0	39,616.0	30,007.0	28,994.0
Other Items	0.0	0.0	0.0	0.0
Income Tax	-13,005.0	-14,453.0	-10,320.0	-9,980.0
Net Income	22,873.0	25,163.0	19,687.0	19,014.0
Cash Flow From Operations	10,434.0	14,736.0	13,513.0	20,080.0
Balance Sheet (000's)				
Cash & Equivalents	6,688.0	3,967.0	4,714.0	12,084.0
Total Current Assets	87,874.0	78,337.0	61,516.0	47,304.0
Fixed Assets, Net	10,538.0	11,490.0	12,462.0	13,180.0
Total Assets	111,609.0	102,282.0	85,979.0	85,179.0
Total Current Liabilities	566.0	568.0	1,242.0	808.0
Long-Term Debt	0.0	0.0	0.0	0.0
Stockholders' Equity	99,773.0	94,296.0	82,437.0	83,263.0
Performance & Financial Condition				
Return on Total Revenues %	53.61	54.20	53.43	51.42
Return on Avg Stockholders' Equity %	23.57	28.48	23.76	23.41
Return on Average Assets %	21.39	26.73	23.00	22.78
Current Ratio	155.25	137.92	49.53	58.54
Debt / Equity %	n.a.	n.a.	n.a.	n.a.

Compound Growth %'s	EPS %	7.85	Net Income %	6.35	Total Revenues %	4.88

Comments

Production and price levels for coal were lower in 1996 causing a decline in net earnings. Oil and gas revenues increased 16%. Deregulation of the utilities industry is expected to increase the demand for coal although the pricing may see further downward pressure. The Company is managing other assets successfully with an investment portfolio that has outperformed the overall market. The Company has always maintained a sound balance sheet and followed conservative accounting practices. Kentucky River Coal is well positioned to capitalize on changes in the market place. Investment Classification: Income & Value

Officers	Position	Ownership Information	
Catesby W. Clay	Chairman	Number of Shares Outstanding	76,728
James G. Kenan III	President, CEO	Market Capitalization	$ 213,303,840
Carroll R. Crouch	Secretary	Frequency of Dividends	Quarterly
Gary I. Conley	Vice President	Number of Shareholders	Under 500
Fred N. Parker	Vice President, Treasurer		

Other Information				
Transfer Agent	Company Office		Where Listed	OTC-BB
Auditor	KPMG Peat Marwick LLP		Symbol	KRIV
Market Maker	Robotti & Co., Inc.	(212)986-0800	SIC Code	1200
	Sharpe Capital Inc.	(800)355-5781	Employees	10
Broker Dealer	Regular Stockbroker			

Kerman State Bank

306 S. Madera Avenue   Kerman, CA 93630   Telephone (209)846-5321   Fax (209)846-7226

Company Description

Since it began business in 1983, the Bank's business activity has been primarily with customers located in the central San Joaquin Valley. Although the Bank has a diversified loan portfolio, a significant portion of its customers' ability to repay the loans is dependent upon the agricultural sector. This is evidenced by the fact that its customer base is centralized in the largest agricultural producing area in the world as well as by the annual report which quotes Daniel Webster: "Let us never forget that the cultivation of the earth is the most important labor of man. When tillage begins, other arts follow. The farmers, therefore, are the founders of civilization."

	12/31/96	12/31/95	12/31/94	12/31/93
Per Share Information				
Stock Price	12.50	14.81	13.74	8.21
Earnings Per Share	0.96	1.11	10.08	0.86
Price / Earnings Ratio	13.02	13.34	1.36	9.55
Book Value Per Share	7.02	6.82	6.19	5.41
Price / Book Value %	178.06	217.16	221.97	151.76
Dividends Per Share	0.74	0.47	0.22	0.20
Annual Financial Data				
Operating Results (000's)				
Net Interest Income	4,058.6	3,902.9	3,612.5	3,153.6
Loan Loss Provision	0.0	-120.0	-80.0	-60.0
Non-Interest Income	517.8	614.2	626.9	543.1
Non-Interest Expense	-2,486.5	-1,988.9	-1,940.4	-1,797.6
Income Before Taxes and Other	2,089.9	2,408.1	2,219.0	1,839.1
Other Items	0.0	0.0	0.0	0.0
Income Tax	-710.2	-880.5	-798.8	-620.8
Net Income	1,379.7	1,527.6	1,420.1	1,218.3
Balance Sheet (000's)				
Cash & Securities	28,441.5	26,471.7	22,066.6	23,076.2
Loans, Net	51,463.5	48,983.7	47,839.3	46,207.6
Total Assets	84,092.7	80,202.8	74,362.4	74,388.7
Deposits	73,779.0	70,147.4	65,217.5	66,347.9
Stockholders' Equity	10,121.5	9,793.1	8,844.6	7,727.3
Performance & Financial Condition				
Return on Avg Stockholders' Equity %	13.86	16.39	17.14	16.78
Return on Average Assets %	1.68	1.98	1.91	1.73
Equity to Assets %	12.04	12.21	11.89	10.39
Net Interest Margin	n.a.	n.a.	n.a.	n.a.
Reserve as a % of Problem Loans	183.96	133.96	93.06	n.a.

Compound Growth %'s	EPS %	3.73	Net Income %	4.24	Net Interest Income %	8.77

Comments

The Bank declared a 2 for 1 stock split in 1994 and 3%, 6%, 6% and 6% stock dividends in 1996, 1995, 1994 and 1993, respectively. All per share amounts have been restated for consistency. 1996 would have been a record year if not for a property writedown of $440,000. A loan production office, opened in Easton in November, 1996, should fuel growth as well as non-interest income as some loans are sold in the secondary market. Investment Classification: Income

Officers	Position	Ownership Information	
Ed Lelandais	President, CEO	Number of Shares Outstanding	1,441,562
Pete Susoev	Exec VP, CFO	Market Capitalization	$ 18,019,525
John R. Royal	Senior VP, Sr Loan Officer	Frequency of Dividends	Semi-Annual
Cathy E. Ponte	Vice President	Number of Shareholders	n.a.
		Where Listed / Symbol	OTC-PS / KMSC

Other Information			Loan Mix	%
Transfer Agent	First Interstate Bank of California Los Angeles, CA		Commerical	49.2
Auditor	Smith & Wilcox		R/E Mortgages	44.8
Market Maker	Hoefer & Arnett, Incorporated	(800)346-5544	Installment	6.0
	A.G. Edwards & Sons, Inc.	(800)325-8197		
Broker Dealer	Regular Stockbroker			
	Hoefer & Arnett, Retail	(800)346-5544 Ext: Lisa		

Keweenaw Land Association, Limited

1801 East Cloverland Drive   Ironwood, MI 49938   Telephone (906)932-3410   Fax (906)932-5823

Company Description

The Company owns and harvests logs on 155,435 acres of forested property in the Upper Peninsula of Michigan. These wood types are classified primarily as "northern hardwoods." Substantial revenue is also generated from land and mineral leases. The Company has been certified as "well managed" by Smartwood, a national program concerned with land management policy. Keweenaw Land Association reacquired approximately 10% of outstanding common shares over the last three years.

	12/31/96	12/31/95	12/31/94	12/31/93
Per Share Information				
Stock Price	36.00	37.00	36.25	30.00
Earnings Per Share	1.32	2.08	2.01	1.62
Price / Earnings Ratio	27.27	17.79	18.03	18.52
Book Value Per Share	17.60	17.32	17.03	15.57
Price / Book Value %	204.55	213.63	212.86	192.68
Dividends Per Share	0.80	0.80	0.80	0.80
Annual Financial Data				
Operating Results (000's)				
Total Revenues	6,469.5	6,027.4	5,177.4	4,341.2
Costs & Expenses	-4,700.6	-3,506.9	-2,558.6	-2,463.5
Income Before Taxes and Other	1,433.9	2,255.8	2,286.2	1,877.7
Other Items	0.0	0.0	0.0	0.0
Income Tax	-483.1	-691.7	-720.3	-567.0
Net Income	950.8	1,564.1	1,565.8	1,310.7
Cash Flow From Operations	703.1	1,509.8	1,232.8	1,214.8
Balance Sheet (000's)				
Cash & Equivalents	267.4	348.5	2,700.1	1,216.6
Total Current Assets	2,586.8	3,284.3	6,131.2	9,699.2
Fixed Assets, Net	8,170.0	8,226.9	5,141.9	801.8
Total Assets	13,161.6	14,336.7	13,740.2	12,593.4
Total Current Liabilities	346.8	494.1	319.5	407.9
Long-Term Debt	0.0	0.0	0.0	0.0
Stockholders' Equity	12,384.1	13,405.4	13,183.6	12,170.9
Performance & Financial Condition				
Return on Total Revenues %	14.70	25.95	30.24	30.19
Return on Avg Stockholders' Equity %	7.37	11.77	12.35	11.08
Return on Average Assets %	6.92	11.14	11.89	10.68
Current Ratio	7.46	6.65	19.19	23.78
Debt / Equity %	n.a.	n.a.	n.a.	n.a.

Compound Growth %'s	EPS %	-6.60	Net Income %	-10.15	Total Revenues %	14.22

Comments

The Company declared a 2 for 1 stock split in 1995. All per share amounts have been adjusted for consistency. Adequate financial strength is maintained for the purpose of property acquisitions. Management has a philosophy of "no net loss of productive timberlands." Noncurrent assets are predominantly comprised of marketable securities. 1995 was the last year of royalty income from the White Pine mine, amounting to over $900,000. The absence of this is the cause of lower 1996 earnings. Timber revenues are expected to increase in 1997 if the market remains stable. Investment Classification: Value

Officers	Position	Ownership Information	
David Ayer	Chairman	Number of Shares Outstanding	703,796
David E. McDonald	Secretary	Market Capitalization	$ 25,336,656
Alan W. Steege	General Manager	Frequency of Dividends	Quarterly
Robert M. Davenport	Controller	Number of Shareholders	Under 500

Other Information			
Transfer Agent	Norwest Shareowner Services South St. Paul, MN	Where Listed	OTC-BB
Auditor	Anderson, Tackman & Company	Symbol	KEWL
Market Maker	A.G. Edwards & Sons, Inc.	(314)289-3000	SIC Code	2410
	Carr Securities Corporation	(800)221-2243	Employees	17
Broker Dealer	Regular Stockbroker		

Kiewit Royalty Trust

FirsTier Bank - 17th & Farnam   Omaha, NE 68102   Telephone (402)348-6000   Fax (402)348-6674

Company Description

The Trust was created in 1982 by Peter Kiewit Sons', Inc. and was organized to provide an efficient, orderly and practical means for the administration of income received from royalty and overriding royalty interests it owned in certain coal leases in Wyoming and Montana. The Trust has no officers or employees and is administered by a trustee, Firstier Bank NA, who collects all income, pays expenses and distributes the remainder to the unit holders quarterly.

	12/31/96	12/31/95	12/31/94	12/31/93
Per Share Information				
Stock Price as of 12/29	6.25	6.25	5.63	5.00
Earnings Per Share	0.46	0.60	0.62	0.66
Price / Earnings Ratio	13.59	10.42	9.08	7.58
Book Value Per Share	0.01	0.01	0.01	0.01
Price / Book Value %	62,500.00	62,500.00	56,300.00	50,000.00
Dividends Per Share	0.46	0.60	0.62	0.66
Annual Financial Data				
Operating Results (000's)				
Total Revenues	5,830.0	7,581.1	7,954.5	8,348.3
Costs & Expenses	-49.6	-47.0	-63.7	-61.2
Income Before Taxes and Other	5,780.3	7,534.1	7,890.8	8,287.1
Other Items	0.0	0.0	0.0	0.0
Income Tax	0.0	0.0	0.0	0.0
Net Income	5,780.3	7,534.1	7,890.8	8,287.1
Cash Flow From Operations	5,780.3	7,534.1	7,890.8	8,287.1
Balance Sheet (000's)				
Cash & Equivalents	244.3	162.0	398.6	383.0
Total Current Assets	335.2	258.9	507.4	512.4
Fixed Assets, Net	0.0	0.0	0.0	0.0
Total Assets	335.2	258.9	507.4	512.4
Total Current Liabilities	244.3	162.0	398.6	383.0
Long-Term Debt	0.0	0.0	0.0	0.0
Stockholders' Equity	90.9	96.9	108.8	129.4
Performance & Financial Condition				
Return on Total Revenues %	99.15	99.38	99.20	99.27
Return on Avg Stockholders' Equity %	6,155.31	7,323.83	6,624.86	6,332.52
Return on Average Assets %	1,945.92	1,966.17	1,547.43	1,312.38
Current Ratio	1.37	1.60	1.27	1.34
Debt / Equity %	n.a.	n.a.	n.a.	n.a.

Compound Growth %'s	EPS % -11.34	Net Income % -11.32	Total Revenues % -11.28

Comments

The Trust's operations and financial position clearly do not lend themselves to traditional analysis. However, based on the quoted unit prices and historical distributions, the units may be a worthwhile investment. Potential investors would, among other things, need to know the size of the coal reserves, the length of time left on the underlying coal leases, whether or not there are any renewal options and what the projected earnings of the royalty interests are for the future. Estimated reserves declined 4% during 1996. The deregulation of the utilities industry is expected to increase the demand for coal. Investment Classification: Income

Officers	Position	Ownership Information	
Not Available		Number of Shares Outstanding	12,633,432
		Market Capitalization	$ 78,958,950
		Frequency of Dividends	Quarterly
		Number of Shareholders	808

Other Information

Transfer Agent	First Bank N.A. Omaha,		Where Listed	OTC-BB
Auditor	Coopers & Lybrand L.L.P.		Symbol	KIRY
Market Maker	Hill Thompson Magid & Co., Inc	(800)631-3083	SIC Code	6795
	The Chicago Corporation	(800)323-1225	Employees	n.a.
Broker Dealer	OTC Specialist			

King Kullen Grocery Co., Inc.

1194 Prospect Avenue   Westbury, NY 11590-2798   Telephone (516)333-7100   Fax (516)333-0012

Company Description

The Company operates a chain of 54 supermarkets in the counties of Queens, Nassau, and Suffolk, all in the New York. Store sizes range from 9,000 to 43,800 square feet. It also owns its own grocery, meat and produce warehouses as well as of a fleet of 15 tractors and 112 trailers. The Company owns two store locations and a 33 acre property in Westbury, New York, the site of its office and warehouse. The Company was formed in 1930, went public in 1961, and is now buying back shares.

	09/28/96	09/30/95	10/01/94	10/02/93
Per Share Information				
Stock Price as of 12/31	90.00	84.50	68.00	68.00
Earnings Per Share	9.14	8.04	10.16	5.58
Price / Earnings Ratio	9.85	10.51	6.69	12.19
Book Value Per Share	122.61	101.99	109.19	99.96
Price / Book Value %	76.67	82.85	62.28	68.03
Dividends Per Share	1.00	0.50	0.50	0.50
Annual Financial Data				
Operating Results (000's)				
Total Revenues	723,896.0	702,780.0	723,372.0	702,279.0
Costs & Expenses	-719,220.0	-698,455.0	-717,897.5	-699,145.0
Income Before Taxes and Other	4,676.0	4,325.0	5,474.5	3,134.0
Other Items	n.a.	n.a.	283.5	n.a.
Income Tax	n.a.	n.a.	n.a.	n.a.
Net Income	4,676.0	4,325.0	5,758.0	3,134.0
Cash Flow From Operations	n.a.	13,801.0	14,797.0	11,089.0
Balance Sheet (000's)				
Cash & Equivalents	n.a.	n.a.	n.a.	n.a.
Total Current Assets	57,647.0	58,901.0	61,175.0	60,506.0
Fixed Assets, Net	n.a.	n.a.	n.a.	n.a.
Total Assets	169,495.0	157,152.0	155,179.0	149,701.0
Total Current Liabilities	70,078.0	57,131.0	56,839.0	57,510.0
Long-Term Debt	20,000.0	20,000.0	20,000.0	20,000.0
Stockholders' Equity	60,078.0	54,862.0	61,883.0	56,144.0
Performance & Financial Condition				
Return on Total Revenues %	0.65	0.62	0.80	0.45
Return on Avg Stockholders' Equity %	8.14	7.41	9.76	n.a.
Return on Average Assets %	2.86	2.77	3.78	n.a.
Current Ratio	0.82	1.03	1.08	1.05
Debt / Equity %	33.29	36.46	32.32	35.62

Compound Growth %'s	EPS %	17.88	Net Income %	14.27	Total Revenues %	1.02

Comments

Only summary information is extracted from the financial statements for the report to shareholders although the Company's auditor expressed an unqualified opinion that the report was accurate. The Company uses LIFO for calculating inventory. Had FIFO been used, the inventory would have been higher by $6.6 million, $6.6 million, $6.2 million and $5.8 million in 1996, 1995, 1994 and 1993, respectively. We estimate cash flow from operations to be in excess of $30 per share. Investment Classification: Value

Officers	Position	Ownership Information	
J. Donald Kennedy	Exec VP, CFO	Number of Shares Outstanding	490,000
Bernard P. Kennedy	Secretary	Market Capitalization	$ 46,058,400
Eugene C. Kennedy	Director	Frequency of Dividends	Annual
Ronald E. Brackett	Director	Number of Shareholders	Under 500
Ronald Conklin	Director		

Other Information				
Transfer Agent	Chemical Bank New York, NY		Where Listed	OTC-BB
Auditor	Grant Thornton LLP		Symbol	KKGR
Market Maker	Tweedy Browne Company L.P.	(212)916-0606	SIC Code	5410
	Carr Securities Corporation	(800)221-2243	Employees	4000
Broker Dealer	OTC Specialist			

This page intentionally left blank.

Kish Bancorp, Inc.

310 East Main Street Belleville, PA 17004 Telephone (717)935-2191 Fax (717)935-5511

Company Description

The Company is the bank holding company of Kishacoquillas Valley National Bank, also referred to as Kish Bank. The Bank provides a full range of banking services to individual and corporate customers in central Pennsylvania. It also offers mutual fund sales and trust and investment services. In 1997, annuities, life insurance, brokerage services, expanded mutual fund sales and property and casualty insurance will be introduced. An advisory board is active in assisting the Bank develop a presence in Huntingdon County. Site selection is in progress. The Bank began business in 1935.

	12/31/96	12/31/95	12/31/94	12/31/93
Per Share Information				
Stock Price	71.00	49.50	42.00	36.50
Earnings Per Share	6.58	5.75	4.92	4.81
Price / Earnings Ratio	10.79	8.61	8.54	7.59
Book Value Per Share	41.41	36.68	30.86	28.01
Price / Book Value %	171.46	134.95	136.10	130.31
Dividends Per Share	1.80	1.55	1.30	1.10
Annual Financial Data				
Operating Results (000's)				
Net Interest Income	5,726.2	5,262.5	4,812.3	4,478.1
Loan Loss Provision	-118.0	-84.0	-60.0	-90.0
Non-Interest Income	623.0	492.4	450.8	469.2
Non-Interest Expense	-3,480.8	-3,317.8	-3,163.6	-2,949.5
Income Before Taxes and Other	2,750.4	2,353.0	2,039.4	1,907.7
Other Items	0.0	0.0	0.0	67.5
Income Tax	-798.0	-652.8	-577.1	-539.9
Net Income	1,952.4	1,700.2	1,462.3	1,435.3
Balance Sheet (000's)				
Cash & Securities	30,380.8	28,179.2	24,447.2	22,575.0
Loans, Net	101,240.8	93,609.3	88,309.1	78,676.9
Total Assets	135,721.4	125,847.4	116,708.4	104,622.7
Deposits	115,161.4	109,475.5	103,408.0	94,130.7
Stockholders' Equity	12,365.6	10,840.9	9,129.0	8,339.1
Performance & Financial Condition				
Return on Avg Stockholders' Equity %	16.83	17.03	16.74	18.42
Return on Average Assets %	1.49	1.40	1.32	1.43
Equity to Assets %	9.11	8.61	7.82	7.97
Net Interest Margin	n.a.	n.a.	n.a.	n.a.
Reserve as a % of Problem Loans	9,717.72	9,412.51	n.a.	2,200.31

Compound Growth %'s	EPS %	11.01	Net Income %	10.80	Net Interest Income %	8.54

Comments

Per share price information is provided by the Company based on actual transactions. These prices are higher than those posted by the market makers but are more representative of fair market value. 1996 was the Corporation's twelfth consecutive year of record profits. Growth in loans ended the year on a strong upward trend. Loan originations were also strong at year end. Management reports excellent loan quality. Investment Classification: Growth

Officers	Position	Ownership Information	
William P. Hayes	President, CEO	Number of Shares Outstanding	298,577
James Shilling, Jr.	Exec VP	Market Capitalization	$ 21,198,967
Donald Smith	Senior VP, Head Cashier	Frequency of Dividends	Semi-Annual
Scott R. Reigle	VP - Finance	Number of Shareholders	413
John A. Cook	VP - Sales	Where Listed / Symbol	OTC-BB / KISB

Other Information			Loan Mix	%
Transfer Agent	Company Office		R/E Mortgages	44.5
Auditor	Boyer & Ritter		Commerical	31.9
Market Maker	F.J. Morrissey & Co., Inc.	(800)842-8928	Installment	19.8
	W.H. Newbold's Son & Co., Inc.	(800)388-3900	Construction	0.9
Broker Dealer	OTC Specialist		Other	2.9
	Dennis Reynolds - Ryan, Beck	(888)231-7226		

Kohler Co.

444 Highland Drive   Kohler, WI 53044   Telephone (414)457-4441   Fax (414)459-1656

Company Description

The Company is an international manufacturer of plumbing products, furniture, engines and generators. These products are marketed through a wide variety of distribution channels. The Company also owns and operates a number of hospitality and real estate businesses in Kohler, Wisconsin. Shares were subject to a 1 for 20 reverse split in 1978. The stock usually trades by auction with only a handful of market makers and broker/dealers involved. Please enjoy a capsule of the history of this great American company, displayed on the opposite page.

	12/31/95	12/31/94	12/31/93	12/31/92
Per Share Information				
Stock Price	125,000.00	90,000.00	80,000.00	75,000.00
Earnings Per Share	7,052.00	8,821.00	2,046.00	6,093.00
Price / Earnings Ratio	17.73	10.20	39.10	12.31
Book Value Per Share	86,936.21	79,479.55	71,238.71	70,344.54
Price / Book Value %	143.78	113.24	112.30	106.62
Dividends Per Share	750.00	850.00	600.00	600.00
Annual Financial Data				
Operating Results (000's)				
Total Revenues	1,833,901.9	1,771,959.2	1,542,113.8	1,472,470.4
Costs & Expenses	-1,721,936.2	-1,636,366.0	-1,442,068.9	-1,391,157.6
Income Before Taxes and Other	94,599.9	113,674.6	80,111.6	78,927.0
Other Items	0.0	0.0	-32,984.2	0.0
Income Tax	-41,199.8	-46,954.9	-31,648.2	-32,818.0
Net Income	53,400.1	66,719.7	15,479.2	46,109.0
Cash Flow From Operations	96,537.4	98,813.3	109,298.4	131,774.2
Balance Sheet (000's)				
Cash & Equivalents	22,329.1	32,955.1	46,252.3	16,009.5
Total Current Assets	626,122.1	583,531.2	540,686.5	482,936.7
Fixed Assets, Net	425,764.2	372,469.0	364,557.2	348,512.0
Total Assets	1,266,465.4	1,099,990.9	1,052,047.8	957,154.7
Total Current Liabilities	281,999.5	251,473.7	262,153.9	254,578.9
Long-Term Debt	202,138.4	132,208.9	140,601.1	104,901.0
Stockholders' Equity	658,281.0	601,183.3	538,992.1	532,156.5
Performance & Financial Condition				
Return on Total Revenues %	2.91	3.77	1.00	3.13
Return on Avg Stockholders' Equity %	8.48	11.70	2.89	8.99
Return on Average Assets %	4.51	6.20	1.54	4.78
Current Ratio	2.22	2.32	2.06	1.90
Debt / Equity %	30.71	21.99	26.09	19.71

Compound Growth %'s	EPS % 4.99	Net Income % 5.02	Total Revenues % 7.59

Comments

1993 results include a $33 million charge to change the method of accounting for postretirement benefits. During 1995, the Company acquired the assets of a domestic manufacturer of mirrored bathroom wall cabinets, acquired a French manufacturer of synthetic baths, whirlpools, and kitchen sinks, and entered into a joint venture with a Chinese manufacturer of vitreous china products. In January, 1996, the Company acquired a Canadian manufacturer of kitchen and bathroom cabinets. 1996 results were not available when we went to press. The annual report is usually available by July. Investment Classification: Value

Officers	Position	Ownership Information	
Herbert V. Kohler, Jr.	Chairman, President	Number of Shares Outstanding	7,572
George R. Tiedens	Senior VP	Market Capitalization	$ 946,500,000
Richard A. Wells	VP - Finance, CFO	Frequency of Dividends	Quarterly
William J. Drew	Secretary	Number of Shareholders	Under 500
Jeffrey P. Cheney	Vice President, Treasurer		

Other Information				
Transfer Agent	Company Office		Where Listed	OTC-PS
Auditor	Arthur Andersen LLP		Symbol	KHCO
Market Maker	Howe Barnes Investments, Inc.	(800)621-2364	SIC Code	3430
	Sharpe Capital Inc.	(800)355-5781	Employees	6000
Broker Dealer	OTC Specialist			
	Standard Investment	(888)783-4688 Ext: Jack		

The Kitchen Sink

How often have you returned from your travels around the world longing for your own commodious, well-equipped bathroom? Americans have John Michael Kohler to thank for these particular creature comforts of ours. When he immigrated from Austria to the United States in the late nineteenth century, Paris had only just constructed sewers and water lines in the decade between 1860-1870. Parisians may not have been enthusiastic about these new conveniences, but Kohler had the vision to embrace a new trend, and began to create bathtubs by applying enamel to cast-iron horse drinking troughs. As it turned out, many people appreciated a hot bath in 1874 as much as we do today, and so America's love affair with the bathroom was born.

Contemporary Americans have come to expect that the bathroom be a key component of their home and a showplace as well. Kohler continues to meet that expectation to this day with style, dominating the American bathroom fixture market and selling overseas in Europe and China. They were the first to manufacture fixtures in colors other than white, viewing their products as elements of furniture design suites. New York's Metropolitan Museum of Art must have agreed, for they put Kohler's innovation on display themselves.

This commitment to quality is undoubtedly one of the traits that helps enable Kohler Co. to stay way ahead of their closest competition, including American Standard, Crane Co., and Eljer Industries. Their 1995 earnings of $53 million on sales of $1.8 billion speak to their success. In addition to bathroom fixtures, Kohler also produces fine furniture, engines and generators and develops real estate. An impressive example of the latter enterprise is the resort complex in Kohler, Wisconsin, which includes the American Club Hotel, a tennis and sports club, a hunting preserve, a spa, a restaurant, shops and two Blackwolf Run golf courses designed by Pete Dye.

Design of the town of Kohler, Wisconsin as a whole was also taken under a Kohler's wing when, in 1917, Walter Kohler, the founder's son, hired the Olmstead Brothers to create a plan for a nurturing environment for Kohler employees. The family has remained committed to the town and remain personal residents themselves. Additional modernization was undertaken in 1977 when Herbert Kohler Jr. hired the Frank Lloyd Wright Foundation to plan for the future of Kohler.

After 123 years of operations, Kohler Co. remains largely privately held by family and employees and is managed by the fourth generation of the Kohler family, but potential estate tax issues could impact the fifth generation's ability to remain closely held. An exciting and forward looking company, Kohler is definitely one to watch as it and we approach the twenty-first century.

LAACO, Ltd.

431 West Seventh Street   Los Angeles, CA 90014-1601   Telephone (213)625-2211   Fax (213)689-1194

Company Description

The Company is a California limited partnership engaged in the ownership and operation of the Los Angeles Athletic Club, the California Yacht Club, and real estate investment and leasing operations. It also owns and operates 17 self storage facilities (located in southern California, Las Vegas, Portland, and Phoenix) and approximately 1,600 acres of partially developed land in the Topanga Canyon area of Los Angeles County. Formed in 1905, the corporate structure was changed to that of a limited partnership in 1986.

	12/31/96	12/31/95	12/31/94	12/31/93
Per Unit Information				
Price Per Unit	281.00	274.50	263.00	245.00
Earnings Per Unit	18.67	40.82	24.40	22.19
Price / Earnings Ratio	15.05	6.72	10.78	11.04
Book Value Per Unit	292.89	295.22	277.90	273.50
Price / Book Value %	95.94	92.98	94.64	89.58
Distributions Per Unit	21.00	23.50	20.00	25.25
Cash Flow Per Unit	36.47	41.93	32.48	48.82
Annual Financial Data				
Operating Results (000's)				
Total Revenues	24,755.0	26,790.0	23,959.0	23,110.0
Costs & Expenses	-20,762.0	-19,610.0	-19,666.0	-20,303.0
Operating Income	3,284.0	7,180.0	4,293.0	2,807.0
Other Items	0.0	0.0	0.0	1,096.0
Net Income	3,284.0	7,180.0	4,293.0	3,903.0
Cash Flow From Operations	6,416.0	7,375.0	5,713.0	8,588.0
Balance Sheet (000's)				
Cash & Equivalents	170.0	373.0	1,620.0	1,167.0
Total Current Assets	7,029.0	18,882.0	16,664.0	16,263.0
Investments	n.a.	n.a.	n.a.	n.a.
Total Assets	62,323.0	60,726.0	57,307.0	56,462.0
Total Current Liabilities	7,655.0	4,058.0	3,784.0	3,736.0
Long-Term Debt	500.0	3,221.0	3,276.0	3,347.0
Partners' Capital	51,521.0	51,931.0	48,885.0	48,110.0
Performance & Financial Condition				
Return on Total Revenues %	13.27	26.80	17.92	16.89
Return on Average Partners' Capital %	6.35	14.24	8.85	8.07
Return on Average Assets %	5.34	12.17	7.55	6.91
Current Ratio	0.92	4.65	4.40	4.35
Debt / Equity %	0.97	6.20	6.70	6.96

Compound Growth %'s	EPU %	-5.59	Net Income %	-5.59	Total Revenues %	2.32

Comments

The expansion of self storage operations continued during 1996 with the acquisition of six new properties. The increased operating costs to bring these properties on line had a dampening effect of reported profits. Working with a team of accountants and attorneys, the Partnership figured a way to retain its status as a pass-through entity after 1997, the year those benefits were scheduled to expire. This should add considerable value over the long-term. Investment Classification: Income & Value

Officers	Position	Ownership Information	
Karen L. Hathaway	President	Number of Units Outstanding	175,907
John K. Hathaway	Senior VP	Market Capitalization	$ 49,429,867
Steven K. Hathaway	Senior VP	Frequency of Distributions	Quarterly
Richard T. LLewellyn	Senior VP	Number of Partners	Under 500
Jeffrey A. Sutton	Controller		

Other Information

Transfer Agent	ChaseMellon Shareholder Services Los Angeles, CA		Where Listed	OTC-BB
Auditor	Coopers & Lybrand L.L.P.		Symbol	LACOZ
Market Maker	Carr Securities Corporation	(800)221-2243	SIC Code	7941
	The Seidler Companies Inc.	(800)421-0164	Employees	375
Broker Dealer	Regular Stockbroker			
	Standard Investment	(888)783-4688 Ext: Jack		

Lab-Volt Systems, Inc.

P.O. Box 686   Farmingdale, NJ 07727   Telephone (908)938-2000   Fax (908)774-8573

Company Description

Lab-Volt Systems, Inc., formerly Buck Engineering Co., Inc., is a manufacturer and supplier of integrated systems for hands-on technical training in electricity, electronics, telecommunications and related fields. With fourteen sales offices and a network of factory-trained representatives strategically located around the world, the Company believes it is well positioned to meet the needs of the educational, industrial, and military technical training communities. Mr. David T. Buck, founder of the Company, died on February 15, 1997. He was ninety-four years old.

	12/31/96	12/31/95	12/31/94	12/31/93
Per Share Information				
Stock Price	3.00	4.75	4.00	2.50
Earnings Per Share	0.44	0.20	1.32	1.02
Price / Earnings Ratio	6.82	23.75	3.03	2.45
Book Value Per Share	7.50	7.12	6.93	n.a.
Price / Book Value %	40.00	66.71	57.72	n.a.
Dividends Per Share	0.0	0.0	0.0	0.0
Annual Financial Data				
Operating Results (000's)				
Total Revenues	27,551.3	28,034.3	29,130.2	19,981.0
Costs & Expenses	-27,216.8	-27,376.6	-27,387.2	-18,956.0
Income Before Taxes and Other	334.6	657.8	1,743.0	1,025.0
Other Items	0.0	0.0	0.0	0.0
Income Tax	126.7	-447.0	-314.0	0.0
Net Income	461.2	210.7	1,429.0	1,025.0
Cash Flow From Operations	1,247.6	-90.2	-261.7	n.a.
Balance Sheet (000's)				
Cash & Equivalents	570.4	650.7	n.a.	n.a.
Total Current Assets	14,812.7	16,307.4	n.a.	n.a.
Fixed Assets, Net	1,320.3	1,308.2	n.a.	n.a.
Total Assets	16,816.4	18,297.7	n.a.	n.a.
Total Current Liabilities	4,586.8	6,507.4	n.a.	n.a.
Long-Term Debt	4,407.0	4,365.8	n.a.	n.a.
Stockholders' Equity	7,822.6	7,424.6	n.a.	n.a.
Performance & Financial Condition				
Return on Total Revenues %	1.67	0.75	4.91	5.13
Return on Avg Stockholders' Equity %	6.05	2.92	n.a.	n.a.
Return on Average Assets %	2.63	1.10	7.54	6.29
Current Ratio	3.23	2.51	n.a.	n.a.
Debt / Equity %	56.34	58.80	n.a.	n.a.

Compound Growth %'s	EPS % -24.44	Net Income % -23.37	Total Revenues % 11.30

Comments

Although total revenues slipped slightly during the last two years, management is encouraged that the quantity of orders has accelerated and remains strong. Export orders accounted for 41% of 1996 revenues. The Company has not had to file with the Securities and Exchange Commission since 1982. To keep the number of shareholders to a minimum, the Company has offered to buy back all lots of less than 100 shares from 145 different shareholders. Investment Classification: Value

Officers	Position	Ownership Information	
Peter M. Schluter	President, CEO	Number of Shares Outstanding	1,043,118
Charles H. Bond	Senior VP, Secretary	Market Capitalization	$ 3,129,354
Shirley L. Barrett	Other	Frequency of Dividends	n.a.
		Number of Shareholders	258

Other Information

Transfer Agent	Reegistrar and Transfer Co. Cranford, NJ		Where Listed	OTC-BB
Auditor	KPMG Peat Marwick LLP		Symbol	LVSY
Market Maker	Robotti & Co., Inc.	(212)986-0800	SIC Code	3600
	Carr Securities Corporation	(800)221-2243	Employees	262
Broker Dealer	Regular Stockbroker			

Lady Baltimore Foods, Inc.

1601 Fairfax Trafficway   Kansas City, KS 66117   Telephone (913)371-8300   Fax (913)621-7217

Company Description

Lady Baltimore Foods, Inc. and its subsidiaries operate primarily as institutional wholesalers of groceries, chemicals, and food service equipment and supplies. Sales are concentrated in the four state region of Kansas, Missouri, Oklahoma and Arkansas. There are no predominant customers. "Nugget" is a private label used for certain Company products.

	06/30/96	06/30/95	06/30/94	06/30/93
Per Share Information				
Stock Price as of 12/31	49.25	62.50	64.00	43.50
Earnings Per Share	4.54	5.41	6.25	6.27
Price / Earnings Ratio	10.85	11.55	10.24	6.94
Book Value Per Share	85.06	78.09	72.83	66.73
Price / Book Value %	57.90	80.04	87.88	65.19
Dividends Per Share	0.15	0.15	0.15	0.12
Annual Financial Data				
Operating Results (000's)				
Total Revenues	183,655.9	166,696.9	156,650.1	148,976.6
Costs & Expenses	-181,538.7	-164,008.0	-153,579.2	-145,846.3
Income Before Taxes and Other	2,117.2	2,688.9	3,070.9	3,130.3
Other Items	0.0	0.0	0.0	0.0
Income Tax	-780.5	-979.5	-1,099.0	-1,150.1
Net Income	1,336.6	1,709.4	1,971.8	1,980.2
Cash Flow From Operations	2,252.1	775.2	1,582.8	3,372.6
Balance Sheet (000's)				
Cash & Equivalents	625.0	2,819.6	3,809.8	3,983.5
Total Current Assets	24,552.2	25,859.7	25,257.9	23,311.7
Fixed Assets, Net	7,950.0	6,924.2	6,524.4	6,587.9
Total Assets	32,795.8	33,169.0	32,266.0	30,530.1
Total Current Liabilities	10,365.1	6,269.8	6,769.2	6,647.9
Long-Term Debt	0.0	572.5	930.4	1,305.8
Stockholders' Equity	20,748.2	24,657.0	22,995.0	21,070.5
Performance & Financial Condition				
Return on Total Revenues %	0.73	1.03	1.26	1.33
Return on Avg Stockholders' Equity %	5.89	7.17	8.95	9.85
Return on Average Assets %	4.05	5.22	6.28	6.69
Current Ratio	2.37	4.12	3.73	3.51
Debt / Equity %	n.a.	2.32	4.05	6.20

Compound Growth %'s	EPS % -10.20	Net Income % -12.28	Total Revenues % 7.22

Comments

Although revenues were higher, the gross profit margin declined from 19.1% in 1995, to 18.3% in 1996. Inventories are stated at LIFO. On a FIFO basis, inventory would have been $1,521,985 higher at June 30, 1996. The Company acquired 71,809 shares of its outstanding stock during the last year for $5,208,806, or an average price of $72.54 per share. It is interesting that this price is higher than even the December 31, 1996, posted ask price of $55 per share. Investment Classification: Value

Officers	Position	Ownership Information	
Melvin Cosner	President, CEO	Number of Shares Outstanding	243,930
Alan Cosner	Secretary, Treasurer	Market Capitalization	$ 12,013,553
Tom Miller	VP - Sales	Frequency of Dividends	Quarterly
Clifford A. Cohen	Other	Number of Shareholders	Under 500

Other Information			
Transfer Agent	Boatman's Trust Company Kansas City, MO	Where Listed	OTC-BB
Auditor	Mayer Hoffman McCann L.C.	Symbol	LDYBA
Market Maker	George K. Baum & Company (800)821-7570	SIC Code	5140
	Howe Barnes Investments, Inc. (800)621-2364	Employees	225
Broker Dealer	Regular Stockbroker		

Lafayette Bancorporation

133 North 4th Street   Lafayette, IN 47902-1130   Telephone (317)423-7100   Fax (317)423-7280

Company Description

Lafayette Bank and Trust Company, founded in 1899, is the wholly-owned subsidiary of this holding company. The Bank offers commercial and retail banking, trust and investment services through its twelve offices in Tippecanoe and White Counties, Indiana. The geographic area is heavily dependent on Purdue University and the agricultural industry. Older established banks are not missing a byte when it comes to the Internet including Lafayette Bank and Trust Company, (http://www.lbtbank.com).

	12/31/96	12/31/95	12/31/94	12/31/93
Per Share Information				
Stock Price	22.25	21.25	18.56	19.19
Earnings Per Share	2.08	1.72	1.64	1.61
Price / Earnings Ratio	10.70	12.35	11.32	11.92
Book Value Per Share	17.63	16.22	14.40	13.60
Price / Book Value %	126.21	131.01	128.89	141.10
Dividends Per Share	0.50	0.40	0.36	0.34
Annual Financial Data				
Operating Results (000's)				
Net Interest Income	14,203.0	12,776.0	12,635.0	12,357.0
Loan Loss Provision	-240.0	-180.0	-600.0	-1,136.0
Non-Interest Income	3,422.0	2,790.0	2,580.0	3,893.0
Non-Interest Expense	-11,191.0	-10,220.0	-9,689.0	-10,198.0
Income Before Taxes and Other	6,194.0	5,166.0	4,926.0	4,916.0
Other Items	0.0	0.0	0.0	-11.0
Income Tax	-2,103.0	-1,791.0	-1,693.0	-1,736.0
Net Income	4,091.0	3,375.0	3,233.0	3,169.0
Balance Sheet (000's)				
Cash & Securities	123,742.0	127,271.0	121,412.0	114,105.0
Loans, Net	271,619.0	225,443.0	221,371.0	214,325.0
Total Assets	414,391.0	372,265.0	360,221.0	340,402.0
Deposits	341,550.0	308,652.0	296,763.0	285,363.0
Stockholders' Equity	34,646.0	31,875.0	28,294.0	26,737.0
Performance & Financial Condition				
Return on Avg Stockholders' Equity %	12.30	11.22	11.75	12.43
Return on Average Assets %	1.04	0.92	0.92	0.96
Equity to Assets %	8.36	8.56	7.85	7.85
Net Interest Margin	n.a.	n.a.	n.a.	n.a.
Reserve as a % of Problem Loans	229.25	174.10	267.94	161.41

Compound Growth %'s	EPS %	8.91	Net Income %	8.89	Net Interest Income %	4.75

Comments

The Company declared a 3 for 1 stock split in 1994 and 20% and 10% stock dividends in 1996 and 1995, respectively. All per share amounts have been adjusted accordingly for consistency. 1996 produced records in nearly every category. Earnings were up 21%, there were large increases in loans and deposits and there was a very impressive growth in non-interest income, the latter being affected by trust fees, the sale of mortgages in the secondary market and other fee income. Management reports that Lafayette has become a regional hub with low unemployment and a strong economy. The Bank believes this will fuel additional growth. Investment Classification: Value

Officers	Position	Ownership Information	
Robert J. Weeder	President	Number of Shares Outstanding	1,965,050
Robert J. Ralston	Senior VP	Market Capitalization	$ 43,722,363
E. James Brisco	Senior VP	Frequency of Dividends	Quarterly
Marvin S. Veatch	Controller	Number of Shareholders	n.a.
		Where Listed / Symbol	OTC-BB / LAYB

Other Information			Loan Mix	%
Transfer Agent	Company Office		Commerical	39.5
Auditor	Crowe, Chizek and Company LLP		R/E Mortgages	38.0
Market Maker	The Chicago Corporation	(312)855-7664	Installment	20.0
	McDonald & Company Securities	(216)443-2350	Other	2.5
Broker Dealer	OTC Specialist			
	Kevin Ryan - Ryan, Beck & Co.	(888)231-7226		

Lake Charles Naval Stores Co., Inc.

203 Carondelet Street, Ste.710   New Orleans, LA 70130   Telephone (504)561-8602   Fax (504)561-8621

Company Description

The Company owns various parcels of land in Louisiana and Mississippi, principally used in harvesting timber, leasing oil and gas rights, and renting for recreational purposes. Lake Charles Naval Stores also sells and trades properties to position itself for additional revenue sources. In August, 1996, a shopping center complex was placed into service.

	12/31/96	12/31/95	12/31/94
Per Share Information			
Stock Price	180.00	180.00	180.00
Earnings Per Share	87.40	221.68	27.33
Price / Earnings Ratio	2.06	0.81	6.59
Book Value Per Share	470.17	394.30	183.61
Price / Book Value %	38.28	45.65	98.03
Dividends Per Share	0.0	0.0	0.0
Annual Financial Data			
Operating Results (000's)			
Total Revenues	1,421.4	2,899.5	434.9
Costs & Expenses	-341.6	-138.7	-101.9
Income Before Taxes and Other	1,079.8	2,760.8	333.0
Other Items	0.0	0.0	0.0
Income Tax	-397.4	-1,025.9	-118.7
Net Income	682.5	1,734.9	214.2
Cash Flow From Operations	n.a.	n.a.	n.a.
Balance Sheet (000's)			
Cash & Equivalents	20.7	100.1	5.3
Total Current Assets	2,148.2	1,272.7	936.7
Fixed Assets, Net	1,279.5	1,275.5	495.2
Total Assets	11,110.6	4,715.1	1,524.7
Total Current Liabilities	201.7	886.9	78.2
Long-Term Debt	6,292.4	0.0	0.0
Stockholders' Equity	3,671.1	3,085.8	1,439.1
Performance & Financial Condition			
Return on Total Revenues %	48.01	59.83	49.26
Return on Avg Stockholders' Equity %	20.20	76.68	n.a.
Return on Average Assets %	8.62	55.61	n.a.
Current Ratio	10.65	1.43	11.99
Debt / Equity %	171.40	n.a.	n.a.

Compound Growth %'s	EPS %	n.a.	Net Income %	n.a.	Total Revenues %	n.a.

Comments

The Company reported that it exchanged timberland for an ownership share of a shopping center in Jacksonville, Florida. There is no indication that the financial statements are audited or that they are prepared under generally accepted accounting principles. Compound growth rates were omitted because of the fluctuations in revenue sources. During 1996, the Company reacquired common shares for $180 per share. Investment Classification: Value

Officers	Position	Ownership Information	
John F. White	President	Number of Shares Outstanding	7,808
		Market Capitalization	$ 1,405,440
		Frequency of Dividends	n.a.
		Number of Shareholders	Under 500

Other Information

				Where Listed	Order Matching Only
Transfer Agent	Company Office			Symbol	n.a.
Auditor	Not indicated			SIC Code	6790
Market Maker	None			Employees	1
Broker Dealer	Standard Investment	(888)783-4688	Ext: Jack		

Lancaster National Bank (The)

P.O.Box 109   Lancaster, NH 03584   Telephone (603)788-4973   Fax (603)788-2636

Company Description

The Lancaster National Bank is an independent bank serving the North Country communities of New Hampshire and Vermont from three offices. The Bank has been providing continuous service since 1881 and is the oldest bank in Coos County. The primary industries in the Bank's market area are wood products and tourism. Although there are only 45,000 shares outstanding, 1,216 and 6,040 shares were traded during 1996 and 1995, respectively.

	12/31/96	12/31/95	12/31/94	12/31/93
Per Share Information				
Stock Price	55.00	44.50	40.00	35.00
Earnings Per Share	10.59	11.14	9.46	6.58
Price / Earnings Ratio	5.19	3.99	4.23	5.32
Book Value Per Share	85.96	77.96	68.14	60.08
Price / Book Value %	63.98	57.08	58.70	58.26
Dividends Per Share	2.00	1.80	1.40	1.10
Annual Financial Data				
Operating Results (000's)				
Net Interest Income	1,776.1	1,883.8	1,683.6	1,489.2
Loan Loss Provision	-15.8	-36.1	-29.6	-60.6
Non-Interest Income	87.1	93.5	93.2	81.2
Non-Interest Expense	-1,125.1	-1,173.3	-1,107.1	-1,056.9
Income Before Taxes and Other	722.4	767.9	640.0	452.9
Other Items	0.0	0.0	0.0	0.0
Income Tax	-245.9	-266.6	-214.2	-156.7
Net Income	476.5	501.3	425.8	296.2
Balance Sheet (000's)				
Cash & Securities	18,003.9	15,321.7	14,690.1	15,260.6
Loans, Net	21,606.8	21,483.8	23,017.6	22,539.2
Total Assets	40,664.9	37,927.5	38,762.9	38,777.3
Deposits	36,646.1	34,250.5	35,543.0	35,947.6
Stockholders' Equity	3,868.3	3,508.1	3,066.3	2,703.5
Performance & Financial Condition				
Return on Avg Stockholders' Equity %	12.92	15.25	14.76	11.61
Return on Average Assets %	1.21	1.31	1.10	0.78
Equity to Assets %	9.51	9.25	7.91	6.97
Net Interest Margin	n.a.	n.a.	n.a.	n.a.
Reserve as a % of Problem Loans	146.18	129.60	76.31	43.44

Compound Growth %'s	EPS %	17.19	Net Income %	17.17	Net Interest Income %	6.05

Comments

The Bank has provided the information as to trading prices for its common shares. The annual report does not contain a management letter. Our side-by-side comparison shows little change from 1995 results. The only significant concentration in loans, according to management, is to motels and bed and breakfast establishments, amounting to $1,230,473 at December 31, 1996. These loans equate to 32% of capital, but are considered by management to be of the highest quality. Investment Classification: Value & Income & Growth

Officers	Position	Ownership Information	
Erling R. Roberts	Chairman	Number of Shares Outstanding	45,000
Lucius C. McIntire	President	Market Capitalization	$ 2,475,000
Jean R. Dion	COO	Frequency of Dividends	Quarterly
J. Edward Perreault	Vice President	Number of Shareholders	110
James A. Seppala	Vice President, Head Cashier	Where Listed / Symbol	OTC-PS / LNCE

Other Information				Loan Mix	%
Transfer Agent	Company Office			R/E Mortgages	82.8
Auditor	Francis J. Dineen, CPA			Consumer	7.8
Market Maker	Legg Mason Wood Walker, Inc.	(212)428-4949		Commerical	7.2
	Forbes Walsh Kelly & Co.	(212)422-1490		Construction	0.8
Broker Dealer	OTC Specialist			Other	1.4
	Norman Kadehjian - Wainwright	(800)727-7176			

Lanxide Corporation

1300 Marrows Road   Newark, DE 19714-6077   Telephone (302)456-6200   Fax (302)454-1712

Company Description

The Company is engaged in the development and commercialization of products based upon a variety of material process technologies which represent a novel approach to the fabrication of ceramic-reinforced composite products. The Company's patented technology has enabled it to engineer a new class of high-performance materials. Since 1983, in excess of $275 million has been expended for research. This has been funded through equity issuances and by joint venture partners. In November, 1995, the Company executed a plan of recapitalization. On November 13, 1996, the Company announced merger talks with Commodore Environmental Services.

	09/30/96	09/30/95	09/30/94
Per Share Information			
Stock Price as of 12/31	10.00	10.00	15.00
Earnings Per Share	0.77	-2.18	-1.55
Price / Earnings Ratio	12.99	n.a.	n.a.
Book Value Per Share	-5.96	-1.40	0.68
Price / Book Value %	n.a.	n.a.	2,205.88
Dividends Per Share	0.0	0.0	0.0
Annual Financial Data			
Operating Results (000's)			
Total Revenues	25,868.0	12,944.0	19,863.0
Costs & Expenses	-24,623.0	-38,325.0	-41,626.0
Income Before Taxes and Other	1,245.0	-25,381.0	-21,763.0
Other Items	487.0	2,664.0	6,079.0
Income Tax	-159.0	0.0	0.0
Net Income	1,573.0	-22,717.0	-15,684.0
Cash Flow From Operations	-11,178.0	-15,142.0	-17,806.0
Balance Sheet (000's)			
Cash & Equivalents	3,458.0	5,212.0	11,453.0
Total Current Assets	8,921.0	9,268.0	18,872.0
Fixed Assets, Net	10,408.0	14,837.0	20,209.0
Total Assets	20,160.0	28,020.0	41,831.0
Total Current Liabilities	4,554.0	8,746.0	5,949.0
Long-Term Debt	15,700.0	19,803.0	14,330.0
Stockholders' Equity	-7,896.0	-14,840.0	6,961.0
Performance & Financial Condition			
Return on Total Revenues %	6.08	-175.50	-78.96
Return on Avg Stockholders' Equity %	n.a.	n.a.	n.a.
Return on Average Assets %	6.53	-65.04	n.a.
Current Ratio	1.96	1.06	3.17
Debt / Equity %	n.a.	n.a.	205.86

Compound Growth %'s	EPS % n.a.	Net Income % n.a.	Total Revenues % 14.12

Comments

Gains of $7.5 million were recognized in 1996 on the sale of venture interests. Other revenues from sales, licensing, and research contracts were up slightly to $18.6 million. Management is tight-lipped about the pending merger including the timetable of events. A thorough understanding of that transaction would be a recommended starting point in any analysis. For the six months ended March 31, 1997, revenue was 46% higher than the previous year. Earnings for the same period slipped to $503,000 from $720,000. Investment Classification: Speculative

Officers	Position	Ownership Information	
Marc S. Newkirk	President, CEO	Number of Shares Outstanding	1,325,595
Mark G. Mortenson	Exec VP, COO	Market Capitalization	$ 13,255,950
Robert J. Ferris	Secretary, Treasurer	Frequency of Dividends	n.a.
Michael J. Hollins	Vice President	Number of Shareholders	190
Christopher R. Kennedy	Vice President		

Other Information

Transfer Agent	Stocktrans, Inc. Ardmore, PA		Where Listed	OTC-BB
Auditor	Price Waterhouse LLP		Symbol	LNXE
Market Maker	Newby & Company	(800)456-3992	SIC Code	3250
	Sharpe Capital Inc.	(800)355-5781	Employees	n.a.
Broker Dealer	Regular Stockbroker			

Lasermedics, Inc.

120 Industrial Boulevard   Sugar Land, TX 77478   Telephone (281)276-7000   Fax (281)276-7176

Company Description

Lasermedics, founded in 1990, is a manufacturer and marketer of diversified products in the physical therapy and rehabilitation industry. The Company provides high quality products and services to healthcare professionals. Its primary goals are to consolidate the largely-fragmented physical medicine and rehabilitation industry and to become a leader in that industry.

	12/31/96	12/31/95	12/31/94	12/31/93
Per Share Information				
Stock Price	5.87	4.25	5.00	7.50
Earnings Per Share	-0.44	-0.98	-3.02	-2.80
Price / Earnings Ratio	n.a.	n.a.	n.a.	n.a.
Book Value Per Share	0.80	-0.24	0.41	0.39
Price / Book Value %	733.75	n.a.	1,219.51	1,923.08
Dividends Per Share	0.0	0.0	0.0	0.0
Annual Financial Data				
Operating Results (000's)				
Total Revenues	12,486.0	538.6	885.5	121.2
Costs & Expenses	-13,257.5	-1,958.2	-4,250.6	-2,283.8
Income Before Taxes and Other	-879.3	-1,419.6	-3,365.1	-2,162.7
Other Items	0.0	0.0	0.0	0.0
Income Tax	0.0	0.0	0.0	0.0
Net Income	-879.3	-1,419.6	-3,365.1	-2,162.7
Cash Flow From Operations	584.3	-582.0	-1,312.2	-1,228.6
Balance Sheet (000's)				
Cash & Equivalents	507.9	203.4	310.7	583.1
Total Current Assets	10,229.4	450.8	630.4	712.6
Fixed Assets, Net	3,488.6	51.1	55.2	34.9
Total Assets	16,225.0	604.2	790.7	889.6
Total Current Liabilities	4,637.4	624.3	210.4	379.8
Long-Term Debt	9,129.0	335.8	0.0	0.0
Stockholders' Equity	2,206.5	-356.0	580.3	509.8
Performance & Financial Condition				
Return on Total Revenues %	-7.04	-263.57	-380.02	-1,785.06
Return on Avg Stockholders' Equity %	-95.03	n.a.	-617.37	n.a.
Return on Average Assets %	-10.45	-203.55	-400.54	n.a.
Current Ratio	2.21	0.72	3.00	1.88
Debt / Equity %	413.73	n.a.	n.a.	n.a.

Compound Growth %'s	EPS % n.a.	Net Income % n.a.	Total Revenues %	368.84

Comments

During 1996, the Company made the following acquisitions: the assets of Henley which provided an expanded and stable base of products and customers as well as manufacturing and marketing infrastructure, the assets of MJH Medical Equipment which added distribution channels to the Company's existing marketing outlets, and all the outstanding stock of Health Career Learning Systems which provides training, safety products and technical support. In January, 1997, the Company completed two additional acquisitions. Management maintains a strong balance sheet despite all of this growth activity. Revenues of $4.8 million were reported for the first quarter of 1997 as well as net income of $153,179, $.06 per share. Investment Classification: Speculative

Officers	Position	Ownership Information	
Chadwick F. Smith, MD	Chairman	Number of Shares Outstanding	2,742,439
Michael M. Barbour	President, CEO	Market Capitalization	$ 16,098,117
Dan D. Sudduth	Exec VP, CFO	Frequency of Dividends	n.a.
Chike J. Ogboenyiya	VP - Finance, Secretary	Number of Shareholders	n.a.
Michael J. Houska	VP - Sales		

Other Information				
Transfer Agent	American Stock & Transfer Co. New York, NY		Where Listed	OTC-BB
Auditor	Goldstein Golub Kessler & Co.		Symbol	LMDX
Market Maker	Havkit Corp.	(212)233-1800	SIC Code	3841
	Mayer & Schweitzer, Inc.	(800)631-3094	Employees	n.a.
Broker Dealer	Regular Stockbroker			

Latshaw Enterprises, Inc.

2533 South West Street   Wichita, KS 67217   Telephone (316)942-7266   Fax (316)942-0518

Company Description

The Company, through its subsidiaries, manufactures and markets mechanical controls, cable devices, wire and screw machine parts, and precision injection molded and vacuum-formed plastic parts for use primarily by original equipment manufacturers. The Company also buys, or manufactures a limited number of consumer products for resale in the retail market. Wescon Products Company, the largest subsidiary, operates two plants in Wichita, Kansas, with three divisions: controls, plastics and consumer products.

	11/02/96	10/28/95	10/29/94	10/30/93
Per Share Information				
Stock Price as of 12/31	375.00	375.00	400.00	262.50
Earnings Per Share	102.43	72.72	64.38	65.00
Price / Earnings Ratio	3.66	5.16	6.21	4.04
Book Value Per Share	677.64	1,154.40	1,026.55	909.28
Price / Book Value %	55.34	32.48	38.97	28.87
Dividends Per Share	0.0	0.0	0.0	0.0
Annual Financial Data				
Operating Results (000's)				
Total Revenues	44,721.0	41,277.0	38,463.0	31,619.0
Costs & Expenses	-41,788.0	-39,143.0	-36,386.0	-29,573.0
Income Before Taxes and Other	2,933.0	2,134.0	2,064.0	2,046.0
Other Items	0.0	0.0	0.0	-681.0
Income Tax	-994.0	-805.0	-871.0	-175.0
Net Income	1,939.0	1,329.0	1,193.0	1,190.0
Cash Flow From Operations	3,769.0	1,676.0	1,938.0	710.0
Balance Sheet (000's)				
Cash & Equivalents	240.0	319.0	184.0	174.0
Total Current Assets	17,808.0	16,818.0	15,327.0	13,011.0
Fixed Assets, Net	7,377.0	7,075.0	6,411.0	5,843.0
Total Assets	25,831.0	24,648.0	21,964.0	19,066.0
Total Current Liabilities	7,165.0	7,827.0	6,900.0	5,379.0
Long-Term Debt	2,717.0	4,994.0	4,686.0	4,630.0
Stockholders' Equity	13,582.0	11,589.0	10,206.0	8,981.0
Performance & Financial Condition				
Return on Total Revenues %	4.34	3.22	3.10	3.76
Return on Avg Stockholders' Equity %	15.41	12.20	12.44	13.93
Return on Average Assets %	7.68	5.70	5.82	6.86
Current Ratio	2.49	2.15	2.22	2.42
Debt / Equity %	20.00	43.09	45.91	51.55

Compound Growth %'s	EPS %	16.37	Net Income %	17.67	Total Revenues %	12.25

Comments

The shareholders approved a 1 for 50 reverse stock split in 1996, and deregistered with the Securities and Exchange Commission. All per share amounts were adjusted for consistency. Included in revenues for 1996 are a full year of revenues attributable to the I.H. Molding Division which was acquired in September, 1995. Higher sales, new product introductions and improved operating efficiencies contributed to the continued growth in net income. Investment Classification: Value & Growth

Officers	Position	Ownership Information	
John Latshaw	Chairman, CEO	Number of Shares Outstanding	20,043
Michael E. Bukaty	President, COO	Market Capitalization	$ 7,516,125
David G. Carr	Senior VP, CFO	Frequency of Dividends	n.a.
		Number of Shareholders	147

Other Information

Transfer Agent	United Missouri Bank, N.A. Kansas City, MO		Where Listed	OTC-BB
Auditor	Ernst & Young LLP		Symbol	LAEI
Market Maker	Carr Securities Corporation	(800)221-2243	SIC Code	3625
	Forbes Walsh Kelly & Co.	(212)422-1490	Employees	500
Broker Dealer	OTC Specialist			

Ledyard National Bank

320 Main Street   Norwich, VT 05055   Telephone (802)649-2050   Fax (802)649-2060

Company Description

Ledyard National Bank provides a variety of investment and trust services in addition to traditional banking through its four office locations to individual and corporate customers in the Upper Connecticut River Valley Region of central New Hampshire and Vermont. The Bank first opened in 1991. We would suggest a visit to this beautiful part of the country, including Dartmouth College, in the fall when the foliage alone is worth the trip. You can also visit them on the internet: (http://www.ledyardbank.com).

	12/31/96	12/31/95	12/31/94	12/31/93
Per Share Information				
Stock Price	16.25	11.00	11.00	9.00
Earnings Per Share	0.86	0.56	0.45	0.52
Price / Earnings Ratio	18.90	19.64	24.44	17.31
Book Value Per Share	11.16	10.50	9.91	9.59
Price / Book Value %	145.61	104.76	111.00	93.85
Dividends Per Share	0.20	0.10	0.0	0.0
Annual Financial Data				
Operating Results (000's)				
Net Interest Income	4,613.7	3,753.6	2,889.2	1,929.3
Loan Loss Provision	-349.0	-355.1	-169.4	-97.1
Non-Interest Income	926.7	552.6	405.6	530.1
Non-Interest Expense	-3,925.4	-3,170.7	-2,527.1	-1,889.5
Income Before Taxes and Other	1,266.0	780.3	598.2	472.8
Other Items	0.0	0.0	0.0	0.0
Income Tax	-475.5	-266.3	-189.3	0.0
Net Income	790.5	514.0	408.9	472.8
Balance Sheet (000's)				
Cash & Securities	50,858.1	32,173.7	29,386.7	30,373.3
Loans, Net	66,024.3	54,789.2	43,890.7	31,329.7
Total Assets	120,703.0	91,125.4	77,263.8	64,081.7
Deposits	101,843.5	74,143.9	55,161.7	43,392.1
Stockholders' Equity	10,249.3	9,628.8	9,083.7	8,798.6
Performance & Financial Condition				
Return on Avg Stockholders' Equity %	7.95	5.49	4.57	5.52
Return on Average Assets %	0.75	0.61	0.58	0.89
Equity to Assets %	8.49	10.57	11.76	13.73
Net Interest Margin	n.a.	n.a.	n.a.	n.a.
Reserve as a % of Problem Loans	341.89	143.45	n.a.	n.a.

Compound Growth %'s	EPS %	18.26	Net Income %	18.69	Net Interest Income %	33.73

Comments

Income tax expense was not required in 1993 because of tax loss carryovers. Per share prices were provided by the Bank and represent the last known transaction price of each respective year. The Bank facilitates trading in its shares by maintaining lists of prospective buyers and sellers. In addition to strong deposit growth, trust department income rose to $265,656 from $118,966 in the prior year, an increase of 123%. Investment Classification: Growth

Officers	Position	Ownership Information	
Peter C. Brown	President, CEO	Number of Shares Outstanding	918,000
Sue G. Shaw	Senior VP, CFO	Market Capitalization	$ 14,917,500
D. Rodman Thomas	Senior VP	Frequency of Dividends	Irregular
William R. Hatch	Vice President, Sr Loan Officer	Number of Shareholders	n.a.
Darcy D. Rogers	Vice President, COO	Where Listed / Symbol	Order Matching Only / n.a.

Other Information		Loan Mix	%
Transfer Agent	Company Office	R/E Mortgages	64.5
Auditor	A.M. Peisch & Company	Commerical	31.6
Market Maker	None - See Note	Consumer	3.9
Broker Dealer	None		

Leslie Building Products, Inc.

200 Mamaroneck Avenue   White Plains, NY 10601   Telephone (914)421-2545   Fax (914)428-4581

Company Description

Leslie Building Products, Inc. is a manufacturer and marketer of a wide variety of specialty building products for the professional and do-it-yourself remodeling and residential construction industry. Its products consist of ornamental iron security products, residential ventilation products, metal and fiberglass air distribution products for the HVAC industry, skylights, a professional line of aluminum rakes, and a full line of door louvers and vision lite products for the architectural door market. The Home Depot, a nationally recognized retailer with 500 stores, is the Company's largest customer accounting for approximately 60% of sales.

	12/31/96	12/31/95	12/31/94
Per Share Information			
Stock Price	2.62	2.12	1.65
Earnings Per Share	0.13	-1.68	-0.93
Price / Earnings Ratio	20.15	n.a.	n.a.
Book Value Per Share	1.77	1.64	3.33
Price / Book Value %	148.02	129.27	49.55
Dividends Per Share	0.0	0.0	0.0
Annual Financial Data			
Operating Results (000's)			
Total Revenues	82,154.0	75,993.0	71,105.0
Costs & Expenses	-81,527.0	-84,062.0	-75,307.0
Income Before Taxes and Other	627.0	-8,069.0	-4,202.0
Other Items	0.0	0.0	0.0
Income Tax	0.0	0.0	-264.0
Net Income	627.0	-8,069.0	-4,466.0
Cash Flow From Operations	-2,439.0	-2,262.0	591.0
Balance Sheet (000's)			
Cash & Equivalents	34.0	15.0	n.a.
Total Current Assets	26,195.0	21,806.0	n.a.
Fixed Assets, Net	15,320.0	16,383.0	n.a.
Total Assets	41,957.0	38,749.0	n.a.
Total Current Liabilities	14,954.0	14,791.0	n.a.
Long-Term Debt	17,598.0	14,749.0	n.a.
Stockholders' Equity	8,563.0	7,868.0	n.a.
Performance & Financial Condition			
Return on Total Revenues %	0.76	-10.62	-6.28
Return on Avg Stockholders' Equity %	7.63	-67.84	-31.12
Return on Average Assets %	1.55	n.a.	n.a.
Current Ratio	1.75	1.47	n.a.
Debt / Equity %	205.51	187.46	n.a.

Compound Growth %'s	EPS % n.a.	Net Income % n.a.	Total Revenues % 7.49

Comments

The 1995 results included nonrecurring expenses of $7.9 million. The loss without those charges would have been $.03 per share. Management was pleased with its return to profitability but cautions not to expect too much in 1997. Rather, an infrastructure is being created to serve the more than 1,000 Home Depot stores that are expected by the year 2000. During December, 1996, the Company was awarded $10 million in contracts for new ventilation products. These products are expected to yield a long term benefit to the Company despite lower profit margins in the near term. Investment Classification: Speculative

Officers	Position	Ownership Information	
Edward W. Rose, III	Chairman	Number of Shares Outstanding	4,833,075
Leigh J. Abrams	President, CEO	Market Capitalization	$ 12,662,657
Fredric M. Zinn	CFO	Frequency of Dividends	n.a.
Harvey J. Kaplan	Secretary, Treasurer	Number of Shareholders	2,447
John F. Cupak	Controller		

Other Information

Transfer Agent	ChaseMellon Shareholder Services Ridgefield Park, NJ		Where Listed	OTC-BB
Auditor	KPMG Peat Marwick LLP		Symbol	LBPI
Market Maker	Carr Securities Corporation	(800)221-2243	SIC Code	3440
	M.H. Meyerson & Co., Inc.	(800)333-3113	Employees	581
Broker Dealer	Regular Stockbroker			

Level Best Golf, Inc.

14561 58th Street North   Clearwater, FL 34620   Telephone (813)535-7770   Fax (813)535-0077

Company Description

Level Best Golf, Inc. markets unique, high quality and effective training aids. The Company's flagship product is Scratch Score Golf (TM) which consists of three 2-hour videos which address almost every facet of the game. It also comes with five training aids designed to work in conjunction with the practice drills demonstrated on the videos. The Company was founded in 1993.

	09/30/96	09/30/95	09/30/94
Per Share Information			
Stock Price as of 12/31	2.75	1.50	0.58
Earnings Per Share	-0.42	-0.74	-0.24
Price / Earnings Ratio	n.a.	n.a.	n.a.
Book Value Per Share	-0.27	-0.13	-0.09
Price / Book Value %	n.a.	n.a.	n.a.
Dividends Per Share	0.0	0.0	0.0
Annual Financial Data			
Operating Results (000's)			
Total Revenues	495.7	98.5	22.3
Costs & Expenses	-1,640.9	-1,571.7	-407.5
Income Before Taxes and Other	-1,145.2	-1,473.2	-385.1
Other Items	0.0	0.0	0.0
Income Tax	0.0	0.0	0.0
Net Income	-1,145.2	-1,473.2	-385.1
Cash Flow From Operations	-506.5	-636.8	-274.4
Balance Sheet (000's)			
Cash & Equivalents	46.9	8.1	n.a.
Total Current Assets	225.4	164.9	n.a.
Fixed Assets, Net	56.1	13.1	n.a.
Total Assets	454.5	188.2	n.a.
Total Current Liabilities	1,229.5	460.1	n.a.
Long-Term Debt	47.4	63.2	n.a.
Stockholders' Equity	-822.3	-348.0	n.a.
Performance & Financial Condition			
Return on Total Revenues %	-231.03	-1,496.01	-1,724.01
Return on Avg Stockholders' Equity %	n.a.	n.a.	n.a.
Return on Average Assets %	-356.35	n.a.	n.a.
Current Ratio	0.18	0.36	n.a.
Debt / Equity %	n.a.	n.a.	n.a.

Compound Growth %'s	EPS % n.a.	Net Income % n.a.	Total Revenues % 371.05

Comments

Although the 1996 increase in revenue was promising, the Company remains far from turning a profit. It used all available resources during the first six months of fiscal 1997 to build inventory and produce advertising for the late spring and summer of 1997. The Company reports many products in the pipe line but we believe it will require cash to execute a successful strategy. Exactly how that will happen remains an uncertainty. Investment Classification: Speculative

Officers	Position	Ownership Information	
Fred L. Solomon	President	Number of Shares Outstanding	3,051,174
Curt L. Rodgers	CFO	Market Capitalization	$ 8,390,729
Patricia A. Sanders	Secretary	Frequency of Dividends	n.a.
James G. Solomon	Vice President	Number of Shareholders	1,068

Other Information				
Transfer Agent	Florida Atlantic Stock Transfer, Inc. Tamarac, FL		Where Listed	OTC-BB
Auditor	Winter, Scheifley & Associates		Symbol	LBGF
Market Maker	J. Alexander Securities, Inc.	(800)421-0258	SIC Code	7200
	Barron Chase Securities Inc.	(800)377-8723	Employees	12
Broker Dealer	Regular Stockbroker			

Lexcom Communications, Inc.

200 North State Street Lexington, NC 27292 Telephone (910)249-9901 Fax (910)243-3026

Company Description

Lexcom Communications, formerly Lexington Telephone Company, provides telephone sales and services to the businesses and residents of Davidson County, North Carolina, and is regulated by state and federal commissions. Having been founded in 1896, the Company just completed its centennial celebration. We hope the Telecommunications Act of 1996 was intended as a present from Congress as local telephone companies will have both challenges and opportunities ahead. Lexcom Wireless was formed in 1996 to provide wireless communication services. Lexcom Cable Services will provide cable television services as early as October, 1997.

	12/31/96	12/31/95	12/31/94	12/31/93
Per Share Information				
Stock Price	385.00	300.00	210.00	175.00
Earnings Per Share	34.24	33.68	26.50	20.67
Price / Earnings Ratio	11.24	8.91	7.92	8.47
Book Value Per Share	230.77	210.28	198.44	181.60
Price / Book Value %	166.83	142.67	105.83	96.37
Dividends Per Share	12.20	11.00	9.80	8.65
Annual Financial Data				
Operating Results (000's)				
Total Revenues	26,156.9	24,394.8	21,819.1	19,721.4
Costs & Expenses	-18,618.2	-16,904.9	-15,126.8	-14,804.4
Income Before Taxes and Other	7,538.7	7,489.9	6,136.5	4,917.0
Other Items	0.0	0.0	0.0	0.0
Income Tax	-2,807.1	-2,823.7	-2,369.1	-1,938.5
Net Income	4,731.6	4,666.2	3,767.4	2,978.5
Cash Flow From Operations	9,728.7	7,475.2	7,576.1	6,398.1
Balance Sheet (000's)				
Cash & Equivalents	1,361.9	529.2	895.4	256.4
Total Current Assets	5,090.7	4,909.6	4,360.0	3,474.7
Fixed Assets, Net	44,072.1	39,834.9	36,716.7	33,606.4
Total Assets	57,882.1	52,356.5	46,628.7	41,476.5
Total Current Liabilities	6,996.0	5,651.1	4,562.4	4,668.8
Long-Term Debt	3,845.0	4,055.0	4,265.0	1,815.0
Stockholders' Equity	32,321.6	29,574.3	28,424.4	26,976.8
Performance & Financial Condition				
Return on Total Revenues %	18.09	19.13	17.27	15.10
Return on Avg Stockholders' Equity %	15.29	16.09	13.60	11.36
Return on Average Assets %	8.58	9.43	8.55	7.64
Current Ratio	0.73	0.87	0.96	0.74
Debt / Equity %	11.90	13.71	15.00	6.73

Compound Growth %'s	EPS %	18.32	Net Income %	16.68	Total Revenues %	9.87

Comments

The Company has investments in a number of emerging communications-related businesses, including 360 Degrees Communications, BellSouth Carolinas PCS, Access/ON Multimedia Services, Inc. and others. These investments are all carried at either cost or under the equity method. None of them are adjusted to fair market value. Revenues and earnings were up slightly during 1996. Investment Classification: Growth

Officers	Position	Ownership Information	
Richard G. Reese	Chairman, President	Number of Shares Outstanding	136,912
B. Earl Hester, Jr.	Exec VP	Market Capitalization	$ 52,711,120
Meredith Harris Mode	Secretary	Frequency of Dividends	Quarterly
Charles D. Harris	Vice President, Treasurer	Number of Shareholders	Under 500
Royster M. Tucker, Jr.	Vice President		

Other Information

Transfer Agent	Company Office		Where Listed	OTC-BB
Auditor	McGladrey & Pullen LLP		Symbol	LENG
Market Maker	J.C. Bradford & Co.	(800)251-1740	SIC Code	4810
	Legg Mason Wood & Walker, Inc.	(800)221-9732	Employees	117
Broker Dealer	OTC Specialist			
	Stephen Schuller - Dorsey	(800)375-5431		

Telephones

Alexander Graham Bell invented the telephone in 1876. He lost no time in getting a patent secured on this curious device, and so he had the next seventeen years to build an industry around a new technology pretty much unhindered by competition. As we all know, Bell Telephone was rather successful in its endeavor to hook up America. Less conspicuous, perhaps, are the many so-called independent telephone companies that sprouted in the years after Bell's patents expired. Telephones were not exactly common at that point: Bell had concentrated its efforts in the larger cities, not in towns and certainly not in rural areas. So when the opportunity became available in 1893, thousands of local companies sprouted in even the smallest of communities; more than 6,000 of them, in fact, before the turn of the century only seven years later.

One of these was Lexington Telephone Company, incorporated in the North Carolina town of the same name in 1896. The 1,200 or so souls of Lexington wanted to reach out and touch someone, too; namely, their own neighbors. Instant global communications was simply not a concern of the six local businessmen who pooled resources to start this venture. It's a good thing — Lexington didn't even get connected to Reeds, not ten miles away, until 1912. And then the link was made *from* Reeds, not Lexington. First one town, then another were brought into the fledgling network, patching together a number of different telephone companies in addition to the towns themselves.

Unlike most of the other 6,000 independents, Lexington Telephone managed to survive its infancy. By 1940 the city of Lexington had ballooned to over 10,000 people, and the telephone company could claim 1,660 of them as customers. But just think: less than 20% of the population had a telephone. It is as though this idea of long-distance communications remained a novelty despite the passage of nearly sixty-five years since its invention. Indeed, the company's 1941 directory included exquisitely detailed instructions on how to dial a phone!

Then came World War II, and communications, like so much else, changed forever. Demand absolutely exploded for telephone service during and after the war, and by the mid-50's Lexington had more than 5,000 of them installed. The company kept up with the aid of technological developments including a 1947 invention called the transistor — from where else? Bell Telephone. Out went the vacuum tube and in came digital transmission and push-button phones. Consider the constant battle with aging infrastructure this company has faced: even while embracing integrated circuits and products made viable by such technology, including fax machines and cellular phones, Lexington only removed the last party lines from its network in 1982.

These days, newly renamed Lexcom Communications is still busy, and they're doing much more than just talk; about fiber optics, for example. As ever, it's not a moment too soon. After all, in 1996 — their centennial — they installed their 30,000th access line. At this rate, they will have to move at almost the speed of light just to keep up with their own growth!

Lexington Precision Corporation

767 Third Avenue   New York, NY 10017   Telephone (212)319-4657   Fax (212)319-4659

Company Description

Lexington Precision Corporation manufactures, to customer specifications, rubber and metal component parts used primarily by manufacturers of automobiles, industrial equipment, office equipment and computers, medical devices and home appliances. During 1995, 65.3% of the Company's sales were to the automobile industry. The Company was formed in 1966.

	12/31/96	12/31/95	12/31/94	12/31/93
Per Share Information				
Stock Price	2.08	3.13	2.00	2.00
Earnings Per Share	-0.02	0.49	0.51	0.13
Price / Earnings Ratio	n.a.	6.39	3.92	15.38
Book Value Per Share	-1.19	-1.18	-1.72	-2.38
Price / Book Value %	n.a.	n.a.	n.a.	n.a.
Dividends Per Share	0.0	0.0	0.0	0.0
Annual Financial Data				
Operating Results (000's)				
Total Revenues	114,872.0	104,939.0	89,068.0	74,976.0
Costs & Expenses	-114,849.0	-102,226.0	-86,702.0	-74,125.0
Income Before Taxes and Other	23.0	2,713.0	2,366.0	851.0
Other Items	0.0	0.0	0.0	0.0
Income Tax	-40.0	-425.0	-34.0	0.0
Net Income	-17.0	2,288.0	2,332.0	851.0
Cash Flow From Operations	8,054.0	7,860.0	5,957.0	9,601.0
Balance Sheet (000's)				
Cash & Equivalents	187.0	118.0	79.0	33.0
Total Current Assets	30,845.0	24,478.0	22,752.0	15,715.0
Fixed Assets, Net	53,300.0	44,938.0	32,594.0	22,093.0
Total Assets	97,030.0	81,876.0	67,396.0	49,983.0
Total Current Liabilities	35,167.0	29,253.0	24,330.0	12,733.0
Long-Term Debt	65,148.0	56,033.0	49,627.0	46,273.0
Stockholders' Equity	-5,057.0	-4,976.0	-7,215.0	-9,623.0
Performance & Financial Condition				
Return on Total Revenues %	-0.01	2.18	2.62	1.14
Return on Avg Stockholders' Equity %	n.a.	n.a.	n.a.	n.a.
Return on Average Assets %	-0.02	3.07	3.97	1.78
Current Ratio	0.88	0.84	0.94	1.23
Debt / Equity %	n.a.	n.a.	n.a.	n.a.

Compound Growth %'s	EPS % n.a.	Net Income % n.a.	Total Revenues % 15.28

Comments

Revenues for 1996 were right in the center of the range predicted by management at the beginning of the year. The Metals Group had lower results because of the required replacement of a long-running air-bag component with new air-bag components, requiring substantial startup expenses. At December 31, 1995, the Company had net operating loss carryforwards for federal income tax purposes of $8.1 million that expire in the years 2004 through 2011. During the first quarter of 1997, the Company refinanced much of its secured debt but reported a loss of $.06 per share as compared to a profit of $.08 per share in the same period of 1996. Investment Classification: Speculative

Officers	Position	Ownership Information	
Michael A. Lubin	Chairman	Number of Shares Outstanding	4,263,036
Warren Delano	President	Market Capitalization	$ 8,867,115
Dennis J. Welhouse	Senior VP, CFO	Frequency of Dividends	n.a.
Kenneth I. Greenstein	Secretary	Number of Shareholders	1,050
Kelly L. MacMillan	Treasurer		

Other Information

Transfer Agent	KeyCorp Shareholder Services, Inc. Cleveland, OH		Where Listed	OTC-BB
Auditor	Ernst & Young LLP		Symbol	LEXP
Market Maker	Robotti & Co., Inc.	(212)986-0800	SIC Code	3060
	Carr Securities Corporation	(800)221-2243	Employees	1200
Broker Dealer	Regular Stockbroker			

Life Insurance Company of Alabama

302 Broad Street   Gadsden, AL 35902   Telephone (205)543-2022   Fax (205)549-0070

Company Description

The Company underwrites life insurance policies. It has two classes of stock: a $5 par voting common and a $1 par nonvoting class A. The dividend is always a stated percent of par value. There are 87,548 shares of voting common and 587,504 shares of class A outstanding. We used a weighted average method for per share calculations and treated each $5 par share as five shares of class A for total outstanding shares of 1,025,244. The Company was founded in 1952.

	12/31/96	12/31/95	12/31/94	12/31/93
Per Share Information				
Stock Price	2.62	2.44	2.37	2.37
Earnings Per Share	0.33	0.74	0.18	0.43
Price / Earnings Ratio	7.94	3.30	13.17	5.51
Book Value Per Share	5.90	5.55	4.41	4.40
Price / Book Value %	44.41	43.96	53.74	53.86
Dividends Per Share	0.09	0.09	0.09	0.09
Annual Financial Data				
Operating Results (000's)				
Total Revenues	26,496.5	26,014.8	24,619.8	23,356.1
Costs & Expenses	-25,769.8	-25,130.2	-24,300.8	-22,869.1
Income Before Taxes and Other	691.9	849.2	283.7	444.9
Other Items	0.0	0.0	0.0	0.0
Income Tax	-357.5	-90.0	-95.3	-7.2
Net Income	334.5	759.2	188.4	437.7
Cash Flow From Operations	n.a.	n.a.	n.a.	n.a.
Balance Sheet (000's)				
Cash & Equivalents	495.6	632.5	2,985.4	1,972.8
Total Current Assets	1,984.4	2,031.6	4,096.6	3,247.3
Fixed Assets, Net	792.2	803.9	812.2	813.7
Total Assets	59,514.5	57,082.1	54,119.7	52,655.4
Total Current Liabilities	911.1	692.7	587.4	542.1
Long-Term Debt	0.0	0.0	0.0	0.0
Stockholders' Equity	6,048.1	5,693.6	4,517.1	4,514.0
Performance & Financial Condition				
Return on Total Revenues %	1.26	2.92	0.77	1.87
Return on Avg Stockholders' Equity %	5.70	14.87	4.17	10.43
Return on Average Assets %	0.57	1.37	0.35	0.85
Current Ratio	2.18	2.93	6.97	5.99
Debt / Equity %	n.a.	n.a.	n.a.	n.a.

Compound Growth %'s	EPS % -8.45	Net Income % -8.58	Total Revenues % 4.29

Comments

Noncurrent assets primarily consist of investments in bonds. These bonds have been issued by government agencies which have a AAA rating. Income taxes were disproportionately low in 1993 because of available net operating loss carryovers which have now been used. This may only be exciting to an investor who likes to buy something for less than one-half of what it is worth. However, exit strategies may be hard to come by. Someday the shareholders will say enough is enough and the business will be sold. Investment Classification: Value

Officers	Position	Ownership Information	
Clarence W. Daugette, III	President	Number of Shares Outstanding	1,025,244
Raymond R. Renfrow, Jr.	Exec VP	Market Capitalization	$ 2,686,139
M. Lynn Lowe	Exec VP, Treasurer	Frequency of Dividends	Annual
Robert W. Echols, Jr.	Exec VP, Secretary	Number of Shareholders	Under 500
Dennis B. Adams	Senior VP		

Other Information			
Transfer Agent	Company Office	Where Listed	OTC-BB
Auditor	Not indicated	Symbol	LINS
Market Maker	Morgan Keegan & Company, Inc. (800)289-5019	SIC Code	6310
	Hill Thompson Magid & Co., Inc (800)631-3083	Employees	75
Broker Dealer	Regular Stockbroker		

Limco Del Mar, Ltd.

1141 Cummings Road   Santa Paula, CA 93060-9708   Telephone (805)525-5541   Fax (805)525-8211

Company Description

The Partnership is in the business of lemon and avocado farming on 211 acres of farmlands that it holds for eventual residential development. The property is located in Ventura, California. The Partnership was formed in 1986. Limoneira Company, a general partner, owns approximately 1% of the limited partner units.

	10/31/96	10/31/95	10/31/94	10/31/93
Per Unit Information				
Price Per Unit as of 12/31	10.00	9.00	7.00	9.00
Earnings Per Unit	1.90	1.56	1.26	0.51
Price / Earnings Ratio	5.26	5.77	5.56	17.65
Book Value Per Unit	6.85	5.62	4.61	3.40
Price / Book Value %	145.99	160.14	151.84	264.71
Distributions Per Unit	0.70	0.50	0.0	0.0
Cash Flow Per Unit	2.14	1.75	1.38	0.62
Annual Financial Data				
Operating Results (000's)				
Total Revenues	1,269.9	1,115.2	764.5	512.8
Costs & Expenses	-601.6	-567.5	-320.4	-335.0
Operating Income	668.4	547.7	444.2	177.8
Other Items	0.0	0.0	0.0	0.0
Net Income	668.4	547.7	444.2	177.8
Cash Flow From Operations	753.8	614.0	485.6	218.7
Balance Sheet (000's)				
Cash & Equivalents	681.1	260.4	8.9	36.6
Total Current Assets	717.8	311.6	35.3	61.2
Investments	n.a.	1,793.1	1,792.2	1,672.0
Total Assets	2,469.6	2,261.8	2,151.8	2,057.0
Total Current Liabilities	1.7	17.3	1.7	1.2
Long-Term Debt	0.0	226.1	501.1	851.1
Partners' Capital	2,467.9	2,018.4	1,648.9	1,204.7
Performance & Financial Condition				
Return on Total Revenues %	52.63	49.11	58.10	34.68
Return on Average Partners' Capital %	24.82	29.87	31.13	15.94
Return on Average Assets %	28.25	24.82	21.11	8.74
Current Ratio	421.52	18.05	20.19	51.28
Debt / Equity %	n.a.	11.20	30.39	70.65

Compound Growth %'s	EPU %	55.02	Net Income %	55.47	Total Revenues %	35.29

Comments

Cash arising from recent profitable years has been used to reduce bank debt and to make a distribution to partners. In November, 1995, a Ventura City initiative was passed by the voters which restricts zoning of the Company's properties to only agricultural usage until the year 2030 unless the zoning change is approved by the majority of Ventura City voters. The Measure is currently being litigated by an alliance of property owners. Compound growth rates are not particularly meaningful to the Partnership and can be misleading. The 1996/1997 crop is expected to produce more lemons than the preceding year. Investment Classification: Value & Speculative

Officers	Position	Ownership Information	
J M. Dickenson	CEO	Number of Units Outstanding	351,450
Volney H. Craig	Other	Market Capitalization	$ 3,514,500
Robert A. Hardison	Other	Frequency of Distributions	n.a.
		Number of Partners	Under 500

Other Information

Transfer Agent	Company Office		Where Listed	OTC-BB
Auditor	Deloitte & Touche LLP		Symbol	LIDM
Market Maker	Seidler Companies, Inc., The	(800)421-0164	SIC Code	0174
	Sharpe Capital Inc.	(888)355-5781	Employees	n.a.
Broker Dealer	OTC Specialist			
	Standard Investment	(888)783-4688 Ext: Jack		

Logan Clay Products Company

P.O. Box 698   Logan, OH 43138-0698   Telephone (614)385-2184   Fax (614)385-9336

Company Description

The Company's primary operation is a clay products manufacturing facility located in Logan, Ohio, but it also operates a gas pipeline and maintains working interests in oil and gas producing activities. Clay products include pipe that is resistant to fire, corrosion, abrasion and deflection making it the natural choice for sanitary sewer systems. The Company also manufacturers clay building materials including flue liners, chimney tops, wall coping and channel pipe. More product information is available on the Company's Web Page: (http//www.loganclaypipe.com)

	11/30/96	11/30/95	11/30/94	11/30/93
Per Share Information				
Stock Price as of 12/31	21.50	20.75	25.50	20.50
Earnings Per Share	1.49	-0.04	0.45	-2.08
Price / Earnings Ratio	14.43	n.a.	56.67	n.a.
Book Value Per Share	46.40	45.13	43.34	41.41
Price / Book Value %	46.34	45.98	58.84	49.50
Dividends Per Share	0.25	0.10	0.0	0.40
Annual Financial Data				
Operating Results (000's)				
Total Revenues	9,039.4	8,217.2	8,989.2	7,974.4
Costs & Expenses	-8,666.9	-8,123.9	-8,761.9	-8,402.5
Income Before Taxes and Other	229.9	11.3	132.2	-527.1
Other Items	0.0	0.0	0.0	0.0
Income Tax	7.6	-18.6	-51.5	143.2
Net Income	237.5	-7.4	80.7	-383.9
Cash Flow From Operations	404.8	336.1	675.2	259.7
Balance Sheet (000's)				
Cash & Equivalents	1,324.8	1,179.9	873.1	730.6
Total Current Assets	5,532.2	4,890.8	4,930.8	4,823.2
Fixed Assets, Net	2,429.1	2,545.1	2,495.8	2,546.8
Total Assets	8,605.9	8,100.2	8,524.2	8,759.8
Total Current Liabilities	796.5	538.9	510.1	342.9
Long-Term Debt	7.9	0.0	0.0	0.0
Stockholders' Equity	7,385.4	7,191.4	7,480.6	7,635.2
Performance & Financial Condition				
Return on Total Revenues %	2.63	-0.09	0.90	-4.81
Return on Avg Stockholders' Equity %	3.26	-0.10	1.07	-4.88
Return on Average Assets %	2.84	-0.09	0.93	-4.22
Current Ratio	6.95	9.08	9.67	14.07
Debt / Equity %	0.11	n.a.	n.a.	n.a.

Compound Growth %'s	EPS % n.a.	Net Income % n.a.	Total Revenues % 4.27

Comments

The 12% increase in sales occurred mostly in the second half. No shut down of the tunnel kiln is expected which may return the Company to significant profit levels in 1997. 1995 results include a one time charge of $243,336 for the cost of pension plan curtailment. The Company has been using excess cash to repurchase shares and invest in other businesses including the construction and rental of a building for a Wendy's franchise. Logan Clay has almost no long-term debt and a very comfortable current ratio. Investment Classification: Value

Officers	Position	Ownership Information	
Barton S. Holl	Chairman	Number of Shares Outstanding	159,179
Richard H. Holl	President, CEO	Market Capitalization	$ 3,422,349
Richard H. Brandt	Exec VP, COO	Frequency of Dividends	Annual
Elizabeth H. Brandt	Other	Number of Shareholders	Under 500

Other Information

			Where Listed	OTC-BB
Transfer Agent	Company Office		Symbol	JGNC
Auditor	Robinson, Caltrider, Associate		SIC Code	3200
Market Maker	Martin Nelson & Co., Inc.	(206)682-6261	Employees	96
	Hill Thompson Magid & Co., Inc	(800)631-3083		
Broker Dealer	OTC Specialist			
	Stephen Schuller - Dorsey	(800)375-5431		

Long Island Commercial Bank

One Suffolk Square   Islandia, NY 11722   Telephone (516)348-0888   Fax (516)348-0542

Company Description

Long Island Commercial Bank is one of the youngest banks in this manual, having opened for business in 1990. The Bank offers a wide range of banking services to small privately owned businesses, professionals, municipalities and non-profit organizations from three offices. It also offers a limited number of consumer products in both Suffolk and Nassau Counties. In February, 1996, the Bank closed a secondary stock offering, issuing 329,700 shares of common stock at $10 per share.

	12/31/96	12/31/95	12/31/94	12/31/93
Per Share Information				
Stock Price	10.50	10.00	4.00	4.00
Earnings Per Share	1.18	1.43	0.71	0.20
Price / Earnings Ratio	8.90	6.99	5.63	20.00
Book Value Per Share	10.60	9.74	8.39	7.90
Price / Book Value %	99.06	102.67	47.68	50.63
Dividends Per Share	0.30	0.25	0.10	0.0
Annual Financial Data				
Operating Results (000's)				
Net Interest Income	4,211.9	2,919.0	2,008.0	1,482.7
Loan Loss Provision	-302.0	-180.0	-180.0	-375.0
Non-Interest Income	364.2	337.8	296.4	392.3
Non-Interest Expense	-2,709.0	-2,217.0	-1,700.0	-1,364.2
Income Before Taxes and Other	1,565.1	859.8	424.3	135.8
Other Items	0.0	0.0	0.0	0.0
Income Tax	-530.5	-172.9	-44.3	-18.0
Net Income	1,034.6	686.8	380.1	117.8
Balance Sheet (000's)				
Cash & Securities	125,173.0	61,993.4	48,645.0	24,366.0
Loans, Net	62,659.7	38,843.4	23,341.0	17,745.7
Total Assets	190,897.7	102,507.4	72,986.0	42,940.7
Deposits	178,313.8	94,683.1	67,425.0	37,959.4
Stockholders' Equity	9,889.9	5,844.6	5,034.0	4,740.8
Performance & Financial Condition				
Return on Avg Stockholders' Equity %	13.15	12.63	7.78	2.52
Return on Average Assets %	0.71	0.78	0.66	0.30
Equity to Assets %	5.18	5.70	6.90	11.04
Net Interest Margin	n.a.	n.a.	n.a.	n.a.
Reserve as a % of Problem Loans	242.28	150.06	125.32	71.51

Compound Growth %'s	EPS % 80.70	Net Income % 106.30	Net Interest Income % 41.63

Comments

The infusion of capital and a rapidly rising deposit base, 88% in 1996, is allowing Long Island Commercial Bank to get off to a running start. All goals were exceeded in 1996, with the exception of opening one office which was just a little late. The Smithtown branch opened on February 3, 1997. Management intends to open another branch in 1997, and one more each year thereafter. Other loans, in the box below, are entirely automobile loans. Investment Classification: Growth & Value

Officers	Position	Ownership Information	
Douglas C. Manditch	President, CEO	Number of Shares Outstanding	933,181
Thomas Buonaiuto	Senior VP, CFO	Market Capitalization	$ 9,798,401
Carmelo Vizzini	Senior VP, Sr Loan Officer	Frequency of Dividends	Semi-Annual
Peter Daloia	Vice President	Number of Shareholders	n.a.
Todd L. Flamenbaum	Vice President	Where Listed / Symbol	OTC-BB / LGCB

Other Information			Loan Mix	%
Transfer Agent	Company Office		Commerical	39.3
Auditor	KPMG Peat Marwick LLP		R/E Mortgages	29.3
Market Maker	Sandler O'Neill & Partners LP	(800)635-6986	Consumer	1.4
Broker Dealer	Regular Stockbroker		Other	30.0

Louisiana Central Net Profits Units

P.O. Box 2009   Amarillo, TX 79105-2009   Telephone (806)378-1000   Fax (806)378-8614

Company Description

The Trust is an entity with no existing activities. Arrangements have been made whereby the unit holders receive their share of royalty payments made to the Trust. Under the terms of a 1966 agreement, Pioneer Natural Gas Company purchased certain property interests from Louisiana Central Oil & Gas Company subject to specified net profits payments. In 1986, Mesa Limited Partnership, now Mesa Inc., acquired Pioneer Natural Gas Company and, accordingly, the obligations under the agreement.

	12/31/96	12/31/95	12/31/94	12/31/93
Per Share Information				
Stock Price	390.00	375.00	350.00	300.00
Earnings Per Share	60.24	57.31	59.93	79.73
Price / Earnings Ratio	6.47	6.54	5.84	3.76
Book Value Per Share	n.a.	n.a.	n.a.	n.a.
Price / Book Value %	n.a.	n.a.	n.a.	n.a.
Dividends Per Share	60.24	57.31	59.93	79.73
Annual Financial Data				
Operating Results (000's)				
Total Revenues	902.2	858.3	897.5	1,194.2
Costs & Expenses	0.0	0.0	0.0	0.0
Income Before Taxes and Other	902.2	858.3	897.5	1,194.2
Other Items	0.0	0.0	0.0	0.0
Income Tax	0.0	0.0	0.0	0.0
Net Income	902.2	858.3	897.5	1,194.2
Cash Flow From Operations	902.2	858.3	897.5	1,194.2
Balance Sheet (000's)				
Cash & Equivalents	n.a.	n.a.	n.a.	n.a.
Total Current Assets	n.a.	n.a.	n.a.	n.a.
Fixed Assets, Net	n.a.	n.a.	n.a.	n.a.
Total Assets	n.a.	n.a.	n.a.	n.a.
Total Current Liabilities	n.a.	n.a.	n.a.	n.a.
Long-Term Debt	n.a.	n.a.	n.a.	n.a.
Stockholders' Equity	n.a.	n.a.	n.a.	n.a.
Performance & Financial Condition				
Return on Total Revenues %	100.00	100.00	100.00	100.00
Return on Avg Stockholders' Equity %	n.a.	n.a.	n.a.	n.a.
Return on Average Assets %	n.a.	n.a.	n.a.	n.a.
Current Ratio	n.a.	n.a.	n.a.	n.a.
Debt / Equity %	n.a.	n.a.	n.a.	n.a.

Compound Growth %'s	EPS %	-8.92	Net Income %	-8.92	Total Revenues %	-8.92

Comments

There is no valuation of the remaining royalty interests. The increase in cash flow during 1996 was due to higher prices for both oil and gas and higher production of gas. Oil production was slightly lower. Payments to the unitholders are considered royalties and may be subject to depletion deductions under current income tax regulations. Investment Classification: Income & Value

Officers	Position	Ownership Information	
Not Available		Number of Shares Outstanding	14,977
		Market Capitalization	$ 5,841,030
		Frequency of Dividends	Semi-Annual
		Number of Shareholders	Under 500

Other Information

			Where Listed	OTC-BB
Transfer Agent	American Stock Transfer & Trust Company New York, NY		Symbol	LCNTU
Auditor	Arthur Andersen LLP		SIC Code	6733
Market Maker	Howe Barnes Investments, Inc.	(800)621-2364	Employees	0
	Hill Thompson Magid & Co., Inc	(800)631-3083		
Broker Dealer	Regular Stockbroker			

Louisville Bedding Company

10400 Bunsen Way   Louisville, KY 40299-2510   Telephone (502)491-3370   Fax (502)495-5346

Company Description

Louisville Bedding Company is engaged in the manufacture of textile home furnishings. Products include quilted mattress pads, pillows, pillow shams, dust ruffles and decorative home furnishings. The Company was incorporated in 1903 as the Louisville Pillow Company, successor to the business of a partnership organized in 1889. The present name was taken in 1917. Please enjoy the brief summary of a wonderful history, displayed on the following page.

	12/31/96	12/29/95	12/30/94	12/31/93
Per Share Information				
Stock Price	33.75	28.50	30.50	19.00
Earnings Per Share	7.32	3.47	6.14	4.05
Price / Earnings Ratio	4.61	8.21	4.97	4.69
Book Value Per Share	45.17	37.66	34.73	29.02
Price / Book Value %	74.72	75.68	87.82	65.47
Dividends Per Share	0.76	0.76	0.73	0.69
Annual Financial Data				
Operating Results (000's)				
Total Revenues	118,415.7	119,487.4	123,162.0	109,524.0
Costs & Expenses	-110,756.3	-116,261.2	-117,318.9	-105,706.8
Income Before Taxes and Other	7,659.3	3,226.2	5,843.0	3,817.2
Other Items	0.0	0.0	0.0	150.0
Income Tax	-2,884.0	-1,036.8	-2,027.0	-1,376.0
Net Income	4,775.3	2,189.4	3,816.0	2,591.2
Cash Flow From Operations	8,668.0	7,715.5	563.4	2,511.1
Balance Sheet (000's)				
Cash & Equivalents	641.8	587.3	765.1	1,040.4
Total Current Assets	33,498.6	33,996.1	40,309.8	33,246.1
Fixed Assets, Net	16,172.1	17,433.1	17,379.3	14,761.7
Total Assets	52,496.6	53,513.1	60,144.9	50,060.2
Total Current Liabilities	10,264.9	12,795.3	17,099.9	14,913.4
Long-Term Debt	13,853.3	17,472.6	20,396.2	15,216.3
Stockholders' Equity	27,441.6	22,186.8	21,246.9	17,647.8
Performance & Financial Condition				
Return on Total Revenues %	4.03	1.83	3.10	2.37
Return on Avg Stockholders' Equity %	19.24	10.08	19.62	14.87
Return on Average Assets %	9.01	3.85	6.93	5.46
Current Ratio	3.26	2.66	2.36	2.23
Debt / Equity %	50.48	78.75	96.00	86.22

Compound Growth %'s	EPS %	21.81	Net Income %	22.60	Total Revenues %	2.64

Comments

The efficiencies of the new distribution center, a stabilization of raw material prices, and lower inventories all contributed to a record year of earnings. Management is still concerned about the decline in sales and is likely to focus more intently on strategic acquisitions. At the same time we are told to expect the elimination of some unprofitable product lines. Because of the wide spread between bid and ask prices, it might be prudent to have a specialist post your own bid price slightly higher than all the others. For the first three months of 1997, the Company reported earnings of $787,000 as compared to $512,000 in the same period of 1996. Investment Classification: Value

Officers	Position	Ownership Information	
Harold C. Forrester, Sr.	Chairman	Number of Shares Outstanding	607,529
John M. Minihan	President, CEO	Market Capitalization	$ 20,504,104
Christian F. Rapp	Senior VP, CFO	Frequency of Dividends	Quarterly
Michael H. Romero	VP - Sales	Number of Shareholders	Under 500
Virginia L. Koernner	Controller		

Other Information			
Transfer Agent	Company Office	Where Listed	OTC-BB
Auditor	KPMG Peat Marwick LLP	Symbol	LBED
Market Maker	Koonce Securities, Inc.	(800)368-2802	SIC Code	2515
	Hill Thompson Magid & Co., Inc	(800)631-3083	Employees	800
Broker Dealer	Regular Stockbroker		

Pillows and Mattresses

Eight years ago, in 1989, the Louisville Bedding Company proudly celebrated its centennial. There was indeed a great deal to celebrate. The company, whose current sales of $118 million are backed by strong financial condition, has been in existence since before automobiles, radios or moving pictures were part of our landscape. It was born in an era of discovery, invention and expansion in America, when telephones were novelties and only forty-two states existed in the United States.

Situated as it is on the southern bank of the Ohio River, Louisville, Kentucky was in 1889 a major industrial and mercantile hub on the border between the north and south. The twentieth largest city in our nation, Louisville boasted the latest in modern conveniences and a pervasive spirit of enterprise. It was a perfect time, Samuel D. Cruse decided, to strike out on his own.

Mr. Cruse had gained early experience working for a mercantile company. He now began to manufacture mattresses and pillows himself by forming the Louisville Pillow and Mattress Company, which later became the Louisville Bedding Company. The business grew and by about 1900, wool as well as cotton comforters had been added to the company's product lines. In 1905 the company, which now had an approximate value of $31,400, was sold to Milburn Kelly.

Over the next two decades Louisville Bedding Company's growth was impressive, with sales reaching $1,000,000 by 1923. Improvements during this time included the purchase of *auto trucks*, which began to replace the mules and wagons commonly used for deliveries in earlier years. The company's prosperity was also reflected in its support of the war effort when, in 1917, it purchased $8,000 worth of Liberty Bonds. After the war, the Roaring Twenties saw America anxious to indulge in material comforts. The Company capitalized on this mood, advertising its wares with the slogan, "Invest in Rest".

By 1930, however, sales had mysteriously declined by over fifty percent. Good times vanished; in fact, the company stopped making *any* money. The Great Depression hit Louisville Bedding hard, and the company struggled simply to survive and keep its workers on the payroll. Their determination paid off. Employees later gratefully recalled that they always had a paycheck and that none were laid off. Not many companies can boast of an accomplishment of this magnitude.

Today, the company has facilities located throughout Kentucky and in California. Sales showrooms exist in New York and Atlanta and all of their products are marketed internationally. The company now has over 800 employees and a book value of $27,400,000. It is clear that Louisville Bedding Company has done much more than simply survive; it is a model for other would-be winners to follow.

Luzerne National Bank Corporation

118 Main Street   Luzerne, PA 18709   Telephone (717)288-4511   Fax (717)283-3419

Company Description

Camp Luzerne was one of only two Union training camps in Pennsylvania during the Civil War. The town Luzerne grew up after the War. The Corporation's subsidiary, Luzerne National Bank, was formed in 1907 by a group of local residents. It now has a branch in Swoyersville as well. Concerned about staying independent, the shareholders approved anti-takeover policies in 1995. The Bank acts as facilitator for investors wishing to buy or sell stock.

	12/31/96	12/31/95	12/31/94	12/31/93
Per Share Information				
Stock Price	25.00	23.00	21.50	20.00
Earnings Per Share	3.48	2.30	1.81	1.05
Price / Earnings Ratio	7.18	10.00	11.88	19.05
Book Value Per Share	21.81	18.92	15.07	15.35
Price / Book Value %	114.63	121.56	142.67	130.29
Dividends Per Share	0.43	0.40	0.40	0.30
Annual Financial Data				
Operating Results (000's)				
Net Interest Income	4,075.0	3,561.0	3,277.0	2,445.0
Loan Loss Provision	-185.0	-245.0	-388.0	-366.0
Non-Interest Income	393.0	177.0	127.0	306.0
Non-Interest Expense	-2,671.0	-2,472.0	-2,243.0	-1,963.0
Income Before Taxes and Other	1,612.0	1,021.0	773.0	422.0
Other Items	0.0	0.0	0.0	0.0
Income Tax	-491.0	-284.0	-198.0	-87.0
Net Income	1,121.0	737.0	575.0	335.0
Balance Sheet (000's)				
Cash & Securities	31,711.0	34,689.0	34,618.0	38,780.0
Loans, Net	49,234.0	44,980.0	43,633.0	36,556.0
Total Assets	84,394.0	82,342.0	80,383.0	77,070.0
Deposits	73,423.0	75,647.0	75,012.0	71,674.0
Stockholders' Equity	6,934.0	6,017.0	4,793.0	4,880.0
Performance & Financial Condition				
Return on Avg Stockholders' Equity %	17.31	13.64	11.89	6.89
Return on Average Assets %	1.34	0.91	0.73	0.47
Equity to Assets %	8.22	7.31	5.96	6.33
Net Interest Margin	n.a.	n.a.	n.a.	n.a.
Reserve as a % of Problem Loans	n.a.	n.a.	n.a.	n.a.

Compound Growth %'s	EPS %	49.10	Net Income %	49.57	Net Interest Income %	18.56

Comments

The Corporation approved a 2 for 1 split in 1995. All per share amounts have been restated for consistency. Compound earnings growth rates are pushed higher by a poor performance in 1993, the base year. But the last three years all produced record earnings and returns on assets and equity reached a fine level in 1996. A third office will be opened in Back Mountain in 1997. Investment Classification: Growth

Officers	Position	Ownership Information	
William V. Leandri	President, CEO	Number of Shares Outstanding	318,000
Alexander T. Kormas	Vice President	Market Capitalization	$ 7,950,000
Michael Kerkowski	Vice President	Frequency of Dividends	Semi-Annual
Michael Mondy	Sr Loan Officer	Number of Shareholders	n.a.
		Where Listed / Symbol	Order Matching Only / n.a.

Other Information		Loan Mix	%
Transfer Agent	Company Office	Not Allocated	100
Auditor	Not indicated		
Market Maker	Company Office - See Note		
Broker Dealer	None		

M.H. Rhodes, Inc.

99 Thompson Road   Avon, CT 06001   Telephone (860)673-3281   Fax (860)673-8633

Company Description

The Company manufactures mechanical and electrical timers. Timers are used in commercial cooking equipment, HVAC applications, bio-medical devices and other special applications. The Company has been in the same line of business since its formation in 1930. The Ripley Company's Photocontrol Division was acquired in 1990. Photocontrols are devices that are inserted on the tops of street and roadway lights. Their prime purpose is to individually turn the light on at certain darkness levels.

	12/31/96	12/31/95	12/31/94	12/31/93
Per Share Information				
Stock Price	3.50	5.50	5.50	3.75
Earnings Per Share	-0.88	-4.38	0.38	0.62
Price / Earnings Ratio	n.a.	n.a.	14.47	6.05
Book Value Per Share	19.21	19.14	16.00	14.84
Price / Book Value %	18.22	28.74	34.38	25.27
Dividends Per Share	0.0	0.0	0.0	0.0
Annual Financial Data				
Operating Results (000's)				
Total Revenues	8,011.1	8,083.7	9,844.0	10,328.3
Costs & Expenses	-8,191.8	-8,968.6	-9,771.5	-10,189.6
Income Before Taxes and Other	-184.8	-884.8	72.6	138.7
Other Items	0.0	0.0	0.0	0.0
Income Tax	7.5	-10.6	6.8	-9.1
Net Income	-177.4	-895.5	79.4	129.5
Cash Flow From Operations	597.8	370.6	2.9	82.8
Balance Sheet (000's)				
Cash & Equivalents	137.8	32.5	6.2	14.3
Total Current Assets	4,107.3	4,470.6	5,962.6	5,559.5
Fixed Assets, Net	759.0	844.3	995.1	1,086.0
Total Assets	4,886.5	5,347.0	6,998.3	6,709.1
Total Current Liabilities	1,503.1	2,384.7	2,380.5	2,520.7
Long-Term Debt	726.5	275.6	1,160.6	1,039.7
Stockholders' Equity	2,483.6	2,564.9	3,330.9	3,120.5
Performance & Financial Condition				
Return on Total Revenues %	-2.21	-11.08	0.81	1.25
Return on Avg Stockholders' Equity %	-7.03	-30.38	2.46	4.35
Return on Average Assets %	-3.47	-14.51	1.16	1.89
Current Ratio	2.73	1.87	2.50	2.21
Debt / Equity %	29.25	10.75	34.84	33.32

Compound Growth %'s	EPS % n.a.	Net Income % n.a.	Total Revenues % -8.12

Comments

Management closed the Canadian operation during 1996 in an effort to become more efficient. A good recovery from the 1995 loss was noted as well as increased cash flow from operations. Although sales have been flat, new orders are arriving. At December 31, 1996, the Company had a backlog of sale orders totaling $3.4 as compared to $2.8 million at the end of the preceding year. Management reports that photocontrol continues to gain market share in the domestic utility market. For the first quarter of 1997, sales were flat and a loss of $122,699, $.61 per share, was reported. Investment Classification: Value & Speculative

Officers	Position	Ownership Information	
J. L. Morelli	President, Chairman	Number of Shares Outstanding	129,278
A. D. Springer	VP - Finance, Treasurer	Market Capitalization	$ 452,473
S. L. Vanasse	Secretary	Frequency of Dividends	n.a.
H. B. Matles	Vice President	Number of Shareholders	667

Other Information

			Where Listed	OTC-BB
Transfer Agent	Mellon Shareholders Services, LLC Ridgefield Park, NJ		Symbol	RHMH
Auditor	Riggs & Associates		SIC Code	3625
Market Maker	Herzog, Heine, Geduld, Inc.	(800)221-3600	Employees	89
	Carr Securities Corporation	(800)221-2243		
Broker Dealer	Regular Stockbroker			

MLX Corp.

1000 Center Place   Norcross, GA 30093   Telephone (770)798-0677   Fax (770)798-0633

Company Description

MLX is engaged in the active search for acquisition opportunities which have attractive valuations and which meet certain financial acquisition criteria. MLX's strategic assets include a federal tax loss carryforward of approximately $275 million, available cash equivalents exceeding $35 million, the public listing of its common stock and management experience in a variety of industries. This current position followed the divestiture of an existing business in 1995.

	12/31/96	12/31/95	12/31/94	12/31/93
Per Share Information				
Stock Price	13.25	9.87	n.a.	n.a.
Earnings Per Share	0.20	7.53	n.a.	n.a.
Price / Earnings Ratio	66.25	1.31	n.a.	n.a.
Book Value Per Share	14.04	13.76	n.a.	n.a.
Price / Book Value %	94.37	71.73	n.a.	n.a.
Dividends Per Share	0.0	0.0	n.a.	n.a.
Annual Financial Data				
Operating Results (000's)				
Total Revenues	1,876.0	1,074.0	17.0	93.0
Costs & Expenses	-997.0	-1,129.0	-1,029.0	-1,708.0
Income Before Taxes and Other	879.0	-73.0	-1,106.0	-1,615.0
Other Items	0.0	20,865.0	3,477.0	6,732.0
Income Tax	-317.0	18.0	376.0	549.0
Net Income	562.0	20,810.0	2,747.0	5,666.0
Cash Flow From Operations	955.0	-1,999.0	5,063.0	n.a.
Balance Sheet (000's)				
Cash & Equivalents	37,927.0	32,903.0	n.a.	n.a.
Total Current Assets	37,973.0	37,119.0	n.a.	n.a.
Fixed Assets, Net	4.0	5.0	n.a.	n.a.
Total Assets	39,431.0	38,509.0	n.a.	n.a.
Total Current Liabilities	669.0	674.0	n.a.	n.a.
Long-Term Debt	0.0	0.0	n.a.	n.a.
Stockholders' Equity	36,764.0	35,878.0	n.a.	n.a.
Performance & Financial Condition				
Return on Total Revenues %	29.96	1,937.62	n.a.	n.a.
Return on Avg Stockholders' Equity %	1.55	n.a.	n.a.	n.a.
Return on Average Assets %	1.44	n.a.	n.a.	n.a.
Current Ratio	56.76	55.07	n.a.	n.a.
Debt / Equity %	n.a.	n.a.	n.a.	n.a.

Compound Growth %'s   EPS % n.a.   Net Income % n.a.   Total Revenues % n.a.

Comments

More than 150 acquisition candidates have been evaluated over the last eighteen months. Corporate funds continue to be invested in overnight repurchase agreements backed by the United States Treasury and federal agency obligations. A large chunk, $144 million, of the tax loss carryover expires in 1997 if not used. The trading range of the shares is very close to the net cash per share equivalent, if not at a slight discount. This is one of the better "blank checks" we have seen; the investment is backed by cash and several bonuses are added. But like all blank checks, we do not know what business will be acquired or the timing. Investment Classification: Speculative

Officers	Position	Ownership Information	
Alfred R. Glancy III	Chairman	Number of Shares Outstanding	2,618,000
Thomas C. Waggoner	President, CEO	Market Capitalization	$ 34,688,500
Theodore R. Kallgren	Secretary, Treasurer	Frequency of Dividends	n.a.
Mary M. McCulley	Other	Number of Shareholders	8,900

Other Information			
Transfer Agent	American Stock & Transfer Co. New York, NY	Where Listed	OTC-BB
Auditor	Ernst & Young LLP	Symbol	MLXR
Market Maker	Robotti & Co., Inc.	(212)986-0800	SIC Code	6770
	Carr Securities Corporation	(800)221-2243	Employees	n.a.
Broker Dealer	Regular Stockbroker		

Magicworks Entertainment Incorporated

930 Washington Avenue, Suite 640   Miami Beach, FL 33139   Telephone (305)532-1566   Fax (305)532-4014

Company Description

Magicworks Entertainment Incorporated acquires domestic and international stage and ancillary rights to theatrical productions, produces and promotes live entertainment, manages and books performances and shows, and merchandises a broad range of products associated with its productions and performers. Prior to 1992, the Company focused primarily on the worldwide production of "The Magic of David Copperfield."

	12/31/96	12/31/95	12/31/94	12/31/93
Per Share Information				
Stock Price	3.00	n.a.	n.a.	n.a.
Earnings Per Share	0.06	n.a.	n.a.	n.a.
Price / Earnings Ratio	50.00	n.a.	n.a.	n.a.
Book Value Per Share	0.19	n.a.	n.a.	n.a.
Price / Book Value %	1,578.95	n.a.	n.a.	n.a.
Dividends Per Share	0.0	n.a.	n.a.	n.a.
Annual Financial Data				
Operating Results (000's)				
Total Revenues	71,953.6	54,439.3	41,010.0	41,654.9
Costs & Expenses	-68,802.4	-49,253.5	-37,021.0	-36,548.9
Income Before Taxes and Other	3,151.2	5,185.8	3,989.0	5,106.1
Other Items	11.7	-1,446.9	-1,460.0	-1,828.4
Income Tax	-1,759.0	-1,458.2	-987.0	-1,278.3
Net Income	1,404.0	2,280.7	1,542.0	1,999.4
Cash Flow From Operations	1,500.2	4,853.4	5,571.0	n.a.
Balance Sheet (000's)				
Cash & Equivalents	6,367.2	5,098.0	0.0	0.0
Total Current Assets	10,429.0	9,005.0	0.0	0.0
Fixed Assets, Net	2,076.3	1,346.0	0.0	0.0
Total Assets	14,854.7	11,717.0	8,396.5	4,152.4
Total Current Liabilities	3,795.9	7,625.0	0.0	0.0
Long-Term Debt	6,177.5	393.0	0.0	0.0
Stockholders' Equity	4,607.1	2,229.0	2,499.1	1,642.0
Performance & Financial Condition				
Return on Total Revenues %	1.95	4.19	3.76	4.80
Return on Avg Stockholders' Equity %	41.08	96.48	74.47	174.11
Return on Average Assets %	10.57	22.68	24.58	54.85
Current Ratio	2.75	1.18	n.a.	n.a.
Debt / Equity %	134.09	17.63	n.a.	n.a.

Compound Growth %'s	EPS % n.a.	Net Income % -11.12	Total Revenues % 19.99

Comments

Over the last several years, the Company has experienced significant growth, primarily as a result of the success of its productions as well as its continued diversification. Management believes that the touring live entertainment industry is a high-growth industry and is seeking touring rights for well-established, popular musicals. Promotion revenue increased by $18.9 million during 1996, primarily as a result of the successful promotion of "The Phantom of the Opera" and the Southeast Asia tour of "David Copperfield." 1997 will have a 50% increase in the number of productions. Investment Classification: Speculative

Officers	Position	Ownership Information	
Brad Krassner	Chairman, CEO	Number of Shares Outstanding	24,394,300
Lee Marshall	President, COO	Market Capitalization	$ 73,182,900
Steven Chaby	CFO	Frequency of Dividends	n.a.
		Number of Shareholders	250

Other Information

			Where Listed	OTC-BB
Transfer Agent	Progressive Transfer Co. Salt Lake city, UT		Symbol	MAJK
Auditor	Arthur Andersen LLP		SIC Code	7900
Market Maker	Alpine Securities Corporation	(800)521-5588	Employees	n.a.
	Acap Financial Inc.	(800)541-3961		
Broker Dealer	Regular Stockbroker			

Main Street Athletic Clubs, Inc.

1901 South Bascom Ave., #1440   Campbell, CA 95008   Telephone (408)371-7144   Fax (408)371-7149

Company Description

Main Street Athletic Clubs owns and operates seven health and fitness clubs in northern California. Four clubs are located in the greater San Jose area and three clubs are located in the Monterey Bay area. The predecessor to the Company was Foxworthy Athletic Club which operated as a partnership until the beginning of 1995. Management is seeking expansion through acquisitions. A public offering of 500,000 shares of common for $10 per share was 86% complete on May 16, 1997.

	12/31/96	12/31/95	12/31/94	12/31/93
Per Share Information				
Stock Price	6.00	n.a.	n.a.	n.a.
Earnings Per Share	0.14	0.19	0.16	0.21
Price / Earnings Ratio	42.86	n.a.	n.a.	n.a.
Book Value Per Share	0.14	0.25	n.a.	n.a.
Price / Book Value %	4,285.71	n.a.	n.a.	n.a.
Dividends Per Share	0.0	0.0	0.0	0.0
Annual Financial Data				
Operating Results (000's)				
Total Revenues	3,974.6	3,837.2	3,511.0	2,483.7
Costs & Expenses	-3,747.8	-3,668.7	-3,275.7	-2,154.1
Income Before Taxes and Other	-154.7	-60.3	235.3	329.6
Other Items	348.1	309.5	0.0	0.0
Income Tax	-5.1	-77.2	-94.1	-131.8
Net Income	188.3	172.0	141.2	197.8
Cash Flow From Operations	486.2	472.0	827.7	757.8
Balance Sheet (000's)				
Cash & Equivalents	162.3	7.9	0.2	3.0
Total Current Assets	277.4	93.2	692.5	504.4
Fixed Assets, Net	3,092.0	2,367.3	1,469.7	1,091.2
Total Assets	4,390.7	3,467.1	3,259.4	1,595.7
Total Current Liabilities	1,663.0	1,720.8	2,031.4	1,601.7
Long-Term Debt	2,539.5	1,518.1	177.3	247.3
Stockholders' Equity	188.2	228.3	777.5	-615.3
Performance & Financial Condition				
Return on Total Revenues %	4.74	4.48	4.02	7.96
Return on Avg Stockholders' Equity %	90.43	34.20	174.07	n.a.
Return on Average Assets %	4.79	5.11	5.82	17.42
Current Ratio	0.17	0.05	0.34	0.31
Debt / Equity %	1349.40	665.01	22.81	n.a.

Compound Growth %'s	EPS % -12.64	Net Income % -1.62	Total Revenues % 16.97

Comments

Chester Billingsley has proven to be a charismatic leader as he has found no shortage of clubs wanting to join his growing empire. The Company has plenty of press coverage too and was 386th on INC. Magazine's 500 fastest-growing private companies. Proceeds from the stock offering, referred to above, will provide working capital and funds for additional acquisitions. Investment Classification: Speculative

Officers	Position	Ownership Information	
Chester Billingsley	Chairman, CEO	Number of Shares Outstanding	1,325,084
Joseph Gigantino	COO	Market Capitalization	$ 7,950,504
Norman P. Monson	CFO	Frequency of Dividends	n.a.
Dave Billingsley	Vice President	Number of Shareholders	n.a.

Other Information				
Transfer Agent	Company Office		Where Listed	OTC-BB
Auditor	Mark Shelley & Associates		Symbol	MFIT
Market Maker	Sharpe Capital Inc.	(800)355-5781	SIC Code	7991
	Wm. V. Frankel & Co., Inc.	(800)631-3091	Employees	n.a.
Broker Dealer	Regular Stockbroker			

Marin, Bank of

1101 Fourth Street San Rafael, CA 94901 Telephone (415)485-2265 Fax (415)485-2256

Company Description

Known for its hot tubs and creative use of peacock features, Marin County, California is also one of the wealthiest counties in the United States on a per capita basis. Lying on the north side of the Golden Gate Bridge over the San Francisco Bay, Bank of Marin has five excellent locations to access this customer base as well as customers from the greater Bay area. The Bank was founded in 1990.

	12/31/96	12/31/95	12/31/94	12/31/93
Per Share Information				
Stock Price	20.00	14.62	12.58	n.a.
Earnings Per Share	1.70	1.36	1.19	n.a.
Price / Earnings Ratio	11.76	10.75	10.57	n.a.
Book Value Per Share	11.72	12.10	10.44	n.a.
Price / Book Value %	170.65	120.83	120.50	n.a.
Dividends Per Share	0.0	0.0	0.0	n.a.
Annual Financial Data				
Operating Results (000's)				
Net Interest Income	9,143.2	7,828.3	6,386.0	4,731.4
Loan Loss Provision	-425.0	-475.0	-450.0	-410.0
Non-Interest Income	779.8	632.0	478.0	402.3
Non-Interest Expense	-6,302.6	-5,490.1	-4,373.9	-3,655.5
Income Before Taxes and Other	3,195.4	2,495.2	2,040.0	1,068.2
Other Items	0.0	0.0	0.0	0.0
Income Tax	-1,189.0	-989.0	-788.0	-233.1
Net Income	2,006.4	1,506.2	1,252.0	835.1
Balance Sheet (000's)				
Cash & Securities	61,839.8	61,839.8	37,614.8	n.a.
Loans, Net	97,831.2	97,831.2	85,636.7	n.a.
Total Assets	164,195.1	164,195.1	126,628.7	n.a.
Deposits	146,795.6	146,795.6	110,676.0	n.a.
Stockholders' Equity	13,568.0	13,568.0	11,401.4	n.a.
Performance & Financial Condition				
Return on Avg Stockholders' Equity %	14.79	12.06	12.31	10.07
Return on Average Assets %	1.22	1.04	1.06	0.90
Equity to Assets %	8.26	8.26	9.00	n.a.
Net Interest Margin	5.71	5.97	5.62	n.a.
Reserve as a % of Problem Loans	n.a.	n.a.	n.a.	n.a.

Compound Growth %'s	EPS %	19.52	Net Income %	33.93	Net Interest Income %	24.56

Comments

The Bank declared 6% and 5% stock dividends in 1996 and 1995, respectively. All per share amounts have been adjusted for consistency. Strong growth in deposits (18.7%) and loans (29.1%) are the primary reasons for the large gain in net interest income. Returns on assets and equity have steadily been rising for this young bank. Management reports excellent quality in its loan portfolio. Compound growth in earnings per share represents the change between 1994 and 1996. Investment Classification: Growth

Officers	Position	Ownership Information	
J. D. Sullivan	Chairman, CEO	Number of Shares Outstanding	1,157,505
W. Robert Griswold, Jr.	President, COO	Market Capitalization	$ 23,150,100
Philip J. Salz	Senior VP	Frequency of Dividends	n.a.
Alexandra E. Souza	Senior VP, Head Cashier	Number of Shareholders	869
Martha W. Hollenbeck	Secretary	Where Listed / Symbol	OTC-BB / BMRC

Other Information			Loan Mix	%
Transfer Agent	Company Office		R/E Mortgages	51.6
Auditor	Not indicated		Commerical	30.2
Market Maker	Hoefer & Arnett, Incorproated	(800)346-5544	Installment	10.5
	A.G. Edwards & Sons, Inc.	(800)325-8197	Construction	7.7
Broker Dealer	Regular Stockbroker			
	Hoefer & Arnett, Retail	(800)346-5544 Ext: Lisa		

Market America, Inc.

7605-A Business Park Drive   Greensboro, NC 27409   Telephone (910)605-0040   Fax (910)605-0041

Company Description

Market America is a product brokerage and direct sales company that uses a proprietary marketing plan called binary marketing. The Company sells a variety of consumer home-use products through a network of part-time independent contract sales people. The Company was formed in 1992 and merged with another company in 1993 via a reverse acquisition. Operations prior to 1993 were minimal. Trading in the Company's common stock began in 1994.

	04/30/96	04/30/95	04/30/94	04/30/93
Per Share Information				
Stock Price as of 12/31	5.12	2.19	1.41	n.a.
Earnings Per Share	0.26	0.04	0.01	n.a.
Price / Earnings Ratio	19.69	54.75	141.00	n.a.
Book Value Per Share	0.31	0.05	0.01	n.a.
Price / Book Value %	1,651.61	4,380.00	14,100.00	n.a.
Dividends Per Share	0.0	0.0	0.0	n.a.
Annual Financial Data				
Operating Results (000's)				
Total Revenues	42,797.9	19,615.6	9,391.9	1,321.9
Costs & Expenses	-34,292.8	-18,287.0	-9,072.5	-1,368.7
Income Before Taxes and Other	8,505.1	1,328.6	319.5	-46.9
Other Items	0.0	0.0	0.0	0.0
Income Tax	-3,351.9	-533.8	-107.3	16.4
Net Income	5,153.2	794.8	212.2	-30.5
Cash Flow From Operations	8,020.6	2,129.2	870.5	-26.5
Balance Sheet (000's)				
Cash & Equivalents	10,455.9	2,830.0	807.9	50.8
Total Current Assets	11,561.4	3,285.8	1,000.7	124.4
Fixed Assets, Net	542.9	327.1	263.3	195.9
Total Assets	12,238.3	3,619.0	1,274.8	325.8
Total Current Liabilities	5,387.1	2,162.0	1,028.4	316.2
Long-Term Debt	324.4	128.3	24.6	0.0
Stockholders' Equity	6,169.7	1,016.5	221.8	9.5
Performance & Financial Condition				
Return on Total Revenues %	12.04	4.05	2.26	-2.30
Return on Avg Stockholders' Equity %	143.42	128.37	183.49	n.a.
Return on Average Assets %	64.99	32.48	26.52	n.a.
Current Ratio	2.15	1.52	0.97	0.39
Debt / Equity %	5.26	12.62	11.09	n.a.

Compound Growth %'s	EPS %	409.90	Net Income %	392.78	Total Revenues %	218.72

Comments

Sales continue to grow rapidly, increasing another 117% in fiscal 1996. Earnings climbed 500%. The Company has been able to execute its growth strategy without the need of either external financing or an equity issue. Health and Nutritional Store sales continue to boom. The BioTech Store and The Automotive Store doubled their sales and The Personal Care Store tripled its sales. 8,000 people attended the third annual convention held in Tyson's Corner, Virginia. Corporate facilities were expanded. Can anything go wrong? Investment Classification: Growth

Officers	Position	Ownership Information	
James H. Ridinger	President, CEO	Number of Shares Outstanding	19,950,000
Dennis Franks	Exec VP	Market Capitalization	$ 102,144,000
Martin Weissman	Exec VP	Frequency of Dividends	n.a.
Loren A. Ridinger	Vice President	Number of Shareholders	n.a.
Edward Faulkner	Controller		

Other Information

Transfer Agent	TranSecurities, International, Inc. Spokane, WA		Where Listed	OTC-BB
Auditor	Terrence J. Dunne, CPA		Symbol	MARK
Market Maker	Wilson-Davis & Co., Inc.	(800)453-5735	SIC Code	7319
	Nash, Weiss & Co.	(800)526-3041	Employees	64
Broker Dealer	Regular Stockbroker			

Market Guide, Inc.

2001 Marcus Ave., Ste. So. 200   Lake Success, NY 11042-1011   Telephone (516)327-2400   Fax (516)327-2420

Company Description

Market Guide, Inc. acquires and publishes financial information on publicly traded companies and markets this information to the financial community. Information is primarily obtained from reports filed by the subject company with the Securities and Exchange Commission. The Company was incorporated in New York in 1983. In the last fiscal year, the Company issued 343,363 shares of common stock in a private placement for $3.50 per share.

	02/28/97	02/29/96	02/28/95	02/28/94
Per Share Information				
Stock Price as of 12/31	3.00	4.50	2.72	1.40
Earnings Per Share	0.06	0.12	0.08	0.08
Price / Earnings Ratio	50.00	37.50	34.00	17.50
Book Value Per Share	0.86	0.58	0.45	0.17
Price / Book Value %	348.84	775.86	604.44	823.53
Dividends Per Share	0.0	0.0	0.0	0.0
Annual Financial Data				
Operating Results (000's)				
Total Revenues	4,807.5	4,024.4	2,688.0	2,001.1
Costs & Expenses	-4,551.6	-3,516.1	-2,332.7	-1,733.8
Income Before Taxes and Other	256.0	508.3	355.3	267.3
Other Items	0.0	0.0	0.0	0.0
Income Tax	2.4	-1.1	-16.8	-19.1
Net Income	258.3	507.2	338.4	248.2
Cash Flow From Operations	827.9	593.5	119.9	395.0
Balance Sheet (000's)				
Cash & Equivalents	1,230.9	680.8	695.1	200.5
Total Current Assets	2,051.9	1,706.4	1,343.8	532.3
Fixed Assets, Net	1,207.0	667.6	426.8	136.9
Total Assets	5,228.6	3,471.7	2,603.1	1,230.8
Total Current Liabilities	604.2	732.3	576.9	625.9
Long-Term Debt	564.3	291.2	182.7	14.1
Stockholders' Equity	4,060.2	2,448.2	1,843.5	590.8
Performance & Financial Condition				
Return on Total Revenues %	5.37	12.60	12.59	12.40
Return on Avg Stockholders' Equity %	7.94	23.64	27.81	53.18
Return on Average Assets %	5.94	16.70	17.66	22.96
Current Ratio	3.40	2.33	2.33	0.85
Debt / Equity %	13.90	11.89	9.91	2.39

Compound Growth %'s	EPS %	-9.14	Net Income %	1.34	Total Revenues %	33.93

Comments

The Company executed a 1 for 4 reverse stock split in August, 1995. All per share amounts have been restated for consistency. Earnings per share growth has been diluted by the issuance of additional shares. The Company has a net operating loss carryforward of approximately $1 million which expires in fiscal years 2000 through 2003. Revenues increased 19% in fiscal year 1997, reflecting improvement in all markets served by the Company. Investment Classification: Speculative

Officers	Position	Ownership Information	
John D. Case	Chairman, Secretary	Number of Shares Outstanding	4,708,186
Homi M. Byramji	President, CEO	Market Capitalization	$ 14,124,558
		Frequency of Dividends	n.a.
		Number of Shareholders	800

Other Information			
Transfer Agent	American Stock Transfer & Trust Company New York, NY	Where Listed	OTC-BB
Auditor	Zerbo & McKiernan P.C.	Symbol	MARG
Market Maker	Herzog, Heine, Geduld, Inc. (800)221-3600	SIC Code	7380
	Mayer & Schweitzer, Inc. (800)631-3094	Employees	87
Broker Dealer	Regular Stockbroker		

Mauch Chunk Trust Company

1111 North Street   Jim Thorpe, PA 18229   Telephone (717)325-2265   Fax (717)325-8368

Company Description

Mauch Chunk Trust Company is a full service bank with four offices serving Carbon County, Pennsylvania. The last office to open was in Redner's Warehouse Market in Nesquehoning during 1996. The Bank also offers a full line of trust services. An interesting comparison could be made between Mauch Chunk Trust Company and JTNB Bancorp (Jim Thorpe National Bank) which operates in the same community and is also presented in this book. 1997 marks the 95th anniversary of the Bank. We extend our congratulations.

	12/31/96	12/31/95	12/31/94	12/31/93
Per Share Information				
Stock Price	48.00	35.42	30.97	27.89
Earnings Per Share	4.14	3.68	3.48	3.30
Price / Earnings Ratio	11.59	0.63	8.90	8.45
Book Value Per Share	37.02	35.14	30.24	27.12
Price / Book Value %	129.66	100.80	102.41	102.84
Dividends Per Share	1.26	0.80	0.66	0.59
Annual Financial Data				
Operating Results (000's)				
Net Interest Income	3,871.6	3,531.3	3,528.6	3,370.3
Loan Loss Provision	-185.5	-42.0	-36.0	-36.5
Non-Interest Income	426.3	328.2	351.9	299.8
Non-Interest Expense	-2,441.9	-2,286.8	-2,254.1	-2,180.4
Income Before Taxes and Other	1,670.5	1,530.8	1,590.4	1,453.2
Other Items	0.0	0.0	0.0	-1.1
Income Tax	-317.0	-328.9	-466.3	-408.1
Net Income	1,353.5	1,201.8	1,124.1	1,043.9
Balance Sheet (000's)				
Cash & Securities	48,571.9	35,378.1	22,758.6	22,841.4
Loans, Net	63,517.4	58,534.0	53,712.6	49,515.7
Total Assets	115,396.2	96,690.8	79,005.1	74,876.7
Deposits	78,621.1	69,379.7	61,221.9	57,820.5
Stockholders' Equity	12,097.7	11,484.7	9,882.6	8,730.1
Performance & Financial Condition				
Return on Avg Stockholders' Equity %	11.48	11.25	12.08	12.71
Return on Average Assets %	1.28	1.37	1.46	1.42
Equity to Assets %	10.48	11.88	12.51	11.66
Net Interest Margin	n.a.	n.a.	n.a.	n.a.
Reserve as a % of Problem Loans	n.a.	1,157.30	150.65	167.88

Compound Growth %'s	EPS %	7.85	Net Income %	9.04	Net Interest Income %	4.73

Comments

The 1996 stock price is the first bid price to have been posted by a market maker. Earlier prices were calculated from dividend reinvestment plan activity as shown in the financial statements. In addition to a healthy increase in net interest income, trust assets under management increased 24% to $11.5 million. Income from trust activity improved 19%. Management expects the current banking environment to continue to evolve at a rapid pace. Investment Classification: Value

Officers	Position	Ownership Information	
Patrick H. Reilly	President, CEO	Number of Shares Outstanding	326,782
Edward J. McElmoyle	Secretary, Treasurer	Market Capitalization	$ 15,685,536
Ray W. Reitz	Vice President	Frequency of Dividends	Quarterly
Melva L. McArdle	Other	Number of Shareholders	n.a.
Linda Snyder	Other	Where Listed / Symbol	OTC-PS / MCTP

Other Information			Loan Mix	%
Transfer Agent	Company Office		R/E Mortgages	60.5
Auditor	Beard & Company, Inc.		Commerical	25.6
Market Maker	Ryan, Beck & Co.	(800)223-8969	Installment	13.9
	F.J. Morrissey & Co., Inc.	(800)842-8928		
Broker Dealer	OTC Specialist			
	Jack Ingold	(412)391-4594		

Maui Land & Pineapple Company, Inc.

120 Kane Street   Kahului, HI 96732   Telephone (808)877-3351   Fax (808)871-0953

Company Description

The Company is both a land-holding and operating company with several wholly-owned subsidiaries, including Maui Pineapple Company, Ltd.("Pineapple") and Kapalua Land Company, Inc.("Kapalua"). The Company owns approximately 28,000 acres on the island of Maui. Pineapple is the sole supplier of private label canned pineapple products to U.S. supermarkets. Kapalua is the developer of a destination resort on Maui. The Company also owns and operates other significant commercial and residential property on Maui. The Company was founded in 1909.

	12/31/96	12/31/95	12/31/94	12/31/93
Per Share Information				
Stock Price	42.50	41.00	55.00	102.50
Earnings Per Share	-0.42	-0.87	-2.18	-6.15
Price / Earnings Ratio	n.a.	n.a.	n.a.	n.a.
Book Value Per Share	32.29	32.76	33.63	35.79
Price / Book Value %	131.62	125.15	163.54	286.39
Dividends Per Share	0.05	0.0	0.0	0.75
Annual Financial Data				
Operating Results (000's)				
Total Revenues	136,335.0	125,577.0	125,882.0	131,172.0
Costs & Expenses	-136,576.0	-128,602.0	-132,620.0	-149,654.0
Income Before Taxes and Other	-1,123.0	-3,025.0	-6,738.0	-18,482.0
Other Items	0.0	0.0	0.0	0.0
Income Tax	376.0	1,466.0	2,829.0	7,423.0
Net Income	-747.0	-1,559.0	-3,909.0	-11,059.0
Cash Flow From Operations	11,754.0	2,142.0	11,536.0	-2,360.0
Balance Sheet (000's)				
Cash & Equivalents	453.0	166.0	2,269.0	1,223.0
Total Current Assets	35,308.0	36,554.0	40,960.0	49,460.0
Fixed Assets, Net	86,610.0	88,557.0	180,194.0	148,774.0
Total Assets	132,851.0	137,085.0	235,411.0	211,588.0
Total Current Liabilities	15,841.0	13,126.0	42,057.0	20,062.0
Long-Term Debt	27,347.0	36,227.0	99,180.0	96,108.0
Stockholders' Equity	58,033.0	58,870.0	60,429.0	64,321.0
Performance & Financial Condition				
Return on Total Revenues %	-0.55	-1.24	-3.11	-8.43
Return on Avg Stockholders' Equity %	-1.28	-2.61	-6.27	-15.74
Return on Average Assets %	-0.55	-0.84	-1.75	-5.68
Current Ratio	2.23	2.78	0.97	2.47
Debt / Equity %	47.12	61.54	164.13	149.42

Compound Growth %'s	EPS % n.a.	Net Income % n.a.	Total Revenues %	1.30

Comments

Most of the Company's land was acquired during the period from 1911 to 1932 and is carried at cost. Management is engineering a return to profitability but was hampered by very dry weather which reduced the pineapple crop. The reduction in loss is actually more significant if one factors in $5 million of non-cash income that was recorded in the preceding year. Good progress is also reported in the development of new products. The overall sluggishness of Hawaii's economy has dampened the real estate and resort business on a temporary basis. Investment Classification: Value

Officers	Position	Ownership Information	
Gary L. Gifford	President, CEO	Number of Shares Outstanding	1,797,125
Paul J. Meyer	Exec VP, CFO	Market Capitalization	$ 76,377,813
Douglas R. Schenk	Exec VP	Frequency of Dividends	n.a.
Donald A. Young	Exec VP	Number of Shareholders	388
Adele H. Sumida	Secretary		

Other Information				
Transfer Agent	ChaseMellon Shareholder Services Ridgefield Park, NJ		Where Listed	OTC-BB
Auditor	Deloitte & Touche LLP		Symbol	MAUI
Market Maker	Martin Nelson & Co., Inc.	(206)682-6261	SIC Code	2033
	Monroe Securities, Inc.	(800)766-5560	Employees	2160
Broker Dealer	Regular Stockbroker			

Mechanics Bank (The)

3170 Hilltop Mall Road   Richmond, CA 94806   Telephone (510)262-7200   Fax (510)262-7959

Company Description

The Mechanics Bank was formed in 1905 and now operates fifteen offices in Contra Costa, Alameda and Napa Counties, California. The Bank's primary source of revenue is providing loans and related banking services to customers who are predominately individuals and small businesses. Investment management and trust services are also provided. At least two new openings will occur in 1997; a Berkeley branch opened in February and a branch in Marin County will open in the second half of the year. The Bank is very proud of its history and financial condition and is already making plans to celebrate its 100th anniversary as an independent community bank.

	12/31/96	12/31/95	12/31/94	12/31/93
Per Share Information				
Stock Price	7,200.00	5,500.00	4,500.00	4,000.00
Earnings Per Share	641.83	585.52	545.86	502.97
Price / Earnings Ratio	11.22	9.39	8.24	7.95
Book Value Per Share	6,039.71	5,603.23	5,118.50	4,694.09
Price / Book Value %	119.21	98.16	87.92	85.21
Dividends Per Share	180.00	165.00	134.00	120.00
Annual Financial Data				
Operating Results (000's)				
Net Interest Income	47,595.1	45,091.4	45,366.1	44,558.2
Loan Loss Provision	-1,400.0	-1,275.0	-2,100.0	-4,300.0
Non-Interest Income	7,263.2	6,657.6	5,888.6	6,775.7
Non-Interest Expense	-35,231.2	-34,585.6	-34,260.6	-32,803.0
Income Before Taxes and Other	18,227.1	15,888.4	14,894.1	14,230.9
Other Items	0.0	0.0	0.0	0.0
Income Tax	-5,390.5	-4,178.0	-3,977.0	-4,171.4
Net Income	12,836.6	11,710.4	10,917.1	10,059.5
Balance Sheet (000's)				
Cash & Securities	374,582.2	396,235.1	358,150.4	337,401.9
Loans, Net	649,626.6	551,963.0	502,617.3	455,161.7
Total Assets	1,054,140.9	980,664.3	890,653.7	822,474.3
Deposits	896,277.1	832,565.2	762,553.2	698,104.1
Stockholders' Equity	120,794.2	112,064.6	102,370.0	93,881.7
Performance & Financial Condition				
Return on Avg Stockholders' Equity %	11.03	10.92	11.13	11.17
Return on Average Assets %	1.26	1.25	1.27	1.27
Equity to Assets %	11.46	11.43	11.49	11.41
Net Interest Margin	n.a.	n.a.	n.a.	n.a.
Reserve as a % of Problem Loans	679.65	1,834.54	n.a.	n.a.

Compound Growth %'s	EPS %	8.47	Net Income %	8.47	Net Interest Income %	2.22

Comments

Net income was at a record high for the eighth consecutive year. Management expects to continue a steady rate of expansion and has targeted key areas of the greater San Francisco Bay area. Fee income from trust and investment management was up 27% as compared to 1995. The Bank has instituted several programs dedicated to nurturing employee excellence. The SIP (Stakeholders in Performance) program now provides immediate cash awards to all employees if financial goals are met. Sounds good. Where do we sign up? Investment Classification: Value

Officers	Position	Ownership Information	
William M. Reid	President, CEO	Number of Shares Outstanding	20,000
Steven I. Barlow	Exec VP	Market Capitalization	$ 144,000,000
Robert B. Leet	Exec VP	Frequency of Dividends	Quarterly
William J. Schwerin	Senior VP	Number of Shareholders	n.a.
John R. Balsiger	CFO	Where Listed / Symbol	OTC-BB / MCHB

Other Information			Loan Mix	%
Transfer Agent	Company Office		R/E Mortgages	50.4
Auditor	Arthur Andersen LLP		Installment	38.0
Market Maker	Hoefer & Arnett, Incorporated	(800)346-5544	Commerical	10.8
	Sutro & Co., Incorporated	(800)227-4422	Other	0.8
Broker Dealer	OTC Specialist			
	Standard Investment	(888)783-4688 Ext: Jack		

Medjet Inc.

1090 King Geroges Post Rd.#201   Edison, NJ 08837   Telephone (908)738-3990   Fax (908)738-3984

Company Description

Medjet Inc., founded in 1993, is engaged in the research and development of medical technology with an emphasis on ophthalmic surgical technology and equipment, and has developed a proprietary technology and derivative devices for corneal surgery. The Company has not tested its HydroBlade (Trademark) Keratome on live human eyes but has tested it on over 1,000 porcine and rabbit corneas, over 24 cadaver eyes and 22 live rabbits. The Company is currently readying its prototype for studies on blind human eyes in a clinical setting.

	12/31/96	12/31/95
Per Share Information		
Stock Price	7.12	n.a.
Earnings Per Share	-0.43	n.a.
Price / Earnings Ratio	n.a.	n.a.
Book Value Per Share	1.15	n.a.
Price / Book Value %	619.13	n.a.
Dividends Per Share	0.0	n.a.
Annual Financial Data		
Operating Results (000's)		
Total Revenues	86.7	7.9
Costs & Expenses	-1,360.3	-685.1
Income Before Taxes and Other	-1,273.6	-677.2
Other Items	0.0	0.0
Income Tax	-0.4	-0.2
Net Income	-1,274.0	-677.4
Cash Flow From Operations	-1,134.6	-706.2
Balance Sheet (000's)		
Cash & Equivalents	4,242.0	n.a.
Total Current Assets	4,290.7	n.a.
Fixed Assets, Net	171.1	n.a.
Total Assets	4,540.3	n.a.
Total Current Liabilities	349.8	n.a.
Long-Term Debt	0.0	n.a.
Stockholders' Equity	4,190.4	n.a.
Performance & Financial Condition		
Return on Total Revenues %	-1,469.37	n.a.
Return on Avg Stockholders' Equity %	n.a.	n.a.
Return on Average Assets %	n.a.	n.a.
Current Ratio	12.26	n.a.
Debt / Equity %	n.a.	n.a.

Compound Growth %'s	EPS % n.a.	Net Income % n.a.	Total Revenues % n.a.

Comments

At December 31, 1996, the Company had sixteen employees all of whom were engaged in research and development activities. Outside professionals have also been engaged to handle various aspects of the developmental process. On August 14, 1996, the Company consummated its initial public offering. The common stock began trading on the OTC Bulletin Board on November 14, 1996. Management believes it has adequate cash reserves for at least the balance of 1997. Investment Classification: Speculative

Officers	Position	Ownership Information	
Eugene I. Gordon	Chairman, President	Number of Shares Outstanding	3,648,666
Thomas M. Handschiegel	VP - Finance, Secretary	Market Capitalization	$ 25,978,502
		Frequency of Dividends	n.a.
		Number of Shareholders	33

Other Information				
Transfer Agent	Continental Stock Transfer & Trust Co. New York, NY		Where Listed	OTC-BB
Auditor	Rosenberg Rich Baker Berman		Symbol	MDJT
Market Maker	Citadel Securities Corp.	(516)378-1000	SIC Code	3841
	Patterson Travis Inc.	(800)377-8625	Employees	16
Broker Dealer	Regular Stockbroker			

Mendocino Brewing Company, Inc.

13351 South Highway 101 Hopland, CA 95449 Telephone (707)744-1015 Fax (707)744-1910

Company Description

The Company produces domestic specialty beers and sells to distributors and other retailers. The Company's operations are located in Mendocino County, approximately 80 miles north of San Francisco. Distribution is primarily in northern California, but also extends to eight other western states. Production has been at capacity since 1988. A new brewery in Ukiah began operations in May, 1997, which is expected to increase capacity from 18,000 barrels per year to 50,000 barrels in the near-term and 200,000 barrels later. The growth of the micro brewing industry, which was growing at a 40% to 50% rate annually, has cooled slightly in 1996. The Company also has retail operations consisting of a brewpub and gift shop. The Company was founded in 1983.

		12/31/96	12/31/95	12/31/94	12/31/93
Per Share Information					
	Stock Price	7.06	7.56	6.00	n.a.
	Earnings Per Share	-0.05	0.08	0.08	n.a.
	Price / Earnings Ratio	n.a.	94.50	75.00	n.a.
	Book Value Per Share	1.75	1.81	1.57	n.a.
	Price / Book Value %	403.43	417.68	382.17	n.a.
	Dividends Per Share	0.0	0.0	0.0	n.a.
Annual Financial Data					
Operating Results (000's)					
	Total Revenues	3,851.3	3,714.1	3,552.1	3,389.4
	Costs & Expenses	-4,012.1	-3,387.5	-3,327.3	-3,168.7
	Income Before Taxes and Other	-202.0	326.6	224.8	220.7
	Other Items	0.0	0.0	0.0	0.0
	Income Tax	78.2	-152.9	-71.5	-81.8
	Net Income	-123.8	173.7	153.3	138.9
	Cash Flow From Operations	224.0	6.4	197.8	391.6
Balance Sheet (000's)					
	Cash & Equivalents	494.8	1,696.1	2,900.8	296.0
	Total Current Assets	1,346.3	2,473.8	3,422.0	757.0
	Fixed Assets, Net	9,270.3	3,954.1	301.0	206.8
	Total Assets	11,144.6	6,514.0	4,038.1	1,079.6
	Total Current Liabilities	4,963.1	1,514.7	314.8	288.2
	Long-Term Debt	0.0	554.9	0.0	7.5
	Stockholders' Equity	4,300.4	4,424.2	3,723.3	783.9
Performance & Financial Condition					
	Return on Total Revenues %	-3.21	4.68	4.31	4.10
	Return on Avg Stockholders' Equity %	-2.84	4.26	6.80	n.a.
	Return on Average Assets %	-1.40	3.29	5.99	n.a.
	Current Ratio	0.27	1.63	10.87	2.63
	Debt / Equity %	n.a.	12.54	n.a.	0.96

Compound Growth %'s	EPS % n.a.	Net Income % n.a.	Total Revenues % 4.35

Comments

The Company undertook a direct public offering of their stock, raising approximately $3.3 million (600,000 shares at an average of $5.52 per share) in the latter part of 1994 and the first part of 1995. In February, 1995, the Company was listed on the Pacific Stock exchange with an opening trade of $8.25. We are not impressed with 1996 results which were dragged down by a $400,000 increase in marketing costs. In May, 1997, Indian beer mogul Vijay Mallya announced plans to invest $3.5 million in the Company. Investment Classification: Speculative

Officers	Position	Ownership Information	
H. Michael Laybourn	CEO, President	Number of Shares Outstanding	2,322,222
Norman H. Franks	CFO, Treasurer	Market Capitalization	$ 16,394,887
Michael F. Lovett	Secretary	Frequency of Dividends	n.a.
		Number of Shareholders	2,435

Other Information			
Transfer Agent	The First National Bank of Boston Boston, MA	Where Listed	PSE
Auditor	Moss Adams LLP	Symbol	MBRP
Market Maker	None	SIC Code	2082
		Employees	72
Broker Dealer	Regular Stockbroker		

Merchants of Shenandoah Ban-Corp

101 N. Main Street   Shenandoah, PA 17976-0110   Telephone (717)462-1983   Fax (717)462-0549

Company Description

Merchants National Bank of Shenandoah, subsidiary of the Corporation, is primarily locally owned and serves the banking needs of a diverse base of residents and businesses in northern Schuylkill and southern Luzerne Counties. This area of Pennsylvania was strictly rural and agricultural when the Bank began operations in 1891. Today it considers itself urban with almost 6,000 residents in the City of Shenandoah alone. This is where one's perspective may make a real difference.

	12/31/96	12/31/95	12/31/94	12/31/93
Per Share Information				
Stock Price	25.50	25.00	24.50	24.50
Earnings Per Share	1.57	1.27	1.03	1.13
Price / Earnings Ratio	16.24	19.69	23.79	21.68
Book Value Per Share	21.76	21.11	18.19	20.54
Price / Book Value %	117.19	118.43	134.69	119.28
Dividends Per Share	0.50	0.46	0.44	0.40
Annual Financial Data				
Operating Results (000's)				
Net Interest Income	2,112.2	2,026.7	2,059.0	1,970.6
Loan Loss Provision	-88.0	-45.0	0.0	-18.0
Non-Interest Income	171.8	177.5	188.3	288.1
Non-Interest Expense	-1,615.0	-1,663.4	-1,860.2	-1,879.7
Income Before Taxes and Other	581.0	495.7	387.0	361.0
Other Items	0.0	0.0	0.0	0.0
Income Tax	-124.4	-126.2	-88.5	-32.3
Net Income	456.6	369.5	298.5	328.7
Balance Sheet (000's)				
Cash & Securities	27,167.9	28,462.1	28,925.0	31,065.3
Loans, Net	29,370.8	29,922.9	31,203.2	24,224.3
Total Assets	58,129.0	59,740.7	61,846.2	56,800.9
Deposits	49,709.0	51,513.0	52,420.8	49,906.9
Stockholders' Equity	6,335.3	6,146.3	5,297.9	5,980.9
Performance & Financial Condition				
Return on Avg Stockholders' Equity %	7.32	6.46	5.29	5.59
Return on Average Assets %	0.77	0.61	0.50	n.a.
Equity to Assets %	10.90	10.29	8.57	10.53
Net Interest Margin	n.a.	n.a.	n.a.	n.a.
Reserve as a % of Problem Loans	n.a.	54.51	72.91	143.82

Compound Growth %'s	EPS %	11.59	Net Income %	11.58	Net Interest Income %	2.34

Comments

The Company declared a 2 for 1 stock split in 1994. 1993 per share amounts were adjusted accordingly. Net income rose 23.55% in 1996. Despite modest declines in total assets, loans and deposits, net interest income was improved by close managing of interest spreads. At year end there were no non-accrual loans. High quality loan growth continues to be management's top priority. Investment Classification: Value

Officers	Position	Ownership Information	
Anthony R. Cali	President, CEO	Number of Shares Outstanding	291,186
Jane A. Mallick	Senior VP, Head Cashier	Market Capitalization	$ 7,425,243
Dwain J. Barlow	Vice President	Frequency of Dividends	Quarterly
Norma J. Barlow	Vice President, CFO	Number of Shareholders	n.a.
Barbara W. Mitchell	Other	Where Listed / Symbol	OTC-BB / MSHN

Other Information			Loan Mix	%
Transfer Agent	Company Office		R/E Mortgages	71.7
Auditor	Jarrett Stokes & Kelly		Commerical	18.4
Market Maker	F.J. Morrissey & Co., Inc.	(800)842-8928	Installment	6.5
	Ryan, Beck & Co.	(800)395-7926	Other	3.4
Broker Dealer	Regular Stockbroker			

Merchants' National Properties, Inc.

708 Third Avenue   New York, NY 10017-4201   Telephone (212)557-1400   Fax (212)983-4532

Company Description

The Company owns and leases real estate to various commercial tenants and invests in various real estate ventures. The properties are located in the United States and Canada. Investments in the ventures are carried under the equity method of accounting, which approximates the Company's share in the underlying net book value of the properties.

	12/31/95	12/31/94	12/31/93
Per Share Information			
Stock Price as of 12/31	184.00	135.00	135.00
Earnings Per Share	40.69	30.35	30.64
Price / Earnings Ratio	4.52	4.45	4.41
Book Value Per Share	449.88	411.30	325.83
Price / Book Value %	40.90	32.82	41.43
Dividends Per Share	20.00	15.00	20.00
Annual Financial Data			
Operating Results (000's)			
Total Revenues	7,632.5	5,755.6	5,719.7
Costs & Expenses	-621.9	-170.0	-195.9
Income Before Taxes and Other	7,010.5	5,564.4	5,497.8
Other Items	-19.1	0.0	0.0
Income Tax	-2,373.3	-2,120.1	-1,995.6
Net Income	4,618.0	3,444.3	3,502.2
Cash Flow From Operations	270.8	1,807.0	-214.7
Balance Sheet (000's)			
Cash & Equivalents	2,380.7	1,437.4	1,482.9
Total Current Assets	15,658.3	7,102.1	8,675.5
Fixed Assets, Net	6,093.7	6,283.1	6,562.9
Total Assets	57,612.7	52,598.3	37,998.2
Total Current Liabilities	867.7	1,356.3	528.7
Long-Term Debt	0.0	0.0	0.0
Stockholders' Equity	51,048.6	46,597.0	36,979.2
Performance & Financial Condition			
Return on Total Revenues %	60.50	59.84	61.23
Return on Avg Stockholders' Equity %	9.46	8.24	9.62
Return on Average Assets %	8.38	7.60	9.47
Current Ratio	18.05	5.24	16.41
Debt / Equity %	n.a.	n.a.	n.a.

Compound Growth %'s	EPS %	15.24	Net Income %	14.83	Total Revenues %	15.52

Comments

Stockholders' equity at the end of 1995 year includes approximately $10 million in order to adopt GAAP reporting for the fair market value of security investments that have appreciated in value. The substantial increase in earnings results from the sale of properties and a rise in joint venture income. The 1996 report was not yet available as we went to press. Investment Classification: Income & Value

Officers	Position	Ownership Information	
Leonard Marx, Sr.	Chairman	Number of Shares Outstanding	113,471
		Market Capitalization	$ 20,878,664
		Frequency of Dividends	Quarterly
		Number of Shareholders	Under 500

Other Information				
Transfer Agent	Company Office		Where Listed	OTC-BB
Auditor	Frank & Zimmerman & Co. LLP		Symbol	MNPP
Market Maker	Hill Thompson Magid & Co., Inc	(800)631-3083	SIC Code	6510
	Herzog, Heine, Geduld, Inc.	(800)221-3600	Employees	3
Broker Dealer	OTC Specialist			

Mercom, Inc.

105 Carnegie Center   Princeton, NJ 08540   Telephone (609)734-3700   Fax (609)951-8632

Company Description

Mercom is a cable television operator with three cable systems in southern Michigan and one in Port St. Lucie, Florida. At December 31, 1996, the systems had 40,000 subscribers. The Company completed the issuance of 2.4 million shares of common stock at $3.60 per share through a rights offering in August, 1995. Proceeds were used primarily to repay outstanding debt.

	12/31/96	12/31/95	12/31/94	12/31/93
Per Share Information				
Stock Price	6.50	5.25	3.38	3.63
Earnings Per Share	0.31	0.16	-0.27	-0.10
Price / Earnings Ratio	20.97	32.81	n.a.	n.a.
Book Value Per Share	-0.61	-0.92	-5.51	-5.24
Price / Book Value %	n.a.	n.a.	n.a.	n.a.
Dividends Per Share	0.0	0.0	0.0	0.0
Annual Financial Data				
Operating Results (000's)				
Total Revenues	15,709.0	14,217.0	12,957.0	12,632.0
Costs & Expenses	-14,172.0	-13,670.0	-12,952.0	-12,841.0
Income Before Taxes and Other	1,500.0	547.0	-662.0	-219.0
Other Items	0.0	0.0	0.0	0.0
Income Tax	-28.0	2.0	4.0	-17.0
Net Income	1,472.0	549.0	-658.0	-236.0
Cash Flow From Operations	4,103.0	2,366.0	2,591.0	3,136.0
Balance Sheet (000's)				
Cash & Equivalents	3,054.0	2,033.0	96.0	989.0
Total Current Assets	3,524.0	2,590.0	697.0	1,310.0
Fixed Assets, Net	14,248.0	15,434.0	16,451.0	17,946.0
Total Assets	19,851.0	20,390.0	19,823.0	22,244.0
Total Current Liabilities	5,340.0	5,851.0	7,093.0	6,598.0
Long-Term Debt	17,430.0	18,930.0	25,926.0	28,184.0
Stockholders' Equity	-2,919.0	-4,391.0	-13,196.0	-12,538.0
Performance & Financial Condition				
Return on Total Revenues %	9.37	3.86	-5.08	-1.87
Return on Avg Stockholders' Equity %	n.a.	n.a.	n.a.	n.a.
Return on Average Assets %	7.32	2.73	-3.13	-1.02
Current Ratio	0.66	0.44	0.10	0.20
Debt / Equity %	n.a.	n.a.	n.a.	n.a.

Compound Growth %'s	EPS %	n.a.	Net Income %	n.a.	Total Revenues %	7.54

Comments

C-TEC Corporation owns approximately 62% of the outstanding stock of the Company. C-TEC intends to spin-off two of its operating divisions as separate companies. One of these will be C-TEC Cable Systems of Michigan which will consist of C-TEC's classic cable television operations and its interest in Mercom. The improved net earnings in 1996 are attributable to higher operating income and lower interest expense because of the repayment of debt in 1995. Investment Classification: Speculative

Officers	Position	Ownership Information	
David C. McCourt	Chairman, CEO	Number of Shares Outstanding	4,787,060
Michael J. Mahoney	President, COO	Market Capitalization	$ 31,115,890
Bruce C. Godfrey	Exec VP, CFO	Frequency of Dividends	n.a.
Raymond B. Ostroski	Exec VP	Number of Shareholders	1,804
John D. Filipowicz	Vice President, Secretary		

Other Information			
Transfer Agent	Boston EquiServe Boston, MA	Where Listed	OTC-BB
Auditor	Coopers & Lybrand L.L.P.	Symbol	MEEO
Market Maker	Gabelli & Company, Inc.	(914)921-5153	SIC Code	4841
	Carr Securities Corporation	(800)221-2243	Employees	52
Broker Dealer	Regular Stockbroker		

Meritage Hospitality Group Inc.

40 Pearl Street N.W.   Grand Rapids, MI 49503   Telephone (616)776-2600   Fax (616)776-2776

Company Description

Meritage Hospitality Group, Inc., formerly Thomas Edison Inns, is engaged in the hospitality business including the operation of hotels and restaurants. The Company owns the Thomas Edison Inn, the St. Clair Inn and the Spring Lake Holiday Inn, all in Michigan, with a total of 348 rooms. Each hotel has a picturesque waterfront setting and seeks business and leisure travelers who desire full service accommodations. The Company also owns a 54% limited partner interest in Wendy's of West Michigan Limited Partnership which operates 26 Wendy's Old-Fashioned Hamburger restaurants.

	11/30/96	11/30/95	11/30/94	11/30/93
Per Share Information				
Stock Price as of 12/31	5.50	6.63	7.50	7.50
Earnings Per Share	-0.62	-1.13	-0.02	0.15
Price / Earnings Ratio	n.a.	n.a.	n.a.	50.00
Book Value Per Share	0.63	2.01	3.44	3.46
Price / Book Value %	873.02	329.85	218.02	216.76
Dividends Per Share	0.50	0.0	0.0	0.0
Annual Financial Data				
Operating Results (000's)				
Total Revenues	17,536.0	15,069.8	15,458.8	14,639.5
Costs & Expenses	-19,502.6	-17,840.3	-15,256.7	-14,244.0
Income Before Taxes and Other	-1,966.6	-2,770.5	202.1	395.5
Other Items	21.1	0.0	-117.3	0.0
Income Tax	20.0	721.4	-112.0	-165.1
Net Income	-1,925.6	-2,049.1	-27.2	230.4
Cash Flow From Operations	-1,496.4	425.3	989.9	1,056.1
Balance Sheet (000's)				
Cash & Equivalents	2,265.5	1,336.9	621.8	450.7
Total Current Assets	4,059.5	3,014.9	1,969.2	1,531.0
Fixed Assets, Net	21,757.1	13,218.3	13,645.0	14,068.6
Total Assets	31,928.9	17,983.5	19,688.4	20,004.0
Total Current Liabilities	3,956.4	2,971.3	1,562.9	1,981.1
Long-Term Debt	21,711.8	11,204.9	12,251.7	12,240.2
Stockholders' Equity	2,021.4	3,055.4	5,225.1	5,252.2
Performance & Financial Condition				
Return on Total Revenues %	-10.98	-13.60	-0.18	1.57
Return on Avg Stockholders' Equity %	-75.86	-49.49	-0.52	4.49
Return on Average Assets %	-7.72	-10.88	-0.14	1.15
Current Ratio	1.03	1.01	1.26	0.77
Debt / Equity %	1074.08	366.73	234.48	233.05

Compound Growth %'s	EPS % n.a.	Net Income % n.a.	Total Revenues % 6.20

Comments

On October 26, 1996, the Company entered into an agreement to acquire the general partnership interest in the Wendy's Partnership. It is anticipated that the agreement will be executed in 1997. It is the Company's intention to ultimately acquire the entire business of the Wendy's Partnership. Revenues increased 16.9% but the Company is still showing a loss. Investment Classification: Speculative

Officers	Position	Ownership Information	
Christopher B. Hewett	President, CEO	Number of Shares Outstanding	3,214,379
Robert E. Schermer, Jr.	Exec VP	Market Capitalization	$ 17,679,085
William D. Badgerow	Vice President, CFO	Frequency of Dividends	n.a.
James R. Saalfeld	Vice President, Secretary	Number of Shareholders	600

Other Information

Transfer Agent	ChaseMellon Shareholder Services Ridgefield Park, NJ		Where Listed	OTC-BB
Auditor	Grant Thornton LLP		Symbol	MHGI
Market Maker	Stifel, Nicolaus & Company	(800)776-6821	SIC Code	7011
	Robert W. Baird & Co., Inc.	(800)562-2288	Employees	142
Broker Dealer	Regular Stockbroker			

Meteor Industries, Inc.

216 Sixteenth Street, Ste. 730   Denver, CO 80202   Telephone (303)572-1135   Fax (303)572-1803

Company Description

The Company is a wholesale and retail distributor of petroleum products primarily in several western states. It also operates retail gasoline and convenience stores in New Mexico and Colorado. The Company was formed in December, 1992, and raised $800,000 in equity capital in 1994 with a Reg. A offering. In June, 1995, Meteor acquired Hillger Oil Company. This acquisition doubled the Company's gasoline sales and improved cash flows. In November, 1995, the Company issued 1,745,000 shares of its stock in the acquisition of Capco Resources whose major assets were a California environmental services firm, a $1.5 million promissory note, and an interest in a company that is involved in the development of a power plant in Pakistan.

	12/31/96	08/31/95	08/31/94
Per Share Information			
Stock Price	5.06	2.50	5.19
Earnings Per Share	0.15	0.12	0.02
Price / Earnings Ratio	33.73	20.83	259.50
Book Value Per Share	1.55	0.80	0.58
Price / Book Value %	326.45	312.50	894.83
Dividends Per Share	0.0	0.0	0.0
Annual Financial Data			
Operating Results (000's)			
Total Revenues	60,380.1	45,372.9	39,159.8
Costs & Expenses	-59,237.0	-45,412.2	-39,169.0
Income Before Taxes and Other	1,143.0	-39.3	-9.2
Other Items	-286.5	0.0	0.0
Income Tax	-394.7	191.7	28.6
Net Income	461.8	152.3	19.4
Cash Flow From Operations	842.0	2,177.1	-702.3
Balance Sheet (000's)			
Cash & Equivalents	1,080.3	244.2	522.6
Total Current Assets	8,487.9	6,682.5	6,556.3
Fixed Assets, Net	8,277.4	5,767.7	4,561.7
Total Assets	20,433.7	14,581.3	12,255.6
Total Current Liabilities	8,942.9	6,950.6	5,606.1
Long-Term Debt	445.8	2,095.7	2,603.6
Stockholders' Equity	5,119.9	1,014.1	482.1
Performance & Financial Condition			
Return on Total Revenues %	0.76	0.34	0.05
Return on Avg Stockholders' Equity %	15.06	20.36	n.a.
Return on Average Assets %	2.64	1.14	n.a.
Current Ratio	0.95	0.96	1.17
Debt / Equity %	8.71	206.66	540.01

Compound Growth %'s	EPS % n.a.	Net Income % n.a.	Total Revenues % 24.17

Comments

The Company changed fiscal years for reporting. We presented the last three full reporting cycles. Since the end of 1996, the Company has announced another acquisition, the receipt of $500,000 net of legal fees on a litigation settlement, the $150 million financing of the power plant in Pakistan and certain income related to consulting services on the plant project. Another stock offering is expected during 1997 to finance the acquisition activity. Investment Classification: Speculative

Officers	Position	Ownership Information	
Ilyas Chaudhary	Chairman, CEO	Number of Shares Outstanding	3,310,138
Edward J. Names	President, COO	Market Capitalization	$ 16,749,298
Dennis R. Staal	CFO	Frequency of Dividends	n.a.
		Number of Shareholders	265

Other Information			
Transfer Agent	American Securities Transfer, Inc. Denver, CO	Where Listed	OTC-BB
Auditor	Coopers & Lybrand L.L.P.	Symbol	METE
Market Maker	Sherwood Securities Corp.	(800)525-3499	SIC Code	5170
	Van Kasper & Company, Inc.	(800)603-5969	Employees	n.a.
Broker Dealer	Regular Stockbroker		

Mexco Energy Corporation

214 W. Texas Avenue, Ste. 1101   Midland, TX 79701   Telephone (915)682-1119   Fax (915)682-1123

Company Description

Mexco Energy Corporation is engaged in the acquisition, exploration and development of oil and gas properties, principally in Texas. The Company operates seven of its producing oil wells and other companies operate the remaining 868 producing wells located on leased property. At March 31, 1996, the Company held leasehold rights to 59,928 gross acres (2,207 net acres). The Company was founded in 1972.

	03/31/96	03/31/95	03/31/94	03/31/93
Per Share Information				
Stock Price as of 12/31	4.50	2.00	1.38	0.75
Earnings Per Share	0.15	0.09	0.88	-0.01
Price / Earnings Ratio	30.00	22.22	1.57	n.a.
Book Value Per Share	1.79	1.57	1.48	0.61
Price / Book Value %	251.40	127.39	93.24	122.95
Dividends Per Share	0.0	0.0	0.0	0.0
Annual Financial Data				
Operating Results (000's)				
Total Revenues	834.1	573.9	1,579.9	352.7
Costs & Expenses	-621.8	-459.1	-491.3	-361.7
Income Before Taxes and Other	212.3	114.8	1,088.6	-9.0
Other Items	0.0	0.0	0.0	0.0
Income Tax	-11.7	-10.0	-59.9	0.0
Net Income	200.6	104.8	1,028.7	-9.0
Cash Flow From Operations	396.4	255.6	1,302.8	80.1
Balance Sheet (000's)				
Cash & Equivalents	172.1	221.0	739.5	10.4
Total Current Assets	280.7	303.4	823.3	64.3
Fixed Assets, Net	2,331.3	1,648.5	1,045.1	753.5
Total Assets	2,612.0	1,951.9	1,868.4	817.8
Total Current Liabilities	32.6	75.6	128.7	81.3
Long-Term Debt	0.0	0.0	0.0	25.5
Stockholders' Equity	2,545.1	1,844.5	1,739.7	711.0
Performance & Financial Condition				
Return on Total Revenues %	24.05	18.27	65.11	-2.54
Return on Avg Stockholders' Equity %	9.14	5.85	83.95	-1.27
Return on Average Assets %	8.79	5.49	76.59	-1.15
Current Ratio	8.61	4.01	6.40	0.79
Debt / Equity %	n.a.	n.a.	n.a.	3.59

Compound Growth %'s	EPS % n.a.	Net Income % n.a.	Total Revenues % 33.23

Comments

During 1996, oil and gas production each increased 33% as a result of additional producing oil and gas properties. Included in the operating results for 1994 are proceeds from the settlement of litigation in the amount of $1.2 million. Revenues for the nine months ended December 31, 1996, were $889,000 and Net Income was $261,000 as compared to $524,000 and $98,000 for the same period in 1995. Investment Classification: Speculative

Officers	Position	Ownership Information	
Nicholas C. Taylor	President, Treasurer	Number of Shares Outstanding	1,423,229
Donna G. Yanko	Vice President, Secretary	Market Capitalization	$ 6,404,531
Teresa C. Mitchell	Controller	Frequency of Dividends	n.a.
		Number of Shareholders	1,476

Other Information			
Transfer Agent	American Securities Transfer, Inc. Denver, CO	Where Listed	OTC-BB
Auditor	Grant Thornton LLP	Symbol	MEXC
Market Maker	Carr Securities Corporation (800)221-2243	SIC Code	1311
		Employees	2
Broker Dealer	OTC Specialist		

Michigan Rivet Corporation

13201 Stephens Road   Warren, MI 48089-2092   Telephone (810)754-5100   Fax (810)754-2750

Company Description

The Company is a domestic manufacturer of cold headed steel fasteners, nuts and components, principally for the automotive industry. The McLaughlin Company, a subsidiary, is a manufacturer of specialized nuts, nut and washer assemblies, and fasteners. Consolidated sales to General Motors, Ford and Chrysler were 33%, 40% and 19%, respectively, of total 1996 sales. The Company was formed in 1969.

	10/31/96	10/31/95	10/31/94	10/31/93
Per Share Information				
Stock Price as of 12/31	6.00	3.25	2.00	3.00
Earnings Per Share	2.09	2.55	0.07	-1.20
Price / Earnings Ratio	2.87	1.27	28.57	n.a.
Book Value Per Share	13.23	11.51	9.19	9.12
Price / Book Value %	45.35	28.24	21.76	32.89
Dividends Per Share	0.37	0.24	0.0	0.0
Annual Financial Data				
Operating Results (000's)				
Total Revenues	41,596.5	40,352.2	38,375.2	33,057.4
Costs & Expenses	-39,553.1	-38,546.5	-38,486.0	-34,124.9
Income Before Taxes and Other	2,043.4	1,805.7	-110.8	-1,067.5
Other Items	0.0	0.0	0.0	0.0
Income Tax	-710.0	-175.8	155.0	300.0
Net Income	1,333.4	1,629.9	44.2	-767.5
Cash Flow From Operations	2,319.5	3,861.3	1,329.9	526.9
Balance Sheet (000's)				
Cash & Equivalents	119.4	110.7	638.3	201.6
Total Current Assets	11,685.0	11,328.4	12,854.3	10,599.4
Fixed Assets, Net	8,910.7	8,821.1	8,815.1	9,380.2
Total Assets	21,299.8	20,654.8	21,736.3	20,041.9
Total Current Liabilities	5,829.2	6,114.5	9,548.5	13,074.5
Long-Term Debt	3,746.6	4,436.8	4,379.6	571.0
Stockholders' Equity	8,444.9	7,346.4	5,866.1	5,821.8
Performance & Financial Condition				
Return on Total Revenues %	3.21	4.04	0.12	-2.32
Return on Avg Stockholders' Equity %	16.89	24.67	0.76	-12.37
Return on Average Assets %	6.36	7.69	0.21	-3.82
Current Ratio	2.00	1.85	1.35	0.81
Debt / Equity %	44.37	60.39	74.66	9.81

Compound Growth %'s	EPS % n.a.	Net Income % n.a.	Total Revenues %	7.96

Comments

In 1995, the Company realized proceeds of $1.2 million from an insurance policy on a former president of the Company who passed away during the year. The net gain of $1.1 million is included in revenues. Net income of $1,333,333 in 1996 was $845,000 greater than the prior year without the nonrecurring insurance income. Compound growth in earnings and earnings per share have not been displayed because of lower than usual earnings in the base year. For the six months ended April 30, 1997, revenue was 8% higher and earnings per share were $1.05 as compared to $.90 in the same period of the preceding year. Investment Classification: Value & Income

Officers	Position	Ownership Information	
William B. Stade	President, Chairman	Number of Shares Outstanding	638,525
William P. Lianos	Exec VP, Treasurer	Market Capitalization	$ 3,831,150
Clark V. Stevens	Secretary	Frequency of Dividends	Quarterly
		Number of Shareholders	310

Other Information			
Transfer Agent	Bank of Boston Boston, MA	Where Listed	OTC-PS
Auditor	Plante & Moran, LLP	Symbol	n.a.
Market Maker	Carr Securities Corporation	(800)221-2243	SIC Code	3452
	Wm. C. Roney & Co.	(800)521-1196	Employees	283
Broker Dealer	OTC Specialist			
	Kevin Ryan - Ryan, Beck & Co.	(888)231-7226		

MidCity Financial Corporation

801 West Madison Street   Chicago, IL 60607   Telephone (312)421-7600   Fax (312)633-0322

Company Description

The Company provides a full range of banking services to individual and corporate customers through its banking subsidiaries, principally in metropolitan Chicago, Illinois and Oklahoma City, Oklahoma. Subsidiaries include The Mid-City National Bank of Chicago (founded in 1911), First National Bank of Morton Grove (founded in 1951), Bank of Elmhurst (founded in 1968), Union Bank and Trust Company (founded in 1952 in Oklahoma City) and MidCity Information Services, Inc. The Company changed its name from Mid-Citco Incorporated in 1995.

	12/31/96	12/31/95	12/31/94	12/31/93
Per Share Information				
Stock Price	3,000.00	2,500.00	2,110.00	1,800.00
Earnings Per Share	295.69	274.33	285.12	276.64
Price / Earnings Ratio	10.15	9.11	7.40	6.51
Book Value Per Share	2,963.44	2,705.70	2,468.48	2,215.91
Price / Book Value %	101.23	92.40	85.48	81.23
Dividends Per Share	44.00	41.00	32.00	26.15
Annual Financial Data				
Operating Results (000's)				
Net Interest Income	50,439.0	47,833.0	49,138.0	50,184.0
Loan Loss Provision	-918.0	-634.0	-837.0	-1,394.0
Non-Interest Income	7,378.0	6,542.0	6,313.0	6,175.0
Non-Interest Expense	-37,524.0	-35,800.0	-35,929.0	-36,306.0
Income Before Taxes and Other	19,375.0	17,941.0	18,685.0	18,659.0
Other Items	0.0	0.0	0.0	-294.0
Income Tax	-5,339.0	-4,878.0	-5,108.0	-5,192.0
Net Income	14,036.0	13,063.0	13,577.0	13,173.0
Balance Sheet (000's)				
Cash & Securities	783,573.0	811,951.0	781,533.0	835,487.0
Loans, Net	631,791.0	600,933.0	577,767.0	501,537.0
Total Assets	1,461,904.0	1,463,347.0	1,408,000.0	1,385,565.0
Deposits	1,304,125.0	1,283,235.0	1,270,279.0	1,264,968.0
Stockholders' Equity	140,485.0	128,840.0	117,544.0	105,517.0
Performance & Financial Condition				
Return on Avg Stockholders' Equity %	10.42	10.60	12.17	11.81
Return on Average Assets %	0.96	0.91	0.97	0.94
Equity to Assets %	9.61	8.80	8.35	7.62
Net Interest Margin	3.95	3.86	n.a.	n.a.
Reserve as a % of Problem Loans	202.27	219.44	228.06	229.90

Compound Growth %'s	EPS %	2.24	Net Income %	2.14	Net Interest Income %	0.17

Comments

After a slight earnings decline in 1995, the Company is back on track producing record earnings growth that has now been achieved in fifteen of the last sixteen years. In addition to what is apparent in the financial statements, management reports success in meeting targeted goals for capital improvements, enhancing customer service, controlling expenditures, engineering and marketing products, and developing employees. The Company's common shares are thinly-traded. Investment Classification: Value

Officers	Position	Ownership Information	
E M. Bakwin	Chairman, CEO	Number of Shares Outstanding	47,406
Kenneth A. Skopec	President	Market Capitalization	$ 142,218,000
Randall J. Yenerich	Exec VP	Frequency of Dividends	Quarterly
Ronald D. Santo	Senior VP, Secretary	Number of Shareholders	n.a.
David E. Greiwe	Vice President, Controller	Where Listed / Symbol	OTC-BB / MCIT

Other Information			Loan Mix	%
Transfer Agent	Company Office		R/E Mortgages	54.6
Auditor	KPMG Peat Marwick LLP		Commerical	31.7
Market Maker	The Chicago Corporation	(800)621-1674	Consumer	13.6
	Howe Barnes Investments, Inc.	(800)621-2364	Other	0.1
Broker Dealer	OTC Specialist			
	Kevin Ryan - Ryan, Beck & Co.	(888)231-7226		

Mills Music Trust

1775 Broadway, Suite 708 New York, NY 10019 Telephone (212)246-7203 Fax (212)246-7217

Company Description

Mills Music Trust was created in 1964 for the purpose of acquiring the rights to receive payment for a deferred contingent purchase price obligation payable to Mills Music, Inc. The payments are determined quarterly and are based on a formula which considers gross royalty income paid to composers, authors and others for the 25,000 titles contained in the "Old Mills Catalogue" of musical compositions. All of the income, less minimal administrative expenses, is distributed. The Trust was created when 277,712 units of beneficial interest were sold to the holders of common stock of Utilities & Industries Corporation.

	12/31/96	12/31/95	12/31/94	12/31/93
Per Share Information				
Stock Price	41.00	40.00	34.00	36.00
Earnings Per Share	4.13	4.42	4.57	3.75
Price / Earnings Ratio	9.93	9.05	7.44	9.60
Book Value Per Share	n.a.	n.a.	n.a.	n.a.
Price / Book Value %	n.a.	n.a.	n.a.	n.a.
Dividends Per Share	4.13	4.42	4.57	3.75
Annual Financial Data				
Operating Results (000's)				
Total Revenues	1,175.5	1,268.4	1,308.1	1,065.5
Costs & Expenses	-27.3	-42.0	-38.6	-23.1
Income Before Taxes and Other	1,148.3	1,226.4	1,269.5	1,042.4
Other Items	0.0	0.0	0.0	0.0
Income Tax	0.0	0.0	0.0	0.0
Net Income	1,148.3	1,226.4	1,269.5	1,042.4
Cash Flow From Operations	1,148.3	1,226.4	1,269.5	1,042.4
Balance Sheet (000's)				
Cash & Equivalents	0.0	0.0	0.8	0.8
Total Current Assets	0.0	0.0	0.8	0.8
Fixed Assets, Net	0.0	0.0	0.0	0.0
Total Assets	0.0	0.0	0.8	0.8
Total Current Liabilities	0.0	0.0	0.0	0.0
Long-Term Debt	0.0	0.0	0.0	0.0
Stockholders' Equity	0.0	0.0	0.8	0.8
Performance & Financial Condition				
Return on Total Revenues %	97.68	96.69	97.05	97.83
Return on Avg Stockholders' Equity %	n.a.	n.a.	n.a.	n.a.
Return on Average Assets %	n.a.	n.a.	n.a.	n.a.
Current Ratio	n.a.	n.a.	n.a.	n.a.
Debt / Equity %	n.a.	n.a.	n.a.	n.a.

Compound Growth %'s	EPS %	3.27	Net Income %	3.28	Total Revenues %	3.33

Comments

Statements of cash receipts and disbursements are the only financial statements prepared. There is no book value per unit because cumulative distributions exceed the initial investment in the trust. The Trust's receipts are derived from copyrights established prior to 1964 and as such, they fluctuate based upon public interest in the nostalgia of older songs. Investment Classification: Income

Officers	Position	Ownership Information	
Bernard D. Fischman	Other	Number of Shares Outstanding	277,712
Marine Midland Bank	Other	Market Capitalization	$ 11,386,192
		Frequency of Dividends	Quarterly
		Number of Shareholders	321

Other Information			
Transfer Agent	Marine Midland Bank N.A. New York, NY	Where Listed	OTC-BB
Auditor	KPMG Peat Marwick LLP	Symbol	MMTRS
Market Maker	Carr Securities Corporation (800)221-2243	SIC Code	6790
	Hill Thompson Magid & Co., Inc (800)631-3083	Employees	n.a.
Broker Dealer	Regular Stockbroker		

Minster State Bank

96 W. Fourth Street   Minster, OH 45865   Telephone (419)628-2351   Fax (419)628-2103

Company Description

Minster State Bank provides banking and other financial services in the west central Ohio counties of Auglaize, Mercer, Darke and Shelby. Five locations dot these rural areas. Management recognizes its relatively high capital ratio and is taking on the challenge of deploying these funds to maximize shareholder value. New markets and additional products are being explored. The Bank was founded in 1914.

	12/31/96	12/31/95	12/31/94	12/31/93
Per Share Information				
Stock Price	48.00	41.00	33.00	30.00
Earnings Per Share	5.18	4.33	3.53	3.14
Price / Earnings Ratio	9.27	9.47	9.35	9.55
Book Value Per Share	35.52	32.27	27.91	25.72
Price / Book Value %	135.14	127.05	118.24	116.64
Dividends Per Share	1.80	1.30	1.05	0.95
Annual Financial Data				
Operating Results (000's)				
Net Interest Income	6,596.8	6,065.9	5,157.9	4,650.4
Loan Loss Provision	-120.0	-225.0	-210.0	-180.0
Non-Interest Income	974.3	750.3	764.9	822.7
Non-Interest Expense	-3,984.9	-3,729.7	-3,462.2	-3,344.9
Income Before Taxes and Other	3,466.1	2,861.5	2,250.7	1,948.2
Other Items	0.0	0.0	0.0	0.0
Income Tax	-955.7	-768.0	-549.2	-439.5
Net Income	2,510.4	2,093.5	1,701.5	1,508.6
Balance Sheet (000's)				
Cash & Securities	36,273.2	38,038.6	32,747.5	29,838.0
Loans, Net	111,743.8	99,052.7	91,888.5	86,294.0
Total Assets	154,202.2	142,835.5	130,494.3	121,273.0
Deposits	129,187.3	122,587.4	114,953.9	107,746.0
Stockholders' Equity	17,252.1	15,675.4	13,555.7	12,493.0
Performance & Financial Condition				
Return on Avg Stockholders' Equity %	15.25	14.32	13.06	12.61
Return on Average Assets %	1.69	1.53	1.35	1.27
Equity to Assets %	11.19	10.97	10.39	10.30
Net Interest Margin	n.a.	n.a.	n.a.	n.a.
Reserve as a % of Problem Loans	566.86	2,271.98	499.39	82.60

Compound Growth %'s	EPS %	18.16	Net Income %	18.50	Net Interest Income %	12.36

Comments

The Bank declared a 2 for 1 stock split in 1996. This may help alleviate the thin market (no sellers) in the shares. Per share amounts were adjusted for the split. 1996 results were outstanding. Management reported that the main contributing factors were strong loan growth, increased fee income, excellent asset quality and better-than-expected interest margins. Investment Classification: Growth & Income

Officers	Position	Ownership Information	
Orval Homan	President, CEO	Number of Shares Outstanding	485,700
Mark Henschen	Exec VP	Market Capitalization	$ 23,313,600
Kenneth Wuebker	CFO	Frequency of Dividends	Quarterly
Dennis York	Other	Number of Shareholders	n.a.
Robert Albers	Other	Where Listed / Symbol	Order Matching Only / n.a.

Other Information		Loan Mix	%
Transfer Agent	Company Office	R/E Mortgages	70.8
Auditor	Not indicated	Commerical	19.9
Market Maker	None	Installment	8.0
		Other	1.3
Broker Dealer	McDonald & Company (800)321-1452 Ext: Chuck		

Mod-U-Kraf Homes, Inc.

822 Pell Avenue   Rocky Mount, VA 24151   Telephone (540)483-0291   Fax (540)483-2228

Company Description

Mod-U-Kraf Homes, Inc. manufactures and sells sectionalized custom single family homes of its own design. The Company also manufactures a commercial line of products consisting of multi-family and diversified specialty structures. The single family homes range in price from $55,000 to $250,000 and range in size from 705 square feet to 2,950 square feet. Products are sold to home builders, developers and realtors in Virginia, Maryland, West Virginia and North Carolina. The Company was formed in 1971 and has built over 7,000 homes.

	12/31/96	12/31/95	12/31/94	12/31/93
Per Share Information				
Stock Price	5.25	4.00	4.88	3.39
Earnings Per Share	0.22	0.46	0.38	0.66
Price / Earnings Ratio	23.86	8.70	12.84	5.14
Book Value Per Share	5.65	5.55	5.25	4.99
Price / Book Value %	92.92	72.07	92.95	67.94
Dividends Per Share	0.12	0.12	0.12	0.10
Annual Financial Data				
Operating Results (000's)				
Total Revenues	11,440.8	9,275.5	9,481.7	8,050.3
Costs & Expenses	-11,048.8	-8,541.0	-8,811.9	-7,522.2
Income Before Taxes and Other	290.1	607.5	555.0	342.8
Other Items	0.0	0.0	0.0	342.2
Income Tax	-112.5	-228.7	-246.8	-147.7
Net Income	177.7	378.8	308.2	537.3
Cash Flow From Operations	-269.1	273.0	883.0	166.6
Balance Sheet (000's)				
Cash & Equivalents	1,077.3	1,426.7	1,226.7	1,110.5
Total Current Assets	4,597.3	4,498.1	4,591.5	4,128.7
Fixed Assets, Net	3,893.8	2,245.6	897.8	911.4
Total Assets	9,617.9	7,845.5	6,329.5	5,883.2
Total Current Liabilities	1,236.5	897.8	863.2	568.7
Long-Term Debt	2,639.8	2,365.3	1,195.3	1,253.5
Stockholders' Equity	4,661.0	4,582.4	4,271.0	4,061.0
Performance & Financial Condition				
Return on Total Revenues %	1.55	4.08	3.25	6.67
Return on Avg Stockholders' Equity %	3.84	8.56	7.40	14.00
Return on Average Assets %	2.03	5.34	5.05	9.66
Current Ratio	3.72	5.01	5.32	7.26
Debt / Equity %	56.64	51.62	27.99	30.87

Compound Growth %'s	EPS %	-30.66	Net Income %	-30.85	Total Revenues %	12.43

Comments

1993 results include a nonrecurring benefit of $342,000, $.50 per share, from the accrual of postretirement benefits in accordance with new accounting standards. This has the effect of unfavorably distorting the compound decline in earnings and earnings per share. A new plant went into production in July, 1996, which has already had a positive effect on revenues. Expenses during 1996 were higher due to overhead for training new employees and other start-up costs associated with the facility. Investment Classification: Growth & Value

Officers	Position	Ownership Information	
Dale H. Powell	Chairman, President	Number of Shares Outstanding	825,649
Edwin J. Campbell	Vice President, Secretary	Market Capitalization	$ 4,334,657
Jeffrey L. Boudreaux	Controller	Frequency of Dividends	Quarterly
		Number of Shareholders	448

Other Information			
Transfer Agent	First Union Bank Charlotte, NC	Where Listed	OTC-BB
Auditor	Brown, Edwards & Company, LLP	Symbol	MODU
Market Maker	Koonce Securities, Inc.	(800)368-2803	SIC Code	2452
	The Chicago Corporation	(800)323-1225	Employees	90
Broker Dealer	Regular Stockbroker		

Monarch Cement Company (The)

P.O. Box 1000   Humboldt, KS 66748-1000   Telephone (316)473-2222   Fax (316)473-2447

Company Description

The Company manufactures and sells portland cement, the basic material used in the production of ready-mixed concrete used in highway, bridge and building construction where strength and durability are primary requirements. The Company is also in the ready-mixed concrete, concrete products and sundry building materials business. Products are distributed in the states of Kansas, Iowa, Nebraska, Missouri, Arkansas and Oklahoma. The Monarch Cement Company was founded in 1908.

	12/31/96	12/31/95	12/31/94	12/31/93
Per Share Information				
Stock Price	14.75	12.63	12.50	7.88
Earnings Per Share	2.50	1.81	0.94	-0.02
Price / Earnings Ratio	5.90	6.98	13.30	n.a.
Book Value Per Share	11.73	9.68	8.11	7.68
Price / Book Value %	125.32	130.48	154.13	102.60
Dividends Per Share	0.52	0.46	0.46	0.40
Annual Financial Data				
Operating Results (000's)				
Total Revenues	87,820.1	81,666.8	73,645.7	66,118.3
Costs & Expenses	-71,294.5	-69,374.8	-67,694.5	-59,579.3
Income Before Taxes and Other	16,525.7	12,073.5	6,373.4	7,406.9
Other Items	0.0	0.0	0.0	-5,080.0
Income Tax	-5,980.0	-4,400.0	-2,375.0	-2,415.0
Net Income	10,545.7	7,673.5	3,998.4	-88.1
Cash Flow From Operations	14,611.6	10,355.3	8,195.9	7,309.1
Balance Sheet (000's)				
Cash & Equivalents	3,242.2	5,071.3	3,668.8	1,665.9
Total Current Assets	39,417.5	31,732.5	26,523.0	28,569.1
Fixed Assets, Net	23,599.4	22,517.8	20,988.2	17,191.0
Total Assets	68,648.4	59,782.8	52,522.0	49,862.8
Total Current Liabilities	6,682.6	6,638.3	6,703.8	6,316.7
Long-Term Debt	0.0	0.0	0.0	0.0
Stockholders' Equity	49,580.7	41,023.8	34,398.4	32,546.7
Performance & Financial Condition				
Return on Total Revenues %	12.01	9.40	5.43	-0.13
Return on Avg Stockholders' Equity %	23.28	20.35	11.95	-0.26
Return on Average Assets %	16.42	13.67	7.81	-0.19
Current Ratio	5.90	4.78	3.96	4.52
Debt / Equity %	n.a.	n.a.	n.a.	n.a.

Compound Growth %'s	EPS % 63.08	Net Income % 62.40	Total Revenues % 9.92

Comments

The Company effectuated a stock split in 1994 with the issuance of a class B stock with greater voting rights. 1993 per share amounts have been restated for consistency. 1993 amounts include a nonrecurring expense of $5.5 million, $1.30 per share, due to the implementation of the new accounting standard requiring accrual of postretirement employee benefits. During 1995, a capital improvement program was completed at the Company's cement plant allowing for increased production at a reduced cost per ton. The positive results of the new plant are evident in the 1996 report. The Company had $16.1 million in short term investments in addition to its cash at December 31, 1996. Investment Classification: Growth & Value & Income

Officers	Position	Ownership Information	
Jack R. Callahan	President	Number of Shares Outstanding	4,226,290
Walter H. Wulf, Jr.	Exec VP	Market Capitalization	$ 62,146,028
Karl Callaway	Secretary	Frequency of Dividends	Irregular
Byron K. Radcliff	Treasurer	Number of Shareholders	700
Robert M. Kissick	Vice President		

Other Information

Transfer Agent	Company Office		Where Listed	OTC-BB
Auditor	Arthur Andersen LLP		Symbol	MCEM
Market Maker	Fahnestock & Co., Inc.	(212)422-7813	SIC Code	3270
	McDonald & Company Securities	(800)321-2190	Employees	555
Broker Dealer	Regular Stockbroker			

Monroe Title Insurance Corporation

47 West Main Street   Rochester, NY 14614-1499   Telephone (716)232-2070   Fax (716)232-4988

Company Description

Monroe Title Insurance Corporation issues title insurance and renders abstracts of title throughout western, central, and upstate New York State. It has established nineteen branches to penetrate the market. The Company also has a wholly-owned subsidiary, MATCO Ventures, Inc. which owns a majority interest in Monroe-Allegany Title Services, Inc.

	12/31/96	12/31/95	12/31/94	12/31/93
Per Share Information				
Stock Price	8.25	9.12	11.50	7.50
Earnings Per Share	2.48	0.53	0.91	2.14
Price / Earnings Ratio	3.33	17.21	12.64	3.50
Book Value Per Share	12.12	9.92	8.82	8.87
Price / Book Value %	68.07	91.94	130.39	84.55
Dividends Per Share	0.40	0.22	0.60	1.09
Annual Financial Data				
Operating Results (000's)				
Total Revenues	17,825.2	13,436.3	17,407.6	19,782.5
Costs & Expenses	-13,832.5	-12,869.3	-15,575.6	-16,648.2
Income Before Taxes and Other	3,690.0	567.1	1,832.1	3,134.2
Other Items	0.0	0.0	-420.0	300.0
Income Tax	-987.4	-1.0	-440.0	-866.0
Net Income	2,702.6	566.1	972.1	2,568.2
Cash Flow From Operations	503.8	-509.7	-508.0	2,358.4
Balance Sheet (000's)				
Cash & Equivalents	123.2	8.3	10.7	109.5
Total Current Assets	17,327.6	15,649.2	15,241.7	18,294.1
Fixed Assets, Net	3,463.5	1,944.5	2,064.9	2,139.6
Total Assets	21,898.5	20,581.2	20,155.7	24,902.4
Total Current Liabilities	1,793.5	2,836.8	2,787.0	5,211.0
Long-Term Debt	557.6	97.6	190.2	489.1
Stockholders' Equity	14,448.8	11,905.3	10,578.6	10,642.0
Performance & Financial Condition				
Return on Total Revenues %	15.16	4.21	5.58	12.98
Return on Avg Stockholders' Equity %	20.51	5.04	9.16	26.08
Return on Average Assets %	12.72	2.78	4.31	11.67
Current Ratio	9.66	5.52	5.47	3.51
Debt / Equity %	3.86	0.82	1.80	4.60

Compound Growth %'s	EPS %	5.04	Net Income %	1.71	Total Revenues %	-3.41

Comments

The Company declared a 4 for 1 stock split in 1994. All per share amounts were adjusted for consistency. 1994 results include a nonrecurring expense of $420,000, $.40 per share, in connection with the adoption of new accounting rules to record postretirement health care benefits. 1993 results include a $300,000, $.25 per share, nonrecurring benefit due to a change in accounting methods. 1996 results were positively affected by a positive adjustment in the reserve for losses which produced $2,680,488 of income (the total reserve for losses was reduced from $4.1 million to $1.3 million). Investment Classification: Value

Officers	Position	Ownership Information	
Thomas A. Podsiadlo	VP - Finance	Number of Shares Outstanding	1,192,459
		Market Capitalization	$ 9,837,787
		Frequency of Dividends	Quarterly
		Number of Shareholders	Under 500

Other Information			
Transfer Agent	Company Office	Where Listed	OTC-BB
Auditor	Arthur Andersen LLP	Symbol	MTTL
Market Maker	PaineWebber Incorporated	(800)221-5532	SIC Code	6540
	Howe Barnes Investments, Inc.	(800)621-2364	Employees	300
Broker Dealer	Regular Stockbroker		

Morris Run Coal Mining Company

P.O. Box 538   Dallas, PA 18612   Telephone (717)675-2831

Company Description

Morris Run Coal Mining Company was once an active coal mining operation in northeast Pennsylvania. Although it stopped operations years ago, it has not been able to liquidate because of an ongoing obligation to pay Medicare premiums of retired employees or their widows. It is believed that negotiations with the United Mine Workers of America will resolve this matter soon.

	12/31/96	12/31/95	12/31/94	12/31/93
Per Share Information				
Stock Price	200.00	190.00	180.00	180.00
Earnings Per Share	2.16	1.53	-6.73	-8.95
Price / Earnings Ratio	92.59	124.18	n.a.	n.a.
Book Value Per Share	289.59	286.56	277.75	291.01
Price / Book Value %	69.06	66.30	64.81	61.85
Dividends Per Share	0.0	0.0	0.0	0.0
Annual Financial Data				
Operating Results (000's)				
Total Revenues	28.3	27.9	25.6	18.9
Costs & Expenses	-23.2	-24.5	-40.4	-38.5
Income Before Taxes and Other	5.2	3.4	-14.8	-19.7
Other Items	0.0	0.0	0.0	0.0
Income Tax	-0.4	0.0	0.0	0.0
Net Income	4.8	3.4	-14.8	-19.7
Cash Flow From Operations	n.a.	n.a.	n.a.	n.a.
Balance Sheet (000's)				
Cash & Equivalents	49.3	44.1	42.9	141.2
Total Current Assets	330.9	383.4	214.4	144.1
Fixed Assets, Net	0.0	0.0	0.0	0.0
Total Assets	639.4	632.3	612.9	642.2
Total Current Liabilities	2.9	2.4	2.4	2.5
Long-Term Debt	0.0	0.0	0.0	0.0
Stockholders' Equity	636.5	629.9	610.5	639.6
Performance & Financial Condition				
Return on Total Revenues %	16.77	12.06	-57.88	-104.40
Return on Avg Stockholders' Equity %	0.75	0.54	-2.37	n.a.
Return on Average Assets %	0.75	0.54	-2.36	n.a.
Current Ratio	113.46	159.81	88.09	57.36
Debt / Equity %	n.a.	n.a.	n.a.	n.a.

Compound Growth %'s	EPS % n.a.	Net Income % n.a.	Total Revenues % 14.55

Comments

Not only is timing of the liquidation important but so is the value of the securities reflected on the Company's balance sheet at cost. The amount of interest and dividend income would suggest that there is a significant amount of appreciation. The few trades that have taken place are well below book value. The ultimate set-aside for miners is still undetermined although the obligation is declining with time. Investment Classification: Value

Officers	Position	Ownership Information	
Darrel Crispell	Chairman	Number of Shares Outstanding	2,198
Tamzon Green	Other	Market Capitalization	$ 439,600
Rodney Robertson, Sr.	Other	Frequency of Dividends	n.a.
Rodney T. Robertson, Jr.	Other	Number of Shareholders	Under 500

Other Information

Transfer Agent	Company Office		Where Listed	OTC-BB
Auditor	Not indicated		Symbol	MRRS
Market Maker	Hill Thompson Magid & Co., Inc	(800)631-3083	SIC Code	6700
			Employees	n.a.
Broker Dealer	OTC Specialist			

Mortgage Oil Company

1545 Wilshire Boulevard   Los Angeles, CA 90017-4501   Telephone (213)483-2742   Fax (213)483-2748

Company Description

Mortgage Oil Company primarily invests in real estate partnerships, holds a number of marketable securities, and holds various oil, gas and mineral rights. The Company was spun-off from the liquidations of Mortgage Guarantee Company and Mortgage Service Co. in 1946 and 1949, respectively. The Company's mineral rights trace back to the 1920's and 1930's. At that time, the rights were carved out of foreclosed farmlands throughout California's San Joaquin Valley.

	12/31/95	12/31/94	12/31/93	12/31/92
Per Share Information				
Stock Price as of 12/31	27.50	23.00	27.00	24.00
Earnings Per Share	2.68	0.92	1.26	0.72
Price / Earnings Ratio	10.26	25.00	21.43	33.33
Book Value Per Share	38.20	29.42	29.70	29.17
Price / Book Value %	71.99	78.18	90.91	82.28
Dividends Per Share	0.92	1.26	0.72	2.00
Annual Financial Data				
Operating Results (000's)				
Total Revenues	190.9	104.4	124.4	92.5
Costs & Expenses	-56.7	-57.3	-54.5	-61.1
Income Before Taxes and Other	134.2	47.2	69.9	31.4
Other Items	0.0	0.0	0.0	0.0
Income Tax	-24.3	-9.4	-17.6	-1.7
Net Income	109.8	37.7	52.3	29.7
Cash Flow From Operations	-49.0	6.8	-69.2	-14.8
Balance Sheet (000's)				
Cash & Equivalents	47.7	0.8	54.7	6.5
Total Current Assets	49.4	384.3	595.4	589.3
Fixed Assets, Net	0.0	0.0	0.0	0.0
Total Assets	1,781.8	1,218.2	1,250.3	1,220.2
Total Current Liabilities	18.0	1.1	5.7	7.1
Long-Term Debt	0.0	0.0	0.0	0.0
Stockholders' Equity	1,566.9	1,207.1	1,234.6	1,212.2
Performance & Financial Condition				
Return on Total Revenues %	57.54	36.12	42.02	32.15
Return on Avg Stockholders' Equity %	7.92	3.09	4.27	n.a.
Return on Average Assets %	7.32	3.06	4.23	n.a.
Current Ratio	2.75	358.19	104.26	83.51
Debt / Equity %	n.a.	n.a.	n.a.	n.a.

Compound Growth %'s	EPS %	45.84	Net Income %	44.98	Total Revenues %	23.88

Comments

The oil, gas and mineral rights are carried on the balance sheet as $2.00. This accounting reflects the formation and spin-off of the Company in the 1940's. Investments in real estate limited partnerships have generally been made from 1991 to the present. These investments are reflected on the financial statements at their adjusted tax basis. Investments in securities are reflected at their fair market value. The annual report is typically mailed to shareholders nine months after year end. The 1996 report was not available when we went to press. Investment Classification: Value

Officers	Position	Ownership Information	
Morgan Adams, Jr.	President	Number of Shares Outstanding	41,015
David V. Adams	Secretary, Treasurer	Market Capitalization	$ 1,127,913
		Frequency of Dividends	Annual
		Number of Shareholders	Under 500

Other Information			
Transfer Agent	Company Office	Where Listed	OTC-BB
Auditor	Oberlies & Pearson, Inc.	Symbol	MGAG
Market Maker	The Seidler Companies Inc.	(800)421-0164	SIC Code	6790
	Sharpe Capital Inc.	(800)355-5781	Employees	1
Broker Dealer	OTC Specialist		

Mt. Bachelor, Inc.

335 S.W. Century Drive   Bend, OR 97709   Telephone (541)382-2442   Fax (541)382-6536

Company Description

Mt. Bachelor, Inc. and its wholly-owned subsidiaries, Mt. Bachelor Super Shuttle, Inc. and Mt. Bachelor Travel Corporation, operate a ski and summer resort in the Deschutes National Forest in central Oregon. The views from the various chair lifts and mountain top are, reportedly, some of the very best in the entire northwest.

	07/31/96	07/31/95	07/31/94
Per Share Information			
Stock Price as of 12/31	10,000.00	9,000.00	8,500.00
Earnings Per Share	1,302.27	1,082.06	1,240.44
Price / Earnings Ratio	7.68	8.32	6.85
Book Value Per Share	9,970.60	8,868.32	8,086.26
Price / Book Value %	100.29	101.48	105.12
Dividends Per Share	200.00	300.00	300.00
Annual Financial Data			
Operating Results (000's)			
Total Revenues	21,021.3	20,121.2	20,077.8
Costs & Expenses	-18,013.3	-17,591.3	-17,434.4
Income Before Taxes and Other	3,008.0	2,529.9	2,643.4
Other Items	0.0	0.0	204.1
Income Tax	-1,121.0	-962.0	-1,050.1
Net Income	1,887.0	1,567.9	1,797.4
Cash Flow From Operations	4,644.3	4,698.3	5,051.7
Balance Sheet (000's)			
Cash & Equivalents	39.3	49.6	n.a.
Total Current Assets	942.2	995.2	n.a.
Fixed Assets, Net	22,445.3	20,890.9	n.a.
Total Assets	23,748.0	22,123.0	n.a.
Total Current Liabilities	1,152.9	1,779.8	n.a.
Long-Term Debt	7,012.9	6,277.6	n.a.
Stockholders' Equity	14,447.4	12,850.2	n.a.
Performance & Financial Condition			
Return on Total Revenues %	8.98	7.79	8.95
Return on Avg Stockholders' Equity %	13.83	12.76	16.29
Return on Average Assets %	8.23	n.a.	n.a.
Current Ratio	0.82	0.56	n.a.
Debt / Equity %	48.54	48.85	n.a.

Compound Growth %'s	EPS %	2.46	Net Income %	2.46	Total Revenues %	2.32

Comments

1996 results were respectable despite a slow start to the 95-96 season. A new express chair is operational for the 96-97 season that is 8,400 feet long with an elevation gain of 2,350 feet. As a result of a five year survey, it was concluded that guests wanted more challenging terrain. The Company responded with a number of new "black diamond" runs. Management is keeping a watchful eye on expenses and we will keep a watchful eye on our skis. Just lead us to the "green circle". Investment Classification: Value

Officers	Position	Ownership Information	
David K. Marsh	President	Number of Shares Outstanding	1,449
Christopher J. Stecher	VP - Finance	Market Capitalization	$ 14,490,000
James E. Petersen	Secretary	Frequency of Dividends	Semi-Annual
Lawrence S. Black	Treasurer	Number of Shareholders	Under 500
Kathleen E. DeGree	Vice President		

Other Information

Transfer Agent	Company Office	Where Listed	Order Matching Only
Auditor	Deloitte & Touche LLP	Symbol	n.a.
Market Maker	None	SIC Code	7999
		Employees	n.a.
Broker Dealer	Standard Investment	(888)783-4688 Ext: Jack	

Mt. Carmel Public Utility Co.

316 Market Street   Mt. Carmel, IL 62863   Telephone (618)262-5151

Company Description

Mt. Carmel Public Utility Company is the supplier of gas and electric power to the residents and businesses of Wabash County in the southeastern corner of Illinois. Only the Ohio River separates this part of the State from neighboring Indiana. The Company is regulated by the Illinois Public Utilities Commission. One major customer accounts for approximately 27% of revenues. The Company was incorporated in 1950.

	12/31/96	12/31/95	12/31/94
Per Share Information			
Stock Price	20.00	20.00	20.00
Earnings Per Share	1.68	0.04	-0.01
Price / Earnings Ratio	11.90	500.00	n.a.
Book Value Per Share	31.21	30.54	31.75
Price / Book Value %	64.08	65.49	62.99
Dividends Per Share	1.00	1.25	2.00
Annual Financial Data			
Operating Results (000's)			
Total Revenues	13,481.9	12,752.3	12,755.0
Costs & Expenses	-12,999.0	-12,782.2	-12,844.0
Income Before Taxes and Other	430.7	-29.9	-97.0
Other Items	0.0	0.0	0.0
Income Tax	-95.4	37.1	95.2
Net Income	335.2	7.2	-1.8
Cash Flow From Operations	n.a.	1,020.4	1,000.0
Balance Sheet (000's)			
Cash & Equivalents	419.3	70.6	90.9
Total Current Assets	1,654.5	1,322.9	1,504.6
Fixed Assets, Net	10,793.9	10,564.6	10,428.6
Total Assets	12,740.6	11,916.7	12,034.7
Total Current Liabilities	1,830.8	2,277.6	1,828.3
Long-Term Debt	3,937.5	2,712.5	3,062.5
Stockholders' Equity	6,243.0	6,107.7	6,350.6
Performance & Financial Condition			
Return on Total Revenues %	2.49	0.06	-0.01
Return on Avg Stockholders' Equity %	5.43	0.12	-0.03
Return on Average Assets %	2.72	0.06	n.a.
Current Ratio	0.90	0.58	0.82
Debt / Equity %	63.07	44.41	48.22

Compound Growth %'s	EPS % n.a.	Net Income % n.a.	Total Revenues % 2.81

Comments

The Company has been named in a lawsuit by a neighboring utility provider which claims that the Company infringed upon its service territory in its sales to its major customer. We also note that the Company maintains life insurance on certain officers which is unusual for a public utility company. The 6% increase in revenues has a substantial effect on net earnings. Compound growth in earnings rates were not displayed because they represented a change between only two years. Investment Classification: Income & Value

Officers	Position	Ownership Information	
Philip Barnhard IV	President	Number of Shares Outstanding	200,000
Barbara A. Springs	Secretary	Market Capitalization	$ 4,000,000
Jack W. Blevins	Vice President	Frequency of Dividends	Annual
Eric Bramlet	Vice President	Number of Shareholders	Under 500

Other Information				
Transfer Agent	Company Office		Where Listed	OTC-BB
Auditor	Deloitte & Touche LLP		Symbol	MCPB
Market Maker	Chicago Corporation, The	(800)621-1674	SIC Code	4910
	Hill Thompson Magid & Co., Inc	(800)631-3083	Employees	40
Broker Dealer	OTC Specialist			

Muncy Bank Financial, Inc.

2 North Main Street   Muncy, PA 17756   Telephone (717)546-2211   Fax (717)546-7358

Company Description

The Company is the holding company of Muncy Bank & Trust Company which was founded in 1893. Muncy is a rural community in central Pennsylvania, about 100 miles north of Harrisburg. The population of Lycoming County is 125,000. The Bank considers itself a "Hometown Bank" and even publishes the names of all of its employees on each quarterly and annual financial report. During 1996, employees, officers and directors spent over 4,800 hours participating in more than 60 civic and charitable organizations.

	12/31/96	12/31/95	12/31/94	12/31/93
Per Share Information				
Stock Price	43.00	40.00	37.12	35.62
Earnings Per Share	5.35	5.01	4.51	4.20
Price / Earnings Ratio	8.04	7.98	8.23	8.48
Book Value Per Share	43.58	40.29	34.95	33.04
Price / Book Value %	98.67	99.28	106.21	107.81
Dividends Per Share	1.65	1.60	1.40	1.35
Annual Financial Data				
Operating Results (000's)				
Net Interest Income	3,622.3	3,484.0	3,158.2	3,079.6
Loan Loss Provision	-18.0	-55.5	-22.0	-25.0
Non-Interest Income	415.8	435.7	367.0	344.0
Non-Interest Expense	-2,158.8	-2,170.5	-2,016.2	-1,957.1
Income Before Taxes and Other	1,861.3	1,693.7	1,487.1	1,441.6
Other Items	0.0	0.0	0.0	0.0
Income Tax	-517.6	-439.8	-361.4	-347.5
Net Income	1,343.7	1,253.9	1,125.6	1,094.0
Balance Sheet (000's)				
Cash & Securities	23,746.0	25,120.2	23,229.6	22,035.0
Loans, Net	62,979.5	61,454.8	58,692.8	53,181.3
Total Assets	88,733.8	88,509.2	84,040.2	77,113.7
Deposits	74,820.1	75,435.3	70,682.2	63,740.5
Stockholders' Equity	10,905.6	10,083.6	8,723.2	8,236.3
Performance & Financial Condition				
Return on Avg Stockholders' Equity %	12.80	13.33	13.27	13.51
Return on Average Assets %	1.52	1.45	1.40	1.44
Equity to Assets %	12.29	11.39	10.38	10.68
Net Interest Margin	n.a.	n.a.	n.a.	n.a.
Reserve as a % of Problem Loans	194.21	336.78	1,497.22	1,523.53

Compound Growth %'s	EPS %	8.40	Net Income %	7.09	Net Interest Income %	5.56

Comments

The Company acquired 14,000 treasury shares in 1993. Richard Lloyd retired after a very successful twenty-seven year stay at the Bank. Daniel Berninger took over as president and CEO. Management is focused on keeping abreast of new technology and has reviewed or upgraded most of its infrastructure. Investment Classification: Value & Income

Officers	Position	Ownership Information	
Richard H. Lloyd	President, CEO	Number of Shares Outstanding	250,265
Daniel C. Berninger	Senior VP	Market Capitalization	$ 10,761,395
Donna L. Yocum	Secretary	Frequency of Dividends	Quarterly
Craig W. Kremser	Vice President	Number of Shareholders	n.a.
Helen M. Smith	Head Cashier	Where Listed / Symbol	OTC-BB / MNCY

Other Information				Loan Mix	%
Transfer Agent	Company Office			R/E Mortgages	79.2
Auditor	Larson, Kellett & Associates			Consumer	16.2
Market Maker	Ryan, Beck & Co.	(800)325-7926		Commerical	4.6
	Hopper Soliday & Co., Inc.	(800)456-9234			
Broker Dealer	OTC Specialist				
	Jack Ingold	(412)391-4594			

Mutual Savings Life Insurance Company

2801 Highway 31, South   Decatur, AL 35603-2222   Telephone (205)552-7011   Fax (205)552-7284

Company Description

Mutual Savings Life Insurance Company is licensed in the states of Alabama, Florida, Georgia, Louisiana, Mississippi and Tennessee and writes life, accident and health insurance. Its subsidiary, Mutual Savings Fire Insurance Company is licensed in Alabama, Georgia, Louisiana and Mississippi and writes fire and allied lines. Marketing operations are conducted through agency personnel and approximately 700 representatives. Over one million policies are outstanding.

	12/31/96	12/31/95	12/31/94	12/31/93
Per Share Information				
Stock Price	15.00	17.00	18.00	22.00
Earnings Per Share	0.74	2.41	1.49	2.27
Price / Earnings Ratio	20.27	7.05	12.08	9.69
Book Value Per Share	14.37	14.70	13.37	13.15
Price / Book Value %	104.38	115.65	134.63	167.30
Dividends Per Share	1.00	1.00	1.00	1.00
Annual Financial Data				
Operating Results (000's)				
Total Revenues	70,641.4	69,700.9	69,655.3	70,163.8
Costs & Expenses	-69,244.1	-66,874.1	-67,565.8	-66,728.5
Income Before Taxes and Other	1,397.3	2,826.8	2,089.5	3,435.3
Other Items	162.7	-1.8	33.1	-8.4
Income Tax	-750.0	-200.0	-525.0	-1,000.0
Net Income	810.0	2,625.0	1,597.6	2,426.8
Cash Flow From Operations	7,713.9	6,872.8	4,548.5	26,115.1
Balance Sheet (000's)				
Cash & Equivalents	1,993.5	334.7	3,705.7	2,021.1
Total Current Assets	10,385.6	10,429.1	11,087.3	9,202.5
Fixed Assets, Net	91.3	82.8	86.3	63.9
Total Assets	273,923.6	266,497.7	260,452.9	256,696.5
Total Current Liabilities	730.4	367.4	1,190.0	1,185.1
Long-Term Debt	0.0	0.0	0.0	0.0
Stockholders' Equity	15,669.2	16,024.8	14,308.9	14,085.5
Performance & Financial Condition				
Return on Total Revenues %	1.15	3.77	2.29	3.46
Return on Avg Stockholders' Equity %	5.11	17.31	11.25	18.25
Return on Average Assets %	0.30	1.00	0.62	1.00
Current Ratio	14.22	28.39	9.32	7.77
Debt / Equity %	n.a.	n.a.	n.a.	n.a.

Compound Growth %'s	EPS %	-31.18	Net Income %	-30.63	Total Revenues %	0.23

Comments

On March 21, 1997, the Company settled the Gibson case involving burial insurance litigation filed in 1984. Plaintiff attorney fees of $2.5 million were paid in 1997 but accrued in 1996. There was also an additional $700,000 of expense associated with the litigation in 1996. Mutual Savings Fire Insurance had a turnaround year after suffering a loss of $294,000 in 1995. Its profit was $5,000 and is expected to rise even more in 1997. Investment Classification: Income & Value

Officers	Position	Ownership Information	
Don A. Johnson	Chairman, President	Number of Shares Outstanding	1,090,292
Don F. Morrison	Senior VP, Secretary	Market Capitalization	$ 16,354,380
Donald L. Williams	Senior VP	Frequency of Dividends	Quarterly
G. Alan Lansdell	Senior VP	Number of Shareholders	Under 500
John H. Parker	Vice President, Treasurer		

Other Information				
Transfer Agent	Company Office - Stock Transfer Dept.		Where Listed	OTC-PS
Auditor	KPMG Peat Marwick LLP		Symbol	MUTS
Market Maker	Dorsey Investment Securities	(800)375-5431	SIC Code	6310
	Hill Thompson Magid & Co., Inc	(800)631-3083	Employees	140
Broker Dealer	Regular Stockbroker			
	Stephen R. Schuller - Dorsey	(800)375-5431		

NCC Industries, Inc.

165 Main Street   Cortland, NY 13045   Telephone (607)756-2841   Fax (607)756-6607

Company Description

The Company designs, manufactures and sells women's undergarments. Sales are made to department, specialty, discount and chain stores throughout the United States. Much of the manufacturing process is performed overseas. In April, 1995, Maidenform Worldwide, Inc. (Maidenform) acquired approximately 92.4% of the Company's outstanding stock. The Company's Chairman and one of its Executive VP's own the majority of Maidenform's outstanding stock.

	12/31/96	12/31/95	12/31/94	12/31/93
Per Share Information				
Stock Price	2.62	9.00	7.88	7.13
Earnings Per Share	-2.90	0.63	1.35	0.85
Price / Earnings Ratio	n.a.	14.29	5.84	8.39
Book Value Per Share	5.92	8.87	8.22	6.89
Price / Book Value %	44.26	101.47	95.86	103.48
Dividends Per Share	0.0	0.0	0.0	0.0
Annual Financial Data				
Operating Results (000's)				
Total Revenues	99,795.1	125,987.3	128,042.4	110,597.8
Costs & Expenses	-114,590.3	-122,183.5	-119,812.2	-105,531.4
Income Before Taxes and Other	-14,795.2	3,803.8	8,230.2	5,066.4
Other Items	0.0	0.0	0.0	0.0
Income Tax	2,097.4	-1,053.1	-2,329.2	-1,351.6
Net Income	-12,697.8	2,750.7	5,901.0	3,714.8
Cash Flow From Operations	-870.5	19,764.9	15,415.4	-6,166.9
Balance Sheet (000's)				
Cash & Equivalents	73.4	725.2	1,034.8	442.1
Total Current Assets	39,485.7	64,628.4	58,591.1	63,939.8
Fixed Assets, Net	7,750.0	10,155.6	11,186.3	11,557.5
Total Assets	47,333.6	75,368.7	71,588.0	76,664.6
Total Current Liabilities	19,581.7	32,955.6	23,442.3	33,029.9
Long-Term Debt	0.0	1,916.4	9,361.4	12,733.7
Stockholders' Equity	25,899.6	38,831.8	35,983.6	30,155.0
Performance & Financial Condition				
Return on Total Revenues %	-12.72	2.18	4.61	3.36
Return on Avg Stockholders' Equity %	-39.23	7.35	17.84	13.09
Return on Average Assets %	-20.70	3.74	7.96	5.34
Current Ratio	2.02	1.96	2.50	1.94
Debt / Equity %	n.a.	4.94	26.02	42.23

Compound Growth %'s	EPS % n.a.	Net Income % n.a.	Total Revenues % -3.37

Comments

Sales decreased 21% as a result of less demand for Company products at Wal-Mart, Mervyn's, J.C. Penney and in branded businesses. The Company discontinued the "Bill Blass" program and failed to replace it with another program. Liquidity constraints have also caused delays in filling orders. Despite a higher backlog of orders at December 31, 1996 as compared to the prior year ($13,084,000 vs. $9,719,000), revenue for the first quarter of 1997 was off 46% and a net loss of $1,318,711, $.30 per share, was recorded. Investment Classification: Speculative

Officers	**Position**	**Ownership Information**	
Elizabeth Coleman	Chairman, CEO	Number of Shares Outstanding	4,375,492
Steven Masket	Exec VP, Secretary	Market Capitalization	$ 11,463,789
Frank Stull	Exec VP, CFO	Frequency of Dividends	n.a.
		Number of Shareholders	358

Other Information			
Transfer Agent	ChaseMellon Shareholder Services Ridgefield Park, NJ	Where Listed	OTC-BB
Auditor	Ernst & Young LLP	Symbol	NCCD
Market Maker	JA Glynn & Company	(800)966-4596	SIC Code	2342
	Koonce Securities, Inc.	(800)368-2802	Employees	491
Broker Dealer	Regular Stockbroker		

National Properties Corporation

4500 Merle Hay Road   Des Moines, IA 50310   Telephone (515)278-1132   Fax (515)278-1168

Company Description

National Properties Corporation is in the business of developing commercial real estate for lease to tenants under net lease arrangements. At December 31, 1996, the Company had 39 properties located in Arizona, Georgia, Iowa, Kansas, Missouri, Nebraska, Oklahoma and Texas. One convenience store property was acquired during 1996 and two additional convenience store properties were acquired on March 4, 1997. The Company was formed in 1960.

	12/31/96	12/31/95	12/31/94	12/31/93
Per Share Information				
Stock Price	20.50	24.51	23.56	23.44
Earnings Per Share	2.30	1.97	1.96	1.68
Price / Earnings Ratio	8.91	12.44	12.02	13.95
Book Value Per Share	28.71	26.49	24.15	21.38
Price / Book Value %	71.40	92.53	97.56	109.64
Dividends Per Share	0.10	0.0	0.18	0.17
Annual Financial Data				
Operating Results (000's)				
Total Revenues	3,404.1	3,334.9	3,234.6	2,882.2
Costs & Expenses	-1,765.1	-1,406.3	-1,348.6	-1,155.3
Income Before Taxes and Other	1,639.1	1,419.5	1,408.4	1,232.4
Other Items	0.0	0.0	0.0	0.0
Income Tax	-600.0	-516.8	-503.2	-440.3
Net Income	1,039.1	902.7	905.2	792.1
Cash Flow From Operations	1,842.3	1,367.1	1,629.8	1,522.7
Balance Sheet (000's)				
Cash & Equivalents	120.8	123.8	238.7	154.4
Total Current Assets	388.3	151.6	270.5	183.7
Fixed Assets, Net	18,102.4	17,394.3	17,681.9	16,351.7
Total Assets	20,115.2	19,117.6	19,599.6	17,411.6
Total Current Liabilities	592.3	1,563.1	1,442.8	1,166.1
Long-Term Debt	6,030.8	5,148.1	6,758.1	6,220.4
Stockholders' Equity	12,899.5	12,070.4	11,142.2	10,025.1
Performance & Financial Condition				
Return on Total Revenues %	30.52	27.07	27.99	27.48
Return on Avg Stockholders' Equity %	8.32	7.78	8.55	8.13
Return on Average Assets %	5.30	4.66	4.89	4.88
Current Ratio	0.66	0.10	0.19	0.16
Debt / Equity %	46.75	42.65	60.65	62.05

Compound Growth %'s	EPS %	11.04	Net Income %	9.47	Total Revenues %	5.70

Comments

Included in Total Assets for the last three years are marketable securities of approximately $1.5 million. The Company has an ongoing stock repurchase program, subject to market prices. Management reported that the tenants of all 39 leased properties were in compliance with the terms of their respective leases. One tenant, who occupies three locations that generate $455,000 of annual income, has been reporting substantial operational losses. That tenant is being watched very closely. A Chapter 11 Reorganization of that tenant, should it occur, would result in a substantial reduction in future lease income. Investment Classification: Value

Officers	Position	Ownership Information	
Raymond Di Paglia	President	Number of Shares Outstanding	449,245
Kristine M. Fasano	Secretary, Treasurer	Market Capitalization	$ 9,209,523
Robert W. Guely	Vice President, CFO	Frequency of Dividends	Irregular
		Number of Shareholders	833

Other Information			
Transfer Agent	Chase Mellon Shareholder Services Ridgefield Park, NJ	Where Listed	OTC-BB
Auditor	Northup, Haines et. al.	Symbol	NAPE
Market Maker	Carr Securities Corporation	(800)221-2243	SIC Code	6512
	Boenning & Scattergood, Inc.	(800)883-8383	Employees	6
Broker Dealer	OTC Specialist		

National Stock Yards Company

Exchange Building   National Stock Yards, IL 62071   Telephone (618)274-6400   Fax (618)274-6402

Company Description

The Company provides marketplaces on its land for the exchange of livestock in the greater St. Louis and Oklahoma City areas. The customer base consists of livestock suppliers who primarily distribute to meat packers and processors throughout the United States. In addition to the Stockyards operations, the Company owns approximately 600 acres of underdeveloped real estate near its St. Louis facility. National Stock Yards was founded in 1872.

	12/31/96	12/31/95	12/31/94	12/31/93
Per Share Information				
Stock Price	77.00	69.50	53.00	39.00
Earnings Per Share	3.24	0.90	1.61	-0.38
Price / Earnings Ratio	23.77	77.22	32.92	n.a.
Book Value Per Share	243.52	240.28	239.38	237.77
Price / Book Value %	31.62	28.92	22.14	16.40
Dividends Per Share	0.0	0.0	0.0	0.0
Annual Financial Data				
Operating Results (000's)				
Total Revenues	5,134.7	4,811.6	5,036.1	5,101.1
Costs & Expenses	-4,898.4	-4,756.3	-4,913.9	-5,115.7
Income Before Taxes and Other	236.3	55.3	122.2	-14.5
Other Items	0.0	0.0	0.0	0.0
Income Tax	-95.0	-16.0	-52.0	-2.0
Net Income	141.3	39.3	70.2	-16.5
Cash Flow From Operations	362.8	339.9	254.0	78.8
Balance Sheet (000's)				
Cash & Equivalents	654.7	434.2	337.6	397.2
Total Current Assets	780.7	673.8	574.0	650.7
Fixed Assets, Net	10,921.3	10,836.2	10,920.3	10,765.2
Total Assets	11,702.0	11,510.0	11,494.9	11,415.9
Total Current Liabilities	442.1	468.9	398.9	497.5
Long-Term Debt	119.3	136.8	155.4	0.0
Stockholders' Equity	10,620.6	10,479.3	10,440.0	10,369.8
Performance & Financial Condition				
Return on Total Revenues %	2.75	0.82	1.39	-0.32
Return on Avg Stockholders' Equity %	1.34	0.38	0.67	-0.16
Return on Average Assets %	1.22	0.34	0.61	-0.14
Current Ratio	1.77	1.44	1.44	1.31
Debt / Equity %	1.12	1.31	1.49	n.a.

Compound Growth %'s	EPS %	41.86	Net Income %	41.87	Total Revenues %	0.22

Comments

Management reports a continuing decline in stock yard operations at the St. Louis facility due to the continued trend of direct buying in the hog market. The Oklahoma City facility reported higher earnings. Management has been investigating alternative uses of the Company's substantial real estate holdings. A considerable gain on the sale of assets enabled the Company to produce its third consecutive profitable year. Investment Classification: Value

Officers	Position	Ownership Information	
Michael Bakwin	Chairman	Number of Shares Outstanding	43,612
George A. Hall	President	Market Capitalization	$ 3,358,124
Patrick Henry	Secretary, Treasurer	Frequency of Dividends	Irregular
Kathryn Kueker	Other	Number of Shareholders	Under 500
Russell J. Porcelli	Other		

Other Information			
Transfer Agent	First National Bank of Chicago Chicago, IL	Where Listed	OTC-BB
Auditor	Lopata Flegel Hoffman & Co.LLP	Symbol	NSYC
Market Maker	S.J. Wolfe & Co.	(800)262-2244	SIC Code	7389
	Herzog, Heine, Geduld, Inc.	(800)221-3600	Employees	40
Broker Dealer	Regular Stockbroker		

Naturade, Inc.

7110 East Jackson Street   Paramount, CA 90723   Telephone (310)531-8120   Fax (310)531-8170

Company Description

Naturade, Inc. manufactures and distributes health related products including vitamins, nutritional supplements and skin and hair care products. Its products are sold primarily to distributors who resell to health and natural food stores. Approximately 7% of the Company's sales were made to foreign customers in fiscal year 1996. The Company was established in 1986 and acquired Naturade Products in 1989. Naturade was established in 1926.

	09/30/96	09/30/95	09/30/94	09/30/93
Per Share Information				
Stock Price as of 12/31	2.12	1.81	0.91	1.25
Earnings Per Share	0.06	0.14	0.18	0.01
Price / Earnings Ratio	35.33	12.93	5.06	125.00
Book Value Per Share	0.42	0.35	0.27	0.02
Price / Book Value %	504.76	517.14	337.04	6,250.00
Dividends Per Share	0.0	0.0	0.0	0.0
Annual Financial Data				
Operating Results (000's)				
Total Revenues	10,118.7	10,096.6	8,139.8	7,616.8
Costs & Expenses	-9,914.6	-9,491.7	-7,752.2	-7,566.9
Income Before Taxes and Other	204.2	336.8	387.6	49.9
Other Items	0.0	0.0	91.0	0.0
Income Tax	-38.0	58.3	29.0	-27.0
Net Income	166.2	395.1	507.6	22.9
Cash Flow From Operations	96.2	90.6	496.6	176.7
Balance Sheet (000's)				
Cash & Equivalents	120.1	116.4	201.9	61.8
Total Current Assets	2,541.3	2,300.2	2,255.2	1,699.9
Fixed Assets, Net	2,201.1	2,182.5	110.4	119.4
Total Assets	5,160.2	4,820.8	2,564.6	2,093.2
Total Current Liabilities	1,661.7	1,367.5	1,602.8	1,632.2
Long-Term Debt	2,418.3	2,555.7	199.1	393.1
Stockholders' Equity	1,080.2	897.6	762.8	68.0
Performance & Financial Condition				
Return on Total Revenues %	1.64	3.91	6.24	0.30
Return on Avg Stockholders' Equity %	16.80	47.59	122.21	248.45
Return on Average Assets %	3.33	10.70	21.80	1.10
Current Ratio	1.53	1.68	1.41	1.04
Debt / Equity %	223.87	284.73	26.10	578.41

Compound Growth %'s	EPS %	81.71	Net Income %	93.71	Total Revenues %	9.93

Comments

The Company redesigned its Aloe Vera 80 Skin & Hair Care Line in the spring of 1996. Eight new products were also added to the line. A new area of distribution for the Company in 1996 was the chain of 2,400 GNC stores. The Company also completed the initial product development and package design for its new Biospec brand of vitamins. Distribution began in the first quarter of 1997. International sales were off because of the reorganization of a customer in Saudi Arabia. Sales to this customer resumed in early 1997. For the six months ended March 31, 1997, sales were up 56% over the same period in the prior year and earnings per share were $.14 as compared to a loss of $.05 in the equivalent period. Investment Classification: Speculative

Officers	Position	Ownership Information	
Allan Schulman	President, CEO	Number of Shares Outstanding	2,593,005
Michael Fernicola	Exec VP	Market Capitalization	$ 5,497,171
Paul D. Shapnick	CFO, Secretary	Frequency of Dividends	n.a.
		Number of Shareholders	596

Other Information

Transfer Agent	Registrar & Transfer Company Cranford, NJ		Where Listed	OTC-BB
Auditor	McGladrey & Pullen LLP		Symbol	NRDC
Market Maker	Nash, Weiss & Co.	(800)526-3041	SIC Code	2844
	Wm. V. Frankel & Co., Inc.	(800)631-3091	Employees	48
Broker Dealer	Regular Stockbroker			

Naylor Pipe Company

1230 East Ninety-Second Street   Chicago, IL 60619   Telephone (773)721-9400   Fax (773)721-9494

Company Description

Naylor Pipe Company is engaged in the business of manufacturing and selling spiral welded steel pipe. The Company was founded in 1925.

	12/31/96	12/31/95	12/31/94	12/31/93
Per Share Information				
Stock Price	151.00	145.00	140.00	135.00
Earnings Per Share	36.90	17.72	18.04	1.12
Price / Earnings Ratio	4.09	8.18	7.76	120.54
Book Value Per Share	564.77	524.88	484.94	458.96
Price / Book Value %	26.74	27.63	28.87	29.41
Dividends Per Share	6.51	6.07	4.01	5.66
Annual Financial Data				
Operating Results (000's)				
Total Revenues	12,419.9	11,154.5	11,364.1	9,428.3
Costs & Expenses	-11,603.3	-10,788.9	-10,950.2	-9,722.2
Income Before Taxes and Other	816.6	365.6	413.9	-294.0
Other Items	0.0	0.0	0.0	211.3
Income Tax	-330.0	-131.1	-160.9	98.5
Net Income	486.6	234.5	253.1	15.9
Cash Flow From Operations	-1,316.8	2,548.5	-308.7	-130.1
Balance Sheet (000's)				
Cash & Equivalents	29.3	113.5	14.9	86.6
Total Current Assets	6,869.3	5,866.5	5,512.1	4,685.1
Fixed Assets, Net	1,645.2	1,769.3	1,938.0	2,110.7
Total Assets	8,850.7	7,966.8	8,004.1	7,347.7
Total Current Liabilities	1,007.1	681.6	868.4	525.1
Long-Term Debt	0.0	0.0	0.0	0.0
Stockholders' Equity	7,447.6	6,945.2	6,802.8	6,508.6
Performance & Financial Condition				
Return on Total Revenues %	3.92	2.10	2.23	0.17
Return on Avg Stockholders' Equity %	6.76	3.41	3.80	n.a.
Return on Average Assets %	5.79	2.94	3.30	n.a.
Current Ratio	6.82	8.61	6.35	8.92
Debt / Equity %	n.a.	n.a.	n.a.	n.a.

Compound Growth %'s	EPS % n.a.	Net Income % n.a.	Total Revenues % 9.62

Comments

The Company's balance sheet is exceptionally strong. Inventory is accounted for under the LIFO method producing a hidden asset of another $1,777,000 as of December 31, 1996. Favorable results achieved in 1996 were due to favorable pricing of pipe products as well as opportunities to purchase a substantial tonnage of coil steel at lower prices. Management reports that there is still over-capacity in the steel pipe and tubing sector which is holding down profit margins. The Company continues to acquire shares and has retired 17% of ownership since 1992. Investment Classification: Value

Officers	Position	Ownership Information	
William B. Skeates	President	Number of Shares Outstanding	13,187
		Market Capitalization	$ 1,991,237
		Frequency of Dividends	Quarterly
		Number of Shareholders	Under 500

Other Information			
Transfer Agent	Company Office	Where Listed	OTC-BB
Auditor	Gray Hunter Steiner	Symbol	NAYP
Market Maker	Ernst & Company (800)845-4330	SIC Code	3317
	Hill Thompson Magid & Co., Inc (800)631-3083	Employees	100
Broker Dealer	OTC Specialist		

Nebraska, First National of

1620 Dodge Street   Omaha, NE 68102   Telephone (402)341-0500   Fax (402)633-3019

Company Description

The Company is a Nebraska-based interstate bank holding company whose primary assets are the following banking subsidiaries: First National Bank of Omaha, The Bank of Boulder, First National Bank (Fort Collins-Loveland), First National Bank and Trust Company of Columbus, First National Bank of Kansas, First National Bank (North Platte), The Fremont National Bank and Trust Company, Platte Valley State Bank & Trust Company, First National Bank South Dakota, and Union Colony Bank. The Company has over 4,500 employees.

	12/31/96	12/31/95	12/31/94	12/31/93
Per Share Information				
Stock Price	3,400.00	3,650.00	2,350.00	1,700.00
Earnings Per Share	202.53	237.17	222.43	202.10
Price / Earnings Ratio	16.79	15.39	10.57	8.41
Book Value Per Share	1,407.19	1,239.54	1,035.90	851.74
Price / Book Value %	241.62	294.46	226.86	199.59
Dividends Per Share	37.22	33.73	38.07	16.86
Annual Financial Data				
Operating Results (000's)				
Net Interest Income	485,183.0	426,923.0	361,975.0	314,990.0
Loan Loss Provision	-180,059.0	-102,767.0	-71,698.0	-67,083.0
Non-Interest Income	180,485.0	137,430.0	115,615.0	96,134.0
Non-Interest Expense	-371,256.0	-331,495.0	-288,779.0	-238,584.0
Income Before Taxes and Other	114,353.0	130,091.0	117,113.0	105,457.0
Other Items	0.0	0.0	0.0	0.0
Income Tax	-44,121.0	-47,850.0	-39,980.0	-35,375.0
Net Income	70,232.0	82,241.0	77,133.0	70,082.0
Balance Sheet (000's)				
Cash & Securities	1,581,632.0	1,465,373.0	1,148,655.0	943,985.0
Loans, Net	4,990,735.0	4,371,687.0	3,878,653.0	3,123,297.0
Total Assets	6,912,057.0	6,110,542.0	5,261,907.0	4,271,853.0
Deposits	5,836,169.0	5,089,880.0	4,383,090.0	3,652,307.0
Stockholders' Equity	487,966.0	429,831.0	359,216.0	295,355.0
Performance & Financial Condition				
Return on Avg Stockholders' Equity %	15.30	20.85	23.57	26.62
Return on Average Assets %	1.08	1.45	1.62	1.79
Equity to Assets %	7.06	7.03	6.83	6.91
Net Interest Margin	n.a.	n.a.	n.a.	n.a.
Reserve as a % of Problem Loans	129.70	122.91	n.a.	n.a.

Compound Growth %'s	EPS %	0.07	Net Income %	0.07	Net Interest Income %	15.49

Comments

The Company has had twenty-five consecutive years of both asset growth and return on equity greater than 15%. Returns on equity and assets have trended downward the last several years. Management attributes the recent decline in profits to the decision to increase the allowance for problem loans. The Company does not disclose total nonperforming loans or impaired loans. It does claim, somewhat inconsistently, that impaired loans are immaterial. There is probably no reason to be concerned, however, as the Company writes-off every debt once 180 days delinquent. Investment Classification: Growth

Officers	Position	Ownership Information	
Bruce R. Lauritzen	President	Number of Shares Outstanding	346,767
Elias J. Eliopoulos	Exec VP	Market Capitalization	$1,179,007,800
J. William Henry	Exec VP	Frequency of Dividends	Quarterly
Dennis A. O'Neal	Exec VP	Number of Shareholders	350
Charles R. Walker	Exec VP	Where Listed / Symbol	OTC-BB / FINN

Other Information			Loan Mix	%
Transfer Agent	First National Bank of Omaha Omaha, NE		Consumer	64.6
Auditor	Deloitte & Touche LLP		Commerical	13.1
Market Maker	Kirkpatrick Pettis Smith et al	(800)776-5778	R/E Mortgages	12.4
	Macallaster Pitfield MacKay	(212)422-9366	Agriculture	5.6
Broker Dealer	Regular Stockbroker		Construction	3.0
	Jerry Stratman	(800)776-5780	Other	1.3

Network Data Processing Corporation

200 Fifth Avenue, S.E. Cedar Rapids, IA 52401-1810 Telephone (319)398-1800 Fax (319)398-1872

Company Description

The Company provides data processing services for the insurance industry throughout the United States, including computer software licensing agreements, system implementation and conversion, and repetitive and special processing. The Company was formed in 1956 to acquire a data processing business that began in 1916 as a consulting actuary firm by the name of Taylor & Taylor. It went public in 1969 and had a 1 for 100 reverse split in 1987.

	03/31/96	03/31/95	03/31/94	03/31/93
Per Share Information				
Stock Price as of 12/31	500.00	501.50	382.15	349.13
Earnings Per Share	104.57	123.81	-201.77	113.04
Price / Earnings Ratio	4.78	4.05	n.a.	3.09
Book Value Per Share	429.33	308.82	158.17	359.75
Price / Book Value %	116.46	162.39	241.61	97.05
Dividends Per Share	0.0	0.0	0.0	0.0
Annual Financial Data				
Operating Results (000's)				
Total Revenues	9,739.0	9,607.3	5,127.1	5,872.7
Costs & Expenses	-8,439.7	-8,559.7	-6,750.3	-4,885.3
Income Before Taxes and Other	1,299.3	1,047.6	-1,623.3	987.3
Other Items	0.0	0.0	0.0	0.0
Income Tax	-532.2	-209.7	364.4	-328.6
Net Income	767.0	837.9	-1,258.9	658.8
Cash Flow From Operations	1,244.1	1,259.7	377.0	873.6
Balance Sheet (000's)				
Cash & Equivalents	212.8	48.1	119.1	190.9
Total Current Assets	2,105.7	2,006.3	1,579.3	1,915.0
Fixed Assets, Net	1,014.7	679.3	807.3	749.2
Total Assets	6,835.6	5,913.0	5,658.4	5,718.3
Total Current Liabilities	2,253.9	2,756.8	3,310.2	2,063.9
Long-Term Debt	276.0	244.5	747.5	618.4
Stockholders' Equity	3,149.1	2,090.1	986.9	2,225.1
Performance & Financial Condition				
Return on Total Revenues %	7.88	8.72	-24.55	11.22
Return on Avg Stockholders' Equity %	29.28	54.47	-78.39	36.02
Return on Average Assets %	12.03	14.48	-22.13	13.78
Current Ratio	0.93	0.73	0.48	0.93
Debt / Equity %	8.77	11.70	75.75	27.79

Compound Growth %'s	EPS %	-2.56	Net Income %	5.20	Total Revenues %	18.37

Comments

During 1996, the Company completed development of ID-3, the most technologically advanced database system available to the life insurance industry. Eighteen companies have already licensed the system and eight companies have it in full production. Management reports that results for fiscal year ending March 31, 1997, are extremely favorable and will exceed fiscal 1996 by 15% in both revenue and pre-tax profits. The Company has issued additional common shares in each of the last three years at approximately $500 per share. The posted bid price is actually lower. Investment Classification: Growth & Value

Officers	Position	Ownership Information	
Howard F. Arner	CEO, President	Number of Shares Outstanding	7,335
John Millard	Senior VP	Market Capitalization	$ 3,667,500
Marian Antin	Senior VP	Frequency of Dividends	n.a.
William Choromanski	Senior VP	Number of Shareholders	Under 500
Connie Michel	Controller		

Other Information			
Transfer Agent	Norwest Shareholder Services South St. Paul, MN	Where Listed	OTC-BB
Auditor	McGladrey & Pullen LLP	Symbol	NTDP
Market Maker	Carr Securities Corporation (800)221-2243	SIC Code	7374
	Hill Thompson Magid & Co., Inc (800)631-3083	Employees	90
Broker Dealer	OTC Specialist		
	Standard Investment (888)783-4688 Ext: Jack		

NeuroCorp., Ltd.

150 White Plains Road   Tarrytown, NY 10591   Telephone (914)631-3316   Fax (914)631-3514

Company Description

NeuroCorp., formerly known as Tamarac Ventures, Ltd., was formed in 1987 as a blind pool for the purpose of acquiring an unknown existing business. On November 23, 1994, the Company acquired HZI Research Center Inc.(HZI), a company that is involved in research and development in preparing new programs related to new drug development, multi-national/multi-center Alzheimer research, and Tele-neuro-psychiatry businesses. The former shareholders of HZII became the majority shareholders of NeuroCorp. In December, 1996, the Company raised $2 million in a private placement to three individuals.

	12/31/96	12/31/95
Per Share Information		
Stock Price	7.75	2.00
Earnings Per Share	-0.24	-0.05
Price / Earnings Ratio	n.a.	n.a.
Book Value Per Share	0.36	0.26
Price / Book Value %	2,152.78	769.23
Dividends Per Share	0.0	0.0
Annual Financial Data		
Operating Results (000's)		
Total Revenues	1,079.2	1,586.4
Costs & Expenses	-2,620.4	-1,878.5
Income Before Taxes and Other	-1,541.2	-292.1
Other Items	-125.7	0.0
Income Tax	32.3	29.6
Net Income	-1,634.7	-262.5
Cash Flow From Operations	-897.4	n.a.
Balance Sheet (000's)		
Cash & Equivalents	1,851.1	n.a.
Total Current Assets	2,605.6	n.a.
Fixed Assets, Net	83.5	n.a.
Total Assets	4,580.4	n.a.
Total Current Liabilities	1,523.0	n.a.
Long-Term Debt	15.5	n.a.
Stockholders' Equity	2,777.9	n.a.
Performance & Financial Condition		
Return on Total Revenues %	-151.47	-16.55
Return on Avg Stockholders' Equity %	-69.63	n.a.
Return on Average Assets %	n.a.	n.a.
Current Ratio	1.71	n.a.
Debt / Equity %	0.56	n.a.

Compound Growth %'s	EPS % n.a.	Net Income % n.a.	Total Revenues % -31.97

Comments

The common stock was first listed on the Electronic Bulletin Board in 1995. Price information is not available for prior years. 1996 revenue declined because of the absence of new contracts. Proceeds from the private placement are largely to be used for the initial development and expansion of Memory Centers. Management intends to set up 100 such centers over the next five years if the pilot program is successful. Investors should be familiar with more of the technical details to properly evaluate whether or not this technology is worthy of a gamble. Investment Classification: Speculative

Officers	Position	Ownership Information	
Turan M. Itll	President, CEO	Number of Shares Outstanding	7,723,806
Pierre LeBars	Exec VP	Market Capitalization	$ 59,859,497
Jonathan E. Raven	Exec VP	Frequency of Dividends	n.a.
Aileen A. Kunitz	Vice President, CFO	Number of Shareholders	382

Other Information				
Transfer Agent	Jersey Transfer & Trust Co. Verona, NJ		Where Listed	OTC-BB
Auditor	Scarano & Lipton, P.C.		Symbol	NURC
Market Maker	Olsen Payne & Co.	(800)453-5321	SIC Code	8090
	Mayer & Schweitzer, Inc.	(800)631-3094	Employees	n.a.
Broker Dealer	Regular Stockbroker			

Nevada Manhattan Mining Incorporated

5038 N. Pkwy Calabasas, Ste 100   Calabasas, CA 91302   Telephone (818)591-4400   Fax (818)591-4411

Company Description

Nevada Manhattan Mining Incorporated, formerly Epic Enterprises, Ltd., was formed in 1985 to acquire, explore, develop, finance and sell mining rights and properties. As of May 31, 1996, the Company was still in the developmental stage. Since May 31, 1996, the Company has acquired certain mining properties in Indonesia and timber properties in Brazil. The Company has made a deliberate shift in emphasis to harvesting timber, with millions of acres under management.

	05/31/96	05/31/95	05/31/94
Per Share Information			
Stock Price as of 12/31	8.87	1.12	0.85
Earnings Per Share	-0.16	-0.12	-0.15
Price / Earnings Ratio	n.a.	n.a.	n.a.
Book Value Per Share	0.43	0.66	0.45
Price / Book Value %	2,062.79	169.70	188.89
Dividends Per Share	0.0	0.0	0.0
Annual Financial Data			
Operating Results (000's)			
Total Revenues	0.0	0.0	0.0
Costs & Expenses	-1,198.5	-611.1	-480.5
Income Before Taxes and Other	-1,198.5	-611.1	-480.5
Other Items	0.0	0.0	0.0
Income Tax	0.0	0.0	0.0
Net Income	-1,198.5	-611.1	-480.5
Cash Flow From Operations	-852.3	-616.0	-749.1
Balance Sheet (000's)			
Cash & Equivalents	234.0	0.0	n.a.
Total Current Assets	234.0	4.4	n.a.
Fixed Assets, Net	3,965.8	3,707.5	n.a.
Total Assets	4,199.8	3,711.9	n.a.
Total Current Liabilities	450.5	630.5	n.a.
Long-Term Debt	115.7	0.0	n.a.
Stockholders' Equity	3,633.6	3,081.3	n.a.
Performance & Financial Condition			
Return on Total Revenues %	n.a.	n.a.	n.a.
Return on Avg Stockholders' Equity %	-35.70	n.a.	n.a.
Return on Average Assets %	-30.30	n.a.	n.a.
Current Ratio	0.52	0.01	n.a.
Debt / Equity %	3.18	n.a.	n.a.

Compound Growth %'s	EPS % n.a.	Net Income % n.a.	Total Revenues % n.a.

Comments

The Company is developing an infrastructure to accomodate a growing timber harvesting operation in Brazil. Although the numbers are far from on paper, management is targeting $2 million in cash flow per month in the near term and $15 million per month at some point in the future. There has been much activity in the Company's shares which rose to over $14 per share before settling down at $4 per share on May 31, 1997. Investment Classification: Speculative

Officers	Position	Ownership Information	
Christopher Michaels	President, CEO	Number of Shares Outstanding	8,353,881
Jeffrey S. Kramer	COO, CFO	Market Capitalization	$ 74,098,924
Stanley J. Mohr	Vice President	Frequency of Dividends	n.a.
William Michaels	Vice President	Number of Shareholders	n.a.

Other Information

Transfer Agent	U.S. Stock Transfer Corp. Glendale, CA		Where Listed	OTC-BB
Auditor	Jackson & Rhodes P.C.		Symbol	NVMH
Market Maker	Kirlin Securities	(516)396-5456	SIC Code	1041
	Marlowe & Co.	(516)231-6426	Employees	9
Broker Dealer	Regular Stockbroker			

New Orleans Cold Storage and Warehouse Company Ltd.

3401 Alvar Street   New Orleans, LA 70126   Telephone (504)944-4400   Fax (504)944-8539

Company Description

New Orleans Cold Storage and Warehouse Ltd. provides cold storage, inspection and transportation services for customers primarily in the southern region of the United States.

	12/31/96	12/31/95	12/31/94
Per Share Information			
Stock Price	50.00	50.00	50.00
Earnings Per Share	14.60	11.55	5.78
Price / Earnings Ratio	3.42	4.33	8.65
Book Value Per Share	111.53	97.93	87.38
Price / Book Value %	44.83	51.06	57.22
Dividends Per Share	1.00	1.00	1.25
Annual Financial Data			
Operating Results (000's)			
Total Revenues	20,947.5	17,837.9	12,166.1
Costs & Expenses	-20,105.5	-17,142.5	-12,754.4
Income Before Taxes and Other	842.1	695.4	-588.3
Other Items	0.0	0.0	0.0
Income Tax	-302.3	-268.2	801.9
Net Income	539.8	427.2	213.6
Cash Flow From Operations	2,506.5	1,550.7	994.4
Balance Sheet (000's)			
Cash & Equivalents	1,470.9	752.3	676.7
Total Current Assets	3,364.9	3,245.3	2,342.3
Fixed Assets, Net	13,714.5	12,686.0	12,495.3
Total Assets	17,142.6	16,014.5	15,068.6
Total Current Liabilities	4,106.2	3,159.6	2,483.8
Long-Term Debt	8,212.5	8,431.0	8,854.9
Stockholders' Equity	4,124.3	3,621.5	3,231.3
Performance & Financial Condition			
Return on Total Revenues %	2.58	2.40	1.76
Return on Avg Stockholders' Equity %	13.94	12.47	6.79
Return on Average Assets %	3.26	2.75	n.a.
Current Ratio	0.82	1.03	0.94
Debt / Equity %	199.13	232.80	274.04

Compound Growth %'s	EPS %	58.93	Net Income %	58.96	Total Revenues %	31.22

Comments

The Company has managed strong increases in revenues of 17.4% and 46.6% in 1996 and 1995, respectively. The largest increases have been posted by the transportation division. Patience and a little professional help may be required to acquire shares for the interested, as only 37,000 shares are outstanding. The latest shares offered were at $55.75 per share. Investment Classification: Value

Officers	Position	Ownership Information	
Gary Escoffier	President	Number of Shares Outstanding	36,980
Lawrence Moloney	Secretary	Market Capitalization	$ 1,849,000
Joseph Paniello	Vice President	Frequency of Dividends	Quarterly
		Number of Shareholders	Under 500

Other Information					
Transfer Agent	Company Office			Where Listed	Order Matching Only
Auditor	Ernst & Young LLP			Symbol	n.a.
Market Maker	Dorsey Investment Securities	(800)375-5431		SIC Code	4200
				Employees	n.a.
Broker Dealer	Stephen Schuller - Dorsey	(800)375-5431			

New Ulm Telecom, Inc.

400 Second Street North   New Ulm, MN 56073   Telephone (507)354-4111   Fax (507)354-1982

Company Description

New Ulm Telecom, Inc.'s principal business is the operation of local phone companies (seven subsidiaries) which provide local exchange telephone service and related access to the long distance network. At December 31, 1996, the Company provided telephone service to over 14,354 access lines in six southern Minnesota cities and one northern Iowa city and adjacent rural areas. Most of the Company's operations are regulated by the state utilities commissions. The Company was formed in 1905.

	12/31/96	12/31/95	12/31/94	12/31/93
Per Share Information				
Stock Price	28.00	8.41	6.13	6.67
Earnings Per Share	1.39	1.30	1.23	1.22
Price / Earnings Ratio	20.14	6.47	4.98	5.47
Book Value Per Share	9.46	8.72	8.00	7.32
Price / Book Value %	295.98	96.44	76.63	91.12
Dividends Per Share	0.65	0.58	0.54	0.49
Annual Financial Data				
Operating Results (000's)				
Total Revenues	9,919.6	9,544.8	8,866.2	7,745.8
Costs & Expenses	-5,929.5	-5,798.9	-5,326.6	-4,573.1
Income Before Taxes and Other	3,990.1	3,745.9	3,539.6	3,172.6
Other Items	0.0	0.0	0.0	0.0
Income Tax	-1,586.5	-1,491.1	-1,412.6	-1,057.9
Net Income	2,403.5	2,254.8	2,127.0	2,114.8
Cash Flow From Operations	4,067.5	3,330.3	3,419.3	2,724.1
Balance Sheet (000's)				
Cash & Equivalents	2,517.9	1,829.2	1,433.8	1,125.6
Total Current Assets	3,939.0	3,478.0	2,748.4	2,931.6
Fixed Assets, Net	12,145.8	12,370.6	12,108.3	12,377.5
Total Assets	22,849.4	22,021.5	20,976.2	21,309.1
Total Current Liabilities	937.5	949.5	821.8	1,574.8
Long-Term Debt	4,033.3	4,400.0	4,766.7	6,505.8
Stockholders' Equity	16,385.4	15,113.7	13,869.5	12,678.1
Performance & Financial Condition				
Return on Total Revenues %	24.23	23.62	23.99	27.30
Return on Avg Stockholders' Equity %	15.26	15.56	16.02	17.56
Return on Average Assets %	10.71	10.49	10.06	11.57
Current Ratio	4.20	3.66	3.34	1.86
Debt / Equity %	24.62	29.11	34.37	51.32

Compound Growth %'s	EPS %	4.44	Net Income %	4.36	Total Revenues %	8.59

Comments

The Company declared a 3 for 1 stock split in 1996. All per share amounts were restated for consistency. The Company has been growing by acquiring interests in cellular phone companies, generally partnerships, and other telephone companies. The Company's most recent acquisition was that of Peoples Telephone Company in Iowa, for a total purchase price of approximately $3.9 million. For the first quarter of 1997, the Company had 12.4% higher revenues and earnings per share of $.41 as compared to $.33 in the first quarter of 1996. Investment Classification: Growth

Officers	Position	Ownership Information	
James Jensen	President	Number of Shares Outstanding	1,732,455
Bill Otis	Exec VP, COO	Market Capitalization	$ 48,508,740
Gary Nelson	Secretary	Frequency of Dividends	Quarterly
Lavern Biebl	Treasurer	Number of Shareholders	909
Mark Retzlaff	Vice President		

Other Information				
Transfer Agent	Company Office		Where Listed	OTC-BB
Auditor	Olsen Thielen & Co.		Symbol	NULM
Market Maker	F.J. Morrissey & Co., Inc.	(800)842-8928	SIC Code	4813
	Sharpe Capital Inc.	(800)355-5781	Employees	43
Broker Dealer	OTC Specialist			

New York and Harlem Railroad Company

One East Fourth Street   Cincinnati, OH 45202   Telephone (513)579-6643

Company Description

The Company owns land under Grand Central Station and various railroad tracks in the New York City area which are leased to the New York Metropolitan Transportation Authority (MTA). MTA has an option to purchase these properties which may be exercised up until the year 2019. The common stock is divided into two groups with differing rights. A preference goes to shares not held by American Premier Underwriters, Inc., the insurance company that is a party to the various agreements. 97% of the common shares are owned by American Financial Group (NYSE) and they now control the distribution of information on The New York and Harlem Railroad Company. They refused to send us information.

	12/31/96	12/31/95	12/31/94	12/31/92
Per Share Information				
Stock Price	125.00	100.00	100.00	n.a.
Earnings Per Share	6.24	7.99	4.25	n.a.
Price / Earnings Ratio	20.03	12.52	23.53	n.a.
Book Value Per Share	26.16	24.93	21.96	n.a.
Price / Book Value %	477.83	401.12	455.37	n.a.
Dividends Per Share	5.00	5.00	5.00	n.a.
Annual Financial Data				
Operating Results (000's)				
Total Revenues	576.7	1,290.8	974.2	33,276.8
Costs & Expenses	-332.8	-374.3	-372.0	-30,588.1
Income Before Taxes and Other	243.9	546.4	-101.0	2,688.7
Other Items	0.0	0.0	0.0	0.0
Income Tax	0.0	0.0	0.0	-1,064.9
Net Income	243.9	546.4	-101.0	1,623.8
Cash Flow From Operations	n.a.	546.4	-101.0	n.a.
Balance Sheet (000's)				
Cash & Equivalents	5,559.7	5,155.7	4,840.2	n.a.
Total Current Assets	14,802.7	5,344.2	5,013.5	n.a.
Fixed Assets, Net	154.7	154.7	154.7	n.a.
Total Assets	15,205.7	14,885.4	15,622.3	n.a.
Total Current Liabilities	276.4	168.6	422.8	n.a.
Long-Term Debt	9,057.0	9,057.0	9,057.0	n.a.
Stockholders' Equity	5,872.4	5,659.9	5,142.6	n.a.
Performance & Financial Condition				
Return on Total Revenues %	42.30	42.33	-10.36	n.a.
Return on Avg Stockholders' Equity %	4.23	10.12	n.a.	n.a.
Return on Average Assets %	1.62	3.58	n.a.	n.a.
Current Ratio	53.56	31.70	11.86	n.a.
Debt / Equity %	154.23	160.02	176.12	n.a.

Compound Growth %'s	EPS % n.a.	Net Income % n.a.	Total Revenues %	-23.06

Comments

The financial statements are very difficult to interpret, primarily because of a $91 million receivable, without interest, that is not due until the year 2274, unless MTA exercises its purchase option. Since the present value of even this large sum is less than $1 million, we have decided to remove it from the balance sheet both as an asset and as shareholders equity. There is a lease which would be appropriate to examine by any serious investor. This may possibly reap benefits in the year 2019 or else be a good asset for the great-great-grandchildren's trust. Earnings per share relate to the preferred common stock (shares not held by APU) including an allocation in 1994. Investment Classification: Speculative

Officers	Position	Ownership Information	
James C. Kennedy	Secretary	Number of Shares Outstanding	173,121
		Market Capitalization	$ 21,640,125
		Frequency of Dividends	n.a.
		Number of Shareholders	Under 500

Other Information

			Where Listed	OTC-BB
Transfer Agent	Girard Bank Philadelphia, PA		Symbol	NYHA
Auditor	Not indicated		SIC Code	6510
Market Maker	Legg Mason Wood Walker, Inc.	(212)428-4949	Employees	n.a.
Broker Dealer	OTC Specialist			

Nichols (J.C.) Company

310 Ward Parkway   Kansas City, MO 64112-2110   Telephone (816)561-3456   Fax (816)960-6211

Company Description

The Company owns and manages numerous retail properties, apartment buildings, office and industrial properties and a residential land development in the greater Kansas City area of Missouri. Barrett Brady, president, has led J.C. Nichols on a new course since former management was removed. This once secretive company has split its shares 80 for 1 and now plans for a NASDAQ listing.

	12/31/96	12/31/95	12/31/94	12/31/93
Per Share Information				
Stock Price	29.00	21.56	7.50	7.18
Earnings Per Share	5.62	-0.74	-0.96	0.04
Price / Earnings Ratio	5.16	n.a.	n.a.	179.50
Book Value Per Share	-5.90	-7.57	-1.64	-21.98
Price / Book Value %	n.a.	n.a.	n.a.	n.a.
Dividends Per Share	0.0	0.0	0.12	0.12
Annual Financial Data				
Operating Results (000's)				
Total Revenues	132,628.0	99,305.0	93,802.0	96,204.0
Costs & Expenses	-87,976.0	-115,803.0	-98,801.0	-96,178.0
Income Before Taxes and Other	44,652.0	-16,498.0	-44,698.0	26.0
Other Items	0.0	0.0	29,136.0	0.0
Income Tax	-16,750.0	5,746.0	1,028.0	484.0
Net Income	27,902.0	-10,752.0	-14,534.0	510.0
Cash Flow From Operations	29,713.0	22,017.0	5,339.0	18,736.0
Balance Sheet (000's)				
Cash & Equivalents	14,454.0	7,209.0	14,186.0	30,520.0
Total Current Assets	67,862.0	54,134.0	50,081.0	54,048.0
Fixed Assets, Net	220,133.0	229,524.0	245,192.0	239,008.0
Total Assets	320,327.0	328,695.0	351,712.0	362,112.0
Total Current Liabilities	39,228.0	32,571.0	19,490.0	19,139.0
Long-Term Debt	309,188.0	326,349.0	351,317.0	342,383.0
Stockholders' Equity	-28,606.0	-36,725.0	-25,821.0	-31,568.0
Performance & Financial Condition				
Return on Total Revenues %	21.04	-10.83	-15.49	0.53
Return on Avg Stockholders' Equity %	n.a.	n.a.	n.a.	n.a.
Return on Average Assets %	8.60	-3.16	-4.07	0.13
Current Ratio	1.73	1.66	2.57	2.82
Debt / Equity %	n.a.	n.a.	n.a.	n.a.

Compound Growth %'s	EPS % n.a.	Net Income % n.a.	Total Revenues % 11.30

Comments

Last year management said "A real estate company, like J.C. Nichols, with many mature and valuable real estate holdings does not get credit for the substantial appreciation in its real estate assets under conventional accounting methods." In 1996, they proved their point by recognizing nearly $35 million in gains on sales of investments and other assets. Cash and temporary investments have increased from $11.8 million to $59.5 million. Management reports that overall occupancy rates have remained high and that rental rates have escalated. All per share amounts have been adjusted for the stock split referred to above. In January, 1997, the Company purchased a block of 948,880 shares because the terms were favorable and would benefit all remaining shareholders. On May 9, 1997, the Company received an unsolicited letter from Realty Capital Corporation proposing to enter discussions to acquire the Company. The proposal was rejected by the Board of Directors. Investment Classification: Value

Officers	Position	Ownership Information	
Barrett Brady	President, CEO	Number of Shares Outstanding	4,852,400
Edward A. de Avila	Senior VP	Market Capitalization	$ 140,719,600
G. Reid Teaney	Senior VP	Frequency of Dividends	Quarterly
Price A. Sloan	Secretary	Number of Shareholders	166
Mark A. Peterson	Vice President, CFO		

Other Information

Transfer Agent	American Stock Transfer and Trust Co. New York, NY		Where Listed	OTC-BB
Auditor	KPMG Peat Marwick LLP		Symbol	NCJC
Market Maker	George K. Baum & Company	(800)821-7570	SIC Code	6510
	The Seidler Companies Inc.	(800)421-0164	Employees	350
Broker Dealer	Regular Stockbroker			

North American Scientific, Inc.

7435 Greenbush Avenue   North Hollywood, CA 91605   Telephone (818)503-9201   Fax (818)503-0764

Company Description

North American Scientific manufactures and markets a broad line of low-level radiation sources and standards. The Company's products are used in the field of nuclear medicine by hospitals, medical centers and universities in connection with imaging examinations and disease detection, and also are utilized by nuclear utility companies, U.S. government facilities and industrial users to assist in the monitoring of effluents being released from their respective facilities in order to ensure the safety of personnel and the surrounding communities. The Company, founded in 1987, moved from Canada to the United States in 1996.

	10/31/96	10/31/95	10/31/94	10/31/93
Per Share Information				
Stock Price as of 12/31	1.62	1.25	1.50	1.00
Earnings Per Share	0.14	0.04	0.09	0.03
Price / Earnings Ratio	11.57	31.25	16.67	33.33
Book Value Per Share	0.54	0.38	0.32	0.21
Price / Book Value %	300.00	328.95	468.75	476.19
Dividends Per Share	0.0	0.0	0.0	0.0
Annual Financial Data				
Operating Results (000's)				
Total Revenues	3,083.4	1,878.5	1,426.4	907.7
Costs & Expenses	-2,419.2	-1,651.8	-1,159.6	-800.7
Income Before Taxes and Other	664.2	226.7	266.8	107.0
Other Items	0.0	0.0	0.0	0.0
Income Tax	-251.0	-95.0	0.0	-11.1
Net Income	413.2	131.7	266.8	95.9
Cash Flow From Operations	555.1	-61.3	n.a.	n.a.
Balance Sheet (000's)				
Cash & Equivalents	866.0	491.0	601.8	400.0
Total Current Assets	1,742.7	1,165.8	1,088.9	561.9
Fixed Assets, Net	215.9	86.1	70.0	60.0
Total Assets	2,000.2	1,291.2	1,187.3	654.4
Total Current Liabilities	397.1	174.7	227.8	80.3
Long-Term Debt	0.0	0.0	0.0	0.0
Stockholders' Equity	1,603.1	1,116.5	959.5	574.1
Performance & Financial Condition				
Return on Total Revenues %	13.40	7.01	18.70	10.57
Return on Avg Stockholders' Equity %	30.39	12.69	34.79	n.a.
Return on Average Assets %	25.11	10.63	28.97	n.a.
Current Ratio	4.39	6.67	4.78	7.00
Debt / Equity %	n.a.	n.a.	n.a.	n.a.

Compound Growth %'s	EPS %	67.11	Net Income %	62.72	Total Revenues %	50.32

Comments

We can't help but glow in the dark as we review the growth and conservative balance sheet over what might be dismissed as a penny stock. Management has established a strong sales momentum which it believes can be maintained. International sales, following attendance at the 1996 International Congress of Radiation Protection in Vienna, increased 300%. 1997 has been labelled as a year of great promise as new market opportunities are under evaluation. The stock broke the $4 per share mark at the end of May, 1997. Investment Classification: Growth

Officers	Position	Ownership Information	
Irwin J. Gruverman	Chairman	Number of Shares Outstanding	2,983,201
L. Michael Cutrer	President, CEO	Market Capitalization	$ 4,832,786
		Frequency of Dividends	n.a.
		Number of Shareholders	33

Other Information				
Transfer Agent	U.S. Stock Transfer Corporation Glendale, CA		Where Listed	OTC-BB
Auditor	Price Waterhouse		Symbol	NASI
Market Maker	Sutro & Co., Incorporated	(800)227-4422	SIC Code	3800
	Wien Securities Corp.	(800)624-0050	Employees	n.a.
Broker Dealer	Regular Stockbroker			

North Carolina Railroad Company

234 Fayetteville Street Mall, Suite 600   Raleigh, NC 27601   Telephone (919)829-7355   Fax (919)829-7356

Company Description

The North Carolina Railroad Company owns and leases approximately 317 miles of railroad lines running from Charlotte to Morehead City, North Carolina. The Company was formed in 1849. From 1856 to 1871 it conducted railroad operations. Since that time it has leased its property to others. Most of the Company's property is currently operated by Norfolk Southern. The Company elected tax status as a real estate investment trust effective for 1996 and beyond.

	12/31/96	12/31/95	12/31/94	12/31/93
Per Share Information				
Stock Price	38.25	27.50	25.25	36.00
Earnings Per Share	2.01	2.07	0.03	-0.01
Price / Earnings Ratio	19.03	13.29	841.67	n.a.
Book Value Per Share	2.96	4.01	1.94	1.95
Price / Book Value %	1,292.23	685.79	1,301.55	1,846.15
Dividends Per Share	3.06	0.03	0.0	0.03
Annual Financial Data				
Operating Results (000's)				
Total Revenues	5,620.5	15,132.6	851.1	777.8
Costs & Expenses	-2,357.0	-988.6	-760.9	-694.9
Income Before Taxes and Other	3,263.5	14,143.9	90.1	82.9
Other Items	0.0	0.0	0.0	-140.9
Income Tax	5,340.5	-5,279.0	17.0	4.0
Net Income	8,604.0	8,864.9	107.1	-54.0
Cash Flow From Operations	3,141.0	13,847.8	194.3	-135.0
Balance Sheet (000's)				
Cash & Equivalents	5,318.9	15,139.5	1,615.3	912.7
Total Current Assets	5,318.9	15,333.9	1,926.7	1,330.9
Fixed Assets, Net	7,826.1	7,790.8	7,792.8	7,799.3
Total Assets	13,145.0	24,480.3	10,084.8	9,640.0
Total Current Liabilities	462.7	6,084.7	549.5	56.3
Long-Term Debt	0.0	0.0	0.0	0.0
Stockholders' Equity	12,682.3	17,185.7	8,320.8	8,342.2
Performance & Financial Condition				
Return on Total Revenues %	153.08	58.58	12.59	-6.95
Return on Avg Stockholders' Equity %	57.61	69.51	1.29	-0.64
Return on Average Assets %	45.74	51.29	1.09	-0.56
Current Ratio	11.50	2.52	3.51	23.62
Debt / Equity %	n.a.	n.a.	n.a.	n.a.

Compound Growth %'s   EPS % n.a.   Net Income % n.a.   Total Revenues % n.a.

Comments

The new lease with Norfolk Southern provides a much improved cash flow and allows the Company the right to withdraw and develop properties that are not essential for railway operations. There is, however, a shareholder derivative action that challenges the approval of the lease. As Norfolk Southern was restrained by the court from making lease payments, 1996 revenue is lower. Compound growth rates are misleading because they reflect nonrecurring changes in lease revenues. Accordingly, they have not been displayed. Investment Classification: Income

Officers	Position	Ownership Information	
R. Samuel Hunt	President	Number of Shares Outstanding	4,283,470
Scott M. Saylor	Exec VP	Market Capitalization	$ 163,842,728
J. Bradley Wilson	Secretary	Frequency of Dividends	n.a.
Lynn T. McConnell	Treasurer	Number of Shareholders	722
J. Melville Broughton, Jr.	Vice President		

Other Information

Transfer Agent	First Citizens Bank & Trust Company Raleigh, NC		Where Listed	OTC-BB
Auditor	Ernst & Young LLP		Symbol	NORA
Market Maker	The Seidler Companies Inc.	(800)421-0164	SIC Code	4011
	Herzog, Heine, Geduld, Inc.	(800)221-3600	Employees	3
Broker Dealer	Regular Stockbroker			

North Coast Bank

8733 Lakewood Drive   Windsor, CA 95492   Telephone (707)838-8000   Fax (707)838-8225

Company Description

North Coast Bank changed its name from Windsor Oaks National Bank in 1997. Management believes that this name change has enhanced the Bank's business image and increased public visibility. The Bank's primary service area, the heart of the famous wine growing region of northern Sonoma County, has seen considerable population growth in recent years. The Bank was organized in 1990.

	12/31/96	12/31/95	12/31/94	12/31/93
Per Share Information				
Stock Price	6.75	6.25	7.50	9.00
Earnings Per Share	0.84	0.54	-0.28	-0.61
Price / Earnings Ratio	8.04	11.57	n.a.	n.a.
Book Value Per Share	8.21	7.43	6.55	7.08
Price / Book Value %	82.22	84.12	114.50	127.12
Dividends Per Share	0.0	0.0	0.0	0.0
Annual Financial Data				
Operating Results (000's)				
Net Interest Income	1,763.0	1,696.4	1,536.3	1,333.1
Loan Loss Provision	-70.5	-81.6	-110.0	-90.9
Non-Interest Income	220.6	264.2	239.8	152.5
Non-Interest Expense	-1,595.6	-1,673.3	-1,769.4	-1,624.7
Income Before Taxes and Other	317.5	205.8	-103.3	-230.1
Other Items	0.0	0.0	0.0	0.0
Income Tax	0.0	-0.8	-0.8	-0.8
Net Income	317.5	205.0	-104.1	-230.9
Balance Sheet (000's)				
Cash & Securities	9,474.0	10,822.9	7,131.3	8,099.1
Loans, Net	19,451.9	19,643.2	17,619.4	17,364.3
Total Assets	29,850.8	31,464.4	25,866.1	26,511.7
Deposits	26,605.2	27,780.2	23,271.9	23,734.3
Stockholders' Equity	3,096.9	2,803.7	2,470.6	2,669.8
Performance & Financial Condition				
Return on Avg Stockholders' Equity %	10.76	7.77	-4.05	-8.29
Return on Average Assets %	1.04	0.72	-0.40	-0.91
Equity to Assets %	10.37	8.91	9.55	10.07
Net Interest Margin	n.a.	n.a.	n.a.	n.a.
Reserve as a % of Problem Loans	1,186.76	151.69	422.49	176.50

Compound Growth %'s	EPS % n.a.	Net Income % n.a.	Net Interest Income % 9.77

Comments

Management attributed the 1993 loss to opening a new office, relocating the first office and weak loan demand. The 1994 loss was not explained. The higher profit in 1996 is mostly attributable to lower overhead costs. Management says there is more of this coming as they tighten their infrastructure. Compound growth rates in earnings were not displayed because of the lack of a significant base period. Investment Classification: Value

Officers	Position	Ownership Information	
Michael D. Arendt	President, CEO	Number of Shares Outstanding	377,334
Robert A. Koch	Senior VP, Sr Loan Officer	Market Capitalization	$ 2,547,005
Kathy Pinkard	Senior VP, CFO	Frequency of Dividends	n.a.
Kristina M. Tyer	Vice President	Number of Shareholders	n.a.
Belinda Novick	Other	Where Listed / Symbol	OTC-PS / WOCA

Other Information				Loan Mix	%
Transfer Agent	Company Office			R/E Mortgages	50.7
Auditor	Richardson & Company			Commerical	33.1
Market Maker	A.G. Edwards & Sons, Inc.	(800)325-8197		Construction	6.4
	Black & Company, Inc.	(800)423-2124		Installment	1.5
Broker Dealer	OTC Specialist			Other	8.3
	Hoefer & Arnett, Retail	(800)346-5544	Ext: Lisa		

North Coast Life Insurance Co.

1116 West Riverside Avenue   Spokane, WA 99210-1445   Telephone (509)838-4235   Fax (509)747-8569

Company Description

North Coast Life Insurance Co. writes a variety of life insurance and annuity products through 212 general agents, agents, and brokers who act as representatives. Business is conducted in twelve western states, although two-thirds of all revenue is generated in California. The Company was founded in 1964. Over one-half of the employees are shareholders.

	12/31/96	12/31/95	12/31/94	12/31/93
Per Share Information				
Stock Price	3.00	5.00	5.00	5.00
Earnings Per Share	0.74	3.60	1.82	-0.57
Price / Earnings Ratio	4.05	1.39	2.75	n.a.
Book Value Per Share	n.a.	n.a.	n.a.	n.a.
Price / Book Value %	n.a.	n.a.	n.a.	n.a.
Dividends Per Share	0.0	0.0	0.0	0.0
Annual Financial Data				
Operating Results (000's)				
Total Revenues	12,679.9	14,054.5	13,558.7	12,337.6
Costs & Expenses	-11,827.8	-12,014.0	-11,863.8	-12,256.1
Income Before Taxes and Other	565.5	1,353.4	862.0	-1,022.2
Other Items	0.0	0.0	0.0	0.0
Income Tax	0.0	0.0	0.0	0.0
Net Income	565.5	1,353.4	862.0	-1,022.2
Cash Flow From Operations	n.a.	n.a.	n.a.	n.a.
Balance Sheet (000's)				
Cash & Equivalents	700.9	538.5	52.1	7.6
Total Current Assets	4,796.4	3,928.1	3,494.4	3,521.8
Fixed Assets, Net	1,489.5	1,852.4	1,430.2	3,545.9
Total Assets	73,966.8	71,573.4	68,102.0	66,468.6
Total Current Liabilities	798.8	277.9	250.5	337.9
Long-Term Debt	0.0	500.0	0.0	0.0
Stockholders' Equity	4,426.1	4,036.9	2,849.0	3,084.1
Performance & Financial Condition				
Return on Total Revenues %	4.46	9.63	6.36	-8.29
Return on Avg Stockholders' Equity %	13.36	39.31	29.06	n.a.
Return on Average Assets %	0.78	1.94	1.28	n.a.
Current Ratio	6.00	14.14	13.95	10.42
Debt / Equity %	n.a.	12.39	n.a.	n.a.

Compound Growth %'s	EPS % n.a.	Net Income % n.a.	Total Revenues % 0.92

Comments

The financial statements are not presented in accordance with GAAP and therefore require insurance industry experience to interpret. The preferred stock, traded on NASDAQ, will probably be redeemed in a few years according to a Company official. Book value was not calculated because of insufficient information. We were told that it would be approximately $11 million, including the preferred, if GAAP accounting were used. Earnings per share are shown based upon the statutory accounting in the report and may be higher than GAAP reporting by 20% to 25%. The compound growth in earnings rates were not presented because 1995 results included a nonrecurring gain of $1.6 million related to a litigation settlement. Investment Classification: Speculative

Officers	Position	Ownership Information	
C. Robert Ogden	President	Number of Shares Outstanding	275,106
Robert E. Blair	Senior VP	Market Capitalization	$ 825,318
Richard D. Hillier	Senior VP	Frequency of Dividends	Quarterly
Clifford D. Kutsch	Secretary	Number of Shareholders	311
Gavin J. Cooley	Treasurer		

Other Information				
Transfer Agent	Company Office		Where Listed	OTC-BB
Auditor	Coopers & Lybrand LLP		Symbol	NCLI
Market Maker	Martin Nelson & Co., Inc.	(206)682-6261	SIC Code	6310
	Empire Securities Inc.	(800)541-5960	Employees	31
Broker Dealer	Regular Stockbroker			
	Stephen Schuller - Dorsey	(800)375-5431		

North Pittsburgh Systems, Inc.

4008 Gibsonia Road   Gibsonia, PA 15044-9311   Telephone (412)443-9600   Fax (412)443-9431

Company Description

The Company, organized in 1985, is the parent of North Pittsburg Telephone Company (NPTC) and PennTelecon, Inc. (PTI). Since 1906, NPTC has been providing telephone service to a 287 square mile area in portions of four western Pennsylvania counties. PTI sells, rents and services telecommunication equipment, message toll services and high capacity intercity facilities. Two other subsidiaries, formed in 1995, provide consulting, computer and Internet access services.

	12/31/96	12/31/95	12/31/94	12/31/93
Per Share Information				
Stock Price	23.50	22.75	16.07	14.00
Earnings Per Share	0.78	0.71	0.66	0.61
Price / Earnings Ratio	30.13	32.04	24.35	22.95
Book Value Per Share	3.68	3.43	3.19	2.97
Price / Book Value %	638.59	663.27	503.76	471.38
Dividends Per Share	0.52	0.48	0.44	0.40
Annual Financial Data				
Operating Results (000's)				
Total Revenues	61,667.0	53,822.5	50,162.2	45,119.1
Costs & Expenses	-42,028.0	-35,343.9	-33,373.0	-29,940.2
Income Before Taxes and Other	19,639.0	17,740.9	16,789.2	14,620.9
Other Items	0.0	0.0	0.0	450.0
Income Tax	-7,909.0	-7,054.2	-6,884.8	-5,906.2
Net Income	11,730.0	10,686.7	9,904.4	9,164.7
Cash Flow From Operations	19,860.0	18,429.8	17,403.6	17,726.4
Balance Sheet (000's)				
Cash & Equivalents	11,313.0	9,359.0	14,778.6	19,045.0
Total Current Assets	24,785.0	28,747.4	32,056.2	34,280.2
Fixed Assets, Net	65,594.0	58,616.4	50,994.1	47,645.9
Total Assets	99,523.0	96,156.1	91,577.9	88,771.2
Total Current Liabilities	10,384.0	10,944.6	9,388.4	9,498.4
Long-Term Debt	20,937.0	27,544.2	28,669.7	28,159.2
Stockholders' Equity	55,306.0	51,527.4	47,911.1	44,624.4
Performance & Financial Condition				
Return on Total Revenues %	19.02	19.86	19.74	20.31
Return on Avg Stockholders' Equity %	21.96	21.49	21.41	21.29
Return on Average Assets %	11.99	11.38	10.98	10.57
Current Ratio	2.39	2.63	3.41	3.61
Debt / Equity %	37.86	53.46	59.84	63.10

Compound Growth %'s	EPS %	8.54	Net Income %	8.57	Total Revenues %	10.98

Comments

The Company declared a 2 for 1 stock split in 1996. All per share amounts have been adjusted for consistency. The Company has been making significant improvements to its facilities and cable systems. During the years 1991 through 1996, the Company made property additions of $66 million and retired property of approximately $20 million. This aggressive rebuilding program should allow the Company to remain competitive in a very dynamic industry. Unprecedented growth in the demand for access lines during 1996 was due to new housing starts in the service area and the demand for Internet connections. Investment Classification: Growth

Officers	Position	Ownership Information	
Charles E. Thomas, Sr.	Chairman	Number of Shares Outstanding	15,040,000
Gerald A. Gorman	President	Market Capitalization	$ 353,440,000
Allen P. Kimble	Secretary, Treasurer	Frequency of Dividends	Quarterly
Harry R. Brown	Vice President	Number of Shareholders	2,845
N. William Barthlow	Vice President		

Other Information				
Transfer Agent	Company Office		Where Listed	OTC-BB
Auditor	KPMG Peat Marwick LLP		Symbol	NORY
Market Maker	Hefren Tillotson, Inc.	(412)434-0990	SIC Code	4813
	Legg Mason Wood & Walker, Inc.	(800)221-9732	Employees	288
Broker Dealer	Regular Stockbroker			

North State Telephone Company

111 North Main Street   High Point, NC 27261   Telephone (910)886-3600   Fax (910)887-7418

Company Description

North State Telephone Company operates entirely in the communications industry, providing telephone service for over 100,000 access lines in four counties located in north central North Carolina. The Company is regulated by the State of North Carolina Utilities Commission and the Federal Communications Commission. The Company remembers its beginnings in 1895 when it had 60 customers using crude, crank telephones and is proud that over 100 years later it still offers the best of technology and customer service. There are two classes of common shares: Class A shares are voting and Class B shares are nonvoting.

	12/31/95	12/31/94	12/31/93
Per Share Information			
Stock Price	420.00	375.00	315.00
Earnings Per Share	33.16	24.05	20.61
Price / Earnings Ratio	12.67	15.59	15.28
Book Value Per Share	204.46	186.93	177.71
Price / Book Value %	205.42	200.61	177.26
Dividends Per Share	15.90	15.22	15.64
Annual Financial Data			
Operating Results (000's)			
Total Revenues	65,570.3	59,321.2	53,428.5
Costs & Expenses	-42,453.5	-41,647.2	-38,788.8
Income Before Taxes and Other	23,116.8	17,674.0	14,639.7
Other Items	0.0	0.0	-137.2
Income Tax	-8,494.8	-6,886.3	-5,112.2
Net Income	14,622.0	10,787.7	9,390.2
Cash Flow From Operations	23,577.5	20,300.4	17,751.7
Balance Sheet (000's)			
Cash & Equivalents	515.6	769.5	1,454.9
Total Current Assets	21,548.7	25,939.3	28,724.6
Fixed Assets, Net	80,733.0	74,776.9	71,642.3
Total Assets	119,341.0	112,340.0	109,423.1
Total Current Liabilities	12,416.7	11,530.3	9,239.4
Long-Term Debt	3,001.5	4,120.0	4,893.5
Stockholders' Equity	89,973.2	82,302.5	82,072.9
Performance & Financial Condition			
Return on Total Revenues %	22.30	18.19	17.58
Return on Avg Stockholders' Equity %	16.98	13.13	11.57
Return on Average Assets %	12.62	9.73	8.94
Current Ratio	1.74	2.25	3.11
Debt / Equity %	3.34	5.01	5.96

Compound Growth %'s	EPS %	26.84	Net Income %	24.79	Total Revenues %	10.78

Comments

The annual report comes out quite late by traditional standards and 1996 results are not included. Only shareholders are entitled to copies. 1995 results continued on a very positive path setting records in every service category. Management has been able to maintain tight control on expenses despite increased customers and revenues. Deregulation of the telecommunications industry has sharpened the Company's focus on reinforcing its position as a primary provider of full-service communications with increased focus on customer relationships. The price per share at December 31, 1996 was $485 bid, $605 ask. Investment Classification: Growth

Officers	Position	Ownership Information	
Royster M. Tucker, Jr.	President	Number of Shares Outstanding	437,607
Coulson S. Mucher	Treasurer, Controller	Market Capitalization	$ 183,794,940
J. Patrick Harman	Vice President	Frequency of Dividends	Quarterly
C. Hayden McKenzie	Vice President, Secretary	Number of Shareholders	Under 500
William H. Dula	Vice President		

Other Information			
Transfer Agent	Company Office	Where Listed	OTC-BB
Auditor	Deloitte & Touche LLP	Symbol	NORSA
Market Maker	Herzog, Heine, Geduld, Inc.	(800)221-3600	SIC Code	4810
	J.C. Bradford & Co.	(800)251-1740	Employees	388
Broker Dealer	Regular Stockbroker		

North Valley Bancorp

P.O. Box 493517   Redding, CA 96049-3517   Telephone (916)221-8400   Fax (916)222-1768

Company Description

North Valley Bank, subsidiary of Bancorp, operates nine offices in Shasta and Trinity Counties in rural northern California. Bancorp also owns Bank Processing, Inc. which provides data processing services to depository institutions. North Valley Bank was formed in 1973 and has an excellent record of community service through its support of many non-profit organizations.

	12/31/96	12/31/95	12/31/94	12/31/93
Per Share Information				
Stock Price	21.00	19.25	13.83	11.00
Earnings Per Share	2.20	2.20	1.74	1.64
Price / Earnings Ratio	9.55	8.75	7.95	6.71
Book Value Per Share	13.11	11.39	9.80	8.65
Price / Book Value %	160.18	169.01	141.12	127.17
Dividends Per Share	0.70	0.64	0.47	0.46
Annual Financial Data				
Operating Results (000's)				
Net Interest Income	10,564.0	9,910.0	8,718.0	7,666.0
Loan Loss Provision	-720.0	-375.0	-240.0	-110.0
Non-Interest Income	2,581.0	2,630.0	2,477.0	2,676.0
Non-Interest Expense	-6,786.0	-6,412.0	-6,404.0	-6,170.0
Income Before Taxes and Other	5,639.0	5,753.0	4,551.0	4,062.0
Other Items	0.0	0.0	0.0	127.0
Income Tax	-1,532.0	-1,670.0	-1,339.0	-1,178.0
Net Income	4,107.0	4,083.0	3,212.0	3,011.0
Balance Sheet (000's)				
Cash & Securities	77,727.0	76,369.0	78,326.0	92,765.0
Loans, Net	166,983.0	147,808.0	125,463.0	99,457.0
Total Assets	256,877.0	235,072.0	213,956.0	201,068.0
Deposits	229,228.0	211,075.0	193,541.0	183,319.0
Stockholders' Equity	23,900.0	20,973.0	17,926.0	15,705.0
Performance & Financial Condition				
Return on Avg Stockholders' Equity %	18.30	20.99	19.10	20.69
Return on Average Assets %	1.67	1.82	1.55	1.59
Equity to Assets %	9.30	8.92	8.38	7.81
Net Interest Margin	5.11	5.23	5.08	4.85
Reserve as a % of Problem Loans	48.01	77.26	258.24	255.02

Compound Growth %'s	EPS %	10.29	Net Income %	10.90	Net Interest Income %	11.28

Comments

The Company declared a 3 for 2 stock split in 1995. All per share amounts have been adjusted for consistency. Expenses associated with new products and a larger loan loss reserve kept earnings relatively flat in 1996. There was still good growth in loans and assets even before the Bank started with its next round of expansion. A new facility in Shasta Lake will open in late 1997 and plans are being formulated for an office in Cottonwood. Investment Classification: Income & Growth

Officers	Position	Ownership Information	
Donald V. Carter	President, CEO	Number of Shares Outstanding	1,823,688
James F. Cowee	Exec VP	Market Capitalization	$ 38,297,448
Fred A. Drake	Senior VP, Head Cashier	Frequency of Dividends	Semi-Annual
Robert G. Jones	Senior VP	Number of Shareholders	917
Sharon L. Benson	Vice President	Where Listed / Symbol	OTC-BB / NOVB

Other Information			Loan Mix	%
Transfer Agent	Bank of America San Francisco, CA		Commerical	38.0
Auditor	Deloitte & Touche LLP		R/E Mortgages	27.7
Market Maker	Hoefer & Arnett, Incorporated	(800)346-5544	Installment	26.1
	Van Kasper & Company, Inc.	(800)652-1747	Construction	0.7
Broker Dealer	Regular Stockbroker		Other	7.5

Northern Empire Bancshares

801 Fourth Street   Santa Rosa, CA 95404   Telephone (707)579-2265   Fax (707)579-5621

Company Description

Northern Empire Bancshares is a bank holding company whose only subsidiary is Sonoma National Bank. The Bank operates three branches in suburban communities in Sonoma County, California. The Bank makes commercial and real estate loans to customers who are predominantly small and middle-market businesses. Sonoma National Bank has benefitted from an expanding economy and an influx of residents during its ten years of existence. Situated just forty-five miles north of the San Francisco Bay, Sonoma County is a significant wine growing region that also offers many recreational activities.

	12/31/96	12/31/95	12/31/94	12/31/93
Per Share Information				
Stock Price	15.25	8.81	8.39	7.34
Earnings Per Share	1.53	1.21	0.98	0.94
Price / Earnings Ratio	9.97	7.28	8.56	7.81
Book Value Per Share	9.81	8.22	7.38	6.76
Price / Book Value %	155.45	107.18	113.69	108.58
Dividends Per Share	0.0	0.19	0.33	0.56
Annual Financial Data				
Operating Results (000's)				
Net Interest Income	9,232.0	7,565.0	6,119.0	5,183.0
Loan Loss Provision	-420.0	-250.0	-280.0	-174.0
Non-Interest Income	1,620.0	1,602.0	2,146.0	1,898.0
Non-Interest Expense	-6,407.0	-5,859.0	-5,666.0	-4,857.0
Income Before Taxes and Other	4,025.0	3,058.0	2,319.0	2,050.0
Other Items	0.0	0.0	0.0	51.0
Income Tax	-1,719.0	-1,338.0	-973.0	-802.0
Net Income	2,306.0	1,720.0	1,346.0	1,299.0
Balance Sheet (000's)				
Cash & Securities	53,290.0	32,306.0	27,269.0	20,762.0
Loans, Net	165,681.0	129,587.0	90,116.0	81,632.0
Total Assets	224,793.0	166,962.0	121,776.0	106,560.0
Deposits	209,235.0	154,221.0	111,083.0	97,332.0
Stockholders' Equity	14,338.0	11,982.0	10,199.0	8,897.0
Performance & Financial Condition				
Return on Avg Stockholders' Equity %	17.52	15.51	14.10	15.10
Return on Average Assets %	1.18	1.19	1.18	1.28
Equity to Assets %	6.38	7.18	8.38	8.35
Net Interest Margin	n.a.	n.a.	n.a.	n.a.
Reserve as a % of Problem Loans	466.21	421.11	706.97	254.11

Compound Growth %'s	EPS %	17.63	Net Income %	21.08	Net Interest Income %	21.22

Comments

The Company declared 5% stock dividends in each of the last three years. All per share amounts were adjusted accordingly. The original goal of becoming Sonoma County's premier independent community bank is largely achieved. The outstanding financial results reflect continuing gains on sales of SBA guaranteed loans and a growing deposit base. Management says it will continue to explore new geographic markets as well as introduce TeleBanc, a 24-hour telephone access service, in 1997.

Officers	Position	Ownership Information	
Deborah A. Meekins	President, CEO	Number of Shares Outstanding	1,461,400
David F. Titus	Exec VP, Senior Loan Officer	Market Capitalization	$ 22,286,350
JoAnn Barton	Senior VP	Frequency of Dividends	Quarterly
Jane M. Baker	Senior VP, CFO	Number of Shareholders	341
		Where Listed / Symbol	OTC-BB / NREB

Other Information		Loan Mix	%
Transfer Agent	Chemical Mellon Shareholder Services Ridgefield Park, NJ	Commerical	50.1
Auditor	Coopers & Lybrand LLP	R/E Mortgages	47.7
Market Maker	Hoefer & Arnett, Incorporated (800)346-5544	Installment	1.3
	Cowles, Sabol & Company, Inc. (818)906-0881	Construction	0.9
Broker Dealer	Regular Stockbroker		

Northern Lehigh Bancorp, Inc.

502 Main Street   Slatington, PA 18080-0008   Telephone (610)767-3887   Fax (610)767-5420

Company Description

The Citizens National Bank of Slatington, subsidiary of this holding company, has been serving this community in eastern Pennsylvania since 1901. Carbon County, located only ten miles northwest of Allentown and fifty miles northwest of Philadelphia, has become very suburban. The Bank has three offices.

	12/31/96	12/31/95	12/31/94	12/31/93
Per Share Information				
Stock Price	45.00	40.87	38.62	34.50
Earnings Per Share	6.67	7.11	4.65	3.51
Price / Earnings Ratio	6.75	5.75	8.31	9.83
Book Value Per Share	55.66	50.50	43.57	40.42
Price / Book Value %	80.85	80.93	88.64	85.35
Dividends Per Share	1.30	1.00	0.87	0.75
Annual Financial Data				
Operating Results (000's)				
Net Interest Income	3,073.4	2,990.0	2,710.2	2,316.3
Loan Loss Provision	-115.0	-70.0	0.0	-108.0
Non-Interest Income	196.0	299.5	120.6	148.9
Non-Interest Expense	-1,968.9	-1,919.4	-1,952.6	-1,691.9
Income Before Taxes and Other	1,185.5	1,300.1	878.2	665.4
Other Items	0.0	0.0	0.0	0.0
Income Tax	-326.6	-369.3	-267.7	-204.1
Net Income	858.8	930.9	610.5	461.3
Balance Sheet (000's)				
Cash & Securities	13,096.6	20,968.9	20,492.2	21,680.3
Loans, Net	55,165.6	46,040.1	41,726.5	38,852.3
Total Assets	69,838.9	68,513.5	64,016.5	62,165.2
Deposits	62,047.1	61,317.0	57,787.4	56,427.0
Stockholders' Equity	7,162.1	6,498.3	5,709.6	5,296.1
Performance & Financial Condition				
Return on Avg Stockholders' Equity %	12.57	15.25	11.09	8.91
Return on Average Assets %	1.24	1.40	0.97	n.a.
Equity to Assets %	10.26	9.48	8.92	8.52
Net Interest Margin	n.a.	n.a.	n.a.	n.a.
Reserve as a % of Problem Loans	26.89	75.33	35.63	24.72

Compound Growth %'s	EPS %	23.86	Net Income %	23.02	Net Interest Income %	9.89

Comments

1995 earnings included nonrecurring benefits of approximately $140,000. Net loans increased 20% in 1996, as compared to only 1.2% in deposit growth. Management has recognized that expanding the Bank's sources of funds, primarily deposits, will be an important objective. A marketing program is underway. Investment Classification: Growth & Value

Officers	Position	Ownership Information	
Joseph G. Bechtel	Chairman	Number of Shares Outstanding	128,676
Francis P. Burbidge	President, CEO	Market Capitalization	$ 5,790,420
Leon A. Rodenbach	Senior VP, COO	Frequency of Dividends	Annual
Stephanie L. Phillips	Senior VP, Sr Loan Officer	Number of Shareholders	n.a.
Michele M. Hunsicker	Controller	Where Listed / Symbol	OTC-BB / NOLE

Other Information			Loan Mix	%
Transfer Agent	Company Office		R/E Mortgages	77.0
Auditor	Jarrett Stokes & Kelly		Commerical	7.4
Market Maker	Ryan, Beck & Co.	(800)395-7926	Installment	5.8
	Hopper Soliday & Co., Inc.	(800)646-8647	Construction	5.6
Broker Dealer	OTC Specialist		Other	4.2
	Dennis Reynolds - Ryan, Beck	(888)231-7226		

Northfield Precision Instrument Corporation

4400 Austin Boulevard   Island Park, NY 11558-0550   Telephone (516)431-1112   Fax (516)431-1928

Company Description

Northfield Precision Instrument Corporation is in the business of manufacturing precision instruments from its plant in Island Park, Long Island, New York. The automobile and aerospace industries represent a large part of the Company's customer base. Northfield was organized in 1952 and went public in 1959. Almost one-half of the shares issued have been reacquired as treasury shares over the years.

	12/31/96	12/31/95	12/31/94	12/31/93
Per Share Information				
Stock Price	7.75	6.00	7.00	7.00
Earnings Per Share	1.33	0.97	0.64	0.32
Price / Earnings Ratio	5.83	6.19	10.94	21.88
Book Value Per Share	10.00	9.66	9.49	9.65
Price / Book Value %	77.50	62.11	73.76	72.54
Dividends Per Share	1.00	0.80	0.80	0.40
Annual Financial Data				
Operating Results (000's)				
Total Revenues	3,920.6	3,438.1	2,876.1	2,858.3
Costs & Expenses	-3,394.4	-3,068.4	-2,642.2	-2,701.8
Income Before Taxes and Other	526.2	369.6	233.9	156.4
Other Items	0.0	0.0	0.0	0.0
Income Tax	-214.5	-141.5	-83.1	-80.6
Net Income	311.7	228.2	150.7	75.9
Cash Flow From Operations	300.7	426.2	311.6	172.8
Balance Sheet (000's)				
Cash & Equivalents	730.6	815.3	717.8	651.0
Total Current Assets	2,057.1	2,215.4	2,159.1	2,165.1
Fixed Assets, Net	361.4	341.1	334.7	407.6
Total Assets	2,462.8	2,594.2	2,520.6	2,593.8
Total Current Liabilities	109.0	302.4	220.5	216.5
Long-Term Debt	0.0	1.8	42.6	86.7
Stockholders' Equity	2,341.2	2,263.8	2,223.0	2,259.7
Performance & Financial Condition				
Return on Total Revenues %	7.95	6.64	5.24	2.65
Return on Avg Stockholders' Equity %	13.54	10.17	6.72	3.34
Return on Average Assets %	12.33	8.92	5.89	2.90
Current Ratio	18.88	7.33	9.79	10.00
Debt / Equity %	n.a.	0.08	1.92	3.84

Compound Growth %'s	EPS %	60.78	Net Income %	60.16	Total Revenues %	11.11

Comments

Net sales increased for the fourth consecutive year and earnings rose 36.6%. Management believes that much of the improvement in earnings is attributable to cost cutting and operational efficiencies. We noted an improvement in gross margin from 51.6% in 1995 to 53.9% in 1996. Management reports that it is particularly encouraged by the growth of the national economy. The high dividend indicates that Northfield cares a great deal about its shareholders. Investment Classification: Value & Income & Growth

Officers	Position	Ownership Information	
Timothy J. Steffen	President	Number of Shares Outstanding	234,237
Donald E. Freedman	Secretary, Treasurer	Market Capitalization	$ 1,815,337
Bernard Rourke	Director	Frequency of Dividends	n.a.
		Number of Shareholders	Under 500

Other Information

			Where Listed	OTC-BB
Transfer Agent	Continental Stock Transfer and Trust New York, NY		Symbol	NFPC
Auditor	Frumkin & Lukin, P.C.		SIC Code	3800
Market Maker	Carr Securities Corporation	(800)221-2243	Employees	30
	The Seidler Companies Inc.	(800)421-0164		
Broker Dealer	Regular Stockbroker			

Nova Technologies, Inc.

89 Cabot Court, Unit L   Hauppauge, NY 11788   Telephone (516)434-8811

Company Description

Nova Technologies, Inc. was founded in 1984 to create a methodology of providing for the unassisted transfer of bedridden patients. Nova's objective is to become a fully integrated design, engineering, manufacturing and marketing company addressing a niche market in the medical equipment and supply field. On June 14, 1996, the Company acquired Comed, a distributor of specialized beds, support surfaces and related equipment in the greater Boston area.

	12/31/96	12/31/95	12/31/94	12/31/93
Per Share Information				
Stock Price	2.00	2.75	2.00	2.50
Earnings Per Share	-0.33	-0.27	-0.31	-0.37
Price / Earnings Ratio	n.a.	n.a.	n.a.	n.a.
Book Value Per Share	0.26	0.10	-0.16	-0.12
Price / Book Value %	769.23	2,750.00	n.a.	n.a.
Dividends Per Share	0.0	0.0	0.0	0.0
Annual Financial Data				
Operating Results (000's)				
Total Revenues	1,695.7	233.6	238.5	14.2
Costs & Expenses	-3,749.5	-1,535.8	-1,449.6	-1,244.7
Income Before Taxes and Other	-2,053.8	-1,302.2	-1,211.1	-1,230.6
Other Items	0.0	0.0	0.0	0.0
Income Tax	0.0	0.0	0.0	0.0
Net Income	-2,053.8	-1,302.2	-1,211.1	-1,230.6
Cash Flow From Operations	-1,663.6	-1,210.2	-790.6	-1,050.4
Balance Sheet (000's)				
Cash & Equivalents	373.5	485.8	102.2	69.4
Total Current Assets	2,434.6	935.2	372.7	298.1
Fixed Assets, Net	1,255.7	136.3	152.9	202.0
Total Assets	5,351.2	1,396.2	542.1	509.3
Total Current Liabilities	1,640.6	383.1	212.2	128.2
Long-Term Debt	1,598.6	378.9	343.9	309.1
Stockholders' Equity	2,008.9	584.2	-702.0	-430.1
Performance & Financial Oondition				
Return on Total Revenues %	-121.11	-557.53	-507.87	-8,685.50
Return on Avg Stockholders' Equity %	-158.40	n.a.	n.a.	n.a.
Return on Average Assets %	-60.88	-134.37	-230.39	n.a.
Current Ratio	1.48	2.44	1.76	2.33
Debt / Equity %	79.57	64.85	n.a.	n.a.

Compound Growth %'s	EPS % n.a.	Net Income % n.a.	Total Revenues % n.a.

Comments

1996 was the first year of revenues which represented sales and rentals of medical equipment. For the three months ended March 31, 1997, the Company had revenues of $815,173 and an operating loss of $655,069, $.09 per share. As of March 31, 1997, the Company has entered into seven distributorship agreements providing for the sale and shipment of Novabeds (R) to each distributor to be sold within an exclusive sales territory. Investment Classification: Speculative

Officers	Position	Ownership Information	
Paul DiMatteo	Chairman	Number of Shares Outstanding	7,669,657
Stephen Fisher	President, CEO	Market Capitalization	$ 15,339,314
Samuel N. Paul	Exec VP	Frequency of Dividends	n.a.
Douglas Drew	Senior VP	Number of Shareholders	375
Harold J. Lash	Vice President, Controller		

Other Information			
Transfer Agent	American Stock Transfer & Trust Co. New York, NY	Where Listed	OTC-BB
Auditor	Richard A. Eisner & Company	Symbol	NOTL
Market Maker	Hill Thompson Magid & Co., Inc (800)631-3083	SIC Code	2590
	Herzog, Heine, Geduld, Inc. (800)221-3600	Employees	n.a.
Broker Dealer	Regular Stockbroker		

O.A.K. Financial Corporation

2445 84th Street SW   Byron Center, MI 49315   Telephone (616)878-1591   Fax (616)878-4007

Company Description

Byron Center State Bank, subsidiary of the Corporation, serves the southern portion of the greater Grand Rapids, Michigan area through its seven branches located in Byron Center, Jamestown, Cutlerville, Hudsonville, Grandville, Moline and Dorr. To commemorate their 75th year of business in 1996, the Bank established a community grant program to help fund non-profit groups serving all of these same communities.

	12/31/96	12/31/95	12/31/94	12/31/93
Per Share Information				
Stock Price	52.44	46.78	38.56	38.00
Earnings Per Share	4.35	3.98	3.66	3.35
Price / Earnings Ratio	12.06	11.75	10.54	11.34
Book Value Per Share	35.33	32.33	27.58	35.14
Price / Book Value %	148.43	144.70	139.81	108.14
Dividends Per Share	1.00	0.75	0.61	0.54
Annual Financial Data				
Operating Results (000's)				
Net Interest Income	10,320.9	9,631.3	8,711.0	7,654.7
Loan Loss Provision	0.0	-275.0	-170.0	-510.0
Non-Interest Income	1,074.9	919.2	665.0	1,523.1
Non-Interest Expense	-5,168.5	-4,511.1	-4,096.5	-3,760.5
Income Before Taxes and Other	6,227.3	5,764.5	5,109.5	4,907.3
Other Items	0.0	0.0	0.0	0.0
Income Tax	-1,852.0	-1,760.0	-1,429.0	-1,511.0
Net Income	4,375.3	4,004.5	3,680.5	3,396.3
Balance Sheet (000's)				
Cash & Securities	64,870.5	62,186.3	54,776.1	55,948.4
Loans, Net	144,626.4	140,687.7	125,429.9	114,692.4
Total Assets	217,526.5	210,880.4	187,244.2	176,913.9
Deposits	170,220.9	170,011.8	151,074.4	144,111.4
Stockholders' Equity	35,543.6	32,558.9	27,900.2	25,932.1
Performance & Financial Condition				
Return on Avg Stockholders' Equity %	12.85	13.25	13.67	13.87
Return on Average Assets %	2.04	2.01	2.02	2.01
Equity to Assets %	16.34	15.44	14.90	14.66
Net Interest Margin	n.a.	n.a.	n.a.	n.a.
Reserve as a % of Problem Loans	198.99	n.a.	n.a.	n.a.

Compound Growth %'s	EPS %	9.10	Net Income %	8.81	Net Interest Income %	10.47

Comments

The Company declared 10% and 25% stock dividends in 1996 and 1994, respectively. All per share amounts have been restated for earlier periods. Share price information was derived from treasury stock transactions reported by the Corporation. It appears that shares have only been repurchased during the last several years. The stock dividend will make more shares available for possible trading. 1996 earnings were fueled by several major loan loss recoveries that, in turn, reduced this year's loan reserve expense to zero. Investment Classification: Value

Officers	Position	Ownership Information	
John Van Singel	President, CEO	Number of Shares Outstanding	1,006,174
John Peterson	Exec VP, Sr Loan Officer	Market Capitalization	$ 52,763,765
Forrest Bowling	Vice President	Frequency of Dividends	Quarterly
Martin Braun	Vice President, CFO	Number of Shareholders	n.a.
Richard Dykstra	Vice President	Where Listed / Symbol	Order Matching Only / n.a.

Other Information		Loan Mix	%
Transfer Agent	Company Office	R/E Mortgages	73.2
Auditor	Rehmann Robson	Commerical	18.7
Market Maker	None	Consumer	8.1
Broker Dealer	Royal Securities Co. (616)538-2550		
	D.H. Brush & Associates, Inc. (800)831-6671		

OPT-Sciences Corporation

1912 Bannard Street   Riverton, NJ 08077   Telephone (609)829-2800   Fax (609)829-0482

Company Description

OPT-Sciences Corporation is engaged principally in the cutting, grinding, polishing, coating and painting of glass lenses and glass for flat panel displays utilized in the custom fabrication of components for aircraft instrument panels. The aircraft industry is retrofitting older airplanes and replacing glass lenses in instrument panels with flat panel displays which the Company manufactures, thus resulting in a build up in demand for the Company's products. However, there are many companies competing in the same marketplace.

	10/26/96	10/28/95
Per Share Information		
Stock Price as of 12/31	4.00	2.75
Earnings Per Share	0.52	0.29
Price / Earnings Ratio	7.69	9.48
Book Value Per Share	4.95	4.42
Price / Book Value %	80.81	62.22
Dividends Per Share	0.0	0.0
Annual Financial Data		
Operating Results (000's)		
Total Revenues	2,730.7	2,003.2
Costs & Expenses	-2,042.0	-1,646.9
Income Before Taxes and Other	688.7	356.2
Other Items	0.0	0.0
Income Tax	-285.4	-134.6
Net Income	403.3	221.7
Cash Flow From Operations	396.3	383.1
Balance Sheet (000's)		
Cash & Equivalents	2,557.3	2,628.3
Total Current Assets	3,843.9	3,297.7
Fixed Assets, Net	393.1	342.1
Total Assets	4,237.0	3,639.8
Total Current Liabilities	398.6	210.0
Long-Term Debt	0.0	0.0
Stockholders' Equity	3,838.4	3,429.8
Performance & Financial Condition		
Return on Total Revenues %	14.77	11.07
Return on Avg Stockholders' Equity %	11.10	6.67
Return on Average Assets %	10.24	n.a.
Current Ratio	9.64	15.70
Debt / Equity %	n.a.	n.a.

Compound Growth %'s	EPS % n.a.	Net Income % n.a.	Total Revenues %	36.32

Comments

The Company's sales increased by 36% and operating profit rose 120% in the most recent year. These results are largely attributable to growing commercial aircraft and military aircraft markets. For the first quarter ended February 1, 1997, revenue increased another 35% and net earnings were $88,832 as compared to $68,091 in the same period of the preceding year. Investment Classification: Speculative

Officers	Position	Ownership Information	
Anderson L. McCabe	President	Number of Shares Outstanding	776,115
Arthur J. Kania	Secretary, Treasurer	Market Capitalization	$ 3,104,460
Harvey Habeck	Other	Frequency of Dividends	n.a.
		Number of Shareholders	1,043

Other Information				
Transfer Agent	Stocktrans, Inc. Ardmore, PA		Where Listed	OTC-BB
Auditor	Max S. Mayer & Co., P.C.		Symbol	OPST
Market Maker	Olsen Payne & Co.	(800)453-5321	SIC Code	3827
	Carr Securities Corporation	(800)221-2243	Employees	41
Broker Dealer	Regular Stockbroker			

Oak Tree Medical Systems ,Inc.

163-03 Horace-Harding Exprwy. Flushing, NY 11365 Telephone (718)460-8400 Fax (718)460-3507

Company Description

Oak Tree Medical Systems, Inc. is engaged in the business of owning, operating and managing physical therapy clinics. Substantially all of the Company's operations are conducted in northeastern Florida. The Company was founded in 1986 and went public in 1993 through the issuance of 656,250 common shares, netting $5.0 million. Additional shares have been issued since for the acquisition of a business and additional working capital.

	05/31/96	05/31/95	05/31/94	05/31/93
Per Share Information				
Stock Price as of 12/31	4.00	3.00	0.18	0.06
Earnings Per Share	0.39	0.11	-0.19	-0.03
Price / Earnings Ratio	10.26	27.27	n.a.	n.a.
Book Value Per Share	3.02	2.51	3.80	3.99
Price / Book Value %	132.45	119.52	4.74	1.50
Dividends Per Share	0.0	0.0	0.0	0.0
Annual Financial Data				
Operating Results (000's)				
Total Revenues	4,945.3	2,652.9	0.0	0.0
Costs & Expenses	-3,419.2	-2,264.9	-234.2	-15.1
Income Before Taxes and Other	1,526.1	388.0	-234.2	-15.1
Other Items	0.0	0.0	0.0	0.0
Income Tax	-486.1	-127.0	0.0	0.0
Net Income	1,040.0	261.0	-234.2	-15.1
Cash Flow From Operations	-158.8	-158.8	-224.9	-6.1
Balance Sheet (000's)				
Cash & Equivalents	292.3	138.2	11.5	6.5
Total Current Assets	3,519.3	1,974.0	11.5	6.5
Fixed Assets, Net	394.1	333.7	0.0	0.0
Total Assets	10,224.2	8,721.3	5,011.5	5,006.5
Total Current Liabilities	1,378.8	1,993.6	267.0	27.9
Long-Term Debt	0.0	0.0	0.0	0.0
Stockholders' Equity	7,646.3	5,128.4	4,744.5	4,978.7
Performance & Financial Condition				
Return on Total Revenues %	21.03	9.84	n.a.	n.a.
Return on Avg Stockholders' Equity %	16.28	5.29	-4.82	-0.61
Return on Average Assets %	10.98	3.80	-4.68	-0.60
Current Ratio	2.55	0.99	0.04	0.23
Debt / Equity %	n.a.	n.a.	n.a.	n.a.

Compound Growth %'s	EPS % n.a.	Net Income % n.a.	Total Revenues % 86.41

Comments

In June, 1995, the Company exchanged gold ore reserves for approximately a 30% interest in the outstanding shares of Accord Futronics Corporation, a gold mining operation. Accord has not yet produced any revenue for the Company. The Company believes that the $5.0 million valuation for their interest, which is included in assets, is appropriate. Revenue growth is a reflection of expanded operations through acquisitions as well as an increase in per patient visits. In March, 1996, the Company opened a 12,000 square foot facility in Jacksonville, Florida, to expand and enhance operations that were previously conducted elsewhere. Investment Classification: Speculative

Officers	Position	Ownership Information	
Michael J. Gerber	President	Number of Shares Outstanding	2,529,169
Irwin B. Stack	COO, Secretary	Market Capitalization	$ 10,116,676
Henry Dubbin	Vice President	Frequency of Dividends	n.a.
		Number of Shareholders	530

Other Information

Transfer Agent	Continental Stock Transfer & Trust Co. New York, NY		Where Listed	OTC-BB
Auditor	Simon Krowitz Bolin & Assoc.		Symbol	MOAK
Market Maker	Fahnestock & Co., Inc.	(212)422-7813	SIC Code	8049
	Wien Securities Corp.	(800)624-0050	Employees	3
Broker Dealer	Regular Stockbroker			

Oak Valley Community Bank

125 North Third Avenue Oakdale, CA 95361   Telephone (209)848-2265   Fax (209)848-1929

Company Description

Oak Valley Community Bank is an independent bank which began operations in 1991. The Bank's primary source of revenue is providing loans to customers who are predominantly small and middle-market businesses and middle-income individuals in Stanislaus County, part of the San Joaquin Valley of California.   The Bank opened its third full service branch in Sonora (Gold Rush Country) in 1996. It has also received approval to open a Modesto location in 1997. All this expansion takes money; the Bank raised $862,284 through a stock offering in 1996.

	12/31/96	12/31/95	12/31/94	12/31/93
Per Share Information				
Stock Price	12.50	10.25	10.00	10.00
Earnings Per Share	1.28	1.33	1.02	0.65
Price / Earnings Ratio	9.77	7.71	9.80	15.38
Book Value Per Share	11.53	10.59	9.21	8.22
Price / Book Value %	108.41	96.79	108.58	121.65
Dividends Per Share	0.25	0.0	0.0	0.0
Annual Financial Data				
Operating Results (000's)				
Net Interest Income	2,850.8	2,444.9	1,930.6	1,299.5
Loan Loss Provision	-60.0	-68.0	-128.0	-80.0
Non-Interest Income	212.1	142.6	85.5	68.3
Non-Interest Expense	-2,020.0	-1,597.9	-1,447.9	-1,139.6
Income Before Taxes and Other	982.8	921.6	440.1	148.1
Other Items	0.0	0.0	0.0	103.0
Income Tax	-382.0	-348.2	-0.8	-0.8
Net Income	600.8	573.4	439.3	250.3
Balance Sheet (000's)				
Cash & Securities	23,027.0	12,319.0	9,833.8	8,745.5
Loans, Net	31,488.4	27,770.2	23,755.5	20,550.5
Total Assets	55,555.8	41,271.2	34,562.9	30,150.7
Deposits	49,320.6	36,269.3	30,292.0	26,405.2
Stockholders' Equity	5,893.8	4,549.7	3,958.0	3,532.7
Performance & Financial Condition				
Return on Avg Stockholders' Equity %	11.51	13.48	11.73	8.22
Return on Average Assets %	1.24	1.51	1.36	0.94
Equity to Assets %	10.61	11.02	11.45	11.72
Net Interest Margin	n.a.	n.a.	n.a.	n.a.
Reserve as a % of Problem Loans	n.a.	n.a.	n.a.	n.a.

Compound Growth %'s	EPS % 25.34	Net Income % 33.88	Net Interest Income % 29.94

Comments

The Bank declared its first cash dividend in 1996 and increased it 20% in 1997. 1993 results include a nonrecurring benefit of $103,000, or $.27 per share, from a change in accounting method. 1993 and 1994 results are also difficult to compare because of a tax benefit and disproportionately low income tax provision, respectively.   Because of these items, compound earnings and earnings per share growth rates may not be very meaningful. Management is very pleased with the performance of this young bank and remain very enthusiastic. Investment Classification: Value & Growth

Officers	Position	Ownership Information	
Ronald C. Martin	President, CEO	Number of Shares Outstanding	511,319
Ramon A. Esslinger	Exec VP, COO	Market Capitalization	$ 6,391,488
Virgil L. Thompson	Senior VP	Frequency of Dividends	Irregular
Vic Berbano	Vice President, CFO	Number of Shareholders	351
Marsha Carr	Vice President	Where Listed / Symbol	OTC-PS / n.a.

Other Information			Loan Mix	%
Transfer Agent	U.S. Stock Transfer Corporation Glendale, CA		R/E Mortgages	50.1
Auditor	Grant Thornton LLP		Commerical	36.5
Market Maker	Hoefer & Arnett, Incorporated	(800)346-5544	Installment	7.8
	Van Kasper & Company, Inc.	(800)652-1747	Construction	5.6
Broker Dealer	OTC Specialist			
	Hoefer & Arnett, Retail	(800)346-5544 Ext: Lisa		

Oakridge Energy, Inc.

4613 Jacksboro Highway   Wichita Falls, TX 76302   Telephone (817)322-4772   Fax (214)733-3048

Company Description

Oakridge Energy, Inc. is engaged in the exploration, development, production and sale of oil and gas, primarily in Texas, Mississippi, and Arkansas and to a lesser extent the exploration and development of coal and gravel in Colorado. In addition, the Company holds certain real estate in Colorado for investment. As a group, officers and directors owned 67.8% of the Company's outstanding common stock, as last reported, and the Company has been acquiring treasury shares. The Company was formed in 1969.

	02/28/97	02/28/96	02/28/95	02/28/94
Per Share Information				
Stock Price as of 12/31	2.00	2.12	1.82	1.82
Earnings Per Share	0.10	-0.17	-0.15	1.11
Price / Earnings Ratio	20.00	n.a.	n.a.	1.64
Book Value Per Share	2.08	1.91	2.16	2.34
Price / Book Value %	96.15	110.99	84.26	77.78
Dividends Per Share	0.0	0.0	0.0	0.25
Annual Financial Data				
Operating Results (000's)				
Total Revenues	3,177.0	1,133.1	721.3	19,367.3
Costs & Expenses	-2,593.2	-2,365.5	-1,679.2	-7,793.2
Income Before Taxes and Other	583.8	-1,232.3	-1,035.3	11,574.1
Other Items	0.0	0.0	0.0	118.8
Income Tax	-84.4	329.8	211.2	-4,321.4
Net Income	499.4	-902.5	-824.1	7,371.4
Cash Flow From Operations	1,391.7	-857.3	-648.7	-3,892.1
Balance Sheet (000's)				
Cash & Equivalents	195.6	44.3	982.1	1,070.4
Total Current Assets	2,738.8	3,470.5	4,357.2	10,876.5
Fixed Assets, Net	6,033.0	4,641.0	3,247.9	3,283.2
Total Assets	11,360.4	11,088.3	12,815.2	15,035.3
Total Current Liabilities	295.9	480.5	1,004.0	1,037.1
Long-Term Debt	0.0	0.0	0.0	0.0
Stockholders' Equity	10,583.2	10,372.6	11,752.7	13,958.8
Performance & Financial Condition				
Return on Total Revenues %	15.72	-79.65	-114.25	38.06
Return on Avg Stockholders' Equity %	4.77	-8.16	-6.41	59.03
Return on Average Assets %	4.45	-7.55	-5.92	49.93
Current Ratio	9.26	7.22	4.34	10.49
Debt / Equity %	n.a.	n.a.	n.a.	n.a.

Compound Growth %'s	EPS % n.a.	Net Income % n.a.	Total Revenues % n.a.

Comments

Significantly higher oil and gas revenues, primarily from the east Texas area, were the reason for the Company's return to profitability in fiscal 1997. During the last three years the Company has purchased interests of varying size in a number of exploration prospects which were originated by others for the purpose of broadening the Company's exploratory activity exposure. The Company has $1.3 million in investment securities that are not classified as current assets in addition to its excellent current ratio. 1994 results included $16.7 million of gains on the disposition of oil and gas properties which distorted compound growth rates. Investment Classification: Speculative & Value

Officers	Position	Ownership Information	
Noel Pautsky	Chairman, President	Number of Shares Outstanding	5,083,359
Sandra Pautsky	Exec VP, Secretary	Market Capitalization	$ 10,166,718
Danny Croker	Vice President	Frequency of Dividends	Irregular
		Number of Shareholders	559

Other Information

Transfer Agent	Stock Transfer Company of America Dallas, TX		Where Listed	OTC-BB
Auditor	KPMG Peat Marwick LLP		Symbol	OKRG
Market Maker	Morgan Keegan & Company, Inc.	(800)289-5019	SIC Code	1311
	Hill Thompson Magid & Co., Inc	(800)631-3083	Employees	8
Broker Dealer	Regular Stockbroker			

Ocean National Corporation

100 Main Street   Kennebunk, ME 04043-0058   Telephone (207)985-3305   Fax (207)985-7030

Company Description

The Company owns 100% interest in Ocean National Bank which provides a full range of banking services to individual and corporate customers in southern Maine. An excerpt from a recent annual report reads "When you walk into Ocean National Bank, you open the door to a world of services coordinated by hundreds of people you may never meet." With the opening of the South Berwick office in 1996, the Bank now has seven separate locations. Ocean National was founded in 1853 and its shares are highly coveted.

	12/31/96	12/31/95	12/31/94	12/31/93
Per Share Information				
Stock Price	75.00	66.00	60.00	50.00
Earnings Per Share	15.27	14.33	11.87	7.47
Price / Earnings Ratio	4.91	4.61	5.05	6.69
Book Value Per Share	88.92	79.41	68.77	62.29
Price / Book Value %	84.35	83.11	87.25	80.27
Dividends Per Share	5.60	5.00	4.10	2.55
Annual Financial Data				
Operating Results (000's)				
Net Interest Income	7,046.1	6,917.5	6,052.7	5,325.3
Loan Loss Provision	-240.0	-200.0	-30.0	-655.2
Non-Interest Income	1,844.7	1,637.6	1,567.6	1,588.9
Non-Interest Expense	-5,200.4	-5,108.3	-4,867.8	-4,673.6
Income Before Taxes and Other	3,450.5	3,246.8	2,722.6	1,585.4
Other Items	0.0	0.0	0.0	60.0
Income Tax	-1,181.0	-1,111.0	-934.0	-520.0
Net Income	2,269.5	2,135.8	1,788.6	1,125.4
Balance Sheet (000's)				
Cash & Securities	59,990.6	62,550.3	56,689.2	54,004.2
Loans, Net	89,433.1	77,005.6	77,473.2	80,837.3
Total Assets	154,653.8	144,335.2	138,314.3	139,279.5
Deposits	128,538.6	120,706.3	115,765.6	119,937.0
Stockholders' Equity	13,217.7	11,803.4	10,363.5	9,386.9
Performance & Financial Condition				
Return on Avg Stockholders' Equity %	18.14	19.27	18.11	12.51
Return on Average Assets %	1.52	1.51	1.29	0.83
Equity to Assets %	8.55	8.18	7.49	6.74
Net Interest Margin	n.a.	n.a.	n.a.	n.a.
Reserve as a % of Problem Loans	90.27	55.77	60.25	78.23

Compound Growth %'s	EPS %	26.91	Net Income %	26.34	Net Interest Income %	9.78

Comments

Price per share information was derived from treasury stock transactions as reported in the annual report. 1996 was the third consecutive year of record earnings. Management is pursuing a strategy of careful and moderate growth with a focus on improving earnings performance and enhancing shareholder value. This makes the returns on equity, assets and compound growth rates even more impressive. A number of new products will be introduced in 1997. Investment Classification: Growth & Value & Income

Officers	Position	Ownership Information	
Russell G. Cole	President	Number of Shares Outstanding	148,646
Mark T. Mickeriz	Senior VP, Treasurer	Market Capitalization	$ 11,148,450
Terrance L. Beers	Senior VP	Frequency of Dividends	Quarterly
Kelvin A. Worthley	Vice President, Head Cashier	Number of Shareholders	n.a.
Deborah A. Upson	Vice President, Controller	Where Listed / Symbol	OTC-PS / n.a.

Other Information			Loan Mix	%
Transfer Agent	Company Office		R/E Mortgages	82.2
Auditor	Baker Newman & Noyes LLC		Consumer	9.4
Market Maker	E.E. Powell & Company, Inc.	(800)282-1940	Commerical	8.4
	Ryan, Beck & Co.	(800)395-7926		
Broker Dealer	OTC Specialist			
	Jack Ingold	(412)391-4594		

Ogden Telephone Company

21 West Avenue   Spencerport, NY 14559-1397   Telephone (716)352-7200   Fax (716)352-0232

Company Description

Ogden Telephone Company provides local exchange and long distance services to both residential and commercial customers in the Towns of Ogden and Parma, Monroe County, New York. In early 1997, the Company announced that it would be acquired by Citizens Utilities, subject to both regulatory and shareholder approvals.

	12/31/96	12/31/95	12/31/94	12/31/93
Per Share Information				
Stock Price	122.00	120.00	75.00	75.00
Earnings Per Share	10.25	10.00	8.80	7.82
Price / Earnings Ratio	11.90	12.00	8.52	9.59
Book Value Per Share	75.38	75.39	67.68	63.52
Price / Book Value %	161.85	159.17	110.82	118.07
Dividends Per Share	4.42	4.04	3.74	3.53
Annual Financial Data				
Operating Results (000's)				
Total Revenues	10,641.2	10,353.5	9,811.3	10,037.8
Costs & Expenses	-8,549.7	-8,335.2	-8,019.6	-7,825.8
Income Before Taxes and Other	2,091.6	2,018.3	1,791.7	2,212.0
Other Items	0.0	0.0	0.0	-437.2
Income Tax	-675.6	-636.2	-571.2	-686.3
Net Income	1,416.0	1,382.1	1,220.5	1,088.5
Cash Flow From Operations	2,920.6	3,924.9	2,298.1	4,625.7
Balance Sheet (000's)				
Cash & Equivalents	722.8	387.8	717.0	191.6
Total Current Assets	2,728.7	2,660.0	2,872.4	2,289.9
Fixed Assets, Net	22,161.1	22,611.4	22,225.9	22,410.3
Total Assets	26,881.8	27,680.2	27,737.1	27,214.3
Total Current Liabilities	2,592.3	3,323.0	3,747.6	3,819.5
Long-Term Debt	8,418.0	9,003.9	9,474.7	9,849.1
Stockholders' Equity	11,532.4	10,680.8	9,819.8	9,087.2
Performance & Financial Condition				
Return on Total Revenues %	13.31	13.35	12.44	10.84
Return on Avg Stockholders' Equity %	12.75	13.48	12.91	12.40
Return on Average Assets %	5.19	4.99	4.44	4.03
Current Ratio	1.05	0.80	0.77	0.60
Debt / Equity %	72.99	84.30	96.49	108.38

Compound Growth %'s	EPS % n.a.	Net Income % n.a.	Total Revenues % 1.97

Comments

1993 results include a one-time charge of $437,231 due to changes in accounting methods. This distorted compound earnings growth rates which, accordingly, were not presented. Management has been tight-lipped about the acquisition and what shareholders will receive. Analysts following the industry are estimating $180 per share. This follows the consolidation in the telecommunications industry that we have witnessed over the last twelve months. Investment Classification: Value

Officers	Position	Ownership Information	
Philip T. Evans	President	Number of Shares Outstanding	108,811
Maxine B. Davison	CEO, Chairman of the Board	Market Capitalization	$ 13,274,942
Timothy J. Bancroft	VP - Finance	Frequency of Dividends	Quarterly
Maureen L. Howard	Secretary, Treasurer	Number of Shareholders	Under 500
Richard M. Daly	Vice President		

Other Information

Transfer Agent	Company Office		Where Listed	OTC-BB
Auditor	Coopers & Lybrand LLP		Symbol	OGDT
Market Maker	Sharpe Capital Inc.	(800)355-5781	SIC Code	4810
	Hill Thompson Magid & Co., Inc	(800)631-3083	Employees	47
Broker Dealer	OTC Specialist			
	Stephen Schuller - Dorsey	(800)375-5431		

Ojai Oil Company

2161 Ventura Boulevard   Oxnard, CA 93030   Telephone (805)988-0300   Fax (805)485-1131

Company Description

The Company's operations include the production and sale of oil and gas, oil royalties, securities investments, self storage facilities and a mobile home park, most of which are located in southern California. The Company was formed in 1966. A car wash business was sold during 1996 and replaced with a new office building in a tax free exchange. The self storage business was greatly expanded during 1996 with improvements to the Oxnard facility and the purchase of the Santa Clarita facility.

	12/31/96	12/31/95	12/31/94	12/31/93
Per Share Information				
Stock Price	9.25	9.00	9.00	9.00
Earnings Per Share	1.15	0.98	0.40	0.83
Price / Earnings Ratio	8.04	9.18	22.50	10.84
Book Value Per Share	7.88	6.99	6.15	6.03
Price / Book Value %	117.39	128.76	146.34	149.25
Dividends Per Share	0.30	0.30	0.28	0.28
Annual Financial Data				
Operating Results (000's)				
Total Revenues	2,389.9	2,495.8	2,503.0	2,475.8
Costs & Expenses	-1,795.4	-2,039.5	-2,315.6	-2,049.4
Income Before Taxes and Other	594.6	456.4	187.4	426.4
Other Items	0.0	0.0	0.0	0.0
Income Tax	-247.7	-159.0	-66.3	-172.3
Net Income	346.8	297.3	121.1	254.1
Cash Flow From Operations	338.9	-15.2	80.3	183.1
Balance Sheet (000's)				
Cash & Equivalents	123.7	93.2	90.7	62.1
Total Current Assets	932.9	1,112.4	698.0	634.1
Fixed Assets, Net	8,451.6	6,105.6	5,299.8	5,460.9
Total Assets	10,080.5	8,064.1	6,771.2	6,830.9
Total Current Liabilities	361.4	453.3	275.2	225.9
Long-Term Debt	6,901.3	5,056.4	4,225.1	4,402.6
Stockholders' Equity	2,375.8	2,126.1	1,870.0	1,834.1
Performance & Financial Condition				
Return on Total Revenues %	14.51	11.91	4.84	10.26
Return on Avg Stockholders' Equity %	15.41	14.88	6.54	n.a.
Return on Average Assets %	3.82	4.01	1.78	n.a.
Current Ratio	2.58	2.45	2.54	2.81
Debt / Equity %	290.48	237.82	225.93	240.04

Compound Growth %'s	EPS %	11.48	Net Income %	10.92	Total Revenues %	-1.17

Comments

The trade into the new office building had the effect of increasing cash flow by 50%. Although showing improvement, problems remain at the mobile home park because of the damage from the Northridge earthquake in 1994. The hillside behind the park has finally been stabilized. Long-term debt has been increased in connection with the expansion of the self storage business. Investment Classification: Speculative

Officers	Position	Ownership Information	
Theodore Off	President	Number of Shares Outstanding	301,362
Ann Dyer	VP - Finance	Market Capitalization	$ 2,787,599
C. Douglas Off	Secretary	Frequency of Dividends	Irregular
Harry J. Edward	Vice President	Number of Shareholders	Under 500
David Edward	Vice President		

Other Information			
Transfer Agent	Company Office	Where Listed	OTC-BB
Auditor	Lee, Sperling, Hisamune	Symbol	OJOC
Market Maker	PaineWebber Incorporated	(800)227-4253	SIC Code	6700
	Carr Securities Corporation	(800)221-2243	Employees	8
Broker Dealer	OTC Specialist		

Old Fashion Foods, Inc.

5521 Collins Boulevard, S.W.   Austell, GA 30001-3653   Telephone (770)948-1177   Fax (770)739-3254

Company Description

Old Fashion Foods, Inc. is the largest independent vending machine company in Georgia, providing complete vending machine and buffet-style food service to major corporations, hospitals and universities throughout metropolitan Atlanta and northwest Georgia. The Company operates over 3,000 pieces of vending equipment in nearly 350 locations. Formed in 1965 as Old Fashion Sandwich Company, the current name was adopted three years later. The Company reacquired over 150,000 of its shares over the last three years.

	05/25/96	05/27/95	05/28/94	05/30/92
Per Share Information				
Stock Price as of 12/31	3.12	3.37	3.00	1.69
Earnings Per Share	0.10	0.23	-0.13	0.14
Price / Earnings Ratio	31.20	14.65	n.a.	12.07
Book Value Per Share	8.33	8.18	7.46	7.02
Price / Book Value %	37.45	41.20	40.21	24.07
Dividends Per Share	0.0	0.0	0.0	0.0
Annual Financial Data				
Operating Results (000's)				
Total Revenues	15,226.5	14,977.1	14,845.8	18,848.8
Costs & Expenses	-15,073.3	-14,492.7	-14,198.3	-18,619.5
Income Before Taxes and Other	153.2	484.4	647.5	227.8
Other Items	6.6	-67.6	-525.3	0.0
Income Tax	-73.5	-198.9	-252.4	-69.0
Net Income	86.4	217.9	-130.2	158.8
Cash Flow From Operations	1,189.8	1,153.1	339.3	1,450.0
Balance Sheet (000's)				
Cash & Equivalents	1,169.9	865.9	670.7	664.9
Total Current Assets	2,321.7	2,363.0	1,669.4	1,548.0
Fixed Assets, Net	5,278.5	4,953.7	5,161.9	10,065.6
Total Assets	10,094.2	9,760.9	10,186.5	13,654.8
Total Current Liabilities	1,278.2	1,151.2	1,399.6	2,448.5
Long-Term Debt	0.0	0.0	229.9	2,247.3
Stockholders' Equity	7,291.5	7,230.8	7,304.9	7,695.4
Performance & Financial Condition				
Return on Total Revenues %	0.57	1.45	-0.88	0.84
Return on Avg Stockholders' Equity %	1.19	3.00	n.a.	n.a.
Return on Average Assets %	0.87	2.18	n.a.	n.a.
Current Ratio	1.82	2.05	1.19	0.63
Debt / Equity %	n.a.	n.a.	3.15	29.20

Compound Growth %'s	EPS % n.a.	Net Income % n.a.	Total Revenues % 1.27

Comments

1994 and 1995 results reflect losses of $67,584 and $525,345, respectively, in connection with the discontinuance and disposal of the restaurant business and its assets. The balance sheet is favorable with no long term debt. The annual report for 1993 was not available. The Company expanded into the coffee and water service market during 1995 and acquired the assets of a vending company in May, 1996, for $376,000. Investment Classification: Value

Officers	**Position**	**Ownership Information**	
Sheldon E. Smith	Chairman, President	Number of Shares Outstanding	875,655
Jerry W. Seneker	Exec VP	Market Capitalization	$ 2,732,044
Joseph C. Hulsey	Senior VP	Frequency of Dividends	n.a.
Billy E. Rogers	Vice President	Number of Shareholders	Under 500
Billy D. Varner	Controller		

Other Information			
Transfer Agent	American Stock Transfer & Trust Company New York, NY	Where Listed	OTC-BB
Auditor	Ernst & Young LLP	Symbol	OFFI
Market Maker	Morgan Keegan & Company, Inc. (800)238-7533	SIC Code	5490
	Monroe Securities, Inc. (800)766-5560	Employees	150
Broker Dealer	Regular Stockbroker		

Old Forge Bank

216 S. Main Street   Old Forge, PA 18518-1691   Telephone (717)457-8345   Fax (717)457-7317

Company Description

Old Forge Bank has seen a lot of change in its community since it began in 1909, the same year of the first edition of Walker's Manual of California Securities. What was a coal mining town has successfully emerged as a nice rural community ten miles northeast of Wilkes-Barre in northeast Pennsylvania. Tourism is gaining momentum with a ski resort, winery tastings and you can even drop yourself into one of those old mines. We prefer mining for good stocks.

	12/31/96	12/31/95	12/31/94	12/31/93
Per Share Information				
Stock Price	54.50	53.00	51.00	50.00
Earnings Per Share	8.23	7.91	7.34	6.80
Price / Earnings Ratio	6.62	6.70	6.95	7.35
Book Value Per Share	64.35	59.98	52.18	49.93
Price / Book Value %	84.69	88.36	97.74	100.14
Dividends Per Share	3.50	3.25	3.00	3.00
Annual Financial Data				
Operating Results (000's)				
Net Interest Income	5,813.3	5,757.0	5,861.1	5,623.3
Loan Loss Provision	0.0	-225.0	-250.0	-275.0
Non-Interest Income	373.9	458.3	379.0	314.1
Non-Interest Expense	-3,140.3	-3,077.5	-3,322.3	-3,209.7
Income Before Taxes and Other	3,047.0	2,912.7	2,667.8	2,452.7
Other Items	0.0	0.0	0.0	0.0
Income Tax	-745.7	-700.9	-616.1	-553.2
Net Income	2,301.2	2,211.8	2,051.6	1,899.5
Balance Sheet (000's)				
Cash & Securities	40,142.2	40,233.7	37,529.3	36,928.0
Loans, Net	89,572.8	84,294.1	82,238.2	79,236.0
Total Assets	134,519.0	128,072.2	124,021.2	120,164.0
Deposits	115,256.8	104,613.9	100,744.8	103,097.0
Stockholders' Equity	17,987.0	16,763.2	14,585.2	13,954.0
Performance & Financial Condition				
Return on Avg Stockholders' Equity %	13.24	14.11	14.38	14.15
Return on Average Assets %	1.75	1.75	1.68	1.62
Equity to Assets %	13.37	13.09	11.76	11.61
Net Interest Margin	n.a.	n.a.	n.a.	n.a.
Reserve as a % of Problem Loans	73.27	49.33	46.36	n.a.

Compound Growth %'s	EPS %	6.57	Net Income %	6.60	Net Interest Income %	1.11

Comments

Old Forge Bank continues making more profits each year while maintaining excellent returns on equity and assets. Equity has climbed to 13.37% of total assets. The posted price by market makers doesn't give a distressed seller fair value for what they have and equates to a dividend yield of 6.4%. This creates an opportunity for the adventuresome to circumvent normal channels. Investment Classification: Income & Value

Officers	Position	Ownership Information	
James Tedesco	President, CEO	Number of Shares Outstanding	279,497
Richard D. Casagrande	Exec VP, COO	Market Capitalization	$ 15,232,587
Eugenia A. Ventre	Secretary	Frequency of Dividends	Quarterly
Michael L. Jake	Vice President, Controller	Number of Shareholders	n.a.
Allen J. Robinson	Vice President	Where Listed / Symbol	OTC-BB / OLDF

Other Information			Loan Mix	%
Transfer Agent	Company Office		R/E Mortgages	47.0
Auditor	McGrail Merkel Quinn & Assoc.		Commerical	41.6
Market Maker	Ryan, Beck & Co.	(800)325-7926	Installment	11.4
	F.J. Morrissey & Co., Inc.	(800)842-8928		
Broker Dealer	OTC Specialist			
	Dennis Reynolds - Ryan, Beck	(888)231-7226		

Olokele Sugar Company, Limited

1 Kaumakani   Kaumakani, HI 96747   Telephone (808)335-3133   Fax (808)335-6424

Company Description

The Company was in the business of growing sugar cane. After substantial damage from Hurricane Iniki in 1992, the Company completed a sale of all sugar-producing assets. C. Brewer and Company owns approximately 87.8% of the Company and has borrowed all cash generated within the Company. The amount borrowed at June 30, 1996, was $34.7 million. Interest is accrued from C. Brewer at a rate of about 8%.

	06/30/96	12/25/94	12/26/93
Per Share Information			
Stock Price as of 12/31	121.00	100.00	75.00
Earnings Per Share	16.93	21.27	24.86
Price / Earnings Ratio	7.15	4.70	3.02
Book Value Per Share	201.40	182.62	162.62
Price / Book Value %	n.a.	54.76	46.12
Dividends Per Share	4.00	3.35	1.40
Annual Financial Data			
Operating Results (000's)			
Total Revenues	3,751.8	2,239.4	10,462.0
Costs & Expenses	0.0	0.0	0.0
Income Before Taxes and Other	3,751.8	2,239.4	10,462.0
Other Items	0.0	1,789.2	-2,634.6
Income Tax	-1,183.4	-789.5	-3,911.4
Net Income	2,568.4	3,239.1	3,916.0
Cash Flow From Operations	3,874.2	3,960.2	847.1
Balance Sheet (000's)			
Cash & Equivalents	0.0	6.6	0.5
Total Current Assets	766.4	34,475.2	29,283.9
Fixed Assets, Net	0.0	0.0	8,399.7
Total Assets	38,059.3	37,775.7	37,689.2
Total Current Liabilities	3,251.2	7,083.0	5,357.7
Long-Term Debt	0.0	0.0	0.0
Stockholders' Equity	30,556.5	27,816.2	25,612.8
Performance & Financial Condition			
Return on Total Revenues %	68.46	144.64	37.43
Return on Avg Stockholders' Equity %	8.80	12.12	n.a.
Return on Average Assets %	6.77	8.58	n.a.
Current Ratio	0.24	4.87	5.47
Debt / Equity %	n.a.	n.a.	n.a.

Compound Growth %'s   EPS %   n.a.   Net Income %   n.a.   Total Revenues %   n.a.

Comments

The Company changed its reporting year to June 30th. We have only presented the full years with a gap between December 26, 1994 and June 30, 1995. 1996 results included income from discontinued operations of $635,065 after taxes. Management would still like to talk to shareholders about its stock repurchase plan but no longer uses the $100 per share standing offer as the posted bid price is considerably higher. Investment Classification: Value

Officers	Position	Ownership Information	
Kent T. Lucien	Chairman, President	Number of Shares Outstanding	151,718
Kathleen F. Oshiro	Secretary	Market Capitalization	$ 18,357,878
James S. Andrasick	Vice President, Treasurer	Frequency of Dividends	Quarterly
Jon T. Iwatani	Other	Number of Shareholders	Under 500

Other Information			
Transfer Agent	Company Office	Where Listed	OTC-BB
Auditor	Coopers & Lybrand L.L.P.	Symbol	OLOK
Market Maker	Abel-Behnke Corp.	(808)537-8500	SIC Code	6790
	Martin Nelson & Co., Inc.	(800)543-3332	Employees	1
Broker Dealer	OTC Specialist		

Original Sixteen to One Mine, Inc.

527 Miners Street   Alleghany, CA 95910   Telephone (916)287-3223   Fax (916)287-3455

Company Description

Original Sixteen To One Mine, Inc. mines for gold on properties it owns or leases or on which it has claims. The Company owns 412 acres of real property and has mineral rights and limited surface rights to an additional 1,300 acres in the Alleghany and French Gulch mining districts in the Sierra Nevada Mountains of northern California. In addition to refined gold bullion sold to gold buyers and investors, the Company sells high-grade gold and quartz specimens and gold jewelry. The Company was incorporated in 1911 and has never been in bankruptcy, receivership or similar proceedings.

	12/31/96	12/31/95	12/31/94	12/31/93
Per Share Information				
Stock Price	3.75	4.31	3.88	4.50
Earnings Per Share	-0.19	0.21	0.04	0.38
Price / Earnings Ratio	n.a.	20.52	97.00	11.84
Book Value Per Share	0.67	0.86	0.69	0.65
Price / Book Value %	559.70	501.16	562.32	692.31
Dividends Per Share	0.0	0.05	0.0	0.0
Annual Financial Data				
Operating Results (000's)				
Total Revenues	1,468.7	2,836.7	1,356.2	3,410.8
Costs & Expenses	-2,390.2	-1,883.6	-1,213.6	-1,494.6
Income Before Taxes and Other	-921.5	953.1	142.7	1,916.1
Other Items	0.0	0.0	0.0	148.0
Income Tax	267.0	-221.0	15.0	-750.3
Net Income	-654.5	732.1	157.7	1,313.9
Cash Flow From Operations	270.3	571.1	628.1	272.3
Balance Sheet (000's)				
Cash & Equivalents	31.6	180.6	146.7	187.0
Total Current Assets	1,215.3	2,431.7	1,959.1	2,508.2
Fixed Assets, Net	1,973.9	1,621.1	1,201.8	439.8
Total Assets	3,217.7	4,087.1	3,200.9	2,993.7
Total Current Liabilities	848.5	1,036.5	767.7	718.2
Long-Term Debt	11.9	15.8	0.0	0.0
Stockholders' Equity	2,357.3	3,034.8	2,433.2	2,275.5
Performance & Financial Condition				
Return on Total Revenues %	-44.56	25.81	11.63	38.52
Return on Avg Stockholders' Equity %	-24.28	26.78	6.70	82.02
Return on Average Assets %	-17.92	20.09	5.09	66.13
Current Ratio	1.43	2.35	2.55	3.49
Debt / Equity %	0.51	0.52	n.a.	n.a.

Compound Growth %'s	EPS % n.a.	Net Income % n.a.	Total Revenues %	-24.49

Comments

Revenues decreased by 46% primarily because 1995 results were augmented by a material discovery which produced $2 million worth of gold in a ten day period. While the vein system owned by the Company is a proven gold deposit, there are no assurances that this production will continue. However, the Sixteen to One Mine has produced more than 1.1 million ounces of gold since 1896 and gold is still the Company's primary operation. Investment Classification: Speculative

Officers	Position	Ownership Information	
Michael M. Miller	President, CEO	Number of Shares Outstanding	3,504,065
Richard C. Sorlien	Secretary	Market Capitalization	$ 13,140,244
Charles I. Brown	Treasurer	Frequency of Dividends	Irregular
		Number of Shareholders	834

Other Information			
Transfer Agent	Securities Registrar and Transfer Corp. Greenvile, CA	Where Listed	PSE
Auditor	Perry-Smith & Co.	Symbol	OAU
Market Maker	Paragon Capital Corporation (800)345-0505	SIC Code	1041
		Employees	46
Broker Dealer	Regular Stockbroker		

PMD Investment Company

10050 Regency Circle, Ste. 315   Omaha, NE 68114   Telephone (402)392-0608   Fax (402)392-0609

Company Description

PMD Investment Company is registered under the Investment Company Act of 1940 as a diversified, closed-end, management investment company. Its investment portfolio consists of federal agency and municipal bonds. The Company makes distributions to its shareholders of all cash flow, exclusive of reinvesting funds as bonds mature or are called. Distributions received by shareholders are partially exempt from income tax.

	12/31/96
Per Share Information	
Stock Price	3.37
Earnings Per Share	0.14
Price / Earnings Ratio	24.07
Book Value Per Share	4.31
Price / Book Value %	78.19
Dividends Per Share	0.27
Annual Financial Data	
Operating Results (000's)	
Total Revenues	606.5
Costs & Expenses	-108.7
Income Before Taxes and Other	497.8
Other Items	0.0
Income Tax	0.0
Net Income	497.8
Cash Flow From Operations	n.a.
Balance Sheet (000's)	
Cash & Equivalents	0.0
Total Current Assets	193.8
Fixed Assets, Net	0.0
Total Assets	15,502.8
Total Current Liabilities	13.0
Long-Term Debt	0.0
Stockholders' Equity	15,489.8
Performance & Financial Condition	
Return on Total Revenues %	82.07
Return on Avg Stockholders' Equity %	n.a.
Return on Average Assets %	n.a.
Current Ratio	14.85
Debt / Equity %	n.a.

Compound Growth %'s	EPS % n.a.	Net Income % n.a.	Total Revenues % n.a.

Comments

Expenses of administering and managing this portfolio approximate 0.7% of average net assets. Noteworthy is that the tax-free yield is quite favorable since the stock sells below book value. Only one year of data was obtainable. Investment Classification: Income

Officers	Position	Ownership Information	
Gayle Sawicki	President	Number of Shares Outstanding	3,596,795
Patrick Witherspoon	Secretary, Treasurer	Market Capitalization	$ 12,121,199
Hebert Underwood	Vice President	Frequency of Dividends	Quarterly
		Number of Shareholders	n.a.

Other Information				
Transfer Agent	First National Bank of Omaha Omaha, NE		Where Listed	OTC-BB
Auditor	Not indicated		Symbol	PMDI
Market Maker	Mayer & Schweitzer, Inc.	(800)631-3094	SIC Code	6790
	Carr Securities Corporation	(800)221-2243	Employees	n.a.
Broker Dealer	Regular Stockbroker			

PSB Holding Corp

239 Main Street   Preston, MD 21655   Telephone (410)673-2401   Fax (410)673-7417

Company Description

Provident State Bank, subsidiary of this recently formed holding company, started business in 1904. It now has offices in Preston, Denton, Secretary, Federalsburg and Ridgely, in rural Maryland about eighty miles west of Washington, D.C. The Ridgely branch was opened in mid-1997. The Company reports that a few shareholders offered several hundred shares of stock for sale since the formation of the holding company and that they were sold quickly.

	12/31/96	12/31/95	12/31/94	12/31/93
Per Share Information				
Stock Price	28.00	25.25	25.00	25.00
Earnings Per Share	4.15	3.70	3.35	2.89
Price / Earnings Ratio	6.75	6.82	7.46	8.65
Book Value Per Share	35.59	32.03	28.72	26.24
Price / Book Value %	78.67	78.83	87.05	95.27
Dividends Per Share	0.65	0.57	0.50	0.45
Annual Financial Data				
Operating Results (000's)				
Net Interest Income	3,018.4	2,990.9	2,983.9	2,717.4
Loan Loss Provision	-113.1	-172.6	-100.0	-131.3
Non-Interest Income	381.3	364.8	312.3	388.8
Non-Interest Expense	-2,089.3	-2,078.6	-2,195.7	-2,095.0
Income Before Taxes and Other	1,197.4	1,104.5	1,000.5	879.8
Other Items	0.0	0.0	0.0	0.0
Income Tax	-367.0	-365.2	-330.5	-301.4
Net Income	830.4	739.2	670.0	578.4
Balance Sheet (000's)				
Cash & Securities	23,026.2	25,002.4	19,489.9	22,643.8
Loans, Net	49,040.4	43,351.0	44,611.5	43,830.5
Total Assets	74,944.8	70,734.3	66,464.0	68,498.0
Deposits	66,287.5	64,008.9	60,518.3	61,125.1
Stockholders' Equity	7,079.4	6,405.3	5,743.6	5,248.0
Performance & Financial Condition				
Return on Avg Stockholders' Equity %	12.32	12.17	12.19	11.56
Return on Average Assets %	1.14	1.08	0.99	0.89
Equity to Assets %	9.45	9.06	8.64	7.66
Net Interest Margin	n.a.	n.a.	n.a.	n.a.
Reserve as a % of Problem Loans	43.10	40.32	70.99	76.11

Compound Growth %'s	EPS %	12.82	Net Income %	12.81	Net Interest Income %	3.56

Comments

With a solid equity to assets ratio that has been inching up to nearly 10%, it seems appropriate that Provident State Bank is expanding. Loan demand was significantly higher in the second half of 1996. The new branch will affect growth in 1997. Expenses are tightly controlled which allows the increases in net interest income to fall to the bottom line. Shares are hard to find, but it's certainly worth a try. Investment Classification: Value

Officers	Position	Ownership Information	
Jesse G. Cunningham	President, CEO	Number of Shares Outstanding	198,940
Renee' D. Smith	Senior VP	Market Capitalization	$ 5,570,320
Frederick E. Spence, Jr.	Senior VP, Sr Loan Officer	Frequency of Dividends	Quarterly
Nancy J. Milligan	Vice President, Secretary	Number of Shareholders	n.a.
Dorothy L. Lane	Vice President, Head Cashier	Where Listed / Symbol	OTC-BB / PSBP

Other Information			Loan Mix	%
Transfer Agent	Company Office		R/E Mortgages	55.2
Auditor	Rowles & Company		Consumer	29.2
Market Maker	Ferris, Baker Watts Inc.	(800)638-7411	Commerical	11.4
	Folger Nolan Fleming Douglas	(800)326-3633	Construction	4.2
Broker Dealer	OTC Specialist			
	Dennis Reynolds - Ryan, Beck	(888)231-7226		

Pacific Northwest Development Corporation

9725 SW Beaverton-Hillsdale Hwy, Suite 110   Beaverton, OR 97005-3364   Telephone (503)626-9999   Fax (503)646-5074

Company Description

Pacific Northwest Development Corporation and its wholly owned subsidiaries, Pete Wilson Realty, Inc., The Mortgage Exchange, Inc. and Pioneer Industries, Inc., are involved in the development of real estate, brokerage of real estate mortgages and contracting and brokerage of real estate sales. Development projects are primarily located in the Portland, Willamette Valley and Bend-Redmond areas of Oregon. The Company went public in 1972.

	03/31/96	03/31/95	03/31/94	03/31/93
Per Share Information				
Stock Price as of 12/31	4.37	5.25	4.75	3.63
Earnings Per Share	-0.28	0.57	1.13	0.16
Price / Earnings Ratio	n.a.	9.21	4.20	22.69
Book Value Per Share	10.77	11.05	11.25	10.12
Price / Book Value %	40.58	47.51	42.22	35.87
Dividends Per Share	0.0	0.0	0.0	0.0
Annual Financial Data				
Operating Results (000's)				
Total Revenues	11,004.1	17,534.4	13,246.3	7,405.7
Costs & Expenses	-11,164.1	-17,102.8	-12,440.1	-7,206.4
Income Before Taxes and Other	-160.0	431.6	806.1	199.3
Other Items	0.0	0.0	0.0	0.0
Income Tax	21.5	-169.7	-283.7	-126.8
Net Income	-138.5	261.8	522.4	72.5
Cash Flow From Operations	-1,376.3	-863.2	-2,787.1	707.1
Balance Sheet (000's)				
Cash & Equivalents	1,003.5	831.4	1,150.6	2,197.7
Total Current Assets	10,892.7	7,792.0	10,264.3	12,711.8
Fixed Assets, Net	113.5	166.8	119.3	123.5
Total Assets	18,682.9	20,795.8	21,957.3	18,784.8
Total Current Liabilities	3,597.3	3,880.2	5,336.6	4,205.9
Long-Term Debt	8,922.2	9,046.6	9,244.7	8,881.7
Stockholders' Equity	5,389.7	5,528.3	5,194.4	4,672.0
Performance & Financial Condition				
Return on Total Revenues %	-1.26	1.49	3.94	0.98
Return on Avg Stockholders' Equity %	-2.54	4.88	10.59	1.56
Return on Average Assets %	-0.70	1.22	2.56	0.38
Current Ratio	3.03	2.01	1.92	3.02
Debt / Equity %	165.54	163.64	177.97	190.11

Compound Growth %'s	EPS % n.a.	Net Income % n.a.	Total Revenues % 14.11

Comments

The Company is developing a major project in Redmond, Oregon known as The Greens at Redmond which consists of a golf course and 227 housing units. The Company has invested $4.4 million in this project as of last year end. The development of the housing units, scheduled to be built in the 1996 fiscal year, was delayed approximately 12 months due to the County zoning and planning process. The golf course is completed and in full operation. Management feels the Company's major projects are now in prime positions with the infrastructure in place. These projects are expected to create solid profits over the next several years. Investment Classification: Value & Speculative

Officers	Position	Ownership Information	
O.M. "Pete" Wilson	President, CEO	Number of Shares Outstanding	500,381
Joan M. Crew	Senior VP	Market Capitalization	$ 2,186,665
Vicki L. Stollberg	Secretary, Treasurer	Frequency of Dividends	n.a.
Steven M. Wilson	Vice President	Number of Shareholders	160
Marvin C. Steadman	Vice President		

Other Information			
Transfer Agent	Chase Mellon Shareholder Services Los Angeles, CA	Where Listed	OTC-BB
Auditor	Moss Adams LLP	Symbol	PNOD
Market Maker	Black & Company, Inc. (503)248-9600	SIC Code	6530
	S.J. Wolfe & Co. (800)262-2244	Employees	18
Broker Dealer	Regular Stockbroker		

Pamet Systems, Inc.

1000 Main Street   Acton, MA 01720   Telephone (508)263-2060   Fax (508)263-4158

Company Description

Pamet Systems, Inc. designs, develops, installs and supports computer software and turnkey computer systems for public safety agencies. The principal product of the Company is PoliceServer (R), a fully integrated information management system developed specifically for law enforcement agencies. PoliceServer provides law enforcement departments with computer aided dispatch, records management, electronic booking and word processing. The Company also markets to fire departments FireServer (R), an information management system that provides fire departments with data on structures, fire suppression plans and hazardous materials.

	12/31/96	12/31/95	12/31/94
Per Share Information			
Stock Price	2.62	1.12	0.58
Earnings Per Share	0.10	-0.29	-0.06
Price / Earnings Ratio	26.20	n.a.	n.a.
Book Value Per Share	0.15	0.02	n.a.
Price / Book Value %	1,746.67	5,600.00	n.a.
Dividends Per Share	0.0	0.0	0.0
Annual Financial Data			
Operating Results (000's)			
Total Revenues	2,473.8	1,098.1	1,694.8
Costs & Expenses	-2,230.1	-1,667.3	-1,806.1
Income Before Taxes and Other	243.7	-569.2	-111.2
Other Items	0.0	0.0	0.0
Income Tax	0.0	0.0	0.0
Net Income	243.7	-569.2	-111.2
Cash Flow From Operations	-36.3	-69.3	49.3
Balance Sheet (000's)			
Cash & Equivalents	55.4	28.3	n.a.
Total Current Assets	764.2	348.0	n.a.
Fixed Assets, Net	918.4	922.6	n.a.
Total Assets	1,709.8	1,298.1	n.a.
Total Current Liabilities	842.5	670.4	n.a.
Long-Term Debt	494.7	509.4	n.a.
Stockholders' Equity	318.4	39.0	n.a.
Performance & Financial Condition			
Return on Total Revenues %	9.85	-51.84	-6.56
Return on Avg Stockholders' Equity %	136.36	n.a.	n.a.
Return on Average Assets %	16.20	n.a.	n.a.
Current Ratio	0.91	0.52	n.a.
Debt / Equity %	155.36	1307.90	n.a.

Compound Growth %'s	EPS % n.a.	Net Income % n.a.	Total Revenues %	20.81

Comments

The Company experienced a 125.4% increase in revenue and reported a profit for 1996. Management attributes these results partially to communities purchasing systems as a result of the 1995 grants of the 1994 Crime Bill. In addition, the Company is experiencing increased demand for its newer products. Management believes demand will remain strong as a result of public funding and a heightened awareness that computer systems can improve the efficiency and effectiveness of public safety resources. Investment Classification: Speculative

Officers	Position	Ownership Information	
Joel B. Searcy	Chairman, President	Number of Shares Outstanding	2,102,250
Richard C. Becker	Treasurer, COO	Market Capitalization	$ 5,507,895
		Frequency of Dividends	n.a.
		Number of Shareholders	71

Other Information

Transfer Agent	Continental Stock Transfer & Trust Co. New York, NY		Where Listed	OTC-BB
Auditor	Carlin, Charron & Rosen LLP		Symbol	PAMT
Market Maker	Van Kasper & Company	(800)603-5969	SIC Code	7373
	Fahnestock & Co., Inc.	(800)223-3012	Employees	11
Broker Dealer	Regular Stockbroker			

Paradise, Inc.

1200 Martin Luther King Jr. Blvd.   Plant City, FL 33566   Telephone (813)752-1155   Fax (813)754-3168

Company Description

Paradise, Inc. has two business segments. The Company produces candied fruit, a basic fruitcake ingredient, sold to manufacturing bakers, institutional users, and retailers for use in home baking. The candied fruit division also processes frozen strawberry products, for sale to commercial and institutional users, and repackages and sells edible nuts. The molded plastics division produces plastic containers for the Company's products and other molded plastics for sale to packaging and various food processors and others. The Company was formed in 1961.

	12/31/96	12/31/95	12/31/94
Per Share Information			
Stock Price	7.25	6.75	6.50
Earnings Per Share	1.63	1.39	0.67
Price / Earnings Ratio	4.45	4.86	9.70
Book Value Per Share	15.20	13.67	12.38
Price / Book Value %	47.70	49.38	52.50
Dividends Per Share	0.10	0.10	0.0
Annual Financial Data			
Operating Results (000's)			
Total Revenues	20,561.8	20,162.1	22,068.1
Costs & Expenses	-19,157.4	-18,961.3	-21,528.2
Income Before Taxes and Other	1,380.3	1,156.4	532.0
Other Items	0.0	0.0	0.0
Income Tax	-532.0	-433.3	-181.6
Net Income	848.3	723.1	350.5
Cash Flow From Operations	1,191.5	2,549.5	3,166.9
Balance Sheet (000's)			
Cash & Equivalents	2,426.9	2,723.4	746.3
Total Current Assets	8,579.6	8,653.9	7,394.2
Fixed Assets, Net	5,432.5	5,257.5	5,651.3
Total Assets	14,624.9	14,422.0	13,484.6
Total Current Liabilities	3,688.1	3,766.9	6,356.0
Long-Term Debt	2,536.2	3,017.9	98.7
Stockholders' Equity	7,892.9	7,096.5	6,425.3
Performance & Financial Condition			
Return on Total Revenues %	4.13	3.59	1.59
Return on Avg Stockholders' Equity %	11.32	10.70	n.a.
Return on Average Assets %	5.84	5.18	n.a.
Current Ratio	2.33	2.30	1.16
Debt / Equity %	32.13	42.53	1.54

Compound Growth %'s	EPS %	55.98	Net Income %	55.58	Total Revenues %	-3.47

Comments

Management estimates that Company brands account for 75-80% of all candied fruit sold in supermarkets in the United States. The latest financial statements are also sweet with another solid increase in net earnings. It is highly unusual for a stock with so few shares outstanding and little trading volume to maintain a listing on NASDAQ. We have elected to include it in the manual because of these characteristics and the resulting value pricing. Investment Classification: Value

Officers	Position	Ownership Information	
Melvin Gordon	President	Number of Shares Outstanding	519,170
Eugene L. Weiner	Exec VP, Secretary	Market Capitalization	$ 3,763,983
Randy S. Gordon	Vice President	Frequency of Dividends	Semi-Annual
Tracy W. Schulis	Vice President	Number of Shareholders	303
Mark H. Gordon	Vice President		

Other Information			
Transfer Agent	Continental Stock Transfer & Trust Co. New York, NY	Where Listed	NASDAQ
Auditor	Bella, Hermida, Gillman et al	Symbol	PARF
Market Maker	None	SIC Code	2060
		Employees	n.a.
Broker Dealer	Regular Stockbroker		

Pardee Resources Company

One Liberty Place, 38th Floor   Philadelphia, PA 19103-7301   Telephone (215)979-1580   Fax (215)979-1581

Company Description

Pardee Resources Company is a natural resources company that operates through its subsidiaries in the coal, oil and gas, and timber industries. The Companies own land and mineral rights principally in Virginia, West Virginia, Kentucky, Louisiana, and Texas. Many of the properties are leased to third parties for coal mining and processing and for oil and gas drilling and production.

	12/31/96	12/31/95
Per Share Information		
Stock Price	24.25	23.00
Earnings Per Share	1.43	2.48
Price / Earnings Ratio	16.96	9.27
Book Value Per Share	21.94	21.53
Price / Book Value %	110.53	106.83
Dividends Per Share	1.05	1.00
Annual Financial Data		
Operating Results (000's)		
Total Revenues	10,102.0	9,676.1
Costs & Expenses	-5,711.0	-5,312.6
Income Before Taxes and Other	4,391.0	4,363.6
Other Items	-1,200.0	-216.0
Income Tax	-1,205.5	-1,235.6
Net Income	1,985.5	2,911.9
Cash Flow From Operations	3,772.2	3,844.6
Balance Sheet (000's)		
Cash & Equivalents	3,414.0	3,166.1
Total Current Assets	5,535.8	5,398.3
Fixed Assets, Net	6,820.8	5,119.9
Total Assets	25,215.2	23,906.6
Total Current Liabilities	1,661.1	548.0
Long-Term Debt	0.0	0.0
Stockholders' Equity	20,953.3	21,510.8
Performance & Financial Condition		
Return on Total Revenues %	19.65	30.09
Return on Avg Stockholders' Equity %	9.35	13.99
Return on Average Assets %	8.08	n.a.
Current Ratio	3.33	9.85
Debt / Equity %	n.a.	n.a.

Compound Growth %'s	EPS %	n.a.	Net Income %	n.a.	Total Revenues %	4.40

Comments

Each of the two years presented included nonrecurring expenses related to providing health care premiums for retired United Mine Workers of America and their dependents. These amounted to $1,200,000, $1.66 per share, in 1996 and $216,000, $.30 per share, in 1995. Accordingly, compound earnings growth rates were not displayed. Management is confident that the outlook for stronger earnings and continued growth over the longer term is virtually undiminished by these items. All operating divisions are performing well with the oil and gas group having had an exceptional year in 1996. Investment Classification: Value & Income

Officers	Position	Ownership Information	
Walter L. Foulke	Chairman, CEO	Number of Shares Outstanding	725,365
Matthew W. Hall	President, COO	Market Capitalization	$ 17,590,101
Harry G. Symons	Senior VP, CFO	Frequency of Dividends	Quarterly
Carleton Erdman	Senior VP	Number of Shareholders	209
Christine A. Mohan	Vice President, Secretary		

Other Information				
Transfer Agent	Company Office		Where Listed	OTC-BB
Auditor	Ernst & Young LLP		Symbol	PDER
Market Maker	Boenning & Scattergood, Inc.	(800)883-8383	SIC Code	1300
	Hill Thompson Magid & Co., Inc	(800)631-3083	Employees	n.a.
Broker Dealer	Regular Stockbroker			

Park-Lexington Company, Inc.

17 E. 47th Street   New York, NY 10017-3808   Telephone (212)371-7773   Fax (212)371-7787

Company Description

The Company owns and manages several residential properties in New York City and also manages a portfolio of marketable securities. The properties include 328-334 East 52nd Street, 260 Seaman Avenue, and 113-115 East 72nd Street. A note receivable of $3.4 million has as collateral a standby letter of credit and all payments are current. The obligor is presently in bankruptcy. Management considers its decision to substitute collateral in 1983 as being lucky. We think it was brilliant.

	03/31/96	03/31/95	03/31/94	03/31/93
Per Share Information				
Stock Price as of 12/31	313.00	300.00	310.00	295.00
Earnings Per Share	26.47	27.33	36.35	29.08
Price / Earnings Ratio	11.82	10.98	8.53	10.14
Book Value Per Share	347.58	339.22	323.64	310.28
Price / Book Value %	90.05	88.44	95.79	95.08
Dividends Per Share	23.00	23.00	23.00	22.00
Annual Financial Data				
Operating Results (000's)				
Total Revenues	1,913.5	1,816.4	1,748.5	1,786.6
Costs & Expenses	-902.3	-760.8	-734.9	-756.3
Income Before Taxes and Other	1,011.2	1,055.6	1,013.6	1,030.2
Other Items	0.0	0.0	212.0	0.0
Income Tax	-366.0	-390.0	-345.0	-323.0
Net Income	645.2	665.6	880.6	707.2
Cash Flow From Operations	482.1	514.9	582.1	520.0
Balance Sheet (000's)				
Cash & Equivalents	125.7	101.1	51.0	126.5
Total Current Assets	4,145.3	3,789.9	5,489.3	5,407.9
Fixed Assets, Net	3,739.4	3,846.2	1,501.3	1,454.3
Total Assets	11,366.0	11,119.9	10,477.6	10,350.2
Total Current Liabilities	361.4	405.4	371.1	334.7
Long-Term Debt	0.0	0.0	0.0	0.0
Stockholders' Equity	8,785.6	8,576.6	8,205.5	7,887.5
Performance & Financial Condition				
Return on Total Revenues %	33.72	36.64	50.36	39.59
Return on Avg Stockholders' Equity %	7.43	7.93	10.94	9.06
Return on Average Assets %	5.74	6.16	8.46	6.88
Current Ratio	11.47	9.35	14.79	16.16
Debt / Equity %	n.a.	n.a.	n.a.	n.a.

Compound Growth %'s	EPS %	-3.09	Net Income %	-3.02	Total Revenues %	2.31

Comments

1994 results reflect a one-time benefit of $212,000 in connection with an accounting change. The 72nd Street property is fully leased and enjoyed a profit of $124,000 before depreciation in its first full year of operation. This has encouraged management to search for additional properties in a very thin real estate market. Investment Classification: Income & Value

Officers	Position	Ownership Information	
Virginia Sloane	President	Number of Shares Outstanding	23,809
Wm. D. Hart, Jr.	Vice President, Treasurer	Market Capitalization	$ 7,452,217
Arthur J. Smadback	Vice President, Secretary	Frequency of Dividends	Quarterly
Howard Rosenbaum	Other	Number of Shareholders	Under 500
Renato Guca	Other		

Other Information

Transfer Agent	United States Trust Company of New York New York, NY		Where Listed	OTC-BB
Auditor	Eisner & Lubin		Symbol	PKLX
Market Maker	Forbes, Walsh, Kelly & Co, Inc	(800)221-3747	SIC Code	6510
	Carr Securities Corporation	(800)221-2243	Employees	8
Broker Dealer	OTC Specialist			

Pay-O-Matic Corp.

160 Oak Drive   Syosset, NY 11791   Telephone (516)496-4900   Fax (516)469-2282

Company Description

The Company provides customers in New York City and surrounding areas with a wide array of financial and currency services on both the consumer and business levels including check cashing, sale of money orders, food stamps, lotteries, bill payment, benefits disbursement, armored transport, coin and currency supply and check processing. The Company was formed in 1950.

	12/31/95	12/31/94	12/31/93	12/31/92
Per Share Information				
Stock Price	10.00	7.50	12.25	12.25
Earnings Per Share	0.60	0.88	1.54	1.59
Price / Earnings Ratio	16.67	8.52	7.95	7.70
Book Value Per Share	21.02	20.42	19.42	17.87
Price / Book Value %	47.57	36.73	63.08	68.55
Dividends Per Share	0.0	0.0	0.0	0.0
Annual Financial Data				
Operating Results (000's)				
Total Revenues	32,515.4	32,725.5	32,133.3	30,290.1
Costs & Expenses	-31,196.9	-30,948.8	-29,670.5	-27,884.3
Income Before Taxes and Other	1,058.2	1,444.8	2,179.1	2,172.9
Other Items	-5.0	0.0	0.0	0.0
Income Tax	-665.7	-873.3	-1,174.0	-1,128.9
Net Income	387.5	571.5	1,005.2	1,044.0
Cash Flow From Operations	3,394.8	3,765.4	1,983.0	5,467.0
Balance Sheet (000's)				
Cash & Equivalents	23,272.2	24,395.4	17,220.6	27,880.9
Total Current Assets	27,665.9	29,273.0	22,529.1	32,304.5
Fixed Assets, Net	7,395.8	7,127.3	6,459.6	6,486.3
Total Assets	36,448.1	37,955.4	30,528.4	40,298.2
Total Current Liabilities	22,253.7	24,373.4	17,425.9	27,892.5
Long-Term Debt	705.2	479.2	477.2	785.6
Stockholders' Equity	13,489.1	13,102.8	12,625.3	11,620.1
Performance & Financial Condition				
Return on Total Revenues %	1.19	1.75	3.13	3.45
Return on Avg Stockholders' Equity %	2.91	4.44	8.29	9.41
Return on Average Assets %	1.04	1.67	2.84	2.68
Current Ratio	1.24	1.20	1.29	1.16
Debt / Equity %	5.23	3.66	3.78	6.76

Compound Growth %'s	EPS %	-27.74	Net Income %	-28.13	Total Revenues %	2.39

Comments

Flat or declining revenues with rising expenses has caused a decline in corporate profits. The report for 1996 was not yet available, but we did obtain the key numbers. Revenue declined from $32.5 million to $32.0 million. A loss for the year of $81,505, $.13 per share, was recorded as compared to profits of $387,504, $.60 per share, in 1995. We were unable to obtain an explanation of the decline. Investment Classification: Value

Officers	Position	Ownership Information	
Michael Barone	Chairman, Vice President	Number of Shares Outstanding	641,636
Antoinette Mustafa	Chairman	Market Capitalization	$ 6,416,360
Rayman Mustafa	President	Frequency of Dividends	n.a.
Murray Wolf	Secretary	Number of Shareholders	Under 500
Stephen Wolf	Treasurer		

Other Information			
Transfer Agent	Registrar & Transfer Company Cranford, NJ	Where Listed	OTC-BB
Auditor	Rothschild, Topal, Miller & Kraft	Symbol	PAYO
Market Maker	Roney & Co.	(800)321-2038	SIC Code	7389
	Carr Securities Corporation	(800)221-2243	Employees	n.a.
Broker Dealer	OTC Specialist		

Peckham Industries, Inc.

20 Haarlem Avenue   White Plains, NY 10603   Telephone (914)949-2000   Fax (914)949-2075

Company Description

Peckham Industries, Inc. is engaged in the production and sale of asphaltic concrete, stone and liquid asphalt used in the construction of roads. In addition, a wholly-owned subsidiary engages in the leasing of commercial real estate. All business is conducted in New York State and Connecticut through sixteen separate facilities. Sales to state and local government units and agencies represented approximately 31% of revenues in 1996. There are preferred shares outstanding in addition to common stock. The Company has been reacquiring its common shares in recent years.

	12/31/96	12/31/95	12/31/94	12/31/93
Per Share Information				
Stock Price	154.00	104.50	75.00	70.00
Earnings Per Share	-3.00	4.52	10.00	3.00
Price / Earnings Ratio	n.a.	23.12	7.50	23.33
Book Value Per Share	172.46	175.55	163.60	169.90
Price / Book Value %	89.30	59.53	45.84	41.20
Dividends Per Share	0.20	0.20	0.20	0.15
Annual Financial Data				
Operating Results (000's)				
Total Revenues	66,625.0	78,536.0	78,756.0	74,769.0
Costs & Expenses	-67,141.0	-77,602.0	-76,101.0	-73,585.0
Income Before Taxes and Other	-516.0	934.0	2,655.0	1,184.0
Other Items	0.0	0.0	0.0	0.0
Income Tax	302.0	20.0	-659.0	-302.0
Net Income	-214.0	954.0	1,996.0	882.0
Cash Flow From Operations	497.0	6,848.0	1,652.0	7,854.0
Balance Sheet (000's)				
Cash & Equivalents	1,349.0	2,611.0	694.0	3,431.0
Total Current Assets	18,659.0	18,626.0	20,088.0	19,796.0
Fixed Assets, Net	30,799.0	31,380.0	32,941.0	34,347.0
Total Assets	50,252.0	50,854.0	54,064.0	55,479.0
Total Current Liabilities	10,373.0	9,270.0	10,587.0	11,425.0
Long-Term Debt	6,065.0	6,959.0	7,066.0	9,070.0
Stockholders' Equity	29,090.0	29,742.0	31,162.0	29,734.0
Performance & Financial Condition				
Return on Total Revenues %	-0.32	1.21	2.53	1.18
Return on Avg Stockholders' Equity %	-0.73	3.13	6.56	3.00
Return on Average Assets %	-0.42	1.82	3.64	1.57
Current Ratio	1.80	2.01	1.90	1.73
Debt / Equity %	20.85	23.40	22.68	30.50

Compound Growth %'s	EPS % n.a.	Net Income % n.a.	Total Revenues % -3.77

Comments

Price per share information for 1996 and 1995 was derived from treasury stock purchases. The December 31, 1996, posted bid price was $12.75 per share by The Chicago Corporation. Earnings per share are computed after the deduction of the preferred stock dividend. The revenue decline of 15% was largely due to poor weather conditions that were adverse to road construction. Investment Classification: Value

Officers	Position	Ownership Information	
Janet G. Peckham	Chairman, CEO	Number of Shares Outstanding	154,000
John R. Peckham	President, COO	Market Capitalization	$ 23,716,000
James V. DeForest	Exec VP	Frequency of Dividends	Annual
Thomas J. Vitti	Secretary, Treasurer	Number of Shareholders	Under 500
Frank J. Franco	Vice President		

Other Information

Transfer Agent	Company Office		Where Listed	OTC-BB
Auditor	BDO Seidman LLP		Symbol	PCKH
Market Maker	The Chicago Corporation	(800)621-1674	SIC Code	5032
	Hill Thompson Magid & Co., Inc	(800)631-3083	Employees	100
Broker Dealer	OTC Specialist			
	Standard Investment	(888)783-4688 Ext: Jack		

Pekin Life Insurance Company

2505 Court Street   Pekin, IL 61558   Telephone (309)346-1161   Fax (309)346-8510

Company Description

The Company underwrites various life, medical, group, disability and other insurance policies as well as providing annuity and retirement programs. Over 1,000 independent agencies, predominately located in Illinois and surrounding states, write policies for Pekin Life. The Company was founded in 1965. The Farmers Automobile Insurance Association and its subsidiary own approximately 49.3% of outstanding shares.

	12/31/96	12/31/95	12/31/94	12/31/93
Per Share Information				
Stock Price	22.50	17.50	12.63	8.63
Earnings Per Share	0.92	1.28	0.98	0.81
Price / Earnings Ratio	24.46	13.67	12.89	10.65
Book Value Per Share	8.91	8.46	7.57	6.86
Price / Book Value %	252.53	206.86	166.84	125.80
Dividends Per Share	0.21	0.17	0.16	0.14
Annual Financial Data				
Operating Results (000's)				
Total Revenues	159,030.0	145,266.4	146,562.3	130,006.1
Costs & Expenses	-147,756.2	-127,130.1	-131,680.9	-118,038.8
Income Before Taxes and Other	11,273.7	18,136.3	14,881.4	11,967.3
Other Items	0.0	0.0	0.0	0.0
Income Tax	-3,167.9	-6,895.7	-6,221.0	-4,838.3
Net Income	8,105.8	11,240.6	8,660.3	7,129.0
Cash Flow From Operations	38,905.0	37,404.9	43,729.4	31,950.3
Balance Sheet (000's)				
Cash & Equivalents	9,025.9	13,863.8	2,098.1	2,544.5
Total Current Assets	20,142.5	24,105.0	12,528.3	36,350.0
Fixed Assets, Net	1,979.6	22,020.6	2,113.2	2,294.9
Total Assets	425,597.0	391,849.6	343,263.0	300,874.6
Total Current Liabilities	7,630.9	8,267.7	7,143.1	5,698.7
Long-Term Debt	0.0	0.0	0.0	0.0
Stockholders' Equity	78,424.3	74,446.4	66,584.5	60,372.3
Performance & Financial Condition				
Return on Total Revenues %	5.10	7.74	5.91	5.48
Return on Avg Stockholders' Equity %	10.60	15.94	13.64	12.26
Return on Average Assets %	1.98	3.06	2.69	2.51
Current Ratio	2.64	2.92	1.75	6.38
Debt / Equity %	n.a.	n.a.	n.a.	n.a.

Compound Growth %'s	EPS %	4.34	Net Income %	4.37	Total Revenues %	6.95

Comments

The Company intends to expand geographically, especially with its managed care products. Pre-need Life and Annuity policies are a hot item and almost tripled during 1996. Annuity policies overall, however, have shown a marked decrease. An increase in payments to policyholders and beneficiaries was affected by the increase in group business. The contribution to profit from this line decreased during 1996; however, rate increases should begin to improve the results as this next year progresses. Investment Classification: Growth

Officers	Position	Ownership Information	
Robert W. Scheffler	President, CEO	Number of Shares Outstanding	8,800,000
Ronnie D. Fry	Senior VP, COO	Market Capitalization	$ 198,000,000
Paul A. Tornatore	Senior VP	Frequency of Dividends	Quarterly
William E. Tunis	Treasurer, Secretary	Number of Shareholders	1,174
Bret A. Conklin	Vice President, Controller		

Other Information			
Transfer Agent	Company Office	Where Listed	OTC-BB
Auditor	Norbert Zabinski & Co.	Symbol	PKIN
Market Maker	Everen Securities Corp.	(800)321-2338	SIC Code	6310
	Howe Barnes Investments, Inc.	(800)621-2364	Employees	703
Broker Dealer	Regular Stockbroker		

Peninsula Bank of Commerce

1001 Broadway   Millbrae, CA 94030   Telephone (415)697-4333   Fax (415)697-4032

Company Description

Peninsula Bank of Commerce, founded in 1981, operates two branches in suburban communities in northern and central San Mateo County, considered part of the greater San Francisco metropolitan area. The Bank's customers are predominantly small and middle-market businesses. The San Mateo County Times awarded the Bank the "Best of San Mateo" honors in 1996, after polling the community.

	12/31/96	12/31/95	12/31/94	12/31/93
Per Share Information				
Stock Price	27.00	20.25	13.25	11.00
Earnings Per Share	2.65	2.67	2.14	1.00
Price / Earnings Ratio	10.19	7.58	6.19	11.00
Book Value Per Share	19.78	18.62	17.09	16.40
Price / Book Value %	136.50	108.75	77.53	67.07
Dividends Per Share	1.35	1.35	1.00	0.50
Annual Financial Data				
Operating Results (000's)				
Net Interest Income	6,148.7	6,156.7	5,527.7	4,601.6
Loan Loss Provision	-120.0	-204.0	-120.0	-160.0
Non-Interest Income	420.1	476.0	459.8	455.4
Non-Interest Expense	-3,568.5	-3,600.4	-3,676.2	-3,898.5
Income Before Taxes and Other	2,880.4	2,828.3	2,191.2	998.5
Other Items	0.0	0.0	0.0	0.0
Income Tax	-1,045.5	-1,046.4	-824.8	-366.7
Net Income	1,834.9	1,781.9	1,366.5	631.8
Balance Sheet (000's)				
Cash & Securities	136,497.0	35,311.5	25,712.5	33,062.5
Loans, Net	64,185.2	58,805.1	60,478.6	58,262.7
Total Assets	204,320.6	98,754.5	89,748.4	94,578.8
Deposits	188,534.5	84,064.5	77,173.0	82,857.5
Stockholders' Equity	13,273.2	12,271.4	10,790.1	10,316.0
Performance & Financial Condition				
Return on Avg Stockholders' Equity %	14.37	15.45	12.95	6.22
Return on Average Assets %	1.21	1.89	1.48	0.67
Equity to Assets %	6.50	12.43	12.02	10.91
Net Interest Margin	n.a.	n.a.	n.a.	n.a.
Reserve as a % of Problem Loans	85.49	135.52	75.60	41.51

Compound Growth %'s	EPS %	38.38	Net Income %	42.67	Net Interest Income %	10.14

Comments

Compound growth rates in earnings are partially distorted by poor 1993 results, the base year for the calculation. Management was pleased with asset, deposit and loan growth. During 1995 and 1996, there were forty-eight mergers involving California banks. Management views this as an excellent opportunity to gain market share. Strategic investments in technology are planned for 1997. Investment Classification: Growth & Income

Officers	Position	Ownership Information	
Mark F. Doiron	President, CEO	Number of Shares Outstanding	670,924
Thomas T. Pangelinan	Senior VP, CFO	Market Capitalization	$ 18,114,948
Michael W. Bondy	Senior VP, Sr Loan Officer	Frequency of Dividends	Semi-Annual
Mark D. Monasch	Vice President	Number of Shareholders	n.a.
Frank A. Hall	Vice President	Where Listed / Symbol	OTC-PS / PEBC

Other Information			Loan Mix	%
Transfer Agent	Company Office		R/E Mortgages	56.0
Auditor	Coopers & Lybrand LLP		Commerical	24.3
Market Maker	Hoefer & Arnett, Incorporated	(800)346-5544	Construction	17.9
	Ryan, Beck & Co.	(800)395-7926	Installment	1.3
Broker Dealer	Regular Stockbroker		Other	0.5
	Hoefer & Arnett, Retail	(800)346-5544 Ext: Lisa		

Penn Fuel Gas, Inc.

55 South Third Street   Oxford, PA 19363   Telephone (610)932-2000   Fax (610)932-5349

Company Description

Penn Fuel Gas, Inc. provides natural gas distribution, transmission and storage services to 70,000 customers from facilities in Pennsylvania and also sells liquefied petroleum gas and merchandise to 70,900 customers located in over half the counties of Pennsylvania. The Company also provides propane gas service to approximately 28,300 customers in Pennsylvania and Maryland.

	12/31/96	12/31/95	12/31/94	12/31/93
Per Share Information				
Stock Price	64.00	59.00	57.00	53.50
Earnings Per Share	8.90	7.07	6.55	5.99
Price / Earnings Ratio	7.19	8.35	8.70	8.93
Book Value Per Share	93.01	86.51	81.44	74.89
Price / Book Value %	68.81	68.20	69.99	71.44
Dividends Per Share	2.40	2.00	0.0	0.0
Annual Financial Data				
Operating Results (000's)				
Total Revenues	113,936.0	106,749.0	123,410.0	115,997.0
Costs & Expenses	-102,801.0	-97,827.0	-114,128.0	-107,090.0
Income Before Taxes and Other	11,135.0	8,922.0	9,147.0	8,907.0
Other Items	0.0	378.0	0.0	0.0
Income Tax	-3,741.0	-3,223.0	-3,442.0	-3,602.0
Net Income	7,394.0	6,077.0	5,705.0	5,305.0
Cash Flow From Operations	11,811.0	12,371.0	17,927.0	15,152.0
Balance Sheet (000's)				
Cash & Equivalents	2,513.0	5,357.0	11,788.0	5,892.0
Total Current Assets	29,271.0	27,437.0	36,744.0	34,306.0
Fixed Assets, Net	141,292.0	132,602.0	122,897.0	115,237.0
Total Assets	196,465.0	184,277.0	174,367.0	159,236.0
Total Current Liabilities	28,150.0	20,482.0	19,376.0	40,702.0
Long-Term Debt	51,694.0	55,644.0	58,904.0	34,995.0
Stockholders' Equity	77,509.0	72,842.0	69,205.0	64,505.0
Performance & Financial Condition				
Return on Total Revenues %	6.49	5.69	4.62	4.57
Return on Avg Stockholders' Equity %	9.84	8.56	8.53	8.51
Return on Average Assets %	3.88	3.39	3.42	3.46
Current Ratio	1.04	1.34	1.90	0.84
Debt / Equity %	66.69	76.39	85.12	54.25

Compound Growth %'s	EPS %	14.11	Net Income %	11.70	Total Revenues %	-0.60

Comments

The Company reported a sharp rise in income, up 36% after excluding a nonrecurring income item reported in the preceding year. In October, 1996, the Pennsylvania Public Utility Commission approved an increase in utility rates of $6,725,000. The full impact of the increase will be reflected in 1997 results. In February, 1997, the Board of Directors juiced up shareholders by increasing the dividend another 20%. Investment Classification: Income & Growth & Value

Officers	Position	Ownership Information	
Terry H. Hunt	President, CEO	Number of Shares Outstanding	717,583
George C. Rhodes, Sr.	Senior VP	Market Capitalization	$ 45,925,312
Eleanor R. Ross	Secretary	Frequency of Dividends	Quarterly
Ronald J. Frederick	Vice President	Number of Shareholders	Under 500
Edward L. McCusker	Vice President, Treasurer		

Other Information				
Transfer Agent	Company Office		Where Listed	OTC-BB
Auditor	KPMG Peat Marwick LLP		Symbol	PFUL
Market Maker	Herzog, Heine, Geduld, Inc.	(800)221-3600	SIC Code	4924
	Hill Thompson Magid & Co., Inc	(800)631-3083	Employees	750
Broker Dealer	OTC Specialist			

Pennichuck Corporation

4 Water Street   Nashua, NH 03061-0448   Telephone (603)882-5191   Fax (603)882-4125

Company Description

Pennichuck Corporation is engaged principally in the gathering and distribution of potable water to approximately 22,000 customers in southern New Hampshire. The Company is a private supplier of water and, therefore, is not regulated by government agencies. The Southwood Corporation, a wholly-owned subsidiary, manages and develops real estate. With less than a million shares outstanding, the Company has characteristics of an over-the-counter stock although it technically is listed on NASDAQ. It, as well as three other stocks of this nature, are included in the manual to test reader interest. The others are Farmer Bros. Co., Paradise Inc. and Birmingham Utilities. Pennichuck Corporation was founded in 1852.

	12/31/96	12/31/95	12/31/94
Per Share Information			
Stock Price	16.25	17.00	15.00
Earnings Per Share	1.68	1.53	1.32
Price / Earnings Ratio	9.67	11.11	11.36
Book Value Per Share	17.70	17.03	16.59
Price / Book Value %	91.81	99.82	90.42
Dividends Per Share	1.03	0.91	0.0
Annual Financial Data			
Operating Results (000's)			
Total Revenues	12,209.9	11,488.1	10,215.8
Costs & Expenses	-10,219.4	-9,709.0	-8,626.3
Income Before Taxes and Other	1,990.6	1,779.1	1,562.8
Other Items	0.0	0.0	0.0
Income Tax	-752.1	-684.1	-590.2
Net Income	1,238.5	1,095.0	972.5
Cash Flow From Operations	2,282.7	3,179.0	2,238.9
Balance Sheet (000's)			
Cash & Equivalents	260.7	202.8	n.a.
Total Current Assets	3,059.0	2,570.0	n.a.
Fixed Assets, Net	43,338.4	41,446.2	n.a.
Total Assets	50,069.7	47,893.2	n.a.
Total Current Liabilities	2,128.6	1,831.2	n.a.
Long-Term Debt	20,995.0	20,881.1	n.a.
Stockholders' Equity	13,196.4	12,247.2	n.a.
Performance & Financial Condition			
Return on Total Revenues %	10.14	9.53	9.52
Return on Avg Stockholders' Equity %	9.74	9.09	n.a.
Return on Average Assets %	2.53	2.32	2.12
Current Ratio	1.44	1.40	n.a.
Debt / Equity %	159.10	170.50	n.a.

Compound Growth %'s	EPS %	12.82	Net Income %	12.85	Total Revenues %	9.33

Comments

Stephen Schuller, analyst with Dorsey Investment Securities considers this a good little water company. He points out that, although net income has been rising, part of this has been due to the sale of excess lands. Also, relative to its peer group, the Company carries a fairly high amount of debt. Like many water companies in the Northeast, a portion of its lines are very old. Still, the Company has made healthy annual increases to its dividend and seems to be well managed. Investment Classification: Income & Value

Officers	Position	Ownership Information	
Maurice L. Arel	President, CEO	Number of Shares Outstanding	745,515
Stephen J. Densberger	Exec VP	Market Capitalization	$ 12,114,619
James L. Sullivan Jr.	Secretary	Frequency of Dividends	Quarterly
Charles J. Staab	Vice President, CFO	Number of Shareholders	753
Bonalyn J. Hartley	Vice President, Controller		

Other Information

Transfer Agent	Company Office		Where Listed	NASDAQ
Auditor	Arthur Andersen LLP		Symbol	PNNW
Market Maker	n.a.		SIC Code	4940
			Employees	56
Broker Dealer	Regular Stockbroker			
	Stephen Schuller - Dorsey	(800)375-5431		

Pennsylvania Manufacturers Corporation

1735 Market Street   Philadelphia, PA 19103-7590   Telephone (215)665-5070   Fax (215)665-5061

Company Description

Pennsylvania Manufacturers Corporation sells property and casualty insurance and reinsurance as well as workers' compensation and other lines of commercial insurance. The Company operates in the Mid-Atlantic and Southern regions of the United States, primarily in Pennsylvania and the six contiguous states. The Company was founded in 1916 and had 316 consecutive quarterly profits. What happened in 1996? Let's take a look.

	12/31/96	12/31/95	12/31/94	12/31/93
Per Share Information				
Stock Price	15.75	17.00	16.25	13.25
Earnings Per Share	-5.68	0.97	2.32	3.37
Price / Earnings Ratio	n.a.	17.53	7.00	3.93
Book Value Per Share	17.86	25.53	22.10	22.23
Price / Book Value %	88.19	66.59	73.53	59.60
Dividends Per Share	0.32	0.36	0.36	0.32
Annual Financial Data				
Operating Results (000's)				
Total Revenues	566,684.0	661,336.0	656,154.0	772,368.0
Costs & Expenses	-758,078.0	-626,423.0	-590,774.0	-682,747.0
Income Before Taxes and Other	-191,394.0	34,913.0	65,380.0	89,621.0
Other Items	0.0	0.0	0.0	14,119.0
Income Tax	56,060.0	-10,783.0	-8,130.0	-21,324.0
Net Income	-135,334.0	24,130.0	57,250.0	82,416.0
Cash Flow From Operations	-115,945.0	15,913.0	2,294.0	479.0
Balance Sheet (000's)				
Cash & Equivalents	7,176.0	9,170.0	13,150.0	1,147.0
Total Current Assets	716,380.0	599,978.0	614,732.0	605,711.0
Fixed Assets, Net	50,861.0	56,649.0	68,071.0	68,792.0
Total Assets	3,117,516.0	3,258,572.0	3,181,979.0	3,197,909.0
Total Current Liabilities	296,958.0	301,465.0	289,026.0	2,358,150.0
Long-Term Debt	204,699.0	203,848.0	203,975.0	194,836.0
Stockholders' Equity	425,828.0	609,668.0	524,862.0	534,383.0
Performance & Financial Condition				
Return on Total Revenues %	-23.88	3.65	8.73	10.67
Return on Avg Stockholders' Equity %	-26.14	4.25	10.81	16.44
Return on Average Assets %	-4.25	0.75	1.79	2.60
Current Ratio	2.41	1.99	2.13	0.26
Debt / Equity %	48.07	33.44	38.86	36.46

Compound Growth %'s   EPS % n.a.   Net Income % n.a.   Total Revenues % -9.81

Comments

Management explains the huge loss as related to a new strategy that required a significantly larger loss reserve on policies written prior to 1992. It appears that this was necessary to retain an A- rating from the A.M. Best Company. Why management had not been more aggressive in providing for losses in earlier years is not explained. 1993 results reflect a nonrecurring benefit of $14 million, or $.58 per share, which is primarily related to a change in accounting methods. Investment Classification: Value

Officers	Position	Ownership Information	
Frederick W. Anton III	Chairman, CEO	Number of Shares Outstanding	23,843,075
John W. Smithson	President, COO	Market Capitalization	$ 375,528,431
Francis W. McDonnell	Senior VP, CFO	Frequency of Dividends	Quarterly
Robert L. Pratter	Secretary	Number of Shareholders	Under 500
Vincent T. Donnelly	Other		

Other Information			
Transfer Agent	Chemical Mellon Shareholder Services New York, NY	Where Listed	OTC-BB
Auditor	Coopers & Lybrand L.L.P.	Symbol	PMFRA
Market Maker	Herzog, Heine, Geduld, Inc. (800)221-3600	SIC Code	6330
	Robotti & Co., Inc. (212)986-0800	Employees	100
Broker Dealer	Regular Stockbroker		

Pennsylvania State Bank

2148 Market Street   Camp Hill, PA 17001-0487   Telephone (717)731-7272   Fax (717)731-7276

Company Description

The Bank began operations in 1989 and provides commercial banking services through two full service offices to the suburban communities of Cumberland and Dauphin Counties in southwestern Pennsylvania. After a detailed personnel review, it was determined that a formalized sales culture and training program was needed in the organization. Sales training and a more efficient telemarketing system are planned for 1997.

	12/31/96	12/31/95	12/31/94	12/31/93
Per Share Information				
Stock Price	6.50	5.75	4.00	4.00
Earnings Per Share	0.52	0.33	0.38	0.26
Price / Earnings Ratio	12.50	17.42	10.53	15.38
Book Value Per Share	5.57	5.27	4.68	4.46
Price / Book Value %	116.70	109.11	85.47	89.69
Dividends Per Share	0.0	0.02	0.0	0.0
Annual Financial Data				
Operating Results (000's)				
Net Interest Income	3,085.4	2,661.9	2,491.4	1,922.0
Loan Loss Provision	-87.9	-72.0	-124.7	-131.5
Non-Interest Income	568.0	342.7	54.9	59.3
Non-Interest Expense	-2,594.3	-2,340.2	-1,997.4	-1,543.2
Income Before Taxes and Other	971.2	592.4	424.2	306.7
Other Items	0.0	0.0	0.0	0.0
Income Tax	-272.0	-179.0	50.0	0.0
Net Income	699.2	413.4	474.2	306.7
Balance Sheet (000's)				
Cash & Securities	20,421.0	20,039.4	16,114.8	15,774.8
Loans, Net	65,209.1	55,208.2	47,700.5	37,980.0
Total Assets	87,114.1	76,640.7	65,323.2	54,532.6
Deposits	76,083.7	66,843.1	58,711.2	48,389.9
Stockholders' Equity	7,123.5	6,568.2	5,791.2	5,515.9
Performance & Financial Condition				
Return on Avg Stockholders' Equity %	10.21	6.69	8.39	6.34
Return on Average Assets %	0.85	0.58	0.79	0.64
Equity to Assets %	8.18	8.57	8.87	10.11
Net Interest Margin	3.80	3.69	3.78	3.60
Reserve as a % of Problem Loans	807.40	1,392.52	n.a.	249.58

Compound Growth %'s	EPS %	25.99	Net Income %	31.62	Net Interest Income %	17.09

Comments

Earnings per share in both 1993 and 1994 are without an income tax expense. Earnings before taxes has risen consistently and 1996 was the first time the Bank has hit a double-digit return on equity. Non-interest income rose 66%. To retain consistency with the Bank's reports, we did not adjust per share numbers for a 2.5% stock dividend in 1996. Investment Classification: Growth & Value

Officers	Position	Ownership Information	
William V. Freeman	President, CEO	Number of Shares Outstanding	1,278,391
Paul H. Weidman, Jr.	Exec VP, COO	Market Capitalization	$ 8,309,542
Patricia A. Husic	Secretary, Controller	Frequency of Dividends	Irregular
Larry D. Miller	Vice President	Number of Shareholders	n.a.
Jeffrey W. Myers	Vice President	Where Listed / Symbol	OTC-PS / n.a.

Other Information			Loan Mix	%
Transfer Agent	Company Office		R/E Mortgages	68.9
Auditor	Greenawalt & Company, P.C.		Commerical	26.3
Market Maker	Legg Mason Wood Walker, Inc.	(212)428-4890	Construction	1.6
	F.J. Morrissey & Co., Inc.	(800)842-8928	Installment	1.3
Broker Dealer	OTC Specialist		Other	1.9
	Dennis Reynolds - Ryan, Beck	(888)231-7226		

Pennsylvania Warehousing and Safe Deposit Company

1518 Walnut Street   Philadelphia, PA 19102-3419   Telephone (215)467-1228

Company Description

Pennsylvania Warehousing and Safe Deposit Company's principal activity is the management of an investment portfolio. The Company continues to look for reinvestment opportunities. Most of the investment assets are held in treasury notes of the United States with short to mid-term maturities.

	12/31/94	12/31/93	12/31/92
Per Share Information			
Stock Price as of 12/31	750.00	750.00	750.00
Earnings Per Share	124.53	279.08	228.79
Price / Earnings Ratio	6.02	2.69	3.28
Book Value Per Share	2,948.02	2,328.37	2,134.29
Price / Book Value %	25.44	32.21	35.14
Dividends Per Share	85.00	85.00	0.0
Annual Financial Data			
Operating Results (000's)			
Total Revenues	811.6	1,836.7	1,328.6
Costs & Expenses	-146.1	-157.1	-121.4
Income Before Taxes and Other	665.4	1,679.6	1,207.3
Other Items	0.0	0.0	0.0
Income Tax	-126.8	-472.6	-217.7
Net Income	538.6	1,207.0	989.5
Cash Flow From Operations	244.9	27.1	139.0
Balance Sheet (000's)			
Cash & Equivalents	999.3	1,523.1	1,147.2
Total Current Assets	1,090.6	1,597.7	1,250.4
Fixed Assets, Net	0.0	0.0	0.0
Total Assets	14,079.8	10,138.6	9,245.1
Total Current Liabilities	37.1	68.4	14.3
Long-Term Debt	0.0	0.0	0.0
Stockholders' Equity	12,750.2	10,070.2	9,230.8
Performance & Financial Condition			
Return on Total Revenues %	66.37	65.72	74.48
Return on Avg Stockholders' Equity %	4.72	12.51	n.a.
Return on Average Assets %	4.45	12.45	n.a.
Current Ratio	29.37	23.35	87.51
Debt / Equity %	n.a.	n.a.	n.a.

Compound Growth %'s	EPS %	n.a.	Net Income %	n.a.	Total Revenues %	n.a.

Comments

In 1994, the Company was required, under accounting rules, to reflect its investment assets at fair market value. Net unrealized gain on investments of $2,508,998, $580 per share, was added as a line item to the shareholder's equity section of the balance sheet. We were unable to obtain more current information other than the stock price, which was bid at $1,300 as of December 31, 1996. Accept this page as an alert that this security is out there and still trading, when it does trade, at a substantial discount to book value. Investment Classification: Value & Income

Officers	Position	Ownership Information	
Not Available		Number of Shares Outstanding	4,325
		Market Capitalization	$ 5,622,500
		Frequency of Dividends	Quarterly
		Number of Shareholders	Under 500

Other Information				
Transfer Agent	Company Office		Where Listed	OTC-PS
Auditor	Price Waterhouse LLP		Symbol	PAWH
Market Maker	F.J. Morrissey & Co., Inc.	(800)842-8928	SIC Code	6790
	Hill Thompson Magid & Co., Inc	(800)631-3083	Employees	1
Broker Dealer	OTC Specialist			
	Standard Investment	(888)783-4688		

Personal Computer Products, Inc.

11031 Via Frontera, Ste. 100   San Diego, CA 92127   Telephone (619)485-8411   Fax (619)487-5809

Company Description

Personal Computer Products, Inc. 1) develops and licenses laser printer technology; 2) manufactures, markets, and distributes laser printer controllers and accessories; and 3) markets and distributes internationally a variety of personal computer accessory products. The Company was founded in 1982. Over the last several years the Company has been in a transitional period from older technology and products to becoming a leading technology-based supplier of state-of-the-art printer controllers to OEM customers.

	06/30/96	06/30/95
Per Share Information		
Stock Price as of 12/31	1.00	0.37
Earnings Per Share	-0.18	-0.15
Price / Earnings Ratio	n.a.	n.a.
Book Value Per Share	0.03	n.a.
Price / Book Value %	3,333.33	n.a.
Dividends Per Share	0.0	0.0
Annual Financial Data		
Operating Results (000's)		
Total Revenues	11,621.0	14,424.0
Costs & Expenses	-15,346.0	-16,923.0
Income Before Taxes and Other	-3,725.0	-2,502.0
Other Items	116.0	365.0
Income Tax	-4.0	-8.0
Net Income	-3,613.0	-2,145.0
Cash Flow From Operations	-1,272.0	-658.0
Balance Sheet (000's)		
Cash & Equivalents	4,390.0	n.a.
Total Current Assets	6,372.0	n.a.
Fixed Assets, Net	359.0	n.a.
Total Assets	6,810.0	n.a.
Total Current Liabilities	2,396.0	n.a.
Long-Term Debt	0.0	n.a.
Stockholders' Equity	4,414.0	n.a.
Performance & Financial Condition		
Return on Total Revenues %	-31.09	-14.87
Return on Avg Stockholders' Equity %	n.a.	n.a.
Return on Average Assets %	n.a.	n.a.
Current Ratio	2.66	n.a.
Debt / Equity %	n.a.	n.a.

Compound Growth %'s	EPS % n.a.	Net Income % n.a.	Total Revenues % -19.43

Comments

Positive results are apparent in the first nine months of fiscal 1997. Total revenue rose 181% to $22,623,000 and net earnings were $155,000. The balance sheet had working capital of $4,773,000 and no long-term debt. The only problem we see is that the large number of shares outstanding, even with a substantial improvement to income, will prevent the share price from really climbing. This may be the reason the Company effectuated a 1 for 5 reverse split on February 24, 1997. No per share amounts have been restated in the presentation above. Investment Classification: Speculative

Officers	Position	Ownership Information	
Harry J. Saal	Chairman	Number of Shares Outstanding	33,824,955
Edward W. Savarese	President, CEO	Market Capitalization	$ 33,824,955
Brian Bonar	Exec VP	Frequency of Dividends	n.a.
Ralph R. Barry	Secretary, CFO	Number of Shareholders	3,100

Other Information

Transfer Agent	Bank of America San Francisco, CA		Where Listed	OTC-BB
Auditor	Boros & Farrington APC		Symbol	PCPI
Market Maker	Wedbush Morgan Securities, Inc	(800)421-0251	SIC Code	5045
	Sherwood Securities Corp.	(800)435-1235	Employees	n.a.
Broker Dealer	Regular Stockbroker			

Petaluma, Bank of

1360 Redwood Way   Petaluma, CA 94954   Telephone (707)765-2222   Fax (707)765-4568

Company Description

Bank of Petaluma is celebrating its 10th anniversary in 1997. Now with four offices, it serves the banking needs in this quickly growing region wedged between Santa Rosa and the San Francisco Bay in northern California. Local businesses include retailing, professional service organizations, real estate, vineyards and the dairy and poultry industries. In 1996, Bank of Petaluma introduced a full line of investment products. If you can't stop by for a glass of wine you can pop the cork at home and tune them in on your computer: (http://www.BofP.com).

	12/31/96	12/31/95	12/31/94	12/31/93
Per Share Information				
Stock Price	17.50	13.33	10.90	9.75
Earnings Per Share	1.66	1.68	0.82	0.72
Price / Earnings Ratio	10.54	7.93	13.29	13.54
Book Value Per Share	15.58	14.55	12.22	11.65
Price / Book Value %	112.32	91.62	89.20	83.69
Dividends Per Share	0.20	0.14	0.09	0.0
Annual Financial Data				
Operating Results (000's)				
Net Interest Income	5,737.0	4,834.7	3,637.8	2,768.3
Loan Loss Provision	-334.5	-312.9	-246.9	-120.0
Non-Interest Income	976.4	941.4	517.6	433.6
Non-Interest Expense	-4,870.2	-4,194.4	-3,452.5	-2,704.5
Income Before Taxes and Other	1,508.7	1,268.8	456.0	377.4
Other Items	0.0	0.0	0.0	0.0
Income Tax	-434.0	-281.0	-4.6	-25.0
Net Income	1,074.7	987.8	451.4	352.4
Balance Sheet (000's)				
Cash & Securities	46,713.1	49,331.0	41,779.0	21,602.5
Loans, Net	76,259.9	56,903.0	48,186.7	40,512.0
Total Assets	129,441.4	111,866.4	95,683.6	65,764.9
Deposits	110,322.9	91,137.9	82,767.7	57,763.4
Stockholders' Equity	9,375.8	8,583.8	7,210.1	5,665.8
Performance & Financial Condition				
Return on Avg Stockholders' Equity %	11.97	12.51	7.01	6.42
Return on Average Assets %	0.89	0.95	0.56	0.58
Equity to Assets %	7.24	7.67	7.54	8.62
Net Interest Margin	4.71	5.49	5.57	5.57
Reserve as a % of Problem Loans	741.94	347.49	317.52	95.82

Compound Growth %'s	EPS %	32.11	Net Income %	45.02	Net Interest Income %	27.49

Comments

The Bank declared 5% stock dividends in 1996 and 1995. All per share amounts have been restated for consistency. Income tax expense has been rising more rapidly than income thereby distorting the real growth in earnings. This is caused by a shift in investment assets to the loan portfolio. Management reports excellent asset quality. The placement of 94,031 shares of common in 1994 has the effect of reducing the compound growth rate in earnings per share below the compound growth rate for net income. Investment Classification: Growth & Value

Officers	Position	Ownership Information	
Daniel G. Libarle	Chairman	Number of Shares Outstanding	601,675
Walter E. Bragdon	President, CEO	Market Capitalization	$ 10,529,313
Donald J. Morris	Exec VP, Other	Frequency of Dividends	Irregular
Arlene A. Brians	Senior VP, COO	Number of Shareholders	672
Pat Wasik	Secretary	Where Listed / Symbol	OTC-BB / BPLU

Other Information			Loan Mix	%
Transfer Agent	U.S. Stock Transfer Corporation Glendale, CA		Commerical	42.1
Auditor	Richardson & Company		R/E Mortgages	38.2
Market Maker	Hoefer & Arnett, Incorporated	(415)362-7111	Installment	11.4
	Cowles, Sabol & Company, Inc.	(818)906-0881	Construction	7.5
Broker Dealer	Regular Stockbroker		Other	0.8

Phil-Good Products Incorporated

3500 West Reno Avenue   Oklahoma City, OK 73107-6136   Telephone (405)942-5527   Fax (405)942-8002

Company Description

Phil-Good Products, Incorporated specializes in the manufacture of precision custom molding plastics. The majority of customers are located in the southwest United States with Little Giant Pump Company as a major account. The Company was founded in 1959. Peggy Phillips, a third generation family member, was elected president during 1996. Seven children in the generation after Peggy may be the reason the Company bought back 43,237 of its shares this last year.

	06/30/96	06/30/95	06/30/94	06/30/93
Per Share Information				
Stock Price as of 12/31	1.62	1.12	0.44	0.31
Earnings Per Share	0.29	0.31	0.18	0.12
Price / Earnings Ratio	5.59	3.61	2.44	2.58
Book Value Per Share	2.67	2.39	1.89	1.56
Price / Book Value %	60.67	46.86	23.28	19.87
Dividends Per Share	0.10	0.10	0.0	0.10
Annual Financial Data				
Operating Results (000's)				
Total Revenues	4,690.3	5,056.7	3,939.6	3,678.2
Costs & Expenses	-4,487.0	-4,671.0	-3,703.4	-3,512.1
Income Before Taxes and Other	203.3	385.7	236.2	166.1
Other Items	0.0	0.0	0.0	0.0
Income Tax	-79.2	-145.8	-83.9	-54.1
Net Income	124.1	239.9	152.3	112.0
Cash Flow From Operations	314.1	458.4	90.0	239.4
Balance Sheet (000's)				
Cash & Equivalents	227.5	280.8	177.7	158.8
Total Current Assets	958.2	1,134.7	846.2	705.7
Fixed Assets, Net	694.8	842.9	935.1	484.6
Total Assets	1,690.0	2,005.2	1,806.2	1,212.9
Total Current Liabilities	273.5	440.9	327.6	368.8
Long-Term Debt	267.8	430.5	598.4	126.9
Stockholders' Equity	1,148.7	1,133.8	880.2	717.2
Performance & Financial Condition				
Return on Total Revenues %	2.65	4.74	3.87	3.04
Return on Avg Stockholders' Equity %	10.88	23.83	19.07	16.35
Return on Average Assets %	6.72	12.59	10.09	10.20
Current Ratio	3.50	2.57	2.58	1.91
Debt / Equity %	23.31	37.97	67.98	17.70

Compound Growth %'s	EPS %	34.20	Net Income %	3.49	Total Revenues %	8.44

Comments

The Company continues to generate good cash flow and uses it wisely. Last year, long-term debt was reduced further and treasury stock was acquired. The latter helped along the increase in compound growth of earnings per share. The reason we elected to cover this stock that trades under $2 for the second consecutive year is that, although small, it is fundamentally a solid company. The financial ratios are strong, growth has been demonstrated, and the family is watching the business. Investment Classification: Speculative & Value

Officers	Position	Ownership Information	
Walter J. Phillips	Chairman	Number of Shares Outstanding	430,353
Peggy L. Phillips	President	Market Capitalization	$ 697,172
Dale H. Roberts	Exec VP	Frequency of Dividends	Irregular
Virginia L. Phillips	Vice President, Secretary	Number of Shareholders	Under 500

Other Information

Transfer Agent	Company Office		Where Listed	OTC-BB
Auditor	William J.Garner, Inc.		Symbol	PHGD
Market Maker	Koonce Securities, Inc.	(800)368-2802	SIC Code	3080
	Hill Thompson Magid & Co., Inc	(800)631-3083	Employees	40
Broker Dealer	Regular Stockbroker			

Pinnacle Data Systems, Inc.

2155 Dublin Road   Columbus, OH 43228   Telephone (614)487-1150   Fax (614)487-8568

Company Description

Pinnacle Data Systems, Inc. is an independent provider of depot repair services for electronic equipment such as computers, peripherals and printed circuit board assemblies. The Company's repair services are focused on UNIX computer equipment manufactured predominately by Sun Microsystems. The Company also provides customized engineering applications and central processing unit board designs and manufacturing for integration into existing systems. During 1996, the Company offered 350,000 common shares in an initial public offering at $5 per share.

	12/31/96	12/31/95
Per Share Information		
Stock Price	7.12	5.00
Earnings Per Share	0.05	0.29
Price / Earnings Ratio	142.40	17.24
Book Value Per Share	1.53	0.69
Price / Book Value %	465.36	724.64
Dividends Per Share	0.0	0.0
Annual Financial Data		
Operating Results (000's)		
Total Revenues	4,679.0	3,956.4
Costs & Expenses	-4,616.8	-3,713.2
Income Before Taxes and Other	62.1	243.2
Other Items	0.0	0.0
Income Tax	-12.0	-12.0
Net Income	50.1	231.2
Cash Flow From Operations	-392.0	-190.3
Balance Sheet (000's)		
Cash & Equivalents	257.7	8.1
Total Current Assets	2,343.0	1,482.3
Fixed Assets, Net	846.3	607.7
Total Assets	3,203.9	2,220.7
Total Current Liabilities	827.4	903.7
Long-Term Debt	541.2	664.7
Stockholders' Equity	1,767.5	548.0
Performance & Financial Condition		
Return on Total Revenues %	1.07	5.84
Return on Avg Stockholders' Equity %	4.33	n.a.
Return on Average Assets %	1.85	n.a.
Current Ratio	2.83	1.64
Debt / Equity %	30.62	121.30

Compound Growth %'s	EPS %	-82.76	Net Income %	-78.32	Total Revenues %	18.26

Comments

Although overall revenue was up 19%, the increase was totally from repair sales. Product sales actually showed a small decline. The proceeds from the offering was used to reduce debt and provide working capital for expansion. More than one-half of current assets was comprised of inventory. Management says that the Company is required to maintain a high level of inventory in order to service its customers for extended periods of time. There is risk that some of this inventory will become obsolete. Investment Classification: Speculative

Officers	Position	Ownership Information	
Robert K. Henkel	President, CEO	Number of Shares Outstanding	1,155,601
John D. Bair	Vice President, COO	Market Capitalization	$ 8,227,879
C. Robert Hahn	VP - Sales	Frequency of Dividends	n.a.
Thomas J. Carr	Controller	Number of Shareholders	n.a.
Bernd Appleby	Other		

Other Information			
Transfer Agent	Huntington National Bank Columbus, OH	Where Listed	OTC-BB
Auditor	Hausser + Taylor	Symbol	PNDS
Market Maker	Sierra Brokerage Services, Inc	(800)837-3351	SIC Code	7378
	Herzog, Heine, Geduld, Inc.	(800)221-3600	Employees	n.a.
Broker Dealer	Regular Stockbroker		

Pioneer Metals, Inc.

3611 N.W. 74th Street   Miami, FL 33147   Telephone (305)696-0830   Fax (305)696-9876

Company Description

Pioneer Metals, Inc. and its subsidiaries are engaged in the representation and distribution of nationally manufactured products to the heating and air conditioning industry in every metropolitan area in the State of Florida. It also has separate subsidiaries that are involved in export sales, are exploring opportunities in the marine industry, and are manufacturing aluminum air distribution products.

	09/30/95	09/25/94	09/30/93	09/30/92
Per Share Information				
Stock Price as of 12/31	200.00	170.00	115.00	90.00
Earnings Per Share	31.30	26.14	25.64	17.33
Price / Earnings Ratio	6.39	6.50	4.49	5.19
Book Value Per Share	249.97	206.24	179.80	n.a.
Price / Book Value %	80.01	82.43	63.96	n.a.
Dividends Per Share	0.0	0.0	0.0	0.0
Annual Financial Data				
Operating Results (000's)				
Total Revenues	104,900.2	91,816.1	86,406.0	69,091.5
Costs & Expenses	-96,884.8	-84,531.8	-79,622.7	-64,521.5
Income Before Taxes and Other	8,015.4	7,284.4	6,783.3	4,570.0
Other Items	0.0	-175.1	0.0	0.0
Income Tax	-2,384.7	-2,396.7	-2,144.1	-1,419.3
Net Income	5,630.7	4,712.7	4,639.2	3,150.8
Cash Flow From Operations	4,700.0	3,554.9	4,841.2	4,064.9
Balance Sheet (000's)				
Cash & Equivalents	15,835.5	12,328.8	12,055.4	n.a.
Total Current Assets	59,064.9	51,003.9	46,433.2	n.a.
Fixed Assets, Net	9,152.2	8,648.4	7,811.4	n.a.
Total Assets	71,599.4	61,608.7	56,115.3	n.a.
Total Current Liabilities	26,371.6	24,323.7	23,497.4	n.a.
Long-Term Debt	34.7	55.5	90.6	n.a.
Stockholders' Equity	44,972.7	37,105.0	32,527.3	n.a.
Performance & Financial Condition				
Return on Total Revenues %	5.37	5.13	5.37	4.56
Return on Avg Stockholders' Equity %	13.72	13.54	n.a.	n.a.
Return on Average Assets %	8.45	8.01	n.a.	n.a.
Current Ratio	2.24	2.10	1.98	n.a.
Debt / Equity %	0.08	0.15	0.28	n.a.

Compound Growth %'s	EPS %	21.78	Net Income %	21.35	Total Revenues %	14.93

Comments

The annual shareholders report is mailed to shareholders of record approximately one year after year end, but not to those who hold the shares in street name. We have been told that management has even made it difficult for shareholder's of record to obtain reports. The Company has clearly been successful in expanding its business and maintaining consistent profitability. The price per share at December 31, 1996, was $215. On September 30, 1996, the Company announced that the Internal Revenue Service had assessed the accumulated earnings tax alleging that Pioneer Metals had accumulated more money than necessary for its normal business needs. While it is true that the Company has an excellent financial position, assets are clearly being put to good use in expanding the business. The I.R.S. should get lost. Investment Classification: Value & Speculative

Officers	Position	Ownership Information	
William H. Hegamyer	President	Number of Shares Outstanding	179,913
Katharine L. Hegamyer	Secretary	Market Capitalization	$ 35,982,600
Charles V. Robinson	Treasurer	Frequency of Dividends	n.a.
Leonora K. Hegamyer	Vice President	Number of Shareholders	Under 500
Douglas C. Marty	VP - Sales		

Other Information

Transfer Agent	Registrar and Transfer Company Cranford, NJ		Where Listed	OTC-BB
Auditor	Larry Wolfe, C.P.A.		Symbol	PMTL
Market Maker	Sharpe Capital Inc.	(800)355-5781	SIC Code	5075
	PaineWebber Inc.	(800)221-5532	Employees	n.a.
Broker Dealer	Regular Stockbroker			

Planet Entertainment Corporation

222 Highway 35   Middleton, NJ 07748   Telephone (908)530-8819   Fax (908)530-1165

Company Description

Planet Entertainment Corporation is currently involved in various areas of the recorded music industry including the production, licensing, acquisition, marketing and distribution of high quality music in a variety of formats such as CDs, video, CD-ROM and, to a lesser extent, tapes. In June, 1996, the Company acquired Maestro Holding Company for stock. Maestro holds title to over 5,000 master recordings, publishing rights to over 300 songs, and a twenty-four track studio. In November, 1996, the Company acquired Higher Ground Records, one of America's foremost gospel production companies. In November, 1996, the Company acquired 10,000 master recordings and a recording studio from Gulf Coast Music. In March, 1997, the company entered into a joint venture agreement with Wilderness Films that will allow access and exclusive marketing rights to a library of 2,700 films.

	12/31/96
Per Share Information	
Stock Price	4.00
Earnings Per Share	-0.02
Price / Earnings Ratio	n.a.
Book Value Per Share	0.81
Price / Book Value %	493.83
Dividends Per Share	0.0
Annual Financial Data	
Operating Results (000's)	
Total Revenues	105.0
Costs & Expenses	-157.4
Income Before Taxes and Other	-52.4
Other Items	0.0
Income Tax	0.0
Net Income	-52.4
Cash Flow From Operations	-63.2
Balance Sheet (000's)	
Cash & Equivalents	7.0
Total Current Assets	141.8
Fixed Assets, Net	47.5
Total Assets	14,057.7
Total Current Liabilities	504.1
Long-Term Debt	1,000.0
Stockholders' Equity	7,953.6
Performance & Financial Condition	
Return on Total Revenues %	-49.95
Return on Avg Stockholders' Equity %	n.a.
Return on Average Assets %	n.a.
Current Ratio	0.28
Debt / Equity %	12.57

Compound Growth %'s	EPS %	n.a.	Net Income %	n.a.	Total Revenues %	n.a.

Comments

Mr. Joseph Venneri, age 58 and president of the company, has thirty-eight years of experience in the entertainment industry. The balance sheet and book value are largely composed of assets acquired for Company stock that have been valued for accounting purposes. Not much real money has changed hands. Shareholders are singing anyway as the stock price climbed to over $8 per share by the end of May, 1997. This would equate to a market capitalization of over $80 million. We would suggest waiting for some operating numbers which are somewhere in the future. Investment Classification: Speculative

Officers	Position	Ownership Information	
Wallace Giakas	Chairman	Number of Shares Outstanding	9,826,055
Joseph Venneri	President, CEO	Market Capitalization	$ 39,304,220
Richard Bluestine	Exec VP, CFO	Frequency of Dividends	n.a.
John Arnone	Secretary	Number of Shareholders	n.a.

Other Information				
Transfer Agent	Idata, Inc. Dallas, TX		Where Listed	OTC-BB
Auditor	A.J. Robbins, P.C.		Symbol	PLNE
Market Maker	Shamrock Partners Ltd.	(800)326-4900	SIC Code	3652
	Investors Associates Inc.	(800)646-0399	Employees	n.a.
Broker Dealer	Regular Stockbroker			

Plumas Bank

35 South Lindan   Quincy, CA 95971   Telephone (916)283-6808   Fax (916)283-3557

Company Description

The Bank was formed in 1980 to serve communities in Plumas, Lassen, Sierra and Modoc Counties in northeastern California. It has nine offices spreading from Alturas in the north to as far south as Portola. The Bank has not paid a cash dividend but is proud that the original investors have realized an average annual rate of return through appreciation of more than 20%.

	12/31/96	12/31/95	12/31/94	12/31/93
Per Share Information				
Stock Price	12.50	11.46	9.03	6.25
Earnings Per Share	1.07	0.97	0.87	0.81
Price / Earnings Ratio	11.68	11.81	10.38	7.72
Book Value Per Share	9.15	8.05	6.94	6.05
Price / Book Value %	136.61	142.36	130.12	103.31
Dividends Per Share	0.0	0.0	0.0	0.0
Annual Financial Data				
Operating Results (000's)				
Net Interest Income	7,183.0	6,804.2	6,134.2	5,556.6
Loan Loss Provision	-220.0	-155.0	-125.0	-220.0
Non-Interest Income	1,292.3	1,231.5	1,071.0	1,153.0
Non-Interest Expense	-5,767.2	-5,589.4	-5,061.2	-4,695.4
Income Before Taxes and Other	2,488.1	2,291.4	2,019.0	1,794.2
Other Items	0.0	0.0	0.0	0.0
Income Tax	-961.0	-919.0	-811.0	-707.0
Net Income	1,527.1	1,372.4	1,208.0	1,087.2
Balance Sheet (000's)				
Cash & Securities	61,811.9	45,047.7	39,420.6	39,326.8
Loans, Net	78,402.7	74,690.4	64,463.5	57,937.1
Total Assets	149,023.6	127,954.9	111,013.2	102,777.7
Deposits	136,452.1	116,891.6	98,839.2	94,722.4
Stockholders' Equity	11,962.1	10,450.3	8,929.8	7,761.3
Performance & Financial Condition				
Return on Avg Stockholders' Equity %	13.63	14.16	14.48	15.06
Return on Average Assets %	1.10	1.15	1.13	1.10
Equity to Assets %	8.03	8.17	8.04	7.55
Net Interest Margin	5.86	6.28	6.28	6.25
Reserve as a % of Problem Loans	387.03	413.42	380.18	350.78

Compound Growth %'s	EPS %	9.72	Net Income %	11.99	Net Interest Income %	8.93

Comments

The Company declared 6 for 5 stock splits in both 1996 and 1995. All per share amounts have been adjusted for consistency. Management is pleased with the record results despite a rather weak local economy. It attributes the success to formalized training in customer service, an incentive bonus program that extends to every employee and to new products and services. Management forecasts a growth in return on assets in 1997. Investment Classification: Growth

Officers	Position	Ownership Information	
William E. Elliott	President, CEO	Number of Shares Outstanding	1,306,820
Douglas N. Biddle	Senior VP	Market Capitalization	$ 16,335,250
Dennis C. Irvine	Senior VP	Frequency of Dividends	n.a.
Peter R. Walker	VP - Sales	Number of Shareholders	n.a.
Rose Mosinski	Other	Where Listed / Symbol	OTC-BB / PLBA

Other Information		Loan Mix	%
Transfer Agent	U.S. Stock Transfer Corp. Glendale, CA	R/E Mortgages	32.4
Auditor	Perry-Smith & Co.	Commerical	32.4
Market Maker	Hoefer & Arnett, Incorporated (800)346-5544	Installment	27.7
	Morgan Keegan & Company, Inc. (800)238-7533	Construction	7.5
Broker Dealer	Regular Stockbroker		

Pocono Hotels Corporation

1209 Orange Street   Wilmington, DE 19801   Telephone (717)226-4506   Fax (717)226-4697

Company Description

The Company is a holding company whose major subsidiary, Skytop Lodges, Inc., owns and operates a resort in Skytop, Pennsylvania. The subsidiary also develops and sells cluster homes. The Company was formed in 1925. There have been discussions regarding the possible legalization of gambling in the area. The resort could clearly benefit from this taking place. The Company has an outstanding preferred stock with $2.1 million of dividend arrearage. Current dividends on the preferred have been paid in all the years presented below.

	12/31/96	12/31/95	12/31/94	12/31/93
Per Share Information				
Stock Price	111.00	95.75	55.00	60.00
Earnings Per Share	34.67	-2.49	3.60	-19.39
Price / Earnings Ratio	3.20	n.a.	15.28	n.a.
Book Value Per Share	168.56	139.68	142.19	132.82
Price / Book Value %	65.85	68.55	38.68	45.17
Dividends Per Share	0.0	0.0	0.0	0.0
Annual Financial Data				
Operating Results (000's)				
Total Revenues	10,957.4	9,396.4	9,659.8	9,276.8
Costs & Expenses	-10,410.0	-9,294.3	-9,442.1	-9,522.8
Income Before Taxes and Other	547.4	102.1	217.6	-246.0
Other Items	0.0	0.0	0.0	68.4
Income Tax	-141.2	-60.6	-116.3	53.2
Net Income	406.2	41.5	101.3	-124.3
Cash Flow From Operations	1,567.4	110.2	1,054.6	750.1
Balance Sheet (000's)				
Cash & Equivalents	614.9	222.7	862.3	183.4
Total Current Assets	1,698.8	1,063.2	1,464.7	830.9
Fixed Assets, Net	4,087.8	3,535.2	3,549.3	3,822.6
Total Assets	6,511.1	5,471.3	5,422.1	5,355.9
Total Current Liabilities	1,708.5	974.8	828.7	763.3
Long-Term Debt	0.0	0.0	0.0	0.0
Stockholders' Equity	4,702.3	4,362.1	4,443.3	4,408.0
Performance & Financial Condition				
Return on Total Revenues %	3.71	0.44	1.05	-1.34
Return on Avg Stockholders' Equity %	8.96	0.94	2.29	-2.77
Return on Average Assets %	6.78	0.76	1.88	-2.15
Current Ratio	0.99	1.09	1.77	1.09
Debt / Equity %	n.a.	n.a.	n.a.	n.a.

Compound Growth %'s	EPS % n.a.	Net Income % n.a.	Total Revenues %	5.71

Comments

The preferred stock arrearage has been deducted from equity in determining book value for common shares. Earnings per share are also calculated after the accrued preferred dividend. Management reports a sharp turnaround in lodge occupancy, up 49.5% from the preceding year. This is good news as cash is available for additional upgrades for a recently implemented, five-year rehabilitation plan. There were no property sales during 1996 but a number of lots and homes are available should there be interest. Investment Classification: Value

Officers	Position	Ownership Information	
Stewart F. Campbell	Chairman, CEO	Number of Shares Outstanding	9,812
John B. Hogan	Secretary	Market Capitalization	$ 1,089,132
Donald H. Miller	Treasurer	Frequency of Dividends	n.a.
John B. Campbell	Vice President	Number of Shareholders	Under 500
Edward F. Mayotte	Vice President, General Manager		

Other Information			
Transfer Agent	Company Office	Where Listed	OTC-BB
Auditor	Parente Randolph Orlando et al	Symbol	PHTL
Market Maker	Forbes, Walsh, Kelly & Co, Inc (800)221-3747	SIC Code	7011
	Legg Mason Wood & Walker, Inc. (800)221-9732	Employees	220
Broker Dealer	OTC Specialist		

Polyplastex United, Inc.

3671 131st Avenue North, Ste.A   Clearwater, FL 34622   Telephone (813)573-1881   Fax (813)572-7865

Company Description

The Company produces large format computer generated graphics, electrostatic printing, hand painting and seaming, primarily for the outdoor advertising industry. This is a change from its former business which was liquidated as a result of continuing losses. The Company was organized as a sole proprietorship in 1943 and became a public company in 1955. A tender offer was proposed by the Company in late 1995 for up to 50,000 shares at $6 per share to be paid in increments over three years.

	06/30/96	06/30/95	06/30/94	06/30/93
Per Share Information				
Stock Price as of 12/31	3.62	4.50	6.75	6.75
Earnings Per Share	0.68	-2.56	-2.35	-0.60
Price / Earnings Ratio	5.32	n.a.	n.a.	n.a.
Book Value Per Share	4.00	4.69	7.32	10.78
Price / Book Value %	90.50	95.95	92.21	62.62
Dividends Per Share	0.0	0.0	0.0	0.0
Annual Financial Data				
Operating Results (000's)				
Total Revenues	3,266.9	1,658.8	1,053.0	12,275.5
Costs & Expenses	-2,940.3	-3,068.2	-1,200.2	-12,684.3
Income Before Taxes and Other	294.0	-1,527.6	-1,362.0	-419.6
Other Items	0.0	0.0	0.0	0.0
Income Tax	0.0	0.0	0.0	0.0
Net Income	294.0	-1,527.6	-1,362.0	70.6
Cash Flow From Operations	723.5	-73.5	3,341.6	253.5
Balance Sheet (000's)				
Cash & Equivalents	183.0	1,191.4	510.9	110.7
Total Current Assets	1,270.3	2,590.2	3,217.7	6,133.6
Fixed Assets, Net	2,319.4	2,321.7	1,721.6	2,659.2
Total Assets	4,732.3	5,811.1	5,958.8	8,946.8
Total Current Liabilities	729.1	517.2	525.6	2,539.4
Long-Term Debt	1,523.5	1,317.1	153.9	0.0
Stockholders' Equity	1,526.7	2,851.8	4,303.6	6,232.5
Performance & Financial Condition				
Return on Total Revenues %	9.00	-92.09	-129.35	-2.84
Return on Avg Stockholders' Equity %	13.43	-42.70	-25.85	-5.45
Return on Average Assets %	5.58	-25.96	-18.28	-3.77
Current Ratio	1.74	5.01	6.12	2.42
Debt / Equity %	99.79	46.19	3.58	n.a.

Compound Growth %'s	EPS % n.a.	Net Income % n.a.	Total Revenues % -35.68

Comments

Management must be satisfied with the math and have confidence in the future as it reacquired 226,685 common shares during the last fiscal year. Not only that, it wants more and will use all available cash as operations have suddenly become profitable. The Company is also selling passive investments to increase cash flow. A net operating loss is still available for income tax purposes. Market makers want $6 for their shares, a more likely value than the posted bid price. Investment Classification: Value & Speculative

Officers	Position	Ownership Information	
Dennis Peskin	President, Secretary	Number of Shares Outstanding	381,570
Toni L. Medjuck	Treasurer	Market Capitalization	$ 1,381,283
Pamela E. Richards	Vice President	Frequency of Dividends	Irregular
		Number of Shareholders	Under 500

Other Information			
Transfer Agent	Continental Stock Transfer & Trust Co. New York, NY	Where Listed	OTC-BB
Auditor	Cherry, Bekaert & Holland, LLP	Symbol	PYPX
Market Maker	Hill Thompson Magid & Co., Inc (800)631-3083	SIC Code	7312
	Monroe Securities, Inc. (800)766-5560	Employees	25
Broker Dealer	Regular Stockbroker		

Pontiac Bancorp, Inc.

300 West Washington   Pontiac, IL 61764   Telephone (815)844-6155   Fax (815)842-2977

Company Description

Bank of Pontiac, subsidiary of the Company, celebrates its 50th anniversary on September 8, 1997, but hasn't wasted time in getting started as it posted record earnings for 1996. Odell State Bank is also a subsidiary of the Company. Each Bank had one office until the opening in April, 1996, of a second location of Bank of Pontiac and a third with the purchase of Bank of Dwight in February, 1997. Most business is conducted with customers located in Livingston County, Illinois. The 1996 annual report is rich in history and carries a 1947 theme. Do you know when the Dow Jones Industrial Average was at 176.39?

	12/31/96	12/31/95	12/31/94	12/31/93
Per Share Information				
Stock Price	65.00	58.00	50.00	46.50
Earnings Per Share	9.68	9.53	7.99	9.52
Price / Earnings Ratio	6.71	6.09	6.26	4.88
Book Value Per Share	85.86	78.97	66.23	62.94
Price / Book Value %	75.70	73.45	75.49	73.88
Dividends Per Share	1.30	1.20	1.15	1.10
Annual Financial Data				
Operating Results (000's)				
Net Interest Income	5,877.9	5,715.7	5,332.0	5,151.6
Loan Loss Provision	-120.0	-120.0	-100.0	-140.0
Non-Interest Income	1,062.5	997.0	903.4	954.1
Non-Interest Expense	-3,711.9	-3,539.3	-3,591.6	-3,598.2
Income Before Taxes and Other	3,108.6	3,053.4	2,543.8	2,367.5
Other Items	0.0	0.0	0.0	495.0
Income Tax	-872.1	-850.3	-696.7	-662.8
Net Income	2,236.5	2,203.1	1,847.1	2,199.7
Balance Sheet (000's)				
Cash & Securities	77,585.1	69,035.0	64,859.8	76,250.7
Loans, Net	97,292.2	91,223.4	78,585.1	67,629.2
Total Assets	180,960.0	165,032.6	147,999.3	148,013.7
Deposits	152,395.3	136,671.2	123,091.4	124,615.6
Stockholders' Equity	20,622.8	18,968.6	15,909.0	15,123.6
Performance & Financial Condition				
Return on Avg Stockholders' Equity %	11.30	12.63	11.90	15.54
Return on Average Assets %	1.29	1.41	1.25	1.55
Equity to Assets %	11.40	11.49	10.75	10.22
Net Interest Margin	n.a.	n.a.	n.a.	n.a.
Reserve as a % of Problem Loans	1,330.57	605.39	427.29	675.84

Compound Growth %'s	EPS %	0.56	Net Income %	0.55	Net Interest Income %	4.49

Comments

1993 results include a nonrecurring benefit of $495,000, $2.14 per share, related to a change in accounting method for reporting income taxes. This has the effect of lowering the compound earnings and earnings per share growth rates from what they otherwise would have been. Per share price information was provided by the Company as to actual transactions. The posted bid prices by market makers are slightly lower. Management attributes record earnings to strong deposit growth. Investment Classification: Value

Officers	Position	Ownership Information	
H. Wayne Taylor	President, CEO	Number of Shares Outstanding	240,200
Myron L. Otto	Senior VP	Market Capitalization	$ 15,613,000
Michael K. McGregor	Senior VP, Head Cashier	Frequency of Dividends	Quarterly
Richard D. Geschwind	Senior VP	Number of Shareholders	n.a.
Jeanne Gernentz	Other	Where Listed / Symbol	OTC-BB / PONT

Other Information			Loan Mix	%
Transfer Agent	Bank of Pontiac Pontiac, IL		R/E Mortgages	52.2
Auditor	McCladrey & Pullen, LLP		Installment	18.9
Market Maker	Stifel, Nicolaus & Company	(312)704-7000	Commerical	16.3
	GBS Financial Corp.	(818)248-5558	Agriculture	12.6
Broker Dealer	OTC Specialist			
	Jack Ingold	(412)391-4594		

PortaCom Wireless, Inc.

8055 W Manchester Avenue Playa Del Rey, CA 90293 Telephone (310)448-4140 Fax (310)448-4141

Company Description

PortaCom Wireless, Inc., formerly Extreme Technologies, Inc., has engaged in initial stage efforts to secure licensing opportunities for the operation of wireless telephone networks. In December, 1996, the Company entered into a joint venture agreement as the managing partner of a company which holds a 25 year renewable license to develop a mobile wireless system in Cambodia. The Company also holds an ownership position in Metromedia Asia Corporation (MAC) which is involved in the build-out of telecommunications projects in China.

	12/31/96	12/31/95	03/31/95
Per Share Information			
Stock Price	3.32	2.00	n.a.
Earnings Per Share	0.41	-0.14	n.a.
Price / Earnings Ratio	8.10	n.a.	n.a.
Book Value Per Share	0.57	-0.06	n.a.
Price / Book Value %	582.46	n.a.	n.a.
Dividends Per Share	0.0	0.0	n.a.
Annual Financial Data			
Operating Results (000's)			
Total Revenues	9,013.9	143.7	780.8
Costs & Expenses	-4,281.6	-2,024.1	-7,925.4
Income Before Taxes and Other	4,732.4	-1,880.4	-7,144.6
Other Items	407.3	545.9	0.0
Income Tax	0.0	0.0	0.0
Net Income	5,139.7	-1,334.5	-7,144.6
Cash Flow From Operations	-1,911.5	-501.3	-4,715.7
Balance Sheet (000's)			
Cash & Equivalents	114.3	165.7	n.a.
Total Current Assets	114.3	172.8	n.a.
Fixed Assets, Net	12.4	0.0	n.a.
Total Assets	8,226.2	988.2	n.a.
Total Current Liabilities	800.1	2,078.4	n.a.
Long-Term Debt	0.0	0.0	n.a.
Stockholders' Equity	7,426.1	-1,090.3	n.a.
Performance & Financial Condition			
Return on Total Revenues %	57.02	-928.97	-914.99
Return on Avg Stockholders' Equity %	n.a.	n.a.	n.a.
Return on Average Assets %	n.a.	n.a.	n.a.
Current Ratio	0.14	0.08	n.a.
Debt / Equity %	n.a.	n.a.	n.a.

Compound Growth %'s	EPS % n.a.	Net Income % n.a.	Total Revenues % n.a.

Comments

The period ended December 31, 1995, is a nine month reporting period. The income recognized in 1996 relates to the receipt of shares in Asian American Telecommunications Corporation which was subsequently exchanged for a 3.43% interest in MAC. The value of these investments, according to management, are established by reference to cash transactions occurring close in proximity to the receipt of shares. Management does not believe that revenues will be realized from the Cambodian joint venture during 1997. Investment Classification: Speculative

Officers	Position	Ownership Information	
Douglas C. MacLellan	President, CEO	Number of Shares Outstanding	13,118,181
Michael A. Richard	VP - Finance	Market Capitalization	$ 43,552,361
Stephen M. Leahy	Secretary	Frequency of Dividends	n.a.
Morris J. Magid	Treasurer	Number of Shareholders	102
Thomas P. Madden	Vice President		

Other Information

Transfer Agent	n.a.		Where Listed	OTC-PS
Auditor	KPMG Peat Marwick LLP		Symbol	PCWR
Market Maker	Herzog, Heine, Geduld, Inc.	(800)221-3600	SIC Code	3669
	M.H. Meyerson & Co., Inc.	(800)333-3113	Employees	n.a.
Broker Dealer	Regular Stockbroker			

Portland Brewing Company

2730 NW 31st Avenue   Portland, OR 97210   Telephone (503)226-7623   Fax (503)226-2702

Company Description

The Company is a regional specialty brewer of lagers and ales with the capacity to brew over 100,000 barrels per year from two breweries. The Company sells its products in twelve western states. The Company also operates a retail establishment known as the Portland Pub which opened for business in 1986. Public offerings in 1995 and 1994 raised $2.4 million each on the sale of 413,177 shares and 698,520 shares, respectively. Portland Brewing has managed its public offerings by itself, something we don't see too much of these days. The Company also tries to be helpful to shareholders who want to sell shares and acts as an order matcher.

	12/31/96	12/31/95	06/30/94	06/30/93
Per Share Information				
Stock Price	9.00	7.00	4.00	3.33
Earnings Per Share	-0.18	0.13	0.05	0.06
Price / Earnings Ratio	n.a.	53.85	80.00	55.50
Book Value Per Share	3.30	3.47	2.70	2.12
Price / Book Value %	272.73	201.73	148.15	157.08
Dividends Per Share	0.0	0.0	0.0	0.0
Annual Financial Data				
Operating Results (000's)				
Total Revenues	12,154.7	11,001.4	4,239.8	2,216.8
Costs & Expenses	-12,663.4	-10,626.3	-4,143.3	-2,176.1
Income Before Taxes and Other	-529.5	358.0	96.5	36.2
Other Items	0.0	0.0	0.0	0.0
Income Tax	149.3	-119.2	-39.3	11.7
Net Income	-380.2	238.8	57.2	47.9
Cash Flow From Operations	803.1	296.5	-106.0	148.0
Balance Sheet (000's)				
Cash & Equivalents	49.1	156.5	1,004.0	107.1
Total Current Assets	2,013.3	2,010.0	1,857.9	572.3
Fixed Assets, Net	9,548.3	6,751.3	2,882.7	1,846.5
Total Assets	11,814.6	8,906.1	4,915.4	2,492.9
Total Current Liabilities	2,070.2	994.5	394.2	469.1
Long-Term Debt	2,904.8	537.7	0.0	0.0
Stockholders' Equity	6,839.6	7,184.4	4,470.0	2,023.8
Performance & Financial Condition				
Return on Total Revenues %	-3.13	2.17	1.35	2.16
Return on Avg Stockholders' Equity %	-5.42	4.10	1.76	2.37
Return on Average Assets %	-3.67	3.46	1.54	1.92
Current Ratio	0.97	2.02	4.71	1.22
Debt / Equity %	42.47	7.48	n.a.	n.a.

Compound Growth %'s	EPS % n.a.	Net Income % n.a.	Total Revenues %	76.34

Comments

During 1994, the Company changed its year end from June 30, to December 31. Accordingly, the operating results for the six months ended December 31, 1994, are not comparable with the other full years and we excluded them from the presentation. The compound annual growth rate in the specialty beer industry is estimated to be approximately 15% from 1996 to 2001. This is lower than what it had been primarily because of intense competition created by a proliferation of new brands. The 1996 loss is primarily attributable to costs associated with the Company's expansion to the midwest United States, expansion of a restaurant, and infrastructure improvements including management systems for the two restaurants. Investment Classification: Speculative

Officers	Position	Ownership Information	
Charles A. Adams	President, Chairman	Number of Shares Outstanding	2,074,943
Glenmore James	Secretary, CFO	Market Capitalization	$ 18,674,487
Frederick L. Bowman	Vice President	Frequency of Dividends	n.a.
G. Eugene Clark	VP - Sales	Number of Shareholders	5,700

Other Information			
Transfer Agent	Chemical Mellon Shareholder Services New York, NY	Where Listed	Order Matching Only
Auditor	Arthur Andersen LLP	Symbol	n.a.
Market Maker	None - See Note	SIC Code	2082
		Employees	124
Broker Dealer	None		

Portsmouth Square, Inc.

2251 San Diego Ave., Ste.A-151   San Diego, CA 92110-2926   Telephone (619)298-7201   Fax (619)298-3418

Company Description

The Company's major asset, in addition to cash and securities, is a 49.8% interest in Justice Investors, a limited partnership which owns and the Financial District Holiday Inn in San Francisco, California. The Company is both a general partner and a limited partner. Santa Fe Financial Corporation holds 480,757 shares, or 64% of the Company.

	12/31/96	12/31/95	12/31/94	12/31/93
Per Share Information				
Stock Price	18.00	17.37	16.37	15.44
Earnings Per Share	1.34	1.15	1.13	1.11
Price / Earnings Ratio	13.43	15.10	14.49	13.91
Book Value Per Share	2.74	2.02	1.57	1.20
Price / Book Value %	656.93	859.90	1,042.68	1,286.67
Dividends Per Share	0.65	0.70	0.75	0.90
Annual Financial Data				
Operating Results (000's)				
Total Revenues	1,960.7	1,643.4	1,621.1	1,565.2
Costs & Expenses	-285.9	-201.0	-211.9	-172.4
Income Before Taxes and Other	1,674.8	1,442.4	1,409.2	1,392.8
Other Items	0.0	0.0	0.0	0.0
Income Tax	-670.7	-578.3	-564.6	-558.2
Net Income	1,004.1	864.1	844.6	834.6
Cash Flow From Operations	-853.6	627.7	425.1	699.2
Balance Sheet (000's)				
Cash & Equivalents	21.2	1,206.1	1,103.4	1,240.8
Total Current Assets	1,232.7	1,269.6	1,147.9	1,284.7
Fixed Assets, Net	0.0	0.0	0.0	0.0
Total Assets	2,206.0	1,635.1	1,217.3	1,287.3
Total Current Liabilities	148.3	117.3	38.6	146.4
Long-Term Debt	0.0	0.0	0.0	0.0
Stockholders' Equity	2,057.6	1,517.8	1,178.6	896.6
Performance & Financial Condition				
Return on Total Revenues %	51.21	52.58	52.10	53.32
Return on Avg Stockholders' Equity %	56.17	64.09	81.40	n.a.
Return on Average Assets %	52.28	60.59	67.44	n.a.
Current Ratio	8.31	10.82	29.70	8.77
Debt / Equity %	n.a.	n.a.	n.a.	n.a.

Compound Growth %'s	EPS %	6.48	Net Income %	6.36	Total Revenues %	7.80

Comments

The Company recently signed a new lease with Holiday Inn which should boost revenue. It has a term of 10 years with a 5 year option. The property itself may have a value of $40 million to $60 million which, if it is ever realized, would equate to between $23 and $37 per share. In the meantime, Portsmouth assumed a more active role in managing Justice Investors as part of its efforts to improve revenues. The result was a 20% increase in income from this venture. Investment Classification: Income & Value

Officers	Position	Ownership Information	
John V. Winfield	President, CEO	Number of Shares Outstanding	750,000
L. Scott Shields	Treasurer, CFO	Market Capitalization	$ 13,500,000
Lawrence I. Kramer, Jr.	Vice President	Frequency of Dividends	Semi-Annual
William J. Nance	Vice President, Secretary	Number of Shareholders	332

Other Information				
Transfer Agent	U.S. Stock Transfer Corporation Glendale, CA		Where Listed	OTC-BB
Auditor	Ernst & Young LLP		Symbol	PRSI
Market Maker	Wedbush Morgan Securities, Inc	(800)421-0251	SIC Code	6510
	Hill Thompson Magid & Co., Inc	(800)631-3083	Employees	2
Broker Dealer	Regular Stockbroker			

Power Test Investors Limited Partnership

125 Jericho Turnpike   Jericho, NY 11753   Telephone (516)338-6000   Fax (516)338-6062

Company Description

Power Test Investors Limited Partnership owns and leases 291 gasoline service stations and 5 petroleum distribution terminals all of which are located in the eastern United States. Getty Petroleum Corp. (NYSE) is the sole lessee. The Partnership was formed in 1985 as a limited partnership to invest in the Power Test Realty Company, an operating partnership formed for the purpose of acquiring and leasing back certain assets of Getty Oil Company. The officers listed are officers and employees of CLS General Partnership Corp. which manages the affairs of both this partnership and the operating partnership.

	12/31/96	12/31/95	12/31/94	12/31/93
Per Unit Information				
Price Per Unit	8.75	8.50	7.62	8.25
Earnings Per Unit	0.96	1.20	0.90	0.80
Price / Earnings Ratio	9.11	7.08	8.47	10.31
Book Value Per Unit	0.91	0.79	0.34	0.18
Price / Book Value %	961.54	1,075.95	2,241.18	4,583.33
Distributions Per Unit	0.84	0.74	0.74	0.74
Cash Flow Per Unit	1.11	0.90	1.05	1.02
Annual Financial Data				
Operating Results (000's)				
Total Revenues	10,227.0	13,391.4	11,088.3	10,546.6
Costs & Expenses	-3,932.3	-5,510.1	-5,168.0	-5,293.7
Operating Income	6,230.4	7,800.3	5,860.6	5,199.8
Other Items	0.0	0.0	0.0	0.0
Net Income	6,230.4	7,800.3	5,860.6	5,199.8
Cash Flow From Operations	7,190.1	5,841.4	6,808.7	6,659.4
Balance Sheet (000's)				
Cash & Equivalents	1,867.1	5,754.5	2,523.7	1,983.6
Total Current Assets	1,867.1	5,754.5	2,523.7	1,983.6
Investments	3,868.6	4,767.1	5,747.2	6,476.3
Total Assets	35,603.9	40,867.2	40,459.5	41,916.3
Total Current Liabilities	194.4	277.5	358.4	335.8
Long-Term Debt	29,509.1	35,456.5	37,908.9	40,440.5
Partners' Capital	5,900.4	5,133.3	2,192.1	1,140.0
Performance & Financial Condition				
Return on Total Revenues %	60.92	58.25	52.85	49.30
Return on Average Partners' Capital %	112.93	212.97	351.76	548.68
Return on Average Assets %	16.29	19.18	14.23	12.24
Current Ratio	9.61	20.74	7.04	5.91
Debt / Equity %	500.12	690.72	1729.30	3547.26

Compound Growth %'s	EPU %	6.27	Net Income %	6.21	Total Revenues %	-1.02

Comments

During 1995, the Partnership sold 14 stations to Getty which resulted in a gain of $3.1 million. It sold 5 stations in 1994 for a gain of $658,000. These sales are the reason that rental income has declined over the four years presented. Mortgages and notes payable were reduced by approximately $6 million during 1996. Investment Classification: Income

Officers	Position	Ownership Information	
Leo Liebowitz	President, Treasurer	Number of Units Outstanding	6,500,306
Milton Safenowitz	Exec VP	Market Capitalization	$ 56,877,678
Milton Cooper	Secretary	Frequency of Distributions	Quarterly
		Number of Partners	567

Other Information			
Transfer Agent	Company Office	Where Listed	OTC-BB
Auditor	Coopers & Lybrand LLP	Symbol	POWNZ
Market Maker	Herzog, Heine, Geduld, Inc. (800)221-3600	SIC Code	6510
	Sharpe Capital Inc. (800)355-5781	Employees	n.a.
Broker Dealer	Regular Stockbroker		

Preformed Line Products Company

660 Beta Drive   Mayfield Village, OH 44143   Telephone (216)461-5200   Fax (216)442-8816

Company Description

Preformed Line Products operates within a single business segment which is the design, manufacture and sale of hardware employed in the construction and maintenance of telecommunications and other utility networks. Principal products include high quality cable anchoring and control hardware and systems, overhead and underground splice cases and related products, and fiber optic splicing and communications systems. The Company was formed in 1947 and has big plans to celebrate its 50th anniversary.

	12/31/96	12/31/95	12/31/94	12/31/93
Per Share Information				
Stock Price	39.25	37.06	36.00	26.00
Earnings Per Share	4.96	3.26	3.15	1.89
Price / Earnings Ratio	7.91	11.37	11.43	13.76
Book Value Per Share	31.76	28.39	25.72	23.05
Price / Book Value %	123.58	130.54	139.97	112.80
Dividends Per Share	0.97	0.88	0.88	0.88
Annual Financial Data				
Operating Results (000's)				
Total Revenues	186,781.0	159,250.0	145,109.0	112,012.0
Costs & Expenses	-163,097.0	-143,851.0	-128,487.0	-102,514.1
Income Before Taxes and Other	22,340.0	15,399.0	15,509.0	9,220.7
Other Items	0.0	0.0	0.0	0.0
Income Tax	-7,095.0	-5,316.0	-5,779.0	-3,377.2
Net Income	15,245.0	10,083.0	9,730.0	5,843.5
Cash Flow From Operations	19,195.0	17,309.0	17,309.0	6,981.4
Balance Sheet (000's)				
Cash & Equivalents	10,465.0	6,526.0	6,266.4	3,506.2
Total Current Assets	65,610.0	54,941.0	57,198.6	42,625.1
Fixed Assets, Net	41,908.0	41,849.0	41,205.6	38,668.5
Total Assets	133,451.0	122,895.0	119,532.8	101,074.2
Total Current Liabilities	20,961.0	17,350.0	18,570.8	18,202.6
Long-Term Debt	15,102.0	16,645.0	20,294.0	10,378.8
Stockholders' Equity	97,388.0	87,709.0	79,437.2	71,195.6
Performance & Financial Condition				
Return on Total Revenues %	8.16	6.33	6.71	5.22
Return on Avg Stockholders' Equity %	16.47	12.06	12.92	8.39
Return on Average Assets %	11.89	8.32	8.82	6.12
Current Ratio	3.13	3.17	3.08	2.34
Debt / Equity %	15.51	18.98	25.55	14.58

Compound Growth %'s	EPS %	37.93	Net Income %	37.66	Total Revenues %	18.58

Comments

A sharp increase in 1996 earnings was attributable to ongoing cost control initiatives, improved gross margins and reduced selling, general and administrative expense as a percent of sales. A long history of maintaining a strong financial position differentiates the Company in markets crowded by less well capitalized competitors. The Company's financial strength, good current ratio and low debt/equity ratio, should enable management to focus on new opportunities with deregulation of the telecommunications industry and the growing demand for fiber optic cables. Investment Classification: Value & Growth

Officers	Position	Ownership Information	
Jon R. Ruhlman	Chairman, CEO	Number of Shares Outstanding	3,066,624
Robert G. Ruhlman	President, COO	Market Capitalization	$ 120,364,992
John J. Herda	VP - Finance	Frequency of Dividends	Quarterly
J. Richard Hamilton	Secretary	Number of Shareholders	Under 500
Jon Barnes	VP - Sales		

Other Information				
Transfer Agent	National City Bank Cleveland, OH		Where Listed	OTC-BB
Auditor	Ernst & Young LLP		Symbol	PLIN
Market Maker	McDonald & Company Securities	(216)413-2350	SIC Code	3699
	Carr Securities Corporation	(800)221-2243	Employees	150
Broker Dealer	Regular Stockbroker			

Pro Tech Communications, Inc.

3311 Industrial 25th Street   Fort Pierce, FL 34946   Telephone (561)464-5100   Fax (561)464-6644

Company Description

Pro Tech Communications, Inc. presently designs, develops, manufactures and markets lightweight telecommunications headsets employing what the Company believes are new concepts in advanced light weight design. The Company presently manufactures and markets its first design for the commercial headset market comprised of fast food restaurants and other large quantity users. It is also in the process of developing a second system more suitable to telephone companies, government agencies and business offices. The Company had a secondary offering during 1996 and placed 1.1 million shares at $.50 per share.

	10/31/96	10/31/95
Per Share Information		
Stock Price as of 12/31	1.75	0.50
Earnings Per Share	0.0	0.02
Price / Earnings Ratio	n.a.	25.00
Book Value Per Share	0.26	0.20
Price / Book Value %	673.08	250.00
Dividends Per Share	n.a.	0.0
Annual Financial Data		
Operating Results (000's)		
Total Revenues	880.6	833.9
Costs & Expenses	-800.3	-776.0
Income Before Taxes and Other	1.2	57.9
Other Items	0.0	0.0
Income Tax	-1.7	-13.9
Net Income	-0.5	44.0
Cash Flow From Operations	-108.3	-14.5
Balance Sheet (000's)		
Cash & Equivalents	596.7	571.3
Total Current Assets	977.3	785.5
Fixed Assets, Net	128.9	90.2
Total Assets	1,110.5	875.7
Total Current Liabilities	99.2	313.0
Long-Term Debt	0.0	0.0
Stockholders' Equity	1,011.4	562.7
Performance & Financial Condition		
Return on Total Revenues %	-0.06	5.27
Return on Avg Stockholders' Equity %	-0.07	n.a.
Return on Average Assets %	-0.05	n.a.
Current Ratio	9.86	2.51
Debt / Equity %	n.a.	n.a.

Compound Growth %'s	EPS % n.a.	Net Income % n.a.	Total Revenues % 5.60

Comments

The Company incurred $79,072 of expense in connection with the registration of a stock offering during 1996 which eliminated the operating profit. Total headset sales were 20,810 in 1996 as compared to 17,599 in the preceding year. This is not reflected in total revenue because of a shift to selling through distributors at a lower price. Revenues were also slightly off for the first quarter of fiscal 1997. Management attributes this slowness to delays in planned product introductions. The Company expects to introduce one new product in the second quarter and two new products in the third quarter of 1997. Investment Classification: Speculative

Officers	Position	Ownership Information	
Keith Larkin	President, Treasurer	Number of Shares Outstanding	3,964,000
Kenneth Campbell	Vice President, Secretary	Market Capitalization	$ 6,937,000
Richard Hennessey	Vice President	Frequency of Dividends	n.a.
		Number of Shareholders	59

Other Information				
Transfer Agent	American Stock Transfer & Trust Co. New York, NY		Where Listed	OTC-BB
Auditor	KPMG Peat Marwick LLP		Symbol	PCTU
Market Maker	Troster Singer Corporation	(800)526-3160	SIC Code	4813
	Paragon Capital Corp.	(800)345-0505	Employees	13
Broker Dealer	Regular Stockbroker			

Profit Financial Corporation

14675 Interurban Avenue South   Seattle, WA 98168   Telephone (206)901-3000   Fax (206)901-3100

Company Description

Profit Financial Corporation, Inc. is a holding company that, through a subsidiary, Wade Cook Seminars (WCSI), conducts educational investment seminars. WCSI produces video tapes, audio tapes, and written materials designed to teach various investment and cash flow strategies for investors in the stock market. In early 1997, the Company formed a real estate subsidiary which it intends to use as an investment vehicle to invest the cash flow from WCSI into hotels, motels and the underlying property.

	12/31/96	12/31/95	12/31/94
Per Share Information			
Stock Price	2.62	1.87	n.a.
Earnings Per Share	0.46	0.02	-0.03
Price / Earnings Ratio	5.70	93.50	n.a.
Book Value Per Share	0.55	0.08	n.a.
Price / Book Value %	476.36	2,337.50	n.a.
Dividends Per Share	0.0	0.0	0.0
Annual Financial Data			
Operating Results (000's)			
Total Revenues	40,913.8	7,560.8	1,801.0
Costs & Expenses	-36,247.9	-7,253.3	-2,004.6
Income Before Taxes and Other	4,665.9	307.5	-203.6
Other Items	0.0	0.0	0.0
Income Tax	-1,601.2	-183.7	7.9
Net Income	3,064.6	123.8	-195.7
Cash Flow From Operations	4,388.4	910.9	47.8
Balance Sheet (000's)			
Cash & Equivalents	635.1	26.8	n.a.
Total Current Assets	6,958.9	577.4	n.a.
Fixed Assets, Net	7,135.2	345.0	n.a.
Total Assets	16,937.7	2,283.1	n.a.
Total Current Liabilities	10,849.6	1,340.6	n.a.
Long-Term Debt	1,768.8	117.8	n.a.
Stockholders' Equity	3,702.0	528.9	n.a.
Performance & Financial Condition			
Return on Total Revenues %	7.49	1.64	-10.87
Return on Avg Stockholders' Equity %	144.87	n.a.	n.a.
Return on Average Assets %	31.89	n.a.	n.a.
Current Ratio	0.64	0.43	n.a.
Debt / Equity %	47.78	22.27	n.a.

Compound Growth %'s	EPS % n.a.	Net Income % n.a.	Total Revenues % 376.63

Comments

The Company declared a 2 for 1 stock split in 1996. 1995 per share amounts have been adjusted for consistency. During 1996, the number of seminars that the Company held increased from one seminar a week to approximately six a week by year end. Management attributes its quick success to increased expenditures on radio advertising in selected markets, the popularity of stock market investment books authored by Wade B. Cook and the audience reception of the Company's "Wall Street Workshop" seminars. Investment Classification: Speculative

Officers	Position	Ownership Information	
Wade B. Cook	Chairman, President	Number of Shares Outstanding	6,680,684
Laura M. Cook	Secretary	Market Capitalization	$ 17,503,392
Caesar Regoso	Treasurer, Controller	Frequency of Dividends	n.a.
		Number of Shareholders	917

Other Information			
Transfer Agent	National Stock Transfer, Inc. Salt Lake City, UT	Where Listed	OTC-BB
Auditor	Not indicated	Symbol	PFNL
Market Maker	Fahnestock & Co., Inc. (800)223-3012	SIC Code	6799
	Wilson-Davis & Co., Inc. (800)453-5735	Employees	75
Broker Dealer	Regular Stockbroker		

Publix Super Markets, Inc.

1936 George Jenkins Boulevard   Lakeland, FL 33815   Telephone (941)688-1188   Fax (941)680-5314

Company Description

Publix Super Markets, Inc. operated 534 supermarkets at the end of 1996, compared with 508 at the beginning of the year. At the end of 1996, an additional 25 stores were under construction. The markets are located in Florida, Georgia, South Carolina and Alabama. The Company's lines of merchandise include a variety of nationally advertised and private label brands. Private label items are produced in the Company's manufacturing facilities or are manufactured for the Company by outside suppliers. The Company was founded in 1921. Publix Super Markets has over 103,000 employees.

	12/28/96	12/30/95	12/31/94	12/25/93
Per Share Information				
Stock Price as of 12/31	15.25	12.00	16.00	15.50
Earnings Per Share	1.20	1.07	1.03	0.76
Price / Earnings Ratio	12.71	11.21	15.53	20.39
Book Value Per Share	7.96	7.15	6.36	5.49
Price / Book Value %	191.58	167.83	251.57	282.33
Dividends Per Share	0.13	0.11	0.09	0.08
Annual Financial Data				
Operating Results (000's)				
Total Revenues	10,525,969.0	9,470,706.0	8,742,488.0	7,553,969.0
Costs & Expenses	-10,109,385.0	-9,089,206.0	-8,364,188.0	-7,265,260.0
Income Before Taxes and Other	416,584.0	381,500.0	378,300.0	288,709.0
Other Items	0.0	0.0	0.0	-3,494.0
Income Tax	-151,408.0	-139,359.0	-139,733.0	-104,898.0
Net Income	265,176.0	242,141.0	238,567.0	180,317.0
Cash Flow From Operations	639,903.0	488,339.0	428,355.0	370,431.0
Balance Sheet (000's)				
Cash & Equivalents	457,405.0	276,700.0	188,885.0	198,997.0
Total Current Assets	1,226,832.0	978,114.0	817,914.0	734,769.0
Fixed Assets, Net	1,510,275.0	1,452,748.0	1,349,743.0	1,109,175.0
Total Assets	2,921,084.0	2,559,365.0	2,302,336.0	2,054,315.0
Total Current Liabilities	909,567.0	745,544.0	657,943.0	597,609.0
Long-Term Debt	108.0	1,765.0	3,031.0	4,930.0
Stockholders' Equity	1,751,179.0	1,614,717.0	1,473,154.0	1,308,009.0
Performance & Financial Condition				
Return on Total Revenues %	2.52	2.56	2.73	2.39
Return on Avg Stockholders' Equity %	15.76	15.68	17.16	14.56
Return on Average Assets %	9.68	9.96	10.95	9.38
Current Ratio	1.35	1.31	1.24	1.23
Debt / Equity %	0.01	0.11	0.21	0.38

Compound Growth %'s	EPS %	16.45	Net Income %	13.72	Total Revenues %	11.69

Comments

The Company continues to expand without the need of outside financing. Approximately 44 new stores are expected to open in 1997. The Company discourages ownership of its shares outside its employees, former employees, their families and various benefit plans established for the Company's employees and has issued restricted stock that is non-transferable (only the Company could buy it). This tends to depress a true market valuation as an investor has to be careful with the legends on the certificates that they are buying. Management reports that based on appraisals, prepared by independent appraisers, the per share value was $20.75 and $16.25 per share at the end of 1996 and 1995, respectively. Investment Classification: Growth & Value & Speculative

Officers	Position	Ownership Information	
Howard M. Jenkins	Chairman, CEO	Number of Shares Outstanding	219,942,912
W. Edwin Crenshaw	President	Market Capitalization	$3,354,129,408
William H. Vass	Exec VP	Frequency of Dividends	Quarterly
Hoyt R. Barnett	Exec VP	Number of Shareholders	67,000
S. Keith Billups	Secretary		

Other Information				
Transfer Agent	Company Office		Where Listed	OTC-BB
Auditor	KPMG Peat Marwick LLP		Symbol	PUSH
Market Maker	Carr Securities Corporation	(800)221-2243	SIC Code	5411
	The Chicago Corporation	(800)323-1225	Employees	103,000
Broker Dealer	OTC Specialist			

Queen City Investments, Inc.

P.O. Box 1370   Long Beach, CA 90801-1370   Telephone (310)437-0011   Fax (310)437-8672

Company Description

The Company might be best described as an investment company. It's major asset is a 27,000 acre ranch in Aroyo Grande, California. The Company also leases 25,000 acres from the U.S. Government and raises cattle on the properties. However, its primary source of income is from managing the trust assets of Farmers and Merchants Bank of Long Beach, also included in this book. The two companies are related through ownership by the Walker family. The Company was formed in 1973.

	12/31/96	12/31/95	12/31/94	12/31/93
Per Share Information				
Stock Price	325.00	266.00	255.00	225.00
Earnings Per Share	32.20	24.77	27.59	24.34
Price / Earnings Ratio	10.09	10.74	9.24	9.24
Book Value Per Share	300.96	268.76	242.86	215.26
Price / Book Value %	107.99	98.97	105.00	104.52
Dividends Per Share	0.0	0.0	0.0	0.0
Annual Financial Data				
Operating Results (000's)				
Total Revenues	4,531.1	3,982.4	3,841.1	3,295.1
Costs & Expenses	-2,363.7	-2,261.5	-1,911.6	-1,658.0
Income Before Taxes and Other	2,167.4	1,720.9	1,929.5	1,637.0
Other Items	0.0	0.0	0.0	0.0
Income Tax	-588.5	-506.4	-577.1	-443.1
Net Income	1,578.9	1,214.5	1,352.4	1,194.0
Cash Flow From Operations	n.a.	n.a.	n.a.	n.a.
Balance Sheet (000's)				
Cash & Equivalents	228.2	185.9	105.6	1,988.3
Total Current Assets	13,299.7	8,864.3	8,143.1	7,028.5
Fixed Assets, Net	3,510.5	2,033.7	1,860.6	2,010.8
Total Assets	19,076.4	15,006.0	15,081.9	11,982.6
Total Current Liabilities	81.9	0.0	1,200.1	1,056.4
Long-Term Debt	3,327.0	1,829.3	1,975.0	372.6
Stockholders' Equity	14,755.2	13,176.7	11,906.7	10,553.7
Performance & Financial Condition				
Return on Total Revenues %	34.85	30.50	35.21	36.23
Return on Avg Stockholders' Equity %	11.31	9.68	12.04	n.a.
Return on Average Assets %	9.27	8.07	9.99	n.a.
Current Ratio	162.30	n.a.	6.79	6.65
Debt / Equity %	22.55	13.88	16.59	3.53

Compound Growth %'s	EPS %	9.78	Net Income %	9.76	Total Revenues %	11.20

Comments

The financial statements are not audited. The outside accountants prepare a compiled report using income tax basis reporting. Marketable securities and the investment in land assets are stated at cost. The trading range was $325 to $375 as we went to press. Jack Norberg, financial analyst with Standard Investment in Tustin, California, estimates the real value at over $700 per share. Investment Classification: Value

Officers	Position	Ownership Information	
Kenneth G. Walker	President	Number of Shares Outstanding	49,027
Marisala Tejeda	Secretary	Market Capitalization	$ 15,933,775
Charles Hagan	Vice President	Frequency of Dividends	n.a.
		Number of Shareholders	Under 500

Other Information				
Transfer Agent	Company Office		Where Listed	OTC-BB
Auditor	Windes & McClaughry		Symbol	QUCT
Market Maker	The Seidler Companies Inc.	(800)421-0164	SIC Code	6790
	Ragen MacKenzie Inc.	(800)426-5964	Employees	n.a.
Broker Dealer	OTC Specialist			
	Standard Investment	(888)783-4688 Ext: Jack		

Quigley Corporation (The)

10 South Clinton Street   Doylestown, PA 18901   Telephone (215)345-0919   Fax (215)345-5920

Company Description

The Quigley Corporation, since its inception in 1989, has conducted research and development into various types of health-related food supplements and homeopathic cold remedies. During the last fiscal year the Company has had increasing and significant revenues from its national marketing program and increasing public awareness of its Cold-Eeze (TM) lozenge product. The Company has exclusive worldwide use, manufacturing, marketing and distribution rights for its Cold-Eeze formulation. The Annals of Internal Medicine published the results of a study that indicate a 42% reduction in the duration and severity of the common cold with use of this product.

	09/30/96	09/30/95	09/30/94
Per Share Information			
Stock Price as of 12/31	9.37	0.05	n.a.
Earnings Per Share	-0.08	-0.02	n.a.
Price / Earnings Ratio	n.a.	n.a.	n.a.
Book Value Per Share	0.13	0.04	n.a.
Price / Book Value %	7,207.69	125.00	n.a.
Dividends Per Share	0.0	0.0	n.a.
Annual Financial Data			
Operating Results (000's)			
Total Revenues	1,056.4	506.0	109.4
Costs & Expenses	-1,777.8	-664.5	-206.8
Income Before Taxes and Other	-721.3	-158.5	-97.3
Other Items	0.0	0.0	21.6
Income Tax	27.1	5.9	2.0
Net Income	-694.3	-152.6	-73.8
Cash Flow From Operations	18.8	-253.2	-18.6
Balance Sheet (000's)			
Cash & Equivalents	370.1	132.7	n.a.
Total Current Assets	1,036.2	367.4	n.a.
Fixed Assets, Net	65.3	36.9	n.a.
Total Assets	1,368.3	437.1	n.a.
Total Current Liabilities	125.3	80.1	n.a.
Long-Term Debt	0.0	0.0	n.a.
Stockholders' Equity	1,243.0	299.1	n.a.
Performance & Financial Condition			
Return on Total Revenues %	-65.72	-30.15	n.a.
Return on Avg Stockholders' Equity %	-90.04	n.a.	n.a.
Return on Average Assets %	-76.91	n.a.	n.a.
Current Ratio	8.27	4.59	n.a.
Debt / Equity %	n.a.	n.a.	n.a.

Compound Growth %'s	EPS % n.a.	Net Income % n.a.	Total Revenues % 210.74

Comments

The Company declared a 2 for 1 stock split on January 15, 1997. All per share amounts have been restated for consistency. The Company is off and running. Revenues for the three months ended March 31, 1997, were $22.2 million. Profits of $6.5 million, $.40 per share, were nothing to sneeze at either. True this quarter reflects the flu season but management is confident that people will catch colds in the Southern Hemisphere as well and also plans to introduce new products and increase marketing. A private placement to raise additional capital was cancelled. Investment Classification: Speculative

Officers	Position	Ownership Information	
Guy J. Quigley	President, CEO	Number of Shares Outstanding	9,539,528
Eric H. Kaytes	VP - Finance, CFO	Market Capitalization	$ 89,385,377
Charles A. Phillips	Vice President, COO	Frequency of Dividends	n.a.
Robert L. Pollack	Other	Number of Shareholders	253

Other Information

			Where Listed	OTC-BB
Transfer Agent	American Stock Transfer & Trust Co. New York, NY		Symbol	QGLY
Auditor	Nachum Blumenfrucht		SIC Code	2060
Market Maker	West America Securities Corp.	(800)310-9378	Employees	n.a.
	J. Alexander Securities Inc.	(800)800-2121		
Broker Dealer	Regular Stockbroker			

RF Industries, LTD

7610 Miramar Road, Bldg. 6000   San Diego, CA 92126-4202   Telephone (619)549-6340   Fax (619)549-6345

Company Description

RF Industries is engaged in the design, manufacture and distribution of coaxial connectors used in professional radio communication applications. The Company also designs and produces radio frequency links which transmit and receive control signals for the remote operation and monitoring of equipment. The Company was formed in 1979 and had its initial public offering in 1984.

	10/31/96	10/31/95	10/31/94	10/31/93
Per Share Information				
Stock Price as of 12/31	5.00	1.25	1.22	0.25
Earnings Per Share	0.18	0.07	0.39	0.06
Price / Earnings Ratio	27.78	17.86	3.13	4.17
Book Value Per Share	1.30	1.07	1.01	0.37
Price / Book Value %	384.62	116.82	120.79	67.57
Dividends Per Share	0.0	0.0	0.0	0.0
Annual Financial Data				
Operating Results (000's)				
Total Revenues	6,141.7	3,425.9	3,252.8	2,049.6
Costs & Expenses	-5,165.3	-3,150.9	-2,480.6	-1,802.1
Income Before Taxes and Other	976.4	274.9	772.2	247.5
Other Items	0.0	0.0	0.0	0.0
Income Tax	-415.0	-103.3	121.0	-24.0
Net Income	561.4	171.6	893.2	223.5
Cash Flow From Operations	212.8	30.0	459.4	253.0
Balance Sheet (000's)				
Cash & Equivalents	403.5	211.3	862.1	456.6
Total Current Assets	3,908.8	2,789.8	2,282.0	1,555.0
Fixed Assets, Net	111.8	127.1	119.0	133.5
Total Assets	4,063.5	2,955.0	2,423.5	1,695.0
Total Current Liabilities	454.3	245.1	184.9	395.8
Long-Term Debt	0.0	0.0	0.0	12.2
Stockholders' Equity	3,609.2	2,709.9	2,238.7	1,287.0
Performance & Financial Condition				
Return on Total Revenues %	9.14	5.01	27.46	10.91
Return on Avg Stockholders' Equity %	17.77	6.94	50.67	19.02
Return on Average Assets %	16.00	6.38	43.37	14.08
Current Ratio	8.60	11.38	12.34	3.93
Debt / Equity %	n.a.	n.a.	n.a.	0.94

Compound Growth %'s	EPS %	44.22	Net Income %	35.93	Total Revenues %	44.17

Comments

The Company has contracted with Hytek International, LTD., a principal shareholder, for technical and marketing services and cash in exchange for shares of the Company's stock at the rate of 200,000 shares per year. This arrangement has one year remaining. The Company posted an 80% increase in sales during 1996 and more than tripled earnings. President Howard Hill is still contemplating a NASDAQ listing but has seen the stock perform well anyway, up 400% since the first edition of Walker's Manual of Unlisted Stocks. For the six months ended April 30, 1997, revenue was $3,678,928 versus $2,179,589 a year ago. Earnings per share were $.11 as compared to $.08. Investment Classification: Growth

Officers	Position	Ownership Information	
Jack A. Benz	Chairman	Number of Shares Outstanding	2,778,191
Howard F. Hill	President, CEO	Market Capitalization	$ 13,890,955
Terry Gross	Secretary	Frequency of Dividends	n.a.
		Number of Shareholders	893

Other Information			
Transfer Agent	Continental Stock Transfer & Trust Co. New York, NY	Where Listed	OTC-BB
Auditor	J.H. Cohn LLP	Symbol	RFIL
Market Maker	Paragon Capital Corporation	(800)729-7173	SIC Code	3678
	Barber & Bronson Inc.	(800)729-7174	Employees	29
Broker Dealer	Regular Stockbroker		

RWC, Inc.

2105 S. Euclid Avenue   Bay City, MI 48707-0920   Telephone (517)684-4030   Fax (517)684-3960

Company Description

The Company designs, builds and provides parts for special machinery primarily in the automotive and appliance industries. They consider themselves to be specialists in high production automatic assembly and metal fabricating equipment. A tender offer to repurchase 60,000 shares, or about 10% of issued shares, at $10 per share was submitted to the shareholders in January, 1996. 41,295 shares were tendered. The Company acquired another 95,382 shares during January, 1997, from the Nichols family for $13.50 per share. Another tender was made in February, 1997, at $13.50 per share. The Company was formed in 1945.

	10/31/96	10/31/95	10/31/94
Per Share Information			
Stock Price as of 12/31	11.75	7.75	7.00
Earnings Per Share	4.68	-1.30	-0.67
Price / Earnings Ratio	2.51	n.a.	n.a.
Book Value Per Share	12.06	7.64	9.23
Price / Book Value %	97.43	101.44	75.84
Dividends Per Share	0.38	0.35	0.0
Annual Financial Data			
Operating Results (000's)			
Total Revenues	32,232.6	34,140.7	25,666.5
Costs & Expenses	-27,998.3	-31,476.7	-26,272.2
Income Before Taxes and Other	4,234.3	2,664.1	-605.6
Other Items	0.0	-2,522.1	0.0
Income Tax	-1,483.0	-945.0	194.0
Net Income	2,751.3	-803.1	-411.6
Cash Flow From Operations	1,304.3	6,428.6	-196.8
Balance Sheet (000's)			
Cash & Equivalents	5,361.6	5,037.2	69.3
Total Current Assets	13,165.2	11,863.6	9,707.2
Fixed Assets, Net	1,760.9	1,906.5	1,738.3
Total Assets	16,654.7	15,263.3	11,796.3
Total Current Liabilities	5,802.7	7,031.8	5,464.3
Long-Term Debt	23.8	43.7	516.7
Stockholders' Equity	6,931.2	4,592.9	5,550.1
Performance & Financial Condition			
Return on Total Revenues %	8.54	-2.35	-1.60
Return on Avg Stockholders' Equity %	47.75	-15.83	n.a.
Return on Average Assets %	17.24	-5.94	n.a.
Current Ratio	2.27	1.69	1.78
Debt / Equity %	0.34	0.95	9.31

Compound Growth %'s	EPS % n.a.	Net Income % n.a.	Total Revenues % 12.06

Comments

1995 results reflect a one-time expense of $2.5 million for postretirement benefits under new accounting principals. Without such charge, earnings were $2.79 per share. 1996 results were a record $4.68 per share, about one-half the tender price of a year ago. Management attributes the improvement to standardization of refrigerator cabinet lines and other efficiencies. Investment Classification: Value

Officers	Position	Ownership Information	
Ricard W. Glenn	President, CEO	Number of Shares Outstanding	574,944
William G. Perlberg	Secretary, Treasurer	Market Capitalization	$ 6,755,592
		Frequency of Dividends	Annual
		Number of Shareholders	Under 500

Other Information

				Where Listed	OTC-BB
Transfer Agent	Company Office			Symbol	RWCI
Auditor	Weinlander, Fitzhugh et al			SIC Code	3599
Market Maker	Hill Thompson Magid & Co., Inc	(800)631-3083		Employees	214
	PaineWebber Inc.	(800)221-5532			
Broker Dealer	OTC Specialist				
	Standard Investment	(888)783-4688	Ext: Jack		

Radio Frequency Company, Inc.

150 Dover Road   Millis, MA 02054-0158   Telephone (617)762-4900   Fax (617)762-4952

Company Description

Radio Frequency Company operates in a single segment within the electronics industry. The Company designs, manufactures and sells advanced technology, high frequency heat processing systems for the industrial market. In the last year, the Company has increased its pace in research and development. It is currently developing new high powered systems for equipment in the rapidly expanding ceramic and bulk material drying categories.

	03/29/97	03/30/96	03/25/95	03/26/94
Per Share Information				
Stock Price as of 12/31	5.00	3.00	3.25	3.00
Earnings Per Share	0.52	0.06	0.10	0.07
Price / Earnings Ratio	9.62	50.00	32.50	42.86
Book Value Per Share	4.01	3.64	3.73	3.75
Price / Book Value %	124.69	82.42	87.13	80.00
Dividends Per Share	0.16	0.16	0.16	0.16
Annual Financial Data				
Operating Results (000's)				
Total Revenues	5,512.2	3,594.0	3,375.9	3,734.4
Costs & Expenses	-4,680.5	-3,523.2	-3,240.0	-3,701.6
Income Before Taxes and Other	831.7	70.8	135.8	32.9
Other Items	0.0	0.0	0.0	43.9
Income Tax	-345.3	-12.0	-44.3	-11.3
Net Income	486.3	58.8	91.5	65.5
Cash Flow From Operations	110.8	152.1	942.3	288.6
Balance Sheet (000's)				
Cash & Equivalents	1,541.5	1,217.9	1,415.4	1,534.4
Total Current Assets	4,180.2	4,288.1	3,966.0	3,481.7
Fixed Assets, Net	397.0	575.1	604.2	499.2
Total Assets	4,648.3	5,237.0	4,871.2	4,023.8
Total Current Liabilities	973.9	1,902.4	1,467.6	609.2
Long-Term Debt	0.0	0.0	0.0	0.0
Stockholders' Equity	3,647.4	3,306.5	3,392.2	3,414.6
Performance & Financial Condition				
Return on Total Revenues %	8.82	1.64	2.71	1.75
Return on Avg Stockholders' Equity %	13.99	1.76	2.69	1.90
Return on Average Assets %	9.84	1.16	2.06	1.56
Current Ratio	4.29	2.25	2.70	5.72
Debt / Equity %	n.a.	n.a.	n.a.	n.a.

Compound Growth %'s	EPS %	95.12	Net Income %	95.13	Total Revenues %	13.86

Comments

The new line of standard RF Processing equipment embodying the latest state-of-the-art features for the ceramic, converting, baking, and textile industries is superior to the competition, according to management. We are told to expect an increase in Company market share. We can't help but be impressed with 1997 results which posted a 55% increase in revenues and a 767% increase in the bottom line. Investment Classification: Growth

Officers	Position	Ownership Information	
Melvyn H. Harris, M.D.	Chairman, Treasurer	Number of Shares Outstanding	910,575
Thomas W. James	President, CEO	Market Capitalization	$ 4,552,875
Richard M. Cotter	Controller	Frequency of Dividends	Annual
		Number of Shareholders	Under 500

Other Information

Transfer Agent	American Stock Transfer & Trust Company New York, NY		Where Listed	OTC-BB
Auditor	Andrew K. Baxter, CPA		Symbol	RFRQ
Market Maker	H.C. Wainwright & Co., Inc.	(800)225-6790	SIC Code	3567
	Carr Securities Corporation	(800)221-2243	Employees	33
Broker Dealer	Regular Stockbroker			
	Norman Kadehjian - Wainwright	(800)225-6790		

Ragar Corp.

100 Maiden Lane, 17th Floor   New York, NY 10038   Telephone (212)898-8888   Fax (212)898-8800

Company Description

Ragar Corp. sells and installs floor coverings for the residential housing market in Nevada. The Company was organized in 1988 to seek a suitable business for acquisition or merger. An initial public offering was completed in 1990. In June, 1995, the Company acquired all of the outstanding stock of Carpet Barns Holdings, Inc., in exchange for 13,217,750 shares of its common stock.

	12/31/96	12/31/95	12/31/94	12/31/93
Per Share Information				
Stock Price	2.25	3.88	n.a.	n.a.
Earnings Per Share	0.0	0.20	n.a.	n.a.
Price / Earnings Ratio	n.a.	19.40	n.a.	n.a.
Book Value Per Share	0.29	0.25	n.a.	n.a.
Price / Book Value %	775.86	1,552.00	n.a.	n.a.
Dividends Per Share	n.a.	0.0	n.a.	n.a.
Annual Financial Data				
Operating Results (000's)				
Total Revenues	42,432.8	40,382.5	42,551.7	34,572.9
Costs & Expenses	-41,524.9	-35,901.4	-36,975.6	-33,451.6
Income Before Taxes and Other	907.9	4,481.1	4,888.3	1,113.8
Other Items	0.0	0.0	0.0	0.0
Income Tax	-317.0	-1,525.2	-1,662.0	-378.7
Net Income	590.9	2,955.9	3,226.3	735.1
Cash Flow From Operations	4,308.3	5,223.1	6,074.4	1,185.9
Balance Sheet (000's)				
Cash & Equivalents	335.1	693.4	n.a.	n.a.
Total Current Assets	4,882.6	4,993.4	n.a.	n.a.
Fixed Assets, Net	549.3	415.7	n.a.	n.a.
Total Assets	23,143.6	24,084.5	n.a.	n.a.
Total Current Liabilities	15,630.8	8,750.0	n.a.	n.a.
Long-Term Debt	110.8	8,811.6	n.a.	n.a.
Stockholders' Equity	4,193.7	3,727.7	n.a.	n.a.
Performance & Financial Condition				
Return on Total Revenues %	1.39	7.32	7.71	2.13
Return on Avg Stockholders' Equity %	14.92	n.a.	n.a.	n.a.
Return on Average Assets %	2.50	n.a.	n.a.	n.a.
Current Ratio	0.31	0.57	1.23	n.a.
Debt / Equity %	2.64	236.38	22.07	n.a.

Compound Growth %'s	EPS %	n.a.	Net Income %	-7.02	Total Revenues %	7.07

Comments

1995 operating results include the seven months ended December 31, 1995 (under new ownership) and the five months ended June 1, 1995 (under former management). The years ended December 31, 1994 and 1993 are for a predecessor company. The results of operations are not comparable to the predecessor operations due to the amortization of intangible assets and interest expense incurred on the acquisition debt. Balance sheets, per share information and statistics are not presented prior to 1995, due to lack of comparability. The Company is going to have to figure a way it can generate income to reduce its massive short-term debt. First quarter results of 1997 were not much help as revenues were off 5.2% from the previous years pace. Investment Classification: Speculative

Officers	Position	Ownership Information	
Philip A. Herman	Chairman, President	Number of Shares Outstanding	14,569,586
William Poccia	CFO	Market Capitalization	$ 32,781,569
Gary Peiffer	Secretary	Frequency of Dividends	n.a.
		Number of Shareholders	369

Other Information				
Transfer Agent	Corporate Stock Transfer, Inc. Denver, CO		Where Listed	OTC-BB
Auditor	McGladrey & Pullen LLP		Symbol	RAGC
Market Maker	A.J. Michaels & Co.	(516)231-3686	SIC Code	5713
	M.H. Meyerson & Co., Inc.	(800)333-3113	Employees	110
Broker Dealer	Regular Stockbroker			

This page intentionally left blank.

Rancho Vista National Bank

1385 East Vista Way   Vista, CA 92084   Telephone (619)631-2500   Fax (619)631-2555

Company Description

The Bank operates two branches in San Diego County and one branch in Orange County, California. The Bank's primary source of revenue is providing loans to customers who are predominately small and middle-market businesses and individuals. In 1995, Rancho Vista National Bank was honored in Washington, D.C. for its unique partnership with the Vista Community Clinic and their Funds for Moms program. Fund for Moms provides zero-interest loans to expectant mothers for medical care to ensure healthy births. These mothers do not otherwise qualify for assistance or traditional loans. The Bank is currently celebrating its 15th anniversary.

	12/31/96	12/31/95	12/31/94	12/31/93
Per Share Information				
Stock Price	16.00	10.88	7.05	6.72
Earnings Per Share	1.88	1.62	0.37	0.14
Price / Earnings Ratio	8.51	6.72	19.05	48.00
Book Value Per Share	16.76	14.89	12.99	12.73
Price / Book Value %	95.47	73.07	54.27	52.79
Dividends Per Share	0.0	0.0	0.0	0.0
Annual Financial Data				
Operating Results (000's)				
Net Interest Income	5,195.4	5,592.2	5,572.0	4,190.0
Loan Loss Provision	-195.0	-461.4	-491.0	-24.0
Non-Interest Income	956.3	2,000.6	2,700.0	3,252.0
Non-Interest Expense	-4,366.9	-6,060.8	-7,603.0	-7,386.0
Income Before Taxes and Other	1,589.8	1,070.6	178.0	32.0
Other Items	0.0	0.0	0.0	0.0
Income Tax	-615.0	-295.0	0.0	37.0
Net Income	974.8	775.6	178.0	69.0
Balance Sheet (000's)				
Cash & Securities	30,341.4	32,937.7	23,038.7	22,960.0
Loans, Net	71,734.1	54,365.2	66,018.7	56,400.0
Total Assets	104,423.6	89,994.7	91,931.8	82,390.0
Deposits	95,195.2	82,130.7	80,526.1	74,839.0
Stockholders' Equity	8,098.7	7,106.4	6,201.6	6,074.0
Performance & Financial Oondition				
Return on Avg Stockholders' Equity %	12.82	11.66	2.90	1.14
Return on Average Assets %	1.00	0.85	0.20	0.08
Equity to Assets %	7.76	7.90	6.75	7.37
Net Interest Margin	n.a.	n.a.	n.a.	n.a.
Reserve as a % of Problem Loans	92.11	81.33	27.93	29.90

Compound Growth %'s	EPS % n.a.	Net Income % n.a.	Net Interest Income % 7.43

Comments

The Company declared an 8% stock dividend in 1996 and 5% stock dividends in each of the preceding three years presented. All per share amounts have been restated for consistency. As 1993 earnings were extremely low, we elected not to present the compound earnings growth rates which uses 1993 as the base year. This young bank boasts thirteen consecutive years of profit and now has assets above $100 million for the first time. Loan and deposit growth are expected to continue at 15% or better. Investment Classification: Value

Officers	Position	Ownership Information	
Judy Stewart	President, CEO	Number of Shares Outstanding	483,286
Richard Revier	Exec VP, Sr Loan Officer	Market Capitalization	$ 7,732,576
Karen Barberio	Vice President	Frequency of Dividends	n.a.
James Burgess	Vice President, CFO	Number of Shareholders	285
Nancy Gebhardt	Vice President	Where Listed / Symbol	OTC-BB / RVSA

Other Information			Loan Mix	%
Transfer Agent	Harris Trust & Savings Bank Chicago, IL		R/E Mortgages	78.0
Auditor	Dayton & Associates		Construction	16.2
Market Maker	Crowell Weedon & Co.	(800)421-8909	Commerical	4.3
	GBS Financial Corp.	(800)765-5558	Consumer	1.5
Broker Dealer	OTC Specialist			
	Hoefer & Arnett, Retail	(800)346-5544 Ext: Lisa		

Rand McNally

8255 North Central Park Avenue   Skokie, IL 60076-2908   Telephone (847)329-8100   Fax (847)673-0813

Company Description

Rand McNally is the world's leading provider of geographic products and information. During 1996, it divested a number of other businesses related to its core business including manufacturing-related operations. Rand McNally, having a history that goes back to 1856, surprised the world with its April 30, 1997 announcement: the Company is up for sale. A desire for future liquidity on the part of family shareholders and attractive valuations for media properties were among the reasons cited. Rand McNally claims that it is a private company even though shares are freely traded in the over-the-counter market. Please take a moment to savor the richness of this magnificent company on the following page.

	12/31/96	12/31/95	12/31/94	12/31/93
Per Share Information				
Stock Price	300.00	345.00	154.00	150.00
Earnings Per Share	9.13	11.06	13.07	6.62
Price / Earnings Ratio	32.86	31.19	11.78	22.66
Book Value Per Share	101.57	108.13	103.24	93.48
Price / Book Value %	295.36	319.06	149.17	160.46
Dividends Per Share	4.60	4.60	4.40	4.20
Annual Financial Data				
Operating Results (000's)				
Total Revenues	164,548.0	145,765.0	438,525.0	395,288.0
Costs & Expenses	-147,656.0	-128,671.0	-410,989.0	-376,177.0
Income Before Taxes and Other	16,892.0	17,878.0	25,124.0	7,797.0
Other Items	-364.0	0.0	0.0	1,487.0
Income Tax	-5,680.0	-5,243.0	-10,870.0	-1,894.0
Net Income	10,848.0	12,635.0	14,254.0	7,390.0
Cash Flow From Operations	n.a.	n.a.	n.a.	n.a.
Balance Sheet (000's)				
Cash & Equivalents	27,545.0	7,556.0	30,010.0	28,750.0
Total Current Assets	192,522.0	176,173.0	182,039.0	153,200.0
Fixed Assets, Net	88,739.0	96,754.0	100,491.0	101,950.0
Total Assets	322,956.0	314,232.0	315,716.0	291,100.0
Total Current Liabilities	87,954.0	75,987.0	84,584.0	62,150.0
Long-Term Debt	50,600.0	66,735.0	67,452.0	70,850.0
Stockholders' Equity	120,681.0	119,639.0	112,592.0	104,350.0
Performance & Financial Condition				
Return on Total Revenues %	6.59	8.67	3.25	1.87
Return on Avg Stockholders' Equity %	9.03	10.88	13.14	n.a.
Return on Average Assets %	3.40	4.01	4.70	n.a.
Current Ratio	2.19	2.32	2.15	2.47
Debt / Equity %	41.93	55.78	59.91	67.90

Compound Growth %'s	EPS %	11.31	Net Income %	13.65	Total Revenues %	n.a.

Comments

There is no indication in the shareholder's report that these numbers have been audited nor are the financial statements as complete as what are traditionally found. Financial information was restated for 1995 to exclude discontinued operations. A number of divisions were sold during 1996 and the Book Service Group was sold in January, 1997. Profits on these sales will be in excess of $25 million after taxes but the final price has not yet been determined. The remaining discontinued operations are anticipated to be sold by mid-1997. Timing of the sale of the core business is not known. Investment Classification: Value

Officers	Position	Ownership Information	
Andrew McNally IV	Chairman, CEO	Number of Shares Outstanding	1,188,171
John S. Bakalar	President, COO	Market Capitalization	$ 356,451,300
Edward C. McNally	Secretary	Frequency of Dividends	Quarterly
		Number of Shareholders	Under 500

Other Information

Transfer Agent	First Trust of Illinois, N.A. Chicago, IL		Where Listed	OTC-BB
Auditor	Not indicated		Symbol	RNMC
Market Maker	Howe Barnes Investments, Inc.	(800)621-2364	SIC Code	2740
	Herzog, Heine, Geduld, Inc.	(800)221-3600	Employees	5000
Broker Dealer	Regular Stockbroker			

Map Making

William Rand and Andrew McNally opened their first print shop on Chicago's Lake Street in 1856, five years before the beginning of the American Civil War. Recognizing that Chicago had become a booming rail center, Messrs. Rand and McNally decided to produce railroad tickets, timetables and other transportation related items. Their business grew and prospered, even side stepping the worst of the Great Chicago Fire of 1871, which put them out of business for only three days. The next year saw the production of Rand McNally's first map, and in 1880 they began to manufacture globes and maps for schools.

The Company had grown to 675 employees by 1899 when, after forty-three years in business with his co-founder, William Rand sold his share of the Company to Andrew McNally. By 1905, both of the founders had passed away (within a year of each other), leaving their heirs to carry on.

And this they did. Within two years, the Company was producing the first *photo-auto guides*, predecessors to modern road maps. These included written directions and photographs of landmarks found along routes covered by the map. Andrew McNally II even managed to supply some of the photos used to illustrate the Chicago-Milwaukee guide while on his honeymoon!

The age of the automobile had obviously arrived, but road maps were still quite cumbersome to use, relying on long road names and difficult graphics to identify highways. The development in 1917 of a system for numbering highways was a welcome enhancement of Rand McNally's product and undoubtedly helped popularize automobile touring in America. Gulf Oil teamed up with the Company to this end as well, distributing Rand McNally maps at its service stations.

While the rise of the automobile greatly augmented the demand for Rand McNally products, other markets existed for their maps as well. Charles Lindbergh even put the Company's product to use, navigating the land portion of his famed transatlantic flight of 1927 with Rand McNally maps at his side. By World War II and Germany's invasion of Poland, public demand for European maps had reached such a pitch that the Company's presses operated overtime for the war's duration.

Today, Rand McNally continues in its business of providing diversified products and services. The Company still supplies transportation tickets and related items for ground and now air travel through its Docu-Systems segment. In addition, they now have three other segments, including Book Services, related to book manufacture; Publishing, which provides complete global geographic information; and Media Services, a provider of digital packaging solutions. As the twentieth century draws to a close, they are well prepared, it seems, to enter into the third century in which they will be doing business.

Randall Bearings, Inc.

Greenlawn Ave. and Lake St.   Lima, OH 45802-1258   Telephone (419)223-1075   Fax (419)228-0200

Company Description

The Company manufactures various types of bearings. It was organized in 1918 and went public in 1946 with an offering of 100,000 shares at $3.50 per share. The Company is one of many parties that have been named as a potentially responsible party under Superfund legislation with respect to the Jack's Creek/Sitken Smelting superfund site. Randall is the supplier of materials sold to Sitken Smelting and has no direct involvement in the site.

	12/31/96	12/31/95	12/31/94	12/31/93
Per Share Information				
Stock Price	9.50	8.69	4.75	4.75
Earnings Per Share	-1.17	1.07	1.10	0.80
Price / Earnings Ratio	n.a.	8.12	4.32	5.94
Book Value Per Share	12.14	13.77	12.93	12.03
Price / Book Value %	78.25	63.11	36.74	39.48
Dividends Per Share	0.28	0.23	0.20	0.20
Annual Financial Data				
Operating Results (000's)				
Total Revenues	8,796.2	8,655.2	7,600.4	6,430.8
Costs & Expenses	-9,402.9	-7,751.5	-6,709.1	-5,784.2
Income Before Taxes and Other	-606.7	753.0	752.6	526.7
Other Items	0.0	0.0	0.0	0.0
Income Tax	88.4	-277.6	-266.4	-167.7
Net Income	-518.3	475.4	486.1	359.0
Cash Flow From Operations	n.a.	n.a.	n.a.	n.a.
Balance Sheet (000's)				
Cash & Equivalents	1,122.4	757.2	909.4	1,083.6
Total Current Assets	4,850.1	4,699.7	4,531.4	4,046.9
Fixed Assets, Net	2,239.0	2,565.4	2,480.5	2,255.9
Total Assets	7,136.8	7,309.8	7,053.7	6,368.5
Total Current Liabilities	971.4	773.4	876.7	690.9
Long-Term Debt	133.5	112.2	183.0	132.1
Stockholders' Equity	5,378.4	6,121.2	5,748.1	5,350.9
Performance & Financial Condition				
Return on Total Revenues %	-5.89	5.49	6.40	5.58
Return on Avg Stockholders' Equity %	-9.01	8.01	8.76	6.88
Return on Average Assets %	-7.18	6.62	7.24	5.70
Current Ratio	4.99	6.08	5.17	5.86
Debt / Equity %	2.48	1.83	3.18	2.47

Compound Growth %'s	EPS % n.a.	Net Income % n.a.	Total Revenues % 11.01

Comments

The Company accrued an estimated $254,000 liability related to the environmental remediation problem noted above. This combined with a reduction in the estimated useful lives of equipment purchased between 1989 and 1993 caused red ink. Management reports good sales in the first quarter of 1997 and foresees a smooth growth path for the next five years. The Company is in excellent financial condition and has strong growth over the years for which we have reports. With the stock trading at below book value, it is clear that low visibility has a real impact on the pricing of a security. Investment Classification: Value

Officers	Position	Ownership Information	
B G. Dickerson	Chairman, President	Number of Shares Outstanding	443,016
R R. Harris	Secretary, Treasurer	Market Capitalization	$ 4,208,652
W R. Buchanan	VP - Manufacturing	Frequency of Dividends	Quarterly
		Number of Shareholders	Under 500

Other Information

Transfer Agent	The First National Bank of Chicago Chicago, IL		Where Listed	OTC-BB
Auditor	Rea & Associates Inc.		Symbol	RBRG
Market Maker	Robotti & Co., Inc.	(212)986-4800	SIC Code	3490
	Carr Securities Corporation	(800)221-2243	Employees	65
Broker Dealer	Regular Stockbroker			

Ravens Metal Products, Inc.

861 East Tallmadge Avenue   Akron, OH 44310   Telephone (216)630-4528   Fax (216)630-4535

Company Description

The Company designs, manufactures, and sells aluminum truck trailers and bodies, including dump trailers and bodies and flatbed trailers used in the transportation industry. These products are sold direct to customers and through a nationwide network of dealerships. The Company also sells a variety of after-market parts for trucks and trailers. In June, 1995, the Company commenced production at a 19.6 acre site in Kent, Ohio. Plans are being made to expand the site from its current 75,000 square feet of ground space. Ravens Metal Products was formed in 1956.

	03/31/96	03/31/95	03/31/94	03/31/93
Per Share Information				
Stock Price as of 12/31	5.00	8.52	8.52	5.00
Earnings Per Share	0.10	0.92	1.04	0.53
Price / Earnings Ratio	50.00	9.26	8.19	9.43
Book Value Per Share	1.77	1.68	0.71	-0.26
Price / Book Value %	282.49	507.14	1,200.00	n.a.
Dividends Per Share	0.0	0.0	0.0	0.0
Annual Financial Data				
Operating Results (000's)				
Total Revenues	40,352.9	42,160.6	25,797.6	20,038.9
Costs & Expenses	-40,047.4	-39,398.6	-24,191.7	-19,354.9
Income Before Taxes and Other	305.5	2,762.0	1,605.9	684.0
Other Items	0.0	0.0	0.0	531.0
Income Tax	-111.0	-960.8	423.2	-284.0
Net Income	194.5	1,801.2	2,029.1	931.0
Cash Flow From Operations	-1,864.2	685.3	1,235.5	193.7
Balance Sheet (000's)				
Cash & Equivalents	441.9	394.0	606.1	587.7
Total Current Assets	11,949.0	9,773.3	6,040.2	4,825.1
Fixed Assets, Net	6,985.0	5,896.8	2,195.6	2,246.5
Total Assets	21,886.5	19,405.2	8,420.3	7,168.7
Total Current Liabilities	6,049.0	6,090.4	3,471.3	3,400.7
Long-Term Debt	6,708.0	9,716.1	3,129.4	3,921.6
Stockholders' Equity	3,440.1	3,267.1	1,373.3	-496.4
Performance & Financial Condition				
Return on Total Revenues %	0.48	4.27	7.87	4.65
Return on Avg Stockholders' Equity %	5.80	77.63	462.79	n.a.
Return on Average Assets %	0.94	12.95	26.03	14.72
Current Ratio	1.98	1.60	1.74	1.42
Debt / Equity %	194.99	297.40	227.87	n.a.

Compound Growth %'s	EPS %	-42.64	Net Income %	-40.66	Total Revenues %	26.28

Comments

The Company executed a 1 for 4 reverse split in 1996. All per share amounts were adjusted for consistency. During the year ended March 31, 1994, the Company realized a gain of $565,000 on the settlement of disputes and collection of life insurance proceeds relating to a previous chairman of the Company. Officers and directors, as a group, owned 88.8% of the Company's outstanding common shares at June 25, 1996. 1996 earnings declined due to costs associated with the startup of the Kent facility and a decline in demand for trailers. However, for the nine months ended December 31, 1996, the Company had sales of $32.7 million and net earnings of $852,000 ($.44 per share) as compared to $28.4 million and a net loss of $28,000 in the comparable period of 1995. Investment Classification: Speculative

Officers	Position	Ownership Information	
Lowell P. Morgan	President	Number of Shares Outstanding	1,943,525
Jacob Pollock	CEO, Treasurer	Market Capitalization	$ 9,717,625
Nicholas T. George	Secretary	Frequency of Dividends	n.a.
John J. Stitz	Vice President, CFO	Number of Shareholders	4,000

Other Information			
Transfer Agent	Company Office	Where Listed	OTC-BB
Auditor	Coopers & Lybrand L.L.P.	Symbol	RVMP
Market Maker	J.C. Bradford & Co.	(800)522-1927	SIC Code	3715
	Carr Securities Corporation	(800)221-2243	Employees	215
Broker Dealer	Regular Stockbroker		

Real Silk Investments, Incorporated

445 N. Pennsylvania St., #500   Indianapolis, IN 46204-1800   Telephone (317)632-7359   Fax (317)632-5104

Company Description

Real Silk Investments is registered under the Investment Company Act of 1940 as a diversified, closed-end, management investment company and, except for certain gains accruing before the election to be a regulated investment company, is not taxed on its income. The Company makes distributions to its shareholders of all cash flow, exclusive of reinvesting funds, as investments are sold. Investments are predominantly a diversified portfolio of common stocks in approximately 70 different companies.

	12/31/96	12/31/95	12/31/94	12/31/93
Per Share Information				
Stock Price	440.00	380.00	300.00	300.00
Earnings Per Share	55.61	85.18	-12.10	73.45
Price / Earnings Ratio	7.91	4.46	n.a.	4.08
Book Value Per Share	615.41	575.03	505.13	531.15
Price / Book Value %	71.50	66.08	59.39	56.48
Dividends Per Share	15.23	15.28	13.92	13.15
Annual Financial Data				
Operating Results (000's)				
Total Revenues	9,816.0	14,414.6	-2,794.5	n.a.
Costs & Expenses	-377.0	-357.3	-317.1	n.a.
Income Before Taxes and Other	9,439.0	14,057.3	-3,111.6	n.a.
Other Items	0.0	0.0	0.0	n.a.
Income Tax	-281.4	-29.7	1,118.8	n.a.
Net Income	9,157.5	14,027.6	-1,992.8	n.a.
Cash Flow From Operations	n.a.	n.a.	n.a.	n.a.
Balance Sheet (000's)				
Cash & Equivalents	12.3	10.4	52.1	n.a.
Total Current Assets	356.0	402.2	392.2	n.a.
Fixed Assets, Net	42.1	44.7	50.6	n.a.
Total Assets	114,485.0	107,555.7	96,038.9	n.a.
Total Current Liabilities	161.1	10.5	34.7	n.a.
Long-Term Debt	0.0	0.0	0.0	n.a.
Stockholders' Equity	101,347.3	94,697.9	83,186.7	n.a.
Performance & Financial Condition				
Return on Total Revenues %	93.29	97.32	71.31	n.a.
Return on Avg Stockholders' Equity %	9.34	15.77	n.a.	n.a.
Return on Average Assets %	8.25	13.78	n.a.	n.a.
Current Ratio	2.21	38.29	11.29	n.a.
Debt / Equity %	n.a.	n.a.	n.a.	n.a.

Compound Growth %'s	EPS % n.a.	Net Income % n.a.	Total Revenues % n.a.

Comments

Compound growth rates were not calculated because of the nature of the business. Operating expenses are less than 0.33% of total assets, an admirable rate for even the simplest of mutual funds. As of December 31, 1996, the Company's largest group of investments were in the financial sector (18.21%), industrial sector (17.59%), energy/natural resources sector (10.88%), and consumer goods sector (10.48%). Investment Classification: Value

Officers	Position	Ownership Information	
Daniel R. Efroymson	President, Treasurer	Number of Shares Outstanding	164,683
L A. Cox	Secretary	Market Capitalization	$ 72,460,520
Loralei M. Efroymson	Vice President	Frequency of Dividends	Quarterly
M A. Singer	Other	Number of Shareholders	Under 500
J D. Hagan	Other		

Other Information

Transfer Agent	ChaseMellon Shareholder Services Ridgefield Park, NJ		Where Listed	OTC-BB
Auditor	KPMG Peat Marwick LLP		Symbol	RSHM
Market Maker	McDonald & Company Securities	(216)443-2350	SIC Code	6799
	Herzog, Heine, Geduld, Inc.	(800)221-3600	Employees	10
Broker Dealer	OTC Specialist			
	Standard Investment	(888)783-4688 Ext: Jack		

Red Oak Hereford Farms, Inc.

P.O. Box 456   Red Oak, IA 51566   Telephone (712)623-9224   Fax (712)623-4533

Company Description

Red Oak Hereford Farms, Inc., formerly Wild Wings, Inc., is engaged in the business of selling premium, branded, fresh beef to retail and food service markets located predominately in the southwest and midwest United States. The Company was a virtual shell that was used by Mid-Ag, LLC to take its recently formed operation public without a formal registration with the Securities and Exchange Commission. On May 27, 1997, the Company announced the acquisition of Midland Cattle Company in exchange for 1,538,462 shares of common stock. Midland, which has been in business for ten years, will add $65 million in annual revenue to operations.

	03/15/97
Per Share Information	
Stock Price	6.50
Earnings Per Share	-0.05
Price / Earnings Ratio	n.a.
Book Value Per Share	-0.05
Price / Book Value %	n.a.
Dividends Per Share	0.0
Annual Financial Data	
Operating Results (000's)	
Total Revenues	7,169.5
Costs & Expenses	-7,683.9
Income Before Taxes and Other	-514.4
Other Items	0.0
Income Tax	0.0
Net Income	-514.4
Cash Flow From Operations	-461.8
Balance Sheet (000's)	
Cash & Equivalents	0.0
Total Current Assets	2,698.7
Fixed Assets, Net	129.5
Total Assets	2,976.9
Total Current Liabilities	2,705.8
Long-Term Debt	477.6
Stockholders' Equity	-506.5
Performance & Financial Condition	
Return on Total Revenues %	-7.17
Return on Avg Stockholders' Equity %	n.a.
Return on Average Assets %	n.a.
Current Ratio	1.00
Debt / Equity %	n.a.

Compound Growth %'s	EPS %	n.a.	Net Income %	n.a.	Total Revenues %	n.a.

Comments

Financial reports have not been provided for Mid-Ag. The promotional literature claims that revenues of $30 million in 1995 doubled to $60 million in 1996. Yet revenue for the first 2.5 months of 1997 was only $7.1 million. The Company claims that this is due to fewer barbecues during the winter. Could this be a bunch of bull? Not so, according to the American Hereford Association, a non-profit organization that promotes beef. They say Red Oak is for real. Investment Classification: Speculative

Officers	Position	Ownership Information	
Gordon Reisinger	President	Number of Shares Outstanding	10,960,000
Charles Kilbe	Secretary	Market Capitalization	$ 71,240,000
John Derner	Vice President, Treasurer	Frequency of Dividends	n.a.
David H. Ellicott	Other	Number of Shareholders	Under 500

Other Information			
Transfer Agent	Company Office	Where Listed	Order Matching Only
Auditor	Not indicated	Symbol	n.a.
Market Maker	None	SIC Code	2010
		Employees	n.a.
Broker Dealer	None		

Redlands Centennial Bank

233 East State Steet   Redlands, CA 92373   Telephone (909)798-3611   Fax (909)335-2363

Company Description

Redlands Centennial Bank began operations on August 1, 1990, after raising $2 million by selling common shares at $5 per share. In 1994 the Bank reported its first annual profit. Management was particularly proud of becoming a full-paying taxpayer in 1995, which is certainly one way to measure success. Redlands is a suburban community of 67,000 residents and is about six miles east of San Bernardino, California.

	12/31/96	12/31/95	12/31/94	12/31/93
Per Share Information				
Stock Price	10.50	9.00	7.00	6.00
Earnings Per Share	1.11	0.90	0.51	-0.38
Price / Earnings Ratio	9.46	10.00	13.73	n.a.
Book Value Per Share	9.24	8.13	6.83	6.71
Price / Book Value %	113.64	1.03	102.49	89.42
Dividends Per Share	0.0	0.0	0.0	0.0
Annual Financial Data				
Operating Results (000's)				
Net Interest Income	2,286.2	2,207.4	1,927.6	1,558.9
Loan Loss Provision	0.0	-116.0	-191.0	-500.0
Non-Interest Income	300.3	346.9	304.3	233.1
Non-Interest Expense	-1,755.5	-1,777.4	-1,771.7	-1,607.7
Income Before Taxes and Other	830.9	660.9	269.2	-315.6
Other Items	0.0	0.0	0.0	0.0
Income Tax	-303.9	-232.7	-26.8	132.2
Net Income	527.0	428.2	242.4	-183.4
Balance Sheet (000's)				
Cash & Securities	21,521.1	15,264.4	17,452.4	11,152.1
Loans, Net	24,571.3	22,303.9	19,820.6	18,775.8
Total Assets	48,598.6	38,497.4	38,017.0	30,983.7
Deposits	43,915.4	34,387.1	34,685.4	27,715.0
Stockholders' Equity	4,394.8	3,858.1	3,245.4	3,185.8
Performance & Financial Condition				
Return on Avg Stockholders' Equity %	12.77	12.05	7.54	-5.61
Return on Average Assets %	1.21	1.12	0.70	-0.59
Equity to Assets %	9.04	10.02	8.54	10.28
Net Interest Margin	6.10	6.31	5.80	5.48
Reserve as a % of Problem Loans	746.02	216.38	734.28	n.a.

Compound Growth %'s	EPS %	47.53	Net Income %	47.44	Net Interest Income %	13.61

Comments

Redlands Centennial Bank declared stock dividends of 8%, 5% and 5% in 1996, 1995 and 1994, respectively. All per share amounts were adjusted for consistency. The Bank had net operating loss carryovers to offset most taxes through 1994. Compound earnings growth rates will be distorted because profitable operations were first reached in 1994 as well as the impact of income tax reporting. No addition was required for the reserve for loan losses which was the major factor in the earnings increase of 23%. Management has hired a number of professionals who will focus on the SBA loan market in 1997. Investment Classification: Growth & Value

Officers	Position	Ownership Information	
Edmond R. McCormick	President, CEO	Number of Shares Outstanding	475,745
Sharon Roberts	Senior VP	Market Capitalization	$ 4,995,323
Roy D. Lewis	Senior VP	Frequency of Dividends	n.a.
Beth Sanders	Senior VP, CFO	Number of Shareholders	365
Sally Flanders	Secretary	Where Listed / Symbol	OTC-PS / REDD

Other Information		Loan Mix	%
Transfer Agent	First Interstate Bank Los Angeles, CA	Commerical	67.3
Auditor	Hutchinson and Bloodgood LLP	Consumer	32.7
Market Maker	Wedbush Securities, Inc. (800)421-0251		
	Sutro & Co., Incorporated (800)227-4422		
Broker Dealer	OTC Specialist		
	Gorian Thornes, Inc. (800)888-7551		

Reinhold Industries Inc.

12827 East Imperial Highway   Santa Fe Springs, CA 90670-4713   Telephone (562)944-3281   Fax (562)944-7238

Company Description

Reinhold Industries, Inc. is a manufacturer of advanced custom composite components and sheet molding compounds for a variety of applications. Reinhold derives revenues from the United States defense contract industry, the aerospace industry and other commercial industries. Reinhold was owned by Keene Corporation from 1984 until 1993, at which time Keene filed for bankruptcy protection because of the demands on Keene of thousands of asbestos-related lawsuits which named Keene as a party. On July 31, 1996, Keene consummated its plan of reorganization and Reinhold was merged into Keene with a subsequent name change back to Reinhold.

	03/31/97	12/31/96	12/31/95	12/31/94
Per Share Information				
Stock Price	3.56	3.25	n.a.	n.a.
Earnings Per Share	0.20	0.20	n.a.	n.a.
Price / Earnings Ratio	n.a.	16.25	n.a.	n.a.
Book Value Per Share	2.90	2.86	n.a.	n.a.
Price / Book Value %	122.76	113.64	n.a.	n.a.
Dividends Per Share	0.0	0.0	n.a.	n.a.
Annual Financial Data				
Operating Results (000's)				
Total Revenues	3,286.0	14,279.0	13,324.0	16,932.0
Costs & Expenses	-3,203.0	-13,103.0	-12,954.0	-13,494.0
Income Before Taxes and Other	83.0	-1,963.0	-9,122.0	-7,792.0
Other Items	0.0	0.0	0.0	0.0
Income Tax	-9.0	-235.0	139.0	0.0
Net Income	74.0	-2,198.0	-8,983.0	-7,792.0
Cash Flow From Operations	374.0	-7,714.0	n.a.	n.a.
Balance Sheet (000's)				
Cash & Equivalents	1,275.0	1,522.0	n.a.	n.a.
Total Current Assets	5,038.0	5,544.0	n.a.	n.a.
Fixed Assets, Net	5,151.0	5,158.0	n.a.	n.a.
Total Assets	11,994.0	12,540.0	n.a.	n.a.
Total Current Liabilities	1,327.0	1,942.0	n.a.	n.a.
Long-Term Debt	0.0	2,591.0	n.a.	n.a.
Stockholders' Equity	5,793.0	5,719.0	n.a.	n.a.
Performance & Financial Condition				
Return on Total Revenues %	2.25	-15.39	-67.42	-46.02
Return on Avg Stockholders' Equity %	1.29	-9.21	-19.27	-14.08
Return on Average Assets %	.60	-5.69	-12.83	-8.21
Current Ratio	3.80	2.85	n.a.	n.a.
Debt / Equity %	n.a.	45.31	n.a.	n.a.

Compound Growth %'s	EPS % n.a.	Net Income % n.a.	Total Revenues % n.a.

Comments

There was a substantial restatement of the Company's balance sheet at July 31, 1996. Earnings per share for 1996 are based on the earnings from August 1, 1996 through December 31, 1996. We also displayed the results for the first quarter of 1997. Management reports that with the bankruptcy behind them, future growth appears positive for all business units. Investment Classification: Speculative

Officers	Position	Ownership Information	
Michael T. Furry	President, CEO	Number of Shares Outstanding	1,998,956
David M. Blakesley	VP - Finance, Secretary	Market Capitalization	$ 7,116,283
		Frequency of Dividends	n.a.
		Number of Shareholders	n.a.

Other Information			
Transfer Agent	Continental Stock Transfer & Trust Co. New York, NY	Where Listed	OTC-BB
Auditor	KPMG Peat Marwick LLP	Symbol	RNHDA
Market Maker	Robotti & Co., Inc. (212)986-0800	SIC Code	3728
	Herzog, Heine, Geduld, Inc. (800)221-3600	Employees	n.a.
Broker Dealer	Regular Stockbroker		

Reo Plastics, Inc.

11850-93rd Avenue North   Maple Grove, MN 55369-3633   Telephone (612)425-4171   Fax (612)425-0735

Company Description

Reo Plastics, Inc.'s operations principally involve the custom injection molding, decorating, and assembling of thermoplastics for customers in various industries nationwide. The Company has one major customer that accounted for 35.2% and 22.9% of sales for 1996 and 1995, respectively. Reo Plastics was founded in 1962.

	04/30/96	04/30/95	04/30/94	04/30/93
Per Share Information				
Stock Price as of 12/31	10.00	10.00	8.50	7.00
Earnings Per Share	1.38	1.49	1.44	1.10
Price / Earnings Ratio	7.25	6.71	5.90	6.36
Book Value Per Share	14.49	13.11	11.62	10.18
Price / Book Value %	69.01	76.28	73.15	68.76
Dividends Per Share	0.0	0.0	0.0	0.0
Annual Financial Data				
Operating Results (000's)				
Total Revenues	17,496.5	14,268.1	12,253.0	10,888.5
Costs & Expenses	-16,313.1	-12,996.0	-11,050.8	-9,963.9
Income Before Taxes and Other	1,183.5	1,272.0	1,202.2	924.6
Other Items	0.0	0.0	0.0	0.0
Income Tax	-448.0	-479.0	-435.0	-337.0
Net Income	735.5	793.0	767.2	587.6
Cash Flow From Operations	1,210.0	-215.4	2,121.2	214.0
Balance Sheet (000's)				
Cash & Equivalents	105.4	77.4	746.5	98.5
Total Current Assets	7,365.4	7,647.8	5,575.2	5,546.1
Fixed Assets, Net	5,279.1	4,858.1	2,754.9	2,684.6
Total Assets	12,644.5	12,543.9	8,430.1	8,420.7
Total Current Liabilities	4,492.1	5,110.0	1,756.2	2,490.0
Long-Term Debt	200.0	200.0	200.0	200.0
Stockholders' Equity	7,714.4	6,979.0	6,185.9	5,418.7
Performance & Financial Condition				
Return on Total Revenues %	4.20	5.56	6.26	5.40
Return on Avg Stockholders' Equity %	10.01	12.05	13.22	11.47
Return on Average Assets %	5.84	7.56	9.11	7.28
Current Ratio	1.64	1.50	3.17	2.23
Debt / Equity %	2.59	2.87	3.23	3.69

Compound Growth %'s	EPS %	7.85	Net Income %	7.77	Total Revenues %	17.13

Comments

Revenue soared 22.7% during fiscal 1996 but net earnings were slightly lower due to reduced operating margins. For the first six months of fiscal 1997, sales were $10.2 million as compared to $9.1 in the same period last year, an 11.5% increase. Profits were up 33.2% to $1.11 per share. Compound growth rates are also favorable for this company that trades below book value. Investment Classification: Value

Officers	Position	Ownership Information	
Earl A. Patch	President	Number of Shares Outstanding	532,500
Jim Wolf	Vice President	Market Capitalization	$ 5,325,000
Jim Swanson	Vice President	Frequency of Dividends	n.a.
Elmer Douglas	Vice President	Number of Shareholders	Under 500
Rollie Curtis	Controller		

Other Information

Transfer Agent	Northwestern Bank North Wilkesboro, NC		Where Listed	OTC-BB
Auditor	McGladrey & Pullen LLP		Symbol	REOP
Market Maker	R.J. Steichen & Co.	(800)328-8217	SIC Code	3089
			Employees	200
Broker Dealer	Regular Stockbroker			

Reserve Petroleum Company (The)

6801 N. Broadway, Suite 300   Oklahoma City, OK 73116-9092   Telephone (405)848-7551   Fax (405)848-7888

Company Description

The Reserve Petroleum Company is engaged principally in the exploration for and the development of oil and natural gas properties. The Company owns mineral interests in approximately 94,180 net acres located in nine states with 57,434 acres being in Texas and Oklahoma. As a result of its mineral ownership the Company has royalty interests in 16 producing gas wells. The Company was founded in 1931.

	12/31/96	12/31/95	12/31/94	12/31/93
Per Share Information				
Stock Price	31.25	21.94	22.07	21.00
Earnings Per Share	4.68	3.50	0.65	1.34
Price / Earnings Ratio	6.68	6.27	33.95	15.67
Book Value Per Share	38.35	34.47	32.10	32.35
Price / Book Value %	81.49	63.65	68.75	64.91
Dividends Per Share	1.00	1.00	1.00	1.00
Annual Financial Data				
Operating Results (000's)				
Total Revenues	3,182.7	2,021.9	1,643.4	1,561.3
Costs & Expenses	-2,257.5	-1,477.1	-1,541.3	-1,399.9
Income Before Taxes and Other	925.2	544.8	102.2	161.4
Other Items	0.0	0.0	0.0	55.9
Income Tax	-133.8	48.3	8.6	10.7
Net Income	791.4	593.0	110.8	228.0
Cash Flow From Operations	1,153.5	786.9	710.9	485.9
Balance Sheet (000's)				
Cash & Equivalents	385.1	175.0	112.6	98.6
Total Current Assets	4,056.7	3,399.9	3,086.9	3,337.9
Fixed Assets, Net	1,997.3	2,026.3	1,998.7	1,959.3
Total Assets	6,863.6	6,200.1	5,798.1	5,947.0
Total Current Liabilities	273.4	165.9	119.5	205.1
Long-Term Debt	0.0	0.0	0.0	0.0
Stockholders' Equity	6,461.7	5,860.0	5,444.2	5,509.0
Performance & Financial Condition				
Return on Total Revenues %	24.86	29.33	6.74	14.60
Return on Avg Stockholders' Equity %	12.85	10.49	2.02	4.15
Return on Average Assets %	12.12	9.89	1.89	3.86
Current Ratio	14.84	20.49	25.82	16.27
Debt / Equity %	n.a.	n.a.	n.a.	n.a.

Compound Growth %'s	EPS %	51.72	Net Income %	51.42	Total Revenues %	26.80

Comments

The Company has won an action in a Texas court to quiet title on an interest it has in mineral rights associated with two producing oil and gas wells. $850,000 of production revenues are held in suspense by the wells' operator pending any possible appeals. The proceeds will be recorded as income when released. In 1996, 73% of oil and gas revenue were from owned mineral properties as compared to 46% in 1995. The Company continues to participate in new prospecting. Investment Classification: Value & Speculative

Officers	Position	Ownership Information	
Mason McLain	President	Number of Shares Outstanding	168,479
Jerry L. Crow	Treasurer, Secretary	Market Capitalization	$ 5,264,969
Robert T. McLain	Vice President	Frequency of Dividends	Annual
		Number of Shareholders	1,431

Other Information			
Transfer Agent	Company Office	Where Listed	OTC-BB
Auditor	Grant Thornton LLP	Symbol	RSRV
Market Maker	Hill Thompson Magid & Co., Inc (800)631-3083	SIC Code	6792
	Boenning & Scattergood, Inc. (800)883-8383	Employees	8
Broker Dealer	OTC Specialist		

Reuter Manufacturing, Inc.

410 11th Avenue South   Hopkins, MN 55343   Telephone (612)935-6921   Fax (612)933-5803

Company Description

Reuter Manufacturing, Inc. is a contract manufacturer of precision machined components, assemblies and devices for medical and industrial original equipment manufacturers. The Company manufactures on a contract basis, among other items, close tolerance bearing-related assemblies for the medical device industry. In order to differentiate itself from its competitors, the Company emphasizes its design engineering and manufacturing engineering support. In 1986, the Company entered the waste processing business which proved unprofitable. By 1996, the Company had refocused its efforts on contract manufacturing.

	12/31/96	12/31/95
Per Share Information		
Stock Price	3.25	0.36
Earnings Per Share	1.52	-0.87
Price / Earnings Ratio	2.14	n.a.
Book Value Per Share	-2.51	-5.04
Price / Book Value %	n.a.	n.a.
Dividends Per Share	0.0	0.0
Annual Financial Data		
Operating Results (000's)		
Total Revenues	14,227.0	11,237.9
Costs & Expenses	-13,457.4	-11,847.5
Income Before Taxes and Other	769.6	-609.6
Other Items	7,249.0	-2,157.9
Income Tax	-20.0	0.0
Net Income	7,998.6	-2,767.5
Cash Flow From Operations	667.2	-32.8
Balance Sheet (000's)		
Cash & Equivalents	75.0	101.0
Total Current Assets	3,959.5	2,973.6
Fixed Assets, Net	4,176.7	4,082.3
Total Assets	8,534.0	7,502.3
Total Current Liabilities	8,767.8	22,879.2
Long-Term Debt	7,689.7	495.7
Stockholders' Equity	-8,067.6	-16,072.2
Performance & Financial Condition		
Return on Total Revenues %	56.22	-24.63
Return on Avg Stockholders' Equity %	n.a.	n.a.
Return on Average Assets %	99.76	n.a.
Current Ratio	0.45	0.13
Debt / Equity %	n.a.	n.a.

Compound Growth %'s	EPS % n.a.	Net Income % n.a.	Total Revenues % 26.60

Comments

During 1996, the Company restructured certain debt obligations which resulted in a nonrecurring gain of $7,249,000 ($1.38 per share). However, the Company did turn a profit of $750,000 ($.14 per share) on a fully-diluted basis. As of December 31, 1996, the Company had negative working capital and was in default under its asset-based short-term financing arrangement. The Company's ability to continue as a going concern is dependent on its ability to cure or obtain waivers of the default conditions. For the first quarter of 1997, the Company reported an 84% increase in revenue and a profit of $649,000 ($.19 per share). As of May 31, 1997, the stock was trading at about $5 per share. Investment Classification: Speculative

Officers	Position	Ownership Information	
Edward E. Strickland	Chairman	Number of Shares Outstanding	3,208,020
James W. Taylor	President, CEO	Market Capitalization	$ 10,426,065
William H. Johnson	Secretary, Controller	Frequency of Dividends	n.a.
Robert D. Klingberg	Vice President	Number of Shareholders	1,316
Thomas L. Beltrand	VP - Manufacturing		

Other Information

Transfer Agent	American Stock & Transfer Co. New York, NY		Where Listed	OTC-BB
Auditor	Coopers & Lybrand LLP		Symbol	RTMF
Market Maker	Furman Selz Inc.	(800)448-3223	SIC Code	3821
	Troster Singer	(800)526-3160	Employees	n.a.
Broker Dealer	Regular Stockbroker			

Reynolds, Smith and Hills, Inc.

4651 Salisbury Road   Jacksonville, FL 32256   Telephone (904)296-2000   Fax (904)279-2491

Company Description

Reynolds, Smith and Hills, Inc. is a professional services firm operating in the engineering, architectural design and environmental services industry. The Company provides a full range of architectural, engineering, planning and environmental services to public and private sector clients primarily in the southeastern United States through nine offices. The Company has grown rapidly since it was founded in 1990.

	03/31/96	03/31/95	03/31/94	03/31/93
Per Share Information				
Stock Price as of 12/31	10.50	8.50	6.50	4.50
Earnings Per Share	0.20	0.78	0.61	0.15
Price / Earnings Ratio	52.50	10.90	10.66	30.00
Book Value Per Share	10.42	10.21	9.44	9.09
Price / Book Value %	100.77	83.25	68.86	49.50
Dividends Per Share	0.0	0.0	0.0	0.0
Annual Financial Data				
Operating Results (000's)				
Total Revenues	25,595.0	23,654.0	22,106.0	23,205.0
Costs & Expenses	-25,355.0	-23,002.0	-21,575.0	-23,053.0
Income Before Taxes and Other	240.0	652.0	531.0	152.0
Other Items	0.0	0.0	0.0	0.0
Income Tax	-148.0	-302.0	-260.0	-90.0
Net Income	92.0	350.0	271.0	62.0
Cash Flow From Operations	900.0	1,533.0	695.0	473.0
Balance Sheet (000's)				
Cash & Equivalents	263.0	577.0	525.0	389.6
Total Current Assets	8,950.0	8,443.0	7,871.0	6,392.4
Fixed Assets, Net	2,456.0	2,216.0	2,070.0	2,113.4
Total Assets	12,521.0	11,858.0	11,203.0	9,901.2
Total Current Liabilities	7,015.0	6,129.0	5,457.0	3,818.5
Long-Term Debt	76.0	524.0	1,035.0	1,460.3
Stockholders' Equity	4,741.0	4,576.0	4,193.0	3,914.8
Performance & Financial Condition				
Return on Total Revenues %	0.36	1.48	1.23	0.27
Return on Avg Stockholders' Equity %	1.97	7.98	6.68	1.61
Return on Average Assets %	0.75	3.04	2.57	0.58
Current Ratio	1.28	1.38	1.44	1.67
Debt / Equity %	1.60	11.45	24.68	37.30

Compound Growth %'s	EPS %	10.06	Net Income %	14.06	Total Revenues %	3.32

Comments

Price per share information was derived from stock issuances by the Company. No public market currently exists so we suggest contacting the Company if there is an interest. The Company's backlog at March 31, 1996 was $38.1 million. For the nine months ended December 31, 1996, revenues were 10.7% higher and net income was $566,000, $1.24 per share, as compared to $90,000, $.20 per share, in the same period of the 1996 fiscal year. Investment Classification: Growth

Officers	Position	Ownership Information	
Leerie T. Jenkins, Jr.	President, CEO	Number of Shares Outstanding	455,000
David K. Robertson	Exec VP, CFO	Market Capitalization	$ 4,777,500
Charles W. Gregg	Exec VP, COO	Frequency of Dividends	n.a.
Darold F. Cole	Senior VP	Number of Shareholders	186
J. Ronald Ratliff	Senior VP		

Other Information			
Transfer Agent	Company Office	Where Listed	Order Matching Only
Auditor	Deloitte & Touche LLP	Symbol	n.a.
Market Maker	None - See Note	SIC Code	8710
		Employees	365
Broker Dealer	None		

Rhinelander Telecommunications, Inc.

53 North Stevens Street   Rhinelander, WI 54501-0340   Telephone (715)369-4641   Fax (715)369-1274

Company Description

Rhinelander Telecommunications, Inc. is a diversified communications company providing local telephone service, business communications services, internet access, paging and cellular telephone service. The primary service area is northern Wisconsin. In January, 1997, the Company successfully bid on seven F-block licenses for Personal Computer Services at a total cost of $1.5 million.

	12/31/96	12/31/95	12/31/94	12/31/93
Per Share Information				
Stock Price	19.00	22.50	21.50	22.75
Earnings Per Share	1.31	1.14	1.40	1.23
Price / Earnings Ratio	14.50	19.74	15.36	18.50
Book Value Per Share	13.41	12.77	11.59	10.64
Price / Book Value %	141.69	176.19	185.50	213.82
Dividends Per Share	0.48	0.46	0.44	0.42
Annual Financial Data				
Operating Results (000's)				
Total Revenues	17,869.7	15,575.6	15,232.7	11,587.9
Costs & Expenses	-14,038.3	-12,101.2	-11,241.0	-8,202.1
Income Before Taxes and Other	3,814.5	3,474.4	3,984.5	3,374.9
Other Items	0.0	0.0	0.0	0.0
Income Tax	-1,465.0	-1,419.6	-1,544.4	-1,234.9
Net Income	2,349.5	2,054.8	2,440.1	2,140.0
Cash Flow From Operations	7,092.5	5,995.1	4,273.5	4,119.7
Balance Sheet (000's)				
Cash & Equivalents	1,445.2	2,639.2	1,297.7	1,489.1
Total Current Assets	4,625.6	6,254.8	4,226.8	4,005.0
Fixed Assets, Net	36,773.4	34,094.8	32,290.0	31,562.9
Total Assets	50,390.0	49,036.5	41,622.9	40,678.1
Total Current Liabilities	5,042.1	4,601.8	2,459.8	3,261.2
Long-Term Debt	14,994.7	15,898.3	13,372.7	13,644.9
Stockholders' Equity	24,115.9	22,629.2	20,239.6	18,576.6
Performance & Financial Condition				
Return on Total Revenues %	13.15	13.19	16.02	18.47
Return on Avg Stockholders' Equity %	10.05	9.59	12.57	11.97
Return on Average Assets %	4.73	4.53	5.93	6.28
Current Ratio	0.92	1.36	1.72	1.23
Debt / Equity %	62.18	70.26	66.07	73.45

Compound Growth %'s	EPS %	2.12	Net Income %	3.16	Total Revenues %	15.53

Comments

In late 1995, Rib Lake Telephone Company was acquired to bring in some new management, increase the customer base, provide entry into the cable industry and increase the Company's wireless position. Revenue would have reflected a 5.3% increase for 1996 without the addition of Rib Lake. The bottom line, however, was a strong 15% increase. Cash flow from operations continues to be well above income levels. We were impressed by the number of our subscribers who were familiar with this company. It appears that its user friendly approach to telephone services has carried through the shareholder relations department as well. This is exactly what we like to see. Investment Classification: Growth

Officers	Position	Ownership Information	
Donald A. Anklam	President	Number of Shares Outstanding	1,798,513
Kirby H. Roen	Secretary, Treasurer	Market Capitalization	$ 34,171,747
Dexter C. Defnet	Vice President	Frequency of Dividends	Quarterly
Lee A. Lappin	Other	Number of Shareholders	349

Other Information

Transfer Agent	Company Office		Where Listed	OTC-BB
Auditor	Kiesling Associates LLP		Symbol	RLND
Market Maker	Howe Barnes Investments, Inc.	(800)621-2364	SIC Code	4810
	Hill Thompson Magid & Co., Inc	(800)631-3083	Employees	83
Broker Dealer	Regular Stockbroker			
	Stephen Schuller - Dorsey	(800)375-5431		

Robroy Industries, Inc.

River Road   Verona, PA 15147-0097   Telephone (412)828-2100   Fax (412)828-3952

Company Description

Robroy Industries is a multinational manufacturer of various products related principally to the electrical industry. The Company's principal lines of businesses are conduit products, enclosure products and computer packaging products. In 1994 and 1995, the Company acquired assets from Keystone/Rees and Sigma Information Systems that added additional product capability to its existing product lines. The Company was formed in 1905.

	06/30/96	06/30/95	06/30/94	06/30/93
Per Share Information				
Stock Price as of 12/31	18.75	17.50	19.00	19.00
Earnings Per Share	1.43	0.68	1.84	1.80
Price / Earnings Ratio	13.11	25.74	10.33	10.56
Book Value Per Share	17.63	16.45	15.94	14.26
Price / Book Value %	106.35	106.38	119.20	133.24
Dividends Per Share	0.24	0.24	0.21	0.19
Annual Financial Data				
Operating Results (000's)				
Total Revenues	123,548.0	111,005.1	104,199.6	94,328.6
Costs & Expenses	-115,488.6	-102,053.9	-93,902.2	-84,287.9
Income Before Taxes and Other	7,353.7	3,836.5	10,297.4	10,040.8
Other Items	0.0	0.0	0.0	0.0
Income Tax	-2,628.0	-1,520.8	-3,840.0	-3,731.7
Net Income	4,725.7	2,315.7	6,457.5	6,309.1
Cash Flow From Operations	7,249.5	4,463.5	8,046.8	4,301.3
Balance Sheet (000's)				
Cash & Equivalents	393.6	7,449.3	2,940.1	3,475.0
Total Current Assets	40,623.0	43,725.0	35,301.3	33,140.9
Fixed Assets, Net	18,960.5	16,688.9	14,247.9	13,922.2
Total Assets	81,856.8	75,021.0	72,496.6	68,630.2
Total Current Liabilities	17,460.8	14,721.0	10,098.7	9,511.8
Long-Term Debt	5,500.0	3,250.0	5,363.3	7,797.7
Stockholders' Equity	58,235.4	56,340.1	55,851.8	49,974.9
Performance & Financial Condition				
Return on Total Revenues %	3.82	2.09	6.20	6.69
Return on Avg Stockholders' Equity %	8.25	4.13	12.20	13.33
Return on Average Assets %	6.02	3.14	9.15	10.54
Current Ratio	2.33	2.97	3.50	3.48
Debt / Equity %	9.44	5.77	9.60	15.60

Compound Growth %'s	EPS %	-7.38	Net Income %	-9.18	Total Revenues %	9.41

Comments

The Company declared a 2.5 to 1 stock split in 1994. 1993 per share amounts have been adjusted accordingly. 1995 included a restructuring charge of $3.5 million, or $1.02 per share. Restructuring included the relocation of the Verona plant, the closure and sale of other facilities, and the acquisition of certain companies and product lines. Management reports that 1996 results are on target with the restructuring program and that the outlook for 1997 continues to be bright. Investment Classification: Value

Officers	Position	Ownership Information	
Peter McIlroy II	President, CEO	Number of Shares Outstanding	3,302,806
Loy B. Goodheart	President	Market Capitalization	$ 61,927,613
David Marshall	President	Frequency of Dividends	Quarterly
McKenna M. Lawrence	President	Number of Shareholders	Under 500
Louis J. Kirchner	Exec VP, CFO		

Other Information			
Transfer Agent	ChaseMellon Shareholder Services New York, NY	Where Listed	OTC-BB
Auditor	Deloitte & Touche LLP	Symbol	RROYA
Market Maker	Legg Mason Wood Walker, Inc. (800)346-5075	SIC Code	5063
	Rodgers Brothers Inc. (412)281-1940	Employees	999
Broker Dealer	Regular Stockbroker		

Rochester & Pittsburgh Coal Company

655 Church Street   Indiana, PA 15701   Telephone (412)349-5800   Fax (412)349-5460

Company Description

Rochester & Pittsburgh Coal Company has been mining bituminous steam coal in western Pennsylvania since 1882. Most sales are made, under long-term supply contracts, to electricity generating plants located adjacent to or near the Company's mines. In 1992, the Company acquired coal properties in southwest Pennsylvania. The Company is developing these properties and it expects development to be complete in 1997. These properties will allow the Company to access the general eastern utility coal market and should constitute a major part of the Company's operations.

	12/31/96	12/31/95	12/31/94	12/31/93
Per Share Information				
Stock Price	26.00	29.32	34.25	39.38
Earnings Per Share	3.27	-1.03	0.72	2.06
Price / Earnings Ratio	7.95	n.a.	47.57	19.12
Book Value Per Share	61.37	59.06	60.33	61.31
Price / Book Value %	42.37	49.64	56.77	64.23
Dividends Per Share	0.60	0.75	1.50	1.50
Annual Financial Data				
Operating Results (000's)				
Total Revenues	217,282.0	225,879.0	196,773.0	161,941.0
Costs & Expenses	-202,052.0	-228,127.0	-191,294.0	-153,893.0
Income Before Taxes and Other	15,230.0	-3,872.0	4,304.0	3,876.0
Other Items	0.0	0.0	0.0	4,709.0
Income Tax	-3,969.0	337.0	-1,838.0	-1,502.0
Net Income	11,261.0	-3,535.0	2,466.0	7,083.0
Cash Flow From Operations	50,319.0	27,615.0	15,844.0	13,049.0
Balance Sheet (000's)				
Cash & Equivalents	34,466.0	27,437.0	30,656.0	23,737.0
Total Current Assets	95,393.0	109,024.0	129,614.0	101,600.0
Fixed Assets, Net	356,625.0	322,363.0	230,169.0	183,009.0
Total Assets	531,398.0	491,407.0	410,994.0	356,884.0
Total Current Liabilities	58,846.0	33,601.0	32,631.0	27,844.0
Long-Term Debt	100,501.0	120,784.0	75,693.0	29,455.0
Stockholders' Equity	211,185.0	203,114.0	207,450.0	210,794.0
Performance & Financial Condition				
Return on Total Revenues %	5.18	-1.57	1.25	4.37
Return on Avg Stockholders' Equity %	5.44	-1.72	1.18	3.37
Return on Average Assets %	2.20	-0.78	0.64	2.07
Current Ratio	1.62	3.24	3.97	3.65
Debt / Equity %	47.59	59.47	36.49	13.97

Compound Growth %'s	EPS % 16.65	Net Income % 16.71	Total Revenues % 10.29

Comments

Although revenues declined in 1996, certain marketing efforts are expected to have a significant positive impact on 1997 revenues. At December 31, 1996, the Company had an accrued liability of approximately $146 million as a reserve for workers' compensation benefits, mine closings, postretirement benefits and health benefits. 1995 operating results were severely impacted by a seven-month-long mine workers strike. Depreciation, depletion and amortization amounted to $11.2 million for 1996. Note the resulting significant amount of cash flow from operations. Investment Classification: Value

Officers	Position	Ownership Information	
Thomas W. Garges, Jr.	President, CEO	Number of Shares Outstanding	3,440,984
Peter Iselin	VP - Finance, Secretary	Market Capitalization	$ 89,465,584
W. Joseph Engler, Jr.	Vice President	Frequency of Dividends	Quarterly
George M. Evans	Vice President, Treasurer	Number of Shareholders	680
Jeffery A. Mack	Controller		

Other Information

Transfer Agent	First Chicago Trust Company of New York New York, NY		Where Listed	OTC-BB
Auditor	Ernst & Young LLP		Symbol	DRAE
Market Maker	Pennsylvania Merchant Group	(800)762-8624	SIC Code	1221
	Legg Mason Wood & Walker, Inc.	(800)346-5075	Employees	1670
Broker Dealer	Regular Stockbroker			

Rockies Fund, Inc. (The)

4465 Northpark Drive, Ste. 400   Colorado Springs, CO 80907   Telephone (719)590-4900   Fax (719)590-4888

Company Description

The Rockies Fund, Inc. was formed in 1983 for the purpose of making venture capital investments in developing companies throughout the United States. The Fund makes managerial assistance available to new and developing companies and follows certain guidelines when identifying potential portfolio companies. The Fund attempts to invest in those companies which are unique with regard to their products or their production or marketing techniques. One of our original subscribers requested that we consider this Fund for inclusion and we were pleased to do exactly that.

	12/31/96	12/31/95	12/31/94	12/31/93
Per Share Information				
Stock Price	4.00	2.00	1.75	1.25
Earnings Per Share	1.60	-0.62	0.09	0.93
Price / Earnings Ratio	2.50	n.a.	19.44	1.34
Book Value Per Share	3.64	2.04	2.67	2.58
Price / Book Value %	109.89	98.04	65.54	48.45
Dividends Per Share	0.0	0.0	0.0	0.0
Annual Financial Data				
Operating Results (000's)				
Total Revenues	1,658.3	37.0	587.2	898.7
Costs & Expenses	-635.2	-436.5	-531.7	-304.1
Income Before Taxes and Other	1,023.2	-399.5	55.5	594.6
Other Items	0.0	0.0	0.0	0.0
Income Tax	0.0	0.0	0.0	0.0
Net Income	1,023.2	-399.5	55.5	594.6
Cash Flow From Operations	-123.8	-195.9	-295.7	-65.2
Balance Sheet (000's)				
Cash & Equivalents	499.4	1.2	37.1	9.1
Total Current Assets	2,530.6	1,471.9	1,767.5	1,843.1
Fixed Assets, Net	764.5	714.9	655.6	661.0
Total Assets	3,470.1	2,186.8	2,423.1	2,504.1
Total Current Liabilities	764.3	458.4	317.6	424.2
Long-Term Debt	315.3	351.8	391.6	428.4
Stockholders' Equity	2,330.7	1,307.6	1,707.0	1,651.6
Performance & Financial Condition				
Return on Total Revenues %	61.70	-1,079.57	9.44	66.16
Return on Avg Stockholders' Equity %	56.24	-26.50	3.30	43.90
Return on Average Assets %	36.17	-17.33	2.25	32.21
Current Ratio	3.31	3.21	5.56	4.35
Debt / Equity %	13.53	26.91	22.94	25.94

Compound Growth %'s	EPS %	19.82	Net Income %	19.83	Total Revenues %	22.65

Comments

At December 31, 1996, the Fund had investments in thirty-four different companies. All investments are reflected at their fair market values at each year end. During 1996, the Fund recognized substantial gains of $1,549,196 from the sale of investments, mainly related to one such holding. Shares can be acquired for a small amount above book value. This is a way for an investor to participate in venture capital investments that might not otherwise be available. The cost, of course, are salaries to the principals and other expenses. Investment Classification: Speculative

Officers	Position	Ownership Information	
Stephen G. Calandrella	President, CEO	Number of Shares Outstanding	640,256
Windy D. Haddad	Secretary	Market Capitalization	$ 2,561,024
Barbara A. Hamstad	Treasurer	Frequency of Dividends	n.a.
		Number of Shareholders	116

Other Information				
Transfer Agent	American Securities Transfer Lakewood, CO		Where Listed	OTC-BB
Auditor	Gelfond Hochstadt Pangburn		Symbol	ROCE
Market Maker	D.A. Davidson & Co.	(406)761-6523	SIC Code	6790
	J.P. Trading Ltd.	(405)842-1992	Employees	4
Broker Dealer	Regular Stockbroker			

Root Company, The A.I.

623 West Liberty Street   Medina, OH 44258   Telephone (330)725-6677   Fax (330)725-5624

Company Description

The A.I. Root Company is a manufacturer, marketer, and distributor of candles, beeswax products and bee keeping accessories and supplies. The Company also publishes and sells "Gleanings In Bee Culture" magazine. Church candles were the predominant product line from when the Company was founded in 1869 until 1993 when decorative candles took the lead. The Company has facilities in Ohio, Iowa, Texas, Georgia and Pennsylvania.

	07/31/96	07/31/95	07/31/94	07/31/93
Per Share Information				
Stock Price as of 12/31	375.00	375.00	375.00	375.00
Earnings Per Share	312.17	282.80	183.57	85.27
Price / Earnings Ratio	1.20	1.33	2.04	4.40
Book Value Per Share	1,678.89	1,368.99	773.00	590.00
Price / Book Value %	22.34	27.39	48.51	63.56
Dividends Per Share	2.25	2.00	1.83	1.78
Annual Financial Data				
Operating Results (000's)				
Total Revenues	n.a.	n.a.	n.a.	n.a.
Costs & Expenses	n.a.	n.a.	n.a.	n.a.
Income Before Taxes and Other	n.a.	n.a.	n.a.	n.a.
Other Items	n.a.	n.a.	n.a.	n.a.
Income Tax	n.a.	n.a.	n.a.	n.a.
Net Income	2,403.0	2,178.0	2,009.0	968.0
Cash Flow From Operations	n.a.	n.a.	n.a.	n.a.
Balance Sheet (000's)				
Cash & Equivalents	528.1	29.2	212.2	1,277.9
Total Current Assets	7,789.0	7,074.0	6,821.9	6,213.7
Fixed Assets, Net	8,013.6	6,881.3	3,702.1	2,199.7
Total Assets	16,264.3	14,554.0	11,020.9	8,885.3
Total Current Liabilities	2,869.5	3,602.8	2,591.0	2,417.2
Long-Term Debt	0.0	0.0	0.0	0.0
Stockholders' Equity	12,692.4	10,349.5	8,230.4	6,276.1
Performance & Financial Condition				
Return on Total Revenues %	n.a.	n.a.	n.a.	n.a.
Return on Avg Stockholders' Equity %	20.86	23.44	27.70	n.a.
Return on Average Assets %	15.59	17.03	20.18	n.a.
Current Ratio	2.71	1.96	2.63	2.57
Debt / Equity %	n.a.	n.a.	n.a.	n.a.

Compound Growth %'s	EPS %	54.12	Net Income %	35.40	Total Revenues %	n.a.

Comments

The Company does not disclose its income statement even to shareholders. We calculated a net earnings number from the change in stockholders' equity. Business has been extremely strong over the last few years, causing the manufacturing facilities to go to 24-hour production schedules on some products. At the end of 1994, a new 70,000 square foot (1.6 acres) production building was added next to an existing building that was, in turn, converted to a distribution warehouse. As shares are sweeter than honey, we don't find the market makers bid price to be at all enticing. This might be an opportunity for someone willing to pay a reasonable price. Investment Classification: Value

Officers	Position	Ownership Information	
John A. Root	President	Number of Shares Outstanding	7,560
Stuart W. Root	Secretary	Market Capitalization	$ 2,835,000
		Frequency of Dividends	Annual
		Number of Shareholders	Under 500

Other Information				
Transfer Agent	Company Office		Where Listed	OTC-PS
Auditor	Not indicated		Symbol	RTAIB
Market Maker	The Chicago Corporation	(800)621-1674	SIC Code	3900
			Employees	230
Broker Dealer	OTC Specialist			
	Standard Investment	(888)783-4688 Ext: Jack		

Roseville Communications Company

211 Lincoln Street Roseville, CA 95678-2614 Telephone (916)786-6141 Fax (916)781-7777

Company Description

Roseville Communications Company, formerly Roseville Telephone Company, provides local and toll telephone service and network access services in an 83 square mile area in Placer and Sacramento Counties in California. Currently, no other local exchange telephone companies operate in the area served by the Company. The region has experienced substantial growth in recent years as a suburban area to the city of Sacramento, the Capitol of the State of California. The Company was founded in 1914.

	12/31/96	12/31/95	12/31/94	12/31/93
Per Share Information				
Stock Price	24.75	24.49	28.75	30.52
Earnings Per Share	1.40	1.20	1.35	1.50
Price / Earnings Ratio	17.68	20.41	21.30	20.35
Book Value Per Share	12.16	11.35	10.72	9.58
Price / Book Value %	203.54	215.77	268.19	318.58
Dividends Per Share	0.58	0.57	0.54	0.51
Annual Financial Data				
Operating Results (000's)				
Total Revenues	117,062.0	111,068.0	106,258.0	100,000.0
Costs & Expenses	-80,948.0	-73,017.0	-67,537.0	-60,479.0
Income Before Taxes and Other	35,979.0	31,141.0	34,221.0	37,902.0
Other Items	0.0	0.0	0.0	0.0
Income Tax	-14,518.0	-12,634.0	-13,866.0	-15,384.0
Net Income	21,461.0	18,507.0	20,355.0	22,518.0
Cash Flow From Operations	32,663.0	32,785.0	36,731.0	36,647.0
Balance Sheet (000's)				
Cash & Equivalents	24,435.0	24,854.0	21,282.0	9,847.0
Total Current Assets	45,918.0	54,126.0	53,379.0	38,498.0
Fixed Assets, Net	184,182.0	178,225.0	173,359.0	168,571.0
Total Assets	267,881.0	256,889.0	246,808.0	226,459.0
Total Current Liabilities	26,251.0	21,638.0	20,322.0	19,143.0
Long-Term Debt	28,036.0	33,750.0	37,321.0	40,000.0
Stockholders' Equity	186,801.0	174,393.0	164,675.0	142,921.0
Performance & Financial Condition				
Return on Total Revenues %	18.33	16.66	19.16	22.52
Return on Avg Stockholders' Equity %	11.88	10.92	13.23	16.61
Return on Average Assets %	8.18	7.35	8.60	10.79
Current Ratio	1.75	2.50	2.63	2.01
Debt / Equity %	15.01	19.35	22.66	27.99

Compound Growth %'s	EPS % -2.27	Net Income % -1.59	Total Revenues % 5.39

Comments

In January, 1997, West Coast PCS, a venture in which Roseville has an 89% interest, was the successful bidder for Block E licenses to offer services in four Basic Trading Areas located in California including Sacramento, Stockton, Modesto and Yuba City. In February, 1997, Roseville commenced operations to produce, publish and distribute Roseville's telephone directory which previously had been published by an unrelated party. The Company also hopes to add long distance services in 1997 and has filed with the Public Utilities Commission accordingly. Investment Classification: Speculative

Officers	Position	Ownership Information	
Robert L. Doyle	Chairman	Number of Shares Outstanding	15,358,720
Brian H. Strom	President, CEO	Market Capitalization	$ 380,128,320
Michael D. Campbell	Exec VP, CFO	Frequency of Dividends	Quarterly
		Number of Shareholders	9,500

Other Information				
Transfer Agent	Company Office		Where Listed	OTC-BB
Auditor	Ernst & Young LLP		Symbol	RVTL
Market Maker	Gabelli & Company, Inc.	(914)921-5154	SIC Code	4813
	Prudential Securities	(916)789-4444	Employees	501
Broker Dealer	Regular Stockbroker			
	Bill Baxter - Prudential	(800)772-9978		

SGI International

1200 Prospect Street, Ste. 325   La Jolla, CA 92037   Telephone (619)551-1090   Fax (619)551-0247

Company Description

SGI International's principal business is developing and marketing energy technologies. The Company developed the patented Liquids From Coal Process (LFC), which upgrades low-rank coal into a higher Btu coal called Coal Derived Liquid and also produces coal gas, a non-condensable gas, that is used for processing heating. During 1996, the Company made significant progress in further developing aspects of marketing the LFC Process. The Company also owns Assembly & Manufacturing Systems, Inc. (AMS) which was acquired in 1995. The common shares, which traded as high as $90 in 1993, gradually lost value to a low point of about $.62 in 1996.

	12/31/96	12/31/95	12/31/94	12/31/93
Per Share Information				
Stock Price	4.30	0.67	0.67	2.30
Earnings Per Share	-0.80	-2.46	-3.02	-3.62
Price / Earnings Ratio	n.a.	n.a.	n.a.	n.a.
Book Value Per Share	0.03	-0.42	0.26	1.28
Price / Book Value %	14,333.33	n.a.	257.69	179.69
Dividends Per Share	0.0	0.0	0.0	0.0
Annual Financial Data				
Operating Results (000's)				
Total Revenues	4,244.3	900.3	552.5	809.9
Costs & Expenses	-8,041.0	-7,437.2	-6,396.6	-6,926.3
Income Before Taxes and Other	-4,259.4	-6,824.9	-5,844.1	-6,116.4
Other Items	0.0	0.0	0.0	0.0
Income Tax	0.0	0.0	0.0	0.0
Net Income	-4,259.4	-6,824.9	-5,844.1	-6,116.4
Cash Flow From Operations	-3,742.2	-2,838.1	-4,423.5	-4,728.2
Balance Sheet (000's)				
Cash & Equivalents	740.0	74.2	551.3	n.a.
Total Current Assets	2,295.2	944.9	717.4	n.a.
Fixed Assets, Net	548.6	249.3	166.6	n.a.
Total Assets	6,628.7	6,592.1	8,198.4	n.a.
Total Current Liabilities	6,310.4	3,314.0	4,065.7	n.a.
Long-Term Debt	123.8	4,631.3	3,575.8	n.a.
Stockholders' Equity	194.6	-1,629.6	556.9	n.a.
Performance & Financial Condition				
Return on Total Revenues %	-100.36	-758.07	-1,057.75	-755.19
Return on Avg Stockholders' Equity %	n.a.	n.a.	-161.42	-420.68
Return on Average Assets %	-64.43	-92.29	n.a.	n.a.
Current Ratio	0.36	0.29	0.18	n.a.
Debt / Equity %	63.60	n.a.	642.14	n.a.

Compound Growth %'s	EPS % n.a.	Net Income % n.a.	Total Revenues % 73.70

Comments

Significant progress toward commercialization of the LFC Process occurred late in 1996 and early in 1997. Mitsubishi International has contracted to build a $460 million LFC plant, making the Company's patents potentially valuable. The increase in revenue is attributable to AMS. Although the market is gaining optimism about the Company's future, the auditors issued a "going concern" qualification in their opinion. For the three months ended March 31, 1997, sales were flat and a loss of $1,143,545 ($.19 per share) was reported. Investment Classification: Speculative

Officers	Position	Ownership Information	
Joseph A. Savoca	President, CEO	Number of Shares Outstanding	6,094,605
John R. Taylor	Secretary	Market Capitalization	$ 26,206,802
Larry Wiese	Vice President	Frequency of Dividends	n.a.
Robert Walty	Other	Number of Shareholders	2,200

Other Information

Transfer Agent	Atlas Stock Transfer Corporation Salt Lake City, UT		Where Listed	OTC-BB
Auditor	Ernst & Young LLP		Symbol	SGII
Market Maker	Fahnestock & Co., Inc.	(800)223-3012	SIC Code	8711
	Alpine Securities Corp.	(800)521-5588	Employees	n.a.
Broker Dealer	Regular Stockbroker			

SLH Corporation

2600 Grand Boulevard, Ste. 500   Kansas City, MO 64108   Telephone (816)842-7000   Fax (816)842-2101

Company Description

SLH Corporation was formed in 1996 and is primarily engaged in the business of managing, developing and disposing of real estate properties and other assets acquired from Seafield Capital Corporation (Seafield). Seafield's business was forced to discontinue and, as a result, the Company was able to acquire all remaining assets subject to assuming a number of liabilities and contingencies. The Company plans to sell all assets in an orderly manner except for its interest in Syntroleum Corporation, a company involved in the development of proprietary technology for the conversion of natural gas into synthetic liquid hydrocarbons.

	12/31/96	12/31/95	12/31/94	12/31/93
Per Share Information				
Stock Price as of 5/19	48.00	n.a.	n.a.	n.a.
Earnings Per Share	-3.45	n.a.	n.a.	n.a.
Price / Earnings Ratio	n.a.	n.a.	n.a.	n.a.
Book Value Per Share	22.08	n.a.	n.a.	n.a.
Price / Book Value %	217.39	n.a.	n.a.	n.a.
Dividends Per Share	0.0	n.a.	n.a.	n.a.
Annual Financial Data				
Operating Results (000's)				
Total Revenues	16,598.0	11,359.0	13,139.0	17,470.0
Costs & Expenses	-20,740.0	-23,855.0	-21,121.0	-21,636.0
Income Before Taxes and Other	-4,142.0	-12,496.0	-7,982.0	-4,166.0
Other Items	-1,400.0	0.0	0.0	0.0
Income Tax	-56.0	1,264.0	1,437.0	0.0
Net Income	-5,598.0	-11,232.0	-6,545.0	-4,166.0
Cash Flow From Operations	8,853.0	-33.0	-4,169.0	n.a.
Balance Sheet (000's)				
Cash & Equivalents	3,925.0	0.0	0.0	0.0
Total Current Assets	5,529.0	4,432.0	3,707.0	6,006.0
Fixed Assets, Net	425.0	630.0	0.0	0.0
Total Assets	38,474.0	51,638.0	64,627.0	70,155.0
Total Current Liabilities	2,165.0	365.0	239.0	2,150.0
Long-Term Debt	0.0	1,289.0	2,689.0	1,153.0
Stockholders' Equity	35,813.0	49,686.0	61,147.0	66,438.0
Performance & Financial Condition				
Return on Total Revenues %	-33.73	-98.88	-49.81	-23.85
Return on Avg Stockholders' Equity %	-13.09	-20.27	-10.26	-5.64
Return on Average Assets %	-12.42	-19.32	-9.71	-5.39
Current Ratio	2.55	12.14	15.51	2.79
Debt / Equity %	n.a.	2.59	4.40	1.74

Compound Growth %'s	EPS % n.a.	Net Income % n.a.	Total Revenues % -1.69

Comments

Balance sheet and income statement numbers are those of Seafield Capital Corporation as the acquisition was not complete until 1997. Revenues are largely from the disposal of real estate assets. For the quarter ended March 31, 1997, the Company reported a profit of $2,176,000, $1.28 per share, and had current assets of $22.6 million. Maybe there's something here after all. Investment Classification: Speculative

Officers	Position	Ownership Information	
P. Anthony Jacobs	Chairman	Number of Shares Outstanding	1,622,276
James R. Seward	President, CEO	Market Capitalization	$ 77,869,248
Steven K. Fitzwater	Vice President, CFO	Frequency of Dividends	n.a.
		Number of Shareholders	1,800

Other Information

Transfer Agent	n.a.		Where Listed	OTC-BB
Auditor	KPMG Peat Marwick LLP		Symbol	SLHO
Market Maker	George K. Baum & Company	(800)821-7570	SIC Code	6500
	Carr Securities Corporation	(800)221-2243	Employees	9
Broker Dealer	Regular Stockbroker			

Sadlier, Inc., William H.

9 Pine Street   New York, NY 10005-1002   Telephone (212)227-2120   Fax (212)312-6080

Company Description

William H. Sadlier, Inc. is engaged in the publishing industry and publishes and distributes a wide variety of textbooks as well as related workbooks, teachers manuals, charts and other visual and audio aids, principally in the subject areas of religion, mathematics, language arts and social sciences. The Company was formed in 1928. It delisted from the NASDAQ market in 1996.

	12/31/96	12/31/95	12/31/94	12/31/93
Per Share Information				
Stock Price	8.75	6.50	4.50	4.25
Earnings Per Share	0.91	0.79	0.22	0.60
Price / Earnings Ratio	9.62	8.23	20.45	7.08
Book Value Per Share	13.91	13.17	12.48	n.a.
Price / Book Value %	62.90	49.35	36.06	n.a.
Dividends Per Share	0.20	0.10	0.20	0.20
Annual Financial Data				
Operating Results (000's)				
Total Revenues	26,365.4	23,722.1	22,178.6	19,920.2
Costs & Expenses	-24,912.3	-22,464.1	-21,829.7	-19,211.8
Income Before Taxes and Other	1,453.1	1,258.1	348.8	708.4
Other Items	0.0	0.0	0.0	138.3
Income Tax	-644.0	-551.0	-148.0	-306.0
Net Income	809.1	707.1	200.8	540.7
Cash Flow From Operations	3,236.5	2,375.9	1,983.3	2,634.1
Balance Sheet (000's)				
Cash & Equivalents	1,814.3	687.8	871.5	n.a.
Total Current Assets	7,988.2	7,200.8	5,823.4	n.a.
Fixed Assets, Net	945.7	1,002.2	1,163.0	n.a.
Total Assets	15,683.4	15,737.1	14,540.2	n.a.
Total Current Liabilities	3,225.4	3,727.6	3,037.8	n.a.
Long-Term Debt	100.0	200.0	300.0	n.a.
Stockholders' Equity	12,354.7	11,778.3	11,160.6	n.a.
Performance & Financial Condition				
Return on Total Revenues %	3.07	2.98	0.91	2.71
Return on Avg Stockholders' Equity %	6.71	6.16	n.a.	n.a.
Return on Average Assets %	5.15	4.67	n.a.	n.a.
Current Ratio	2.48	1.93	1.92	n.a.
Debt / Equity %	0.81	1.70	2.69	n.a.

Compound Growth %'s	EPS %	14.89	Net Income %	14.38	Total Revenues %	9.79

Comments

Since 1991 sales have grown by 35% and net income by 56%. Efforts to reach the public school market had substantial success in 1996. Management hopes to continue sales growth without the same degree of marketing expense required this past year. The balance sheet is exceptionally strong. Investment Classification: Value & Growth

Officers	Position	Ownership Information	
Frank S. Dinger	Chairman, COO	Number of Shares Outstanding	888,058
William S. Dinger	President, Secretary	Market Capitalization	$ 7,770,508
Gerard F. Baumbach	Exec VP	Frequency of Dividends	Semi-Annual
Joseph F. Brophy	Exec VP	Number of Shareholders	Under 500
Henry E. Christel	Vice President, Treasurer		

Other Information

Transfer Agent	American StockTransfer & Trust Co. New York, NY		Where Listed	OTC-BB
Auditor	KPMG Peat Marwick LLP		Symbol	SADL
Market Maker	Robotti & Co., Inc.	(212)986-0800	SIC Code	2731
	Carr Securities Corporation	(800)221-2243	Employees	n.a.
Broker Dealer	Regular Stockbroker			

Salient Systems, Inc.

4330 Tuller Road   Dublin, OH 43017-5008   Telephone (614)792-5800   Fax (614)792-5888

Company Description

Salient Systems, Inc. is engaged in the manufacturing of wheel impact load detectors and other products for the railroad industry. Tricon Lubricants, Inc., a wholly-owned subsidiary, is a manufacturer of grease and lubricants that it sells as additives for other products. The Company was formed in 1984. It completed a secondary stock offering in 1996, raising $1.1 million on the placement of 251,615 shares.

	12/31/96	12/31/95	12/31/94	12/31/93
Per Share Information				
Stock Price	6.75	5.50	5.50	5.12
Earnings Per Share	-0.03	0.04	0.04	0.06
Price / Earnings Ratio	n.a.	137.50	137.50	85.33
Book Value Per Share	0.67	0.49	0.29	0.24
Price / Book Value %	1,007.46	1,122.45	1,896.55	2,133.33
Dividends Per Share	0.0	0.0	0.0	0.0
Annual Financial Data				
Operating Results (000's)				
Total Revenues	1,766.2	1,979.8	1,572.2	1,863.0
Costs & Expenses	-1,940.1	-1,781.2	-1,420.4	-1,665.6
Income Before Taxes and Other	-173.9	191.7	151.8	197.4
Other Items	0.0	0.0	0.0	68.8
Income Tax	66.5	-54.6	-31.7	-63.8
Net Income	-107.3	137.1	120.1	202.4
Cash Flow From Operations	-199.0	508.2	-268.6	715.9
Balance Sheet (000's)				
Cash & Equivalents	1,061.6	737.3	539.6	906.3
Total Current Assets	1,894.6	1,962.2	1,207.3	1,623.0
Fixed Assets, Net	338.3	289.8	107.0	131.9
Total Assets	3,038.6	2,256.3	1,322.6	1,763.4
Total Current Liabilities	634.8	567.0	353.4	868.4
Long-Term Debt	0.0	0.0	0.0	118.1
Stockholders' Equity	2,403.8	1,689.3	969.2	776.8
Performance & Financial Condition				
Return on Total Revenues %	-6.08	6.92	7.64	10.87
Return on Avg Stockholders' Equity %	-5.24	10.31	13.76	37.21
Return on Average Assets %	-4.05	7.66	7.78	n.a.
Current Ratio	2.98	3.46	3.42	1.87
Debt / Equity %	n.a.	n.a.	n.a.	15.21

Compound Growth %'s	EPS % n.a.	Net Income % n.a.	Total Revenues % -1.76

Comments

Sales of wheel impact load detectors have dropped as a percentage of total sales, largely as a result of product expansion in other areas. Much focus has been on developing and marketing state-of-the-art data management and measurement/detection systems. Management launched a vigorous sales effort during the third quarter of 1996 and has won a major contract. Negotiations also look promising with China as a major order may be in the pipeline. Management believes the stage is set for an improved 1997 both in terms of sales and net earnings. Investment Classification: Speculative

Officers	Position	Ownership Information	
Harold D. Harrison	CEO	Number of Shares Outstanding	3,601,615
Jack Morgan	COO	Market Capitalization	$ 24,310,901
Sharron A. Harrison	CFO	Frequency of Dividends	n.a.
Warren Jamison	Vice President	Number of Shareholders	Under 500

Other Information

Transfer Agent	Oxford Transfer & Registry Agency, Inc. Glendale, CA	Where Listed	OTC-BB
Auditor	Groner, Boyle & Quillin, PLL	Symbol	SLTS
Market Maker	Paragon Capital Corporation	(800)345-0505	SIC Code	8731
	Sierra Brokerage Service, Inc.	(800)837-3351	Employees	15
Broker Dealer	Regular Stockbroker		

Samarnan Investment Corporation

P.O. Box 651   Cleburne, TX 76033-0134   Telephone (817)641-7881   Fax (817)641-7884

Company Description

Samarnan Investment Corporation is registered under the Investment Company Act of 1940 as a diversified, closed-end, management investment company. Its investment portfolio consists of municipal bonds.

	12/31/96	12/31/95	12/31/94
Per Share Information			
Stock Price	10.50	10.25	9.75
Earnings Per Share	0.58	1.32	-0.11
Price / Earnings Ratio	18.10	7.77	n.a.
Book Value Per Share	15.12	15.25	14.68
Price / Book Value %	69.44	67.21	66.42
Dividends Per Share	0.72	0.75	0.80
Annual Financial Data			
Operating Results (000's)			
Total Revenues	793.7	1,676.2	-46.5
Costs & Expenses	-91.6	-89.2	-90.0
Income Before Taxes and Other	702.1	1,587.0	-136.5
Other Items	0.0	0.0	0.0
Income Tax	0.0	0.0	0.0
Net Income	702.1	1,587.0	-136.5
Cash Flow From Operations	702.1	1,587.0	-136.5
Balance Sheet (000's)			
Cash & Equivalents	678.9	68.6	85.6
Total Current Assets	948.3	340.0	417.0
Fixed Assets, Net	0.0	0.0	0.0
Total Assets	18,182.5	18,345.4	17,657.7
Total Current Liabilities	14.3	14.0	12.0
Long-Term Debt	0.0	0.0	0.0
Stockholders' Equity	18,168.2	18,331.4	17,645.7
Performance & Financial Condition			
Return on Total Revenues %	88.46	94.68	293.62
Return on Avg Stockholders' Equity %	3.85	8.82	n.a.
Return on Average Assets %	3.84	8.82	n.a.
Current Ratio	66.22	24.29	34.75
Debt / Equity %	n.a.	n.a.	n.a.

Compound Growth %'s	EPS % n.a.	Net Income % n.a.	Total Revenues % n.a.

Comments

Expenses of administering and managing the investment portfolio approximate .5% of average assets. Gains and losses on sale or redemption of bonds vary from year to year. Accordingly, compound growth rates were not displayed. Distributions to shareholders are largely tax-free income. Noteworthy is that the tax-free yield is quite favorable since the stock sells below book value. Investment Classification: Income & Value

Officers	Position	Ownership Information	
George S. Walls, Jr.	President	Number of Shares Outstanding	1,201,768
Jerry D. Wheatley	Secretary, Treasurer	Market Capitalization	$ 12,618,564
		Frequency of Dividends	Quarterly
		Number of Shareholders	155

Other Information			
Transfer Agent	Securities Transfer Corporation Dallas, TX	Where Listed	OTC-BB
Auditor	Cheshier & Fuller, L.L.P.	Symbol	SMAV
Market Maker	Carr Securities Corporation	(800)221-2243	SIC Code	6790
	Robotti & Co., Inc.	(212)986-0800	Employees	n.a.
Broker Dealer	Regular Stockbroker		

Savers Life Insurance Company

8064 North Point Boulevard   Winston Salem, NC 27106   Telephone (910)759-3888   Fax (910)759-3999

Company Description

Savers Life Insurance Company provides life, accident and health insurance services in North Carolina, South Carolina, Virginia and Florida. Even though the Company has managed excellent growth, it is moving ahead with marketing alliances that will enable the generation of fee income without capital constraints. The Company's stock is not listed on any exchange and it has been reacquiring shares in recent years. The best way to acquire shares is through a local broker or advertisement in a local newspaper.

	12/31/95	12/31/94	12/31/93	12/31/92
Per Share Information				
Stock Price	6.50	6.75	7.00	7.00
Earnings Per Share	0.53	1.79	0.78	1.05
Price / Earnings Ratio	12.26	3.77	8.97	6.67
Book Value Per Share	9.71	8.84	6.72	7.25
Price / Book Value %	66.94	76.36	104.17	96.55
Dividends Per Share	0.0	0.06	0.06	0.06
Annual Financial Data				
Operating Results (000's)				
Total Revenues	58,003.5	53,605.8	37,890.4	23,435.8
Costs & Expenses	-56,926.6	-49,278.6	-35,694.1	-21,134.4
Income Before Taxes and Other	1,076.9	4,327.2	2,196.3	2,301.4
Other Items	0.0	0.0	0.0	0.0
Income Tax	-115.9	-1,086.0	-782.0	-288.6
Net Income	960.9	3,241.2	1,414.3	2,012.8
Cash Flow From Operations	-202.3	4,563.0	1,247.1	1.1
Balance Sheet (000's)				
Cash & Equivalents	15,004.7	12,769.7	28,759.7	17,172.1
Total Current Assets	15,952.8	14,149.1	30,585.6	17,172.1
Fixed Assets, Net	105.5	151.0	203.3	91.7
Total Assets	83,342.3	84,431.5	77,557.9	72,642.0
Total Current Liabilities	1,010.2	1,672.1	1,163.1	3,035.9
Long-Term Debt	0.0	0.0	0.0	0.0
Stockholders' Equity	17,250.1	15,781.5	11,909.3	10,863.5
Performance & Financial Condition				
Return on Total Revenues %	1.66	6.05	3.73	8.59
Return on Avg Stockholders' Equity %	5.82	23.41	12.42	n.a.
Return on Average Assets %	1.15	4.00	1.88	n.a.
Current Ratio	15.79	8.46	26.30	5.66
Debt / Equity %	n.a.	n.a.	n.a.	n.a.

Compound Growth %'s	EPS %	-20.38	Net Income %	-21.84	Total Revenues %	35.27

Comments

1996 results were not yet released when we went to press. 1995 earnings suffered from higher than expected claims. New marketing efforts were being investigated for 1996 including long term care, home health care, and group life and disability. Management was expecting positive results from these new products in the second half of 1996. Investment Classification: Value

Officers	Position	Ownership Information	
Jerry D. Stoltz, Sr.	President, Treasurer	Number of Shares Outstanding	1,775,903
Jerry E. Francis	Senior VP	Market Capitalization	$ 11,543,370
Patricia G. Landy	Secretary	Frequency of Dividends	Irregular
David A. Roberson	Vice President	Number of Shareholders	Under 500
Debra P. Berg	Controller		

Other Information			
Transfer Agent	Company Office	Where Listed	Order Matching Only
Auditor	D.E. Gatewood and Company	Symbol	n.a.
Market Maker	None - See Note	SIC Code	6310
		Employees	n.a.
Broker Dealer	None		

Scioto Downs, Inc.

6000 South High Street   Columbus, OH 43207   Telephone (614)491-2515   Fax (614)491-4626

Company Description

The Company's sole business is the ownership and operation of a harness horse racing facility in Columbus, Ohio, where it has conducted racing since 1959. Revenues are earned from commissions on pari-mutuel wagering and various other related operations, including admissions, concessions and parking.

	10/31/96	10/31/95	10/31/94	10/31/93
Per Share Information				
Stock Price as of 12/31	12.25	13.75	13.00	15.94
Earnings Per Share	-0.56	-0.22	-0.33	-0.31
Price / Earnings Ratio	n.a.	n.a.	n.a.	n.a.
Book Value Per Share	7.50	8.18	8.49	8.99
Price / Book Value %	163.33	168.09	153.12	177.31
Dividends Per Share	0.10	0.10	0.10	0.10
Annual Financial Data				
Operating Results (000's)				
Total Revenues	5,923.7	6,332.7	6,053.3	6,050.7
Costs & Expenses	-6,440.6	-6,568.5	-6,396.5	-6,327.9
Income Before Taxes and Other	-516.9	-235.9	-343.1	-277.2
Other Items	0.0	0.0	41.0	0.0
Income Tax	185.0	106.0	104.0	90.0
Net Income	-331.9	-129.9	-198.1	-187.2
Cash Flow From Operations	219.2	478.4	484.7	602.6
Balance Sheet (000's)				
Cash & Equivalents	621.6	787.8	685.1	669.1
Total Current Assets	787.6	995.9	879.4	817.4
Fixed Assets, Net	7,307.0	7,799.9	8,293.2	8,804.3
Total Assets	8,094.6	8,795.8	9,172.6	9,621.8
Total Current Liabilities	503.0	3,665.2	493.2	428.1
Long-Term Debt	3,025.9	0.0	3,263.2	3,369.3
Stockholders' Equity	4,470.9	4,871.2	5,059.0	5,357.7
Performance & Financial Condition				
Return on Total Revenues %	-5.60	-2.05	-3.27	-3.09
Return on Avg Stockholders' Equity %	-7.11	-2.62	-3.80	-3.42
Return on Average Assets %	-3.93	-1.45	-2.11	-1.91
Current Ratio	1.57	0.27	1.78	1.91
Debt / Equity %	67.68	n.a.	64.50	62.89

Compound Growth %'s	EPS % n.a.	Net Income % n.a.	Total Revenues % -0.70

Comments

For good news, shareholders must look forward as the racing industry in the state of Ohio was successful in seeking legislation that now permits full card simulcasting. The new law went into effect after the Company was closed for the season. The early returns at operating tracks look promising for the viability of Ohio harness racing, for the purse structure at Ohio tracks, and for the bottom line for all of Ohio racing. An agreement was also reached with nearby Beulah Park so that the two tracks would not be open for simulcasting at the same time. For investors, the bank is the finish line; we must wait for next year's results. Investment Classification: Speculative

Officers	Position	Ownership Information	
Robert S. Steele	President, COO	Number of Shares Outstanding	595,767
Roderick H. Willcox	Secretary	Market Capitalization	$ 7,298,146
William C. Heer	Treasurer	Frequency of Dividends	Semi-Annual
Laverne A. Hill	Vice President	Number of Shareholders	1,697
Timothy V. Luther	Controller		

Other Information				
Transfer Agent	Company Office		Where Listed	OTC-BB
Auditor	Coopers & Lybrand LLP		Symbol	SCDO
Market Maker	Paragon Capital Corporation	(800)345-0505	SIC Code	7948
	Sierra Brokerage Services, Inc	(800)837-3351	Employees	350
Broker Dealer	Regular Stockbroker			

Scripps Bank

7817 Ivanhoe Avenue, Suite 201   La Jolla, CA 92038   Telephone (619)456-2265   Fax (619)459-2156

Company Description

Scripps Bank has thirteen offices serving affluent La Jolla and surrounding communities in and near San Diego, California. It offers a full range of bank and trust services. Management is in the midst of a major expansion to double the number of offices serving the area. During both 1996 and 1995, stock offerings were oversubscribed. The Bank placed 680,000 and 185,000 shares at prices ranging from $12 to $15, in 1996 and 1995, respectively. An Employee Stock Ownership Plan owns a portion of the Bank which started business in 1984.

	12/31/96	12/31/95	12/31/94	12/31/93
Per Share Information				
Stock Price	18.25	14.62	10.45	8.18
Earnings Per Share	1.34	1.26	0.79	0.60
Price / Earnings Ratio	13.62	11.60	13.23	13.63
Book Value Per Share	12.53	10.73	8.85	8.39
Price / Book Value %	145.65	136.25	118.08	97.50
Dividends Per Share	0.20	0.17	0.11	0.09
Annual Financial Data				
Operating Results (000's)				
Net Interest Income	14,475.0	12,389.0	10,294.0	7,920.0
Loan Loss Provision	-805.0	-971.0	-724.0	-1,277.0
Non-Interest Income	3,366.0	2,810.0	2,364.0	2,132.0
Non-Interest Expense	-12,689.0	-11,016.0	-10,134.0	-7,568.0
Income Before Taxes and Other	4,347.0	3,212.0	1,800.0	1,207.0
Other Items	0.0	0.0	0.0	100.0
Income Tax	-1,746.0	-1,360.0	-760.0	-560.0
Net Income	2,601.0	1,852.0	1,040.0	747.0
Balance Sheet (000's)				
Cash & Securities	118,990.0	94,812.0	56,247.0	38,675.0
Loans, Net	175,972.0	128,815.0	117,335.0	103,355.0
Total Assets	301,489.0	229,342.0	179,803.0	147,541.0
Deposits	271,830.0	211,746.0	167,526.0	135,490.0
Stockholders' Equity	27,658.0	16,277.0	11,479.0	10,598.0
Performance & Financial Condition				
Return on Avg Stockholders' Equity %	11.84	13.34	9.42	7.39
Return on Average Assets %	0.98	0.91	0.64	0.56
Equity to Assets %	9.17	7.10	6.38	7.18
Net Interest Margin	n.a.	n.a.	n.a.	n.a.
Reserve as a % of Problem Loans	368.36	95.91	2,949.15	251.74

Compound Growth %'s	EPS %	30.71	Net Income %	51.57	Net Interest Income %	22.26

Comments

The Bank declared a 10% stock dividend in 1995. All per share amounts were adjusted for consistency. During 1996, assets increased 31%, deposits grew 28%, net loans climbed 37% and trust assets under administration increased 85%. Additional growth is imminent as the Kearney Mesa and North County Coastal offices opened in January, 1997, and the Encinitas office moved into a permanent location in mid-1997. Investment Classification: Growth

Officers	Position	Ownership Information	
Ronald J. Carlson	President, CEO	Number of Shares Outstanding	2,208,000
Douglas H. Evans	Exec VP	Market Capitalization	$ 40,296,000
James S. Hartung	Exec VP	Frequency of Dividends	Semi-Annual
Richard J. Roncaglia	Exec VP	Number of Shareholders	n.a.
Mark E. Oemcke	Senior VP, CFO	Where Listed / Symbol	OTC-BB / SCPP

Other Information			Loan Mix	%
Transfer Agent	Chemical Mellon shareholder Services Ridgefield Park, NJ		Commerical	50.3
Auditor	Price Waterhouse LLP		R/E Mortgages	33.0
Market Maker	Wedbush Securities, Inc.	(800)421-0251	Installment	15.3
	Torrey Pines Securities, Inc.	(800)688-8679	Other	1.4
Broker Dealer	Regular Stockbroker			

Sea Pines Associates, Inc.

32 Greenwood Drive   Hilton Head Island, SC 29938   Telephone (803)785-3333   Fax (803)842-1927

Company Description

The Company owns and operates a full-service resort in Sea Pines Plantation on Hilton Head, Island, South Carolina. The resort consists of three golf courses, tennis courts and various other recreational facilities, home and villa rentals and food and beverage services. The Company is also involved in real estate brokerage, country club operations and the development of a retirement community. The Company was formed in 1987.

	10/31/96	10/31/95	10/31/94	10/31/93
Per Share Information				
Stock Price as of 12/31	5,400.00	5,400.00	5,250.00	5,250.00
Earnings Per Share	2,197.40	-118.84	367.93	209.20
Price / Earnings Ratio	2.46	n.a.	14.27	25.10
Book Value Per Share	5,904.76	4,068.38	4,548.23	4,541.31
Price / Book Value %	91.45	132.73	115.43	115.61
Dividends Per Share	360.00	360.00	360.00	360.00
Annual Financial Data				
Operating Results (000's)				
Total Revenues	42,859.0	33,105.0	34,428.0	35,577.0
Costs & Expenses	-34,120.0	-33,522.0	-33,197.0	-34,753.0
Income Before Taxes and Other	8,739.0	-417.0	1,193.0	824.0
Other Items	0.0	0.0	0.0	0.0
Income Tax	-3,340.0	125.0	-289.0	-310.0
Net Income	5,399.0	-292.0	904.0	514.0
Cash Flow From Operations	2,026.0	1,708.0	2,542.0	2,090.0
Balance Sheet (000's)				
Cash & Equivalents	1,428.0	1,968.0	1,847.0	1,687.0
Total Current Assets	3,827.0	5,249.0	5,190.0	5,539.0
Fixed Assets, Net	38,039.0	40,954.0	35,998.0	36,132.0
Total Assets	46,257.0	51,706.0	45,161.0	44,601.0
Total Current Liabilities	5,331.0	6,631.0	5,992.0	5,836.0
Long-Term Debt	18,719.0	17,902.0	14,115.0	14,515.0
Stockholders' Equity	14,508.0	9,996.0	11,175.0	11,158.0
Performance & Financial Condition				
Return on Total Revenues %	12.60	-0.88	2.63	1.44
Return on Avg Stockholders' Equity %	44.07	-2.76	8.10	4.53
Return on Average Assets %	11.02	-0.60	2.01	1.17
Current Ratio	0.72	0.79	0.87	0.95
Debt / Equity %	129.03	179.09	126.31	130.09

Compound Growth %'s	EPS %	n.a.	Net Income %	n.a.	Total Revenues %	6.40

Comments

The Company's capital stock was originally issued in units consisting of 500 shares of preferred stock and 750 shares of common stock. Virtually all stock transactions have been in units as originally issued. All share and per share amounts are converted to units. The preferred stock has a liquidation preference of $7.60 per share ($3,800 per unit) and annual dividends per share of $.72 per share ($360 per unit). The Country Club was turned over to its members in May, 1996, causing a gain of $7.7 million. Because this is nonrecurring, compound earnings growth rates have not been displayed. A new conference center, which has long been considered essential, is being constructed during 1997. Real estate sales and golf operations both had excellent years. Investment Classification: Value

Officers	Position	Ownership Information	
Charles W. Flynn	Chairman	Number of Shares Outstanding	2,457
Michael E. Lawrence	CEO	Market Capitalization	$ 13,267,800
Angus Cotton	Secretary	Frequency of Dividends	Quarterly
Thomas C. Morton	Treasurer	Number of Shareholders	697
Norman P. Harberger	Other		

Other Information			
Transfer Agent	Wachovia Bank of North Carolina, N.A.	Where Listed	OTC-PS
Auditor	Ernst & Young LLP	Symbol	SPSU
Market Maker	Robinson-Humphrey Company Inc. (800)241-0445	SIC Code	7997
		Employees	265
Broker Dealer	Dean Witter Reynolds Inc. (212)392-3790		

Seven J Stock Farm, Inc.

808 Travis Street, Ste. 1453   Houston, TX 77002-5701   Telephone (713)228-8900   Fax (713)228-8913

Company Description

The principal operations of the Company consist of producing and selling field crops, leasing pastures, and gathering and transporting natural gas through pipelines. The Company also receives oil and gas royalties on the 11,140 acres of land it owns in Houston County, Texas. Seven J Stock Farm, Inc. was formed in 1948.

	10/31/96	10/31/95	10/31/94	10/31/93
Per Share Information				
Stock Price as of 12/31	3.50	3.50	3.50	2.75
Earnings Per Share	0.05	0.11	0.12	0.10
Price / Earnings Ratio	70.00	31.82	29.17	27.50
Book Value Per Share	1.08	1.06	0.95	0.83
Price / Book Value %	324.07	330.19	368.42	331.33
Dividends Per Share	0.04	0.0	0.0	0.0
Annual Financial Data				
Operating Results (000's)				
Total Revenues	561.0	686.0	600.0	546.0
Costs & Expenses	-452.0	-459.0	-385.0	-358.0
Income Before Taxes and Other	109.0	227.0	215.0	188.0
Other Items	0.0	0.0	0.0	0.0
Income Tax	-32.0	-65.0	-34.0	-39.0
Net Income	77.0	162.0	181.0	149.0
Cash Flow From Operations	-74.0	299.0	158.0	345.0
Balance Sheet (000's)				
Cash & Equivalents	97.0	487.0	376.0	86.0
Total Current Assets	437.0	631.0	525.0	594.0
Fixed Assets, Net	1,353.0	1,168.0	1,046.0	853.0
Total Assets	1,798.0	1,807.0	1,579.0	1,455.0
Total Current Liabilities	159.0	176.0	132.0	184.0
Long-Term Debt	0.0	0.0	0.0	0.0
Stockholders' Equity	1,560.0	1,541.0	1,379.0	1,198.0
Performance & Financial Condition				
Return on Total Revenues %	13.73	23.62	30.17	27.29
Return on Avg Stockholders' Equity %	4.97	11.10	14.05	13.26
Return on Average Assets %	4.27	9.57	11.93	10.43
Current Ratio	2.75	3.59	3.98	3.23
Debt / Equity %	n.a.	n.a.	n.a.	n.a.

Compound Growth %'s	EPS %	-20.63	Net Income %	-19.75	Total Revenues %	0.91

Comments

Revenues from the production of cotton decreased 84% from the previous year directly as a result of the extreme drought conditions followed by unseasonably heavy rains. The Company's land is stated at a cost of $303,000, which computes to an average cost of $27.20 per acre. 7,442 acres are presently leased for $16 per acre. Another 2,612 acres are leased under a crop sharing arrangement. Investment Classification: Speculative

Officers	Position	Ownership Information	
John R. Parten	Chairman, President	Number of Shares Outstanding	1,451,000
Valerie Coulter	Secretary	Market Capitalization	$ 5,078,500
R.F. Pratka	Vice President, Treasurer	Frequency of Dividends	Irregular
		Number of Shareholders	851

Other Information				
Transfer Agent	Company Office		Where Listed	OTC-BB
Auditor	Mattison and Riquelmy		Symbol	SEVJ
Market Maker	Carr Securities Corporation	(800)221-2243	SIC Code	6792
	Hill Thompson Magid & Co., Inc	(800)631-3083	Employees	10
Broker Dealer	Regular Stockbroker			

Seven-Up/RC Bottling Co. of Southern Calif., Inc.

3220 East 26th Street   Los Angeles, CA 90023   Telephone (213)268-7779   Fax (213)267-6226

Company Description

Seven-Up/RC Bottling Company of Southern California, Inc. is among the largest beverage distributors in the United States. The Company manufactures and distributes a broad range of beverage products in southern and central California and in portions of Nevada and New Mexico. The Company has the exclusive right within its territories to manufacture many of the beverages. The Company was privately owned until it filed for bankruptcy protection in May, 1996.

	12/31/96	12/31/95	12/31/94	12/31/93
Per Share Information				
Stock Price	9.87	n.a.	n.a.	n.a.
Earnings Per Share	1.47	n.a.	n.a.	n.a.
Price / Earnings Ratio	6.71	n.a.	n.a.	n.a.
Book Value Per Share	10.53	n.a.	n.a.	n.a.
Price / Book Value %	93.73	n.a.	n.a.	n.a.
Dividends Per Share	0.0	n.a.	n.a.	n.a.
Annual Financial Data				
Operating Results (000's)				
Total Revenues	328,850.0	396,935.0	413,935.0	371,480.0
Costs & Expenses	-307,590.0	-424,114.0	-429,650.0	-384,998.0
Income Before Taxes and Other	7,702.0	-32,194.0	-15,715.0	-13,518.0
Other Items	0.0	0.0	0.0	-826.0
Income Tax	-345.0	0.0	-185.0	0.0
Net Income	7,357.0	-32,194.0	-15,900.0	-14,344.0
Cash Flow From Operations	21,845.0	5,767.0	n.a.	n.a.
Balance Sheet (000's)				
Cash & Equivalents	3,813.0	5,949.0	n.a.	n.a.
Total Current Assets	58,128.0	85,515.0	n.a.	n.a.
Fixed Assets, Net	56,790.0	79,945.0	n.a.	n.a.
Total Assets	121,370.0	192,133.0	n.a.	n.a.
Total Current Liabilities	46,724.0	253,466.0	n.a.	n.a.
Long-Term Debt	19,527.0	0.0	n.a.	n.a.
Stockholders' Equity	52,663.0	-61,333.0	n.a.	n.a.
Performance & Financial Condition				
Return on Total Revenues %	2.24	-8.11	-3.84	-3.86
Return on Avg Stockholders' Equity %	n.a.	n.a.	n.a.	n.a.
Return on Average Assets %	4.69	n.a.	n.a.	n.a.
Current Ratio	1.24	0.34	n.a.	n.a.
Debt / Equity %	37.08	n.a.	n.a.	n.a.

Compound Growth %'s	EPS % n.a.	Net Income % n.a.	Total Revenues % -3.98

Comments

An extraordinary gain of $54.6 million was recorded in connection with the reorganization in bankruptcy which we excluded from the presentation above. Furthermore, we combined the periods before and after reorganization to present the entire year. Nonrecurring items in the 1996 year amount to a net gain of about $21.3 million, $4.26 per share. Revenues declined due to the sale of certain operating divisions. As we went to press, Dr. Pepper Bottling Company of Texas made an offer to purchase all shares at $12 per share subject to a number of conditions. Management did not want to speculate on the outcome of this transaction. Investment Classification: Speculative

Officers	Position	Ownership Information	
Barton S. Brodkin	President, CEO	Number of Shares Outstanding	5,000,000
Richard D. Ferguson	Exec VP, CFO	Market Capitalization	$ 49,350,000
Roy S. Breneman	Exec VP	Frequency of Dividends	n.a.
Louis Janicich	Senior VP	Number of Shareholders	29
F. L. Joseph Chalmers	Senior VP		

Other Information

Transfer Agent	Fleet national Bank Hartford, CT		Where Listed	OTC-BB
Auditor	Arthur Andersen LLP		Symbol	SURC
Market Maker	Merit Capital Associates	(800)405-1000	SIC Code	2086
	Troster Singer	(800)222-0890	Employees	n.a.
Broker Dealer	Regular Stockbroker			

Shenandoah Telecommunications Company

124 South Main Street   Edinburg, VA 22824   Telephone (540)984-4141   Fax (540)984-1892

Company Description

Shenandoah Telecommunications Company is a holding company that through its subsidiaries provides local and long distance telephone, cable television, mobile communications, business radio, cellular telephone and unregulated communications services, as well as other communications related products and services, to the northern Shenandoah Valley area of Virginia and surrounding areas. The Company was founded in 1902.

	12/31/96	12/31/95	12/31/94	12/31/93
Per Share Information				
Stock Price	21.00	24.50	22.00	20.38
Earnings Per Share	1.33	1.66	1.29	1.22
Price / Earnings Ratio	15.79	14.76	17.05	16.70
Book Value Per Share	11.47	10.44	9.20	8.29
Price / Book Value %	183.09	234.67	239.13	245.84
Dividends Per Share	0.42	0.48	0.38	0.30
Annual Financial Data				
Operating Results (000's)				
Total Revenues	26,774.0	22,910.4	20,531.6	18,245.0
Costs & Expenses	-18,288.5	-13,713.4	-12,709.6	-12,077.1
Income Before Taxes and Other	8,485.5	10,338.3	7,822.0	7,153.9
Other Items	-669.3	-534.7	-393.3	-69.5
Income Tax	-2,821.6	-3,573.0	-2,577.6	-2,481.8
Net Income	4,994.6	6,230.7	4,851.0	4,602.6
Cash Flow From Operations	8,740.1	8,161.3	7,281.6	6,634.1
Balance Sheet (000's)				
Cash & Equivalents	3,763.5	7,348.7	9,505.5	8,410.8
Total Current Assets	14,551.1	15,308.9	15,165.0	13,629.4
Fixed Assets, Net	49,193.4	36,826.2	31,896.2	31,503.9
Total Assets	79,374.1	59,897.0	52,464.2	49,652.1
Total Current Liabilities	4,552.4	4,258.8	2,386.2	3,854.6
Long-Term Debt	24,176.8	10,097.0	9,517.9	9,051.9
Stockholders' Equity	43,127.9	39,271.3	34,616.7	31,176.0
Performance & Financial Condition				
Return on Total Revenues %	18.65	27.20	23.63	25.23
Return on Avg Stockholders' Equity %	12.12	16.87	14.75	15.63
Return on Average Assets %	7.17	11.09	9.50	9.74
Current Ratio	3.20	3.59	6.36	3.54
Debt / Equity %	56.06	25.71	27.50	29.03

Compound Growth %'s	EPS %	2.92	Net Income %	2.76	Total Revenues %	13.64

Comments

Telephone revenues increased a modest 6% during 1996, while revenues from other services grew a whopping 30.1%. Deregulation of the telecommunications industry will present many opportunities for this well capitalized company that has already established itself in many different markets. During 1996, the Shenandoah River flooded the Valley on two separate occasions which destroyed Company property in low-lying locations. Service to residents was restored within four days and the Company was able to equip the residents of those areas with cellular telephones to use until normal service was restored. Investment Classification: Growth

Officers	Position	Ownership Information	
Christopher E. French	President, CEO	Number of Shares Outstanding	3,760,760
Laurence F. Paxton	VP - Finance	Market Capitalization	$ 78,975,960
Harold Morrison, Jr.	Secretary	Frequency of Dividends	Annual
Dick D. Bowman	Treasurer	Number of Shareholders	3,399
Noel M. Borden	Vice President		

Other Information				
Transfer Agent	Company Office		Where Listed	OTC-BB
Auditor	McGladrey & Pullen LLP		Symbol	SHET
Market Maker	Carr Securities Corporation	(800)221-2243	SIC Code	4813
	Scott & Stringfellow, Inc.	(800)446-7074	Employees	152
Broker Dealer	Regular Stockbroker			

Shepmyers Investment Company

P.O. Box 339   Hanover, PA 17331   Telephone (717)637-8931   Fax (717)637-6766

Company Description

Shepmeyers Investment Company is registered under the Investment Company Act of 1940 as a diversified, closed-end management company and intends to meet the requirements of a regulated investment company. This enables it to not be subject to federal or state income taxes. The Company's objective is to seek as high a level of income as is consistent with preservation of capital. Its investment portfolio consists largely of municipal bonds.

	12/31/96	12/31/95	12/31/94
Per Share Information			
Stock Price	15.00	13.50	13.50
Earnings Per Share	0.79	1.69	0.05
Price / Earnings Ratio	18.99	7.99	270.00
Book Value Per Share	20.25	20.49	19.81
Price / Book Value %	74.07	65.89	68.15
Dividends Per Share	1.03	1.01	1.06
Annual Financial Data			
Operating Results (000's)			
Total Revenues	719.6	1,410.1	152.7
Costs & Expenses	-114.9	-110.0	-112.3
Income Before Taxes and Other	604.6	1,300.1	40.4
Other Items	0.0	0.0	0.0
Income Tax	0.0	0.0	0.0
Net Income	604.6	1,300.1	40.4
Cash Flow From Operations	604.6	1,300.1	40.4
Balance Sheet (000's)			
Cash & Equivalents	1.0	1.0	1.0
Total Current Assets	245.5	253.8	238.9
Fixed Assets, Net	0.0	0.0	0.0
Total Assets	15,911.2	15,890.5	15,501.3
Total Current Liabilities	355.6	145.9	280.9
Long-Term Debt	0.0	0.0	0.0
Stockholders' Equity	15,555.6	15,744.5	15,220.4
Performance & Financial Condition			
Return on Total Revenues %	84.03	92.20	26.44
Return on Avg Stockholders' Equity %	3.86	8.40	n.a.
Return on Average Assets %	3.80	8.28	n.a.
Current Ratio	0.69	1.74	0.85
Debt / Equity %	n.a.	n.a.	n.a.

Compound Growth %'s	EPS % n.a.	Net Income % n.a.	Total Revenues % n.a.

Comments

Expenses of administering and managing the investment portfolio comprise approximately .7% of average assets. Gains and losses on sale or redemption of bonds vary from year to year. Accordingly, compound growth rates were not displayed. Distributions to shareholders are largely tax-free income. Noteworthy is that the tax-free yield is quite favorable since the stock sells below book value. Investment Classification: Income

Officers	**Position**	**Ownership Information**	
P. E. Spears	Chairman, President	Number of Shares Outstanding	768,238
W. Bruce McConnel, III	Secretary	Market Capitalization	$ 11,523,570
G. P. King	Vice President, Treasurer	Frequency of Dividends	Quarterly
		Number of Shareholders	n.a.

Other Information				
Transfer Agent	Investors Trust Company Wyomissing, PA		Where Listed	OTC-PS
Auditor	Ernst & Young LLP		Symbol	SHYI
Market Maker	The Chicago Corporation	(800)621-1674	SIC Code	6790
	Carr Securities Corporation	(800)221-2243	Employees	n.a.
Broker Dealer	OTC Specialist			

Shopsmith, Inc.

6530 Poe Avenue   Dayton, OH 45414   Telephone (513)898-6070   Fax (513)890-5197

Company Description

Shopsmith, Inc. produces and markets quality woodworking tools and other woodworking products. Products are distributed directly to consumers through demonstration and mail selling channels. The name "Shopsmith" is a registered trademark which the Company applies to the majority of its products. During fiscal 1994, as an element of a restructuring plan, the Company sold 12 and closed the remainder of its 44 retail stores in order to generate cash for operations.

	03/30/96	04/01/95	04/02/94	04/03/93
Per Share Information				
Stock Price as of 12/31	2.37	1.19	1.44	2.75
Earnings Per Share	1.13	0.56	-3.58	-0.59
Price / Earnings Ratio	2.10	2.13	n.a.	n.a.
Book Value Per Share	0.68	-0.46	-1.17	2.43
Price / Book Value %	348.53	n.a.	n.a.	113.17
Dividends Per Share	0.0	0.0	0.0	0.0
Annual Financial Data				
Operating Results (000's)				
Total Revenues	17,466.7	17,728.9	48,045.6	51,113.0
Costs & Expenses	-15,952.8	-16,391.6	-56,538.5	-52,686.5
Income Before Taxes and Other	1,513.9	1,420.7	-8,675.0	-1,573.5
Other Items	770.8	0.0	19.0	0.0
Income Tax	743.0	0.0	0.0	185.0
Net Income	3,027.7	1,420.7	-8,656.0	-1,388.5
Cash Flow From Operations	1,233.4	2,041.2	923.6	-504.4
Balance Sheet (000's)				
Cash & Equivalents	560.2	360.9	749.3	202.9
Total Current Assets	3,849.5	3,799.2	6,058.1	12,026.9
Fixed Assets, Net	608.6	613.0	932.8	4,161.6
Total Assets	5,024.2	4,415.3	7,032.5	16,380.2
Total Current Liabilities	3,214.7	4,717.0	8,191.3	8,894.6
Long-Term Debt	0.0	426.4	0.0	1,742.3
Stockholders' Equity	1,809.5	-1,224.7	-2,802.8	5,743.3
Performance & Financial Condition				
Return on Total Revenues %	17.33	8.01	-18.02	-2.72
Return on Avg Stockholders' Equity %	1,035.50	n.a.	-588.75	-21.75
Return on Average Assets %	64.15	24.82	-73.94	-8.52
Current Ratio	1.20	0.81	0.74	1.35
Debt / Equity %	n.a.	n.a.	n.a.	30.34

Compound Growth %'s	EPS % n.a.	Net Income % n.a.	Total Revenues % n.a.

Comments

1996 results include a nonrecurring gain of $770,824 ($.29 per share) from the extinguishment of debt. Included in the loss for 1994 is $4.3 million for discontinued operations and restructuring. As a result of its restructuring efforts, the Company showed profits in fiscal years 1995 and 1996. For the first nine months of fiscal year 1997, the Company had similar sales as the prior year and Net Income of $1.1 million ($.39 per share) as compared to $2.3 million ($.87 per share) for the same period in 1996. Investment Classification: Speculative

Officers	Position	Ownership Information	
John R. Folkerth	President, CEO	Number of Shares Outstanding	2,659,175
William C. Becker	VP - Finance, CFO	Market Capitalization	$ 6,302,245
Robert L. Folkerth	VP - Sales	Frequency of Dividends	n.a.
		Number of Shareholders	2,703

Other Information

Transfer Agent	Huntington National Bank Columbus, OH		Where Listed	OTC-BB
Auditor	Crowe, Chizek and Company LLP		Symbol	SHOP
Market Maker	Wedbush Morgan Securities, Inc	(800)421-0251	SIC Code	3550
	Wm. V. Frankel & Co., Inc.	(800)631-3091	Employees	122
Broker Dealer	Regular Stockbroker			

Simi Valley Bank

1475 E. Los Angeles Avenue   Simi Valley, CA 93065   Telephone (805)581-2800   Fax (805)522-6412

Company Description

Simi Valley Bank, with a main office and one branch, primarily serves the greater Simi Valley/Moorpark area and Ventura County, California. In the first quarter of 1997, the Bank was approved as a Preferred Lender by the Small Business Administration. Although the Bank participated in SBA lending over the last four years, the new status will make the loan approval process more efficient. The Bank was founded in 1981.

	12/31/96	12/31/95	12/31/94	12/31/93
Per Share Information				
Stock Price	10.62	8.25	4.25	5.00
Earnings Per Share	1.01	1.44	0.55	0.18
Price / Earnings Ratio	10.51	5.73	7.73	27.78
Book Value Per Share	9.56	9.01	8.06	7.51
Price / Book Value %	111.09	91.56	52.73	66.58
Dividends Per Share	0.50	0.50	0.0	0.0
Annual Financial Data				
Operating Results (000's)				
Net Interest Income	5,844.0	5,740.8	4,590.8	3,681.6
Loan Loss Provision	-313.5	-245.0	-595.6	-933.6
Non-Interest Income	1,565.5	1,910.2	1,775.1	2,323.0
Non-Interest Expense	-5,445.6	-5,271.7	-5,002.7	-4,874.0
Income Before Taxes and Other	1,650.4	2,134.2	767.6	197.0
Other Items	0.0	0.0	0.0	0.0
Income Tax	-683.6	-809.2	-264.0	-35.7
Net Income	966.8	1,325.0	503.6	161.3
Balance Sheet (000's)				
Cash & Securities	36,594.2	32,432.6	36,307.5	29,723.4
Loans, Net	52,728.1	52,236.4	48,136.1	40,365.5
Total Assets	96,537.0	90,578.3	90,065.2	76,370.6
Deposits	87,001.6	81,254.2	82,065.7	69,197.3
Stockholders' Equity	8,741.6	8,226.4	7,349.6	6,848.4
Performance & Financial Condition				
Return on Avg Stockholders' Equity %	11.40	17.01	7.09	2.38
Return on Average Assets %	1.03	1.47	0.61	n.a.
Equity to Assets %	9.06	9.08	8.16	8.97
Net Interest Margin	n.a.	n.a.	n.a.	n.a.
Reserve as a % of Problem Loans	43.81	164.35	n.a.	n.a.

Compound Growth %'s	EPS %	77.70	Net Income %	81.64	Net Interest Income %	16.65

Comments

Management reports the successful conversion to a new computer system with state of the art technology. The decline in earnings was not directly addressed. Our side-by-side analysis shows a decline in non-interest income and a rise in non-interest expense. Compound earnings growth rates are distorted by poor results in 1993, the base year for the calculations. Investment Classification: Growth & Value & Income

Officers	Position	Ownership Information	
R.A. "Tony" Palmer	President, CEO	Number of Shares Outstanding	914,405
Robert D. Scott	Exec VP	Market Capitalization	$ 9,710,981
Janice France-Pettit	Senior VP, CFO	Frequency of Dividends	Quarterly
Teri Bingham	Senior VP	Number of Shareholders	n.a.
Susan Deese	Vice President	Where Listed / Symbol	OTC-BB / SIVY

Other Information		Loan Mix	%
Transfer Agent	Chemical Mellon Shareholder Services Ridgefield Park, NJ	R/E Mortgages	58.6
Auditor	Grant Thornton LLP	Commerical	33.7
Market Maker	J. Alexander Securities, Inc. (800)421-0258	Consumer	7.7
	GBS Financial Corp. (818)248-5558		
Broker Dealer	Regular Stockbroker		

Sims-Agricultural Products Company

3795 County Road 29   Mt. Gilead, OH 43338   Telephone (419)946-2015   Fax (419)946-6571

Company Description

Sims Agriculture Products Company is primarily in the business of manufacturing and marketing a complete line of micronutrients and granular nitrogen sulfate used in agriculture. It also is involved in the conversion of zinc filter cake into granulated and powdered finished products. Products are sold throughout the United States and Canada. The Company was founded in 1991 and went public in October, 1993, at $5 per share.

	06/30/96	06/30/95	06/30/94	06/30/93
Per Share Information				
Stock Price as of 12/31	4.50	3.00	2.50	2.50
Earnings Per Share	0.09	0.11	0.11	0.07
Price / Earnings Ratio	50.00	27.27	22.73	35.71
Book Value Per Share	0.84	0.74	0.61	0.12
Price / Book Value %	535.71	405.41	409.84	2,083.33
Dividends Per Share	0.0	0.0	0.0	0.0
Annual Financial Data				
Operating Results (000's)				
Total Revenues	6,095.3	5,476.3	3,965.0	3,453.7
Costs & Expenses	-5,780.8	-5,057.5	-3,643.1	-3,264.6
Income Before Taxes and Other	314.5	379.6	306.2	109.9
Other Items	0.0	0.0	0.0	0.0
Income Tax	-113.6	-133.4	-114.0	0.0
Net Income	200.9	246.1	192.2	109.9
Cash Flow From Operations	141.8	51.4	-78.4	-9.7
Balance Sheet (000's)				
Cash & Equivalents	140.0	5.5	11.8	20.3
Total Current Assets	2,877.2	1,817.0	1,746.6	1,040.5
Fixed Assets, Net	3,280.3	3,048.0	2,092.1	1,653.3
Total Assets	6,387.8	5,042.6	4,057.1	2,933.6
Total Current Liabilities	2,614.2	1,787.5	1,046.7	928.0
Long-Term Debt	1,053.3	1,255.9	1,347.5	1,461.2
Stockholders' Equity	2,499.0	1,830.3	1,542.0	544.5
Performance & Financial Condition				
Return on Total Revenues %	3.30	4.49	4.85	3.18
Return on Avg Stockholders' Equity %	9.28	14.60	18.42	224.67
Return on Average Assets %	3.51	5.41	5.50	4.15
Current Ratio	1.10	1.02	1.67	1.12
Debt / Equity %	42.15	68.62	87.38	268.36

Compound Growth %'s	EPS %	8.74	Net Income %	22.26	Total Revenues %	20.85

Comments

The Company declared a 2 for 1 stock split in 1996. All per share amounts have been adjusted for consistency. The issuance of additional new shares has diluted the compound growth in earnings per share. The Company continues to build its revenue base and strengthen its balance sheet as well. For the nine months ended March 31, 1997, revenue had risen another 14% over the prior year and earnings were $.07 per share. The latest financial information can be accessed on the Company's website: (http://www.simsag.com). Investment Classification: Speculative

Officers	Position	Ownership Information	
Dallas Paul	President	Number of Shares Outstanding	2,066,600
John Bowen	Secretary, Treasurer	Market Capitalization	$ 9,299,700
		Frequency of Dividends	n.a.
		Number of Shareholders	300

Other Information			
Transfer Agent	Huntington Bank Columbus, OH	Where Listed	OTC-BB
Auditor	Robert J. LeHew & Associates	Symbol	SAGG
Market Maker	Wien Securities Corp.	(800)624-0050	SIC Code	2873
	J. Alexander Securities Inc.	(800)421-0258	Employees	35
Broker Dealer	Regular Stockbroker		
	CORNA Securities	(800)934-2676	

Siuslaw Valley Bank

777 Highway 101   Florence, OR 97439-0280   Telephone (541)997-3486   Fax (541)997-2549

Company Description

Siuslaw Valley Bank operates from six retail banking offices and a combined commercial banking/mortgage office serving the rural communities of Lane County, located in southwestern and coastal Oregon. The Bank also originates and sells mortgage loans in the secondary market. The Bank was formed in 1964 and now has 112 employees.

	12/31/96	12/31/95	12/31/94	12/31/93
Per Share Information				
Stock Price	14.50	10.00	8.00	8.00
Earnings Per Share	1.75	1.53	1.16	1.22
Price / Earnings Ratio	8.29	6.54	6.90	6.56
Book Value Per Share	7.83	6.93	5.82	5.07
Price / Book Value %	185.19	144.30	137.46	157.79
Dividends Per Share	0.75	0.60	0.40	0.40
Annual Financial Data				
Operating Results (000's)				
Net Interest Income	7,852.8	7,561.1	6,531.7	5,728.1
Loan Loss Provision	-100.0	-150.0	-300.0	0.0
Non-Interest Income	2,411.2	1,717.8	2,226.1	2,831.6
Non-Interest Expense	-5,161.2	-4,862.3	-5,141.0	-5,094.4
Income Before Taxes and Other	5,002.8	4,266.6	3,316.8	3,465.4
Other Items	0.0	0.0	0.0	0.0
Income Tax	-1,860.0	-1,515.0	-1,225.3	-1,271.0
Net Income	3,142.8	2,751.6	2,091.5	2,194.4
Balance Sheet (000's)				
Cash & Securities	45,107.9	30,004.5	23,018.8	31,636.8
Loans, Net	90,867.1	94,110.7	84,982.0	75,026.3
Total Assets	141,300.6	128,693.0	112,554.0	111,023.7
Deposits	123,201.9	111,802.9	99,201.7	98,294.0
Stockholders' Equity	14,089.5	12,478.3	10,467.4	9,125.7
Performance & Financial Condition				
Return on Avg Stockholders' Equity %	23.66	23.98	21.35	26.16
Return on Average Assets %	2.33	2.28	1.87	2.07
Equity to Assets %	9.97	9.70	9.30	8.22
Net Interest Margin	6.64	6.33	5.97	5.97
Reserve as a % of Problem Loans	898.76	687.27	245.12	501.09

Compound Growth %'s	EPS %	12.78	Net Income %	12.72	Net Interest Income %	11.09

Comments

Management attributes the strong price movement in the Bank's common shares to a "market observation" of the sustained earning performance over the last several years. To us it is remarkable that this community bank has escaped attention with some of the best performance numbers we've seen. Part of it may have to do with the fact that, up until now, only local people knew of this as an investment. The placement and sale of mortgage loans was the key to 1996's record year, pushing non-interest income up 40.4%. But all else looks well too, especially the returns on assets and equity. Investment Classification: Income

Officers	Position	Ownership Information	
Johan Mehlum	President	Number of Shares Outstanding	1,800,000
Lonnie Iholts	Exec VP	Market Capitalization	$ 26,100,000
Lindsey Johnson	Vice President	Frequency of Dividends	Quarterly
Marilla Kessel	Vice President	Number of Shareholders	n.a.
Margaret Lessor	Head Cashier	Where Listed / Symbol	Order Matching Only / n.a.

Other Information			Loan Mix	%
Transfer Agent	Company Office		R/E Mortgages	73.6
Auditor	Symonds, Evans & Larson, P.C.		Commerical	16.2
Market Maker	Black & Company, Inc.	(800)423-2124	Construction	5.3
			Installment	4.5
Broker Dealer	John Ballantyne	(503)248-9600	Other	0.4

Six Rivers National Bank

402 F Street   Eureka, CA 95501   Telephone (707)443-8400   Fax (707)443-3631

Company Description

Six Rivers National Bank operates four branches in beautiful Humboldt and Del Norte Counties in northern California. The Bank opened at the end of 1989. In April, 1996, the downtown Eureka office was opened and now functions as the head office. The Bank became the dominant Small Business Administration lender in the region and has expanded the product mix to offer other various government guaranteed loan products. Six Rivers can also be found on the Internet: (http://www.sixrivers.com).

	12/31/96	12/31/95	12/31/94	12/31/93
Per Share Information				
Stock Price	14.00	10.00	7.00	3.00
Earnings Per Share	1.35	1.00	0.37	0.40
Price / Earnings Ratio	10.37	10.00	18.92	7.50
Book Value Per Share	10.19	8.92	7.59	7.62
Price / Book Value %	137.39	112.11	92.23	39.37
Dividends Per Share	0.0	0.0	0.0	0.0
Annual Financial Data				
Operating Results (000's)				
Net Interest Income	5,073.6	4,053.8	3,380.3	2,875.0
Loan Loss Provision	-276.0	-225.0	-228.5	-172.3
Non-Interest Income	1,066.6	972.4	733.6	907.5
Non-Interest Expense	-4,482.5	-3,820.0	-3,679.9	-3,564.7
Income Before Taxes and Other	1,381.7	981.2	205.4	45.5
Other Items	0.0	0.0	0.0	161.5
Income Tax	-580.2	-412.1	0.0	0.0
Net Income	801.5	569.1	205.4	207.0
Balance Sheet (000's)				
Cash & Securities	23,138.9	28,519.9	25,768.2	23,932.3
Loans, Net	72,654.4	54,664.5	42,990.5	34,097.0
Total Assets	100,019.3	87,189.5	72,196.0	62,710.3
Deposits	91,986.2	79,887.7	66,948.5	57,470.9
Stockholders' Equity	5,754.0	5,037.2	4,206.3	4,219.8
Performance & Financial Condition				
Return on Avg Stockholders' Equity %	14.86	12.31	4.88	5.31
Return on Average Assets %	0.86	0.71	0.30	0.34
Equity to Assets %	5.75	5.78	5.83	6.73
Net Interest Margin	n.a.	n.a.	n.a.	n.a.
Reserve as a % of Problem Loans	45.46	101.09	57.89	39.52

Compound Growth %'s	EPS % 50.00	Net Income % 57.03	Net Interest Income % 20.84

Comments

The Bank tacked on another 15% to asset and deposit growth following last year's 20% increase. But management states that profitability is the strategic focus for the next two years and has been for the last two as well. There is no doubt that the returns on assets and equity confirm this emphasis. Enough loans are being generated to allow for the sale of some on the secondary market, producing non-interest income. This could have a significant impact on future results if the Bank can maintain their dominant position under federally insured programs. Investment Classification: Growth

Officers	Position	Ownership Information	
John F. Burger	President, CEO	Number of Shares Outstanding	564,840
Michael Martinez	Senior VP, CFO	Market Capitalization	$ 7,907,760
Marjorie L. Plum	Senior VP	Frequency of Dividends	n.a.
Gene Ulrich	Senior VP, Sr Loan Officer	Number of Shareholders	n.a.
Kathryn Brown	Vice President	Where Listed / Symbol	OTC-PS / SIXR

Other Information			Loan Mix	%
Transfer Agent	Company Office		Commerical	55.3
Auditor	Deloitte & Touche LLP		Installment	24.2
Market Maker	Sutro & Co., Incorporated	(800)227-4422	R/E Mortgages	13.9
	Hoefer & Arnett, Incorporated	(800)346-5544	Construction	2.8
Broker Dealer	Regular Stockbroker		Other	3.8
	Hoefer & Arnett, Retail	(800)346-5544 Ext: Lisa		

Slade's Ferry Bancorp

100 Slade's Ferry Avenue   Somerset, MA 02726   Telephone (508)675-2121   Fax (508)675-1751

Company Description

Slade's Ferry Bancorp, formerly Weetamoe Bancorp, is the holding company of Slade's Ferry Trust Company, a bank. The Bank was formed in 1959 and operates its business from ten locations in and around Somerset, Massachusetts. The National Bank of Fairhaven was acquired in August, 1996, thereby allowing access to the greater New Bedford marketplace. The Bank has active personal involvement in more than 85 civic, charitable, municipal and church organizations.

	12/31/96	12/31/95	12/31/94	12/31/93
Per Share Information				
Stock Price	8.25	7.86	7.86	7.49
Earnings Per Share	0.86	0.60	0.57	0.49
Price / Earnings Ratio	9.59	13.10	13.79	15.29
Book Value Per Share	7.12	6.49	5.46	5.70
Price / Book Value %	115.87	121.11	143.96	131.40
Dividends Per Share	0.24	0.17	0.15	0.09
Annual Financial Data				
Operating Results (000's)				
Net Interest Income	10,416.9	8,776.9	8,602.4	8,033.2
Loan Loss Provision	-400.0	-550.0	-645.0	-1,455.0
Non-Interest Income	1,305.5	1,056.0	1,099.1	1,226.2
Non-Interest Expense	-7,380.2	-6,631.5	-6,701.6	-5,853.1
Income Before Taxes and Other	3,942.2	2,651.4	2,354.9	1,951.4
Other Items	0.0	0.0	0.0	39.5
Income Tax	-1,564.0	-1,005.8	-887.7	-723.3
Net Income	2,378.2	1,645.6	1,467.2	1,267.6
Balance Sheet (000's)				
Cash & Securities	81,120.2	77,106.3	50,975.6	64,705.9
Loans, Net	194,934.8	148,069.4	133,481.5	123,811.3
Total Assets	291,342.5	233,421.7	193,909.3	196,475.5
Deposits	267,791.0	214,220.7	177,314.8	179,566.8
Stockholders' Equity	19,847.3	17,826.7	14,847.7	15,379.7
Performance & Financial Condition				
Return on Avg Stockholders' Equity %	12.63	10.07	9.71	8.64
Return on Average Assets %	0.91	0.77	0.75	0.66
Equity to Assets %	6.81	7.64	7.66	7.83
Net Interest Margin	4.44	4.36	4.78	4.59
Reserve as a % of Problem Loans	59.14	91.89	66.99	43.31

Compound Growth %'s	EPS %	20.62	Net Income %	23.34	Net Interest Income %	9.05

Comments

The Company declared 5% stock dividends in each of the last three years and a 3 for 2 stock split in 1995. All per share amounts have been adjusted for consistency. 1996 was a record year spurred by increased asset growth, the largest net interest spreads in recent history and a record amount of loan loss recoveries. Management is focused on efforts to expand the Bank's presence in the greater New Bedford marketplace during 1997. The acquisition referred to above was accounted for as a purchase, hence, only operations from the date of purchase are included in the Company's financial statements. Investment Classification: Growth & Value

Officers	Position	Ownership Information	
James D. Carey	President, CEO	Number of Shares Outstanding	2,789,142
Ralph S. Borges	Senior VP, Treasurer	Market Capitalization	$ 23,010,422
Susan R. Hajder	Senior VP	Frequency of Dividends	Quarterly
Carol A. Martin	Senior VP	Number of Shareholders	868
Manuel J. Tavares	Senior VP	Where Listed / Symbol	OTC-PS / SFBC

Other Information			Loan Mix	%
Transfer Agent	Company Office		R/E Mortgages	77.4
Auditor	Shatswell, MacLeod & Co, PC		Commerical	15.8
Market Maker	First Albany Corporation	(800)541-5061	Construction	3.5
	Advest, Inc.	(800)998-9834	Consumer	3.3
Broker Dealer	Regular Stockbroker			

Smith Investment Company

11270 West Park Place   Milwaukee, WI 53223-0972   Telephone (414)359-4030   Fax (414)359-4198

Company Description

Smith Investment Company is involved in a wide range of industries including feed storage systems, ceramic coating, barber and beauty salon furniture and fixtures, commercial warehousing and packaging, and multicolor printing. Through its investment in A. O. Smith Corporation (NYSE), the Company also is involved in fractional horsepower and hermetic electric motors, residential and commercial water heaters, fiberglass piping systems, and water, waste water and dry storage tanks.

	12/31/96	12/31/95	12/31/94	12/31/93
Per Share Information				
Stock Price	63.00	63.00	52.50	49.00
Earnings Per Share	13.23	11.81	10.15	5.77
Price / Earnings Ratio	4.76	5.33	5.17	8.49
Book Value Per Share	89.06	76.99	64.28	56.39
Price / Book Value %	70.74	81.83	81.67	86.89
Dividends Per Share	1.20	1.10	1.00	1.00
Annual Financial Data				
Operating Results (000's)				
Total Revenues	121,821.0	136,240.0	127,735.0	104,147.0
Costs & Expenses	-107,364.0	-112,816.0	-107,125.0	-92,233.0
Income Before Taxes and Other	12,353.0	21,046.0	17,883.0	8,887.0
Other Items	12,319.0	0.0	0.0	0.0
Income Tax	-2,734.0	-1,354.0	-959.0	727.0
Net Income	21,938.0	19,692.0	16,924.0	9,614.0
Cash Flow From Operations	15,578.0	10,318.0	6,193.0	4,528.0
Balance Sheet (000's)				
Cash & Equivalents	280.0	199.0	394.0	185.0
Total Current Assets	30,895.0	31,003.0	30,468.0	23,224.0
Fixed Assets, Net	44,205.0	44,080.0	42,526.0	41,742.0
Total Assets	207,973.0	194,108.0	175,641.0	157,987.0
Total Current Liabilities	39,411.0	43,551.0	37,378.0	32,005.0
Long-Term Debt	15,100.0	17,622.0	26,894.0	27,914.0
Stockholders' Equity	147,702.0	127,690.0	107,195.0	94,033.0
Performance & Financial Condition				
Return on Total Revenues %	18.01	14.45	13.25	9.23
Return on Avg Stockholders' Equity %	15.93	16.77	16.82	10.45
Return on Average Assets %	10.91	10.65	10.15	6.19
Current Ratio	0.78	0.71	0.82	0.73
Debt / Equity %	10.22	13.80	25.09	29.69

Compound Growth %'s	EPS %	31.86	Net Income %	31.65	Total Revenues %	5.36

Comments

Other assets include a 30.7% equity interest in the A.O. Smith Corporation. At December 31, 1996, the fair market value of that investment was $188 million and it was reflected on the books as $130 million. This difference equates to $35 per share of unrecognized book value. The Company reported the fifth consecutive year of higher operating profit from wholly-owned businesses. A. O. Smith Corporation reported a fourth consecutive year of record earnings. On January 27, 1997, A. O. Smith Corporation announced the sale of its Automotive Products Company. This will generate a significant gain to Smith Investment Company in 1997. Investment Classification: Value

Officers	Position	Ownership Information	
Arthur O. Smith	Chairman, CEO	Number of Shares Outstanding	1,658,533
Bruce M. Smith	President	Market Capitalization	$ 104,487,579
Glen R. Bomberger	VP - Finance	Frequency of Dividends	Quarterly
Wesley A. Ulrich	Secretary, Treasurer	Number of Shareholders	Under 500

Other Information			
Transfer Agent	Firstar Trust Company Milwaukee, WI	Where Listed	OTC-BB
Auditor	Ernst & Young LLP	Symbol	SMIC
Market Maker	Robert W. Baird & Co., Inc. (800)562-2288	SIC Code	3621
	Boenning & Scattergood, Inc. (800)883-8383	Employees	5
Broker Dealer	Regular Stockbroker		

Snow Summit Ski Corporation

880 Summit Boulevard   Big Bear Lake, CA 92315   Telephone (909)866-5766   Fax (909)866-3201

Company Description

The Company is the owner and operator of Snow Summit ski area and Sierra Summit ski area in southern California. The Company has been granted the right to use National Forest Service land as the sites for its ski operations, but these permits have expiration dates of May 30, 2024, at Snow Summit and December 31, 2003, at Sierra Summit. Permits of this nature are usually extended. Snow Summit is regarded as offering the finest skiing in southern California. Owners of at least 60 shares of stock are allowed special privileges to use the facilities.

	04/30/96	04/30/95	04/30/94	04/30/93
Per Share Information				
Stock Price as of 12/31	160.00	170.00	170.00	165.00
Earnings Per Share	5.89	17.37	12.31	2.17
Price / Earnings Ratio	27.16	9.79	13.81	76.04
Book Value Per Share	139.31	134.43	118.05	105.74
Price / Book Value %	114.85	126.46	144.01	156.04
Dividends Per Share	1.00	1.00	0.0	1.00
Annual Financial Data				
Operating Results (000's)				
Total Revenues	21,033.6	24,665.2	23,894.1	21,231.9
Costs & Expenses	-20,362.8	-22,639.6	-22,521.1	-20,942.4
Income Before Taxes and Other	670.8	2,025.6	1,373.0	289.5
Other Items	0.0	0.0	0.0	0.0
Income Tax	-269.7	-841.7	-534.0	-141.8
Net Income	401.1	1,183.9	839.0	147.8
Cash Flow From Operations	534.5	3,440.1	3,381.7	1,028.2
Balance Sheet (000's)				
Cash & Equivalents	790.3	1,338.5	1,619.1	643.7
Total Current Assets	4,834.0	3,616.2	4,002.0	2,776.9
Fixed Assets, Net	17,489.3	15,220.3	14,865.2	16,155.9
Total Assets	23,594.1	20,145.7	20,214.9	20,319.1
Total Current Liabilities	3,801.7	1,309.4	4,454.8	3,561.0
Long-Term Debt	10,230.2	5,769.4	7,046.5	8,704.2
Stockholders' Equity	9,494.0	9,161.1	8,045.4	7,206.3
Performance & Financial Condition				
Return on Total Revenues %	1.91	4.80	3.51	0.70
Return on Avg Stockholders' Equity %	4.30	13.76	11.00	2.06
Return on Average Assets %	1.83	5.87	4.14	0.77
Current Ratio	1.27	2.76	0.90	0.78
Debt / Equity %	107.75	62.98	87.59	120.79

Compound Growth %'s	EPS %	39.49	Net Income %	39.50	Total Revenues %	-0.31

Comments

Despite being subject to the forces of Mother Nature, the Company has consistently returned a profit and is constantly looking for ways to improve operations. After three years of intense negotiations, management has concluded a lease/purchase agreement for 2.7 acres of property adjacent to the Snow Summit base area. Plans are in the works to expand and provide a large number of new and improved services intended to greatly enhance Snow Summit which should be ready for the 1997/1998 season. The 1995/1996 ski season was one of the worst on record which accounts for lower earnings. Investment Classification: Value

Officers	Position	Ownership Information	
Richard C. Kun	President	Number of Shares Outstanding	68,150
Steven Trainor	VP - Finance	Market Capitalization	$ 10,904,000
Greg Ralph	Vice President	Frequency of Dividends	Quarterly
Thomas Banish	Vice President	Number of Shareholders	Under 500
Robert Tarras	Controller		

Other Information

Transfer Agent	U.S. Stock Transfer Corporation Glendale, CA	Where Listed	OTC-PS
Auditor	Grant Thornton LLP	Symbol	SSNS
Market Maker	The Seidler Companies Inc.	(800)421-0164	SIC Code	7999
	Sharpe Capital Inc.	(800)355-5781	Employees	n.a.
Broker Dealer	OTC Specialist		
	Standard Investment	(888)783-4688 Ext: Jack	

Solid Controls, Inc.

820 South Fifth Street   Hopkins, MN 55343   Telephone (612)933-9053   Fax (612)933-8961

Company Description

Solid Controls, Inc. designs and manufactures a diversified line of integrated machine controls, providing modern technology to the plastic machine industry. Much of the demand for sophisticated plastic machinery relates directly to the automotive industry. The Company has paid dividends for 24 consecutive years.

	03/31/96	03/31/95	03/31/94	03/31/93
Per Share Information				
Stock Price as of 12/31	1.62	2.19	2.37	2.50
Earnings Per Share	0.05	-0.07	0.04	0.09
Price / Earnings Ratio	32.40	n.a.	59.25	27.78
Book Value Per Share	2.22	2.33	2.55	2.59
Price / Book Value %	72.97	93.99	92.94	96.53
Dividends Per Share	0.13	0.13	0.13	0.13
Annual Financial Data				
Operating Results (000's)				
Total Revenues	2,699.1	3,381.2	2,864.2	3,179.8
Costs & Expenses	-2,698.1	-3,490.0	-2,804.2	-3,038.6
Income Before Taxes and Other	1.0	-108.8	60.0	141.2
Other Items	0.0	0.0	0.0	0.0
Income Tax	47.4	20.0	-9.0	-40.4
Net Income	48.4	-88.8	51.0	100.8
Cash Flow From Operations	277.1	166.0	-45.3	268.4
Balance Sheet (000's)				
Cash & Equivalents	868.8	1,217.0	1,222.6	1,369.2
Total Current Assets	2,043.2	2,509.9	2,694.2	2,777.5
Fixed Assets, Net	39.7	44.4	59.3	59.8
Total Assets	2,296.5	2,902.1	3,166.7	3,283.2
Total Current Liabilities	92.3	132.1	126.4	179.2
Long-Term Debt	0.0	0.0	0.0	0.0
Stockholders' Equity	2,170.4	2,768.5	3,020.2	3,065.4
Performance & Financial Condition				
Return on Total Revenues %	1.79	-2.63	1.78	3.17
Return on Avg Stockholders' Equity %	1.96	-3.07	1.68	3.26
Return on Average Assets %	1.86	-2.93	1.58	3.03
Current Ratio	22.15	19.01	21.31	15.50
Debt / Equity %	n.a.	n.a.	n.a.	n.a.

Compound Growth %'s	EPS %	-17.79	Net Income %	-21.71	Total Revenues %	-5.32

Comments

Fiscal 1996 results include nonrecurring income of $177,356 from the proceeds of life insurance. The money was used to fulfill a commitment to retire 206,400 shares of stock at $2.50 per share. The Company is more aggressively trying to expand markets and has made dramatic cost reductions. Although sales were off again in the six months ended September 30, 1996, the loss was reduced to $72,000, $.07 per share. The Company is still financially strong and expects profitability in the second half of fiscal 1997. Investment Classification: Speculative & Value

Officers	Position	Ownership Information	
Ronald A. Kokesh	President	Number of Shares Outstanding	979,404
A. Larry Katz	Secretary	Market Capitalization	$ 1,586,634
Kevin R. Kokesh	VP - Sales	Frequency of Dividends	Semi-Annual
Alan E. Wenker	Controller	Number of Shareholders	Under 500

Other Information

Transfer Agent	ChaseMellon Shareholder Services Ridgefield Park, NJ		Where Listed	OTC-BB
Auditor	Deloitte & Touche LLP		Symbol	SLDC
Market Maker	Hill Thompson Magid & Co., Inc	(800)631-3083	SIC Code	5063
	R.J. Steichen and Co.	(800)328-8217	Employees	n.a.
Broker Dealer	Regular Stockbroker			

Sonoma Valley Bank

202 West Napa Street   Sonoma, CA 95476   Telephone (707)935-3200   Fax (707)935-3899

Company Description

Sonoma Valley Bank, located in the heart of the California wine region, commenced operations in 1988. The Bank's lending activities are directed towards granting short and medium-term commercial loans, customized lines of credit for such purposes as operating capital, business start-ups and inventory, etc., and interim construction financing. The Bank has two locations.

	12/31/96	12/31/95	12/31/94	12/31/93
Per Share Information				
Stock Price	20.25	15.91	9.92	11.02
Earnings Per Share	2.17	1.81	1.25	0.90
Price / Earnings Ratio	9.33	8.79	7.94	12.24
Book Value Per Share	14.31	12.20	9.89	9.01
Price / Book Value %	141.51	130.41	100.30	122.31
Dividends Per Share	0.0	0.0	0.0	0.0
Annual Financial Data				
Operating Results (000's)				
Net Interest Income	4,567.2	4,129.3	3,486.2	2,947.2
Loan Loss Provision	-184.0	-190.0	-250.0	-328.9
Non-Interest Income	643.0	499.9	429.3	404.1
Non-Interest Expense	-3,183.9	-2,930.1	-2,606.4	-2,260.6
Income Before Taxes and Other	1,842.3	1,509.2	1,059.2	761.7
Other Items	0.0	0.0	0.0	0.0
Income Tax	-672.3	-532.8	-382.3	-288.9
Net Income	1,170.0	976.4	676.9	472.9
Balance Sheet (000's)				
Cash & Securities	36,961.4	25,368.4	24,027.5	22,096.7
Loans, Net	50,854.0	47,672.5	37,826.1	36,792.5
Total Assets	90,787.1	75,923.8	64,465.5	59,852.0
Deposits	82,218.8	68,694.6	58,667.0	54,751.4
Stockholders' Equity	7,722.2	6,582.9	5,337.6	4,864.1
Performance & Financial Condition				
Return on Avg Stockholders' Equity %	16.36	16.38	13.27	10.65
Return on Average Assets %	1.40	1.39	1.09	0.86
Equity to Assets %	8.51	8.67	8.28	8.13
Net Interest Margin	6.23	6.75	6.06	5.98
Reserve as a % of Problem Loans	209.08	209.98	n.a.	893.47

Compound Growth %'s	EPS %	34.09	Net Income %	35.25	Net Interest Income %	15.72

Comments

The Bank has declared 10%, 10%, 5% and 5% stock dividends in 1996, 1995, 1994 and 1993, respectively. All per share amounts have been adjusted for consistency. You might expect strong growth from a young bank. However, Sonoma Valley Bank has also been producing high returns on equity and assets. Most of the 20% increase in earnings traces to the increase in net interest income as deposits grew 19% and total assets grew 20%. Non-interest income is also providing an added boost to the bottom line. Investment Classification: Growth

Officers	Position	Ownership Information	
Mel Switzer, Jr.	President, CEO	Number of Shares Outstanding	539,609
Mary Quade Dieter	Exec VP, CFO	Market Capitalization	$ 10,927,082
Jean Hopeman	Senior VP, Sr Loan Officer	Frequency of Dividends	n.a.
Ray Sullivan	Vice President	Number of Shareholders	1,086
Juan Martinez	Vice President	Where Listed / Symbol	OTC-BB / SOVY

Other Information		Loan Mix	%
Transfer Agent	American Stock Transfer & Trust Company New York, NY	Commerical	63.2
Auditor	Richardson & Company	Consumer	20.7
Market Maker	Robert Thomas Securities (707)935-9778	Construction	9.0
	Raymond, James & Associates (800)237-5621	R/E Mortgages	7.1
Broker Dealer	Regular Stockbroker		

South Chester Tube Company

210 N. Brinton Lake Road   Concordville, PA 19331   Telephone (215)459-4000   Fax (215)358-6350

Company Description

South Chester Tube Company is primarily engaged in manufacturing and selling access hardware and latching devices. The Company's marketing effort covers the United States. It also has international sales through five operating subsidiaries in England, France, Germany, Italy and Australia. An Employee Stock Ownership Plan (ESOP) owned a 21.5% interest in the Company as of July, 1993. At that time, the ESOP offered to purchase an additional 1,300 shares for a cash price of $6,267 per share so as to increase its ownership to 30%.

	06/30/93	06/30/92
Per Share Information		
Stock Price as of 12/31	5,900.00	5,900.00
Earnings Per Share	344.81	263.85
Price / Earnings Ratio	17.11	22.36
Book Value Per Share	4,447.43	4,151.85
Price / Book Value %	132.66	142.11
Dividends Per Share	60.00	54.00
Annual Financial Data		
Operating Results (000's)		
Total Revenues	42,952.9	76,476.1
Costs & Expenses	-34,722.6	-63,161.6
Income Before Taxes and Other	8,230.3	13,314.5
Other Items	0.0	0.0
Income Tax	-3,030.5	-4,789.2
Net Income	5,199.8	8,525.3
Cash Flow From Operations	n.a.	8,630.1
Balance Sheet (000's)		
Cash & Equivalents	22,093.0	19,381.5
Total Current Assets	52,166.7	48,176.0
Fixed Assets, Net	18,412.7	17,495.0
Total Assets	73,800.9	68,748.2
Total Current Liabilities	5,721.5	5,618.7
Long-Term Debt	0.0	0.0
Stockholders' Equity	67,067.3	62,609.9
Performance & Financial Condition		
Return on Total Revenues %	12.11	11.15
Return on Avg Stockholders' Equity %	8.02	n.a.
Return on Average Assets %	7.30	n.a.
Current Ratio	9.12	8.57
Debt / Equity %	n.a.	n.a.

Compound Growth %'s	EPS % n.a.	Net Income % n.a.	Total Revenues % n.a.

Comments

We have been trying to track down this financial statement for almost two years and will keep trying. The bid price for the shares rose to $7,000 by the end of 1995, and $8,100 at the end of 1996. Investment Classification: Value

Officers	Position	Ownership Information	
Stephen J. Kelly	Chairman, President	Number of Shares Outstanding	15,080
C.I. Murphy	VP - Finance	Market Capitalization	$ 122,148,000
C.G. Gibbon	Secretary	Frequency of Dividends	Quarterly
C. Robert Ganskopp	VP - Sales	Number of Shareholders	Under 500

Other Information			
Transfer Agent	Company Office	Where Listed	OTC-BB
Auditor	Deloitte & Touche LLP	Symbol	SOUC
Market Maker	F.J. Morrissey & Co., Inc. (800)842-8928	SIC Code	3429
	Hill Thompson Magid & Co., Inc (800)631-3083	Employees	n.a.
Broker Dealer	OTC Specialist		
	Standard Investment (888)783-4688 Ext: Jack		

Southern Scottish Inns, Inc.

1726 Montreal Circle   Tucker, GA 30084   Telephone (770)938-5966   Fax (770)938-6382

Company Description

Southern Scottish Inns, Inc. franchises, finances, owns and leases motels as well as restaurants in association with the motels. At December 31, 1995, the Company held franchises on 269 motels, including Passport Inns, Red Carpet Inns, Scottish Inns and Master Hosts Inns. The motels are located in the southern United States. The Company was founded in 1971.

	12/31/95	12/31/94	12/31/93	12/31/92
Per Share Information				
Stock Price	1.50	1.32	1.07	1.01
Earnings Per Share	0.37	0.18	0.12	0.16
Price / Earnings Ratio	4.05	7.33	8.92	6.31
Book Value Per Share	3.77	3.45	3.26	3.37
Price / Book Value %	39.79	38.26	32.82	29.97
Dividends Per Share	0.0	0.0	0.0	0.0
Annual Financial Data				
Operating Results (000's)				
Total Revenues	6,193.2	4,986.6	4,151.3	3,982.9
Costs & Expenses	-4,673.1	-4,134.9	-3,591.2	-3,607.1
Income Before Taxes and Other	1,520.2	851.6	560.1	375.9
Other Items	-84.4	-172.1	-191.6	60.0
Income Tax	-584.5	-256.8	-96.5	-75.8
Net Income	851.2	422.7	272.0	360.0
Cash Flow From Operations	277.8	550.3	182.9	399.0
Balance Sheet (000's)				
Cash & Equivalents	138.6	83.4	148.2	112.1
Total Current Assets	1,547.2	1,382.0	1,260.0	1,080.4
Fixed Assets, Net	3,821.0	4,089.2	3,794.3	3,998.8
Total Assets	16,259.4	14,344.4	13,915.5	13,928.2
Total Current Liabilities	2,654.7	2,142.4	1,979.7	1,614.8
Long-Term Debt	2,710.6	2,125.0	2,356.5	2,853.7
Stockholders' Equity	8,764.8	8,003.3	7,580.6	7,797.4
Performance & Financial Condition				
Return on Total Revenues %	13.74	8.48	6.55	9.04
Return on Avg Stockholders' Equity %	10.15	5.43	3.54	4.55
Return on Average Assets %	5.56	2.99	1.95	2.55
Current Ratio	0.58	0.65	0.64	0.67
Debt / Equity %	30.93	26.55	31.09	36.60

Compound Growth %'s	EPS %	32.24	Net Income %	33.22	Total Revenues %	15.85

Comments

The Company's financial statements are typically filed very late and were not yet available for 1996. For the nine months ended September 30, 1996, the Company reported profits of $791,868, $.34 per share. Current assets were strengthened to $2.0 million which is encouraging. The price per share at December 31, 1996, was $1.30 bid/$1.82 ask. Investment Classification: Value & Speculative

Officers	Position	Ownership Information	
Harry C. McIntire	Chairman	Number of Shares Outstanding	2,322,466
Jack M. Dubard	President	Market Capitalization	$ 3,483,699
Bobby E. Guimbellot	CEO	Frequency of Dividends	n.a.
		Number of Shareholders	910

Other Information

Transfer Agent	First National Bank of Commerce New Orleans, LA		Where Listed	OTC-BB
Auditor	Robert J. Clark, C.P.A.		Symbol	SOHS
Market Maker	Morgan Keegan & Company, Inc.	(800)238-7533	SIC Code	6794
	Carr Securities Corporation	(800)221-2243	Employees	144
Broker Dealer	Regular Stockbroker			

Southern Webbing Mills, Inc.

4701 Southern Webbing Mill Rd. Greensboro, NC 27405 Telephone (910)375-3103 Fax (910)621-2136

Company Description

Southern Webbing Mills, Inc. is engaged in the manufacture and sale of quality woven and knitted narrow elastic and non-elastic fabrics, primarily for use in apparel and orthopedic appliances. The Company was founded in 1924.

	12/31/96	12/31/95	12/31/94	12/31/93
Per Share Information				
Stock Price	6.75	6.50	6.00	n.a.
Earnings Per Share	-2.24	-1.13	0.30	-0.28
Price / Earnings Ratio	n.a.	n.a.	20.00	n.a.
Book Value Per Share	6.77	9.26	10.56	n.a.
Price / Book Value %	99.70	70.19	56.82	n.a.
Dividends Per Share	0.20	0.20	0.16	0.64
Annual Financial Data				
Operating Results (000's)				
Total Revenues	11,758.1	16,460.5	18,432.3	19,522.3
Costs & Expenses	-12,984.7	-17,126.5	-17,692.8	-19,773.4
Income Before Taxes and Other	-1,226.6	-913.5	342.6	-251.1
Other Items	0.0	0.0	0.0	0.0
Income Tax	-34.8	253.0	-158.7	73.5
Net Income	-1,261.4	-660.6	183.9	-177.6
Cash Flow From Operations	n.a.	409.9	1,666.0	n.a.
Balance Sheet (000's)				
Cash & Equivalents	0.0	0.0	199.4	n.a.
Total Current Assets	4,917.6	5,201.3	6,288.7	n.a.
Fixed Assets, Net	1,735.5	3,070.7	3,549.3	n.a.
Total Assets	7,083.2	8,741.9	10,296.7	n.a.
Total Current Liabilities	3,034.5	1,798.2	2,271.2	n.a.
Long-Term Debt	0.0	1,169.4	1,267.5	n.a.
Stockholders' Equity	3,692.0	5,339.9	6,267.8	n.a.
Performance & Financial Condition				
Return on Total Revenues %	-10.73	-4.01	1.00	-0.91
Return on Avg Stockholders' Equity %	-27.93	-11.38	n.a.	n.a.
Return on Average Assets %	-15.94	-6.94	n.a.	n.a.
Current Ratio	1.62	2.89	2.77	n.a.
Debt / Equity %	n.a.	21.90	20.22	n.a.

Compound Growth %'s	EPS % n.a.	Net Income % n.a.	Total Revenues % -15.55

Comments

The last annual report reported very difficult times caused by the decline in the medical safety belt business, a decision to reduce the woven suspender and belt customer base, and the loss of a large customer. The management team has been restructured which caused substantial severance costs. The medical textiles operation was also consolidated into the Greensboro location. The good news is that first quarter results for 1997 were on target for a net profit of $101,000 as compared to a loss of $228,000 in the same period of 1996. April results were ahead of plan. Investment Classification: Speculative

Officers	Position	Ownership Information	
William B. Barnhardt	President, CEO	Number of Shares Outstanding	545,112
William T. Linton	Senior VP	Market Capitalization	$ 3,679,506
Edwin M. Chapman	Secretary, Treasurer	Frequency of Dividends	n.a.
Ann C. McDougald	Vice President	Number of Shareholders	Under 500
Steven W. King	VP - Manufacturing		

Other Information			
Transfer Agent	Company Office	Where Listed	OTC-BB
Auditor	Not indicated	Symbol	SOUM
Market Maker	Hill Thompson Magid & Co., Inc (800)631-3083	SIC Code	2200
	Carr Securities Corporation (800)221-2243	Employees	50
Broker Dealer	Regular Stockbroker		

Spartan Mills

463 Howard Street   Spartanburg, SC 29303   Telephone (803)574-0211   Fax (803)587-0291

Company Description

Spartan Mills is a multinational manufacturer of textile and related products. The Company's principal lines of business include apparel fabrics, home furnishing fabrics, industrial and decorative fabrics, health care fabrics and products, knit apparel fabrics and dyeing, finishing and printing of textile fabrics. The principal markets for these products are in the United States and Europe.

	11/30/96	12/02/95	12/03/94	11/27/93
Per Share Information				
Stock Price as of 12/31	40.00	84.00	88.00	87.00
Earnings Per Share	-16.37	-21.15	-3.82	8.80
Price / Earnings Ratio	n.a.	n.a.	n.a.	9.89
Book Value Per Share	106.91	119.43	137.56	139.05
Price / Book Value %	37.41	70.33	63.97	62.57
Dividends Per Share	0.0	0.0	1.00	1.00
Annual Financial Data				
Operating Results (000's)				
Total Revenues	n.a.	n.a.	n.a.	n.a.
Costs & Expenses	n.a.	n.a.	n.a.	n.a.
Income Before Taxes and Other	n.a.	n.a.	n.a.	n.a.
Other Items	n.a.	n.a.	n.a.	n.a.
Income Tax	n.a.	n.a.	n.a.	N.a.
Net Income	-21,051.0	-28,070.0	-6,544.0	10,716.0
Cash Flow From Operations	n.a.	n.a.	n.a.	n.a.
Balance Sheet (000's)				
Cash & Equivalents	1,614.0	454.0	313.0	2,339.0
Total Current Assets	109,617.0	128,578.0	136,740.0	137,047.0
Fixed Assets, Net	140,075.0	156,575.0	144,291.0	145,256.0
Total Assets	259,725.0	291,585.0	293,376.0	293,024.0
Total Current Liabilities	51,899.0	50,702.0	57,915.0	43,869.0
Long-Term Debt	4,336.0	16,230.0	23,901.0	27,714.0
Stockholders' Equity	137,482.0	158,533.0	186,603.0	190,837.0
Performance & Financial Condition				
Return on Total Revenues %	n.a.	n.a.	n.a.	n.a.
Return on Avg Stockholders' Equity %	-14.22	-16.27	-3.47	5.81
Return on Average Assets %	-7.64	-9.60	-2.23	3.62
Current Ratio	2.11	2.54	2.36	3.12
Debt / Equity %	3.15	10.24	12.81	14.52

Compound Growth %'s	EPS % n.a.	Net Income % n.a.	Total Revenues % n.a.

Comments

The continuing increase in the level of imported garments has and may continue to have a substantial negative impact on the Company's apparel businesses. Net income for the years shown was estimated by looking at the change in retained earnings. The Company does not present an income statement as part of its annual report. The balance sheet numbers are the only firm numbers available. LIFO is used to calculate inventory. At the November, 1996 year end, inventory was valued $37.4 million lower than current costs. Investment Classification: Speculative & Value

Officers	Position	Ownership Information	
Walter S. Montgomery	President, CEO	Number of Shares Outstanding	1,285,919
Perry Conley	CFO	Market Capitalization	$ 51,436,760
		Frequency of Dividends	n.a.
		Number of Shareholders	Under 500

Other Information

Transfer Agent	Company Office			
Auditor	Ernst & Young LLP		Where Listed	OTC-BB
Market Maker	Hill Thompson Magid & Co., Inc	(800)631-3083	Symbol	SNML
	The Chicago Corporation	(800)323-1225	SIC Code	2200
Broker Dealer	Regular Stockbroker		Employees	n.a.

Sportsman's Guide, Inc. (The)

411 Farwell Avenue   South St. Paul, MN 55075   Telephone (612)451-3030   Fax (612)450-6130

Company Description

The Sportsman's Guide, Inc. is an outdoor consumer catalog marketer, offering a variety of merchandise such as apparel, footwear, hunting and shooting accessories, fishing and camping goods, optics, collectibles, and a variety of gift items. Operations are conducted from one facility in South St. Paul, Minnesota, with catalogs being distributed throughout the United States. About one million customers purchased from the Company's catalogs during 1996. Approximately 45 million catalogs were mailed to existing and prospective customers during that year. The Company was formed in 1977.

	12/29/96	12/30/95	12/31/94	12/31/93
Per Share Information				
Stock Price	2.00	2.00	9.10	2.10
Earnings Per Share	0.91	-0.75	1.01	-0.20
Price / Earnings Ratio	2.20	n.a.	9.01	n.a.
Book Value Per Share	1.66	0.66	1.41	0.24
Price / Book Value %	120.48	303.03	645.39	875.00
Dividends Per Share	0.0	0.0	0.0	0.0
Annual Financial Data				
Operating Results (000's)				
Total Revenues	112,281.0	101,905.0	96,398.0	60,191.0
Costs & Expenses	-108,967.0	-104,004.0	-93,248.0	-60,654.0
Income Before Taxes and Other	3,086.0	-2,099.0	3,107.0	-478.0
Other Items	0.0	0.0	0.0	0.0
Income Tax	-759.0	355.0	-385.0	0.0
Net Income	2,327.0	-1,744.0	2,722.0	-478.0
Cash Flow From Operations	662.0	1,276.0	-125.0	1,120.0
Balance Sheet (000's)				
Cash & Equivalents	0.0	0.0	653.0	0.0
Total Current Assets	23,535.0	19,411.0	17,891.0	12,851.5
Fixed Assets, Net	4,355.0	4,298.0	3,288.0	1,808.5
Total Assets	27,890.0	23,709.0	21,179.0	14,660.0
Total Current Liabilities	19,923.0	21,874.0	13,940.0	11,554.4
Long-Term Debt	1,795.0	220.0	3,773.0	1,774.0
Stockholders' Equity	3,875.0	1,548.0	3,292.0	570.0
Performance & Financial Condition				
Return on Total Revenues %	2.07	-1.71	2.82	-0.79
Return on Avg Stockholders' Equity %	85.82	-72.07	140.96	-59.08
Return on Average Assets %	9.02	-7.77	15.19	-4.11
Current Ratio	1.18	0.89	1.28	1.11
Debt / Equity %	46.32	14.21	114.61	311.22

Compound Growth %'s	EPS %	-5.08	Net Income %	-7.54	Total Revenues %	23.10

Comments

During early 1997, the Company executed a 1 for 10 reverse stock split. All per share amounts have been adjusted for consistency. Revenues were higher by 10%. The fact that marketing and administrative costs were held firm is great news for a mail order catalog company. The balance sheet improved and management announced a three-year renewal of the credit line. This will allow working capital to take advantage of trade discounts and special buying opportunities as they appear. Investment Classification: Speculative

Officers	Position	Ownership Information	
Gary Olen	President, CEO	Number of Shares Outstanding	2,333,600
Gregory Binkley	Exec VP, COO	Market Capitalization	$ 4,667,200
William G. Luth	Senior VP	Frequency of Dividends	n.a.
Charles B. Lingen	CFO, Senior VP	Number of Shareholders	300
John Casler	Vice President		

Other Information				
Transfer Agent	Corporate Stock Transfer, Inc. Denver, CO		Where Listed	OTC-BB
Auditor	Grant Thornton LLP		Symbol	GIDE
Market Maker	R.J. Steichen & Co.	(800)328-8217	SIC Code	5961
	John G. Kinnard and Co., Inc.	(800)825-5466	Employees	750
Broker Dealer	Regular Stockbroker			

Spring Street Brewing Company, Inc.

826 Broadway, 6th floor   New York, NY 10003   Telephone (212)253-4455   Fax (212)253-4494

Company Description

Spring Street Brewing Company, Inc. produces and markets Wit, Amber Wit and Black Wit which are hand-crafted Belgian recipe wheat ales. Plans are in process for developing additional beers. The products are currently sold through distributors in fifteen states. After raising $2.2 million through a direct public offering in 1995, the Company gained additional notoriety by establishing an order matching service on the Internet. In early 1997, the Company completed a secondary offering of 1.2 million shares at $2.75 per share.

	03/31/96	09/30/95	09/30/94
Per Share Information			
Stock Price as of 12/31	2.75	1.85	0.56
Earnings Per Share	-0.01	-0.07	-0.07
Price / Earnings Ratio	n.a.	n.a.	n.a.
Book Value Per Share	0.10	0.08	0.05
Price / Book Value %	2,750.00	2,312.50	1,120.00
Dividends Per Share	0.0	0.0	0.0
Annual Financial Data			
Operating Results (000's)			
Total Revenues	463.6	419.1	330.8
Costs & Expenses	-566.0	-903.0	-788.5
Income Before Taxes and Other	-143.0	-528.4	-488.0
Other Items	33.1	17.3	0.0
Income Tax	-0.7	0.0	0.0
Net Income	-110.6	-511.1	-488.0
Cash Flow From Operations	-514.3	-345.8	-345.8
Balance Sheet (000's)			
Cash & Equivalents	1,104.6	644.8	200.8
Total Current Assets	1,666.6	985.3	414.9
Fixed Assets, Net	46.0	39.2	35.2
Total Assets	1,727.2	1,029.4	455.3
Total Current Liabilities	187.1	352.2	165.7
Long-Term Debt	0.0	0.0	0.0
Stockholders' Equity	819.1	611.8	289.6
Performance & Financial Condition			
Return on Total Revenues %	-23.85	-121.96	-147.51
Return on Avg Stockholders' Equity %	-15.45	-113.40	n.a.
Return on Average Assets %	-8.02	-68.85	n.a.
Current Ratio	8.91	2.80	2.50
Debt / Equity %	n.a.	n.a.	n.a.

Compound Growth %'s	EPS % n.a.	Net Income % n.a.	Total Revenues % n.a.

Comments

The period ended March 31, 1996, is a six-month partial year. More current numbers were not available. In 1996, the Securities and Exchange Commission may have thought the Company was going a little too far by having shares trade on Cyber Street rather than on Wall Street. The Company complied with the Government's request to come back down to earth. As of now, there is no mechanism for trading, but management intends to fix that soon. Latest developments are available on a World Wide Web site: (http://www.witcap.com). Investment Classification: Speculative

Officers	Position	Ownership Information	
Andrew D. Klein	Chairman, Treasurer	Number of Shares Outstanding	7,926,637
Delos W. Lander	President	Market Capitalization	$ 21,798,252
Peter G. Weinberg	Vice President, Secretary	Frequency of Dividends	n.a.
Barry A. Osherow	Vice President	Number of Shareholders	Under 500

Other Information

Transfer Agent	Company Office		Where Listed	Order Matching Only
Auditor	Arthur Andersen LLP		Symbol	n.a.
Market Maker	None - See Note		SIC Code	2082
			Employees	8
Broker Dealer	None			

St. Lawrence Seaway Corporation (The)

320 N. Meridian St., Ste. 818   Indianapolis, IA 46204   Telephone (317)639-5292   Fax (317)632-7142

Company Description

The St. Lawrence Seaway Corporation, since it was formed in 1959, has principally engaged in farming, timber harvesting and other traditional agricultural activities. During the last six years, the Company's only other operating activity has been the sale of certain farming acreage, and investment of its remaining liquid assets, primarily in interest bearing cash equivalent securities.

	03/31/96	03/31/95	03/31/94	03/31/93
Per Share Information				
Stock Price as of 12/31	2.50	2.25	2.50	2.50
Earnings Per Share	-0.21	-0.22	0.04	0.07
Price / Earnings Ratio	n.a.	n.a.	62.50	35.71
Book Value Per Share	3.32	3.53	3.74	3.60
Price / Book Value %	75.30	63.74	66.84	69.44
Dividends Per Share	0.0	0.0	0.0	0.0
Annual Financial Data				
Operating Results (000's)				
Total Revenues	69.0	65.1	137.6	148.0
Costs & Expenses	-150.4	-156.3	-113.5	-109.7
Income Before Taxes and Other	-81.5	-91.2	24.1	38.3
Other Items	0.0	0.0	0.0	0.0
Income Tax	-0.7	5.4	-8.0	-10.3
Net Income	-82.2	-85.7	16.1	28.0
Cash Flow From Operations	-26.4	-43.3	-142.7	n.a.
Balance Sheet (000's)				
Cash & Equivalents	1,232.5	1,260.9	n.a.	n.a.
Total Current Assets	1,246.1	1,290.6	n.a.	n.a.
Fixed Assets, Net	124.7	124.2	n.a.	n.a.
Total Assets	1,370.9	1,414.8	n.a.	n.a.
Total Current Liabilities	62.1	23.9	n.a.	n.a.
Long-Term Debt	0.0	0.0	n.a.	n.a.
Stockholders' Equity	1,308.8	1,391.0	n.a.	n.a.
Performance & Financial Condition				
Return on Total Revenues %	-119.15	-131.66	11.69	18.93
Return on Avg Stockholders' Equity %	-6.09	-5.98	1.09	1.92
Return on Average Assets %	-5.90	-5.87	1.07	1.87
Current Ratio	20.07	54.09	n.a.	n.a.
Debt / Equity %	n.a.	n.a.	n.a.	n.a.

Compound Growth %'s	EPS % n.a.	Net Income % n.a.	Total Revenues % -22.47

Comments

The Company has not yet found the right opportunity for investing its cash which is the largest asset. The Board of Directors is evaluating opportunities to become a "blank-check" company, which seeks the acquisition of an operating business, as well as transactions with operating businesses themselves. For the nine months ended December 31, 1996, a loss of $36,922, $.09 per share, was reported. Although a price below book value may look attractive, an assessment of management's ability to execute a reasonable acquisition would be prudent. Investment Classification: Value & Speculative

Officers	Position	Ownership Information	
Joel M. Greenblatt	Chairman	Number of Shares Outstanding	393,735
Daniel L. Nir	President, Treasurer	Market Capitalization	$ 984,338
Jack C. Brown	Secretary	Frequency of Dividends	n.a.
		Number of Shareholders	1,382

Other Information			
Transfer Agent	Continental Stock Transfer & Trust Co. New York, NY	Where Listed	OTC-BB
Auditor	Sallee & Company	Symbol	STLS
Market Maker	Carr Securities Corporation	(800)221-2243	SIC Code	6519
	Koonce Securities, Inc.	(800)368-2802	Employees	1
Broker Dealer	Regular Stockbroker			

St. Louis Steel Casting Inc.

2300 Falling Springs Road   Sauget, IL 62206-1102   Telephone (618)353-5800   Fax (618)337-2277

Company Description

St. Louis Steel Casting Inc. is engaged in the foundry industry, specifically in the production of carbon, low alloy steel castings. Hydraulic Press Brick Company, a 56% owned subsidiary, produces expanded shale aggregate which is used principally in the construction industry in the components of walls, floors and structural elements. A significant portion of Hydraulic's sales is delivered to purchasers located in the Midwestern United States. The accounts of Hydraulic are consolidated with those of the Company. St. Louis Steel Casting was founded in 1926.

	09/30/96	09/30/95	09/30/94	09/30/93
Per Share Information				
Stock Price as of 12/31	28.50	23.00	17.50	12.50
Earnings Per Share	4.77	5.50	6.26	1.93
Price / Earnings Ratio	5.97	4.18	2.80	6.48
Book Value Per Share	34.90	30.98	26.24	20.50
Price / Book Value %	n.a.	74.24	66.69	60.98
Dividends Per Share	0.85	0.75	0.52	0.40
Annual Financial Data				
Operating Results (000's)				
Total Revenues	25,498.0	26,820.0	21,334.0	12,945.0
Costs & Expenses	-22,316.0	-23,150.0	-17,901.0	-11,878.0
Income Before Taxes and Other	3,182.0	3,556.0	3,401.0	1,051.0
Other Items	-686.0	-502.0	-336.0	-106.0
Income Tax	-1,073.0	-1,414.0	-1,199.0	-369.0
Net Income	1,423.0	1,640.0	1,866.0	576.0
Cash Flow From Operations	3,098.0	2,393.0	3,995.0	705.0
Balance Sheet (000's)				
Cash & Equivalents	3,205.0	1,368.0	2,576.0	1,238.0
Total Current Assets	10,414.0	9,550.0	8,384.0	6,148.0
Fixed Assets, Net	6,063.0	5,036.0	4,506.0	3,481.0
Total Assets	16,797.0	14,998.0	13,511.0	9,767.0
Total Current Liabilities	2,353.0	2,352.0	2,032.0	1,327.0
Long-Term Debt	0.0	0.0	726.0	58.0
Stockholders' Equity	10,409.0	9,239.0	7,824.0	6,115.0
Performance & Financial Condition				
Return on Total Revenues %	5.58	6.11	8.75	4.45
Return on Avg Stockholders' Equity %	14.48	19.22	26.77	9.79
Return on Average Assets %	8.95	11.51	16.03	6.17
Current Ratio	4.43	4.06	4.13	4.63
Debt / Equity %	n.a.	n.a.	9.28	0.95

Compound Growth %'s	EPS %	35.20	Net Income %	35.18	Total Revenues %	25.35

Comments

1995 results include approximately $767,000 of gain from property transactions. 1994 and 1993 results include income from the receipt of insurance proceeds of $1,284,000 and $282,000, respectively. The Company entered the 1997 fiscal year with a substantial level of backlogs and shipments of foundry products. For the six months ended March 31, 1997, the Company reported net earnings of $606,000, $2.03 per share, as compared to $300,000, $1.01 per share, in the same period of 1996. Investment Classification: Growth & Value

Officers	Position	Ownership Information	
Christian B. Peper, Jr.	Chairman	Number of Shares Outstanding	298,225
Earl J. Bewig	President, COO	Market Capitalization	$ 8,499,413
Robert H. Schnellbacher	Secretary	Frequency of Dividends	Quarterly
Robert N. Stewart	Treasurer	Number of Shareholders	190
Gregory D. Fore	VP - Sales		

Other Information			
Transfer Agent	KeyCorp Shareholder Services, Inc. Cleveland, OH	Where Listed	OTC-BB
Auditor	Kerber, Eck & Braeckel LLP	Symbol	STLO
Market Maker	Burns, Pauli & Co., Inc. (800)325-3373	SIC Code	3320
	Koonce Securities, Inc. (800)368-2802	Employees	75
Broker Dealer	Regular Stockbroker		

Standard Electronics, Inc.

215 John Glenn Drive   Amherst, NY 14228-2227   Telephone (716)691-3061   Fax (716)691-3170

Company Description

Standard Electronics, Inc. is a wholesale distributor of electronic parts and equipment primarily to retailers located in western New York. It is also the Sony franchisee for its geographic area. The Company has been buying back its shares. The price it paid in 1996 was $6 per share, up from $5 a year earlier. These amounts represent a substantial discount from book value.

	06/30/96	06/30/95	06/30/94	06/30/93
Per Share Information				
Stock Price as of 12/31	4.00	5.00	6.00	6.00
Earnings Per Share	0.11	0.01	1.26	-3.59
Price / Earnings Ratio	36.36	500.00	4.76	n.a.
Book Value Per Share	12.07	11.88	11.86	10.58
Price / Book Value %	33.14	42.09	50.59	56.71
Dividends Per Share	0.0	0.0	0.0	0.0
Annual Financial Data				
Operating Results (000's)				
Total Revenues	11,268.6	10,285.4	10,503.6	11,422.5
Costs & Expenses	-11,229.9	-10,283.7	-10,431.7	-12,031.1
Income Before Taxes and Other	38.7	1.7	71.9	-610.8
Other Items	0.0	0.0	0.0	0.0
Income Tax	-23.0	0.0	116.0	74.0
Net Income	15.7	1.7	187.9	-536.8
Cash Flow From Operations	151.8	234.7	588.5	-368.7
Balance Sheet (000's)				
Cash & Equivalents	3,300.0	18.6	66.7	14.3
Total Current Assets	3,300.0	3,332.0	3,128.5	3,273.0
Fixed Assets, Net	785.6	780.0	903.7	966.5
Total Assets	4,508.4	4,833.3	4,682.8	4,835.5
Total Current Liabilities	2,343.3	2,587.4	2,359.4	2,625.2
Long-Term Debt	396.4	481.4	559.6	631.5
Stockholders' Equity	1,768.7	1,764.4	1,763.7	1,578.8
Performance & Financial Condition				
Return on Total Revenues %	0.14	0.02	1.79	-4.70
Return on Avg Stockholders' Equity %	0.89	0.09	11.24	-29.03
Return on Average Assets %	0.34	0.03	3.95	-10.56
Current Ratio	1.41	1.29	1.33	1.25
Debt / Equity %	22.41	27.29	31.73	40.00

Compound Growth %'s	EPS % n.a.	Net Income % n.a.	Total Revenues % -0.45

Comments

1994 results include a nonoperating benefit of $116,000 arising from a change in the accounting for income taxes. This distorted compound growth rates in earnings so we did not display them. The Company stabilized after losses in 1991, 1992 and 1993. Management does not provide an explanation of results or a description of the current economic environment. Investment Classification: Value

Officers	Position	Ownership Information	
William Humston	President	Number of Shares Outstanding	146,558
Mercy Degain	Controller	Market Capitalization	$ 586,232
		Frequency of Dividends	n.a.
		Number of Shareholders	Under 500

Other Information

Transfer Agent	Manufacturers & Traders Trust Co.		Where Listed	OTC-PS
Auditor	BDO Seidman LLP		Symbol	SDEL
Market Maker	Hill Thompson Magid & Co., Inc	(800)631-3083	SIC Code	5065
	The Chicago Corporation	(800)323-1225	Employees	40
Broker Dealer	OTC Specialist			
	Standard Investment	(888)783-4688 Ext: Jack		

Startech Environmental Corporation

79 Old Ridgefield Road   Wilton, CT 06897   Telephone (203)762-2499   Fax (203)761-0839

Company Description

Startech Environmental Corporation, formerly Kapalua Acquisitions, Inc., was investigating possible business opportunities until November 17, 1995, when it completed the acquisition of Startech Corporation. Startech designs and manufactures machinery to recover, recycle, reduce and remediate hazardous and nonhazardous waste materials. The Startech Plasma Waste Converter (PWC) is a closed-loop recycling system that converts materials formerly regarded as hazardous wastes into useful commodity products. The Company is targeting the hazardous waste industry as its initial market.

	10/31/96	10/31/95
Per Share Information		
Stock Price as of 12/31	3.75	5.00
Earnings Per Share	-0.12	-0.04
Price / Earnings Ratio	n.a.	n.a.
Book Value Per Share	-0.01	-0.04
Price / Book Value %	n.a.	n.a.
Dividends Per Share	0.0	0.0
Annual Financial Data		
Operating Results (000's)		
Total Revenues	29.4	0.0
Costs & Expenses	-699.4	-36.7
Income Before Taxes and Other	-670.0	-36.7
Other Items	0.0	0.0
Income Tax	-0.5	0.0
Net Income	-670.5	-36.7
Cash Flow From Operations	-484.1	-17.1
Balance Sheet (000's)		
Cash & Equivalents	280.8	83.2
Total Current Assets	291.6	85.0
Fixed Assets, Net	0.0	0.0
Total Assets	391.6	85.0
Total Current Liabilities	444.7	121.4
Long-Term Debt	0.0	0.0
Stockholders' Equity	-53.1	-36.4
Performance & Financial Condition		
Return on Total Revenues %	-2,278.19	n.a.
Return on Avg Stockholders' Equity %	n.a.	n.a.
Return on Average Assets %	-281.34	n.a.
Current Ratio	0.66	0.70
Debt / Equity %	n.a.	n.a.

Compound Growth %'s	EPS %	n.a.	Net Income %	n.a.	Total Revenues %	n.a.

Comments

Revenues in 1996 were for services and not for product sales. The Company does not presently have any product for sale. It intends to manufacture or engage others to manufacture PWCs. Management states that customer deposits, proceeds from the further sale of stock, and the utilization of a loan facility will satisfy capital needs for the foreseeable future. This may be a generously optimistic assessment. Investors should absolutely make sure there is a reasonable product development and introduction schedule. A private placement of 638,917 shares in the first quarter of fiscal 1997 raised an additional $958,376. Investment Classification: Speculative

Officers	Position	Ownership Information	
Joseph F. Longo	President, Treasurer	Number of Shares Outstanding	5,850,374
Leonard V. Knap	Vice President	Market Capitalization	$ 21,938,903
Kevin M. Black	Vice President, Secretary	Frequency of Dividends	n.a.
John D. Watts	Vice President, CFO	Number of Shareholders	260

Other Information

Transfer Agent	Corporate Stock Transfer, Inc. Denver, CO		Where Listed	OTC-BB
Auditor	Kostin, Ruffkess & Company LLC		Symbol	STHK
Market Maker	Allen & Company, Inc.	(800)221-2246	SIC Code	3590
	Troster Singer	(800)526-3160	Employees	8
Broker Dealer	Regular Stockbroker			

Stein Industries, Inc.

7135-53 Northland Drive North   Brooklyn Park, MN 55428   Telephone (612)504-3500   Fax (612)375-1905

Company Description

The Company's primary businesses are the manufacture and sale of display fixtures and materials to a wide range of store retailers throughout the United States and the marketing of electronic components, primarily switches, to national and international manufacturers. The two divisions operate under the Carlson Store Fixture Company trade name. The Company was formed in 1907 and assumed its present name in 1971.

	12/31/96	12/31/95	12/31/94	12/31/93
Per Share Information				
Stock Price	12.00	4.00	3.50	4.00
Earnings Per Share	2.04	1.42	1.13	0.93
Price / Earnings Ratio	5.88	2.82	3.10	4.30
Book Value Per Share	9.09	7.05	5.63	4.50
Price / Book Value %	132.01	56.74	62.17	88.89
Dividends Per Share	0.0	0.0	0.0	0.0
Annual Financial Data				
Operating Results (000's)				
Total Revenues	30,274.9	23,669.2	18,343.6	13,364.6
Costs & Expenses	-27,466.2	-21,665.3	-16,585.1	-11,960.9
Income Before Taxes and Other	2,616.3	1,805.8	1,549.7	1,239.0
Other Items	0.0	0.0	0.0	0.0
Income Tax	-926.3	-630.1	-610.9	-464.3
Net Income	1,690.1	1,175.7	938.7	774.7
Cash Flow From Operations	1,332.6	760.6	-241.6	359.3
Balance Sheet (000's)				
Cash & Equivalents	1,869.4	1,172.4	451.2	903.5
Total Current Assets	9,030.8	7,858.3	6,175.9	4,942.2
Fixed Assets, Net	749.4	315.7	305.6	221.9
Total Assets	9,857.2	8,217.0	6,493.0	5,188.2
Total Current Liabilities	2,205.5	2,272.1	1,763.7	1,414.1
Long-Term Debt	122.6	86.9	55.9	41.5
Stockholders' Equity	7,528.1	5,838.0	4,662.3	3,723.6
Performance & Financial Condition				
Return on Total Revenues %	5.58	4.97	5.12	5.80
Return on Avg Stockholders' Equity %	25.29	22.39	22.39	22.95
Return on Average Assets %	18.70	15.99	16.07	15.76
Current Ratio	4.09	3.46	3.50	3.50
Debt / Equity %	1.63	1.49	1.20	1.12

Compound Growth %'s	EPS %	29.93	Net Income %	29.70	Total Revenues %	31.33

Comments

In 1996, sales increased 27.6% and net earnings increased 44.9%. While each operating unit performed well, management reports significant remaining challenges and opportunities in the immediate future. The focal point continues to be on increasing sales and developing marketing and product/market strategies, while controlling costs and expenses. The financial strength of the Company continues to grow impressively. Investment Classification: Growth

Officers	Position	Ownership Information	
Norman R. Stein	Chairman	Number of Shares Outstanding	827,893
Michael J. Stein	President, CEO	Market Capitalization	$ 9,934,716
Thomas A. Meyers	COO	Frequency of Dividends	n.a.
Philip B. Halverson	Treasurer, CFO	Number of Shareholders	Under 500

Other Information

			Where Listed	OTC-BB
Transfer Agent	Chase Mellon Shareholder Services New York, NY		Symbol	SNND
Auditor	Abdo, Abdo & Eick		SIC Code	2540
Market Maker	Koonce Securities, Inc.	(800)368-2802	Employees	110
	Robb, Peck, McCooey Clearing	(212)482-3535		
Broker Dealer	Regular Stockbroker			

Sterling Chemicals Holdings, Inc.

1200 Smith, Suite 1900   Houston, TX 77002-4312   Telephone (713)650-3700   Fax (713)654-9551

Company Description

Sterling Chemicals Holdings, Inc. is a holding company that, through its operating subsidiaries, is a major producer of petrochemicals and pulp chemicals. The Company's petrochemical business operates at a facility in Texas. The pulp chemical business manufactures sodium chlorate at four locations in Canada and sodium chlorite at one location in Canada. In January, 1997, the Company started producing sodium chlorate at a new plant located in Georgia. The pulp chemical business is also the world's leading supplier of large-scale chlorine dioxide generators for the pulp and paper industry.

	09/30/96	09/30/95	09/30/94	09/30/93
Per Share Information				
Stock Price as of 12/31	11.25	8.12	13.12	4.00
Earnings Per Share	0.62	2.70	0.34	-0.10
Price / Earnings Ratio	18.15	3.01	38.59	n.a.
Book Value Per Share	-25.70	4.30	1.61	1.27
Price / Book Value %	n.a.	188.84	814.91	314.96
Dividends Per Share	0.0	0.0	0.0	0.06
Annual Financial Data				
Operating Results (000's)				
Total Revenues	790,465.0	1,030,198.0	703,446.0	518,821.0
Costs & Expenses	-740,063.0	-802,040.0	-675,192.0	-525,789.0
Income Before Taxes and Other	50,402.0	228,158.0	28,254.0	-6,968.0
Other Items	-1,900.0	-3,104.0	0.0	0.0
Income Tax	-16,898.0	-75,005.0	-9,122.0	1,548.0
Net Income	31,604.0	150,049.0	19,132.0	-5,420.0
Cash Flow From Operations	63,601.0	191,838.0	75,249.0	48,114.0
Balance Sheet (000's)				
Cash & Equivalents	5,609.0	30,882.0	2,013.0	1,352.0
Total Current Assets	209,018.0	220,351.0	211,508.0	144,721.0
Fixed Assets, Net	365,765.0	309,084.0	291,126.0	314,315.0
Total Assets	689,684.0	609,939.0	580,925.0	539,705.0
Total Current Liabilities	132,085.0	145,731.0	190,699.0	113,769.0
Long-Term Debt	714,632.0	103,581.0	192,621.0	256,845.0
Stockholders' Equity	-272,439.0	239,318.0	89,734.0	70,336.0
Performance & Financial Condition				
Return on Total Revenues %	4.00	14.57	2.72	-1.04
Return on Avg Stockholders' Equity %	n.a.	91.20	23.90	-6.87
Return on Average Assets %	4.86	25.20	3.41	n.a.
Current Ratio	1.58	1.51	1.11	1.27
Debt / Equity %	n.a.	43.28	214.66	365.17

Compound Growth %'s	EPS %	35.04	Net Income %	28.53	Total Revenues %	15.07

Comments

The most significant event during fiscal 1996 was the merger of Sterling Chemicals with STX Acquisition Corp., which resulted in a recapitalization of the Company. Over the next few years, management anticipates that the business will generate sufficient cash flow to service the Company's debt. After the current industry downturn is over, the Company intends to reduce debt when cash flow is at peak levels. The market outlook for sodium chlorate, however, appears favorable for fiscal 1997. Growth in demand is driven by the continuing substitution of chlorine dioxide for elemental chlorine. Investment Classification: Speculative

Officers	Position	Ownership Information	
Robert W. Roten	President, CEO	Number of Shares Outstanding	10,599,000
Jim P. Wise	VP - Finance, CFO	Market Capitalization	$ 119,238,750
Robert N. Bannon	Vice President	Frequency of Dividends	n.a.
Richard K. Crump	Vice President	Number of Shareholders	280
F. Maxwell Evans	Vice President, Secretary		

Other Information			
Transfer Agent	KeyCorp Shareholder Services, Inc. Houston, TX	Where Listed	OTC-BB
Auditor	Deloitte & Touche LLP	Symbol	STXX
Market Maker	Stifel, Nicolaus & Company	(800)776-6821	SIC Code	2800
	CS First Boston Corp.	(800)752-5114	Employees	1200
Broker Dealer	Regular Stockbroker		

Sterling Sugars, Inc.

P.O. Box 572   Franklin, LA 70538   Telephone (318)828-0620   Fax (318)838-1757

Company Description

Sterling Sugars, Inc. is a grower and processor of sugarcane from which it produces raw sugar and molasses. The Company's raw sugar factory is located on 65 acres of land outside the city of Franklin, Louisiana. Farming acreage includes 11,607 acres of owned land and 1,560 acres of leased land. The Company also leases oil and gas rights and has two producing wells on its property from which it receives royalties. The Company has been growing and processing sugarcane in Louisiana since 1807.

	01/31/97	01/31/96	01/31/95	01/31/94
Per Share Information				
Stock Price as of 12/31	6.50	5.63	4.94	3.94
Earnings Per Share	0.81	0.85	0.30	-0.40
Price / Earnings Ratio	8.02	6.62	16.47	n.a.
Book Value Per Share	6.27	5.45	4.63	4.33
Price / Book Value %	103.67	103.30	106.70	90.99
Dividends Per Share	0.0	0.0	0.0	0.0
Annual Financial Data				
Operating Results (000's)				
Total Revenues	39,415.2	29,644.6	34,250.6	13,932.8
Costs & Expenses	-36,183.5	-26,429.9	-32,952.7	-15,831.1
Income Before Taxes and Other	3,231.6	3,214.6	1,297.9	-1,898.3
Other Items	0.0	0.0	0.0	200.0
Income Tax	-1,194.7	-1,095.0	-555.5	715.0
Net Income	2,037.0	2,119.6	742.4	-983.3
Cash Flow From Operations	3,566.4	-1,135.9	8,508.7	-3,829.4
Balance Sheet (000's)				
Cash & Equivalents	110.3	134.1	623.2	544.0
Total Current Assets	14,508.2	14,794.6	8,827.5	14,290.5
Fixed Assets, Net	18,970.8	11,980.5	11,027.2	11,926.6
Total Assets	35,584.6	27,969.6	20,879.6	26,513.3
Total Current Liabilities	9,303.3	9,625.6	4,333.8	11,168.9
Long-Term Debt	9,615.2	4,017.5	4,371.4	4,694.2
Stockholders' Equity	15,665.5	13,628.5	11,346.4	10,604.0
Performance & Financial Condition				
Return on Total Revenues %	5.17	7.15	2.17	-7.06
Return on Avg Stockholders' Equity %	13.91	16.97	6.76	-8.86
Return on Average Assets %	6.41	8.68	3.13	-4.15
Current Ratio	1.56	1.54	2.04	1.28
Debt / Equity %	61.38	29.48	38.53	44.27

Compound Growth %'s	EPS %	64.32	Net Income %	65.64	Total Revenues %	41.43

Comments

The Company acquired 8,519 acres of additional land during 1996 at an average price of approximately $1,000 per acre. Last year we commented that land on the books was recorded at a cost of $1.8 million, which amounts to approximately $156 per acre at December 31, 1995. If the land holdings alone were adjusted to fair market value, book value would likely double. Revenue increased 33% during 1996. Investment Classification: Growth & Value

Officers	Position	Ownership Information	
Craig P. Caillier	President, CEO	Number of Shares Outstanding	2,500,000
Stanley H. Pipes	Vice President, Treasurer	Market Capitalization	$ 16,250,000
Williard E. Legendre	Vice President	Frequency of Dividends	n.a.
Carl W. Bauer	Vice President, Secretary	Number of Shareholders	720
Randall K. Romero	Controller		

Other Information			
Transfer Agent	Whitney National Bank of New Orleans New Orleans, LA	Where Listed	OTC-BB
Auditor	LeGlue & Company	Symbol	SSUG
Market Maker	Legg Mason Wood Walker, Inc.	(800)221-9732	SIC Code	2060
	Carr Securities Corporation	(800)221-2243	Employees	223
Broker Dealer	Regular Stockbroker		
	Stephen Schuller - Dorsey	(800)375-5431	

Stonecutter Mills Corporation

P.O. Box 157   Spindale, NC 28160   Telephone (704)286-2341   Fax (704)287-7280

Company Description

The primary business of Stonecutter Mills consists of the weaving of greige goods which, in turn, are sold to the fabric converting trade. The eventual end use of these goods is in the ladies' sportswear and home furnishing markets. The Company also derives revenue from the sale of yarn as well as from commission processing by its Dyeing and Finishing Division. Other businesses include wood products, trucking and warehousing. The history of the Company proudly dates back to 1920. Please enjoy our historical vignette.

	06/29/96	07/01/95	07/02/94	07/01/93
Per Share Information				
Stock Price as of 12/31	275.00	276.00	83.00	79.00
Earnings Per Share	12.62	71.07	61.07	42.28
Price / Earnings Ratio	21.79	3.88	1.36	1.87
Book Value Per Share	386.75	389.27	330.75	274.93
Price / Book Value %	71.11	70.90	25.09	28.73
Dividends Per Share	15.20	12.60	7.80	6.20
Annual Financial Data				
Operating Results (000's)				
Total Revenues	107,874.4	126,553.5	n.a.	n.a.
Costs & Expenses	-105,195.3	-110,660.9	n.a.	n.a.
Income Before Taxes and Other	2,679.1	15,892.6	n.a.	n.a.
Other Items	0.0	0.0	n.a.	n.a.
Income Tax	-978.9	-6,315.4	n.a.	n.a.
Net Income	1,700.2	9,577.2	8,230.3	5,698.5
Cash Flow From Operations	8,705.0	19,082.6	n.a.	n.a.
Balance Sheet (000's)				
Cash & Equivalents	11,204.7	10,301.6	7,965.8	376.8
Total Current Assets	39,728.5	45,379.3	40,145.7	34,983.8
Fixed Assets, Net	20,605.4	20,750.6	16,655.4	16,759.0
Total Assets	60,729.7	66,536.5	57,305.2	52,182.7
Total Current Liabilities	8,504.8	13,026.9	10,552.9	11,575.7
Long-Term Debt	107.1	1,052.0	2,180.2	3,557.9
Stockholders' Equity	52,117.8	52,457.7	44,572.1	37,049.2
Performance & Financial Condition				
Return on Total Revenues %	1.58	7.57	n.a.	n.a.
Return on Avg Stockholders' Equity %	3.25	19.74	20.17	16.46
Return on Average Assets %	2.67	15.47	15.03	11.48
Current Ratio	4.67	3.48	3.80	3.02
Debt / Equity %	0.21	2.01	4.89	9.60

Compound Growth %'s	EPS % -33.17	Net Income % -33.18	Total Revenues % n.a.

Comments

Management didn't explain the decline in 1996 revenues. The balance sheet remains excessively strong. Inventories are valued on a Last-in, First-out basis which typically undervalues the balance sheet value. Investment Classification: Income & Value

Officers	Position	Ownership Information	
James R. Cowan	Chairman, President	Number of Shares Outstanding	134,760
Dan Briscoe	Senior VP	Market Capitalization	$ 37,059,000
Gerald N. Rodelli	Senior VP	Frequency of Dividends	Quarterly
T P. Walker	Secretary	Number of Shareholders	Under 500
James M. Perry	Treasurer		

Other Information				
Transfer Agent	Company Office		Where Listed	OTC-BB
Auditor	Dixon, Odom & Co., LLP		Symbol	STCMA
Market Maker	Koonce Securities, Inc.	(800)368-2802	SIC Code	2399
	Hill Thompson Magid & Co., Inc	(800)631-3083	Employees	1000
Broker Dealer	OTC Specialist			

Textiles

In the mid-nineteenth century, large scale mechanization of the textile industry launched the Industrial Revolution in Europe. It was then that textiles migrated from a cottage industry to factory production. In America, this transition naturally began in areas located close to the cotton fields. Stonecutter's founder, Kenneth Tanner, is credited with the transformation of one of these areas, Spindale, North Carolina, from an agrarian economy to a textile complex.

Stonecutter is named after a nearby creek bearing the same name. It was originally constructed on a hill making it a highly visible landmark in the surrounding rural landscape. Mr. Tanner's vision for the area extended far beyond his first mill and encompassed a completely modern village, replete with electric lights, water, sewerage, baths, landscape design, a movie theater, a dairy, a steam laundry and other public buildings. He founded his new company in 1920 with $1,250,000 of stock subscriptions and proceeded to move dirt with mules and drag pans to prepare the site.

Before Stonecutter was established, Spindale had been a quiet rural outpost with people either living and working on their farms or cutting timber for local companies. Cash resources were for the most part minimal. People grew their own food and an informal barter system existed for the procurement of other goods. Stonecutter changed all of this, and Spindale became an industrial center where people could work for wages and improve their standard of living.

Tanner began his enterprise by looming cotton; rayon followed five years later. It wasn't long, unfortunately, before America fell into the Great Depression. The company only survived this difficult era because of attributes that also account for its long-term success: conservatism, determination and a commitment to quality. They continued to keep pace with new technologies and at the same time to prize their employees, focusing on a supportive workplace and ongoing training. A testimony to this commitment was the establishment in 1943 of a profit sharing plan in recognition of employees' contributions to the company's ongoing success.

One day in 1950, twenty-five years after the first rayon came off Stonecutter's looms, employees were surprised, but perhaps delighted as well to find that their weekly wages had been delivered in the form of small pouches sewn of rayon and filled with silver coins! Can you imagine the three tons of coins it took to fulfill this obligation arriving from the Federal Reserve under armed guard and the commotion it must have caused in Spindale?

In 1997, after seventy-seven years in business, Stonecutter is not only viable, but has become a fully integrated and successful operation that includes fabric manufacture, retail sales of cloth and timber products and a trucking company. The company has truly succeeded in living up to Kenneth Tanner's vision.

Strategia Corporation

10301 Linn Station Road   Louisville, KY 40233   Telephone (502)426-3434   Fax (502)426-3028

Company Description

Strategia Corporation, formerly Dataguard Recovery Services, provides disaster recovery, consulting, information processing and outsourcing services to users of large-scale computer systems in North America and Europe. Since inception in 1984, the Company has specialized in assisting clients to prepare for and avert the consequences of unknown, unplanned interruptions in data processing. During the next several years the Company expects to devote substantial resources to assisting clients prepare their computers for the Year 2000 Problem. The Company's wholly-owned subsidiary, Twinsys Dataguard SA, offers similar services in France.

	12/31/96	12/31/95	12/31/94
Per Share Information			
Stock Price	6.75	0.88	n.a.
Earnings Per Share	-0.29	0.01	-0.01
Price / Earnings Ratio	n.a.	88.00	n.a.
Book Value Per Share	0.47	0.74	n.a.
Price / Book Value %	1,436.17	118.92	n.a.
Dividends Per Share	0.0	0.0	0.0
Annual Financial Data			
Operating Results (000's)			
Total Revenues	9,454.7	8,972.4	4,617.1
Costs & Expenses	-10,020.3	-8,486.8	-4,610.8
Income Before Taxes and Other	-565.6	485.5	6.3
Other Items	0.0	0.0	0.0
Income Tax	-158.1	-443.6	0.0
Net Income	-723.7	42.0	6.3
Cash Flow From Operations	1,835.5	2,679.7	772.3
Balance Sheet (000's)			
Cash & Equivalents	338.4	170.6	n.a.
Total Current Assets	1,495.8	1,789.2	n.a.
Fixed Assets, Net	8,483.6	8,761.4	n.a.
Total Assets	10,745.4	10,787.7	n.a.
Total Current Liabilities	4,483.9	5,084.4	n.a.
Long-Term Debt	978.6	1,024.4	n.a.
Stockholders' Equity	2,072.3	1,279.3	n.a.
Performance & Financial Condition			
Return on Total Revenues %	-7.65	0.47	0.14
Return on Avg Stockholders' Equity %	-43.19	n.a.	n.a.
Return on Average Assets %	-6.72	n.a.	n.a.
Current Ratio	0.33	0.35	n.a.
Debt / Equity %	47.22	80.07	n.a.

Compound Growth %'s	EPS % n.a.	Net Income % n.a.	Total Revenues % 43.10

Comments

The Company declared a 1 for 2 reverse split during 1996. 1995 per share amounts have been adjusted accordingly. The Company issued 266,000 shares of common at $6 per share during 1996. In February, 1997, the Company began offering up to 1,500,000 shares of common at $7 per share and placed 1,366,000 of the shares. There are also preferred shares outstanding as well as employee stock options. Revenue from disaster recovery backup and contingency planning services represented approximately 98% of the Company's revenue in 1996 and 1995. Investment Classification: Speculative

Officers	Position	Ownership Information	
Richard W. Smith	President	Number of Shares Outstanding	3,038,885
James P. Buren	Exec VP, Treasurer	Market Capitalization	$ 20,512,474
John P. Snyder	Secretary	Frequency of Dividends	n.a.
		Number of Shareholders	620

Other Information

Transfer Agent	ChaseMellon Shareholder Services Ridgefield Park, NJ		Where Listed	OTC-BB
Auditor	Ernst & Young LLP		Symbol	STGI
Market Maker	S.W. Ryan & Company Inc.	(610)668-8241	SIC Code	7370
	Troster Singer	(800)526-3160	Employees	n.a.
Broker Dealer	Regular Stockbroker			

Superior Supplements, Inc.

270 Oser Avenue Hauppauge, NY 11788 Telephone (516)231-0783 Fax (516)231-3515

Company Description

Superior Supplements, Inc. was formed on April 24, 1996. The Company is engaged in the development, manufacture, marketing and sale of dietary supplements including vitamins, minerals, herbs and specialty nutritional supplements, in bulk tablet, capsule and powder form. The Company intends to manufacture a wide variety of products for companies which package and sell through many different channels of distribution, including health food, drug, convenience and mass market stores. Prior to completion of its manufacturing facility, the Company was operating as a wholesaler for these products.

	06/30/96
Per Share Information	
Stock Price as of 12/31	12.00
Earnings Per Share	0.01
Price / Earnings Ratio	1,200.00
Book Value Per Share	0.37
Price / Book Value %	3,243.24
Dividends Per Share	0.0
Annual Financial Data	
Operating Results (000's)	
Total Revenues	857.4
Costs & Expenses	-809.0
Income Before Taxes and Other	48.4
Other Items	0.0
Income Tax	-13.2
Net Income	35.2
Cash Flow From Operations	280.5
Balance Sheet (000's)	
Cash & Equivalents	594.2
Total Current Assets	1,086.0
Fixed Assets, Net	341.3
Total Assets	2,565.5
Total Current Liabilities	1,085.4
Long-Term Debt	200.0
Stockholders' Equity	1,280.1
Performance & Financial Condition	
Return on Total Revenues %	4.10
Return on Avg Stockholders' Equity %	n.a.
Return on Average Assets %	n.a.
Current Ratio	1.00
Debt / Equity %	15.62

Compound Growth %'s	EPS % n.a.	Net Income % n.a.	Total Revenues % n.a.

Comments

The first year was a partial year from April 24, 1996 through June 30, 1996. Manufacturing operations for tableting and encapsulating of single ingredient products commenced on October 1, 1996, although the facility was not fully operational until 1997. For the nine months ended March 31, 1997, the Company reported sales of $2.6 million and a net loss of $615,000, $.15 per share. At that date, the Company had current assets of $3.4 million and current liabilities of $1.7 million. The stock price has fallen from the offering price of $12 per share to $5.50, as of May 31, 1997. Investment Classification: Speculative

Officers	Position	Ownership Information	
Lawrence D. Simon	President, CFO	Number of Shares Outstanding	3,500,000
Matthew L. Harriton	Secretary	Market Capitalization	$ 42,000,000
		Frequency of Dividends	n.a.
		Number of Shareholders	n.a.

Other Information				
Transfer Agent	American Stock Transfer & Trust Company New York, NY		Where Listed	OTC-BB
Auditor	Holtz Rubenstein & Co., LLP		Symbol	SPSU
Market Maker	J. Alexander Securities, Inc.	(800)421-0258	SIC Code	2833
	Comprehensive Capital Corp.	(800)338-3014	Employees	8
Broker Dealer	Regular Stockbroker			

Sutter Basin Corporation, Ltd.

10982 Knights Road   Robbins, CA 95676   Telephone (916)738-4456   Fax (916)738-4151

Company Description

The Company is a diversified agricultural operation which provides custom farming services, raises various crops and provides drying and storage services. The property is located in California's Sacramento Valley. There are only 2,077 shares outstanding as the Company has reacquired 25,390 treasury shares.

	12/31/96	12/31/95	12/31/94
Per Share Information			
Stock Price	62.00	62.00	60.00
Earnings Per Share	-15.71	8.11	2.20
Price / Earnings Ratio	n.a.	7.64	27.27
Book Value Per Share	65.01	80.72	72.62
Price / Book Value %	95.37	76.81	82.62
Dividends Per Share	0.0	0.0	0.0
Annual Financial Data			
Operating Results (000's)			
Total Revenues	775.0	770.2	866.5
Costs & Expenses	-806.0	-751.8	-859.9
Income Before Taxes and Other	-31.8	18.3	5.8
Other Items	0.0	0.0	0.0
Income Tax	-0.8	-1.4	-1.3
Net Income	-32.6	16.8	4.6
Cash Flow From Operations	21.7	-67.1	19.4
Balance Sheet (000's)			
Cash & Equivalents	24.5	22.3	27.3
Total Current Assets	34.0	28.3	37.6
Fixed Assets, Net	433.5	339.9	181.2
Total Assets	467.9	368.9	222.0
Total Current Liabilities	47.9	16.3	70.7
Long-Term Debt	285.0	185.0	0.5
Stockholders' Equity	135.0	167.7	150.8
Performance & Financial Condition			
Return on Total Revenues %	-4.21	2.19	0.53
Return on Avg Stockholders' Equity %	-21.56	10.57	n.a.
Return on Average Assets %	-7.80	5.70	n.a.
Current Ratio	0.71	1.74	0.53
Debt / Equity %	211.06	110.34	0.32

Compound Growth %'s	EPS % n.a.	Net Income % n.a.	Total Revenues % -5.43

Comments

A substantial amount of the custom farming is provided by five related entities. It is possible that the remaining property has substantial appreciation. The Company will not comment. However, we did determine that fully-depreciated equipment with an original cost of $242,000 was sold during 1995 for cash at a gain of $68,150, or $32.81 per share. A more difficult task may be in finding shares available for purchase. We rate this security as "value" because the underlying property values are believed to exceed the trading price, and "speculative" because related parties may be able to control the destiny of this Company. Investment Classification: Value & Speculative

Officers	Position	Ownership Information	
Luther C. Anderson	Chairman	Number of Shares Outstanding	2,077
Thomas A. Butler	President	Market Capitalization	$ 128,774
N H. Bruggman	Secretary	Frequency of Dividends	n.a.
		Number of Shareholders	Under 500

Other Information			
Transfer Agent	Company Office	Where Listed	OTC-BB
Auditor	Tenney and Company	Symbol	SUBC
Market Maker	The Chicago Corporation	(800)621-1674	SIC Code	0700
	Robotti & Co., Inc.	(212)986-0800	Employees	n.a.
Broker Dealer	OTC Specialist		

T/F Purifiner, Inc.

3036 High Ridge Road, Ste. 100   Boyton Beach, FL 33426   Telephone (561)547-9499   Fax (561)547-4025

Company Description

T/F Purifiner, Inc. owns the rights to manufacture, market and distribute worldwide the Purifiner (R), a bypass oil purification system for use with most internal combustion engines, generators and other types of equipment that use lubricating oil. Although this product has been around for over ten years, it has been the subject of litigation and other delays in a successful implementation strategy.

	12/31/96	12/31/95
Per Share Information		
Stock Price	7.90	n.a.
Earnings Per Share	-0.60	n.a.
Price / Earnings Ratio	n.a.	n.a.
Book Value Per Share	0.36	n.a.
Price / Book Value %	2,194.44	n.a.
Dividends Per Share	0.0	n.a.
Annual Financial Data		
Operating Results (000's)		
Total Revenues	1,329.1	1,480.0
Costs & Expenses	-3,312.3	-1,889.8
Income Before Taxes and Other	-1,983.3	-409.8
Other Items	0.0	0.0
Income Tax	0.0	0.0
Net Income	-1,983.3	-409.8
Cash Flow From Operations	-1,609.1	-177.7
Balance Sheet (000's)		
Cash & Equivalents	929.0	n.a.
Total Current Assets	2,555.6	n.a.
Fixed Assets, Net	172.4	n.a.
Total Assets	3,039.7	n.a.
Total Current Liabilities	827.7	n.a.
Long-Term Debt	0.0	n.a.
Stockholders' Equity	1,814.6	n.a.
Performance & Financial Condition		
Return on Total Revenues %	-149.22	n.a.
Return on Avg Stockholders' Equity %	n.a.	n.a.
Return on Average Assets %	n.a.	n.a.
Current Ratio	3.09	n.a.
Debt / Equity %	n.a.	n.a.

Compound Growth %'s	EPS % n.a.	Net Income % n.a.	Total Revenues % -10.20

Comments

The Company declared a 2.5 to 1 stock split in 1997. The 1996 per share amounts have been adjusted for consistency. The Company reports having 75 distributors in the United States and Canada as well as 17 overseas distributors. Yet we do not see any increase in revenue. For the first quarter ended March 31, 1997, revenue declined 3% and the Company lost $672,330 on the quarter. The market capitalization doesn't make much sense for a company this small and with so little in the way of results. Investment Classification: Speculative

Officers	Position	Ownership Information	
Richard C. Ford	President, CEO	Number of Shares Outstanding	5,097,080
		Market Capitalization	$ 40,266,932
		Frequency of Dividends	n.a.
		Number of Shareholders	278

Other Information				
Transfer Agent	Florida Atlantic Stock Transfer, Inc. Tamarac, FL		Where Listed	OTC-PS
Auditor	Richard A. Eisner & Company		Symbol	TFPU
Market Maker	Wm. V. Frankel & Co., Inc.	(800)631-3091	SIC Code	3714
	Herzog, Heine, Geduld, Inc.	(800)221-3600	Employees	n.a.
Broker Dealer	Regular Stockholder			

TIF Instruments, Inc.

9101 N.W. 7th Avenue   Miami, FL 33150   Telephone (305)757-8811   Fax (305)757-3105

Company Description

TIF Instruments, Inc. is in the business of manufacturing electronic testing and measurement equipment primarily for the automotive, air conditioning and refrigeration industries. The Company also deals directly with the needs of contractors and wholesalers. The Company went public in 1960 but maintains a quiet profile. Only shareholders are entitled to financial information about the Company.

	06/30/96	06/30/95	06/30/94	06/30/93
Per Share Information				
Stock Price as of 12/31	43.25	32.00	29.50	25.00
Earnings Per Share	0.17	8.42	4.81	1.94
Price / Earnings Ratio	254.41	3.80	6.13	12.89
Book Value Per Share	59.52	60.92	52.38	50.44
Price / Book Value %	72.66	52.53	56.32	49.56
Dividends Per Share	0.0	0.0	0.0	0.0
Annual Financial Data				
Operating Results (000's)				
Total Revenues	17,454.4	25,302.8	21,312.5	18,847.6
Costs & Expenses	-17,390.1	-21,703.6	-19,253.7	-18,131.5
Income Before Taxes and Other	64.3	3,599.2	2,058.8	716.1
Other Items	0.0	0.0	0.0	0.0
Income Tax	-17.9	-1,360.3	-779.8	-200.0
Net Income	46.4	2,238.9	1,279.0	516.1
Cash Flow From Operations	n.a.	n.a.	n.a.	n.a.
Balance Sheet (000's)				
Cash & Equivalents	7,378.0	7,166.3	5,675.4	n.a.
Total Current Assets	18,354.0	19,589.5	16,643.4	n.a.
Fixed Assets, Net	266.4	340.5	335.4	n.a.
Total Assets	18,620.4	19,930.0	16,978.8	n.a.
Total Current Liabilities	1,287.9	2,451.4	1,994.6	n.a.
Long-Term Debt	0.0	0.0	0.0	n.a.
Stockholders' Equity	16,244.5	16,199.2	13,928.3	n.a.
Performance & Financial Condition				
Return on Total Revenues %	0.27	8.85	6.00	2.74
Return on Avg Stockholders' Equity %	0.29	14.86	n.a.	n.a.
Return on Average Assets %	0.24	12.13	n.a.	n.a.
Current Ratio	14.25	7.99	8.34	n.a.
Debt / Equity %	n.a.	n.a.	n.a.	n.a.

Compound Growth %'s	EPS %	-55.58	Net Income %	-55.20	Total Revenues %	-2.53

Comments

The Company does not release the full financial statements to its shareholders, but instead prepares a one page condensed version from the audited statements. 1996 was a most difficult year for the Company. An unusually cool spring was only partially to blame as the Company took inventory adjustments for slow moving products and raw materials. Management is actively improve product mix and hopes to introduce new products and reduce material, design and manufacturing costs. The balance sheet is the envy of any company that has had a bad year. Investment Classification: Value

Officers	Position	Ownership Information	
Thomas Gerard	President	Number of Shares Outstanding	272,941
Jamie Gerard	Treasurer	Market Capitalization	$ 11,804,698
Elliot Gerard	VP - Manufacturing	Frequency of Dividends	n.a.
Thomas Wolff	VP - Sales	Number of Shareholders	Under 500

Other Information

Transfer Agent	Sun Trust Bank Atlanta, GA		Where Listed	OTC-BB
Auditor	Not indicated		Symbol	TIFS
Market Maker	Koonce Securities, Inc.	(800)368-2802	SIC Code	3820
	Carr Securities Corporation	(800)221-2243	Employees	400
Broker Dealer	Regular Stockbroker			

TNR Technical, Inc.

279 Douglas Avenue, Ste. 1112   Altamonte Springs, FL 32714   Telephone (407)682-4311   Fax (407)682-4469

Company Description

TNR Technical, Inc. is an authorized distributor for several battery manufacturers, including Sanyo, Eveready, Duracell, and Sony, and stocks one of the largest battery inventories in the southeastern United States. In addition, the Company designs, assembles and markets batteries and multi-cell battery packs to a wide variety of industrial markets. The Company began business in 1979.

	07/31/96	07/31/95	07/31/94	07/31/93
Per Share Information				
Stock Price as of 12/31	3.00	3.25	1.63	1.75
Earnings Per Share	0.52	1.67	0.56	0.50
Price / Earnings Ratio	5.77	1.95	2.91	3.50
Book Value Per Share	7.20	6.69	5.02	4.45
Price / Book Value %	41.67	48.58	32.47	39.33
Dividends Per Share	0.0	0.0	0.0	0.0
Annual Financial Data				
Operating Results (000's)				
Total Revenues	3,823.1	3,745.3	3,605.2	2,821.5
Costs & Expenses	-3,638.6	-3,546.3	-3,449.5	-2,691.6
Income Before Taxes and Other	184.4	199.0	155.7	130.0
Other Items	0.0	0.0	0.0	0.0
Income Tax	-49.0	239.0	-7.5	0.0
Net Income	135.4	438.0	148.2	130.0
Cash Flow From Operations	242.9	-83.0	51.5	122.7
Balance Sheet (000's)				
Cash & Equivalents	426.3	100.3	353.8	362.6
Total Current Assets	1,677.2	1,709.7	1,488.7	1,325.4
Fixed Assets, Net	109.8	56.9	37.5	33.0
Total Assets	1,997.4	2,022.6	1,532.2	1,364.3
Total Current Liabilities	107.6	268.2	215.8	196.1
Long-Term Debt	0.0	0.0	0.0	0.0
Stockholders' Equity	1,889.8	1,754.4	1,316.4	1,168.2
Performance & Financial Condition				
Return on Total Revenues %	3.54	11.69	4.11	4.61
Return on Avg Stockholders' Equity %	7.43	28.53	11.93	11.78
Return on Average Assets %	6.74	24.64	10.24	10.03
Current Ratio	15.59	6.38	6.90	6.76
Debt / Equity %	n.a.	n.a.	n.a.	n.a.

Compound Growth %'s	EPS % 1.32	Net Income % 1.37	Total Revenues % 10.66

Comments

Net Income for 1995 includes a credit of $239,000 resulting from a change in accounting method for income taxes. Other than that, 1996 results are very similar. For the six months ended January 31, 1997, revenues were up slightly and Net Income was $84,990 ($.32 per share) as compared to $33,366 ($.13 per share) for the same period in the prior fiscal year. The Company maintains a comfortable pile of cash and short-term investments which totalled $774,000 at the last year end. Investment Classification: Value

Officers	Position	Ownership Information	
Jerrold Lazarus	Chairman, CEO	Number of Shares Outstanding	262,437
Wayne Thaw	President, COO	Market Capitalization	$ 787,311
		Frequency of Dividends	n.a.
		Number of Shareholders	1,622

Other Information

Transfer Agent	American Stock Transfer & Trust Company New York, NY	Where Listed	OTC-BB
Auditor	James, Park, Tschopp et al	Symbol	TNRK
Market Maker	Carr Securities Corporation	(800)221-2243	SIC Code	3691
	Paragon Capital Corp.	(800)345-0505	Employees	21
Broker Dealer	Regular Stockbroker		

Talbot Bank of Easton, Maryland (The)

18 East Dover Steet   Easton, MD 21601   Telephone (410)822-1400   Fax (410)820-7180

Company Description

The Talbot Bank of Easton, Maryland is a commercial bank founded in 1885. Its service areas are Talbot and Dorchester Counties, Maryland. The Bank has three locations in Easton, one location in St. Michaels, and the 1996 addition of a Supermarket branch at the Metro Market in Cambridge. The Bank also has an office in cyberspace: (http://www.talbot-bank.com).

	12/31/96	12/31/95	12/31/94	12/31/93
Per Share Information				
Stock Price	50.50	45.00	38.00	38.00
Earnings Per Share	5.44	4.55	3.85	1.57
Price / Earnings Ratio	9.28	9.89	9.87	24.20
Book Value Per Share	47.07	42.64	37.72	37.19
Price / Book Value %	107.29	105.53	100.74	102.18
Dividends Per Share	1.40	1.25	1.00	0.95
Annual Financial Data				
Operating Results (000's)				
Net Interest Income	10,571.1	9,228.4	8,273.9	7,870.0
Loan Loss Provision	-955.0	-540.0	-525.0	-2,911.0
Non-Interest Income	574.2	617.0	632.7	982.0
Non-Interest Expense	-5,218.8	-5,083.5	-4,886.7	-4,540.0
Income Before Taxes and Other	4,971.5	4,221.9	3,495.0	1,401.0
Other Items	0.0	0.0	0.0	0.0
Income Tax	-1,751.2	-1,537.6	-1,232.4	-483.0
Net Income	3,220.3	2,684.3	2,262.6	918.0
Balance Sheet (000's)				
Cash & Securities	77,396.0	67,991.4	84,342.0	75,277.0
Loans, Net	168,972.2	160,207.1	141,358.0	146,264.6
Total Assets	253,184.0	234,405.5	231,700.0	226,621.6
Deposits	215,101.4	195,447.0	193,364.0	199,143.1
Stockholders' Equity	27,920.0	25,193.5	22,204.0	21,797.6
Performance & Financial Condition				
Return on Avg Stockholders' Equity %	12.13	11.33	10.28	4.28
Return on Average Assets %	1.32	1.15	0.99	0.42
Equity to Assets %	11.03	10.75	9.58	9.62
Net Interest Margin	4.53	4.22	3.81	n.a.
Reserve as a % of Problem Loans	123.73	71.76	61.27	120.27

Compound Growth %'s	EPS %	51.32	Net Income %	51.94	Net Interest Income %	10.34

Comments

The 1996 earnings were at record levels. Increased loan volume was cited as the largest single factor. We believe that earnings may have deliberately been depressed to create a cushion for future years. A bank can conceivably show a desired growth rate by making adjustment to its loan loss reserve. You be the judge as we quote the president from his letter to shareholders: "The Board is always mindful of the ability to sustain growth over long periods of time. That is why in 1996 they voted to make addition to the provision for loan losses which resulted in an increase in the allowance for loan losses to a level more consistent with it's peer group." Investment Classification: Growth & Value

Officers	Position	Ownership Information	
W. Moorhead Vermilye	President, CEO	Number of Shares Outstanding	593,121
Jerome M. McConnell	Exec VP	Market Capitalization	$ 29,952,611
G. Rodney Taylor	Senior VP	Frequency of Dividends	Quarterly
Susan E. Leaverton	VP - Finance	Number of Shareholders	499
Robert J. Meade	Vice President	Where Listed / Symbol	OTC-BB / TBES

Other Information			Loan Mix	%
Transfer Agent	Company Office		R/E Mortgages	72.9
Auditor	Stegman & Company		Commerical	17.0
Market Maker	Ferris, Baker Watts Inc.	(800)638-7411	Consumer	5.5
	Legg Mason Wood & Walker, Inc.	(800)221-9732	Construction	4.0
Broker Dealer	OTC Specialist		Agriculture	0.1
	Jack Ingold	(412)391-4594	Other	0.5

Technology 80 Inc.

658 Mendelssohn Avenue North   Minneapolis, MN 55427   Telephone (612)542-9545   Fax (612)542-9785

Company Description

Technology 80 Inc. designs, manufactures, and markets motion control components and systems for original equipment manufacturers, machine and instrument builders and end users located worldwide. Products are sold through direct sales, manufacturers representatives and distributors.   The Company was formed in 1980.

	08/31/96	08/31/95	08/31/94	08/31/93
Per Share Information				
Stock Price as of 12/31	2.56	1.63	1.50	1.25
Earnings Per Share	0.39	0.37	0.60	0.30
Price / Earnings Ratio	6.56	4.41	2.50	4.17
Book Value Per Share	2.77	2.47	2.01	1.50
Price / Book Value %	92.42	65.99	74.63	83.33
Dividends Per Share	0.0	0.0	0.0	0.0
Annual Financial Data				
Operating Results (000's)				
Total Revenues	4,417.4	3,899.3	3,254.8	2,797.7
Costs & Expenses	-3,430.3	-2,914.2	-2,603.4	-2,311.7
Income Before Taxes and Other	987.0	985.2	651.3	486.0
Other Items	0.0	0.0	580.0	0.0
Income Tax	-321.7	-340.1	-271.1	-5.0
Net Income	665.4	645.1	960.2	481.0
Cash Flow From Operations	680.0	761.3	377.7	266.2
Balance Sheet (000's)				
Cash & Equivalents	419.1	926.2	458.4	1,199.0
Total Current Assets	2,158.2	3,233.0	2,959.6	2,474.0
Fixed Assets, Net	84.0	90.2	66.4	64.2
Total Assets	4,897.6	4,195.4	3,392.5	2,538.2
Total Current Liabilities	547.1	265.5	278.8	230.9
Long-Term Debt	0.0	0.0	0.0	0.0
Stockholders' Equity	4,350.4	3,857.8	3,113.6	2,307.3
Performance & Financial Condition				
Return on Total Revenues %	15.06	16.54	29.50	17.19
Return on Avg Stockholders' Equity %	16.21	18.51	35.43	23.27
Return on Average Assets %	14.63	17.00	32.38	21.51
Current Ratio	3.94	12.18	10.61	10.72
Debt / Equity %	n.a.	n.a.	n.a.	n.a.

Compound Growth %'s	EPS %	9.14	Net Income %	11.42	Total Revenues %	16.44

Comments

Revenue continues to increase annually, 14.7% in 1996, because of increased interest in the Company's product line. The order backlog at the end of fiscal 1996 was $1,288,792 as compared to $525,631 in the prior year. For the six months ended February 28, 1997, the Company had sales of $2.1 million and Net Income of $433,000 ($.25 per share) as compared to $1.9 million and $247,000 ($.14 per share) for the same period in 1996. Investment Classification: Value

Officers	Position	Ownership Information	
Duane A. Markus	President, CEO	Number of Shares Outstanding	1,571,170
James A. Burkett	COO	Market Capitalization	$ 4,022,195
Thomas L. Gould	Secretary	Frequency of Dividends	n.a.
		Number of Shareholders	178

Other Information			
Transfer Agent	First National Bank of Minneapolis Minneapolis, MN	Where Listed	OTC-BB
Auditor	Lurie, Besikof, Lapidus & Co.	Symbol	TKAT
Market Maker	R.J. Steichen & Co. (612)341-6200	SIC Code	3679
	John G. Kinnard and Co., Inc. (800)825-5466	Employees	23
Broker Dealer	Regular Stockbroker		

Tehama Bank

P.O.Box 890   Red Bluff, CA 96080   Telephone (916)529-0436   Fax (916)529-0908

Company Description

Tehama Bank, formerly Tehama County Bank, serves the northern California area with six branch offices in Shasta and Glenn Counties. Red Bluff is an area rich in recreation, farming and lumber. Two of the offices, Orland and Willows, were acquired in early 1997. The Bank also has a Dealer Loan Center that focuses on financing autos, trucks and other vehicles. A loan production office was opened in 1996. The Bank commenced business in 1984.

	12/31/96	12/31/95	12/31/94	12/31/93
Per Share Information				
Stock Price	11.75	12.27	9.50	7.89
Earnings Per Share	1.18	1.12	1.08	1.00
Price / Earnings Ratio	9.96	10.96	8.80	7.89
Book Value Per Share	9.38	8.20	6.93	5.94
Price / Book Value %	125.27	149.63	137.09	132.83
Dividends Per Share	0.0	0.0	0.0	0.0
Annual Financial Data				
Operating Results (000's)				
Net Interest Income	5,917.3	5,545.2	4,426.7	3,520.6
Loan Loss Provision	-570.0	-330.0	-180.0	-182.5
Non-Interest Income	1,859.8	1,775.1	1,654.9	1,382.3
Non-Interest Expense	-4,308.7	-4,102.7	-3,335.1	-2,491.9
Income Before Taxes and Other	2,898.5	2,887.7	2,566.4	2,228.6
Other Items	0.0	0.0	0.0	0.0
Income Tax	-959.0	-1,039.0	-890.7	-708.0
Net Income	1,939.5	1,848.7	1,675.7	1,520.6
Balance Sheet (000's)				
Cash & Securities	40,979.1	42,408.5	28,087.3	26,492.8
Loans, Net	91,687.4	80,582.2	73,423.4	58,320.7
Total Assets	138,122.2	127,826.5	106,390.2	88,690.9
Deposits	121,602.7	113,586.7	94,645.8	78,925.7
Stockholders' Equity	15,113.2	13,085.9	10,758.0	8,862.2
Performance & Financial Condition				
Return on Avg Stockholders' Equity %	13.76	15.51	17.08	19.26
Return on Average Assets %	1.46	1.58	1.72	1.88
Equity to Assets %	10.94	10.24	10.11	9.99
Net Interest Margin	4.73	5.03	4.85	n.a.
Reserve as a % of Problem Loans	729.05	595.30	279.29	81.63

Compound Growth %'s	EPS %	5.67	Net Income %	8.45	Net Interest Income %	18.90

Comments

The Bank declared a 2 for 1 stock split in 1994 and 10% stock dividends in each of the last three years. All per share amounts have been adjusted accordingly. Tehama Bank continues to produce excellent results. With new offices, a newly formed leasing partnership, and a decision to pursue opportunities in the SBA lending market, we will probably see a stepped-up growth rate. Management will have to pay close attention not to sacrifice earnings during this period. All indications are that they are prepared for the challenge. Investment Classification: Value

Officers	Position	Ownership Information	
William P. Ellison	President, CEO	Number of Shares Outstanding	1,610,940
W. Steven Gilman	Senior VP, COO	Market Capitalization	$ 18,928,545
Frank S. Onions	Senior VP, CFO	Frequency of Dividends	Irregular
David L. Roberts	Senior VP, Senior Loan Officer	Number of Shareholders	975
Helen M. McIntosh	Vice President	Where Listed / Symbol	OTC-BB / THMC

Other Information			Loan Mix	%
Transfer Agent	U.S. Stock Transfer Corporation Glendale, CA		R/E Mortgages	43.7
Auditor	Perry-Smith & Co.		Installment	38.7
Market Maker	Hoefer & Arnett, Incorporated	(800)346-5544	Commerical	11.4
	Sutro & Co., Incorporated	(800)288-2811	Construction	6.2
Broker Dealer	Regular Stockbroker			
	L. Jack Block	(415)954-0689		

Temco Service Industries, Inc.

One Park Avenue   New York, NY 10016-5802   Telephone (212)889-6353   Fax (212)213-9854

Company Description

Temco is an acknowledged leader in facility maintenance services in the United States and Europe providing a full range of janitorial, mechanical maintenance, gardening, pest control, security and indoor air quality consulting. It is also involved in the design and manufacture of sophisticated advertising and display signs. The Company was founded in 1917 and now has over 7,000 employees.

	09/30/96	09/30/95	09/30/94	09/30/93
Per Share Information				
Stock Price as of 12/31	18.00	32.00	27.00	21.50
Earnings Per Share	1.51	1.89	2.67	2.12
Price / Earnings Ratio	11.92	16.93	10.11	10.14
Book Value Per Share	38.46	38.83	34.75	29.93
Price / Book Value %	46.80	82.41	77.70	71.83
Dividends Per Share	0.0	0.0	0.0	0.0
Annual Financial Data				
Operating Results (000's)				
Total Revenues	191,258.5	175,348.2	135,539.4	129,151.1
Costs & Expenses	-188,878.3	-173,101.4	-133,376.2	-126,501.2
Income Before Taxes and Other	1,945.5	2,246.7	2,163.2	2,296.2
Other Items	0.0	0.0	531.7	0.0
Income Tax	-1,108.7	-1,196.2	-1,212.4	-1,131.4
Net Income	836.8	1,050.5	1,482.5	1,164.8
Cash Flow From Operations	5,695.8	-3,367.6	5,204.5	4,449.0
Balance Sheet (000's)				
Cash & Equivalents	5,589.2	3,531.1	9,980.1	7,976.6
Total Current Assets	36,311.5	35,479.4	32,034.5	29,414.4
Fixed Assets, Net	14,471.1	16,008.8	14,441.3	12,364.6
Total Assets	58,523.5	57,645.3	52,013.6	46,294.3
Total Current Liabilities	24,069.4	23,400.4	19,721.5	19,850.0
Long-Term Debt	5,230.7	4,173.0	5,375.6	4,120.0
Stockholders' Equity	21,244.7	21,586.6	19,318.1	16,640.8
Performance & Financial Condition				
Return on Total Revenues %	0.44	0.60	1.09	0.90
Return on Avg Stockholders' Equity %	3.91	5.14	8.25	6.85
Return on Average Assets %	1.44	1.92	3.02	2.40
Current Ratio	1.51	1.52	1.62	1.48
Debt / Equity %	24.62	19.33	27.83	24.76

Compound Growth %'s	EPS % -10.69	Net Income % -10.44	Total Revenues % 13.98

Comments

1996 results include a nonrecurring expense related to the write-off of intangible assets of $434,683, or $.78 per share. 1994 results include a nonrecurring benefit of $531,700 from a change in accounting method. 1995 showed a sharp increase in revenue of $40 million, a 29% increase over the prior year, partially due to two acquisitions in 1994. Revenue increased 9% in 1996. There is no explanation for the large decline in stock price. Investment Classification: Growth & Value

Officers	Position	Ownership Information	
Herman J. Hellman	Chairman, CEO	Number of Shares Outstanding	552,402
Edward Valenti	Secretary, Treasurer	Market Capitalization	$ 9,943,236
Joseph Bailey	Vice President	Frequency of Dividends	Irregular
Ann Marie McVey	Vice President, CFO	Number of Shareholders	Under 500

Other Information			
Transfer Agent	American Stock Transfer & Trust Company New York, NY	Where Listed	OTC-BB
Auditor	KPMG Peat Marwick LLP	Symbol	TMCS
Market Maker	Herzog, Heine, Geduld, Inc. (800)221-3600	SIC Code	7349
		Employees	7000
Broker Dealer	Regular Stockbroker		

Terre Aux Boeufs Land Co., Inc.

228 St. Charles Avenue   New Orleans, LA 70130   Telephone (504)552-4720   Fax (504)586-3658

Company Description

The Company holds U.S. Government securities and 14,000 acres of swamp land in St. Bernard Parish outside the city of New Orleans. Over the years there has been exploration for oil and gas and some has been found on adjacent properties. Some seismic activity has been reported but, so far, only a few hunters are making use of the property.

	12/31/96	12/31/95	12/31/94	12/31/93
Per Share Information				
Stock Price	20.00	20.00	22.00	22.00
Earnings Per Share	0.57	0.47	0.25	-0.03
Price / Earnings Ratio	35.09	42.55	88.00	n.a.
Book Value Per Share	31.73	31.16	30.69	30.44
Price / Book Value %	63.03	64.18	71.68	72.27
Dividends Per Share	0.0	0.0	0.0	0.0
Annual Financial Data				
Operating Results (000's)				
Total Revenues	39.1	39.8	26.8	20.9
Costs & Expenses	-24.5	-27.4	-23.3	-23.8
Income Before Taxes and Other	14.7	12.4	3.4	-2.9
Other Items	0.0	0.0	0.0	0.0
Income Tax	-2.2	-2.1	2.0	2.3
Net Income	12.5	10.3	5.4	-0.6
Cash Flow From Operations	15.5	8.5	6.7	-8.1
Balance Sheet (000's)				
Cash & Equivalents	29.8	22.2	20.6	10.3
Total Current Assets	43.5	362.1	661.4	656.0
Fixed Assets, Net	0.0	9.9	9.9	9.9
Total Assets	694.3	681.6	671.3	665.9
Total Current Liabilities	0.3	0.0	0.0	0.0
Long-Term Debt	0.0	0.0	0.0	0.0
Stockholders' Equity	694.0	681.6	671.3	665.9
Performance & Financial Condition				
Return on Total Revenues %	31.87	25.78	20.18	-2.81
Return on Avg Stockholders' Equity %	1.81	1.52	0.81	-0.09
Return on Average Assets %	1.81	1.52	0.81	-0.09
Current Ratio	174.10	n.a.	n.a.	n.a.
Debt / Equity %	n.a.	n.a.	n.a.	n.a.

Compound Growth %'s	EPS % n.a.	Net Income % n.a.	Total Revenues % n.a.

Comments

The property rights are of an unknown value. Land is on the books at $9,925 but annual property taxes of an almost equal amount are paid. A little research here may yield a big reward. Compound growth rates are not meaningful and have not been displayed. Anyone want to take a walk in a swamp? Investment Classification: Value

Officers	Position	Ownership Information	
Edward Grimball	President	Number of Shares Outstanding	21,875
Phillip Zollinger	Secretary	Market Capitalization	$ 437,500
M. Cleland Powell, III	Vice President, Treasurer	Frequency of Dividends	n.a.
		Number of Shareholders	Under 500

Other Information

Transfer Agent	Company Office		Where Listed	OTC-BB
Auditor	Doody and Doody		Symbol	TAUX
Market Maker	Hill Thompson Magid & Co., Inc	(800)631-3083	SIC Code	6790
	Herzog, Heine, Geduld, Inc.	(800)221-3600	Employees	n.a.
Broker Dealer	OTC Specialist			
	Stephen R. Schuller	(800)375-5431		

Thanksgiving Coffee Company, Inc.

19100 S. Noyo Harbor Drive   Fort Bragg, CA 95437   Telephone (707)964-0118   Fax (707)964-0351

Company Description

Thanksgiving Coffee Company, Inc. roasts and blends high-quality Arabica coffee and high-quality teas. These products are sold primarily through its own distribution network to restaurants, grocery stores and other retail outlets in the northern California area. The Company was founded in 1972 and had an initial public offering in 1995 at which time it sold 256,039 shares at $5 per share. A stock broker has been engaged to assist buyers and sellers with stock transactions.

	12/31/96	12/31/95	12/31/94	12/31/93
Per Share Information				
Stock Price	5.00	5.00	n.a.	n.a.
Earnings Per Share	0.63	-1.80	0.06	0.02
Price / Earnings Ratio	7.94	n.a.	n.a.	n.a.
Book Value Per Share	1.28	0.42	0.80	0.72
Price / Book Value %	390.63	1,190.48	n.a.	n.a.
Dividends Per Share	0.0	0.0	0.0	0.0
Annual Financial Data				
Operating Results (000's)				
Total Revenues	4,339.0	4,134.8	3,584.1	4,452.8
Costs & Expenses	-4,330.9	-4,202.8	-3,479.6	-4,425.4
Income Before Taxes and Other	8.0	-68.1	104.5	27.4
Other Items	0.0	0.0	0.0	0.0
Income Tax	17.5	4.0	-44.0	-8.0
Net Income	25.5	-64.1	60.5	19.4
Cash Flow From Operations	-66.7	202.6	116.2	160.2
Balance Sheet (000's)				
Cash & Equivalents	399.0	128.3	206.4	181.9
Total Current Assets	1,346.5	1,093.6	1,098.1	1,065.1
Fixed Assets, Net	915.0	701.4	692.2	676.2
Total Assets	2,585.2	1,835.2	1,847.2	1,806.9
Total Current Liabilities	431.8	1,079.2	735.9	881.0
Long-Term Debt	515.1	174.8	297.0	229.0
Stockholders' Equity	1,586.9	523.3	787.9	702.8
Performance & Financial Condition				
Return on Total Revenues %	0.59	-1.55	1.69	0.44
Return on Avg Stockholders' Equity %	2.42	-9.77	8.12	2.80
Return on Average Assets %	1.15	-3.48	3.31	n.a.
Current Ratio	3.12	1.01	1.49	1.21
Debt / Equity %	32.46	33.40	37.69	32.58

Compound Growth %'s	EPS %	n.a.	Net Income %	n.a.	Total Revenues %	-0.86

Comments

1996 results include a tax benefit of $17,474, $.43 per share. Because this distorts income, we did not display compound earnings growth rates. The Company is now well capitalized and is cautiously moving on expansion plans including mail order, slotting fees to retailers and new products. In 1996, the Company acquired a bakery for $50,000 in cash and a note for $300,000. This is called horizontal growth, particularly for the waistline. Investment Classification: Speculative

Officers	Position	Ownership Information	
Joan Katzeff	President, CFO	Number of Shares Outstanding	1,237,039
Paul Katzeff	CEO, Secretary	Market Capitalization	$ 6,185,195
Rick Moon	General Manager	Frequency of Dividends	n.a.
		Number of Shareholders	Under 500

Other Information				
Transfer Agent	Company Office		Where Listed	Order Matching Only
Auditor	Percy S. Yang, C.P.A.		Symbol	n.a.
Market Maker	Ted Prescott	(707)468-8646	SIC Code	2095
			Employees	n.a.
Broker Dealer	None - See Note			

Tidelands Royalty Trust "B"

P.O. Box 830241   Dallas, TX 75283-0241   Telephone (800)985-0794   Fax (214)508-3969

Company Description

The Trust was established in 1954 through a transfer into it of contract rights to certain properties in exchange for units of beneficial interest. The contract rights enable the Trust to receive an interest in any oil, gas or other mineral leases obtained by Chevron during a 50-year period beginning in 1951. At December 31, 1996, Marine Petroleum Trust (NASDAQ) owned 32.6% of Tidelands Royalty Trust "B".

	12/31/96	12/31/95	12/31/94
Per Share Information			
Stock Price	5.25	6.25	7.75
Earnings Per Share	0.78	0.70	1.08
Price / Earnings Ratio	6.73	8.93	7.18
Book Value Per Share	0.53	0.50	n.a.
Price / Book Value %	990.57	1,250.00	n.a.
Dividends Per Share	0.74	0.69	1.55
Annual Financial Data			
Operating Results (000's)			
Total Revenues	1,176.8	1,057.6	1,610.9
Costs & Expenses	-83.1	-76.0	-101.1
Income Before Taxes and Other	1,093.6	981.7	1,509.8
Other Items	0.0	0.0	0.0
Income Tax	-17.3	-16.7	-10.6
Net Income	1,076.3	965.0	1,499.2
Cash Flow From Operations	1,090.6	912.1	1,352.7
Balance Sheet (000's)			
Cash & Equivalents	1,763.0	1,706.8	n.a.
Total Current Assets	1,945.3	1,905.2	n.a.
Fixed Assets, Net	0.0	0.0	n.a.
Total Assets	1,945.3	1,905.2	n.a.
Total Current Liabilities	1,210.3	1,217.1	n.a.
Long-Term Debt	0.0	0.0	n.a.
Stockholders' Equity	734.9	688.1	n.a.
Performance & Financial Condition			
Return on Total Revenues %	91.47	91.24	93.07
Return on Avg Stockholders' Equity %	151.28	n.a.	n.a.
Return on Average Assets %	55.91	n.a.	n.a.
Current Ratio	1.61	1.57	n.a.
Debt / Equity %	n.a.	n.a.	n.a.

Compound Growth %'s	EPS % -15.02	Net Income % -15.27	Total Revenues % -14.53

Comments

Revenues and distributions fluctuate from period to period based on factors beyond the control of the Trust. Tidelands is due to commence receiving royalties in 1997 from a new gas well completed by Burlington Resources. The Trust believes that it will continue to have revenues sufficient to permit distributions to be made to unitholders for the foreseeable future. Investment Classification: Income

Officers	Position	Ownership Information	
R. Ray Bell	Controller	Number of Shares Outstanding	1,386,375
Chas G. McBurney	Other	Market Capitalization	$ 7,278,469
		Frequency of Dividends	Quarterly
		Number of Shareholders	n.a.

Other Information

Transfer Agent	Bank of New York New York, NY		Where Listed	OTC-BB
Auditor	KPMG Peat Marwick LLP		Symbol	TIRTZK
Market Maker	Herzog, Heine, Geduld, Inc.	(800)221-3600	SIC Code	6730
	Sharpe Capital Inc.	(800)355-5781	Employees	1
Broker Dealer	Regular Stockbroker			

Tidewater, Bank of

1548 Laskin Road   Virginia Beach, VA 23451   Telephone (757)422-0000   Fax (757)491-6303

Company Description

Bank of Tidewater, founded in 1985, is a community bank serving the communities of Virginia Beach, Virginia and surrounding areas. The bank has seven locations, four of which are in Virginia Beach. Two of the branches, Greenbrier and Shore Drive, opened in the fourth quarter of 1996. The Bank also formed a wholly-owned subsidiary to own an interest in a title insurance company. Management has engaged a market research firm to help intensify sales efforts in 1997.

	12/31/96	12/31/95	12/31/94	12/31/93
Per Share Information				
Stock Price	16.60	13.00	13.30	13.20
Earnings Per Share	1.27	1.07	1.00	0.76
Price / Earnings Ratio	13.07	12.15	13.30	17.37
Book Value Per Share	8.50	7.96	7.91	7.48
Price / Book Value %	195.29	163.32	168.14	176.47
Dividends Per Share	0.80	1.44	0.48	0.35
Annual Financial Data				
Operating Results (000's)				
Net Interest Income	7,680.8	6,760.6	6,214.8	5,087.3
Loan Loss Provision	-240.0	-180.0	-188.0	-190.0
Non-Interest Income	2,494.2	2,307.5	2,081.8	1,826.9
Non-Interest Expense	-6,457.3	-6,063.7	-5,598.2	-4,840.6
Income Before Taxes and Other	3,477.7	2,824.4	2,510.4	1,883.5
Other Items	0.0	0.0	0.0	26.7
Income Tax	-1,190.6	-976.0	-817.5	-644.3
Net Income	2,287.1	1,848.4	1,692.9	1,265.9
Balance Sheet (000's)				
Cash & Securities	47,410.6	50,275.3	37,367.0	55,572.0
Loans, Net	98,849.2	86,923.5	75,101.4	62,369.7
Total Assets	153,373.4	141,950.1	117,320.6	122,392.2
Deposits	133,458.0	126,390.1	102,934.5	109,634.3
Stockholders' Equity	14,908.7	13,528.3	12,983.9	12,176.5
Performance & Financial Condition				
Return on Avg Stockholders' Equity %	16.09	13.94	13.46	10.84
Return on Average Assets %	1.55	1.43	1.41	1.11
Equity to Assets %	9.72	9.53	11.07	9.95
Net Interest Margin	5.90	5.87	5.58	4.95
Reserve as a % of Problem Loans	1,295.68	414.18	486.60	321.43

Compound Growth %'s	EPS %	18.67	Net Income %	21.79	Net Interest Income %	14.72

Comments

The Bank declared a 5 for 4 stock split in February, 1997. All per share amounts have been adjusted to be consistent with the current pricing of the stock. 1996 was a record year with net income jumping 24%. Most of the growth was attributable to a large increase in net interest income. Management did not repeat a special dividend of $1 per share paid in 1995, probably because of the new expansion. Most shareholders would prefer the Bank to retain capital, having demonstrated excellent returns on assets and equity. Investment Classification: Growth & Income

Officers	**Position**	**Ownership Information**	
Elizabeth A. Duke	President, CEO	Number of Shares Outstanding	1,753,426
Larry G. Harcum	Exec VP, COO	Market Capitalization	$ 29,106,872
W. Kevin King	Exec VP, Senior Loan Officer	Frequency of Dividends	Quarterly
Neal A. Petrovich	Exec VP, CFO	Number of Shareholders	931
Owne J. Moore	Senior VP	Where Listed / Symbol	OTC-BB / BKTI

Other Information			**Loan Mix**	**%**
Transfer Agent	Company Office		R/E Mortgages	57.4
Auditor	KPMG Peat Marwick LLP		Commerical	17.8
Market Maker	Wheat, First Securities, Inc.	(800)446-1016	Installment	10.5
	McKinnon & Company, Inc.	(800)846-4391	Consumer	7.4
Broker Dealer	OTC Specialist		Construction	6.9
	Jack Ingold	(412)391-4594		

Tork, Inc.

1 Grove Street   Mount Vernon, NY 10550   Telephone (914)664-3542   Fax (914)664-5052

Company Description

Tork, Inc. manufactures electronic and electromechanical time switches, photoelectric controls, and occupancy sensors to control the demand and use of energy. It also manufactures horns, bells, strobes, etc. for visible and audible signaling. These products are used in commercial and industrial buildings. The primary customers of the Company are electrical distributors, who in turn sell to electrical contractors and consulting engineers. Tork Electro Sistemas, S.A. de C.V. is a subsidiary that operates in Mexico.

	07/31/96	07/31/95	07/31/94	07/31/93
Per Share Information				
Stock Price as of 12/31	10.50	11.12	6.50	6.25
Earnings Per Share	0.76	0.78	0.97	0.66
Price / Earnings Ratio	13.82	14.26	6.70	9.47
Book Value Per Share	13.25	12.21	12.11	11.26
Price / Book Value %	79.25	91.07	53.67	55.51
Dividends Per Share	0.0	0.0	0.0	0.0
Annual Financial Data				
Operating Results (000's)				
Total Revenues	15,201.3	15,290.8	15,826.0	14,831.8
Costs & Expenses	-14,518.6	-14,502.7	-14,902.5	-14,208.0
Income Before Taxes and Other	682.6	788.1	903.8	582.5
Other Items	0.0	0.0	0.0	0.0
Income Tax	-260.9	-298.0	-298.9	-172.7
Net Income	421.7	490.1	604.9	409.9
Cash Flow From Operations	564.2	5.9	911.2	-98.9
Balance Sheet (000's)				
Cash & Equivalents	1,770.5	2,467.7	2,719.1	1,659.7
Total Current Assets	7,274.6	8,015.3	8,042.4	6,698.2
Fixed Assets, Net	859.3	880.9	1,057.5	949.5
Total Assets	9,160.1	9,965.4	10,055.2	8,864.5
Total Current Liabilities	2,388.3	2,463.5	2,537.8	1,855.1
Long-Term Debt	0.0	0.0	0.0	0.0
Stockholders' Equity	6,771.8	7,501.8	7,517.4	7,009.4
Performance & Financial Condition				
Return on Total Revenues %	2.77	3.20	3.82	2.76
Return on Avg Stockholders' Equity %	5.91	6.53	8.33	6.00
Return on Average Assets %	4.41	4.90	6.39	4.62
Current Ratio	3.05	3.25	3.17	3.61
Debt / Equity %	n.a.	n.a.	n.a.	n.a.

Compound Growth %'s	EPS %	4.81	Net Income %	0.95	Total Revenues %	0.82

Comments

1996 and 1995 results were negatively affected by the Company's Mexican subsidiary which was hurt by the devaluation of the peso. Management reports that commercial construction and renovation have remained slow during 1996. The current ratio would even be better than reported if the extra cash squirreled away in stock mutual funds of in the amount of $696,000 were reported as a current asset. The Company acquired 105,944 common shares during 1996 which represents 17% of all shares outstanding. There is no long-term debt outstanding. Investment Classification: Value

Officers	Position	Ownership Information	
Victoria White	Chairman, CEO	Number of Shares Outstanding	511,110
R. Sam Shankar	President, CEO	Market Capitalization	$ 5,366,655
Carmen Caputo	VP - Finance, Treasurer	Frequency of Dividends	n.a.
Leonard Caponigro	Vice President	Number of Shareholders	Under 500
Michael Bizzoco	VP - Sales		

Other Information			
Transfer Agent	Registrar & Transfer Company Cranford, NJ	Where Listed	OTC-BB
Auditor	KPMG Peat Marwick LLP	Symbol	TORK
Market Maker	Wachtel & Co., Inc.	(202)898-1018	SIC Code	5063
	Hill Thompson Magid & Co., Inc	(800)631-3083	Employees	120
Broker Dealer	Regular Stockbroker		

Torrington Water Company (The)

110 Prospect Street   Torrington, CT 06790-0867   Telephone (203)489-4149   Fax (860)496-7889

Company Description

The Torrington Water Company provides water to approximately 8,500 residential and business customers in Torrington, Connecticut, and surrounding communities. The City of Torrington accounts for 25% of total revenue. The Company is regulated by the Connecticut Department of Public Utilities. The Torrington Water Company was founded in 1878.

	12/31/96	12/31/95	12/31/94	12/31/93
Per Share Information				
Stock Price	75.25	70.50	80.00	80.00
Earnings Per Share	9.19	11.82	8.30	9.92
Price / Earnings Ratio	8.19	5.96	9.64	8.06
Book Value Per Share	78.26	71.15	61.41	55.19
Price / Book Value %	96.15	99.09	130.27	144.95
Dividends Per Share	2.08	2.08	2.08	2.08
Annual Financial Data				
Operating Results (000's)				
Total Revenues	4,502.2	3,915.1	3,070.9	2,720.0
Costs & Expenses	-3,366.1	-2,520.9	-2,194.1	-1,867.1
Income Before Taxes and Other	1,136.0	1,394.2	876.8	852.9
Other Items	0.0	0.0	0.0	169.6
Income Tax	-474.3	-543.4	-278.9	-308.1
Net Income	661.8	850.8	597.9	714.4
Cash Flow From Operations	533.0	7,021.1	-4,381.5	843.7
Balance Sheet (000's)				
Cash & Equivalents	99.5	152.7	829.3	38.5
Total Current Assets	1,082.7	1,765.2	7,160.3	755.0
Fixed Assets, Net	24,807.2	24,405.1	16,829.9	12,312.4
Total Assets	26,960.0	27,180.5	25,045.5	14,324.1
Total Current Liabilities	2,613.5	3,354.3	1,717.3	1,234.7
Long-Term Debt	10,810.0	11,155.0	11,500.0	2,128.0
Stockholders' Equity	5,634.6	5,122.6	4,421.5	3,973.4
Performance & Financial Condition				
Return on Total Revenues %	14.70	21.73	19.47	26.26
Return on Avg Stockholders' Equity %	12.30	17.83	14.24	19.35
Return on Average Assets %	2.44	3.26	3.04	5.18
Current Ratio	0.41	0.53	4.17	0.61
Debt / Equity %	191.85	217.76	260.09	53.56

Compound Growth %'s	EPS %	n.a.	Net Income %	n.a.	Total Revenues %	18.29

Comments

1993 results include a one-time benefit of $169,627, or $2.35 per share, because of a change in accounting for income taxes. The compound earnings growth rates were not displayed because of the distortion in the base year. Management reports that the new filtration plant is functioning flawlessly and is producing water with excellent physical characteristics. On January 7, 1997, approvals were received to extend the system to Bridgeport Hydraulic Company. Construction of the extension has begun and is expected to be operational in the summer, 1997. Investment Classification: Value

Officers	Position	Ownership Information	
Richard D. Calhoun	President	Number of Shares Outstanding	72,000
Thomas K. Hubbard	Vice President, Secretary	Market Capitalization	$ 5,418,000
Mary J. Treusch	Vice President, Treasurer	Frequency of Dividends	Quarterly
Frederick D. Griswold	Vice President	Number of Shareholders	Under 500
Catherine C. Roscello	Controller		

Other Information			
Transfer Agent	Company Office	Where Listed	OTC-BB
Auditor	David R. Daggett	Symbol	TORW
Market Maker	Fahnestock & Co., Inc.	(800)223-3012	SIC Code	4940
	Legg Mason Wood & Walker, Inc.	(800)221-9732	Employees	16
Broker Dealer	OTC Specialist		
	Norman Kadehjian - Wainwright	(800)727-7176	

Tower Properties Company

911 Main Street, Ste. 100   Kansas City, MO 64105   Telephone (816)421-8255   Fax (816)374-0611

Company Description

Tower Properties Company owns, develops, leases and manages real property in the greater Kansas City metropolitan area including Johnson County, Kansas and Jackson County, Missouri. The improved real estate owned by the Company consists of 17 properties which include office buildings, apartment complexes, a warehouse/office facility and automobile parking lots and garages. The Company was founded in 1971.

	12/31/96	12/31/95	12/31/94	12/31/93
Per Share Information				
Stock Price	96.00	75.00	65.00	65.00
Earnings Per Share	8.80	8.84	4.75	2.90
Price / Earnings Ratio	10.91	8.48	13.68	22.41
Book Value Per Share	131.92	120.66	108.90	101.43
Price / Book Value %	72.77	62.16	59.69	64.08
Dividends Per Share	0.0	0.0	0.0	0.0
Annual Financial Data				
Operating Results (000's)				
Total Revenues	16,492.2	13,152.9	11,697.1	9,870.7
Costs & Expenses	-14,157.2	-10,787.9	-10,402.7	-9,316.4
Income Before Taxes and Other	2,335.0	2,365.0	1,294.4	554.3
Other Items	-12.5	-27.0	-28.7	135.2
Income Tax	-817.3	-827.8	-453.9	-194.0
Net Income	1,505.2	1,510.2	811.8	495.5
Cash Flow From Operations	3,778.2	3,982.0	2,778.3	2,341.8
Balance Sheet (000's)				
Cash & Equivalents	52.8	5.6	23.2	18.7
Total Current Assets	1,355.1	1,400.6	772.5	817.7
Fixed Assets, Net	53,472.9	45,102.4	35,918.1	30,982.7
Total Assets	63,624.2	56,504.1	42,497.9	36,669.5
Total Current Liabilities	989.5	1,355.4	957.2	832.7
Long-Term Debt	26,905.1	19,300.9	17,820.5	10,313.2
Stockholders' Equity	22,544.2	20,635.3	18,618.0	17,327.2
Performance & Financial Condition				
Return on Total Revenues %	9.13	11.48	6.94	5.02
Return on Avg Stockholders' Equity %	6.97	7.69	4.52	2.90
Return on Average Assets %	2.51	3.05	2.05	1.42
Current Ratio	1.37	1.03	0.81	0.98
Debt / Equity %	119.34	93.53	95.72	59.52

Compound Growth %'s	EPS %	44.78	Net Income %	44.83	Total Revenues %	18.66

Comments

Management reports that 1996 was a good year for real estate investments with demand equaling supply and a gradual appreciation in real estate values. During 1996, the Company acquired a 100,000 square foot warehouse and a small office building. The downtown properties have been enhanced by the restoration of parts of the downtown area including Quality Hill. Downtown office rentals continue to be extremely competitive. Investment Classification: Value

Officers	Position	Ownership Information	
James M. Kemper, Jr.	President, CEO	Number of Shares Outstanding	170,895
Benjamin F. Bryan	Exec VP	Market Capitalization	$ 16,405,920
Chester A. Wittwer, Jr.	Vice President, Secretary	Frequency of Dividends	n.a.
Margaret V. Allinder	Controller	Number of Shareholders	571

Other Information

Transfer Agent	UMB Bank, n.a. Kansas City, MO		Where Listed	OTC-BB
Auditor	Arthur Andersen LLP		Symbol	TPOP
Market Maker	George K. Baum & Company	(816)474-1100	SIC Code	6512
	Howe Barnes Investments, Inc.	(800)621-2364	Employees	45
Broker Dealer	OTC Specialist			
	Standard Investment	(888)783-4688 Ext: Jack		

Transnational Industries, Inc.

P.O. Box 198, U.S. Route 1   Chadds Ford, PA 19317   Telephone (610)459-5200   Fax (610)459-3830

Company Description

Through its subsidiary, the Company produces astronomical simulation equipment (planetariums) and simulation domes. The Company also services such equipment under maintenance contracts. Its principal customers are domestic and international museums, educational facilities, defense contractors, and the entertainment industry. The Company was incorporated in Delaware in 1985, and in 1986 it acquired Spitz Space Systems, Inc., which was founded in 1944. Recently, Spitz introduced new video projection products for planetarium theaters using immersive multimedia displays for wide audiences.

	01/31/97	01/31/96	01/31/95	01/31/94
Per Share Information				
Stock Price as of 12/31	1.50	2.32	3.10	3.00
Earnings Per Share	0.51	0.39	29.18	-8.00
Price / Earnings Ratio	2.94	5.95	0.11	n.a.
Book Value Per Share	6.49	4.78	4.11	-68.92
Price / Book Value %	19.38	48.54	75.43	n.a.
Dividends Per Share	0.0	0.0	0.0	0.0
Annual Financial Data				
Operating Results (000's)				
Total Revenues	6,842.0	5,761.0	5,310.0	5,713.0
Costs & Expenses	-6,563.0	-5,545.0	-5,041.0	-5,705.0
Income Before Taxes and Other	279.0	216.0	269.0	8.0
Other Items	0.0	0.0	8,767.0	-832.0
Income Tax	-6.0	0.0	-7.0	-23.0
Net Income	273.0	216.0	9,029.0	-847.0
Cash Flow From Operations	1,185.0	-299.0	491.0	240.0
Balance Sheet (000's)				
Cash & Equivalents	953.0	339.0	670.0	524.0
Total Current Assets	3,136.0	2,825.0	2,790.0	2,472.0
Fixed Assets, Net	585.0	584.0	545.0	869.0
Total Assets	6,059.0	5,842.0	5,891.0	5,790.0
Total Current Liabilities	2,571.0	1,872.0	2,078.0	1,962.0
Long-Term Debt	979.0	1,734.0	1,793.0	11,148.0
Stockholders' Equity	2,509.0	2,236.0	2,020.0	-7,320.0
Performance & Financial Condition				
Return on Total Revenues %	3.99	3.75	170.04	-14.83
Return on Avg Stockholders' Equity %	11.51	10.15	n.a.	n.a.
Return on Average Assets %	4.59	3.68	154.59	-11.66
Current Ratio	1.22	1.51	1.34	1.26
Debt / Equity %	39.02	77.55	88.76	n.a.

Compound Growth %'s	EPS % n.a.	Net Income % n.a.	Total Revenues % 6.20

Comments

During 1994, the Company completed a comprehensive debt and equity restructuring and for the fiscal year ended January 31, 1995, recognized a gain on the elimination of debt of $8.8 million. Also, in conjunction with the restructuring, the Company issued warrants, purchased and repurchased certain preferred and common stock, implemented a reverse 20 to 1 stock split and made other changes to its equity structure. The Company appears to have been reasonably profitable ever since. The preferred stock has liquidation preference and dividend requirements. Compound earnings growth rates were distorted by the 1994 year and have not been displayed. Investment Classification: Speculative

Officers	Position	Ownership Information	
Charles F. Huber	Chairman	Number of Shares Outstanding	324,220
Charles H. Holmes, Jr.	President, CEO	Market Capitalization	$ 486,330
Paul L. Dailey	Secretary, CFO	Frequency of Dividends	n.a.
		Number of Shareholders	100

Other Information			
Transfer Agent	American Stock Transfer & Trust Company New York, NY	Where Listed	OTC-BB
Auditor	Stockton Bates & Company, P.C.	Symbol	TRSN
Market Maker	Carr Securities Corporation (800)221-2243	SIC Code	3699
	Furman Selz Inc. (800)448-3223	Employees	52
Broker Dealer	Regular Stockbroker		

This page intentionally left blank.

Tremont Advisors, Inc.

555 Theodore Fremd Avenue   Rye, NY 10580   Telephone (914)921-3400   Fax (914)921-3499

Company Description

Tremont Advisors Inc. is a holding company which, through its subsidiaries, renders consulting and specialized investment services to investment funds, investment managers, institutional investors, and high net worth individuals, with respect to the organization and management of their investment portfolios or programs, as well as sponsoring its own multi- manager funds. In addition, the Company offers marketing and business development consulting services to investment management firms and to individual investment advisors. There are two classes of common stock.

	12/31/96	12/31/95	12/31/94	12/31/93
Per Share Information				
Stock Price	3.75	0.94	1.34	0.50
Earnings Per Share	0.14	0.0	-0.04	0.03
Price / Earnings Ratio	26.79	n.a.	n.a.	16.67
Book Value Per Share	0.53	0.38	0.38	0.03
Price / Book Value %	707.55	247.37	352.63	1,666.67
Dividends Per Share	0.0	n.a.	0.0	0.0
Annual Financial Data				
Operating Results (000's)				
Total Revenues	5,472.2	3,462.8	3,826.3	1,690.8
Costs & Expenses	-4,750.1	-3,452.7	-4,019.1	-1,559.3
Income Before Taxes and Other	722.1	10.1	-197.9	127.8
Other Items	0.0	0.0	0.0	0.0
Income Tax	-196.5	-2.3	29.7	-44.6
Net Income	525.5	7.8	-168.2	83.2
Cash Flow From Operations	443.0	-135.3	123.8	215.2
Balance Sheet (000's)				
Cash & Equivalents	551.7	455.1	901.1	65.5
Total Current Assets	2,002.9	1,208.0	1,437.4	498.0
Fixed Assets, Net	233.7	231.8	233.8	56.5
Total Assets	3,481.7	2,202.1	2,172.0	637.1
Total Current Liabilities	1,397.1	745.6	723.3	524.5
Long-Term Debt	0.0	0.0	0.0	0.0
Stockholders' Equity	2,062.1	1,456.5	1,448.7	112.6
Performance & Financial Condition				
Return on Total Revenues %	9.60	0.23	-4.40	4.92
Return on Avg Stockholders' Equity %	29.87	0.54	-21.55	36.77
Return on Average Assets %	18.49	0.36	-11.98	14.92
Current Ratio	1.43	1.62	1.99	0.95
Debt / Equity %	n.a.	n.a.	n.a.	n.a.

Compound Growth %'s	EPS % 67.11	Net Income % 84.86	Total Revenues % 47.92

Comments

1996 was a significant year of achievement for the Company. Revenues increased 55%, resulting from major changes in infrastructure, computer technology, business strategies and key additions to staff. Record earnings occurred despite considerable increases in capital investment for technology and new employees. Some people thought it was foolish of us to list Tremont last year in the first edition of Walker's Manual as the share price was under a dollar. It is now 400% higher. Investment Classification: Speculative

Officers	Position	Ownership Information	
Sandra L. Manzke	Chairman, CEO	Number of Shares Outstanding	3,884,457
Robert I. Schulman	President, COO	Market Capitalization	$ 14,566,714
Stephen T. Clayton	CFO	Frequency of Dividends	n.a.
Suzanne S. Hammond	Secretary, Treasurer	Number of Shareholders	70

Other Information			
Transfer Agent	ChaseMellon Shareholder Services New York, NY	Where Listed	OTC-BB
Auditor	Ernst & Young LLP	Symbol	TMAVA
Market Maker	Gabelli & Company, Inc.	(914)921-5154	SIC Code	6282
	Robotti & Co., Inc.	(212)986-0800	Employees	20
Broker Dealer	Regular Stockbroker		

Troy Mills, Inc.

30 Monadnock Street   Troy, NH 03465-1000   Telephone (603)242-7711   Fax (603)242-6896

Company Description

Troy Mills, which was founded in 1865, is engaged in the manufacture of non-woven textiles used as components of the interior trim in automobiles, lining for apparel, media for industrial filters, and wall coverings for commercial interiors. Most employees are part of an Employee Stock Ownership Plan sponsored by the Company. The Company has a glorious history, part of which we tried to capture on the next page.

	10/26/96	10/28/95	10/29/94	10/30/93
Per Share Information				
Stock Price as of 12/31	1.75	2.12	6.00	7.00
Earnings Per Share	0.15	-2.65	0.26	0.97
Price / Earnings Ratio	11.67	n.a.	23.08	7.22
Book Value Per Share	8.53	8.38	11.03	10.99
Price / Book Value %	20.52	25.30	54.40	63.69
Dividends Per Share	0.0	0.0	0.22	0.25
Annual Financial Data				
Operating Results (000's)				
Total Revenues	40,915.7	42,030.9	45,831.5	44,152.0
Costs & Expenses	-40,590.1	-44,412.9	-47,145.7	-42,799.6
Income Before Taxes and Other	325.6	-2,670.8	-1,364.1	1,244.8
Other Items	0.0	0.0	1,085.0	0.0
Income Tax	-213.0	650.1	479.6	-503.8
Net Income	112.6	-2,020.7	200.5	740.9
Cash Flow From Operations	2,570.1	1,267.3	1,048.8	2,430.4
Balance Sheet (000's)				
Cash & Equivalents	0.0	5,904.2	6,326.0	663.0
Total Current Assets	8,690.1	10,603.1	11,734.9	11,124.4
Fixed Assets, Net	10,871.0	11,397.3	11,409.0	8,644.8
Total Assets	19,672.2	22,478.9	23,863.6	20,378.8
Total Current Liabilities	6,559.5	6,137.7	5,454.4	4,072.9
Long-Term Debt	3,786.4	7,312.7	5,454.4	4,072.9
Stockholders' Equity	6,500.1	6,387.5	8,408.2	8,379.2
Performance & Financial Condition				
Return on Total Revenues %	0.28	-4.81	0.44	1.68
Return on Avg Stockholders' Equity %	1.75	-27.32	2.39	9.16
Return on Average Assets %	0.53	-8.72	0.91	3.93
Current Ratio	1.32	1.73	2.15	2.73
Debt / Equity %	58.25	114.49	84.85	74.99

Compound Growth %'s	EPS % -46.32	Net Income % -46.64	Total Revenues % -2.51

Comments

1994 results include a one-time benefit of $1.1 million, or $1.42 per share, created by retroactively changing depreciation methods to slower methods. Having experienced two difficult years, management restructured in 1995 with a major emphasis on reducing product costs. Some of the payoff is demonstrated in 1996, although the Company was also helped by more stable markets that provided lower material prices. Troy Mills is betting that it can now deliver price competitive products by utilizing lower cost materials. It also has new products that are doing well. There are still some environmental issues not yet resolved in which the Company may have liability. Although the Company still has a strong balance sheet, investors are approaching the bargain stock price with caution. Investment Classification: Speculative & Value

Officers	Position	Ownership Information	
Barrett F. Ripley	President, CEO	Number of Shares Outstanding	762,201
John S. Goodnow	Secretary	Market Capitalization	$ 1,333,852
Martin W. Ballen	Vice President	Frequency of Dividends	n.a.
Frederick W. MacMillan	Vice President, CFO	Number of Shareholders	Under 500
James A. Cuddy	VP - Manufacturing		

Other Information

Transfer Agent	John R. Goodnow & Co. Keene, NH		Where Listed	OTC-BB
Auditor	Ernst & Young LLP		Symbol	TMIL
Market Maker	Forbes, Walsh, Kelly & Co, Inc	(800)221-3747	SIC Code	5199
	R.A. Mackie & Co., L.P.	(800)328-1550	Employees	402
Broker Dealer	Regular Stockbroker			

Horses to Automobiles

Troy Mills has the distinction of holding the New Hampshire state record for continuity of family ownership in the textile industry and is third overall in the United States. Five generations of the Ripley family have been at the helm, beginning with Barrett Ripley in 1865. But Troy's history actually starts even a few years earlier than that.

An immigrant from Yorkshire County, England, Thomas Goodall had an idea in 1857 for an improved and more economical horse blanket. Historically, horse blankets had been square in shape, woolen, imported, and expensive. Functionally, it was difficult to keep a square blanket on a horse, so Mr. Goodall improved the design by tapering the blanket. He also made it more affordable to purchase by loom-weaving a combination of cotton and wool into an inexpensive fabric. Horse blankets were then a basic necessity, so these cheaper ones found a ready market in 1857 despite the poor economy.

Goodall's mill was located in Troy, New Hampshire. This site had evolved early on from eighteenth century settlers' needs for a variety of milled products, including those made from textiles. The Ripley family legacy began when Barrett Ripley formed a partnership to acquire Mr. Goodall's mill. He renamed it the Troy Blanket Mill and began to run the manufacturing operation. In those days, before the advent of *horseless* carriages, a farmer was judged by his horse team and the way in which he cared for his animals. Thus it came to pass that having a well-fitting, colorful plaid or patterned Troy blanket for one's horse was a status symbol.

As modes of transportation have changed, Troy has evolved and diversified as well. Having once simply supplied the textile needs of horses, the company now markets its synthetic fabrics to many and diverse industries. Chief among them, however, is the automotive industry. Troy allows automobile manufacturers to define specific product requirements, to color match under multiple lighting conditions and to test color fastness of their fabrics, thereby ensuring the customer's satisfaction with their product.

In the meantime, certain clothing fads have positively impacted the company as well. A few years ago you may have noticed colorfully lined denim and cotton work jackets popularized by rap singers. It was Troy that made the linings for these jackets. Earlier on, when western wear was quite popular, Troy's business in imitation sheepskin was strong. These fleeting fashions boost Troy's sales and demonstrate their versatility, but do not impair the emphasis on their main customer, the automotive industry. Troy Mills remains loyal to the transportation industry, and after more than 131 years of being in business has not wavered in its focus.

Turbotville National Bancorp, Inc.

P.O.Box 37 Turbotville, PA 17772 Telephone (717)649-5118 Fax (717)649-5788

Company Description

Turbotville National Bancorp, Inc. is the holding company of Turbotville National Bank, founded in 1910. The Bank provides standard banking services at its one location in the rural community of Turbotville, central Pennsylvania.

	12/31/96	12/31/95	12/31/94	12/31/93
Per Share Information				
Stock Price	401.00	315.00	315.00	310.00
Earnings Per Share	56.19	52.55	54.16	50.73
Price / Earnings Ratio	7.14	5.99	5.82	6.11
Book Value Per Share	523.20	488.28	431.84	403.93
Price / Book Value %	76.64	64.51	72.94	76.75
Dividends Per Share	14.50	14.00	14.00	13.25
Annual Financial Data				
Operating Results (000's)				
Net Interest Income	2,025.2	1,910.6	1,990.2	1,961.5
Loan Loss Provision	-82.0	-42.0	-82.0	-110.0
Non-Interest Income	160.4	180.2	163.3	164.7
Non-Interest Expense	-1,159.1	-1,158.0	-1,192.0	-1,154.3
Income Before Taxes and Other	944.5	890.8	879.6	862.0
Other Items	0.0	0.0	0.0	0.0
Income Tax	-247.8	-239.1	-208.0	-233.0
Net Income	696.7	651.7	671.6	629.0
Balance Sheet (000's)				
Cash & Securities	16,751.8	16,043.3	14,863.0	17,609.5
Loans, Net	37,514.1	35,687.3	33,779.1	31,533.4
Total Assets	55,086.0	52,536.2	49,521.8	50,104.3
Deposits	48,004.1	46,022.0	43,765.4	44,870.9
Stockholders' Equity	6,487.6	6,054.6	5,354.9	5,008.7
Performance & Financial Condition				
Return on Avg Stockholders' Equity %	11.11	11.42	12.96	13.19
Return on Average Assets %	1.29	1.28	1.35	1.28
Equity to Assets %	11.78	11.52	10.81	10.00
Net Interest Margin	n.a.	n.a.	n.a.	n.a.
Reserve as a % of Problem Loans	81.51	373.97	307.91	132.54

Compound Growth %'s	EPS %	3.47	Net Income %	3.47	Net Interest Income %	1.07

Comments

Although growth ratios are not high, the Bank continues to have favorable earnings when expressed as a percentage of total assets or equity. 1996 was a record year, largely attributable to an improvement in net interest income. The Bank has already completed the process of providing imaging technology to demand deposit customers and will be introducing the debit card in 1997. Investment Classification: Value

Officers	Position	Ownership Information	
James W. Foust	Chairman	Number of Shares Outstanding	12,400
P. Thomas Yoder, Jr.	President, CEO	Market Capitalization	$ 4,972,400
Charles A. Wright	Secretary, Head Cashier	Frequency of Dividends	Irregular
Paul R. Ranck	Vice President	Number of Shareholders	235
Brentha J. Snyder	Other	Where Listed / Symbol	OTC-BB / TVNB

Other Information			Loan Mix	%
Transfer Agent	Company Office		R/E Mortgages	78.7
Auditor	Larson, Kellett & Associates		Consumer	17.1
Market Maker	F.J. Morrissey & Co., Inc.	(800)842-8928	Commerical	3.3
	Ryan, Beck & Co.	(800)325-7926	Construction	0.9
Broker Dealer	OTC Specialist			
	Dennis Reynolds - Ryan, Beck	(888)231-7226		

U.S. Plastic Lumber Corporation

2300 Glades Road, Ste. 440 W.   Boca Raton, FL 33431   Telephone (561)394-3511   Fax (561)394-5335

Company Description

U.S. Plastic Lumber Corporation is engaged in the manufacturing of recycled plastic lumber from post-consumer plastic waste and the recycling of soils which have been exposed to hydrocarbons. The Company's plastic lumber consumers are located throughout the United States and account for 28% of 1996 sales. The Company's soil recycling customers are located primarily in the northeastern United States and account for 72% of 1996 sales. On December 30, 1996, the Company acquired Clean Earth Inc. through the issuance of 5.4 million shares of Company stock. Additional shares will be issued in connection with that transaction if certain production and sales goals are met.

	12/31/96	12/31/95
Per Share Information		
Stock Price	4.62	2.00
Earnings Per Share	-0.32	-0.19
Price / Earnings Ratio	n.a.	n.a.
Book Value Per Share	0.18	0.47
Price / Book Value %	2,566.67	425.53
Dividends Per Share	0.0	0.0
Annual Financial Data		
Operating Results (000's)		
Total Revenues	6,683.5	7,258.0
Costs & Expenses	-10,363.0	-8,393.9
Income Before Taxes and Other	-3,679.5	-1,135.9
Other Items	66.9	0.0
Income Tax	61.5	-310.0
Net Income	-3,551.1	-1,445.9
Cash Flow From Operations	-606.7	-1,164.0
Balance Sheet (000's)		
Cash & Equivalents	854.3	1,199.6
Total Current Assets	3,087.6	4,702.3
Fixed Assets, Net	1,198.2	1,486.0
Total Assets	4,510.7	6,434.9
Total Current Liabilities	2,376.0	2,214.8
Long-Term Debt	6.7	0.0
Stockholders' Equity	2,127.9	4,220.1
Performance & Financial Condition		
Return on Total Revenues %	-53.13	-19.92
Return on Avg Stockholders' Equity %	-111.88	-39.03
Return on Average Assets %	-64.89	n.a.
Current Ratio	1.30	2.12
Debt / Equity %	0.32	n.a.

Compound Growth %'s	EPS % n.a.	Net Income % n.a.	Total Revenues %	-7.92

Comments

The transaction referred to above was recorded as a pooling of interests. The numbers presented above have been restated to show the new combined entity. On January 27, 1997, Recycled Plastics Industries, Inc. was acquired for $1.2 million in cash and one million shares of Company stock. Management is pursuing additional acquisitions which is consistent with its growth strategy. The common share price was over $5 per share on May 31, 1997. Investment Classification: Speculative

Officers	Position	Ownership Information	
Harold H. Gebert	Chairman	Number of Shares Outstanding	11,672,349
Mark S. Alsentzer	President, CEO	Market Capitalization	$ 53,926,252
David A. Farrow	COO	Frequency of Dividends	n.a.
Lionel A. Marquis	CFO	Number of Shareholders	n.a.
Bruce C. Rosetto	Other		

Other Information			
Transfer Agent	Interwest Transfer Co., Inc. Salt Lake City, UT	Where Listed	OTC-BB
Auditor	Kuntz Lesher Siegrist Martini	Symbol	ECPL
Market Maker	Olsen Payne & Co.	(800)453-5321	SIC Code	3080
	Alpine Securities Corp.	(800)521-5588	Employees	n.a.
Broker Dealer	Regular Stockbroker		

UTZ Engineering, Inc.

101 Industrial East   Clifton, NJ 07012-1707   Telephone (201)778-4560   Fax (201)778-4239

Company Description

UTZ Engineering, Inc., formerly Donald Utz Engineering, offers products and services to the hybrid electronics and circuit board industries. The principal products include solder printing stencils, thick-film printing screens, metal masks, computer artwork generation, and custom photo-plotting. Working closely with IBM and AT&T, UTZ Engineering pioneered the development of the first sol-der printing stencils in 1984, and has been the leading supplier ever since. The Company was formed in 1971 and went public in 1985.

	03/31/96	03/31/95	03/31/94	03/31/93
Per Share Information				
Stock Price as of 12/31	1.00	2.00	2.00	2.00
Earnings Per Share	0.22	0.40	0.43	0.21
Price / Earnings Ratio	4.55	5.00	4.65	9.52
Book Value Per Share	2.74	2.65	2.41	2.11
Price / Book Value %	36.50	75.47	82.99	94.79
Dividends Per Share	0.15	0.15	0.15	0.10
Annual Financial Data				
Operating Results (000's)				
Total Revenues	5,663.5	6,143.2	5,403.7	4,712.1
Costs & Expenses	-5,289.3	-5,447.3	-4,649.6	-4,335.4
Income Before Taxes and Other	374.2	694.3	735.2	376.7
Other Items	0.0	0.0	-9.0	0.0
Income Tax	-163.1	-301.5	-307.3	-177.7
Net Income	211.1	392.8	418.9	199.0
Cash Flow From Operations	269.4	601.5	449.5	316.2
Balance Sheet (000's)				
Cash & Equivalents	729.0	694.3	286.5	444.4
Total Current Assets	2,253.1	2,230.8	2,049.4	1,658.1
Fixed Assets, Net	485.0	504.0	524.5	696.5
Total Assets	2,780.4	2,771.5	2,605.1	2,396.0
Total Current Liabilities	99.6	157.0	202.6	246.2
Long-Term Debt	0.0	17.8	39.9	60.2
Stockholders' Equity	2,680.8	2,596.7	2,362.6	2,065.4
Performance & Financial Condition				
Return on Total Revenues %	3.73	6.39	7.75	4.22
Return on Avg Stockholders' Equity %	8.00	15.84	18.92	10.19
Return on Average Assets %	7.61	14.61	16.75	8.52
Current Ratio	22.61	14.21	10.12	6.73
Debt / Equity %	n.a.	0.69	1.69	2.91

Compound Growth %'s	EPS %	1.56	Net Income %	1.99	Total Revenues %	6.32

Comments

Although small, the Company continues to demonstrate solid growth and is financially well positioned to benefit from the explosion of the new communication superhighway. Current assets include cash and marketable securities of slightly over $1 million as of March 31, 1996. The sales decrease was attributable to a market demand down-turn and over-supply in the cellular telephone manufacturing industry. Management reports expanded sales efforts as well as the installation of new laser technology in the manufacturing process. Investment Classification: Value & Income

Officers	Position	Ownership Information	
Donald L. Utz	Chairman, Treasurer	Number of Shares Outstanding	980,000
Frank Colonese	President, CEO	Market Capitalization	$ 980,000
Raynal W. Andrews, III	VP - Manufacturing	Frequency of Dividends	n.a.
		Number of Shareholders	Under 500

Other Information			
Transfer Agent	Jersey Transfer Verona, NJ	Where Listed	OTC-BB
Auditor	Fallon & Fallon	Symbol	DONU
Market Maker	Pars Securities, Inc.	(201)670-0700	SIC Code	3679
	Ernst & Co.	(800)845-4330	Employees	62
Broker Dealer	Regular Stockbroker		

Unidyne Corporation

118 Pickering Way, Ste. 104   Exton, PA 19341   Telephone (610)363-8237   Fax (610)524-8715

Company Description

Unidyne Corporation manufacturers vehicle testing equipment, including emissions testing and post-manufacturing testing, and specialized electric motors and variable speed drives and controls utilizing the Eddy Current Drive operating principle to control drive speed. Substantially all of the assets of the Eddy Current Drive Division of Eaton Corporation were acquired on September 1, 1995. The Company had been involved in other businesses prior to this acquisition.

	12/31/96	12/31/95
Per Share Information		
Stock Price	4.75	n.a.
Earnings Per Share	-0.18	-0.01
Price / Earnings Ratio	n.a.	n.a.
Book Value Per Share	-0.27	n.a.
Price / Book Value %	n.a.	n.a.
Dividends Per Share	0.0	0.0
Annual Financial Data		
Operating Results (000's)		
Total Revenues	16,605.0	6,111.0
Costs & Expenses	-17,826.0	-6,171.0
Income Before Taxes and Other	-1,221.0	-60.0
Other Items	0.0	0.0
Income Tax	-102.0	-40.0
Net Income	-1,323.0	-100.0
Cash Flow From Operations	2,514.0	-512.0
Balance Sheet (000's)		
Cash & Equivalents	46.0	n.a.
Total Current Assets	5,621.0	n.a.
Fixed Assets, Net	8,915.0	n.a.
Total Assets	17,237.0	n.a.
Total Current Liabilities	4,544.0	n.a.
Long-Term Debt	4,767.0	n.a.
Stockholders' Equity	2,655.0	n.a.
Performance & Financial Condition		
Return on Total Revenues %	-7.97	-1.64
Return on Avg Stockholders' Equity %	n.a.	n.a.
Return on Average Assets %	n.a.	n.a.
Current Ratio	1.24	n.a.
Debt / Equity %	179.55	n.a.

Compound Growth %'s	EPS % n.a.	Net Income % n.a.	Total Revenues % n.a.

Comments

1995 results reflect a five-month short period from the date of acquisition referred to above. In addition to the common shares, there is $5 million of preferred shares outstanding. Revenues were lower in the first quarter of 1997, declining 20%. Management attributes this decline to a lower volume of large press drive sales combined with decreased net selling prices. A loss of $156,000, $.03 per share, was reported for the quarter. Investment Classification: Speculative

Officers	Position	Ownership Information	
C. Eugene Hutcheson	President, CEO	Number of Shares Outstanding	8,525,360
David E. Ingram	Exec VP	Market Capitalization	$ 40,495,460
Timothy M. Flynn	Senior VP, CFO	Frequency of Dividends	n.a.
Charlotte E. Doremus	Secretary	Number of Shareholders	885
Delbert A. Warosh	Other		

Other Information

Transfer Agent	Progressive Transfer Co. Salt Lake City, UT			Where Listed	OTC-BB
Auditor	Arthur Andersen LLP			Symbol	UDYN
Market Maker	Shamrock Partners Ltd.		(800)326-4900	SIC Code	3820
	Wien Securities Corp.		(800)624-0050	Employees	n.a.
Broker Dealer	Regular Stockbroker				

Union Bancorp of Evansville, Inc.

P.O. Box 15   Evansville, WI 53536   Telephone (608)882-5200   Fax (608)882-6889

Company Description

Union Bank & Trust Company, subsidiary of this holding company, is celebrating its 100 year anniversary. For many years it was content to simply serve the Evansville community, and a trust department was added in 1940. More recently the Bank has started a geographic expansion to neighboring Brooklyn, Wisconsin, with the acquisition of The Bank of Brooklyn. Another branch opened in the Village of Belleville in 1997. Occasionally we like to blow the whistle on what we believe is unfair treatment of shareholders. Please see what it is that we have to say in the comments below.

	12/31/96	12/31/95	12/31/94	12/31/93
Per Share Information				
Stock Price	2,000.00	2,000.00	2,000.00	2,000.00
Earnings Per Share	351.91	319.47	302.52	257.11
Price / Earnings Ratio	5.68	6.26	6.61	7.78
Book Value Per Share	3,742.68	3,326.59	2,913.02	2,779.54
Price / Book Value %	53.44	60.12	68.66	71.95
Dividends Per Share	0.0	43.00	40.00	36.00
Annual Financial Data				
Operating Results (000's)				
Net Interest Income	1,877.0	1,536.0	1,550.0	1,563.0
Loan Loss Provision	-20.0	0.0	0.0	-180.0
Non-Interest Income	204.0	205.0	105.0	149.0
Non-Interest Expense	-1,345.0	-993.0	-953.0	-912.0
Income Before Taxes and Other	716.0	748.0	702.0	620.0
Other Items	0.0	0.0	0.0	0.0
Income Tax	-91.0	-164.0	-149.0	-150.0
Net Income	625.0	584.0	553.0	470.0
Balance Sheet (000's)				
Cash & Securities	21,913.0	22,536.0	18,406.0	18,200.0
Loans, Net	34,144.0	22,568.0	22,120.0	21,670.0
Total Assets	58,604.0	45,992.0	41,527.0	40,730.0
Deposits	51,099.0	39,135.0	35,325.0	35,428.0
Stockholders' Equity	6,647.0	6,081.0	5,325.0	5,081.0
Performance & Financial Condition				
Return on Avg Stockholders' Equity %	9.82	10.24	10.63	9.63
Return on Average Assets %	1.20	1.33	1.34	1.19
Equity to Assets %	11.34	13.22	12.82	12.47
Net Interest Margin	n.a.	n.a.	n.a.	n.a.
Reserve as a % of Problem Loans	371.60	136.27	113.99	105.41

Compound Growth %'s	EPS %	11.03	Net Income %	9.97	Net Interest Income %	6.29

Comments

As you might expect from the list of officers, the Eager family owns majority control of the Bank, approximately 60%. But that is not good enough, as they want to buy shares back from outsiders. In June, 1995, they offered $2,000 per share, a fraction of book value, and actually received 71 shares. They tried it again in June, 1996; that time there were no takers. They are trying a third time in 1997 at $2,500 per share. We have a group of subscribers that love these situations although our preference would be to stay away as this is clearly a family affair. Investment Classification: Value & Speculative

Officers	Position	Ownership Information	
Leonard P. Eager, Jr.	President	Number of Shares Outstanding	1,776
Alan S. Eager	Senior VP	Market Capitalization	$ 3,552,000
Stephen J. Eager	Vice President	Frequency of Dividends	Quarterly
David E. Fahey	Vice President	Number of Shareholders	n.a.
Christopher A. Eager	Vice President	Where Listed / Symbol	Order Matching Only / n.a.

Other Information		Loan Mix	%
Transfer Agent	Company Office	R/E Mortgages	56.5
Auditor	Not indicated	Agriculture	20.3
Market Maker	None - See Note	Commerical	12.5
		Installment	6.9
Broker Dealer	None	Construction	1.2
		Other	2.6

United Security Bank, National Association

2151 West Shaw Avenue   Fresno, CA 93711   Telephone (209)225-0101   Fax (209)428-4949

Company Description

The Bank, founded in 1987, operates six branches in the Fresno and Oakhurst areas which are in the San Joaquin Valley of California. Effective August 25, 1995, the Bank consummated a merger with Golden Oak Bank. The merger was accounted for as a pooling of interests; financial statements were restated to reflect the financial condition as if they had been together in earlier years. In connection with that merger, 197,533 shares of common stock were issued to the shareholders of Golden Oak Bank.

	12/31/96	12/31/95	12/31/94	12/31/93
Per Share Information				
Stock Price	22.00	16.00	13.00	12.25
Earnings Per Share	1.94	1.44	1.51	1.07
Price / Earnings Ratio	11.34	11.11	8.61	11.45
Book Value Per Share	11.35	9.82	8.58	6.50
Price / Book Value %	193.83	162.93	151.52	188.46
Dividends Per Share	0.74	0.41	0.45	0.38
Annual Financial Data				
Operating Results (000's)				
Net Interest Income	8,852.3	8,673.2	7,633.1	5,972.4
Loan Loss Provision	-700.0	-410.0	-340.6	-315.6
Non-Interest Income	2,138.4	1,726.8	1,099.8	1,128.6
Non-Interest Expense	-4,688.2	-5,430.7	-4,140.4	-3,728.8
Income Before Taxes and Other	5,602.5	4,559.3	4,251.9	3,056.6
Other Items	0.0	0.0	0.0	0.0
Income Tax	-2,275.8	-2,119.3	-1,734.3	-1,272.7
Net Income	3,326.7	2,440.1	2,517.6	1,783.9
Balance Sheet (000's)				
Cash & Securities	30,773.6	44,980.8	41,523.2	32,646.2
Loans, Net	125,441.3	104,871.3	97,082.6	54,629.0
Total Assets	161,732.9	155,334.6	143,915.8	89,588.0
Deposits	141,783.6	137,797.0	129,086.9	76,899.1
Stockholders' Equity	18,590.6	16,501.1	14,325.2	10,786.2
Performance & Financial Condition				
Return on Avg Stockholders' Equity %	18.96	15.83	20.05	17.35
Return on Average Assets %	2.10	1.63	2.16	1.86
Equity to Assets %	11.49	10.62	9.95	12.04
Net Interest Margin	5.98	6.05	6.08	5.33
Reserve as a % of Problem Loans	27.52	38.59	109.42	31.91

Compound Growth %'s	EPS %	21.94	Net Income %	23.09	Net Interest Income %	14.02

Comments

The Bank declared a 2 for 1 stock dividend in 1996. All per share amounts have been adjusted for consistency. Financial information has been restated to reflect the acquisition of Golden Oak Bank, except for the 1993 balance sheet which is not available on a restated basis. Earnings jumped an impressive 34.7% during 1996. Management reports that aggressive plans for growth are in place and that they will continue to seek acquisition opportunities that make sense for the shareholders. Investment Classification: Growth

Officers	Position	Ownership Information	
Dennis R. Woods	President, CEO	Number of Shares Outstanding	1,638,238
Kathy F. Karst	Vice President	Market Capitalization	$ 36,041,236
Kenneth L. Donahue	Vice President, CFO	Frequency of Dividends	Quarterly
David L. Eytcheson	Vice President, COO	Number of Shareholders	n.a.
Rhodlee A. Braa	Vice President, Sr Loan Officer	Where Listed / Symbol	OTC-BB / UBFO

Other Information			Loan Mix	%
Transfer Agent	First Interstate Bank San Francisco, CA		R/E Mortgages	46.5
Auditor	Deloitte & Touche LLP		Commerical	26.3
Market Maker	Van Kasper & Company	(800)652-1747	Construction	22.3
	Sutro & Co., Incorporated	(800)227-4422	Installment	2.8
Broker Dealer	OTC Specialist		Agriculture	2.1
	Hoefer & Arnett, Retail	(800)346-5544 Ext: Lisa		

United Vanguard Homes, Inc.

4 Cedar Swamp Road   Glen Cove, NY 11542   Telephone (516)759-1188   Fax (516)759-1219

Company Description

United Vanguard Homes Inc. owns and operates three residential retirement centers in the state of Michigan, which provide living and extended care services for residents on a month-to-month basis. The Company also provides management and other services for companies affiliated with its majority stockholder, Vanguard Ventures, Inc. On April 19, 1996, the Company entered into an agreement to purchase Harvest Village for $17.4 million, contingent on certain events. During 1996, a public offering of up to 2,070,000 shares at $8.50 per share and a note offering of up to $14,375,000 in debentures were commenced, the proceeds of which would be used to finance the purchase of Harvest Village. These offerings were subsequently cancelled due to adverse market conditions relating to the senior living facility industry sector at the time of the offering.

	03/31/96	03/31/95	03/31/94	03/31/93
Per Share Information				
Stock Price as of 12/31	8.00	6.00	n.a.	n.a.
Earnings Per Share	-0.41	-0.27	n.a.	n.a.
Price / Earnings Ratio	n.a.	n.a.	n.a.	n.a.
Book Value Per Share	-1.82	-2.80	n.a.	n.a.
Price / Book Value %	n.a.	n.a.	n.a.	n.a.
Dividends Per Share	0.0	0.0	n.a.	n.a.
Annual Financial Data				
Operating Results (000's)				
Total Revenues	8,634.2	8,310.4	7,524.2	8,359.0
Costs & Expenses	-7,602.5	-8,937.1	-8,105.9	-6,884.0
Income Before Taxes and Other	1,031.7	-626.7	-581.7	1,475.0
Other Items	0.0	0.0	0.0	434.5
Income Tax	-420.0	0.0	0.0	-480.0
Net Income	611.7	-626.7	-581.7	1,429.5
Cash Flow From Operations	588.8	-2,009.7	-833.1	1,342.0
Balance Sheet (000's)				
Cash & Equivalents	210.2	249.6	n.a.	n.a.
Total Current Assets	1,828.0	2,759.8	n.a.	n.a.
Fixed Assets, Net	2,361.7	2,637.8	n.a.	n.a.
Total Assets	6,087.5	6,101.4	n.a.	n.a.
Total Current Liabilities	1,927.9	3,584.5	n.a.	n.a.
Long-Term Debt	7,173.0	6,975.6	n.a.	n.a.
Stockholders' Equity	-3,328.1	-4,760.7	n.a.	n.a.
Performance & Financial Condition				
Return on Total Revenues %	7.08	-7.54	-7.73	17.10
Return on Avg Stockholders' Equity %	n.a.	n.a.	n.a.	n.a.
Return on Average Assets %	10.04	n.a.	n.a.	n.a.
Current Ratio	0.95	0.77	n.a.	n.a.
Debt / Equity %	n.a.	n.a.	n.a.	n.a.

Compound Growth %'s	EPS % n.a.	Net Income % -24.65	Total Revenues % 1.09

Comments

During 1996, the Company executed a 1 for 1.6667 reverse split. All per share amounts have been adjusted for consistency. For the nine months ended December 31, 1996, the Company reported a loss of $866,572, or $.39 per share. All of the loss can be attributed to $1,000,000 of nonrecurring expense related to the aborted public offering. The Company has an overly-complicated capital structure which should be analyzed by any serious investor. The Company will attempt to help shareholders who want to buy or sell shares by facilitating such transactions. Investment Classification: Speculative

Officers	Position	Ownership Information	
Carl G. Paffendorf	Chairman, CEO	Number of Shares Outstanding	1,827,833
Larry L. Laird	President, COO	Market Capitalization	$ 14,622,664
Paul D'Andrea	VP - Finance	Frequency of Dividends	n.a.
Alan Guttman	Treasurer	Number of Shareholders	800
Teresa Govier	Vice President, Secretary		

Other Information

Transfer Agent	Continental Stock Transfer & Trust Co. New York, NY	Where Listed	Order Matching Only
Auditor	Grant Thornton LLP	Symbol	n.a.
Market Maker	None - See Note	SIC Code	6513
		Employees	n.a.
Broker Dealer	None		

Unity First Acquisition Corp.

245 Fifth Avenue   New York, NY 10016   Telephone (212)696-4282   Fax (212)532-8293

Company Description

Unity First Acquisition Corp. was formed on May 30, 1996, to serve as a vehicle to effect a merger, exchange of capital stock, asset acquisition or other similar business combination with an operating business which the Company believes has significant growth potential. The Company completed a public offering of one million shares of common stock at $6.50 per share. This is known as a "blank check" enterprise, as investors are betting on the skills of management without knowing what the actual business will be.

	01/31/97	07/31/96
Per Share Information		
Stock Price as of 12/31	4.37	n.a.
Earnings Per Share	-0.01	-0.02
Price / Earnings Ratio	n.a.	n.a.
Book Value Per Share	3.92	-0.02
Price / Book Value %	42.84	n.a.
Dividends Per Share	0.0	0.0
Annual Financial Data		
Operating Results (000's)		
Total Revenues	67.7	0.0
Costs & Expenses	-78.7	-15.0
Income Before Taxes and Other	-11.0	-15.0
Other Items	0.0	0.0
Income Tax	0.0	0.0
Net Income	-11.0	-15.0
Cash Flow From Operations	116.5	-15.0
Balance Sheet (000's)		
Cash & Equivalents	407.7	0.6
Total Current Assets	6,478.7	0.6
Fixed Assets, Net	0.0	0.0
Total Assets	6,478.7	250.6
Total Current Liabilities	102.5	265.5
Long-Term Debt	0.0	0.0
Stockholders' Equity	6,376.2	-14.9
Performance & Financial Condition		
Return on Total Revenues %	-16.26	n.a.
Return on Avg Stockholders' Equity %	n.a.	n.a.
Return on Average Assets %	n.a.	n.a.
Current Ratio	63.19	n.a.
Debt / Equity %	n.a.	n.a.

Compound Growth %'s	EPS %	n.a.	Net Income %	n.a.	Total Revenues %	n.a.

Comments

Thus far, the Company has had little operational expense outside the costs of the public offering. At January 31, 1997, the Company had $6,478,695 in cash equivalents. Management has not yet announced any acquisition candidates. Norman Leben has a history of involvement in blank check companies which may be reviewed prior to making an investment in Unity First. Investment Classification: Speculative

Officers	Position	Ownership Information	
Lawrence Burstein	President, Treasurer	Number of Shares Outstanding	1,625,125
Norman Leben	Secretary	Market Capitalization	$ 2,731,250
		Frequency of Dividends	n.a.
		Number of Shareholders	n.a.

Other Information			
Transfer Agent	American Stock Transfer & Trust Co. New York, NY	Where Listed	OTC-BB
Auditor	Arthur Andersen LLP	Symbol	UFAC
Market Maker	Sharpe Capital Inc. (800)355-5781	SIC Code	6770
	Gaines Berland Inc. (800)513-2775	Employees	2
Broker Dealer	Regular Stockbroker		

Universal Metals & Machinery, Inc.

5906 Armour Drive   Houston, TX 77020-8104   Telephone (713)675-6361   Fax (713)675-7819

Company Description

Universal Metals & Machinery, Inc. is engaged principally in the sale of machine tools and related parts and service, stainless steel products (plate, bar, pipe, flanges, and fittings) and nickel alloy products, principally to the chemical, petrochemical and food processing industries worldwide. In 1993, the Company entered into a 50-50 joint venture with Dynamic Products, Inc. to acquire stainless steel inventory from a third party.

	06/30/96	06/30/95	06/30/94	06/30/93
Per Share Information				
Stock Price as of 12/31	2.25	2.25	2.19	2.12
Earnings Per Share	-0.47	0.33	0.15	0.22
Price / Earnings Ratio	n.a.	6.82	14.60	9.64
Book Value Per Share	8.91	9.37	9.05	8.90
Price / Book Value %	25.25	24.01	24.20	23.82
Dividends Per Share	0.0	0.0	0.0	0.0
Annual Financial Data				
Operating Results (000's)				
Total Revenues	8,964.8	11,520.8	8,351.4	7,692.6
Costs & Expenses	-9,246.8	-11,215.9	-8,243.6	-7,522.9
Income Before Taxes and Other	-293.2	305.0	107.8	169.8
Other Items	0.0	0.0	0.0	10.0
Income Tax	74.1	-152.4	-38.2	-77.8
Net Income	-219.0	152.6	69.5	102.0
Cash Flow From Operations	-519.6	-559.3	70.4	34.5
Balance Sheet (000's)				
Cash & Equivalents	111.5	124.2	139.1	128.9
Total Current Assets	6,764.6	6,973.5	6,123.7	5,866.8
Fixed Assets, Net	807.4	871.8	805.5	866.7
Total Assets	7,970.1	8,423.6	7,698.7	6,952.8
Total Current Liabilities	3,756.2	3,565.9	2,995.4	2,754.4
Long-Term Debt	39.8	464.6	462.7	27.4
Stockholders' Equity	4,174.1	4,393.1	4,240.5	4,171.0
Performance & Financial Condition				
Return on Total Revenues %	-2.44	1.32	0.83	1.33
Return on Avg Stockholders' Equity %	-5.11	3.53	1.65	2.48
Return on Average Assets %	-2.67	1.89	0.95	1.50
Current Ratio	1.80	1.96	2.04	2.13
Debt / Equity %	0.95	10.58	10.91	0.66

Compound Growth %'s	EPS % n.a.	Net Income % n.a.	Total Revenues % 5.23

Comments

1995 results include a nonrecurring gain of $178,516 from the sale of a building. Pre-tax earnings from the joint venture were $142,876 and $82,682 for the years 1995 and 1994, respectively, which basically accounts for all Net Income. In 1996, the joint venture registered a loss of $11,181 and Company sales were off the preceding year record mark by 20%. The Company is supported by a strong balance sheet to weather stormy times. Investment Classification: Value

Officers	**Position**	**Ownership Information**	
Michael Feinstein	President	Number of Shares Outstanding	468,720
Julius Feinstein	CEO	Market Capitalization	$ 1,054,620
Larry Cole	Controller	Frequency of Dividends	n.a.
		Number of Shareholders	Under 500

Other Information				
Transfer Agent	ChaseMellon Shareholder Services Ridgefield Park, NJ		Where Listed	OTC-BB
Auditor	Coopers & Lybrand LLP		Symbol	UVMM
Market Maker	Newby & Company	(800)456-3992	SIC Code	5084
	Carr Securities Corporation	(800)221-2243	Employees	30
Broker Dealer	Regular Stockbroker			

VASCO Corp.

1919 S. Highland Avenue, #118C   Lombard, IL 60148   Telephone (630)495-0755   Fax (630)495-0279

Company Description

VASCO Corp. manufactures and sells a variety of products related to security, including hand-held tokens, smart cards, and biometrics. Computer related products include extended end user authentication and virus protection for financial institutions, industry and government. The Company holds patents on a number of these products. The primary market for these products is Europe. The Company also offers consulting services for implementing new software applications in a variety of areas. These services are targeted towards domestic companies. The Company went public in 1985 and has since raised additional capital by issuing preferred stock.

	12/31/95	12/31/94	12/31/93	12/31/92
Per Share Information				
Stock Price as of 12/31	6.87	0.37	0.50	0.25
Earnings Per Share	-0.03	0.01	n.a.	0.02
Price / Earnings Ratio	n.a.	37.00	n.a.	12.50
Book Value Per Share	0.08	0.08	0.02	0.02
Price / Book Value %	8,587.50	462.50	2,500.00	1,250.00
Dividends Per Share	0.0	0.0	0.0	0.0
Annual Financial Data				
Operating Results (000's)				
Total Revenues	3,800.1	2,751.2	2,199.3	2,302.0
Costs & Expenses	-4,408.2	-2,526.5	-2,118.9	-1,802.8
Income Before Taxes and Other	-608.0	224.7	80.4	499.1
Other Items	0.0	0.0	0.0	-16.1
Income Tax	251.0	-87.0	-30.0	-193.9
Net Income	-357.0	137.7	50.4	289.1
Cash Flow From Operations	58.7	-436.1	453.8	318.7
Balance Sheet (000's)				
Cash & Equivalents	744.6	38.1	209.2	2.8
Total Current Assets	2,213.8	1,429.8	917.5	913.9
Fixed Assets, Net	123.3	79.1	104.0	63.6
Total Assets	2,494.5	2,111.0	1,521.8	1,339.7
Total Current Liabilities	1,059.6	665.9	403.8	434.9
Long-Term Debt	7.3	60.0	745.9	512.3
Stockholders' Equity	1,416.9	1,363.7	340.0	242.8
Performance & Financial Condition				
Return on Total Revenues %	-9.40	5.00	2.29	12.56
Return on Avg Stockholders' Equity %	-25.68	16.16	17.28	243.52
Return on Average Assets %	-15.50	7.58	3.52	22.55
Current Ratio	2.09	2.15	2.27	2.10
Debt / Equity %	0.51	4.40	219.39	210.97

Compound Growth %'s	EPS % n.a.	Net Income % n.a.	Total Revenues %	18.19

Comments

When we went to press, the Company was projecting that its 1996 statement would be available on June 30, 1997. For the nine months ended September 30, 1996, the Company reported revenues of $6.2 million, up 170% over the same period of 1995. A loss of $510,703 was also reported for the nine month period. There are a lot of shares outstanding which detracts from upside potential of the stock price. Our calculations were made assuming full conversion of the preferred shares. At May 31, 1997, the stock price was in the $3 per share range. Investment Classification: Speculative

Officers	Position	Ownership Information	
John C. Haggard	President	Number of Shares Outstanding	17,638,539
Ken Hunt	CEO	Market Capitalization	$ 121,176,763
Michael B. Wiggen	Vice President, CFO	Frequency of Dividends	n.a.
		Number of Shareholders	Under 500

Other Information

				Where Listed	OTC-BB
Transfer Agent	Fidelity Transfer Co. Salt Lake City, UT			Symbol	VASC
Auditor	Price Waterhouse LLP			SIC Code	3695
Market Maker	Paragon Capital Corporation	(800)521-8877		Employees	20
	Herzog, Heine, Geduld, Inc.	(800)221-3600			
Broker Dealer	Regular Stockbroker				

VRB Bancorp

110 Pine Street   Rogue River, OR 97537   Telephone (541)582-3216   Fax (541)582-4161

Company Description

Valley of the Rogue Bank, subsidiary of this holding company was founded in 1968. The Bank has grown from a main office in Rogue River to eight additional branch offices serving Josephine and Jackson Counties in southwestern Oregon. Management's objective of increasing shareholder value by 15% a year may sound aggressive. So far, however, they are doing even better than that. A building moratorium is scheduled to end in the fall of 1997 which may spark additional growth in the region.

	12/31/96	12/31/95	12/31/94	12/31/93
Per Share Information				
Stock Price	11.25	6.37	8.01	6.16
Earnings Per Share	0.92	0.82	0.71	0.58
Price / Earnings Ratio	12.23	7.77	11.28	10.62
Book Value Per Share	5.65	4.99	4.30	3.74
Price / Book Value %	199.12	127.66	186.28	164.71
Dividends Per Share	0.25	0.16	0.14	0.12
Annual Financial Data				
Operating Results (000's)				
Net Interest Income	9,560.6	8,983.7	8,355.2	6,503.6
Loan Loss Provision	-250.0	0.0	0.0	0.0
Non-Interest Income	1,370.6	1,380.5	1,511.7	1,631.6
Non-Interest Expense	-5,828.0	-6,061.1	-6,022.1	-4,978.1
Income Before Taxes and Other	4,853.3	4,303.1	3,844.8	3,157.1
Other Items	0.0	0.0	0.0	0.0
Income Tax	-1,602.0	-1,395.0	-1,335.0	-1,104.0
Net Income	3,251.3	2,908.1	2,509.8	2,053.1
Balance Sheet (000's)				
Cash & Securities	69,501.6	55,180.4	46,257.9	56,357.3
Loans, Net	99,775.8	88,972.5	88,441.5	78,583.3
Total Assets	177,106.7	151,485.5	141,536.6	141,969.9
Deposits	155,568.5	132,744.5	125,472.3	127,997.6
Stockholders' Equity	20,188.1	17,469.7	15,000.6	12,973.4
Performance & Financial Condition				
Return on Avg Stockholders' Equity %	17.27	17.91	17.94	16.91
Return on Average Assets %	1.98	1.98	1.77	1.63
Equity to Assets %	11.40	11.53	10.60	9.14
Net Interest Margin	6.02	6.37	6.02	5.98
Reserve as a % of Problem Loans	2,805.76	1,981.36	1,221.27	503.48

Compound Growth %'s	EPS %	16.62	Net Income %	16.56	Net Interest Income %	13.70

Comments

The Company has declared 3 for 2 stock splits in both 1996 and 1994, and 4% stock dividends in 1995 and 1994. All per share amounts have been restated for comparability. 1996 was another record year with an increase in net interest income and a reduction to noninterest expense as the leading two contributors. The Bank even provided $250,000 as a provision for loan losses in 1996, the only such provision in all four years presented. The returns on assets and equity are some of the very best we have seen. Investment Classification: Growth

Officers	Position	Ownership Information	
William A. Haden	President, CEO	Number of Shares Outstanding	3,574,682
Tom Anderson	Exec VP, COO	Market Capitalization	$ 40,215,173
Virgil Syverson	Senior VP	Frequency of Dividends	Annual
Brad Copeland	Senior VP	Number of Shareholders	n.a.
Sharon Warburton	Vice President	Where Listed / Symbol	OTC-BB / VRBA

Other Information			Loan Mix	%
Transfer Agent	Company Office		R/E Mortgages	65.4
Auditor	Moss Adams LLP		Commerical	13.0
Market Maker	Black & Company, Inc.	(800)423-2124	Installment	12.6
	Hill Thompson Magid & Co., Inc	(800)631-3083	Construction	9.0
Broker Dealer	Regular Stockbroker			

Valley Fair Corporation (The)

260 Bergen Turnpike   Little Ferry, NJ 07643   Telephone (201)440-4000   Fax (201)807-0043

Company Description

The Company operates two discount stores under the name "Valley Fair" in the state of New Jersey. The stores sell hard and soft goods as well as health and beauty aids and groceries. Through its wholly-owned subsidiary, L.F. Widmann, Inc., the Company operates 127 retail drug and health and beauty aid stores, primarily in Pennsylvania and also 11 other Mid-Atlantic and Mid-Western states.

	01/28/96	01/29/95	01/30/94	01/31/93
Per Share Information				
Stock Price as of 12/31	26.00	26.00	26.00	28.50
Earnings Per Share	0.0	0.07	1.97	1.71
Price / Earnings Ratio	n.a.	371.43	13.20	16.67
Book Value Per Share	50.19	50.18	50.10	48.12
Price / Book Value %	51.80	51.81	51.90	59.23
Dividends Per Share	0.0	0.0	0.0	0.0
Annual Financial Data				
Operating Results (000's)				
Total Revenues	72,997.7	75,562.6	74,530.5	71,759.0
Costs & Expenses	-72,910.7	-75,552.6	-73,228.1	-70,672.5
Income Before Taxes and Other	87.0	10.0	1,302.5	1,086.5
Other Items	0.0	0.0	0.0	0.0
Income Tax	-86.0	16.0	-577.4	-455.0
Net Income	1.0	26.0	725.1	631.5
Cash Flow From Operations	768.8	184.4	-140.3	2,389.7
Balance Sheet (000's)				
Cash & Equivalents	3,608.6	3,652.6	4,977.5	4,432.2
Total Current Assets	29,429.1	30,908.3	31,637.7	28,873.8
Fixed Assets, Net	4,265.9	4,579.3	4,991.0	5,307.1
Total Assets	34,031.1	35,784.2	36,889.0	34,512.6
Total Current Liabilities	14,719.3	16,062.9	6,409.5	6,026.2
Long-Term Debt	233.6	701.9	11,098.9	9,766.8
Stockholders' Equity	18,468.2	18,469.0	18,447.4	17,728.1
Performance & Financial Condition				
Return on Total Revenues %	0.0	0.03	0.97	0.88
Return on Avg Stockholders' Equity %	0.01	0.14	4.01	n.a.
Return on Average Assets %	0.0	0.07	2.03	n.a.
Current Ratio	2.00	1.92	4.94	4.79
Debt / Equity %	1.26	3.80	60.17	55.09

Compound Growth %'s	EPS %	-79.77	Net Income %	-88.32	Total Revenues %	0.57

Comments

The Company operates on the basis of a 52/53 week year. As we went to print, the operating results for the year ended January 31, 1997, were not available. For the thirty-nine weeks ended October 29, 1996, the Company had revenues of $43.7 million and a net loss of $1,096,000 ($2.98 per share), as compared to $47.9 million and profit of $130,000 ($.35 per share) for the same period in 1995. As in the past, the poor results were attributable to competition and economic uncertainties which continue to affect consumer buying patterns. Investment Classification: Speculative & Value

Officers	Position	Ownership Information	
Edwin Lehr	President, CEO	Number of Shares Outstanding	367,983
Thomas R. Ketteler	Secretary	Market Capitalization	$ 9,567,558
Ross N. Alfieri	Treasurer, CFO	Frequency of Dividends	n.a.
Saul S. Schottenstein	Vice President	Number of Shareholders	1,161
Philip J. Ganguzza	Vice President		

Other Information			
Transfer Agent	Registrar & Transfer Company Cranford, NJ	Where Listed	OTC-BB
Auditor	Alpern, Rosenthal & Co.	Symbol	VALL
Market Maker	Macallaster Pitfield Mackay (212)422-9366	SIC Code	5411
	Carr Securities Corporation (800)221-2243	Employees	690
Broker Dealer	Regular Stockbroker		

Valley Water Systems, Inc.

17 Pierce Street   Plainville, CT 06062-0248   Telephone (860)747-2734   Fax (860)747-5954

Company Description

Valley Water Systems, Inc., formerly The Plainville Water Company, is a public utility distributing water to approximately 5,900 customers in Plainville, Connecticut. The largest customer, the Town of Plainville, accounts for approximately 15% of the Company's total revenue. The Company is regulated by the State of Connecticut Department of Public Utility Control. The Company listed its shares on the OTC bulletin board in 1996 to improve the liquidity of its common shares.

	12/31/96	12/31/95	12/31/94	12/31/93
Per Share Information				
Stock Price	25.00	20.00	20.00	20.00
Earnings Per Share	2.02	1.83	2.66	2.87
Price / Earnings Ratio	12.38	10.93	7.52	6.97
Book Value Per Share	24.89	23.13	21.80	19.39
Price / Book Value %	100.44	86.47	91.74	103.15
Dividends Per Share	0.32	0.15	0.20	0.15
Annual Financial Data				
Operating Results (000's)				
Total Revenues	1,930.2	1,694.6	1,640.8	1,574.2
Costs & Expenses	-1,688.6	-1,500.7	-1,330.6	-1,326.4
Income Before Taxes and Other	226.7	181.5	310.2	247.8
Other Items	0.0	0.0	0.0	0.0
Income Tax	-73.7	-59.2	-187.9	-75.4
Net Income	153.0	122.3	122.3	172.4
Cash Flow From Operations	465.8	35.5	n.a.	n.a.
Balance Sheet (000's)				
Cash & Equivalents	69.7	179.0	n.a.	n.a.
Total Current Assets	500.2	596.6	n.a.	n.a.
Fixed Assets, Net	7,252.6	7,053.0	n.a.	n.a.
Total Assets	8,596.0	8,499.0	n.a.	n.a.
Total Current Liabilities	511.5	692.6	n.a.	n.a.
Long-Term Debt	2,885.0	2,759.9	n.a.	n.a.
Stockholders' Equity	1,888.3	1,755.1	n.a.	n.a.
Performance & Financial Condition				
Return on Total Revenues %	7.93	7.21	7.45	10.95
Return on Avg Stockholders' Equity %	8.40	7.98	9.90	15.94
Return on Average Assets %	1.79	n.a.	n.a.	n.a.
Current Ratio	0.98	0.86	n.a.	n.a.
Debt / Equity %	152.78	157.25	n.a.	n.a.

Compound Growth %'s	EPS % -11.05	Net Income % -3.89	Total Revenues % 7.03

Comments

The anticipated sale of a reservoir to the Town of Southington continues to be tangled in Connecticut's bureaucratic permit regulations. Management intends to persevere because the significant equity that would be freed would be helpful for other infrastructure improvements. At the same time, on-going merger discussions with other water systems may flush through some real benefits to customers, employees and shareholders. Investment Classification: Value

Officers	Position	Ownership Information	
Raymond G. Corsini	President	Number of Shares Outstanding	75,878
		Market Capitalization	$ 1,896,950
		Frequency of Dividends	Quarterly
		Number of Shareholders	Under 500

Other Information				
Transfer Agent	Company Office		Where Listed	OTC-PS
Auditor	David R. Daggett, C.P.A.		Symbol	PLAV
Market Maker	H.C. Wainwright & Co., Inc.	(800)225-6790	SIC Code	4940
			Employees	n.a.
Broker Dealer	Regular Stockbroker			
	Norman Hadehjian - Wainwright	(800)225-6790		

Verdugo Banking Company

500 North Brand Boulevard   Glendale, CA 91203   Telephone (818)549-1000   Fax (818)549-4196

Company Description

Verdugo Banking Company opened its first office in 1991 in Glendale, California. The Bank has demonstrated five strong years despite the weak economic climate in southern California for most of this period. The region has seen a gradual shift away from many of the manufacturing enterprises that were dependent on the defense industry. These have largely been replaced by service providers and an enormous growth in the entertainment industry, primarily due to Glendale's close proximity to Burbank.

	12/31/96	12/31/95	12/31/94	12/31/93
Per Share Information				
Stock Price	13.25	12.00	11.00	10.00
Earnings Per Share	1.19	1.29	0.89	0.26
Price / Earnings Ratio	11.13	9.30	12.36	38.46
Book Value Per Share	11.16	10.00	8.69	7.80
Price / Book Value %	118.73	120.00	126.58	128.21
Dividends Per Share	0.0	0.0	0.0	0.0
Annual Financial Data				
Operating Results (000's)				
Net Interest Income	3,470.1	3,177.7	2,463.8	1,823.0
Loan Loss Provision	-218.3	-324.9	-326.0	-195.0
Non-Interest Income	219.2	215.9	177.8	130.5
Non-Interest Expense	-2,463.3	-2,147.5	-1,849.5	-1,624.0
Income Before Taxes and Other	1,007.8	921.3	466.2	134.5
Other Items	0.0	0.0	0.0	0.0
Income Tax	-384.3	-255.5	-8.0	-0.8
Net Income	623.5	665.8	458.2	133.7
Balance Sheet (000's)				
Cash & Securities	14,218.2	10,734.0	10,964.7	7,948.5
Loans, Net	42,356.1	35,522.7	29,415.7	26,351.3
Total Assets	57,856.4	47,374.6	41,327.2	35,061.6
Deposits	51,645.1	41,308.6	36,582.3	30,813.8
Stockholders' Equity	5,878.6	5,199.2	4,485.8	4,027.6
Performance & Financial Condition				
Return on Avg Stockholders' Equity %	11.26	13.75	10.76	3.38
Return on Average Assets %	1.18	1.50	1.20	0.43
Equity to Assets %	10.16	10.97	10.85	11.49
Net Interest Margin	7.00	7.30	6.80	6.70
Reserve as a % of Problem Loans	303.68	377.89	907.03	n.a.

Compound Growth %'s	EPS %	66.03	Net Income %	67.08	Net Interest Income %	23.93

Comments

Compound earnings growth rates are affected by the lower earnings level in 1993, which is the base period for the calculation, and the absence of an income tax expense in 1993. Irrespective of the actual number, Verdugo continues with an impressive record as total assets, loans and deposits grew 22%, 22% and 25%, respectively, during 1996. Demand deposits grew 40% during the year and comprise 36% of total deposits, explaining in part the high net interest margin percentage. Management characterizes the market as a sea of people and businesses that are "disenfranchised" by the larger institutions. Investment Classification: Growth & Value

Officers	Position	Ownership Information	
Raymond C. Dumser	President, CEO	Number of Shares Outstanding	526,675
Cole W. Minnick	Senior VP, CFO	Market Capitalization	$ 6,978,444
Charles E. Fenton	Senior VP, Sr Loan Officer	Frequency of Dividends	n.a.
Robert A. Hunt	Vice President	Number of Shareholders	n.a.
Robert S. Nolin	Vice President	Where Listed / Symbol	Order Matching Only / VGOB

Other Information			Loan Mix	%
Transfer Agent	Company Office		Commerical	56.1
Auditor	Hutchinson and Bloodgood LLP		R/E Mortgages	39.4
Market Maker	Schroder Wertheim & Co.	(310)443-0500	Installment	4.5
Broker Dealer	OTC Specialist			
	Robert Litter	(310)443-0549		

Virginia Hot Springs, Incorporated

c/o The Homestead   Hot Springs, VA 24445   Telephone (540)839-5500   Fax (540)839-7656

Company Description

The Company was owner and operator of The Homestead, a famous resort in Hot Springs, Virginia. Because of operational difficulties, it transferred the resort to a new management company operated and financed by Club Corporation International (ClubCorp.). The Company owns an 80% interest in the new venture and various parcels of land. ClubCorp will acquire the 80% interest in 1999 using a price formula generally based on a multiple of operating cash flow in the fifth year of the agreement with certain provisions should the calculated amount be less than $15 million. It is the stated intention of management to have an orderly liquidation of the Company over the next ten years or so.

	12/31/96	12/31/95	12/31/94
Per Share Information			
Stock Price	3.00	9.50	15.00
Earnings Per Share	0.09	0.59	-0.02
Price / Earnings Ratio	33.33	16.10	n.a.
Book Value Per Share	3.64	3.55	3.08
Price / Book Value %	82.42	267.61	487.01
Dividends Per Share	0.0	0.0	0.0
Annual Financial Data			
Operating Results (000's)			
Total Revenues	308.9	428.9	271.5
Costs & Expenses	-201.6	-155.9	-281.2
Income Before Taxes and Other	51.7	272.9	-12.9
Other Items	0.0	0.0	0.0
Income Tax	0.0	0.0	0.0
Net Income	51.7	272.9	-12.9
Cash Flow From Operations	157.3	n.a.	n.a.
Balance Sheet (000's)			
Cash & Equivalents	44.8	285.1	11.3
Total Current Assets	44.8	285.1	11.3
Fixed Assets, Net	2,105.6	1,752.5	1,753.3
Total Assets	2,192.7	2,088.8	1,815.9
Total Current Liabilities	0.0	0.0	0.0
Long-Term Debt	0.0	0.0	0.0
Stockholders' Equity	2,130.5	2,078.8	1,805.9
Performance & Financial Condition			
Return on Total Revenues %	16.73	63.62	-4.75
Return on Avg Stockholders' Equity %	2.46	14.05	n.a.
Return on Average Assets %	2.41	13.98	n.a.
Current Ratio	n.a.	n.a.	n.a.
Debt / Equity %	n.a.	n.a.	n.a.

Compound Growth %'s	EPS % n.a.	Net Income % n.a.	Total Revenues % n.a.

Comments

We travelled to The Homestead to find out firsthand what was happening at the resort that has hosted fifteen American presidents. A tour is offered daily to show all the renovations and plans of ClubCorp. They are doing an impressive job and have invested over $20 million in capital improvements. We enjoyed our stay. The first tee on the golf course is the oldest in continuous use in the United States. For 1996, operational results were ahead of plan. Gross operating revenues were $40.4 million, exceeding budget by $2.4 million. Net income from operations was $3,358,000. The formula buyout is difficult to understand but it is becoming apparent that there may indeed be a reward to the shareholders of Virginia Hot Springs. Investment Classification: Speculative & Value

Officers	Position	Ownership Information	
Daniel H. H. Ingalls	President	Number of Shares Outstanding	585,390
Pasco H. Merrill	Secretary	Market Capitalization	$ 1,756,170
Abbie I. Calder	Director	Frequency of Dividends	n.a.
Hebert E. Jones	Director	Number of Shareholders	Under 500
Truman T. Semans	Director		

Other Information

Transfer Agent	Company Office		Where Listed	OTC-BB
Auditor	Pannell Kerr Forster PC		Symbol	VHSI
Market Maker	Scott & Stringfellow, Inc.	(800)446-7074	SIC Code	6790
	Hill Thompson Magid & Co., Inc	(800)631-3083	Employees	n.a.
Broker Dealer	Regular Stockbroker			

Hospitality

The first Homestead was built in Virginia in 1755 when portions of the Shenandoah Valley became noted for the medicinal value of local natural hot springs. For some time, it remained a modest resort, unlikely to grow due to the lack of direct railroad service.

M.E. Ingalls was to change that. In the 1880's he convinced J.P. Morgan to buy the Chesapeake and Ohio line. Ingalls then became its president. He decided to rent a farm at the midpoint of the line, only three miles away from Hot Springs, to escape the smog and summer heat of the city. He fell in love with the area.

Ingalls convinced Morgan to add a line directly to Hot Springs and acquired 17,250 acres of surrounding property in preparation for the anticipated boon. A modern hotel was constructed in 1891, equipped with a few public toilets, heated by open fires and lighted with oil lamps. Unfortunately, it was being further improved in 1901 when a fire reduced the structure to ashes. Within two days, however, architects were on the scene preparing for its reconstruction.

After M.E. Ingalls died in 1914, Fay Ingalls and other family members continued to operate the resort. It was Fay who had the vision to build the Tower, which survives to this day as a remarkable section of The Homestead. It was near completion in 1929 when the stock market crash knocked the bottom out of the resort business. Most of The Homestead's former clientele could no longer afford such luxuries, and the Ingalls family had to reach deep into their own pockets to help the resort stay afloat. Original bond indebtedness was scheduled to mature in 1941, and had unfortunately been acquired by the owner of the resort's largest competitor. As operating debts continued to mount, The Homestead was forced to file for bankruptcy protection.

But the operation turned around, and in 1940 the properties were returned to the family. Soon afterwards the United States government ordered all guests removed so that The Homestead could be used to house 363 Japanese internees. Again the Ingalls family suffered the loss of a small fortune. Their fate was less severe, however, than competing Greenbrier at White Sulfur, which was appropriated by the army for use as a hospital. The Homestead was saved from a similar fate when the State Department chose it as the site of an international war conference to be held there in 1943.

After a number of tumultuous years, The Homestead finally regained financial strength, and is today a world-class resort. Aside from Franklin Delano Roosevelt, who presided over the war conference, it has been visited by dignitaries including fourteen other U.S. presidents and the Duke and Duchess of Windsor. Not all of these high profile visits have been profitable. When King Edward VIII was presented with his bill in 1943, for example, he responded, "What do I do with this? I am not used to paying bills."

The Ingalls family decided to exit their involvement in the resort business and in 1993 entered into an agreement transferring management of The Homestead to Club Corporation International. But if ever there has been a royal family in the resort industry, certainly it will turn out to have been the four generations of Ingalls who built the magnificence of The Homestead.

Viskon-Aire Corporation

410 Winfield Avenue   Salisbury, MD 21801   Telephone (410)543-8800   Fax (410)860-5894

Company Description

Viskon-Aire Corporation manufactures and sells about a dozen different lines of air filters. Distribution is throughout the United States. The Company was formed in 1979 and was distributed to shareholders of Drico Industrial Corp. in its liquidation in 1983.

	12/31/96	12/31/95	12/31/94	12/31/93
Per Share Information				
Stock Price	5.00	9.00	9.00	9.00
Earnings Per Share	0.39	-0.84	-0.59	0.77
Price / Earnings Ratio	12.82	n.a.	n.a.	11.69
Book Value Per Share	12.52	12.13	12.97	12.38
Price / Book Value %	39.94	74.20	69.39	72.70
Dividends Per Share	0.0	0.0	0.0	0.0
Annual Financial Data				
Operating Results (000's)				
Total Revenues	7,359.5	6,884.3	7,099.1	6,785.5
Costs & Expenses	-7,224.4	-7,101.6	-6,955.2	-6,592.1
Income Before Taxes and Other	79.2	-217.3	143.9	193.4
Other Items	0.0	0.0	0.0	0.0
Income Tax	-18.7	87.3	-52.6	-64.2
Net Income	60.5	-129.9	91.3	129.2
Cash Flow From Operations	316.0	88.2	234.3	45.6
Balance Sheet (000's)				
Cash & Equivalents	286.9	121.6	292.4	159.8
Total Current Assets	1,988.4	2,052.8	2,066.6	1,974.7
Fixed Assets, Net	1,271.2	1,363.8	1,140.2	1,159.8
Total Assets	3,360.8	3,511.3	3,298.0	3,225.0
Total Current Liabilities	650.6	811.6	390.8	390.8
Long-Term Debt	769.3	819.2	896.8	915.1
Stockholders' Equity	1,941.0	1,880.5	2,010.4	1,919.1
Performance & Financial Condition				
Return on Total Revenues %	0.82	-1.89	1.29	1.90
Return on Avg Stockholders' Equity %	3.17	-6.68	4.65	6.53
Return on Average Assets %	1.76	-3.82	2.80	3.92
Current Ratio	3.06	2.53	5.29	5.05
Debt / Equity %	39.63	43.57	44.61	47.68

Compound Growth %'s	EPS %	-20.29	Net Income %	-22.35	Total Revenues %	2.74

Comments

After two consecutive years of red ink, the Company posted a modest profit, further strengthening a firm balance sheet. The Company uses the LIFO method in accounting for inventory. The LIFO reserve at December 31, 1996, was not disclosed but was $219,119 in the preceding year. Management does not offer comments with the annual financial statements. Investment Classification: Speculative & Value

Officers	Position	Ownership Information	
Henry Zenzie	President	Number of Shares Outstanding	154,987
Stephen M. Mulinos	Exec VP, Treasurer	Market Capitalization	$ 774,935
Mary Rowin	Secretary	Frequency of Dividends	n.a.
George C. Alpaugh	Other	Number of Shareholders	Under 500

Other Information

Transfer Agent	American Stock Transfer & Trust Company New York, NY		Where Listed	OTC-BB
Auditor	Twilley, Rommel & Moore, P.A.		Symbol	VIAI
Market Maker	The Chicago Corporation	(800)321-1674	SIC Code	3990
	Hill Thompson Magid & Co., Inc	(800)631-3083	Employees	50
Broker Dealer	OTC Specialist			

W.T.B. Financial Corporation

715 W. Sprague Avenue   Spokane, WA 99210-2127   Telephone (509)353-5670   Fax (509)353-3885

Company Description

Washington Trust Bank is the bank subsidiary of W.T.B. Financial Corporation. Northern State Bank, another subsidiary, was merged into Washington Trust in March, 1997. The Company also owns Reardon, Rivard & Associates, Inc., an investment advisory firm with offices in Spokane and Seattle. In 1994, the Corporation attempted but failed to acquire The Wheatland Bank headquartered in Davenport, Washington. Washington Trust Bank serves eastern, north central and the Columbia Basin, Washington with twenty-eight offices and serves northern Idaho with four offices. The Bank was founded in 1902.

	12/31/96	12/31/95	12/31/94	12/31/93
Per Share Information				
Stock Price	36.00	36.00	36.00	23.00
Earnings Per Share	5.94	5.03	5.11	6.21
Price / Earnings Ratio	6.06	7.16	7.05	3.70
Book Value Per Share	48.30	43.55	38.52	35.04
Price / Book Value %	74.53	82.66	93.46	65.64
Dividends Per Share	1.10	0.92	0.78	0.68
Annual Financial Data				
Operating Results (000's)				
Net Interest Income	61,155.3	57,016.5	54,551.0	51,050.7
Loan Loss Provision	-4,242.0	-4,014.0	-3,144.0	-3,179.0
Non-Interest Income	11,849.6	10,847.7	12,171.5	17,189.9
Non-Interest Expense	-50,200.7	-48,016.8	-47,492.6	-44,852.4
Income Before Taxes and Other	18,562.2	15,833.4	16,085.9	20,209.1
Other Items	0.0	0.0	0.0	0.0
Income Tax	-3,957.1	-3,468.2	-3,543.7	-4,917.4
Net Income	14,605.1	12,365.2	12,542.2	15,291.7
Balance Sheet (000's)				
Cash & Securities	413,425.8	374,064.6	344,797.2	347,934.5
Loans, Net	868,568.5	859,224.8	763,726.4	656,613.8
Total Assets	1,346,368.4	1,297,862.4	1,171,389.7	1,063,557.8
Deposits	1,078,212.1	1,054,753.7	937,549.9	891,633.3
Stockholders' Equity	118,760.5	107,050.8	94,663.6	86,037.7
Performance & Financial Condition				
Return on Avg Stockholders' Equity %	12.94	12.26	13.88	19.24
Return on Average Assets %	1.10	1.00	1.12	1.45
Equity to Assets %	8.82	8.25	8.08	8.09
Net Interest Margin	5.38	5.38	5.78	5.88
Reserve as a % of Problem Loans	419.89	406.57	372.84	480.79

Compound Growth %'s	EPS %	-1.47	Net Income %	-1.52	Net Interest Income %	6.20

Comments

Five branches were opened in 1995, a new supermarket location was opened in 1996, and an office in Rathdrum, Idaho opened in March, 1997. The merger of Northern Sate Bank into Washington Trust is expected to be cost effective. Management reports that a number of new services and delivery techniques are being studied. The increase in 1996 earnings was largely attributable to continued strength in the margin on earning assets. Investment Classification: Value

Officers	Position	Ownership Information	
Philip H. Stanton	President, CEO	Number of Shares Outstanding	2,458,820
Albert G. Buss	Senior VP	Market Capitalization	$ 88,517,520
Walker H. Collins	CFO, Treasurer	Frequency of Dividends	Quarterly
R. Calvin Cathcart	Vice President, Secretary	Number of Shareholders	n.a.
Peter F. Stanton	Vice President	Where Listed / Symbol	OTC-BB / WTBFA

Other Information			Loan Mix	%
Transfer Agent	Company Office		R/E Mortgages	51.0
Auditor	Ernst & Young LLP		Commerical	32.4
Market Maker	Ragen MacKenzie Incorporated	(800)426-5964	Consumer	10.0
	Hill Thompson Magid & Co., Inc	(800)631-3083	Construction	6.6
Broker Dealer	OTC Specialist			
	John Ballantyne - Black & Co.	(503)248-9600		

Wailuku Agribusiness Co., Inc.

P.O. Box 520   Wailuku, HI 96793   Telephone (808)244-9570   Fax (808)242-7068

Company Description

The Company grows and sells macadamia nuts and owns agricultural properties on the island of Maui, Hawaii. It is also a 36.83% general partner in The Hawaii Tropical Plantation, a tourist operation for people to visit the different fields of tropical fruits, plants and trees with a final stop at the retail store. C. Brewer and Company, Limited, a subsidiary of Buyco, Inc., owns an 90.4% interest in the Company, increased from 87.7% in 1995. Wailuku has been in business since 1875.

	06/30/96	12/25/94	12/25/93	12/26/92
Per Share Information				
Stock Price as of 12/31	411.00	515.00	450.00	389.00
Earnings Per Share	52.18	35.52	2.79	38.57
Price / Earnings Ratio	7.88	14.50	161.29	10.09
Book Value Per Share	500.46	431.15	398.79	365.29
Price / Book Value %	82.12	119.45	112.84	106.49
Dividends Per Share	7.50	5.00	3.00	3.00
Annual Financial Data				
Operating Results (000's)				
Total Revenues	13,957.5	11,293.5	8,498.8	11,385.3
Costs & Expenses	-3,091.2	-3,258.8	-3,152.2	-3,866.5
Income Before Taxes and Other	10,866.3	8,034.7	2,269.3	7,518.8
Other Items	1,014.4	0.0	0.0	0.0
Income Tax	-4,053.7	-2,706.7	-1,794.5	-1,733.6
Net Income	7,827.0	5,328.0	474.7	5,785.3
Cash Flow From Operations	8,021.6	5,029.1	2,600.9	11,371.9
Balance Sheet (000's)				
Cash & Equivalents	0.7	0.7	0.7	0.7
Total Current Assets	71,711.9	60,225.1	56,653.6	54,493.1
Fixed Assets, Net	11,559.8	13,205.2	13,933.8	13,116.7
Total Assets	84,206.2	74,564.2	71,605.1	68,623.5
Total Current Liabilities	4,177.1	4,337.0	5,042.1	5,953.3
Long-Term Debt	0.0	0.0	0.0	0.0
Stockholders' Equity	75,068.6	64,672.8	59,818.0	54,793.2
Performance & Financial Condition				
Return on Total Revenues %	56.08	47.18	5.59	50.81
Return on Avg Stockholders' Equity %	11.20	8.56	0.83	11.10
Return on Average Assets %	9.86	7.29	0.68	8.80
Current Ratio	17.17	13.89	11.24	9.15
Debt / Equity %	n.a.	n.a.	n.a.	n.a.

Compound Growth %'s	EPS % n.a.	Net Income % n.a.	Total Revenues % 5.22

Comments

In 1995, the Company changed its reporting period to June 30. We only reported full years above. 1993 results reflect the cost of discontinuing pineapple operations at $3,077,397, or $20.52 per share. Financial results are not sent to the shareholders until after the shareholders meeting in November or December. Management reported that current negotiations are being conducted for the possible sale of The Hawaii Tropical Plantation which, if completed, would create substantially more profitability to the shareholders. Investment Classification: Value

Officers	Position	Ownership Information	
Avery B. Chumbley	President	Number of Shares Outstanding	150,000
Kathleen F. Oshiro	Secretary	Market Capitalization	$ 61,650,000
James S. Andrasick	Vice President	Frequency of Dividends	Quarterly
Kent T. Lucien	Vice President, Treasurer	Number of Shareholders	Under 500
Kim L. Peterson	Vice President		

Other Information

Transfer Agent	C. Brewer and Co., Ltd. Honolulu, HI		Where Listed	OTC-BB
Auditor	Coopers & Lybrand L.L.P.		Symbol	WKUA
Market Maker	Abel-Behnke Corp.	(808)536-2341	SIC Code	0173
	Sharpe Capital Inc.	(800)355-5781	Employees	35
Broker Dealer	OTC Specialist			
	Standard Investment	(888)783-4688 Ext: Jack		

Walker International Industries, Inc.

4 Ken-Anthony Pl., S.Lake Blvd.   Mahopac, NY 10541   Telephone (914)628-9404   Fax (914)628-9403

Company Description

Walker International Industries is engaged in various aspects of the photography business including film processing and maintaining a portrait studio. Approximately 26% of sales are generated through the portrait studio which is operated under a licensing agreement with a national retailer. The Company was founded in 1947. Happy 50th to our friends at the other Walkers.

	11/30/96	11/30/95	11/30/94	11/30/93
Per Share Information				
Stock Price as of 12/31	1.62	2.20	1.62	0.87
Earnings Per Share	0.25	0.23	0.05	-0.34
Price / Earnings Ratio	6.48	9.57	32.40	n.a.
Book Value Per Share	4.01	3.69	3.39	3.16
Price / Book Value %	40.40	59.62	47.79	27.53
Dividends Per Share	0.0	0.0	0.0	0.0
Annual Financial Data				
Operating Results (000's)				
Total Revenues	1,513.1	1,550.1	1,400.4	1,506.7
Costs & Expenses	-1,429.6	-1,489.4	-1,383.6	-1,628.0
Income Before Taxes and Other	83.5	60.7	16.7	-121.2
Other Items	0.0	10.3	0.0	0.0
Income Tax	-8.0	-2.0	0.0	0.0
Net Income	75.5	69.0	16.7	-121.2
Cash Flow From Operations	-23.3	96.4	71.9	n.a.
Balance Sheet (000's)				
Cash & Equivalents	286.2	332.5	0.0	0.0
Total Current Assets	546.4	1,015.5	1,116.0	1,140.1
Fixed Assets, Net	178.9	203.8	151.5	167.7
Total Assets	1,342.5	1,320.6	1,267.5	1,307.9
Total Current Liabilities	186.0	220.4	135.3	182.9
Long-Term Debt	0.0	0.0	0.0	0.0
Stockholders' Equity	1,156.5	1,100.3	1,132.3	1,125.0
Performance & Financial Condition				
Return on Total Revenues %	4.99	4.45	1.19	-8.05
Return on Avg Stockholders' Equity %	6.69	6.18	1.48	n.a.
Return on Average Assets %	5.67	5.33	1.30	n.a.
Current Ratio	2.94	4.61	8.25	6.23
Debt / Equity %	n.a.	n.a.	n.a.	n.a.

Compound Growth %'s	EPS % n.a.	Net Income % n.a.	Total Revenues % 0.14

Comments

The Company is highly liquid with total cash and investments of $969,000, or $3.36 per share. This may explain why the Company has been buying back shares over recent years at prices below book value. However, management maintains that it is continuing to investigate other potentially profitable opportunities. Compound earnings growth rates have not been displayed because they were distorted by a below average performance in 1994 and a loss in 1993. Investment Classification: Value

Officers	Position	Ownership Information	
Peter Walker	Chairman, President	Number of Shares Outstanding	288,711
Richard Norris	Secretary, Treasurer	Market Capitalization	$ 467,712
Ronald Whitworth	General Manager	Frequency of Dividends	n.a.
Mona Schwartz	General Manager	Number of Shareholders	n.a.
Charles Snow	Director		

Other Information			
Transfer Agent	American Stock Transfer & Trust Company New York, NY	Where Listed	OTC-BB
Auditor	Kofler, Levenstein, Romanotto	Symbol	WINT
Market Maker	M.H. Meyerson & Co., Inc. (800)333-3113	SIC Code	7220
	Paragon Capital Corp. (800)345-0505	Employees	n.a.
Broker Dealer	Regular Stockbroker		

Warwick Valley Telephone Co.

49 Main Street   Warwick, NY 10990   Telephone (201)764-8181   Fax (914)986-3299

Company Description

Warwick Valley Telephone Co. is an independent telephone company providing telephone service to customers in the towns of Warwick and Goshen, New York and the townships of Vernon and West Milford, New Jersey. The Company provides local telephone service to residential and business customers, access and billing and collection services to interexchange carriers and the sale and leasing of telecommunications equipment, paging and Internet access. The Company was founded in 1907 and has paid a dividend in every year of its existence.

	12/31/96	12/31/95	12/31/94	12/31/93
Per Share Information				
Stock Price	57.25	48.50	47.50	40.25
Earnings Per Share	4.94	3.45	2.82	2.66
Price / Earnings Ratio	11.59	14.06	16.84	15.13
Book Value Per Share	26.07	23.01	21.19	19.94
Price / Book Value %	219.60	210.78	224.16	201.86
Dividends Per Share	1.95	1.74	1.68	1.64
Annual Financial Data				
Operating Results (000's)				
Total Revenues	15,614.2	13,561.2	12,579.2	11,393.2
Costs & Expenses	-9,815.5	-9,862.6	-9,494.2	-8,409.4
Income Before Taxes and Other	4,247.6	2,737.8	2,062.0	2,018.9
Other Items	0.0	0.0	0.0	0.0
Income Tax	-1,152.1	-584.5	-312.5	-376.2
Net Income	3,095.5	2,153.4	1,749.5	1,642.6
Cash Flow From Operations	4,254.0	3,264.3	2,818.8	2,726.7
Balance Sheet (000's)				
Cash & Equivalents	728.5	482.0	422.0	1,529.5
Total Current Assets	5,777.6	5,975.5	4,690.0	5,324.6
Fixed Assets, Net	22,822.5	21,940.4	21,983.4	19,641.8
Total Assets	30,243.6	29,418.0	27,657.6	25,792.7
Total Current Liabilities	3,723.7	4,720.2	3,801.7	2,663.4
Long-Term Debt	7,000.0	7,000.0	7,370.0	7,490.0
Stockholders' Equity	16,710.5	14,744.2	13,499.2	12,636.3
Performance & Financial Condition				
Return on Total Revenues %	19.82	15.88	13.91	14.42
Return on Avg Stockholders' Equity %	19.68	15.25	13.39	13.41
Return on Average Assets %	10.38	7.55	6.55	6.73
Current Ratio	1.55	1.27	1.23	2.00
Debt / Equity %	41.89	47.48	54.60	59.27

Compound Growth %'s	EPS %	22.92	Net Income %	23.52	Total Revenues %	11.08

Comments

1996 was the fourth straight year with significant growth in earnings; they have more than doubled in those four years. Earnings have increased from the addition of newer services but also from growth in additional lines per customer. New dwellings are typically having six lines installed. A much higher productivity is also keeping costs in check in telephone operations. Management reported that 1996 bore the brunt of Warwick Online's start-up costs but the new division is ready to make a significant contribution to 1997 earnings. Investment Classification: Income & Growth

Officers	Position	Ownership Information	
Howard Conklin, Jr.	Chairman	Number of Shares Outstanding	621,771
Fred M. Knipp	President, CEO	Market Capitalization	$ 35,596,390
Philip P. Demarest	Secretary, Treasurer	Frequency of Dividends	Quarterly
Herbert Gareiss, Jr.	Vice President	Number of Shareholders	612
Henry L. Nielsen, Jr.	Other		

Other Information			
Transfer Agent	Company Office	Where Listed	OTC-BB
Auditor	Bush & Germain, P.C.	Symbol	WWVY
Market Maker	Dorsey Investment Securities (800)375-5431	SIC Code	4813
	Ryan, Beck & Co. (800)325-7926	Employees	92
Broker Dealer	Regular Stockbroker		
	Stephen Schuller - Dorsey (800)375-5431		

Waste Recovery, Inc.

309 S. Pearl Expressway   Dallas, TX 75201   Telephone (214)741-3865   Fax (214)741-8945

Company Description

Waste Recovery Inc. is in the tire recovery business, specializing in the processing of scrap tires into a refined fuel supplement referred to as tire-derived fuel. Income is generated from the sale of this fuel and fees charged for the disposal of tires. More than 28 million scrap tires were received for processing at the Company's seven plants during 1996. Domino Salvage was acquired in 1995 and U.S. Tires Recycling Partners was acquired in 1996. Waste Recovery was formed in 1982 and now believes it is the largest firm in its field.

	12/31/96	12/31/95	12/31/94	12/31/93
Per Share Information				
Stock Price	2.06	1.27	1.27	1.72
Earnings Per Share	0.01	-0.12	0.06	-0.08
Price / Earnings Ratio	206.00	n.a.	21.17	n.a.
Book Value Per Share	0.31	0.01	-0.22	-0.72
Price / Book Value %	664.52	12,700.00	n.a.	n.a.
Dividends Per Share	0.0	0.0	0.0	0.0
Annual Financial Data				
Operating Results (000's)				
Total Revenues	17,013.9	14,580.8	12,622.6	8,822.8
Costs & Expenses	-16,722.0	-15,185.0	-12,253.1	-8,930.8
Income Before Taxes and Other	292.0	-926.8	163.0	-108.0
Other Items	0.0	0.0	447.5	-87.6
Income Tax	-8.9	0.0	0.0	0.0
Net Income	283.1	-926.8	610.6	-195.6
Cash Flow From Operations	523.9	487.6	400.2	907.8
Balance Sheet (000's)				
Cash & Equivalents	1,892.4	726.6	261.1	140.0
Total Current Assets	7,286.2	3,415.3	4,422.1	1,842.6
Fixed Assets, Net	16,302.5	4,859.4	3,339.0	3,264.4
Total Assets	28,391.8	10,732.4	8,745.1	5,876.1
Total Current Liabilities	7,313.2	3,177.8	3,483.7	5,038.9
Long-Term Debt	11,637.3	4,409.2	4,002.6	359.2
Stockholders' Equity	8,329.1	2,899.0	1,258.8	-362.9
Performance & Financial Condition				
Return on Total Revenues %	1.66	-6.36	4.84	-2.22
Return on Avg Stockholders' Equity %	5.04	-44.58	136.30	n.a.
Return on Average Assets %	1.45	-9.52	8.35	-3.47
Current Ratio	1.00	1.07	1.27	0.37
Debt / Equity %	139.72	152.10	317.96	n.a.

Compound Growth %'s	EPS % -59.18	Net Income % -31.91	Total Revenues % 24.47

Comments

Included in stockholder's equity is 203,580 share of cumulative preferred stock with a total liquidation preference of $3.0 million. Undeclared cumulative preferred stock dividends of $143,000 per year are used in determining earnings (loss) per common share. In April, 1996, the Company announced that it had been awarded a $2 million contract to clean up an abandoned tire pile in Washington State. Management says that 1996 reflects the Company's move toward its goal of achieving positive operating results and improved cash flow. Management is expected to steer a course towards consistent profitability and, please, no brakes. Investment Classification: Speculative

Officers	Position	Ownership Information	
Thomas L. Earnshaw	President, CEO	Number of Shares Outstanding	17,322,121
Mark W. Hope	Senior VP	Market Capitalization	$ 35,683,569
Robert L. Thelen	Senior VP	Frequency of Dividends	n.a.
C. Ron McNutt	Senior VP	Number of Shareholders	454
David G. Greenstein	Senior VP		

Other Information

Transfer Agent	Securities Transfer Corporation Dallas, TX		Where Listed	OTC-BB
Auditor	Price Waterhouse LLP		Symbol	WRII
Market Maker	Paragon Capital Corporation	(800)521-8877	SIC Code	4953
	Herzog, Heine, Geduld, Inc.	(800)221-3600	Employees	200
Broker Dealer	Regular Stockbroker			

Watson Land Company

22010 South Wilmington Avenue   Carson, CA 90745   Telephone (310)952-6400   Fax (310)522-8788

Company Description

Watson Land Company is engaged in the construction and leasing of industrial commercial properties in southern California. As a real estate investment trust it is exempt from federal income tax. To qualify for this exemption, the Company must distribute 95% of its income to shareholders. In 1995, the Company entered into an agreement to purchase 441,513 shares of common stock from a shareholder at $26 per share over a four year period. As of December 31, 1996, 211,538 shares had been acquired. Watson Land is one of the oldest companies in southern California and traces its roots back to the Spanish land grants.

	12/31/96	12/31/95	12/31/94	12/31/93
Per Share Information				
Stock Price	26.00	26.00	26.00	26.00
Earnings Per Share	1.64	1.37	1.60	1.40
Price / Earnings Ratio	15.85	18.98	16.25	18.57
Book Value Per Share	1.76	2.20	2.52	2.82
Price / Book Value %	1,477.27	1,181.82	1,031.75	921.99
Dividends Per Share	1.80	1.37	1.70	1.24
Annual Financial Data				
Operating Results (000's)				
Total Revenues	44,819.4	43,046.9	45,228.7	43,913.9
Costs & Expenses	-33,463.0	-31,987.9	-32,123.2	-32,421.5
Income Before Taxes and Other	11,356.4	11,059.0	13,105.5	11,492.4
Other Items	1,744.0	0.0	0.0	0.0
Income Tax	-297.0	-264.4	-310.0	-125.0
Net Income	12,803.4	10,794.6	12,795.5	11,367.4
Cash Flow From Operations	20,850.6	16,553.0	19,403.9	16,977.1
Balance Sheet (000's)				
Cash & Equivalents	2,369.5	2,898.3	4,019.7	3,905.3
Total Current Assets	9,439.2	10,605.8	9,346.1	7,320.5
Fixed Assets, Net	147,081.6	147,597.5	150,730.4	155,645.5
Total Assets	170,572.9	171,393.7	174,000.5	176,901.6
Total Current Liabilities	17,508.2	6,010.9	6,035.6	5,959.5
Long-Term Debt	124,803.9	139,025.5	143,203.8	143,256.4
Stockholders' Equity	13,681.8	17,315.6	20,073.0	22,653.0
Performance & Financial Condition				
Return on Total Revenues %	28.57	25.08	28.29	25.89
Return on Avg Stockholders' Equity %	82.61	57.74	59.90	48.42
Return on Average Assets %	7.49	6.25	7.29	6.38
Current Ratio	0.54	1.76	1.55	1.23
Debt / Equity %	912.19	802.89	713.42	632.40

Compound Growth %'s	EPS %	5.42	Net Income %	4.05	Total Revenues %	0.68

Comments

A weakness in the real estate markets, particularly in southern California, caused a slight dip in earnings and cash flow in 1995. The markets are recovering and cash flow from operations have shown a strong rebound. At December 31, 1996, twenty-six of the Company's buildings (2,723,000 square feet) were free of long-term debt. The Company has one of the last undeveloped properties in the greater Los Angeles area which could be a four million square foot industrial park. Jack Norberg, analyst with Standard Investment, compliments management for running the company for the benefit of the shareholders. Investment Classification: Income & Value

Officers	Position	Ownership Information	
William T. Huston	Chairman	Number of Shares Outstanding	7,753,423
Richard M. Cannon	President, CEO	Market Capitalization	$ 201,588,998
Bradley D. Frazier	Secretary	Frequency of Dividends	Quarterly
		Number of Shareholders	Under 500

Other Information			
Transfer Agent	Company Office	Where Listed	Order Matching Only
Auditor	Coopers & Lybrand LLP	Symbol	n.a.
Market Maker	None	SIC Code	6510
		Employees	30
Broker Dealer	None		
	Standard Investment	(888)783-4688 Ext: Jack	

West Virginia-American Water Company

500 Summers Street   Charleston, WV 25301   Telephone (304)340-2007   Fax (304)340-2076

Company Description

The Company, a majority-owned subsidiary of American Water Works, provides water service to 135,122 customers in 151 communities in 12 counties in West Virginia. Although there are other water providers in the State, the Company is aggressively seeking to expand markets through acquisition and normal growth. In early 1996, the Company offered to buy back the shares of a shareholder for book value of $39.51 per share. We heard a report that the company has frozen the buy back price as a disincentive to continuing ownership by the remaining outside shareholders. The Company claims that there are only about 1,500 shares held by outsiders.

	12/31/96	12/31/95	12/31/94	12/31/93
Per Share Information				
Stock Price	21.00	39.51	38.35	37.20
Earnings Per Share	3.87	4.22	3.61	3.21
Price / Earnings Ratio	5.43	9.36	10.62	11.59
Book Value Per Share	40.60	39.51	38.35	37.20
Price / Book Value %	51.72	100.00	100.00	100.00
Dividends Per Share	3.32	2.99	2.47	2.53
Annual Financial Data				
Operating Results (000's)				
Total Revenues	62,976.0	58,360.5	56,322.6	52,550.7
Costs & Expenses	-42,190.0	-47,067.0	-46,999.9	-44,284.2
Income Before Taxes and Other	12,425.0	11,096.4	9,206.9	8,143.6
Other Items	0.0	0.0	0.0	0.0
Income Tax	-4,757.0	-4,134.5	-3,613.3	-3,101.0
Net Income	7,668.0	6,961.9	5,593.7	5,042.6
Cash Flow From Operations	11,905.0	11,491.0	11,032.5	8,488.5
Balance Sheet (000's)				
Cash & Equivalents	188.0	235.3	382.5	5,637.1
Total Current Assets	10,960.0	10,443.5	9,995.1	14,787.0
Fixed Assets, Net	232,712.0	205,082.4	181,737.2	167,297.9
Total Assets	278,360.0	249,323.5	219,081.7	208,697.6
Total Current Liabilities	20,273.0	28,998.2	19,966.5	10,529.3
Long-Term Debt	103,758.0	85,364.9	77,966.1	82,187.4
Stockholders' Equity	80,528.0	66,078.2	59,399.3	58,070.9
Performance & Financial Condition				
Return on Total Revenues %	12.18	11.93	9.93	9.60
Return on Avg Stockholders' Equity %	10.46	11.10	9.52	9.21
Return on Average Assets %	2.91	2.97	2.62	2.68
Current Ratio	0.54	0.36	0.50	1.40
Debt / Equity %	128.85	129.19	131.26	141.53

Compound Growth %'s	EPS %	6.43	Net Income %	14.99	Total Revenues %	6.22

Comments

Management reports the implementation of a $2.4 million rate increase in early 1996, as well as other favorable regulatory developments. Approvals have also been obtained for the first public/private partnership, the Boone County Regional Water Project, whereby property taxes from the private sector will be used to pay for debt service on the public sector portion of the project. The Company hopes it can use this as a model for other regional water projects within the state. The market makers have dropped the bid price for the stock following managements intention to freeze the value mentioned above. $40 per share is a more realistic trading range. Investment Classification: Value & Income

Officers	Position	Ownership Information	
C E. Jarrett	President	Number of Shares Outstanding	1,888,313
Stephen N. Chambers	Secretary	Market Capitalization	$ 39,654,573
D K. Carr	Vice President	Frequency of Dividends	Quarterly
M A. Miller	Vice President, Treasurer	Number of Shareholders	Under 500
T R. Bailey	Controller		

Other Information

Transfer Agent	United National Bank Charlston, WV		Where Listed	OTC-BB
Auditor	Price Waterhouse LLP		Symbol	WVAW
Market Maker	Herzog, Heine, Geduld, Inc.	(800)221-3600	SIC Code	4940
	Monroe Securities, Inc.	(800)766-5560	Employees	368
Broker Dealer	OTC Specialist			
	Standard Investment	(888)783-4688 Ext: Jack		

Westar Financial Services Incorporated

505 East Union, Suite 300   Olympia, WA 98507   Telephone (360)754-6227   Fax (360)754-7028

Company Description

Westar Financial Services Incorporated, successor to Republic Leasing Incorporated, specializes in producing lease products. Prior to 1994, the Company offered lease products to commercial clients only. In December, 1993, the Company expanded its product line by introducing its Dealer Direct Retail Leasing (DDRL) program to a select group of dealers. Through DDRL, the Company acquires leases from selected automobile dealers which have been pre-approved by the Company's experienced retail lease personnel. The Company launched full-scale DDRL operations in October 1995.

	03/31/96	03/31/95	03/31/94	03/31/93
Per Share Information				
Stock Price as of 12/31	7.50	3.25	1.50	1.75
Earnings Per Share	-0.82	-0.43	-0.48	-0.11
Price / Earnings Ratio	n.a.	n.a.	n.a.	n.a.
Book Value Per Share	-1.30	-0.54	-0.11	0.38
Price / Book Value %	n.a.	n.a.	n.a.	460.53
Dividends Per Share	0.0	0.0	0.0	0.0
Annual Financial Data				
Operating Results (000's)				
Total Revenues	1,672.2	2,137.6	1,054.1	4,903.4
Costs & Expenses	-3,189.1	-3,006.9	-1,864.3	-5,096.4
Income Before Taxes and Other	-1,516.8	-869.3	-810.2	-193.0
Other Items	0.0	0.0	-29.3	0.0
Income Tax	665.3	401.7	160.7	33.6
Net Income	-851.6	-467.6	-678.8	-159.4
Cash Flow From Operations	-1,266.3	-495.2	-536.1	233.5
Balance Sheet (000's)				
Cash & Equivalents	190.8	55.3	183.9	926.5
Total Current Assets	403.7	380.4	1,121.6	4,583.0
Fixed Assets, Net	32.0	199.2	649.5	434.7
Total Assets	8,210.2	4,311.0	4,058.5	7,050.3
Total Current Liabilities	409.7	123.0	86.7	250.7
Long-Term Debt	4,357.9	1,880.6	3,084.6	6,034.0
Stockholders' Equity	-1,853.4	-751.6	-149.4	529.4
Performance & Financial Condition				
Return on Total Revenues %	-50.92	-21.88	-64.40	-3.25
Return on Avg Stockholders' Equity %	n.a.	n.a.	-357.22	-26.17
Return on Average Assets %	-13.60	-11.17	-12.22	-1.63
Current Ratio	0.99	3.09	12.94	18.28
Debt / Equity %	n.a.	n.a.	n.a.	1139.71

Compound Growth %'s	EPS % n.a.	Net Income % n.a.	Total Revenues % -30.13

Comments

In May, 1996, the Company declared a 2 for 1 stock split. All per share amounts were adjusted for consistency. Management described the last fiscal year as dynamic and successful. A number of milestones were passed as the Company established a total focus on the DDRL program. Whereas it is easy to see an increase in lease volume, as evidenced by the investment in direct financing leases, it is not easy to understand when profits will begin to flow. If and when that starts to happen, the Company will be able to utilize $4 million in tax loss carryovers. Investment Classification: Speculative

Officers	Position	Ownership Information	
Robert W. Christensen, Jr.	Chairman, CEO	Number of Shares Outstanding	1,430,500
Cathy L. Carlson	Vice President	Market Capitalization	$ 10,728,750
Steven R. Murphy	Vice President	Frequency of Dividends	n.a.
		Number of Shareholders	382

Other Information

Transfer Agent	TransSecurities International Inc. Spokane, WA		Where Listed	OTC-BB
Auditor	BDO Seidman, LLP		Symbol	WEST
Market Maker	Hopper Soliday & Co.,Inc.	(800)646-8647	SIC Code	6140
	Pacific Crest Securities	(800)345-3565	Employees	n.a.
Broker Dealer	Regular Stockbroker			

Westbrook-Thompson Agency

c/o NationsBank, P.O. Box 1317   Fort Worth, TX 76101-1317   Telephone (817)390-6930   Fax (817)390-6767

Company Description

The Agency, through a disbursing agent, collects and distributes, to its unit holders, royalty payments from producing oil and gas properties, after deducting from such receipts amounts to satisfy taxes and other expenses. The Agency was formed upon the dissolution of Westbrook-Thompson Holding Corp. in 1966.

	12/31/96	12/31/95	12/31/94	12/31/93
Per Share Information				
Stock Price	16.25	15.00	14.25	14.00
Earnings Per Share	5.03	3.57	2.79	2.71
Price / Earnings Ratio	3.23	4.20	5.11	5.17
Book Value Per Share	n.a.	n.a.	n.a.	n.a.
Price / Book Value %	n.a.	n.a.	n.a.	n.a.
Dividends Per Share	5.03	3.57	2.79	2.71
Annual Financial Data				
Operating Results (000's)				
Total Revenues	1,056.4	756.3	609.7	602.7
Costs & Expenses	-133.7	-100.9	-96.8	-104.6
Income Before Taxes and Other	922.6	655.4	512.9	498.1
Other Items	0.0	0.0	0.0	0.0
Income Tax	0.0	0.0	0.0	0.0
Net Income	922.6	655.4	512.9	498.1
Cash Flow From Operations	922.6	655.4	512.9	498.1
Balance Sheet (000's)				
Cash & Equivalents	583.3	348.8	269.8	252.6
Total Current Assets	583.3	348.8	269.8	252.6
Fixed Assets, Net	0.0	0.0	0.0	0.0
Total Assets	583.4	348.8	269.9	252.6
Total Current Liabilities	583.3	348.8	269.8	252.6
Long-Term Debt	0.0	0.0	0.0	0.0
Stockholders' Equity	0.0	0.1	0.1	0.1
Performance & Financial Condition				
Return on Total Revenues %	87.34	86.66	84.12	82.64
Return on Avg Stockholders' Equity %	n.a.	n.a.	n.a.	n.a.
Return on Average Assets %	197.94	211.88	196.31	n.a.
Current Ratio	1.00	1.00	1.00	1.00
Debt / Equity %	n.a.	n.a.	n.a.	n.a.

Compound Growth %'s	EPS %	22.89	Net Income %	22.81	Total Revenues %	20.57

Comments

Unit holders generally receive approximately a 20% annual return on current unit price. This fluctuates with both production levels and oil and gas prices. During 1996, a significantly higher gas production and higher oil and gas pricing had a very positive impact on cash flow and distributions. There are also some tax advantages in the depletion deduction allowed unit holders. Investment Classification: Income

Officers	Position	Ownership Information	
Not Available		Number of Shares Outstanding	183,510
		Market Capitalization	$ 2,982,038
		Frequency of Dividends	Semi-Annual
		Number of Shareholders	Under 500

Other Information			
Transfer Agent	NationsBank Fort Worth, TX	Where Listed	OTC-BB
Auditor	Deloitte & Touche LLP	Symbol	WBTMU
Market Maker	Carr Securities Corporation	(800)221-2243	SIC Code	1300
	Hill Thompson Magid & Co., Inc	(800)631-3083	Employees	n.a.
Broker Dealer	OTC Specialist		

Western Lime Corporation

206 N. 6th Avenue West Bend, WI 53095-0057 Telephone (414)334-3005 Fax (414)334-2874

Company Description

Western Lime Corporation is engaged in the manufacture and sale of various lime products used in the paper, construction and chemical industries. The lime industry has emerged from an oversupply position which has had a favorable impact on the Company and the industry as a whole. The Company is struggling to keep up with demand. The two facilities, in Eden and Green Bay, Wisconsin, are being operated at or near capacity. The Company was founded in 1871.

	12/31/96	12/31/95	12/31/94	12/31/93
Per Share Information				
Stock Price	160.00	160.00	155.00	155.00
Earnings Per Share	120.44	147.02	114.61	93.89
Price / Earnings Ratio	1.33	1.09	1.35	1.65
Book Value Per Share	1,335.08	1,202.07	1,060.55	950.44
Price / Book Value %	11.98	13.31	14.62	16.31
Dividends Per Share	5.50	5.50	4.50	4.00
Annual Financial Data				
Operating Results (000's)				
Total Revenues	15,807.8	16,539.7	13,603.1	10,592.3
Costs & Expenses	-13,401.6	-13,479.3	-11,223.0	-9,306.3
Income Before Taxes and Other	2,406.2	3,060.4	2,380.2	1,286.0
Other Items	0.0	0.0	0.0	400.1
Income Tax	-835.0	-1,089.2	-843.5	-427.2
Net Income	1,571.2	1,971.2	1,536.7	1,258.9
Cash Flow From Operations	2,882.5	3,506.5	2,543.0	1,577.8
Balance Sheet (000's)				
Cash & Equivalents	6.8	1,834.0	2.4	1.6
Total Current Assets	4,176.1	5,750.1	3,385.6	2,429.1
Fixed Assets, Net	15,360.0	14,015.8	14,239.8	13,236.9
Total Assets	22,342.0	20,302.4	18,153.0	16,194.1
Total Current Liabilities	1,811.7	1,612.5	1,920.9	1,974.5
Long-Term Debt	66.7	0.0	0.0	0.0
Stockholders' Equity	17,416.2	16,117.3	14,219.8	12,743.5
Performance & Financial Condition				
Return on Total Revenues %	9.94	11.92	11.30	11.89
Return on Avg Stockholders' Equity %	9.37	13.00	11.40	n.a.
Return on Average Assets %	7.37	10.25	8.95	n.a.
Current Ratio	2.31	3.57	1.76	1.23
Debt / Equity %	0.38	n.a.	n.a.	n.a.

Compound Growth %'s	EPS % 8.66	Net Income % 7.67	Total Revenues % 14.28

Comments

After four years of higher sales and earnings, 1996 was slightly off. A decline in gross margins and lower sales were the cause. The Company has been able to reacquire some of its shares for $550 per share, a price that is more reasonable than what is posted by the market makers. The auditors provide a review report rather than a full audit. Investment Classification: Value

Officers	Position	Ownership Information	
V. Fred Nast III	CEO	Number of Shares Outstanding	13,045
John Nast	Other	Market Capitalization	$ 2,087,200
		Frequency of Dividends	Quarterly
		Number of Shareholders	Under 500

Other Information

Transfer Agent	Company Office		Where Listed	OTC-BB
Auditor	Muehl, Steffes & Krueger, S.C.		Symbol	WLIC
Market Maker	Carr Securities Corporation	(800)221-2243	SIC Code	3274
	Hill Thompson Magid & Co., Inc	(800)631-3083	Employees	n.a.
Broker Dealer	OTC Specialist			
	Standard Investment	(888)783-4688 Ext: Jack		

Western Sierra Bancorp

4011 Plaza Goldorado Circle   Cameron Park, CA 95682   Telephone (916)677-5600   Fax (916)677-5075

Company Description

Western Sierra Bank, subsidiary of this recently formed holding company, operates six locations in the "Gold Country" of northern California. (There's still gold in them there hills but its easier to go to the Bank.) The last office to open (February, 1997) was a facility acquired from Wells Fargo in Lincoln. The Bank has been operating since 1984. In 1996, Western Sierra Bank had a secondary offering of 200,000 shares at $10 per share. The proceeds were used for increasing the capital base and providing for additional branch offices.

	12/31/96	12/31/95	12/31/94	12/31/93
Per Share Information				
Stock Price	11.75	8.75	6.00	6.00
Earnings Per Share	1.13	1.11	0.41	0.18
Price / Earnings Ratio	10.40	7.88	14.63	33.33
Book Value Per Share	9.69	8.62	7.55	7.23
Price / Book Value %	121.26	101.51	79.47	82.99
Dividends Per Share	0.0	0.0	0.0	0.0
Annual Financial Data				
Operating Results (000's)				
Net Interest Income	4,256.1	3,809.4	2,972.6	2,335.7
Loan Loss Provision	-457.5	-80.0	-36.0	-130.0
Non-Interest Income	1,691.8	1,227.0	657.2	833.0
Non-Interest Expense	-4,282.5	-3,928.3	-3,222.9	-2,871.0
Income Before Taxes and Other	1,207.9	1,028.0	370.9	167.7
Other Items	0.0	0.0	0.0	7.3
Income Tax	-470.0	-377.0	-134.0	-68.0
Net Income	737.9	651.0	236.9	107.0
Balance Sheet (000's)				
Cash & Securities	16,282.0	16,416.4	13,409.7	18,081.0
Loans, Net	61,650.2	49,888.3	41,205.9	29,026.0
Total Assets	83,460.5	71,050.2	58,214.0	50,107.0
Deposits	74,927.2	63,105.9	52,906.5	45,853.0
Stockholders' Equity	7,720.3	5,155.5	4,300.4	4,116.0
Performance & Financial Condition				
Return on Avg Stockholders' Equity %	11.46	13.77	5.63	2.63
Return on Average Assets %	0.96	1.01	0.44	0.22
Equity to Assets %	9.25	7.26	7.39	8.21
Net Interest Margin	n.a.	n.a.	n.a.	n.a.
Reserve as a % of Problem Loans	49.45	86.73	41.61	n.a.

Compound Growth %'s	EPS % 84.47	Net Income % 90.35	Net Interest Income % 22.14

Comments

The Company declared two stock dividends in 1995 totalling 11%. All per share amounts have been adjusted for consistency. Compound earnings growth rates are affected by a low income level in 1993, the base year for that calculation. The stock offering in 1996 reduces the compound earnings per share growth rate as compared to compound earnings. Management reports significant activity in both Small Business Administration and mortgage lending. Investment Classification: Growth

Officers	Position	Ownership Information	
Gary D. Gall	President, CEO	Number of Shares Outstanding	796,948
Blair Weimer	Senior VP	Market Capitalization	$ 9,364,139
Stephanie Marsh	Senior VP	Frequency of Dividends	n.a.
Lesa Fynes	Vice President, Controller	Number of Shareholders	n.a.
Daniel Henning	Vice President, Sr Loan Officer	Where Listed / Symbol	OTC-BB / WESA

Other Information				Loan Mix	%
Transfer Agent	Company Office			R/E Mortgages	53.6
Auditor	Perry-Smith & Co.			Construction	22.2
Market Maker	Hoefer & Arnett, Incorporated	(800)346-5544		Commerical	20.9
	Black & Company, Inc.	(800)423-2124		Installment	1.1
Broker Dealer	Regular Stockbroker			Other	2.2

Westmoreland Coal Company

2 North Cascade Ave., 14th Fl.   Colorado Springs, CO 80903   Telephone (719)442-2600   Fax (719)448-5825

Company Description

Westmoreland Coal Company's principal activities are the production and sale of coal from the Powder River Basin in eastern Montana, the ownership of interests in cogeneration and other non-regulated independent power plants, the provision of repair and maintenance services to utilities and power projects, and the leasing of capacity at Dominion Terminal Associates, a coal storage and vessel loading facility. On December 23, 1996, the Company filed a voluntary petition for reorganization under Chapter 11 of the United States Bankruptcy Code. The shares were suspended from being traded on the New York Stock Exchange.

	12/31/96	12/31/95	12/31/94	12/31/93
Per Share Information				
Stock Price	1.00	6.37	6.75	5.25
Earnings Per Share	4.80	-13.11	2.19	-14.74
Price / Earnings Ratio	0.21	n.a.	3.08	n.a.
Book Value Per Share	0.03	-5.47	n.a.	n.a.
Price / Book Value %	3,333.33	n.a.	n.a.	n.a.
Dividends Per Share	0.0	0.0	0.0	0.0
Annual Financial Data				
Operating Results (000's)				
Total Revenues	97,533.0	140,831.0	417,828.0	474,653.0
Costs & Expenses	-72,097.0	-224,361.0	-394,801.0	-490,814.0
Income Before Taxes and Other	25,436.0	-83,530.0	23,027.0	-95,411.0
Other Items	13,482.0	-1,368.0	-583.0	-748.0
Income Tax	-575.0	-1,488.0	-2,291.0	-1,487.0
Net Income	38,343.0	-86,386.0	20,153.0	-97,646.0
Cash Flow From Operations	-14,949.0	8,174.0	13,622.0	n.a.
Balance Sheet (000's)				
Cash & Equivalents	8,791.0	11,711.0	n.a.	n.a.
Total Current Assets	17,090.0	18,985.0	n.a.	n.a.
Fixed Assets, Net	42,700.0	59,868.0	n.a.	n.a.
Total Assets	153,971.0	167,107.0	n.a.	n.a.
Total Current Liabilities	6,905.0	35,443.0	n.a.	n.a.
Long-Term Debt	881.0	3,131.0	n.a.	n.a.
Stockholders' Equity	237.0	-38,106.0	n.a.	n.a.
Performance & Financial Condition				
Return on Total Revenues %	39.31	-61.34	4.82	-20.57
Return on Avg Stockholders' Equity %	n.a.	n.a.	n.a.	n.a.
Return on Average Assets %	23.88	n.a.	n.a.	n.a.
Current Ratio	2.48	0.54	n.a.	n.a.
Debt / Equity %	371.73	n.a.	n.a.	n.a.

Compound Growth %'s	EPS % n.a.	Net Income % n.a.	Total Revenues % -40.99

Comments

Recognizing that it would not be able to meet its retiree benefit obligations to the United Mine Workers pension funds, the Company tried to renegotiate its agreements but failed. Filing under Chapter 11 became the only possible way to save the Company. Because of the ongoing nature of the reorganization cases, the outcome of which is not presently determinable, care should be taken to monitor all of the latest developments. At May 31, 1997, there was an active market at between $.75 and $1.00 per share. There is also a preferred stock that trades at a higher price. Investment Classification: Speculative

Officers	Position	Ownership Information	
Christopher K. Seglem	President, CEO	Number of Shares Outstanding	6,965,328
Ronald W. Stucki	Senior VP	Market Capitalization	$ 6,965,328
Theodore E. Worcester	Senior VP, Secretary	Frequency of Dividends	n.a.
Robert J. Jaeger	Senior VP, Treasurer	Number of Shareholders	1,832

Other Information

Transfer Agent	First Chicago Trust Co. of New York Jersey City, NJ		Where Listed	OTC-PS
Auditor	KPMG Peat Marwick LLP		Symbol	WMCLQ
Market Maker	Herzog, Heine, Geduld, Inc.	(800)221-3600	SIC Code	1220
	Oscar Gruss & Son, Inc.	(212)943-6418	Employees	70
Broker Dealer	OTC Specialist			

Westwood Group, Inc. (The)

190 V.F.W. Parkway   Revere, MA 02151   Telephone (617)284-2600   Fax (617)284-7895

Company Description

The Westwood Group operates primarily through its pari-mutuel racing subsidiaries. Wonderland Greyhound Park is a greyhound racing facility located in Revere, Massachusetts, which adjoins the City of Boston. Foxboro Park is a harness racing facility located in Foxboro, Massachusetts, about 25 miles southwest of Boston. Both facilities provide its patrons with a variety of enertainment options including live racing and full card simulcast wagering.

	12/31/96	12/31/95	12/31/94
Per Share Information			
Stock Price	5.00	4.00	5.00
Earnings Per Share	0.41	-1.64	9.63
Price / Earnings Ratio	12.20	n.a.	0.52
Book Value Per Share	-3.56	-3.91	-2.35
Price / Book Value %	n.a.	n.a.	n.a.
Dividends Per Share	0.0	0.0	0.0
Annual Financial Data			
Operating Results (000's)			
Total Revenues	33,663.9	32,949.7	39,625.3
Costs & Expenses	-33,139.1	-35,004.1	-38,547.8
Income Before Taxes and Other	524.8	-2,054.4	1,077.5
Other Items	0.0	0.0	11,159.6
Income Tax	-13.0	0.0	-145.0
Net Income	511.8	-2,054.4	12,092.1
Cash Flow From Operations	2,335.1	781.7	1,039.3
Balance Sheet (000's)			
Cash & Equivalents	2,055.1	1,852.8	n.a.
Total Current Assets	2,894.8	2,919.6	n.a.
Fixed Assets, Net	11,957.5	16,611.8	n.a.
Total Assets	20,830.0	25,607.6	n.a.
Total Current Liabilities	20,000.1	23,399.3	n.a.
Long-Term Debt	3,434.8	5,773.7	n.a.
Stockholders' Equity	-4,464.2	-4,912.7	n.a.
Performance & Financial Condition			
Return on Total Revenues %	1.52	-6.24	30.52
Return on Avg Stockholders' Equity %	n.a.	n.a.	n.a.
Return on Average Assets %	2.20	-7.69	26.71
Current Ratio	0.14	0.12	n.a.
Debt / Equity %	n.a.	n.a.	n.a.

Compound Growth %'s	EPS % n.a.	Net Income % n.a.	Total Revenues % -7.83

Comments

The Company is experiencing a decline in total attendance, caused by a variety of factors including a general decline in the pari-mutuel racing industry and strong competition for the wagered dollar from the Massachusetts State Lottery and from the introduction of casino gambling and slot machines in neighboring states. Losses from operations were reported for four of the last five years. 1996 and 1994 were profitable only because of nonrecurring gains on the sale of assets and other restructuring activity. The balance sheet looks terrible. Investment Classification: Speculative

Officers	Position	Ownership Information	
Charles Sarkis	Chairman	Number of Shares Outstanding	1,255,225
Richard P. Dalton	President, CEO	Market Capitalization	$ 6,276,125
A. Paul Sarkis	Exec VP	Frequency of Dividends	n.a.
Richard G. Egan, Jr.	Secretary, CFO	Number of Shareholders	484
Anthony V. Boschetto	Controller		

Other Information			
Transfer Agent	Progressive Transfer Co. Salt Lake City, UT	Where Listed	OTC-PS
Auditor	BDO Seidman, LLP	Symbol	TWGI
Market Maker	H.C. Wainwright & Co., Inc. (800)727-7176	SIC Code	7948
		Employees	600
Broker Dealer	OTC Specialist		
	Norman Kadehjian - Wainright (800)727-7176		

Westwood Incorporated

30 Mill Street   Southbridge, MA 01550   Telephone (508)764-3252   Fax (508)764-6586

Company Description

Westwood Incorporated's operations are exclusively the design, manufacture, importing, converting and sale of fabrics of wool worsted fibers, cotton fibers, synthetic fibers or a combination of synthetic and natural fibers for sale to apparel manufacturers, to the upholstery trade, to piece good wholesalers, and directly to retail stores and department stores for the home sewing market. The Company's subsidiary was formerly engaged in the manufacturing and sale of women's sportswear.

	09/28/96	09/30/95	10/01/94	10/02/93
Per Share Information				
Stock Price as of 12/31	6.12	3.75	4.00	4.20
Earnings Per Share	-0.94	-0.84	0.38	1.08
Price / Earnings Ratio	n.a.	n.a.	10.53	3.89
Book Value Per Share	11.24	12.17	13.10	12.70
Price / Book Value %	54.45	30.81	30.53	33.07
Dividends Per Share	0.0	0.0	0.0	0.0
Annual Financial Data				
Operating Results (000's)				
Total Revenues	45,938.4	46,566.3	59,776.5	55,931.3
Costs & Expenses	-45,858.6	-46,502.7	-58,901.3	-54,316.3
Income Before Taxes and Other	79.8	63.5	875.2	1,615.0
Other Items	-886.1	-774.6	-29.8	-66.7
Income Tax	-22.0	-31.3	-512.8	-580.3
Net Income	-828.4	-742.4	332.6	967.9
Cash Flow From Operations	-131.6	459.2	-9.6	812.8
Balance Sheet (000's)				
Cash & Equivalents	391.5	882.4	501.2	615.2
Total Current Assets	11,840.3	16,731.8	18,365.6	16,665.4
Fixed Assets, Net	622.9	621.1	819.2	891.0
Total Assets	12,607.9	17,524.9	19,360.2	17,723.2
Total Current Liabilities	2,657.6	6,725.2	7,656.7	6,408.0
Long-Term Debt	0.0	0.0	0.0	0.0
Stockholders' Equity	9,950.3	10,781.4	11,486.6	11,138.2
Performance & Financial Condition				
Return on Total Revenues %	-1.80	-1.59	0.56	1.73
Return on Avg Stockholders' Equity %	-7.99	-6.67	2.94	9.02
Return on Average Assets %	-5.50	-4.03	1.79	n.a.
Current Ratio	4.46	2.49	2.40	2.60
Debt / Equity %	n.a.	n.a.	n.a.	n.a.

Compound Growth %'s	EPS % n.a.	Net Income % n.a.	Total Revenues % -6.35

Comments

The Company had losses of $886,125 and $774,645 in 1996 and 1995, respectively, related to the discontinuance of women's sportswear. Fixed assets are almost fully depreciated, but are said to be in excellent condition. The president is 75 years old and not active in the business. The CEO and major shareholder (60% of shares) is 73 years old and has no family in the business. A number of employees also own shares. Compound earnings growth rates were omitted because of the discontinuance of a business segment. Investment Classification: Value

Officers	Position	Ownership Information	
Howard Olian	Chairman, CEO	Number of Shares Outstanding	885,527
Louis C. Broughton	President	Market Capitalization	$ 5,419,425
Jerome T. Kocur	Secretary, Treasurer	Frequency of Dividends	n.a.
		Number of Shareholders	Under 500

Other Information

Transfer Agent	Company Office		Where Listed	OTC-BB
Auditor	Cole, Samsel & Bernstein LLC		Symbol	WWOD
Market Maker	Carr Securities Corporation	(800)221-2243	SIC Code	2290
	Hill Thompson Magid & Co., Inc	(800)631-3083	Employees	80
Broker Dealer	OTC Specialist			
	Standard Investment	(888)783-4688 Ext: Jack		

Wichita National Life Insurance Company

711 D Avenue   Lawton, OK 73502-1709   Telephone (405)353-5776   Fax (405)353-6482

Company Description

Wichita National Life Insurance Company underwrites life, accident and health insurance. The Company boasts a safety for its customers by comparing itself to the twenty-five largest insurance companies in the United States using standard industry formulas including solvency, surplus funds, net gain ratio and surplus to life insurance in force.

	12/31/96	12/31/95	12/31/94	12/31/93
Per Share Information				
Stock Price	4.00	5.50	4.00	4.00
Earnings Per Share	0.19	0.16	-0.27	0.27
Price / Earnings Ratio	21.05	34.38	n.a.	14.81
Book Value Per Share	5.00	4.89	5.21	5.54
Price / Book Value %	80.00	112.47	76.78	72.20
Dividends Per Share	0.20	0.15	0.10	0.10
Annual Financial Data				
Operating Results (000's)				
Total Revenues	6,464.7	6,164.8	5,214.6	5,078.2
Costs & Expenses	-6,197.1	-5,907.0	-5,574.0	-4,634.1
Income Before Taxes and Other	267.6	257.8	-359.4	444.1
Other Items	0.0	0.0	0.0	0.0
Income Tax	-25.2	-54.5	21.0	-103.2
Net Income	242.4	203.3	-338.4	340.9
Cash Flow From Operations	n.a.	n.a.	n.a.	n.a.
Balance Sheet (000's)				
Cash & Equivalents	11,875.6	10,750.2	10,262.8	9,671.7
Total Current Assets	12,009.1	12,124.5	11,766.7	11,210.3
Fixed Assets, Net	480.7	470.2	460.6	490.8
Total Assets	14,911.5	13,924.4	13,501.1	12,995.6
Total Current Liabilities	540.1	513.2	506.0	373.5
Long-Term Debt	0.0	0.0	0.0	0.0
Stockholders' Equity	6,250.4	6,163.9	6,560.8	6,977.1
Performance & Financial Condition				
Return on Total Revenues %	3.75	3.30	-6.49	6.71
Return on Avg Stockholders' Equity %	3.90	3.19	-5.00	n.a.
Return on Average Assets %	1.68	1.48	-2.55	n.a.
Current Ratio	22.23	23.62	23.25	30.02
Debt / Equity %	n.a.	n.a.	n.a.	n.a.

Compound Growth %'s	EPS %	-11.05	Net Income %	-10.75	Total Revenues %	8.38

Comments

There is no indication that the financial statements have been audited nor do we consider them of sufficient detail to rely upon. Some information that we have received from the Company appears contradictory. Net investment income has been increasing over the years because of a strong balance sheet but adequate disclosures are not made for a prospective investor to determine the degree of risk in investment assets. Investment Classification: Speculative

Officers	Position	Ownership Information	
L B. McClung	Chairman	Number of Shares Outstanding	1,250,000
Randy B. Gilliland	President	Market Capitalization	$ 5,000,000
Ronnie J. Denham	Secretary, Treasurer	Frequency of Dividends	n.a.
Myron G. McChurin	Other	Number of Shareholders	Under 500
Eldon J. Proctor	Other		

Other Information				
Transfer Agent	Company Office		Where Listed	OTC-PS
Auditor	Not indicated		Symbol	n.a.
Market Maker	J.B. Ricards Securities Corp.	(800)621-5253	SIC Code	6310
	Howe Barnes Investments, Inc.	(800)621-2364	Employees	11
Broker Dealer	Regular Stockbroker			

Williams Industries, Incorporated

2849 Meadow View Road   Falls Church, VA 22042   Telephone (703)560-5196   Fax (703)876-9443

Company Description

From its inception in 1970, Williams Industries quickly became an industry leader, specializing in steel erection and the rental of construction equipment. By the mid-1980's, the Company had grown from the original steel erection company to a conglomerate with 27 subsidiaries and affiliates. During the past several years, the Company has downsized and restructured in order to return to profitability and pay debt.

	07/31/96	07/31/95	07/31/94	07/31/93
Per Share Information				
Stock Price as of 12/31	4.12	3.12	0.56	2.00
Earnings Per Share	1.15	1.35	-5.21	-5.21
Price / Earnings Ratio	3.58	2.31	n.a.	n.a.
Book Value Per Share	-0.86	-2.06	-3.42	0.36
Price / Book Value %	n.a.	n.a.	n.a.	555.56
Dividends Per Share	0.0	0.0	0.0	0.0
Annual Financial Data				
Operating Results (000's)				
Total Revenues	29,667.4	31,850.5	45,686.0	50,583.2
Costs & Expenses	-27,511.7	-36,465.7	-50,705.6	-58,509.8
Income Before Taxes and Other	2,155.7	-4,615.2	-5,019.6	-7,926.7
Other Items	867.6	8,100.1	-4,518.2	-5,149.9
Income Tax	-62.5	-50.0	-34.3	-34.2
Net Income	2,960.8	3,434.9	-9,572.1	-13,110.8
Cash Flow From Operations	474.5	3,790.1	-489.6	-451.4
Balance Sheet (000's)				
Cash & Equivalents	1,300.9	819.7	658.4	n.a.
Total Current Assets	14,580.1	12,417.6	20,311.7	n.a.
Fixed Assets, Net	9,452.3	8,487.6	12,369.0	n.a.
Total Assets	28,011.8	24,594.1	38,440.8	n.a.
Total Current Liabilities	12,731.0	12,382.9	16,326.3	n.a.
Long-Term Debt	15,142.3	16,366.9	27,535.0	n.a.
Stockholders' Equity	-2,224.1	-5,240.9	-8,676.3	n.a.
Performance & Financial Condition				
Return on Total Revenues %	9.98	10.78	-20.95	-25.92
Return on Avg Stockholders' Equity %	n.a.	n.a.	n.a.	-177.17
Return on Average Assets %	11.26	10.90	-23.08	-29.20
Current Ratio	1.15	1.00	1.24	n.a.
Debt / Equity %	n.a.	n.a.	n.a.	n.a.

Compound Growth %'s	EPS % -14.81	Net Income % -13.80	Total Revenues % -16.29

Comments

The 1995 net earnings was a result of income on the extinguishment of debt rather than operational in nature. 1996 results included a $2 million gain on the sale of property. The decline in revenues is largely attributable to the downsizing referred to above. Although the Company still has some obstacles, it is making a sincere attempt to restructure. For the six months ended January 31, 1997, the Company posted a real profit of $369,000, $.14 per share, on revenues that were 14% higher than those of the preceding year. Investment Classification: Speculative

Officers	Position	Ownership Information	
Frank E. Williams, III	President, CEO	Number of Shares Outstanding	2,576,017
George R. Pocock	Vice President	Market Capitalization	$ 10,613,190
		Frequency of Dividends	n.a.
		Number of Shareholders	514

Other Information

Transfer Agent	First Union National Bank of N. Carolina Charlotte, NC		Where Listed	OTC-BB
Auditor	Deloitte & Touche LLP		Symbol	WMSI
Market Maker	Koonce Securities, Inc.	(800)368-2802	SIC Code	1700
	Troster Singer	(800)526-3160	Employees	n.a.
Broker Dealer	Regular Stockbroker			

Wilton Bank (The)

47 Old Ridgefield Road   Wilton, CT 06897   Telephone (203)762-2265   Fax (203)761-9662

Company Description

The Wilton Bank was organized in 1987 and operates from one office in the center of Wilton, Connecticut. A picture of the Old Town Hall, which was built in 1832, is on the cover of each annual report and is used as the logo as well. Unfortunately, that is not the Bank's office but, rather, a local church. The Bank ties itself closely to the activities in the community even if it can't get the best real estate in town.

	12/31/96	12/31/95	12/31/94	12/31/93
Per Share Information				
Stock Price	17.00	12.50	9.00	9.00
Earnings Per Share	2.51	2.24	1.73	0.90
Price / Earnings Ratio	6.77	5.58	5.20	10.00
Book Value Per Share	17.00	15.08	13.18	11.84
Price / Book Value %	100.00	82.89	68.29	76.01
Dividends Per Share	0.50	0.40	0.30	0.20
Annual Financial Data				
Operating Results (000's)				
Net Interest Income	4,257.1	4,145.2	3,530.4	2,984.8
Loan Loss Provision	-740.0	-855.0	-797.0	-981.1
Non-Interest Income	276.2	277.0	223.0	213.0
Non-Interest Expense	-2,127.0	-2,076.0	-1,862.8	-1,704.0
Income Before Taxes and Other	1,666.3	1,491.2	1,093.5	512.7
Other Items	0.0	0.0	0.0	0.0
Income Tax	-659.1	-590.0	-397.3	-151.3
Net Income	1,007.2	901.2	696.2	361.5
Balance Sheet (000's)				
Cash & Securities	22,514.5	17,656.4	14,242.7	13,849.0
Loans, Net	49,677.9	48,442.2	46,655.2	40,929.2
Total Assets	73,929.0	67,856.4	61,987.5	55,606.2
Deposits	66,677.5	58,741.6	54,024.0	48,438.1
Stockholders' Equity	6,843.5	6,055.2	5,293.0	4,756.0
Performance & Financial Condition				
Return on Avg Stockholders' Equity %	15.62	15.88	13.86	7.86
Return on Average Assets %	1.42	1.39	1.18	0.65
Equity to Assets %	9.26	8.92	8.54	8.55
Net Interest Margin	n.a.	n.a.	n.a.	n.a.
Reserve as a % of Problem Loans	145.62	92.69	75.56	80.88

Compound Growth %'s	EPS %	40.76	Net Income %	40.72	Net Interest Income %	12.56

Comments

The growth and earnings trend is quite remarkable for this young Bank. Management was very pleased with all financial ratios in 1996, its ninth full year of operations, as well as having a net income after taxes in excess of $1 million. They continue to see great potential for locally focused financial institutions. Few stockholders are willing to sell their shares. Investment Classification: Growth & Value

Officers	Position	Ownership Information	
Nicki Brown	President, CEO	Number of Shares Outstanding	402,600
Frances M. Charney	Exec VP	Market Capitalization	$ 6,844,200
James D. Tenney	Senior VP, Sr Loan Officer	Frequency of Dividends	Annual
Carole M. Elliott	Vice President	Number of Shareholders	400
Edward H. Raff, Jr.	Vice President	Where Listed / Symbol	OTC-BB / WIBW

Other Information			Loan Mix	%
Transfer Agent	Registrar & Transfer Company Cranford, NJ		Commerical	60.8
Auditor	Deloitte & Touche LLP		R/E Mortgages	35.9
Market Maker	Ryan, Beck & Co.	(800)342-2325	Installment	2.6
	First Albany Corporation	(800)541-5061	Other	0.7
Broker Dealer	OTC Specialist			
	John E. Simpson	(203)762-5581		

Wisconsin Fuel & Light Company

211 Forest Street   Wausau, WI 54402-1627   Telephone (715)845-2141   Fax (715)847-6208

Company Description

Wisconsin Fuel and Light Company is a public utility engaged in the distribution of natural gas to a diversified base of residential, commercial and industrial customers, primarily in the communities of Manitowac and Wausau, Wisconsin. It is subject to regulation by the Public Service Commission of Wisconsin. During 1996, the Company formed a wholly-owned non-utility subsidiary that is involved in the consulting and sales of energy products and services. In 1994, the Company issued $2 million of redeemable preferred stock through a private placement.

	12/31/96	12/31/95	12/31/94	12/31/93
Per Share Information				
Stock Price	39.00	40.00	36.00	38.00
Earnings Per Share	4.58	3.31	2.41	3.82
Price / Earnings Ratio	8.52	12.08	14.94	9.95
Book Value Per Share	50.04	26.34	25.35	25.35
Price / Book Value %	77.94	151.86	142.01	149.90
Dividends Per Share	2.38	2.32	2.32	2.30
Annual Financial Data				
Operating Results (000's)				
Total Revenues	53,662.2	45,915.3	47,702.3	51,397.6
Costs & Expenses	-49,074.4	-43,146.3	-45,870.3	-48,478.1
Income Before Taxes and Other	3,704.5	2,768.9	1,832.0	2,888.0
Other Items	0.0	0.0	0.0	0.0
Income Tax	-1,340.9	-1,025.2	-572.5	-1,027.0
Net Income	2,363.6	1,743.7	1,259.5	1,861.0
Cash Flow From Operations	4,628.2	4,914.9	4,083.2	-1,445.6
Balance Sheet (000's)				
Cash & Equivalents	293.4	213.7	34.9	252.2
Total Current Assets	15,801.6	12,287.0	11,264.2	13,820.6
Fixed Assets, Net	26,704.5	25,566.1	24,630.8	23,180.2
Total Assets	47,420.0	43,476.4	44,518.4	46,626.5
Total Current Liabilities	14,990.9	10,697.2	8,366.1	10,417.6
Long-Term Debt	0.0	11,650.0	12,720.0	13,290.0
Stockholders' Equity	26,607.0	14,905.9	14,418.9	12,391.8
Performance & Financial Condition				
Return on Total Revenues %	4.40	3.80	2.64	3.62
Return on Avg Stockholders' Equity %	11.39	11.89	9.40	15.51
Return on Average Assets %	5.20	3.96	2.76	4.34
Current Ratio	1.05	1.15	1.35	1.33
Debt / Equity %	n.a.	78.16	88.22	107.25

Compound Growth %'s	EPS %	6.23	Net Income %	8.30	Total Revenues %	1.45

Comments

The Company has paid a dividend for 42 straight years and boasts of the fact that it has never been reduced. The new subsidiary incurred a loss of $88,680 during 1996, but that didn't dampen extremely strong record results. A combination of extremely cold weather and a rate increase which became effective in late 1995 played a significant role in fueling the bottom line. Management thinks a repeat in 1997 is unlikely. The Company has been seeking regulatory approval for a new design in the way it bills its customers. This would be a fairly high monthly charge and a lower unit energy charge. The Commission asked for some changes and a more modest version of the original proposal has been submitted for approval. Investment Classification: Income

Officers	Position	Ownership Information	
Mark T. Maranger	President, CEO	Number of Shares Outstanding	491,710
Hugh H. Bell	Secretary	Market Capitalization	$ 19,176,690
Paul C. Baird	Treasurer	Frequency of Dividends	Quarterly
Edward C. Vallis	Vice President	Number of Shareholders	171
Monte K. Gehring	Vice President		

Other Information

Transfer Agent	Firstar Trust Company Milwaukee, WI		Where Listed	OTC-BB
Auditor	Arthur Andersen LLP		Symbol	WIFL
Market Maker	B.C. Ziegler and Company	(414)258-3244	SIC Code	4920
	Robert W. Baird & Co., Inc.	(800)562-2288	Employees	160
Broker Dealer	OTC Specialist			

Woodbury Telephone Company (The)

299 Main Street South   Woodbury, CT 06798   Telephone (203)263-2121   Fax (203)263-2770

Company Description

The Woodbury Telephone Company furnishes local exchange telephone services, intrastate toll services, and access to long distance telephone services. The Company also sells telephone equipment and is an Internet provider. The primary service area is the towns of Woodbury, Southbury, and Bethlehem, Connecticut and portions of the towns of Oxford and Roxbury Connecticut. In late 1996, Southern New England Telecommunications Corporation acquired a 36.5% interest in the Company and has entered into a plan of merger by offering shareholders of Woodbury stock worth $43 per share. The transaction has to be approved by the Connecticut Department of Public Utilities which may happen as early as August, 1997. The Woodbury Telephone Company was founded in 1899.

	12/31/96	12/31/95	12/31/94	12/31/93
Per Share Information				
Stock Price	38.75	25.00	24.00	26.00
Earnings Per Share	3.43	2.38	2.11	1.69
Price / Earnings Ratio	11.30	10.50	11.37	15.38
Book Value Per Share	18.56	16.64	15.78	15.19
Price / Book Value %	208.78	150.24	152.09	171.17
Dividends Per Share	1.52	1.52	1.52	1.52
Annual Financial Data				
Operating Results (000's)				
Total Revenues	14,620.3	13,080.8	12,337.5	11,715.1
Costs & Expenses	-10,518.1	-10,073.2	-9,720.6	-9,710.8
Income Before Taxes and Other	4,102.2	3,007.5	2,616.9	2,004.3
Other Items	0.0	0.0	0.0	0.0
Income Tax	-1,460.9	-1,175.7	-992.7	-701.8
Net Income	2,641.3	1,831.8	1,624.2	1,302.5
Cash Flow From Operations	4,846.1	3,540.6	4,493.0	3,569.2
Balance Sheet (000's)				
Cash & Equivalents	2,102.8	2,238.8	1,942.9	2,154.5
Total Current Assets	6,410.8	5,555.3	5,541.2	5,326.8
Fixed Assets, Net	21,451.4	20,398.8	20,971.4	19,893.8
Total Assets	29,028.8	27,323.2	28,083.9	26,994.3
Total Current Liabilities	2,579.9	1,938.7	2,915.2	1,953.4
Long-Term Debt	9,000.0	9,000.0	9,000.0	9,000.0
Stockholders' Equity	14,273.9	12,801.7	12,139.0	11,683.8
Performance & Financial Condition				
Return on Total Revenues %	18.07	14.00	13.16	11.12
Return on Avg Stockholders' Equity %	19.51	14.69	13.64	11.21
Return on Average Assets %	9.37	6.61	5.90	4.86
Current Ratio	2.48	2.87	1.90	2.73
Debt / Equity %	63.05	70.30	74.14	77.03

Compound Growth %'s	EPS %	26.61	Net Income %	26.57	Total Revenues %	7.66

Comments

The Company produced strong results with revenues gaining 14%, led mostly by network services. The acquisition referred to above is likely to happen and has been approved by shareholders. It clearly demonstrates that there are substantial valuations for many of these telephone companies not reflected in their current stock prices. The trick appears to be in finding them, buying them and holding them. The $43 per share transaction value is 72% greater than the stock price at the close of the preceding year. Investment Classification: Income & Growth

Officers	Position	Ownership Information	
J. Garry Mitchell	Chairman	Number of Shares Outstanding	769,107
Donald E. Porter	President, CEO	Market Capitalization	$ 29,802,896
Harmon L. Andrews	Secretary	Frequency of Dividends	Quarterly
		Number of Shareholders	688

Other Information				
Transfer Agent	Company Office		Where Listed	OTC-BB
Auditor	Ernst & Young LLP		Symbol	WBTL
Market Maker	Dorsey Investment Securities	(800)375-5431	SIC Code	4813
	Roney & Co.	(800)521-1196	Employees	73
Broker Dealer	Regular Stockbroker			
	Stephen R. Schuller - Dorsey	(800)375-5431		

Workforce Systems Corp.

8870 Cedar Spring Lane, Ste. 5   Knoxville, TN 37423   Telephone (423)769-2380   Fax (423)769-2668

Company Description

Workforce Systems Corp. is a diversified holding company. Through several subsidiaries, it provides specialized labor services on a contract basis to businesses, manufactures thawing trays and other consumer products, and provides specialized fabrication services. The Company is also an authorized distributor for a full line of power transmission products. The Company was formed in 1992. In 1993, it completed a public offering and began to seek acquisition candidates. During the last three years, the Company acquired a controlling interest in four different companies.

	06/30/96	06/30/95	06/30/94
Per Share Information			
Stock Price as of 12/31	2.75	8.25	8.25
Earnings Per Share	-0.84	0.33	0.15
Price / Earnings Ratio	n.a.	25.00	55.00
Book Value Per Share	2.46	2.93	0.22
Price / Book Value %	111.79	281.57	3,750.00
Dividends Per Share	0.0	0.0	0.0
Annual Financial Data			
Operating Results (000's)			
Total Revenues	3,820.7	2,825.0	1,840.1
Costs & Expenses	-4,928.3	-2,192.6	-1,551.6
Income Before Taxes and Other	-1,107.6	632.5	288.6
Other Items	0.0	45.0	-26.9
Income Tax	-260.3	-239.4	-99.4
Net Income	-1,367.9	438.1	162.3
Cash Flow From Operations	724.4	-528.8	153.1
Balance Sheet (000's)			
Cash & Equivalents	938.5	91.7	11.3
Total Current Assets	3,696.1	1,992.9	116.4
Fixed Assets, Net	2,676.4	2,027.4	1.7
Total Assets	7,702.8	7,366.2	528.4
Total Current Liabilities	955.9	1,123.3	200.6
Long-Term Debt	539.2	720.5	0.0
Stockholders' Equity	5,949.5	4,409.4	327.8
Performance & Financial Condition			
Return on Total Revenues %	-35.80	15.51	8.82
Return on Avg Stockholders' Equity %	-26.41	18.50	n.a.
Return on Average Assets %	-18.16	11.10	n.a.
Current Ratio	3.87	1.77	0.58
Debt / Equity %	9.06	16.34	n.a.

Compound Growth %'s	EPS % n.a.	Net Income % n.a.	Total Revenues %	44.09

Comments

The Company changed its year end from January 31, to June 30 during 1994. Accordingly, the statement of operations for the period ended June 30, 1994, is for a 17 month period. Operations prior to that period were not significant. The Company issued 920,000 additional common shares during 1996 for an average price of about $5 per share. Most of the 1996 loss relates to start-up expenses and $700,000 sunk into mineral exploration. For the nine months ended March 31, 1997, the Company had total revenues of $3.6 million and Net Income of $463,000 which were approximately the same as the numbers reported for the same period of fiscal 1996. Investment Classification: Speculative

Officers	Position	Ownership Information	
Ella B. Chesnutt	President, CEO	Number of Shares Outstanding	2,420,836
Jayme Dorrough	Vice President, Secretary	Market Capitalization	$ 6,657,299
		Frequency of Dividends	n.a.
		Number of Shareholders	70

Other Information			
Transfer Agent	Florida Atlantic Stock Transfer, Inc. Tamarac, FL	Where Listed	OTC-BB
Auditor	Lyle H. Cooper, C.P.A.	Symbol	WFSC
Market Maker	Investors Associate Inc.	(800)646-0399	SIC Code	7363
	Allen & Company, Inc.	(800)221-2246	Employees	76
Broker Dealer	Regular Stockbroker		

Wundies Industries, Inc.

1501 West Third Street   Williamsport, PA 17701   Telephone (717)326-2451   Fax (717)326-9332

Company Description

Wundies Industries, Inc. is a wholesaler and distributor of women's and children's clothing with its main facilities located in Williamsport, Pennsylvania. Shares were issued in 1985 to all of the shareholders of Panex Industries, Inc. The Company has since issued a cumulative preferred stock that accrues a dividend at the annual rate of 13.25%.

	09/29/96	10/01/95	10/02/94	10/03/93
Per Share Information				
Stock Price as of 12/31	2.00	2.82	5.00	6.87
Earnings Per Share	1.22	0.38	1.29	0.82
Price / Earnings Ratio	1.64	7.42	3.88	8.38
Book Value Per Share	4.63	3.43	3.06	1.83
Price / Book Value %	43.20	82.22	163.40	375.41
Dividends Per Share	0.0	0.0	0.0	0.0
Annual Financial Data				
Operating Results (000's)				
Total Revenues	85,139.0	82,292.0	84,555.0	83,647.0
Costs & Expenses	-79,875.0	-79,537.0	-78,779.0	-79,285.0
Income Before Taxes and Other	5,264.0	2,755.0	5,776.0	4,362.0
Other Items	0.0	0.0	0.0	0.0
Income Tax	-1,969.0	-1,207.0	-2,339.0	-1,891.0
Net Income	3,295.0	1,548.0	3,437.0	2,471.0
Cash Flow From Operations	7,935.0	-3,614.0	12,166.0	-2,988.0
Balance Sheet (000's)				
Cash & Equivalents	150.0	145.0	159.0	233.0
Total Current Assets	40,229.0	41,520.0	35,001.0	42,070.0
Fixed Assets, Net	6,020.0	6,591.0	6,246.0	6,566.0
Total Assets	47,761.0	49,667.0	42,488.0	50,072.0
Total Current Liabilities	26,478.0	28,742.0	20,449.0	27,995.0
Long-Term Debt	0.0	2,978.0	5,980.0	9,750.0
Stockholders' Equity	19,487.0	16,250.0	14,713.0	11,380.0
Performance & Financial Condition				
Return on Total Revenues %	3.87	1.88	4.06	2.95
Return on Avg Stockholders' Equity %	18.44	10.00	26.34	23.81
Return on Average Assets %	6.76	3.36	7.43	5.20
Current Ratio	1.52	1.44	1.71	1.50
Debt / Equity %	n.a.	18.33	40.64	85.68

Compound Growth %'s	EPS % 14.16	Net Income % 10.07	Total Revenues % 0.59

Comments

Cumulative dividends on the preferred stock totalled $6,600,000 at the last year end which does not appear as a balance sheet liability. We have subtracted these year end amounts in arriving at book value per common share. Gross profit margins increased from 21.76% to 24.07% making a substantial difference in the bottom line. Earnings per common share are calculated after the effect of the preferred dividend as if it had been declared. All we can say is that it is quite remarkable what you can find for a couple dollars per share. Investment Classification: Value & Speculative

Officers	Position	Ownership Information	
Michael Fitzgerald	President, CEO	Number of Shares Outstanding	2,082,168
Steven Lockcuff	CFO	Market Capitalization	$ 4,164,336
Michael Nightingale	Vice President	Frequency of Dividends	n.a.
Judith Moore	Vice President	Number of Shareholders	Under 500
Thomas Garson	Vice President		

Other Information				
Transfer Agent	Trust Co. of New Jersey Jersey City, NJ		Where Listed	OTC-BB
Auditor	Ernst & Young LLP		Symbol	WUDS
Market Maker	Gruntal & Co., Incorporated	(800)223-7632	SIC Code	5137
	Carr Securities Corporation	(800)221-2243	Employees	n.a.
Broker Dealer	Regular Stockbroker			
	Norman Kadehjian - Wainwright	(800)727-7176		

This page intentionally left blank.

York Corrugating Co.

P.O. Box 1192   York, PA 17405-1192   Telephone (717)845-3511   Fax (717)854-0193

Company Description

York Corrugating Co. is a distributor of plumbing, heating and sheet metal supplies and a manufacturer of metal stampings with two warehouses in Pennsylvania. The main service area is the middle Atlantic states. The Company has reacquired 154,429 shares of the 194,140 originally outstanding, or 80%. No shares were acquired during 1996. The Company was founded in 1902.

	12/31/96	12/31/95	12/31/94	12/31/93
Per Share Information				
Stock Price	72.25	58.50	51.00	50.50
Earnings Per Share	11.06	15.00	9.96	-11.99
Price / Earnings Ratio	6.53	3.90	5.12	n.a.
Book Value Per Share	171.67	161.81	144.34	132.50
Price / Book Value %	42.09	36.15	35.33	38.11
Dividends Per Share	1.20	1.00	0.56	0.45
Annual Financial Data				
Operating Results (000's)				
Total Revenues	17,942.5	18,230.3	16,787.0	15,826.4
Costs & Expenses	-17,406.5	-17,301.5	-16,349.2	-16,331.7
Income Before Taxes and Other	536.0	928.9	437.8	-505.2
Other Items	0.0	0.0	0.0	0.0
Income Tax	-96.7	-333.4	-23.8	-12.8
Net Income	439.3	595.5	414.0	-518.0
Cash Flow From Operations	-157.5	564.9	601.8	-363.5
Balance Sheet (000's)				
Cash & Equivalents	516.1	955.8	472.5	249.7
Total Current Assets	6,677.0	6,520.9	6,258.1	5,597.4
Fixed Assets, Net	1,309.3	1,272.7	1,280.6	1,138.7
Total Assets	8,117.5	7,928.5	7,685.7	6,948.4
Total Current Liabilities	1,206.6	1,402.0	1,591.3	1,083.4
Long-Term Debt	0.0	0.0	0.0	0.0
Stockholders' Equity	6,817.4	6,425.7	6,000.2	5,723.2
Performance & Financial Condition				
Return on Total Revenues %	2.45	3.27	2.47	-3.27
Return on Avg Stockholders' Equity %	6.63	9.58	7.06	-8.64
Return on Average Assets %	5.48	7.63	5.66	-7.23
Current Ratio	5.53	4.65	3.93	5.17
Debt / Equity %	n.a.	n.a.	n.a.	n.a.

Compound Growth %'s	EPS %	5.38	Net Income %	3.01	Total Revenues %	4.27

Comments

After losses in 1991, 1992 and 1993, the Company appears to have restabilized itself. The Company sold its Maryland warehouse in 1995, producing nonrecurring income of approximately $400,000, approximately $10 per share, further strengthening the balance sheet. 1996 results are consistent with the preceding year without the nonrecurring income. Investment Classification: Value

Officers	Position	Ownership Information	
K P. Raub	President, Treasurer	Number of Shares Outstanding	39,711
J E. Hovis	Secretary	Market Capitalization	$ 2,869,120
T R. Miller	Vice President	Frequency of Dividends	Quarterly
		Number of Shareholders	Under 500

Other Information

Transfer Agent	Company Office		Where Listed	OTC-BB
Auditor	Philip R. Friedman and Assoc.		Symbol	YCRG
Market Maker	Robotti & Co., Inc.	(212)986-0800	SIC Code	5074
	Carr Securities Corporation	(800)221-2243	Employees	116
Broker Dealer	OTC Specialist			
	Norman Kadehjian - Wainwright	(800)727-7176		

York Water Company (The)

130 East Market Street   York, PA 17405   Telephone (717)845-3601   Fax (717)852-0058

Company Description

The business of the The York Water Company is to impound, purify and distribute water within its franchised territory located in York County, Pennsylvania. The Company's operations, which serve a population of approximately 143,000 (45,800 customers), are subject to regulation by the Pennsylvania Public Utility Commission. During 1996, the Company acquired the Jefferson Borough water system which added 253 customers and a one million gallon tank to the Company's system. Further expansion is planned for 1997. The York Water Company was founded in 1816.

	12/31/96	12/31/95	12/31/94	12/31/93
Per Share Information				
Stock Price	69.00	66.00	62.00	57.75
Earnings Per Share	4.20	3.66	3.91	4.13
Price / Earnings Ratio	16.43	18.03	15.86	13.98
Book Value Per Share	38.62	34.16	33.75	33.12
Price / Book Value %	178.66	193.21	183.70	174.37
Dividends Per Share	3.60	3.60	3.60	3.60
Annual Financial Data				
Operating Results (000's)				
Total Revenues	16,247.0	15,449.3	14,755.7	14,201.8
Costs & Expenses	-11,228.0	-11,130.4	-10,815.2	-10,786.8
Income Before Taxes and Other	4,018.5	3,732.2	3,500.1	3,836.7
Other Items	0.0	0.0	0.0	0.0
Income Tax	-1,258.7	-1,419.9	-1,055.4	-1,285.8
Net Income	2,759.8	2,312.2	2,444.7	2,550.9
Cash Flow From Operations	4,310.2	3,000.0	3,754.2	3,673.0
Balance Sheet (000's)				
Cash & Equivalents	694.5	0.0	0.0	42.6
Total Current Assets	3,962.8	3,015.7	2,685.8	3,065.1
Fixed Assets, Net	80,755.3	77,245.7	73,537.3	68,338.8
Total Assets	96,736.4	90,459.7	86,967.3	84,738.2
Total Current Liabilities	3,494.6	7,002.6	4,829.6	3,560.4
Long-Term Debt	32,000.0	32,000.0	32,000.0	32,000.0
Stockholders' Equity	28,002.8	21,771.8	21,251.9	20,597.4
Performance & Financial Condition				
Return on Total Revenues %	16.99	14.97	16.57	17.96
Return on Avg Stockholders' Equity %	11.09	10.75	11.68	12.62
Return on Average Assets %	2.95	2.61	2.85	3.09
Current Ratio	1.13	0.43	0.56	0.86
Debt / Equity %	114.27	146.98	150.57	155.36

Compound Growth %'s	EPS %	0.56	Net Income %	2.66	Total Revenues %	4.59

Comments

On August 8, 1996, the Company offered its common shareholders non-transferable subscription rights to purchase up to 80,000 shares of common stock at a purchase price of $67.45 per share. Within 45 days, 79,981 shares were exercised. Overall consumption was lower during 1996, in large part, to the greater than normal precipitation experienced throughout the year, the second highest in recorded history. A 6% rate increase became effective in September, 1996. With a little blue sky we may see record results again in 1997. Investment Classification: Income

Officers	Position	Ownership Information	
William T. Morris	President, CEO	Number of Shares Outstanding	725,131
Jeffrey S. Osman	VP - Finance, Secretary	Market Capitalization	$ 50,034,039
Duane R. Close	Vice President	Frequency of Dividends	Quarterly
Jeffrey R. Hines	Vice President	Number of Shareholders	1,281
Lois L. Shultz	Other		

Other Information			
Transfer Agent	Company Office		
Auditor	KPMG Peat Marwick LLP	Where Listed	OTC-BB
Market Maker	Legg Mason Wood Walker, Inc.	(212)428-4949	Symbol	YORW
	F.J. Morrissey & Co., Inc.	(800)842-8928	SIC Code	4941
Broker Dealer	Regular Stockbroker	Employees	91

Fire and Water

In 1816, the very thought of fire terrified the people of York. The Pennsylvania town was pieced together largely of wooden buildings tightly clustered over just a few blocks. Even a small fire could spread quickly, and local water supplies would never be enough to douse the flames. Somehow, York needed to transport more water into town to guard against this threat. And so the town's citizens decided to put together one of the first public water systems in America, The York Water Company, to do just that.

Their solution was elegant: with locomotion provided by gravity itself, spring water was brought into town through mains manufactured from locally harvested oak trees. Logs were bored out one by one, cut to 13-foot lengths and set end-to-end over the three miles it took to bridge the distance from town to the water source. A massive undertaking for the time, the system was so well crafted that it provided York with water for more than a generation.

By then York found itself in need of a major system upgrade. The population had grown and was spreading, and not always in directions that lay downhill from the spring. Wooden mains had given way to iron in 1840, and eight years later the first pumping station went in, providing newcomers both uphill and further away with piped water and adequate pressure. These new and improved facilities managed to fill York's water needs for nearly fifty more years.

Then, in 1891, typhoid broke out. It happened that private wells were the culprits this time, but public water supplies too were at risk for contamination. Water known for certain to be safe was nearly unheard of in late nineteenth century York or anywhere else. Germ theory had only recently been developed and public health standards were almost nonexistent, yet the company responded to this threat as early as 1899 by installing and using new filtration technology. In doing so they became the first to successfully process water in the entire state of Pennsylvania. It would be almost half a century before comparable sanitary drinking supplies were available throughout America.

The York Water Company's early commitment to public health and well-being manifested itself in yet another way as well — even as Congress was dedicating some of our first National Parks, the company was putting aside an admittedly more modest piece of land as a "public breathing spot" for the people of York in 1903. By turn of the century standards the gesture was environmentally and socially well ahead of its time, but totally in keeping with the company's dedication to their community.

The York Water Company of today is enormous compared to that of 1816 or even of 1916, but it still helps protect the many people of York from fire. Now, within nineteen years of celebrating its own bicentennial, the high standards York continues to uphold will no doubt help to ferry the company comfortably into the 21st century.

Yosemite Bank

P.O. Box 5000   Mariposa, CA 95338   Telephone (209)966-3777   Fax (209)966-4195

Company Description

In the shadows of Half Dome and El Capitan, Yosemite Bank operates three offices located in Mariposa, Groveland and Oakhurst, California. The Bank began operations in 1977 and grew to five offices by 1991. However, as part of an overall strategy to reconcentrate resources to certain mountain areas, two branches were sold in 1993. The Bank has since replaced the volume that left with the sale. An original shareholder who invested $1,000 in Yosemite Bank stock when the Bank was formed in 1977 would now hold shares valued in excess of $7,000.

	12/31/96	12/31/95	12/31/94	12/31/93
Per Share Information				
Stock Price	12.00	9.05	8.16	8.64
Earnings Per Share	1.02	0.62	0.38	1.20
Price / Earnings Ratio	11.76	14.60	21.47	7.20
Book Value Per Share	12.02	11.11	9.20	9.79
Price / Book Value %	99.83	81.46	88.70	88.25
Dividends Per Share	0.0	0.0	0.0	0.0
Annual Financial Data				
Operating Results (000's)				
Net Interest Income	3,498.8	3,162.9	3,020.9	3,285.4
Loan Loss Provision	-80.0	-80.0	-30.0	-6.2
Non-Interest Income	1,116.1	1,017.5	1,279.0	1,851.9
Non-Interest Expense	-3,598.2	-3,618.2	-4,049.7	-3,969.1
Income Before Taxes and Other	936.6	482.2	220.1	1,162.0
Other Items	0.0	0.0	0.0	0.0
Income Tax	-255.0	-75.0	25.0	-385.0
Net Income	681.6	407.2	245.1	777.0
Balance Sheet (000's)				
Cash & Securities	35,905.2	32,494.5	30,931.2	n.a.
Loans, Net	36,545.5	34,019.4	29,585.3	n.a.
Total Assets	80,379.3	73,937.5	67,838.9	n.a.
Deposits	72,028.1	66,139.4	59,483.8	n.a.
Stockholders' Equity	8,025.7	7,344.4	6,011.2	n.a.
Performance & Financial Condition				
Return on Avg Stockholders' Equity %	8.87	6.10	3.58	12.95
Return on Average Assets %	0.88	0.57	0.37	1.27
Equity to Assets %	9.98	9.93	8.86	n.a.
Net Interest Margin	n.a.	n.a.	n.a.	n.a.
Reserve as a % of Problem Loans	262.06	114.64	1,021.27	n.a.

Compound Growth %'s	EPS %	-5.27	Net Income %	-4.27	Net Interest Income %	2.12

Comments

The Bank has declared 5% stock dividends in each of the years presented. All per share amounts have been adjusted for consistency. 1996 results reflect the successful replacement of the deposit base after the sale referred to above. During the first week of 1997, a combination of heavy rains and rapid snow melt combined to produce the worst floods in the recorded history of Yosemite National Park. Economic devastation will temporarily pervade the entire market area. Management predicts lower profits in 1997 because of this tragedy but, like a good community bank, it is helping its customers work through their difficulties with understanding and flexibility. Longer term benefits may be the ultimate reward as the Park rebuilds. Investment Classification: Value

Officers	Position	Ownership Information	
T C. Dowlan	President, CEO	Number of Shares Outstanding	667,558
Glenn E. Sutherland	Senior VP, CFO	Market Capitalization	$ 8,010,696
Lorelei Begley	Senior VP	Frequency of Dividends	n.a.
Robert Eckart	Vice President	Number of Shareholders	850
		Where Listed / Symbol	OTC-BB / YOBK

Other Information			Loan Mix	%
Transfer Agent	U.S. Stock Transfer Corp. Glendale, CA		R/E Mortgages	84.8
Auditor	Arthur Andersen LLP		Consumer	5.5
Market Maker	GBS Financial Corp.	(818)248-5558	Commerical	4.7
	Sutro & Co., Incorporated	(800)227-4422	Construction	4.4
Broker Dealer	Regular Stockbroker		Agriculture	0.6

ZEVEX International, Inc.

4314 Zevex Park Avenue   Salt Lake City, UT 84123   Telephone (801)264-1001   Fax (801)264-1051

Company Description

ZEVEX International designs, manufactures, and sells custom and standard products utilizing ultrasonic transducers and related signal processing instrumentation. Products are sold primarily to original equipment manufacturers serving the medical, industrial and aerospace instrumentation markets. Zevex's products are currently sold directly, through independent manufacturer's representatives, and through distributors worldwide. The Company was founded in 1987.

	12/31/96	12/31/95	12/31/94	12/31/93
Per Share Information				
Stock Price	3.00	3.63	2.63	5.25
Earnings Per Share	0.25	0.24	-0.02	0.36
Price / Earnings Ratio	12.00	15.13	n.a.	14.58
Book Value Per Share	2.47	2.12	2.26	2.28
Price / Book Value %	121.46	171.23	116.37	230.26
Dividends Per Share	0.0	0.0	0.0	0.0
Annual Financial Data				
Operating Results (000's)				
Total Revenues	5,920.7	5,336.6	3,368.6	3,153.0
Costs & Expenses	-5,368.9	-4,892.6	-3,459.9	-2,574.6
Income Before Taxes and Other	551.7	443.9	-91.4	578.3
Other Items	0.0	0.0	0.0	0.0
Income Tax	-206.2	-127.1	66.7	-196.9
Net Income	345.6	316.8	-24.7	381.4
Cash Flow From Operations	-175.1	214.4	-461.7	110.3
Balance Sheet (000's)				
Cash & Equivalents	2,085.1	870.3	864.3	1,462.8
Total Current Assets	5,108.8	2,874.9	2,543.7	2,642.1
Fixed Assets, Net	1,207.0	363.8	276.2	268.1
Total Assets	6,368.7	3,247.4	2,824.0	2,912.1
Total Current Liabilities	588.0	346.5	273.7	337.1
Long-Term Debt	0.0	0.0	0.0	0.0
Stockholders' Equity	3,701.4	2,900.9	2,550.3	2,575.0
Performance & Financial Condition				
Return on Total Revenues %	5.84	5.94	-0.73	12.10
Return on Avg Stockholders' Equity %	10.47	11.62	-0.96	20.06
Return on Average Assets %	7.19	10.44	-0.86	17.65
Current Ratio	8.69	8.30	9.29	7.84
Debt / Equity %	n.a.	n.a.	n.a.	n.a.

Compound Growth %'s	EPS %	-11.45	Net Income %	-3.23	Total Revenues %	23.37

Comments

1996 produced record sales but more good news is on the way. During 1996, ZEVEX became a complete systems manufacturer with the successful fulfillment of a large OEM development contract. The Company also introduced a second proprietary product. With two major manufacturing contracts in hand, management anticipates that sales will increase by 60% or better in 1997. In May, 1997, the Company moved to a new 51,000 square foot facility that will allow for improved efficiencies and greater production growth. There has also been growth in the stock price: $7.25 as of May 12, 1997. Investment Classification: Speculative

Officers	Position	Ownership Information	
Dean G. Constantine	President, CEO	Number of Shares Outstanding	1,495,716
Phillip L. McStotts	Secretary, CFO	Market Capitalization	$ 4,487,148
David J. McNally	Vice President	Frequency of Dividends	n.a.
		Number of Shareholders	509

Other Information			
Transfer Agent	Colonial Stock Transfer Salt Lake City, UT	Where Listed	OTC-BB
Auditor	Daines and Rasmussen	Symbol	ZVXI
Market Maker	Alpine Securities Corporation	(800)521-5588	SIC Code	3845
	Wm. V. Frankel & Co., Inc.	(800)631-3091	Employees	73
Broker Dealer	Regular Stockbroker		

ZAP Power Systems

117 Morris Street   Sebastopol, CA 95472   Telephone (707)824-4150   Fax (707)824-4159

Company Description

The Company manufactures an electric motor system that is sold as a kit to be installed by the customer on their own bicycle. The Company also installs the motor system on bicycles it buys and resells to customers. The electric motor kit has 62 unique parts which the Company manufacturers except for the motor itself, which is acquired from a third party. On November 29, 1996, the Company began to offer up to 500,000 shares at $5.25 per share in a direct public offering. The proceeds are to be used for working capital and expansion.

	12/31/96	12/31/95	12/31/94
Per Share Information			
Stock Price	5.25	1.00	n.a.
Earnings Per Share	-0.45	-0.01	-0.15
Price / Earnings Ratio	n.a.	n.a.	n.a.
Book Value Per Share	0.05	0.04	-0.12
Price / Book Value %	10,500.00	2,500.00	n.a.
Dividends Per Share	0.0	0.0	0.0
Annual Financial Data			
Operating Results (000's)			
Total Revenues	1,190.4	880.8	61.6
Costs & Expenses	-2,006.1	-885.3	-134.3
Income Before Taxes and Other	-815.7	-12.5	-72.7
Other Items	0.0	0.0	0.0
Income Tax	-1.6	-3.5	-0.8
Net Income	-817.3	-16.0	-73.5
Cash Flow From Operations	-618.6	-14.0	13.4
Balance Sheet (000's)			
Cash & Equivalents	161.6	21.8	14.2
Total Current Assets	584.6	110.9	41.1
Fixed Assets, Net	100.3	66.3	15.0
Total Assets	770.2	191.4	56.1
Total Current Liabilities	629.4	131.0	114.6
Long-Term Debt	4.7	0.0	0.0
Stockholders' Equity	112.4	60.4	-58.5
Performance & Financial Condition			
Return on Total Revenues %	-68.66	-1.82	-119.32
Return on Avg Stockholders' Equity %	-945.95	-1,684.20	n.a.
Return on Average Assets %	-169.99	-12.93	n.a.
Current Ratio	0.93	0.85	0.36
Debt / Equity %	4.18	n.a.	n.a.

Compound Growth %'s	EPS % n.a.	Net Income % n.a.	Total Revenues % n.a.

Comments

On February 11, 1997, the Company announced an alliance with a Chinese bicycle manufacturer whereby Zap will supply its drive systems to Forever Bicycle Co. of Shanghai, a government-owned company that produces more than three million bicycles a year. For the quarter ended March 31, 1997, the Company reported higher sales by 26.5% and a net loss of $293,400, $.14 per share. The Company intends to create a market mechanism or facilitator for its shares at the earliest time possible. In the meantime, inquiries can be directed to the Company. Investment Classification: Speculative

Officers	Position	Ownership Information	
James McGreen	President	Number of Shares Outstanding	2,076,500
Nancy K. Cadigan	Secretary	Market Capitalization	$ 10,901,625
Dave Workman	Vice President, CFO	Frequency of Dividends	n.a.
Gary Starr	Other	Number of Shareholders	202

Other Information

Transfer Agent	Company Office		Where Listed	Order Matching Only
Auditor	Moss Adams LLP		Symbol	n.a.
Market Maker	None - See Note		SIC Code	3750
			Employees	35
Broker Dealer	None			

Zimmerman Sign Company

9846 Highway 31 East   Tyler, TX 75705   Telephone (903)535-7400   Fax (903)535-7401

Company Description

Zimmerman Sign Company operates as a leading manufacturer of site identification products with a primary focus on serving large, national and regional retailers. From its plant locations in Texas, Zimmerman manufacturers and sells a variety of signage products which range from large highway-located site identification signs to medium-sized brand and product identification signs and building fascia as well as smaller signs for automatic teller machines, gasoline pump toppers, and other specialty purposes. The Company was founded in 1901.

	12/31/96	12/31/95	12/31/94	12/31/93
Per Share Information				
Stock Price	3.37	n.a.	n.a.	n.a.
Earnings Per Share	0.62	1.28	1.12	0.80
Price / Earnings Ratio	5.44	n.a.	n.a.	n.a.
Book Value Per Share	-5.32	4.69	3.41	n.a.
Price / Book Value %	n.a.	n.a.	n.a.	n.a.
Dividends Per Share	10.62	0.0	1.54	0.0
Annual Financial Data				
Operating Results (000's)				
Total Revenues	41,275.5	41,666.6	36,426.7	33,001.0
Costs & Expenses	-39,545.1	-38,065.6	-33,283.8	-30,755.0
Income Before Taxes and Other	1,730.3	3,600.9	3,142.8	2,246.0
Other Items	0.0	0.0	0.0	0.0
Income Tax	-588.3	-1,224.3	-1,068.6	-768.0
Net Income	1,142.0	2,376.6	2,074.2	1,478.0
Cash Flow From Operations	-1,100.4	-1,498.8	1,171.8	n.a.
Balance Sheet (000's)				
Cash & Equivalents	132.5	107.8	n.a.	n.a.
Total Current Assets	24,364.0	22,808.2	n.a.	n.a.
Fixed Assets, Net	3,152.9	3,068.6	n.a.	n.a.
Total Assets	28,153.9	25,957.1	n.a.	n.a.
Total Current Liabilities	9,461.7	7,838.7	n.a.	n.a.
Long-Term Debt	28,555.0	9,422.2	n.a.	n.a.
Stockholders' Equity	-9,862.8	8,696.2	n.a.	n.a.
Performance & Financial Condition				
Return on Total Revenues %	2.77	5.70	5.69	4.48
Return on Avg Stockholders' Equity %	n.a.	n.a.	n.a.	n.a.
Return on Average Assets %	n.a.	n.a.	n.a.	n.a.
Current Ratio	2.58	2.91	n.a.	n.a.
Debt / Equity %	n.a.	108.35	n.a.	n.a.

Compound Growth %'s	EPS % n.a.	Net Income % n.a.	Total Revenues % n.a.

Comments

The Company became public when Independence Holding Company, the parent company of Zimmerman, declared a 3,863.94 to 1 stock split of Zimmerman shares and distributed them to its shareholders in a tax-free distribution. Before it did that, however, Independence had Zimmerman borrow about $21 million and pay a $19.3 million dividend to Independence, also on a tax-free basis since Zimmerman was a majority-owned company. The net result is that Independence nets the same amount of money it would have netted if Zimmerman had been sold for $30 million (a hefty price) and the shareholders of Independence end up with stock worth $6 million. Investment Classification: Value

Officers	Position	Ownership Information	
Tom E. Boner	President, Treasurer	Number of Shares Outstanding	1,854,692
Jeffrey P. Johnson	Secretary, CFO	Market Capitalization	$ 6,250,312
Michael F. St. Onge	Vice President	Frequency of Dividends	n.a.
John T. Griggs	VP - Manufacturing	Number of Shareholders	n.a.
Michael W. Coppinger	VP - Sales		

Other Information				
Transfer Agent	Company Office		Where Listed	OTC-BB
Auditor	KPMG Peat Marwick LLP		Symbol	ZSCO
Market Maker	Carr Securities Corporation	(800)221-2243	SIC Code	5099
	Pennsylvania Merchant Group	(800)762-8624	Employees	n.a.
Broker Dealer	Regular Stockbroker			

Zions Cooperative Mercantile Institution

2200 South 900 West   Salt Lake City, UT 84137   Telephone (801)579-6179   Fax (801)579-6275

Company Description

More commonly referred to as ZCMI, the Company was organized in 1868 and was the first full-line department store in the United States. Their retail lines of business include both full-line conventional department stores, men's and women's ready-to-wear specialty stores and outlet stores. The full-line conventional department stores are located in the Salt Lake City and Ogden, Utah, areas and in Pocatello and Idaho Falls, Idaho. The specialty and outlet stores are located in Provo and St. George, Utah. Please enjoy our historical vignette on the opposite page.

	02/01/97	02/03/96	01/28/95	01/29/94
Per Share Information				
Stock Price as of 12/31	11.87	11.00	9.82	9.38
Earnings Per Share	0.84	0.27	1.69	1.46
Price / Earnings Ratio	14.13	40.74	5.81	6.42
Book Value Per Share	23.92	23.64	24.91	23.92
Price / Book Value %	49.62	46.53	39.42	39.21
Dividends Per Share	0.60	0.60	0.60	0.60
Annual Financial Data				
Operating Results (000's)				
Total Revenues	259,599.5	254,371.3	244,923.6	235,318.9
Costs & Expenses	-257,078.2	-253,588.9	-240,630.0	-228,281.2
Income Before Taxes and Other	2,521.3	782.4	4,293.6	5,137.7
Other Items	0.0	0.0	1,373.7	0.0
Income Tax	-683.7	-200.8	-2,043.0	-1,984.8
Net Income	1,837.6	581.6	3,624.3	3,152.9
Cash Flow From Operations	6,766.0	1,571.0	-3,874.6	-1,237.2
Balance Sheet (000's)				
Cash & Equivalents	1,467.3	2,698.1	2,698.9	5,315.5
Total Current Assets	103,693.7	102,633.2	105,840.3	99,971.6
Fixed Assets, Net	33,103.0	33,273.9	38,191.7	35,332.3
Total Assets	137,618.4	136,504.9	144,629.9	135,947.2
Total Current Liabilities	37,797.7	24,856.1	35,646.9	40,171.9
Long-Term Debt	26,246.0	56,406.3	50,974.2	40,367.7
Stockholders' Equity	51,775.9	51,062.1	53,570.7	51,092.8
Performance & Financial Condition				
Return on Total Revenues %	0.71	0.23	1.48	1.34
Return on Avg Stockholders' Equity %	3.57	1.11	6.93	6.27
Return on Average Assets %	1.34	0.41	2.58	2.38
Current Ratio	2.74	4.13	2.97	2.49
Debt / Equity %	50.69	110.47	95.15	79.01

Compound Growth %'s	EPS %	-16.83	Net Income %	-16.47	Total Revenues %	3.33

Comments

Although nationwide retail profits reflected a difficult year, ZCMI has reported higher earnings. Most of the increase to the bottom line is attributable to higher sales. Also noted, however, is that the prior year was relatively weak. Management credits the increase in income to more cost-effective systems for conducting business. We can't find evidence of that in the numbers other than the maintenance of gross margins. ZCMI maintains excellent strength in the balance sheet which supports an overall strategy of careful growth. Investment Classification: Income & Growth & Value

Officers	Position	Ownership Information	
Richard H. Madsen	President, CEO	Number of Shares Outstanding	2,164,483
Keith C. Saunders	Exec VP, CFO	Market Capitalization	$ 25,692,413
Nancy Mortensen	Vice President	Frequency of Dividends	Quarterly
R. Barry Arnold	Vice President	Number of Shareholders	1,725
Darrell L. Robinette	Vice President		

Other Information

Transfer Agent	Company Office		Where Listed	OTC-BB
Auditor	Deloitte & Touche LLP		Symbol	ZNCO
Market Maker	Wilson-Davis & Co., Inc.	(800)453-5735	SIC Code	5311
	Neuberger & Berman	(800)543-8481	Employees	2602
Broker Dealer	Regular Stockbroker			

The People's Store

America's first department store... that would be Macy's, right? Or maybe Marshall Field & Company? Location? Must have been New York City, I guess. Any idea who ran it?

Try Brigham Young, Salt Lake City and ZCMI: Zions Cooperative Mercantile Institution. Probably not your first guess, but, according to some, it was actually this dusty outpost of America's wild west that was the true setting for the birth of American retailing on a grand scale. And the moving force behind it was none other than the powerful president of the Mormon church.

It was 1868, and Young was frankly worried. His Mormon settlers had been busy building communities and taming the forbidding Utah wilderness since migrating there some twenty-two years before. Though never exactly cut off from""Gentil"" influence, this tightly knit group was about to be utterly inundated, in Youn''s judgment, when the new Transcontinental Railroad opened an artery from both east and west right into their backyard. He feared the resulting diversity would weaken Mormon solidarity, and wished to guard against this dilution in every way possible. What better solution than to become utterly self-sufficient? How better to attain this independence than by conducting trade only within the community?

To that end leaders of the faith organized Zions. First intended to be strictly wholesale, ZCMI quickly evolved into a retail operation as well, and they sold everything. Dry goods, groceries and hardware were made available at prices consistently lower than those charged by Gentiles. Branches in towns as far away as South Dakota were stocked with inventory identical to that in the Salt Lake store, and no matter how distant or isolated, uniform pricing in every branch was the rule.

Goods "imported" from eastern cities were on the shelves, but church member/customers were exhorted to buy those of so-called home manufacture whenever possible. Supporting local industries sprouted overnight, dutifully turning out everything from soap to shoes. Often the quality of these goods didn't quite match that of imports: homespun was coarse, soap easily disintegrated and brooms could hardly be lifted by a woman, but they were scooped up anyway. The "all-seeing eye" of the store's logo probably helped remind any wavering souls not to forget: on no account were they to conduct trade anywhere else, under threat of excommunication. With these admittedly special circumstances, the "People's Store" sprang into operation, generating a 10 percent cash dividend in its first year of operations and effectively putting many competing Gentile stores right out of business.

What a difference a century can make — ZCMI has arguably moved much closer to Macy's than Brigham Young ever intended, both in terms of merchandising and philosophy. Now a publicly-traded company, it is decidedly more commercial in orientation and does compete with other major retailers for business. Yet company stores remain closed on Sundays and church leaders still populate the board of directors. And the company remains an integral part of the community; as of 1991 it was the state's fourth largest employer. While Young's vision of separatism may not have survived, surely he would recognize his early influence in the continued success of ZCMI today.

Indices

T

U

V

W

X, Y & Z

This page intentionally left blank.

This page intentionally left blank.

4000 - 4999
Transportation & Public Utilities

5000 - 5199
Wholesale Trade

5200 - 5999
Retail Trade

6000 - 6299
Banking

6300 - 6499
Insurance

6500 - 6799
Real Estate & Other Investing

7000 - 8999
Services

This page intentionally left blank.

Over $100,000,000

Publix Super Markets, Inc.	10,525,969,000
Bruno's, Inc.	2,899,044,000
Kohler Co.	1,833,901,900
Crowley Maritime Corporation	1,093,343,000
Sterling Chemicals Holdings, Inc.	790,465,000
King Kullen Grocery Co., Inc.	723,896,000
Benjamin Moore & Co.	625,190,000
Central Steel and Wire Company	594,100,000
Pennsylvania Manufacturers Corporation	566,684,000
Cowles Media Company	497,889,000
Ash Grove Cement Company	417,526,569
Bozzuto's Inc.	379,169,530
Seven-Up/RC Bottling Co. of Southern Calif., Inc.	328,850,000
Americold Corporation	311,699,000
Houlihan's Restaurant Group, Inc.	279,214,000
Irex Corporation	271,232,000
Davey Tree Expert Company (The)	267,206,000
Fisher Companies Inc.	265,220,000
Hanover Foods Corporation	263,560,000
Boswell (J.G.) Company	262,291,000
Zions Cooperative Mercantile Institution	259,599,500
Farmer Bros. Co.	233,766,000
Harriet & Henderson Yarns, Inc.	232,942,800
Finch, Pruyn & Company, Incorporated	227,309,000
Rochester & Pittsburgh Coal Company	217,282,000
Hayward Industries, Inc.	205,574,000
Temco Service Industries, Inc.	191,258,497
Preformed Line Products Company	186,781,000
Lady Baltimore Foods, Inc.	183,655,878
Conbraco Industries, Inc.	171,070,480
Carolina Mills Inc.	169,937,269
Rand McNally	164,548,000
Burnham Corporation	160,233,000
Pekin Life Insurance Company	159,029,950
Maui Land & Pineapple Company, Inc.	136,335,000
Hammett (J.L.) Co.	134,448,700
Nichols (J.C.) Company	132,628,000
Continental Resources, Inc.	126,946,400
Robroy Industries, Inc.	123,548,026
Best Lock Corporation	122,630,694
Smith Investment Company	121,821,000
Bulova Corporation	120,792,000
Louisville Bedding Company	118,415,678
Roseville Communications Company	117,062,000
Amelco Corporation	116,220,000
Lexington Precision Corporation	114,872,000
CBR Brewing Company, Inc. (9 mos.)	114,690,724
Penn Fuel Gas, Inc.	113,936,000
Sportsman's Guide, Inc. (The)	112,281,000
Stonecutter Mills Corporation	107,874,372
E*Capital Corporation	105,103,000
Pioneer Metals, Inc.	104,900,200

$100,000,000 - $50,000,000

NCC Industries, Inc.	99,795,086
Westmoreland Coal Company	97,533,000
Blue Diamond Coal Company	89,966,839
Monarch Cement Company (The)	87,820,131
Frederick Trading Company	87,564,732
Broughton Foods Company	87,162,960
Wundies Industries, Inc.	85,139,000

Erie Family Life Insurance Company	82,720,238
Leslie Building Products, Inc.	82,154,000
Anderson-Tully Company	80,837,488
Exolon-ESK Company	78,462,000
Hershey Creamery Company	77,426,989
Valley Fair Corporation (The)	72,997,734
Magicworks Entertainment Incorporated	71,953,633
First of Michigan Capital Corporation	71,707,443
Case, Pomeroy & Company, Inc.	70,856,000
Continental Health Affiliates, Inc.	70,651,000
Mutual Savings Life Insurance Company	70,641,395
CT Communications, Inc.	69,100,171
Peckham Industries, Inc.	66,625,000
North State Telephone Company	65,570,300
West Virginia-American Water Company	62,976,000
North Pittsburgh Systems, Inc.	61,667,000
Meteor Industries, Inc.	60,380,093
Savers Life Insurance Company	58,003,500
Boston Sand & Gravel Company	57,112,752
Connectivity Technologies Inc.	57,099,749
Keller Manufacturing Company, Inc.	54,168,278
Wisconsin Fuel & Light Company	53,662,197
Adrian Steel Company	52,979,208
Investment Properties Associates	52,290,744
Colorado Gaming & Entertainment Co.	50,817,000
Burke-Parsons-Bowlby Corporation	50,202,952

$49,999,999 - $20,000,000

Fall River Gas Company	49,756,344
Kentucky Investors, Inc.	47,961,664
Investors Heritage Life Insurance Company	47,779,596
Westwood Incorporated	45,938,404
Watson Land Company	44,819,400
Latshaw Enterprises, Inc.	44,721,000
Horizon Telcom, Inc.	44,618,104
First Republic Corporation of America (The)	43,545,947
South Chester Tube Company	42,952,900
Sea Pines Associates, Inc.	42,859,000
Market America, Inc.	42,797,937
Kentucky River Coal Corporation	42,662,000
Ragar Corp.	42,432,818
Auric Corporation	41,613,622
Michigan Rivet Corporation	41,596,542
Zimmerman Sign Company	41,275,477
Cloverleaf Kennel Club	40,968,988
Troy Mills, Inc.	40,915,717
Profit Financial Corporation	40,913,807
Ravens Metal Products, Inc.	40,352,884
Sterling Sugars, Inc.	39,415,200
Chatham Corporation	38,539,000
Computer Services, Inc.	38,027,900
B.B. Walker Company	37,549,000
Bresler & Reiner, Inc.	35,143,000
Fair Grounds Corporation	34,505,723
Westwood Group, Inc. (The)	33,663,862
EMC Corporation	32,579,451
Pay-O-Matic Corp.	32,515,400
RWC, Inc.	32,232,571
Stein Industries, Inc.	30,274,943
Hilliard Corporation (The)	29,869,524
Williams Industries, Incorporated	29,667,376
Biochem International Inc.	29,377,494

American Public Life Insurance Company	28,822,596
Lab-Volt Systems, Inc.	27,551,321
AFA Protective Systems, Inc..	27,416,651
Homasote Company	27,147,793
Shenandoah Telecommunications Company	26,773,992
Life Insurance Company of Alabama.	26,496,538
Sadlier, Inc., William H.	26,365,421
Lexcom Communications, Inc.	26,156,892
Guaranty Corporation.	26,134,000
Lanxide Corporation	25,868,000
Reynolds, Smith and Hills, Inc..	25,595,000
St. Louis Steel Casting Inc.	25,498,000
Fremont Corporation	25,184,000
LAACO, Ltd.	24,755,000
Allstar Inns, Inc.	24,743,000
Du Art Film Laboratories, Inc.	24,637,633
DHB Capital Group Inc.	23,853,553
Athanor Group, Inc..	23,652,690
Bryan Steam Corporation.	22,733,418
Columbian Rope Company	22,299,207
Decker Manufacturing Corporation	22,073,725
BFC Financial Corporation.	21,953,000
Corning Natural Gas Corporation	21,581,709
Snow Summit Ski Corporation	21,033,587
Mt. Bachelor, Inc..	21,021,300
New Orleans Cold Storage and Warehouse Co. Ltd	20,947,508
Paradise, Inc.	20,561,845

$19,999,999 - $10,000,000

York Corrugating Co.	17,942,541
Rhinelander Telecommunications, Inc..	17,869,713
Monroe Title Insurance Corporation	17,825,197
Meritage Hospitality Group Inc.	17,535,969
Reo Plastics, Inc.	17,496,515
Shopsmith, Inc.	17,466,692
TIF Instruments, Inc.	17,454,400
Waste Recovery, Inc.	17,013,906
Unidyne Corporation	16,605,000
SLH Corporation	16,598,000
Tower Properties Company.	16,492,245
York Water Company (The)	16,246,959
Western Lime Corporation	15,807,806
Mercom, Inc.	15,709,000
Warwick Valley Telephone Co.	15,614,170
Crown City Plating Co..	15,565,792
Blue Ridge Real Estate Company	15,397,046
Old Fashion Foods, Inc..	15,226,528
Tork, Inc.	15,201,257
Goodheart-Willcox Company, Inc. (The).	14,872,000
Ellensburg Telephone Company	14,809,600
Woodbury Telephone Company (The)	14,620,253
Reinhold Industries Inc..	14,279,000
Reuter Manufacturing, Inc..	14,226,951
Detroit Legal News Company	14,100,936
Wailuku Agribusiness Co., Inc..	13,957,517
Alaska Power & Telephone Company	13,796,336
First Real Estate Investment Trust of New Jersey	13,678,000
A.D. Makepeace Company	13,608,111
Mt. Carmel Public Utility Co.	13,481,852
Bismarck Hotel Company	13,065,205
Hunter Manufacturing Corp.	12,696,507
North Coast Life Insurance Co..	12,679,939

Lasermedics, Inc..	12,485,961
Naylor Pipe Company	12,419,944
Pennichuck Corporation	12,209,937
Portland Brewing Company	12,154,707
American Industrial Loan Association	11,898,500
Health International, Inc.	11,766,727
Southern Webbing Mills, Inc..	11,758,092
AMCOR Capital Corporation.	11,698,629
Hydraulic Press Brick Company	11,690,000
Personal Computer Products, Inc.	11,621,000
Blue Fish Clothing, Inc..	11,610,855
Mod-U-Kraf Homes, Inc..	11,440,836
Standard Electronics, Inc..	11,268,645
Components Specialties, Inc.	11,261,487
Information Analysis Incorporated	11,231,561
Audio Communications Network, Inc..	11,177,893
Pacific Northwest Development Corporation.	11,004,075
Pocono Hotels Corporation	10,957,406
Ogden Telephone Company	10,641,238
Florafax International, Inc.	10,415,000
Power Test Investors Limited Partnership	10,226,955
Dover Investments Corporation	10,160,000
Naturade, Inc..	10,118,712
Pardee Resources Company	10,101,995

Under $10,000,000

Adams (R.P.) Company, Inc.	9,925,163
New Ulm Telecom, Inc..	9,919,559
Real Silk Investments, Incorporated.	9,816,016
Network Data Processing Corporation	9,739,007
Strategia Corporation	9,454,713
Auto-Graphics, Inc.	9,251,917
Carco Electronics	9,248,993
Logan Clay Products Company	9,039,385
PortaCom Wireless, Inc..	9,013,943
Universal Metals & Machinery, Inc..	8,964,811
HomeCapital Investment Corporation.	8,913,603
Chromaline Corporation.	8,857,529
Citizens' Electric Company	8,849,340
CMP Industries, Inc..	8,834,517
Randall Bearings, Inc..	8,796,225
Hytek Microsystems, Inc..	8,650,975
United Vanguard Homes, Inc..	8,634,173
Century Realty Trust	8,384,732
Cable Link, Inc..	8,253,479
Home-Stake Royalty Corporation (The)	8,213,464
M.H. Rhodes, Inc..	8,011,086
Arthur Treacher's, Inc..	7,873,160
Cherokee Equity Corporation	7,788,073
Finance Company of Pennsylvania	7,748,976
Home-Stake Oil & Gas Company (The)	7,742,074
Viskon-Aire Corporation	7,359,508
Henry County Plywood Corporation	7,274,070
Addvantage Media Group, Inc.	7,044,015
Ainslie Corporation	6,908,582
Transnational Industries, Inc.	6,842,000
Chambersburg Engineering Company.	6,770,596
U.S. Plastic Lumber Corporation	6,683,514
Keweenaw Land Association, Limited	6,469,483
Wichita National Life Insurance Company	6,464,709
Acap Corporation	6,270,767
Community Service Communications, Inc..	6,254,570

Advantage Marketing Systems, Inc..	6,163,740
RF Industries, LTD	6,141,698
Sims-Agricultural Products Company.	6,095,323
Call Now, Inc..	6,027,481
Scioto Downs, Inc.	5,923,701
ZEVEX International, Inc.	5,920,661
InterUnion Financial Corporation.	5,915,435
Kiewit Royalty Trust	5,829,963
UTZ Engineering, Inc..	5,663,510
North Carolina Railroad Company	5,620,469
CVF Corp..	5,611,043
Fifty Associates	5,545,181
Radio Frequency Company, Inc.	5,512,200
Tremont Advisors, Inc.	5,472,227
Christian Brothers, Inc.	5,461,514
Indiana Natural Gas Corporation	5,141,291
National Stock Yards Company	5,134,686
Birmingham Utilities, Inc..	5,112,693
Indians, Inc.	5,085,910
DeltaPoint, Inc.	5,024,000
Oak Tree Medical Systems ,Inc..	4,945,280
Annie's Homegrown, Inc.	4,819,963
Market Guide, Inc..	4,807,500
Phil-Good Products Incorporated	4,690,270
Pinnacle Data Systems, Inc..	4,678,968
Dynamic Associates, Inc.	4,582,263
Queen City Investments, Inc.	4,531,061
Torrington Water Company (The).	4,502,163
Technology 80 Inc.	4,417,353
Thanksgiving Coffee Company, Inc.	4,338,963
SGI International	4,244,268
Connohio, Inc..	3,980,825
Main Street Athletic Clubs, Inc..	3,974,554
Garden City Company.	3,936,300
Northfield Precision Instrument Corporation	3,920,598
Batterymarch Trust (The)	3,869,387
Mendocino Brewing Company, Inc..	3,851,300
TNR Technical, Inc..	3,823,075
Workforce Systems Corp.	3,820,680
VASCO Corp.	3,800,100
Olokele Sugar Company, Limited.	3,751,779
Clinicor, Inc..	3,631,253
National Properties Corporation.	3,404,124
Kahiki Foods, Inc..	3,325,999
Polyplastex United, Inc..	3,266,944
Biddeford and Saco Water Company	3,193,585
Reserve Petroleum Company (The).	3,182,712
Oakridge Energy, Inc..	3,177,000
Carc, Inc.	3,169,900
Hosoi Garden Mortuary, Inc.	3,140,326
Elk Associates Funding Corporation	3,128,704
Bison Instruments, Inc..	3,091,843
North American Scientific, Inc..	3,083,400
Best Universal Lock Co..	2,975,453
Hamburg Industries, Inc.	2,883,306
Cimetrix Incorporated	2,874,000
Central Coal & Coke Corporation.	2,871,772
Colorocs Information Technologies, Inc.	2,863,448
Eyemakers, Inc..	2,794,795
Capital Properties, Inc.	2,793,000
OPT-Sciences Corporation	2,730,742
Solid Controls, Inc.	2,699,053
Best, Inc., Frank E.	2,486,397

Pamet Systems, Inc..	2,473,816
Ojai Oil Company.	2,389,933
ENDOcare, Inc.	2,259,278
Buck Hill Falls Company	2,196,870
Beaver Coal Company, Limited.	2,149,796
Coal Creek Mining and Manufacturing Company	2,120,701
Barnstable Holding Co., Inc.	2,099,684
D.H. Marketing & Consulting, Inc.	2,033,402
Portsmouth Square, Inc..	1,960,718
Valley Water Systems, Inc.	1,930,179
Park-Lexington Company, Inc.	1,913,472
MLX Corp.	1,876,000
Holobeam, Inc.	1,856,218
Salient Systems, Inc..	1,766,236
Nova Technologies, Inc..	1,695,743
Westar Financial Services Incorporated.	1,672,241
Rockies Fund, Inc. (The)	1,658,348
California-Michigan Land and Water Company	1,637,030
Walker International Industries, Inc.	1,513,145
Belle Isle Net Profits Units	1,488,486
Calcasieu Real Estate & Oil Co., Inc.	1,479,172
Original Sixteen to One Mine, Inc.	1,468,737
Lake Charles Naval Stores Co., Inc..	1,421,435
Alterman Investment Fund, Inc..	1,337,175
T/F Purifiner, Inc.	1,329,073
ExperTelligence, Inc.	1,283,335
Limco Del Mar, Ltd..	1,269,944
Zap Power Systems	1,190,400
Tidelands Royalty Trust "B"	1,176,769
Mills Music Trust	1,175,543
NeuroCorp., Ltd..	1,079,193
Quigley Corporation (The)	1,056,442
Westbrook-Thompson Agency	1,056,354
California Orchard Company	1,006,185
Geo Petroleum, Inc..	1,005,946
Chesapeake Investors, Inc.	1,004,733
Danbury Industrial Corporation	1,002,957
Cuban Electric Company.	955,163
Asha Corporation.	941,628
Food Extrusion, Inc.	907,802
Louisiana Central Net Profits Units	902,150
Pro Tech Communications, Inc.	880,553
Superior Supplements, Inc..	857,398
Ammonia Hold, Inc..	841,357
Mexco Energy Corporation	834,073
Continental Investment Corporation.	827,924
Avoca, Incorporated	827,494
Samarnan Investment Corporation.	793,696
Sutter Basin Corporation, Ltd.	774,991
DK Investors, Inc.	721,045
Shepmyers Investment Company	719,567
PMD Investment Company	606,490
Covol Technologies, Inc..	597,730
Golden Cycle Gold Corporation	596,044
New York and Harlem Railroad Company.	576,666
Seven J Stock Farm, Inc..	561,000
Level Best Golf, Inc..	495,681
Spring Street Brewing Company, Inc. (6 mos.)	463,600
Gaming Venture Corp., U.S.A..	423,271
Chequemate International, Inc..	382,137
Virginia Hot Springs, Incorporated	308,928
Hendrick Ranch Royalties, Inc.	305,620
Aztec Land and Cattle Company, Limited	240,368

Conectisys Corporation	209,519
Cass County Iron Company	170,789
American Bio Medica Corporation	158,461
International Automated Systems, Inc.	106,109
Planet Entertainment Corporation	105,000
Medjet Inc.	86,702
Alden Lee Company, Inc..	76,716
Alydaar Software Corporation	69,475
St. Lawrence Seaway Corporation (The)	68,978
Terre Aux Boeufs Land Co., Inc.	39,118
Startech Environmental Corporation	29,431
Morris Run Coal Mining Company.	28,338
Citizens Growth Properties	17,539
Cable-Sat Systems, Inc..	11,246
American Tire Corporation	7,161

Over $10,000,000

Nebraska, First National of	485,183,000
First Citizens Bancorporation of South Carolina	76,665,000
Anchorage, The First National Bank of	76,237,000
Farmers & Merchants Bank of Long Beach	72,356,306
W.T.B. Financial Corporation	61,155,275
MidCity Financial Corporation	50,439,000
Mechanics Bank (The)	47,595,055
Amboy Bancorporation	46,720,000
FCFT, Inc.	38,008,000
Exchange Bank	35,935,000
Burke & Herbert Bank & Trust Company	26,104,578
Chemung Financial Corporation	22,468,113
Bar Harbor Bankshares	16,241,473
Adirondack Trust Company (The)	15,970,990
Hawaii National Bancshares, Inc.	15,372,384
Drovers Bancshares Corporation	15,264,000
InterCounty Bancshares, Inc.	15,009,000
Scripps Bank	14,475,000
BSM Bancorp	14,408,183
Lafayette Bancorporation	14,203,000
Colony Bankcorp, Inc.	13,366,546
IBT Bancorp, Inc.	12,505,371
Herkimer Trust Corporation, Inc.	12,019,000
Humboldt Bancorp	11,013,000
Talbot Bank of Easton, Maryland (The)	10,571,065
North Valley Bancorp	10,564,000
Slade's Ferry Bancorp	10,416,860
O.A.K. Financial Corporation	10,320,879
Borel Bank and Trust Company	10,051,201
Charter National Bancorp, Inc.	10,024,000

$10,000,000 - $5,000,000

First Guaranty Bank	9,827,000
VRB Bancorp	9,560,637
Northern Empire Bancshares	9,232,000
Marin, Bank of	9,143,172
United Security Bank, National Association	8,852,347
DNB Financial Corporation	8,702,837
Hamlin Bank and Trust Company	8,475,891
Heritage Bank of Commerce	7,879,000
Siuslaw Valley Bank	7,852,774
County Bank Corp	7,843,000
Tidewater, Bank of	7,680,770
East Carolina Bank (The)	7,372,669
American River Holdings	7,351,000
Iron and Glass Bancorp, Inc.	7,284,526
Plumas Bank	7,183,022
First Morris Bank	7,183,000
Ocean National Corporation	7,046,121
First Miami Bancorp, Inc.	6,989,836
Columbia Financial Corporation	6,936,692
Connecticut River Bancorp, Inc.	6,796,554
Factory Point Bancorp, Inc.	6,627,166
Minster State Bank	6,596,757
Benchmark Bankshares, Inc.	6,567,571
Four Oaks Bank & Trust Company	6,554,742
Fiduciary Trust Company International	6,161,817
Peninsula Bank of Commerce	6,148,688
Tehama Bank	5,917,295
Pontiac Bancorp, Inc.	5,877,917
Simi Valley Bank	5,843,955

Old Forge Bank	5,813,322
Petaluma, Bank of	5,737,000
Kish Bancorp, Inc.	5,726,189
Citizens National Bancorp, Inc.	5,670,761
Honat Bancorp, Inc.	5,662,996
Hollywood, The Bank of	5,456,000
Cardinal Bancorp, Inc.	5,433,585
Bay Commercial Services	5,369,000
EvergreenBank	5,252,000
Rancho Vista National Bank	5,195,417
Harford National Bank	5,125,301
Six Rivers National Bank	5,073,579

Under $5,000,000

Central Sierra Bank	4,801,951
Butte Community Bank	4,630,000
Ledyard National Bank	4,613,689
Akron, Bank of	4,583,242
Sonoma Valley Bank	4,567,201
First Star Bancorp, Inc.	4,472,709
Gloucester Bank & Trust Company	4,261,000
Wilton Bank (The)	4,257,133
Western Sierra Bancorp	4,256,072
Long Island Commercial Bank	4,211,894
Luzerne National Bank Corporation	4,075,000
Kerman State Bank	4,058,643
Delhi Bank Corp	4,019,343
Central Financial Corporation	3,884,135
Mauch Chunk Trust Company	3,871,625
Muncy Bank Financial, Inc.	3,622,264
Yosemite Bank	3,498,772
Verdugo Banking Company	3,470,125
Citizens Bancorp, Inc.	3,257,626
Pennsylvania State Bank	3,085,377
Investors Financial Corporation	3,084,915
Northern Lehigh Bancorp, Inc.	3,073,387
PSB Holding Corp	3,018,425
Oak Valley Community Bank	2,850,774
Community Independent Bank, Inc.	2,594,010
Redlands Centennial Bank	2,286,204
Merchants of Shenandoah Ban-Corp	2,112,186
Turbotville National Bancorp, Inc.	2,025,177
Union Bancorp of Evansville, Inc.	1,877,000
Lancaster National Bank (The)	1,776,140
North Coast Bank	1,763,017

This page intentionally left blank.

Over $100,000,000

Publix Super Markets, Inc.	3,354,129,408
Nebraska, First National of	1,179,007,800
Kohler Co.	946,500,000
Benjamin Moore & Co.	505,880,760
Ash Grove Cement Company	448,169,619
Bruno's, Inc.	424,337,917
Fisher Companies Inc.	416,366,091
Roseville Communications Company	380,128,320
Pennsylvania Manufacturers Corporation	375,528,431
Rand McNally	356,451,300
North Pittsburgh Systems, Inc.	353,440,000
Cowles Media Company	338,748,148
Anchorage, The First National Bank of	321,000,000
Farmers & Merchants Bank of Long Beach	302,921,500
Farmer Bros. Co.	283,182,858
Erie Family Life Insurance Company	262,237,500
Continental Investment Corporation	240,338,733
CT Communications, Inc.	237,660,160
Boswell (J.G.) Company	235,310,880
Kentucky River Coal Corporation	213,303,840
Watson Land Company	201,588,998
Pekin Life Insurance Company	198,000,000
Case, Pomeroy & Company, Inc.	191,884,126
North State Telephone Company	183,794,940
Fiduciary Trust Company International	178,442,479
Amboy Bancorporation	174,890,678
North Carolina Railroad Company	163,842,728
Central Steel and Wire Company	161,304,175
First Citizens Bancorporation of South Carolina	160,706,340
Alydaar Software Corporation	159,689,080
FCFT, Inc.	153,679,864
Mechanics Bank (The)	144,000,000
MidCity Financial Corporation	142,218,000
Nichols (J.C.) Company	140,719,600
Conbraco Industries, Inc.	124,727,550
South Chester Tube Company	122,148,000
VASCO Corp.	121,176,763
Preformed Line Products Company	120,364,992
Cimetrix Incorporated	119,964,670
Sterling Chemicals Holdings, Inc.	119,238,750
Hayward Industries, Inc.	111,647,983
Exchange Bank	110,758,680
Crowley Maritime Corporation	108,415,375
Finch, Pruyn & Company, Incorporated	107,925,902
Smith Investment Company	104,487,579
International Automated Systems, Inc.	102,506,175
Market America, Inc.	102,144,000

$100,000,000 - $50,000,000

Covol Technologies, Inc.	93,227,069
Food Extrusion, Inc.	90,003,755
Rochester & Pittsburgh Coal Company	89,465,584
Quigley Corporation (The)	89,385,377
W.T.B. Financial Corporation	88,517,520
Carolina Mills Inc.	80,008,005
Shenandoah Telecommunications Company	78,975,960
Kiewit Royalty Trust	78,958,950
SLH Corporation	77,869,248
Maui Land & Pineapple Company, Inc.	76,377,813
Nevada Manhattan Mining Incorporated	74,098,924
Magicworks Entertainment Incorporated	73,182,900

Chequemate International, Inc.	72,829,805
Real Silk Investments, Incorporated	72,460,520
Red Oak Hereford Farms, Inc.	71,240,000
Chemung Financial Corporation	69,419,169
Americold Corporation	69,036,716
Davey Tree Expert Company (The)	68,143,760
Burnham Corporation	65,629,594
A.D. Makepeace Company	64,639,200
Biochem International Inc.	63,732,638
Monarch Cement Company (The)	62,146,028
Burke & Herbert Bank & Trust Company	62,000,000
Hershey Creamery Company	61,987,845
Robroy Industries, Inc.	61,927,613
Bar Harbor Bankshares	61,856,532
Wailuku Agribusiness Co., Inc.	61,650,000
DHB Capital Group Inc.	60,642,541
NeuroCorp., Ltd.	59,859,497
Drovers Bancshares Corporation	58,290,485
E*Capital Corporation	58,099,030
Anderson-Tully Company	58,000,000
Power Test Investors Limited Partnership	56,877,678
Computer Services, Inc.	56,831,166
U.S. Plastic Lumber Corporation	53,926,252
Houlihan's Restaurant Group, Inc.	53,689,324
HomeCapital Investment Corporation	52,872,155
O.A.K. Financial Corporation	52,763,765
Lexcom Communications, Inc.	52,711,120
Spartan Mills	51,436,760
Computer Services, Inc.	50,632,920
York Water Company (The)	50,034,039

$49,999,999 - $25,000,000

LAACO, Ltd.	49,429,867
Seven-Up/RC Bottling Co. of Southern Calif., Inc.	49,350,000
New Ulm Telecom, Inc.	48,508,740
King Kullen Grocery Co., Inc.	46,058,400
Penn Fuel Gas, Inc.	45,925,312
American Bio Medica Corporation	43,764,211
Lafayette Bancorporation	43,722,363
PortaCom Wireless, Inc.	43,552,361
Finance Company of Pennsylvania	43,280,250
Ellensburg Telephone Company	43,164,954
BSM Bancorp	42,600,430
Superior Supplements, Inc.	42,000,000
InterCounty Bancshares, Inc.	41,581,053
Unidyne Corporation	40,495,460
Scripps Bank	40,296,000
T/F Purifiner, Inc.	40,266,932
VRB Bancorp	40,215,173
EMC Corporation	40,195,690
West Virginia-American Water Company	39,654,573
CVF Corp.	39,603,150
Dynamic Associates, Inc.	39,516,425
Planet Entertainment Corporation	39,304,220
Adirondack Trust Company (The)	38,726,820
North Valley Bancorp	38,297,448
IBT Bancorp, Inc.	37,680,000
Keller Manufacturing Company, Inc.	37,262,819
Connectivity Technologies Inc.	37,176,371
Stonecutter Mills Corporation	37,059,000
United Security Bank, National Association	36,041,236
Waste Recovery, Inc.	35,683,569

Warwick Valley Telephone Co.	35,596,390
MLX Corp.	34,688,500
Hamlin Bank and Trust Company	34,600,044
Rhinelander Telecommunications, Inc.	34,171,747
Personal Computer Products, Inc.	33,824,955
Alden Lee Company, Inc.	33,705,000
First Real Estate Investment Trust of New Jersey	33,535,442
Fremont Corporation	33,474,424
Arthur Treacher's, Inc.	33,355,860
Adrian Steel Company	32,834,240
Ragar Corp.	32,781,569
Borel Bank and Trust Company	32,560,157
D.H. Marketing & Consulting, Inc.	32,077,293
Colony Bankcorp, Inc.	31,874,524
Cable-Sat Systems, Inc.	31,671,640
Genetic Vectors, Inc.	31,585,059
Investment Properties Associates	31,160,000
Mercom, Inc.	31,115,890
Information Analysis Incorporated	31,104,839
Bresler & Reiner, Inc.	30,719,183
Horizon Telcom, Inc.	30,516,156
Geo Petroleum, Inc.	30,413,296
Talbot Bank of Easton, Maryland (The)	29,952,611
Woodbury Telephone Company (The)	29,802,896
Humboldt Bancorp	29,626,107
Tidewater, Bank of	29,106,872
Fifty Associates	29,098,140
Fall River Gas Company	28,933,808
BFC Financial Corporation	28,514,105
First Morris Bank	27,993,000
Continental Health Affiliates, Inc.	27,858,648
Boston Sand & Gravel Company	27,110,070
Iron and Glass Bancorp, Inc.	27,072,000
Allstar Inns, Inc.	26,860,598
Heritage Bank of Commerce	26,610,920
First Guaranty Bank	26,501,077
Annie's Homegrown, Inc.	26,212,806
SGI International	26,206,802
Siuslaw Valley Bank	26,100,000
Decker Manufacturing Corporation	25,992,278
Medjet Inc.	25,978,502
Exolon-ESK Company	25,867,192
Zions Cooperative Mercantile Institution	25,692,413
Keweenaw Land Association, Limited	25,336,656
Blue Fish Clothing, Inc.	25,295,600
Cuban Electric Company	25,200,077
Addvantage Media Group, Inc.	25,044,859
Benchmark Bankshares, Inc.	25,010,706

$24,999,999 - $10,000,000

Alaska Power & Telephone Company	24,976,793
Asha Corporation	24,766,760
Salient Systems, Inc.	24,310,901
Hawaii National Bancshares, Inc.	24,174,000
AMCOR Capital Corporation	23,888,926
Investors Heritage Life Insurance Company	23,865,211
County Bank Corp	23,729,440
Peckham Industries, Inc.	23,716,000
Hanover Foods Corporation	23,627,835
Minster State Bank	23,313,600
Marin, Bank of	23,150,100
American Tire Corporation	23,043,852

Slade's Ferry Bancorp	23,010,422
AFA Protective Systems, Inc.	22,425,004
Spring Street Brewing Company, Inc.	22,310,030
Northern Empire Bancshares	22,286,350
Startech Environmental Corporation	21,938,903
Bulova Corporation	21,845,250
Colorado Gaming & Entertainment Co.	21,840,274
Spring Street Brewing Company, Inc.	21,798,252
Ammonia Hold, Inc.	21,734,102
New York and Harlem Railroad Company	21,640,125
Blue Diamond Coal Company	21,510,060
DNB Financial Corporation	21,434,082
Columbia Financial Corporation	21,411,743
Kish Bancorp, Inc.	21,198,967
First of Michigan Capital Corporation	21,068,264
Strategia Corporation	20,512,474
Louisville Bedding Company	20,504,104
First Republic Corporation of America (The)	20,168,070
Four Oaks Bank & Trust Company	20,110,776
Golden Cycle Gold Corporation	19,635,525
Florafax International, Inc.	19,457,053
Wisconsin Fuel & Light Company	19,176,690
Cardinal Bancorp, Inc.	19,057,500
Tehama Bank	18,928,545
Market Guide, Inc.	18,847,103
Portland Brewing Company	18,674,487
East Carolina Bank (The)	18,395,958
Olokele Sugar Company, Limited	18,357,878
ENDOcare, Inc.	18,346,702
Factory Point Bancorp, Inc.	18,298,425
Goodheart-Willcox Company, Inc. (The)	18,271,875
Peninsula Bank of Commerce	18,114,948
Kerman State Bank	18,019,525
Meritage Hospitality Group Inc.	17,679,085
Pardee Resources Company	17,590,101
Profit Financial Corporation	17,503,392
Meteor Industries, Inc.	16,749,298
Tower Properties Company	16,405,920
Mendocino Brewing Company, Inc.	16,394,887
Mutual Savings Life Insurance Company	16,354,380
Clinicor, Inc.	16,345,600
Plumas Bank	16,335,250
Al-Zar, Ltd.	16,250,000
Sterling Sugars, Inc.	16,250,000
Du Art Film Laboratories, Inc.	16,179,064
Honat Bancorp, Inc.	16,113,500
Lasermedics, Inc.	16,098,117
CBR Brewing Company, Inc.	16,000,026
Queen City Investments, Inc.	15,933,775
Herkimer Trust Corporation, Inc.	15,750,000
Mauch Chunk Trust Company	15,685,536
Pontiac Bancorp, Inc.	15,613,000
DeltaPoint, Inc.	15,534,625
Citizens National Bancorp, Inc.	15,468,190
Century Realty Trust	15,440,832
Nova Technologies, Inc.	15,339,314
Alterman Investment Fund, Inc.	15,251,208
Old Forge Bank	15,232,587
Ledyard National Bank	14,917,500
Charter National Bancorp, Inc.	14,869,346
Harford National Bank	14,777,914
Auric Corporation	14,623,400
United Vanguard Homes, Inc.	14,622,664

Tremont Advisors, Inc..	14,566,714
Mt. Bachelor, Inc.	14,490,000
American River Holdings	14,472,716
Market Guide, Inc.	14,124,558
Continental Resources, Inc.	14,085,967
Citizens Bancorp, Inc.	14,082,244
Call Now, Inc.	14,061,278
RF Industries, LTD.	13,890,955
Conectisys Corporation	13,878,645
Blue Ridge Real Estate Company	13,527,095
Portsmouth Square, Inc.	13,500,000
Ogden Telephone Company	13,274,942
Sea Pines Associates, Inc.	13,267,800
Lanxide Corporation	13,255,950
Original Sixteen to One Mine, Inc.	13,140,244
Bozzuto's Inc.	12,917,650
Butte Community Bank	12,766,054
Leslie Building Products, Inc.	12,662,657
Samarnan Investment Corporation.	12,618,564
Harriet & Henderson Yarns, Inc..	12,341,260
Chesapeake Investors, Inc..	12,297,870
Coal Creek Mining and Manufacturing Company	12,149,880
PMD Investment Company	12,121,199
Pennichuck Corporation	12,114,619
Best Lock Corporation	12,065,400
Lady Baltimore Foods, Inc.	12,013,553
TIF Instruments, Inc..	11,804,698
Advantage Marketing Systems, Inc.	11,788,926
Beaver Coal Company, Limited	11,692,660
Delhi Bank Corp.	11,632,608
Savers Life Insurance Company	11,543,370
Oakridge Energy, Inc.	11,541,708
Shepmyers Investment Company	11,523,570
Best Universal Lock Co..	11,508,384
NCC Industries, Inc..	11,463,789
Batterymarch Trust (The)	11,443,500
Mills Music Trust.	11,386,192
Ocean National Corporation	11,148,450
Central Coal & Coke Corporation	11,052,322
Sonoma Valley Bank.	10,927,082
Snow Summit Ski Corporation.	10,904,000
Zap Power Systems	10,901,625
Connecticut River Bancorp, Inc..	10,894,303
Bay Commercial Services	10,767,200
Muncy Bank Financial, Inc.	10,761,395
Westar Financial Services Incorporated	10,728,750
Guaranty Corporation.	10,650,500
Best, Inc., Frank E..	10,627,103
Williams Industries, Incorporated	10,613,190
Colorocs Information Technologies, Inc.	10,606,305
Kentucky Investors, Inc..	10,574,213
Petaluma, Bank of	10,529,313
Reuter Manufacturing, Inc..	10,426,065
Oakridge Energy, Inc..	10,166,718
DK Investors, Inc.	10,134,224
Oak Tree Medical Systems ,Inc.	10,116,676

$9,999,999 - $5,000,000

Temco Service Industries, Inc.	9,943,236
Stein Industries, Inc.	9,934,716
Corning Natural Gas Corporation	9,890,000
Monroe Title Insurance Corporation	9,837,787

Long Island Commercial Bank	9,798,401
Ravens Metal Products, Inc.	9,717,625
Simi Valley Bank	9,710,981
Valley Fair Corporation (The)	9,567,558
Hollywood, The Bank of	9,407,925
American Industrial Loan Association.	9,403,540
Western Sierra Bancorp.	9,364,139
Sims-Agricultural Products Company	9,299,700
Garden City Company	9,223,543
National Properties Corporation	9,209,523
Central Sierra Bank.	9,198,349
Akron, Bank of	9,000,000
Lexington Precision Corporation	8,867,115
Home-Stake Royalty Corporation (The)	8,592,864
Home-Stake Oil & Gas Company (The)	8,592,864
American Public Life Insurance Company	8,573,615
St. Louis Steel Casting Inc..	8,499,413
Level Best Golf, Inc.	8,390,729
Capital Properties, Inc.	8,370,000
EvergreenBank	8,367,168
Pennsylvania State Bank	8,309,542
Pinnacle Data Systems, Inc.	8,227,879
Gloucester Bank & Trust Company	8,155,041
Community Service Communications, Inc..	8,053,134
Yosemite Bank	8,010,696
Irex Corporation	7,998,254
First Star Bancorp, Inc..	7,976,592
Main Street Athletic Clubs, Inc.	7,950,504
Luzerne National Bank Corporation	7,950,000
Six Rivers National Bank.	7,907,760
Hilliard Corporation (The)	7,874,404
Sadlier, Inc., William H.	7,770,508
Rancho Vista National Bank	7,732,576
Frederick Trading Company	7,709,928
Cherokee Equity Corporation.	7,652,108
Health International, Inc.	7,581,384
Latshaw Enterprises, Inc..	7,516,125
Park-Lexington Company, Inc..	7,452,217
Merchants of Shenandoah Ban-Corp	7,425,243
Hytek Microsystems, Inc..	7,332,728
Scioto Downs, Inc.	7,298,146
Tidelands Royalty Trust "B"	7,278,469
Bryan Steam Corporation.	7,268,792
Gaming Venture Corp., U.S.A.	7,258,763
Belle Isle Net Profits Units	7,168,750
Reinhold Industries, Inc..	7,116,283
Investors Financial Corporation	7,050,000
Verdugo Banking Company	6,978,444
Westmoreland Coal Company	6,965,328
Pro Tech Communications, Inc.	6,937,000
B.B. Walker Company	6,906,136
Avoca, Incorporated.	6,851,625
Wilton Bank (The)	6,844,200
Burke-Parsons-Bowlby Corporation	6,756,016
RWC, Inc..	6,755,592
Workforce Systems Corp..	6,657,299
Eyemakers, Inc..	6,543,805
Reinhold Industries Inc..	6,500,000
Birmingham Utilities, Inc.	6,442,082
Pay-O-Matic Corp..	6,416,360
Mexco Energy Corporation.	6,404,531
Oak Valley Community Bank.	6,391,488
Hammett (J.L.) Co.	6,390,996

Hosoi Garden Mortuary, Inc.	6,368,005
Audio Communications Network, Inc.	6,350,308
Shopsmith, Inc.	6,302,245
Westwood Group, Inc. (The)	6,276,125
Zimmerman Sign Company	6,250,312
Thanksgiving Coffee Company, Inc.	6,185,195
Amelco Corporation	6,133,124
Elk Associates Funding Corporation	6,097,100
Community Independent Bank, Inc.	5,920,879
Fair Grounds Corporation	5,857,250
Central Financial Corporation	5,841,079
Louisiana Central Net Profits Units	5,841,030
Northern Lehigh Bancorp, Inc.	5,790,420
Pennsylvania Warehousing and Safe Deposit Company	5,622,500
Chromaline Corporation	5,606,983
PSB Holding Corp	5,570,320
Hydraulic Press Brick Company	5,511,631
Pamet Systems, Inc.	5,507,895
Naturade, Inc.	5,497,171
Calcasieu Real Estate & Oil Co., Inc.	5,492,498
Westwood Incorporated	5,419,425
Torrington Water Company (The)	5,418,000
Tork, Inc.	5,366,655
Homasote Company	5,361,577
Dover Investments Corporation	5,328,378
Reo Plastics, Inc.	5,325,000
Reserve Petroleum Company (The)	5,264,969
Biddeford and Saco Water Company	5,146,044
Broughton Foods Company	5,115,245
Seven J Stock Farm, Inc.	5,078,500
Wichita National Life Insurance Company	5,000,000

Under $5,000,000

Redlands Centennial Bank	4,995,323
Turbotville National Bancorp, Inc.	4,972,400
First Miami Bancorp, Inc.	4,936,000
Carco Electronics	4,909,633
North American Scientific, Inc.	4,832,786
Reynolds, Smith and Hills, Inc.	4,777,500
Sportsman's Guide, Inc. (The)	4,667,200
Radio Frequency Company, Inc.	4,552,875
ZEVEX International, Inc.	4,487,148
Mod-U-Kraf Homes, Inc.	4,334,657
ExperTelligence, Inc.	4,326,793
Indians, Inc.	4,240,000
Randall Bearings, Inc.	4,208,652
Wundies Industries, Inc.	4,164,336
Technology 80 Inc.	4,022,195
Mt. Carmel Public Utility Co.	4,000,000
Citizens' Electric Company	3,973,883
Aztec Land and Cattle Company, Limited	3,882,384
Michigan Rivet Corporation	3,831,150
Paradise, Inc.	3,763,983
Chatham Corporation	3,727,100
Southern Webbing Mills, Inc.	3,679,506
Network Data Processing Corporation	3,667,500
CMP Industries, Inc.	3,567,300
Union Bancorp of Evansville, Inc.	3,552,000
Detroit Legal News Company	3,522,678
Limco Del Mar, Ltd.	3,514,500
Logan Clay Products Company	3,422,349
National Stock Yards Company	3,358,124

Crown City Plating Co.	3,197,835
Holobeam, Inc.	3,135,190
Lab-Volt Systems, Inc.	3,129,354
InterUnion Financial Corporation	3,116,511
Bison Instruments, Inc.	3,114,615
OPT-Sciences Corporation	3,104,460
Westbrook-Thompson Agency	2,982,038
Chambersburg Engineering Company	2,894,408
Kahiki Foods, Inc.	2,891,103
York Corrugating Co.	2,869,120
Root Company, The A.I.	2,835,000
Carc, Inc.	2,814,000
Ojai Oil Company	2,787,599
Cloverleaf Kennel Club	2,784,207
Athanor Group, Inc.	2,751,432
Old Fashion Foods, Inc.	2,732,044
Unity First Acquisition Corp.	2,731,250
Life Insurance Company of Alabama	2,686,139
Rockies Fund, Inc. (The)	2,561,024
North Coast Bank	2,547,005
Indiana Natural Gas Corporation	2,499,120
Auto-Graphics, Inc.	2,495,876
Lancaster National Bank (The)	2,475,000
Christian Brothers, Inc.	2,412,465
Pacific Northwest Development Corporation	2,186,665
Acap Corporation	2,103,452
Western Lime Corporation	2,087,200
Buck Hill Falls Company	2,027,454
Naylor Pipe Company	1,991,237
Valley Water Systems, Inc.	1,896,950
Adams (R.P.) Company, Inc.	1,896,586
New Orleans Cold Storage and Warehouse Co. Ltd	1,849,000
Northfield Precision Instrument Corporation	1,815,337
Virginia Hot Springs, Incorporated	1,756,170
Bismarck Hotel Company	1,698,880
Components Specialties, Inc.	1,652,960
Solid Controls, Inc.	1,586,634
Hunter Manufacturing Corp.	1,564,179
Connohio, Inc.	1,536,430
Citizens Growth Properties	1,437,423
Lake Charles Naval Stores Co., Inc.	1,405,440
Polyplastex United, Inc.	1,381,283
Danbury Industrial Corporation	1,370,065
Troy Mills, Inc.	1,333,852
California-Michigan Land and Water Company	1,298,400
Hendrick Ranch Royalties, Inc.	1,287,796
Cable Link, Inc.	1,258,932
California Orchard Company	1,237,644
Pocono Hotels Corporation	1,089,132
Barnstable Holding Co., Inc.	1,074,000
Henry County Plywood Corporation	1,069,002
Universal Metals & Machinery, Inc.	1,054,620
Ainslie Corporation	1,001,228
St. Lawrence Seaway Corporation (The)	984,338
UTZ Engineering, Inc.	980,000
Hamburg Industries, Inc.	921,803
Cass County Iron Company	907,556
North Coast Life Insurance Co.	825,318
TNR Technical, Inc.	787,311
Viskon-Aire Corporation	774,935
Phil-Good Products Incorporated	697,172
Standard Electronics, Inc.	586,232
Transnational Industries, Inc.	486,330

Walker International Industries, Inc.	467,712
M.H. Rhodes, Inc..	452,473
Morris Run Coal Mining Company	439,600
Terre Aux Boeufs Land Co., Inc.	437,500
Columbian Rope Company	388,101
Sutter Basin Corporation, Ltd..	128,774

This page intentionally left blank.

Over 20%	
Shopsmith, Inc..	1035.50
Florafax International, Inc.	305.47
Addvantage Media Group, Inc..	208.95
Advantage Marketing Systems, Inc.	184.15
Tidelands Royalty Trust "B"	151.28
Profit Financial Corporation	144.87
Market America, Inc.	143.42
Pamet Systems, Inc..	136.36
Power Test Investors Limited Partnership	112.93
HomeCapital Investment Corporation	104.07
Main Street Athletic Clubs, Inc..	90.43
Sportsman's Guide, Inc. (The)	85.82
Watson Land Company	82.61
Hytek Microsystems, Inc.	80.78
Continental Health Affiliates, Inc..	76.84
Holobeam, Inc.	65.91
D.H. Marketing & Consulting, Inc.	60.89
North Carolina Railroad Company	57.61
Beaver Coal Company, Limited	57.34
Rockies Fund, Inc. (The)	56.24
Portsmouth Square, Inc..	56.17
Indians, Inc.	54.49
RWC, Inc.	47.75
Health International, Inc.	46.14
Sea Pines Associates, Inc..	44.07
Cowles Media Company	43.79
Biochem International Inc.	41.95
Magicworks Entertainment Incorporated	41.08
Columbian Rope Company	38.33
Fifty Associates	37.84
Call Now, Inc.	37.60
ExperTelligence, Inc.	34.75
Auric Corporation	33.27
North American Scientific, Inc.	30.39
Tremont Advisors, Inc.	29.87
Network Data Processing Corporation	29.28
Calcasieu Real Estate & Oil Co., Inc.	28.14
Broughton Foods Company	26.99
Boston Sand & Gravel Company	26.50
Gaming Venture Corp., U.S.A.	26.29
Irex Corporation	26.28
Chambersburg Engineering Company.	25.52
Components Specialties, Inc.	25.37
Stein Industries, Inc..	25.29
Exolon-ESK Company	24.05
Athanor Group, Inc..	23.70
Siuslaw Valley Bank.	23.66
Kentucky River Coal Corporation.	23.57
Eyemakers, Inc.	23.51
Hydraulic Press Brick Company	23.43
Cloverleaf Kennel Club	23.42
Monarch Cement Company (The).	23.28
Chromaline Corporation.	22.80
First Guaranty Bank	22.80
North Pittsburgh Systems, Inc.	21.96
Audio Communications Network, Inc.	21.87
Horizon Telcom, Inc.	21.58
Birmingham Utilities, Inc..	21.10
Keller Manufacturing Company, Inc.	20.87
Root Company, The A.I.	20.86
Home-Stake Oil & Gas Company (The)	20.84

Monroe Title Insurance Corporation	20.51
Lake Charles Naval Stores Co., Inc..	20.20
Goodheart-Willcox Company, Inc. (The)	20.07

20 - 10%	
Connohio, Inc..	19.93
Continental Resources, Inc.	19.76
Avoca, Incorporated	19.75
Warwick Valley Telephone Co.	19.68
American Industrial Loan Association	19.64
Woodbury Telephone Company (The)	19.51
Louisville Bedding Company	19.24
United Security Bank, National Association	18.96
Blue Diamond Coal Company.	18.93
Bar Harbor Bankshares	18.86
Benjamin Moore & Co.	18.82
Burke & Herbert Bank & Trust Company.	18.67
Wundies Industries, Inc..	18.44
North Valley Bancorp	18.30
Benchmark Bankshares, Inc.	18.21
Ocean National Corporation.	18.14
Butte Community Bank	18.10
Home-Stake Royalty Corporation (The)	17.98
BFC Financial Corporation	17.90
E*Capital Corporation.	17.81
RF Industries, LTD	17.77
Davey Tree Expert Company (The).	17.69
Northern Empire Bancshares	17.52
Luzerne National Bank Corporation	17.31
VRB Bancorp	17.27
North State Telephone Company	16.98
Michigan Rivet Corporation.	16.89
Kish Bancorp, Inc..	16.83
Naturade, Inc.	16.80
FCFT, Inc.	16.77
Preformed Line Products Company	16.47
Hilliard Corporation (The)	16.44
Sonoma Valley Bank	16.36
Humboldt Bancorp	16.29
Oak Tree Medical Systems ,Inc..	16.28
Amboy Bancorporation	16.26
Ash Grove Cement Company	16.23
Technology 80 Inc.	16.21
Fiduciary Trust Company International	16.10
Tidewater, Bank of	16.09
Smith Investment Company	15.93
County Bank Corp.	15.86
Publix Super Markets, Inc.	15.76
IBT Bancorp, Inc.	15.67
Wilton Bank (The).	15.62
First Citizens Bancorporation of South Carolina	15.49
Ojai Oil Company	15.41
Latshaw Enterprises, Inc.	15.41
Nebraska, First National of	15.30
Lexcom Communications, Inc.	15.29
New Ulm Telecom, Inc.	15.26
Minster State Bank	15.25
AMCOR Capital Corporation	15.23
Best, Inc., Frank E.	15.17
DNB Financial Corporation	15.16
Meteor Industries, Inc..	15.06
Connecticut River Bancorp, Inc.	14.98

Rhinelander Telecommunications, Inc.	10.05
Reo Plastics, Inc.	10.01

10 - 0%

Penn Fuel Gas, Inc.	9.84
Union Bancorp of Evansville, Inc.	9.82
Pennichuck Corporation	9.74
Cherokee Equity Corporation	9.71
East Carolina Bank (The)	9.64
Finch, Pruyn & Company, Incorporated	9.55
CBR Brewing Company, Inc.	9.50
Conbraco Industries, Inc.	9.45
Anchorage, The First National Bank of	9.44
Case, Pomeroy & Company, Inc.	9.43
Western Lime Corporation	9.37
Auto-Graphics, Inc.	9.36
Pardee Resources Company	9.35
Real Silk Investments, Incorporated	9.34
Hayward Industries, Inc.	9.32
Sims-Agricultural Products Company	9.28
Citizens' Electric Company	9.15
Mexco Energy Corporation	9.14
Bryan Steam Corporation	9.08
Farmers & Merchants Bank of Long Beach	9.06
Rand McNally	9.03
Crowley Maritime Corporation	9.00
Pocono Hotels Corporation	8.96
Golden Cycle Gold Corporation	8.92
Yosemite Bank	8.87
Olokele Sugar Company, Limited	8.80
Hollywood, The Bank of	8.66
Hosoi Garden Mortuary, Inc.	8.52
Kohler Co.	8.48
Heritage Bank of Commerce	8.40
Valley Water Systems, Inc.	8.40
National Properties Corporation	8.32
Hershey Creamery Company	8.29
Robroy Industries, Inc.	8.25
Homasote Company	8.16
King Kullen Grocery Co., Inc.	8.14
Elk Associates Funding Corporation	8.07
South Chester Tube Company	8.02
UTZ Engineering, Inc.	8.00
Fremont Corporation	8.00
Ledyard National Bank	7.95
Market Guide, Inc.	7.94
AFA Protective Systems, Inc.	7.80
Hamburg Industries, Inc.	7.76
Carolina Mills Inc.	7.72
Fair Grounds Corporation	7.70
Leslie Building Products, Inc.	7.63
EvergreenBank	7.62
Cass County Iron Company	7.61
Park-Lexington Company, Inc.	7.43
TNR Technical, Inc.	7.43
Keweenaw Land Association, Limited	7.37
Merchants of Shenandoah Ban-Corp.	7.32
Central Coal & Coke Corporation	7.27
Houlihan's Restaurant Group, Inc.	7.14
American Public Life Insurance Company	7.13
Tower Properties Company	6.97
Biddeford and Saco Water Company	6.83

CMP Industries, Inc.	6.80
Naylor Pipe Company	6.76
Sadlier, Inc., William H.	6.71
Walker International Industries, Inc.	6.69
York Corrugating Co.	6.63
LAACO, Ltd.	6.35
Hunter Manufacturing Corp.	6.30
Lab-Volt Systems, Inc.	6.05
Tork, Inc.	5.91
First of Michigan Capital Corporation	5.91
Lady Baltimore Foods, Inc.	5.89
Savers Life Insurance Company	5.82
Ravens Metal Products, Inc.	5.80
Life Insurance Company of Alabama	5.70
Chesapeake Investors, Inc.	5.62
Rochester & Pittsburgh Coal Company	5.44
Mt. Carmel Public Utility Co.	5.43
Alterman Investment Fund, Inc.	5.25
Mutual Savings Life Insurance Company	5.11
Waste Recovery, Inc.	5.04
Seven J Stock Farm, Inc.	4.97
Hendrick Ranch Royalties, Inc.	4.89
Oakridge Energy, Inc.	4.77
Kentucky Investors, Inc.	4.70
Amelco Corporation	4.68
First Miami Bancorp, Inc.	4.59
Pinnacle Data Systems, Inc.	4.33
Snow Summit Ski Corporation	4.30
New York and Harlem Railroad Company	4.23
InterUnion Financial Corporation	4.21
Investors Heritage Life Insurance Company	4.20
Boswell (J.G.) Company	4.06
Bozzuto's Inc.	4.00
Temco Service Industries, Inc.	3.91
Wichita National Life Insurance Company	3.90
Shepmyers Investment Company	3.86
Samarnan Investment Corporation	3.85
A.D. Makepeace Company	3.84
Mod-U-Kraf Homes, Inc.	3.84
Herkimer Trust Corporation, Inc.	3.74
Zions Cooperative Mercantile Institution	3.57
DK Investors, Inc.	3.54
Cuban Electric Company	3.39
Logan Clay Products Company	3.26
Stonecutter Mills Corporation	3.25
Viskon-Aire Corporation	3.17
Cable Link, Inc.	2.91
Pay-O-Matic Corp.	2.91
Connectivity Technologies Inc.	2.86
Danbury Industrial Corporation	2.64
Hawaii National Bancshares, Inc.	2.59
Capital Properties, Inc.	2.51
Virginia Hot Springs, Incorporated	2.46
Thanksgiving Coffee Company, Inc.	2.42
Frederick Trading Company	2.19
Reynolds, Smith and Hills, Inc.	1.97
Solid Controls, Inc.	1.96
Terre Aux Boeufs Land Co., Inc.	1.81
Troy Mills, Inc.	1.75
MLX Corp.	1.55
Chatham Corporation	1.47
National Stock Yards Company	1.34
Old Fashion Foods, Inc.	1.19

Hanover Foods Corporation	0.97
Standard Electronics, Inc.	0.89
Ammonia Hold, Inc.	0.85
Morris Run Coal Mining Company	0.75
Henry County Plywood Corporation	0.58
Blue Ridge Real Estate Company	0.45
TIF Instruments, Inc.	0.29
Valley Fair Corporation (The)	0.01

Under 0%

Pro Tech Communications, Inc.	-0.07
Citizens Growth Properties	-0.60
Peckham Industries, Inc.	-0.73
Dover Investments Corporation	-0.90
Maui Land & Pineapple Company, Inc.	-1.28
Bison Instruments, Inc.	-1.51
Blue Fish Clothing, Inc.	-1.56
CVF Corp.	-1.73
Pacific Northwest Development Corporation	-2.54
Mendocino Brewing Company, Inc.	-2.84
Adams (R.P.) Company, Inc.	-3.29
Carco Electronics	-3.30
Universal Metals & Machinery, Inc.	-5.11
Salient Systems, Inc.	-5.24
Hammett (J.L.) Co.	-5.35
Portland Brewing Company	-5.42
St. Lawrence Seaway Corporation (The)	-6.09
First Republic Corporation of America (The)	-6.61
M.H. Rhodes, Inc.	-7.03
Scioto Downs, Inc.	-7.11
Christian Brothers, Inc.	-7.32
Information Analysis Incorporated	-7.94
Westwood Incorporated	-7.99
Randall Bearings, Inc.	-9.01
Reinhold Industries Inc.	-9.21
Kahiki Foods, Inc.	-10.07
Buck Hill Falls Company	-12.88
SLH Corporation	-13.09
Dynamic Associates, Inc.	-13.77
Spartan Mills	-14.22
Crown City Plating Co.	-14.70
Geo Petroleum, Inc.	-15.02
Spring Street Brewing Company, Inc.	-15.45
Harriet & Henderson Yarns, Inc.	-15.77
Sutter Basin Corporation, Ltd.	-21.56
Original Sixteen to One Mine, Inc.	-24.28
VASCO Corp.	-25.68
Pennsylvania Manufacturers Corporation	-26.14
Workforce Systems Corp.	-26.41
Southern Webbing Mills, Inc.	-27.93
Alden Lee Company, Inc.	-35.52
Nevada Manhattan Mining Incorporated	-35.70
DHB Capital Group Inc.	-39.17
NCC Industries, Inc.	-39.23
Cimetrix Incorporated	-41.37
Strategia Corporation	-43.19
B.B. Walker Company	-61.81
NeuroCorp., Ltd.	-69.63
Meritage Hospitality Group Inc.	-75.86
Asha Corporation	-79.96
Annie's Homegrown, Inc.	-87.66
Quigley Corporation (The)	-90.04

Lasermedics, Inc.	-95.03
Cable-Sat Systems, Inc.	-109.67
U.S. Plastic Lumber Corporation	-111.88
American Tire Corporation	-139.10
Nova Technologies, Inc.	-158.40
Conectisys Corporation	-176.37
Clinicor, Inc.	-185.74
DeltaPoint, Inc.	-215.95
Colorocs Information Technologies, Inc.	-303.50
International Automated Systems, Inc.	-429.68
ENDOcare, Inc.	-468.56
Zap Power Systems	-945.95

Under 10	
Columbian Rope Company	0.23
Root Company, The A.I.	1.20
Western Lime Corporation	1.33
Allstar Inns, Inc.	1.53
Wundies Industries, Inc.	1.64
Lake Charles Naval Stores Co., Inc.	2.06
Broughton Foods Company	2.10
Shopsmith, Inc.	2.10
Reuter Manufacturing, Inc.	2.14
Sportsman's Guide, Inc. (The)	2.20
First Miami Bancorp, Inc.	2.27
Ainslie Corporation	2.34
Sea Pines Associates, Inc.	2.46
Boston Sand & Gravel Company	2.47
Rockies Fund, Inc. (The)	2.50
RWC, Inc.	2.51
Michigan Rivet Corporation	2.87
Transnational Industries, Inc.	2.94
Bulova Corporation	3.13
Pocono Hotels Corporation	3.20
Westbrook-Thompson Agency	3.23
Horizon Telcom, Inc.	3.26
Connohio, Inc.	3.27
Monroe Title Insurance Corporation	3.33
Indians, Inc.	3.33
New Orleans Cold Storage and Warehouse Company Ltd.	3.42
Best Lock Corporation	3.52
Hydraulic Press Brick Company	3.53
Chambersburg Engineering Company	3.53
Williams Industries, Incorporated	3.58
Best, Inc., Frank E.	3.63
Latshaw Enterprises, Inc.	3.66
Cherokee Equity Corporation	3.77
Auric Corporation	3.80
Best Universal Lock Co.	3.95
Hilliard Corporation (The)	4.02
Hytek Microsystems, Inc.	4.03
North Coast Life Insurance Co.	4.05
Naylor Pipe Company	4.09
Blue Diamond Coal Company	4.10
BFC Financial Corporation	4.11
Guaranty Corporation	4.18
Bresler & Reiner, Inc.	4.23
Exolon-ESK Company	4.30
Irex Corporation	4.32
Acap Corporation	4.35
Paradise, Inc.	4.45
UTZ Engineering, Inc.	4.55
Indiana Natural Gas Corporation	4.57
Louisville Bedding Company	4.61
Call Now, Inc.	4.68
Batterymarch Trust (The)	4.73
Detroit Legal News Company	4.74
Components Specialties, Inc.	4.76
Smith Investment Company	4.76
Network Data Processing Corporation	4.78
Barnstable Holding Co., Inc.	4.78
Belle Isle Net Profits Units	4.81
Ocean National Corporation	4.91
California-Michigan Land and Water Company	5.01
Nichols (J.C.) Company	5.16

Hunter Manufacturing Corp.	5.16
E*Capital Corporation	5.16
Lancaster National Bank (The)	5.19
Athanor Group, Inc.	5.19
Continental Resources, Inc.	5.22
Limco Del Mar, Ltd.	5.26
Polyplastex United, Inc.	5.32
West Virginia-American Water Company	5.43
Charter National Bancorp, Inc.	5.44
Zimmerman Sign Company	5.44
Phil-Good Products Incorporated	5.59
Union Bancorp of Evansville, Inc.	5.68
Profit Financial Corporation	5.70
TNR Technical, Inc.	5.77
Northfield Precision Instrument Corporation	5.83
Stein Industries, Inc.	5.88
Monarch Cement Company (The)	5.90
St. Louis Steel Casting Inc.	5.97
Home-Stake Royalty Corporation (The)	5.98
Home-Stake Oil & Gas Company (The)	5.98
Pennsylvania Warehousing and Safe Deposit Company	6.02
W.T.B. Financial Corporation	6.06
Burke & Herbert Bank & Trust Company	6.13
Finch, Pruyn & Company, Incorporated	6.20
Crowley Maritime Corporation	6.22
Bryan Steam Corporation	6.32
Pioneer Metals, Inc.	6.39
Finance Company of Pennsylvania	6.43
Louisiana Central Net Profits Units	6.47
Investment Properties Associates	6.48
Walker International Industries, Inc.	6.48
Elk Associates Funding Corporation	6.51
York Corrugating Co.	6.53
Technology 80 Inc.	6.56
Old Forge Bank	6.62
Reserve Petroleum Company (The)	6.68
Fair Grounds Corporation	6.68
Pontiac Bancorp, Inc.	6.71
Seven-Up/RC Bottling Co. of Southern Calif., Inc.	6.71
Tidelands Royalty Trust "B"	6.73
Northern Lehigh Bancorp, Inc.	6.75
PSB Holding Corp	6.75
Florafax International, Inc.	6.77
Wilton Bank (The)	6.77
Burke-Parsons-Bowlby Corporation	6.82
Akron, Bank of.	6.82
Lab-Volt Systems, Inc.	6.82
Calcasieu Real Estate & Oil Co., Inc.	6.88
Connecticut River Bancorp, Inc.	6.93
Adirondack Trust Company (The)	6.99
Central Financial Corporation	7.05
Turbotville National Bancorp, Inc.	7.14
Olokele Sugar Company, Limited	7.15
Luzerne National Bank Corporation	7.18
Penn Fuel Gas, Inc.	7.19
Garden City Company	7.22
Reo Plastics, Inc.	7.25
Burnham Corporation	7.47
InterUnion Financial Corporation	7.50
Beaver Coal Company, Limited	7.55
Homasote Company	7.58
Ash Grove Cement Company	7.63
Mt. Bachelor, Inc.	7.68

10 - 20

Butte Community Bank	11.86
Biochem International Inc.	11.88
Ogden Telephone Company	11.90
Mt. Carmel Public Utility Co.	11.90
Temco Service Industries, Inc.	11.92
Borel Bank and Trust Company	11.92
Benjamin Moore & Co.	11.99
Drovers Bancshares Corporation	11.99
Carolina Mills Inc.	12.00
ZEVEX International, Inc.	12.00
O.A.K. Financial Corporation	12.06
AMCOR Capital Corporation	12.12
First of Michigan Capital Corporation	12.12
Farmer Bros. Co.	12.12
Westwood Group, Inc. (The)	12.20
VRB Bancorp	12.23
Savers Life Insurance Company	12.26
Valley Water Systems, Inc.	12.38
Cardinal Bancorp, Inc.	12.50
Alaska Power & Telephone Company	12.50
Pennsylvania State Bank	12.50
First Real Estate Investment Trust of New Jersey	12.57
American Public Life Insurance Company	12.65
North State Telephone Company	12.67
Computer Services, Inc.	12.70
Publix Super Markets, Inc.	12.71
Viskon-Aire Corporation	12.82
Corning Natural Gas Corporation	12.95
Hershey Creamery Company	12.95
Lanxide Corporation	12.99
Kerman State Bank	13.02
Tidewater, Bank of	13.07
Alterman Investment Fund, Inc.	13.08
Robroy Industries, Inc.	13.11
Portsmouth Square, Inc.	13.43
California Orchard Company	13.57
Kiewit Royalty Trust	13.59
Scripps Bank	13.62
East Carolina Bank (The)	13.78
Tork, Inc.	13.82
First Morris Bank	13.90
Cowles Media Company	13.92
Case, Pomeroy & Company, Inc.	14.01
Hamburg Industries, Inc.	14.06
Zions Cooperative Mercantile Institution	14.13
Central Coal & Coke Corporation	14.20
Logan Clay Products Company	14.43
Rhinelander Telecommunications, Inc.	14.50
Addvantage Media Group, Inc.	14.57
Goodheart-Willcox Company, Inc. (The)	14.67
Fiduciary Trust Company International	14.71
Chesapeake Investors, Inc.	14.77
Erie Family Life Insurance Company	14.84
Investors Heritage Life Insurance Company	14.89
Iron and Glass Bancorp, Inc.	14.99
LAACO, Ltd.	15.05
Century Realty Trust	15.17
Biddeford and Saco Water Company	15.25
Eyemakers, Inc.	15.63
Shenandoah Telecommunications Company	15.79
Watson Land Company	15.85
Hosoi Garden Mortuary, Inc.	15.91
Fisher Companies Inc.	15.95

Avoca, Incorporated	16.18
Merchants of Shenandoah Ban-Corp	16.24
Reinhold Industries Inc.	16.25
York Water Company (The)	16.43
Heritage Bank of Commerce	16.56
Pay-O-Matic Corp.	16.67
Nebraska, First National of	16.79
Pardee Resources Company	16.96
South Chester Tube Company	17.11
Roseville Communications Company	17.68
Kohler Co.	17.73
Samarnan Investment Corporation	18.10
Bozzuto's Inc.	18.15
Sterling Chemicals Holdings, Inc.	18.15
DK Investors, Inc.	18.34
Ledyard National Bank	18.90
Advantage Marketing Systems, Inc.	18.97
Danbury Industrial Corporation	18.98
Shepmyers Investment Company	18.99
North Carolina Railroad Company	19.03
Chatham Corporation	19.21
Coal Creek Mining and Manufacturing Company	19.62
Market America, Inc.	19.69
Oakridge Energy, Inc.	20.00

Over 20

New York and Harlem Railroad Company	20.03
New Ulm Telecom, Inc.	20.14
Leslie Building Products, Inc.	20.15
Mutual Savings Life Insurance Company	20.27
Fall River Gas Company	20.31
Mercom, Inc.	20.97
Wichita National Life Insurance Company	21.05
AFA Protective Systems, Inc.	21.36
Stonecutter Mills Corporation	21.79
Boswell (J.G.) Company	22.25
EMC Corporation	22.84
CT Communications, Inc.	22.92
National Stock Yards Company	23.77
Mod-U-Kraf Homes, Inc.	23.86
Frederick Trading Company	24.00
PMD Investment Company	24.07
HomeCapital Investment Corporation	24.17
Herkimer Trust Corporation, Inc.	24.41
Pekin Life Insurance Company	24.46
Fremont Corporation	25.00
Capital Properties, Inc.	25.36
Pamet Systems, Inc.	26.20
Tremont Advisors, Inc.	26.79
Snow Summit Ski Corporation	27.16
Keweenaw Land Association, Limited	27.27
RF Industries, LTD	27.78
Mexco Energy Corporation	30.00
North Pittsburgh Systems, Inc.	30.13
Gaming Venture Corp., U.S.A.	30.40
Cuban Electric Company	30.43
Old Fashion Foods, Inc.	31.20
Solid Controls, Inc.	32.40
Rand McNally	32.86
Continental Health Affiliates, Inc.	33.33
Virginia Hot Springs, Incorporated	33.33
Meteor Industries, Inc.	33.73

Under 50 %

Columbian Rope Company	7.51
First Miami Bancorp, Inc.	9.89
Western Lime Corporation	11.98
M.H. Rhodes, Inc.	18.22
Transnational Industries, Inc.	19.38
Troy Mills, Inc.	20.52
Harriet & Henderson Yarns, Inc.	22.66
Root Company, The A.I.	22.34
South Chester Tube Company	22.36
Universal Metals & Machinery, Inc.	25.25
Pennsylvania Warehousing and Safe Deposit Company	25.44
Naylor Pipe Company	26.74
Ainslie Corporation	27.45
Dover Investments Corporation	27.90
Chatham Corporation	28.23
Bulova Corporation	30.18
Hunter Manufacturing Corp.	31.39
National Stock Yards Company	31.62
Standard Electronics, Inc.	33.14
Cherokee Equity Corporation	34.19
UTZ Engineering, Inc.	36.50
Spartan Mills	37.41
Old Fashion Foods, Inc.	37.45
Lake Charles Naval Stores Co., Inc.	38.28
Guaranty Corporation	38.93
Viskon-Aire Corporation	39.94
Lab-Volt Systems, Inc.	40.00
Amelco Corporation	40.21
Walker International Industries, Inc.	40.40
Pacific Northwest Development Corporation	40.58
TNR Technical, Inc.	41.67
York Corrugating Co.	42.09
Rochester & Pittsburgh Coal Company	42.37
Wundies Industries, Inc.	43.20
Kentucky Investors, Inc.	43.77
Best Lock Corporation	44.26
NCC Industries, Inc.	44.26
Life Insurance Company of Alabama	44.41
Adams (R.P.) Company, Inc.	44.48
New Orleans Cold Storage and Warehouse Company Ltd	44.83
Michigan Rivet Corporation	45.35
Logan Clay Products Company	46.34
Hammett (J.L.) Co.	46.59
Temco Service Industries, Inc.	46.80
Bresler & Reiner, Inc.	47.09
Connohio, Inc.	47.17
Pay-O-Matic Corp.	47.57
Paradise, Inc.	47.70
Henry County Plywood Corporation	48.83
Fair Grounds Corporation	49.25
Zions Cooperative Mercantile Institution	49.62
First Republic Corporation of America (The)	49.87

50 - 100 %

West Virginia-American Water Company	51.72
Broughton Foods Company	51.79
Valley Fair Corporation (The)	51.80
Hendrick Ranch Royalties, Inc.	51.96
Acap Corporation	52.00
Frederick Trading Company	52.31
Best Universal Lock Co.	52.75

Horizon Telcom, Inc.	53.27
Union Bancorp of Evansville, Inc.	53.44
Westwood Incorporated	54.45
Indiana Natural Gas Corporation	54.95
Latshaw Enterprises, Inc.	55.34
Crowley Maritime Corporation	55.52
Bryan Steam Corporation	55.53
Elk Associates Funding Corporation	55.95
California-Michigan Land and Water Company	56.21
Finch, Pruyn & Company, Incorporated	56.57
Hanover Foods Corporation	56.63
Barnstable Holding Co., Inc.	57.04
Citizens Growth Properties	57.78
Lady Baltimore Foods, Inc.	57.90
Boston Sand & Gravel Company	58.03
Herkimer Trust Corporation, Inc.	58.08
Homasote Company	59.95
Phil-Good Products Incorporated	60.67
Crown City Plating Co.	61.02
Batterymarch Trust (The)	61.48
Best, Inc., Frank E.	61.48
Hilliard Corporation (The)	62.03
Detroit Legal News Company	62.49
CMP Industries, Inc.	62.66
Sadlier, Inc., William H.	62.90
Terre Aux Boeufs Land Co., Inc.	63.03
Investors Heritage Life Insurance Company	63.35
Capital Properties, Inc.	63.75
Lancaster National Bank (The)	63.98
Mt. Carmel Public Utility Co.	64.08
DK Investors, Inc.	65.45
Pocono Hotels Corporation	65.85
Savers Life Insurance Company	66.94
Akron, Bank of	67.22
Irex Corporation	67.85
Monroe Title Insurance Corporation	68.07
BFC Financial Corporation	68.78
Penn Fuel Gas, Inc.	68.81
Alterman Investment Fund, Inc.	68.87
Reo Plastics, Inc.	69.01
Morris Run Coal Mining Company	69.06
Samarnan Investment Corporation	69.44
Charter National Bancorp, Inc.	69.86
Burke-Parsons-Bowlby Corporation	69.97
First of Michigan Capital Corporation	70.55
Smith Investment Company	70.74
Blue Diamond Coal Company	70.92
Stonecutter Mills Corporation	71.11
EvergreenBank	71.17
Houlihan's Restaurant Group, Inc.	71.22
Bozzuto's Inc.	71.24
National Properties Corporation	71.40
Real Silk Investments, Incorporated	71.50
Citizens' Electric Company	71.62
Central Financial Corporation	72.41
TIF Instruments, Inc.	72.66
Tower Properties Company	72.77
Solid Controls, Inc.	72.97
Shepmyers Investment Company	74.07
W.T.B. Financial Corporation	74.53
Louisville Bedding Company	74.72
Hydraulic Press Brick Company	75.02
InterUnion Financial Corporation	75.25

St. Lawrence Seaway Corporation (The)	75.30
First Star Bancorp, Inc.	75.46
Pontiac Bancorp, Inc.	75.70
Turbotville National Bancorp, Inc.	76.64
King Kullen Grocery Co., Inc.	76.67
Northfield Precision Instrument Corporation	77.50
Cass County Iron Company	77.73
Chesapeake Investors, Inc.	77.75
Wisconsin Fuel & Light Company	77.94
PMD Investment Company	78.19
Randall Bearings, Inc.	78.25
PSB Holding Corp.	78.67
Tork, Inc.	79.25
Wichita National Life Insurance Company	80.00
Pioneer Metals, Inc.	80.01
Chambersburg Engineering Company.	80.46
OPT-Sciences Corporation	80.81
Northern Lehigh Bancorp, Inc.	80.85
Reserve Petroleum Company (The)	81.49
Wailuku Agribusiness Co., Inc.	82.12
North Coast Bank	82.22
Virginia Hot Springs, Incorporated	82.42
Farmers & Merchants Bank of Long Beach.	83.62
E*Capital Corporation.	84.29
Ocean National Corporation.	84.35
Old Forge Bank	84.69
Hayward Industries, Inc.	86.55
Hawaii National Bancshares, Inc.	86.96
Hamlin Bank and Trust Company.	87.48
Boswell (J.G.) Company	88.14
Pennsylvania Manufacturers Corporation	88.19
Adirondack Trust Company (The)	88.75
Peckham Industries, Inc.	89.30
Hollywood, The Bank of	89.39
Park-Lexington Company, Inc.	90.05
Polyplastex United, Inc.	90.50
Anchorage, The First National Bank of	90.55
Finance Company of Pennsylvania	90.60
Carolina Mills Inc.	91.11
Sea Pines Associates, Inc.	91.45
Exolon-ESK Company	91.55
American Public Life Insurance Company	91.78
Pennichuck Corporation	91.81
Community Independent Bank, Inc.	91.99
Technology 80 Inc.	92.42
Auric Corporation	92.80
Mod-U-Kraf Homes, Inc.	92.92
Investors Financial Corporation	93.34
Honat Bancorp, Inc.	93.48
Seven-Up/RC Bottling Co. of Southern Calif., Inc.	93.73
Continental Resources, Inc.	93.88
CBR Brewing Company, Inc.	94.34
MLX Corp.	94.37
Garden City Company	95.03
Auto-Graphics, Inc.	95.34
Sutter Basin Corporation, Ltd.	95.37
Rancho Vista National Bank	95.47
LAACO, Ltd.	95.94
Oakridge Energy, Inc.	96.15
Torrington Water Company (The)	96.15
RWC, Inc.	97.43
Citizens National Bancorp, Inc.	97.98
Components Specialties, Inc.	98.52

Muncy Bank Financial, Inc.	98.67
Long Island Commercial Bank	99.06
Southern Webbing Mills, Inc.	99.70
Yosemite Bank.	99.83
Wilton Bank (The)	100.00

101 - 150 %

Christian Brothers, Inc.	101.20
MidCity Financial Corporation	101.23
Central Coal & Coke Corporation	101.89
Hershey Creamery Company	103.38
Gloucester Bank & Trust Company	103.51
Sterling Sugars, Inc.	103.67
Biddeford and Saco Water Company	104.03
Burnham Corporation.	104.24
Conbraco Industries, Inc.	104.34
Mutual Savings Life Insurance Company	104.38
Hamburg Industries, Inc.	106.13
Robroy Industries, Inc.	106.35
Talbot Bank of Easton, Maryland (The)	107.29
Burke & Herbert Bank & Trust Company	107.86
Queen City Investments, Inc.	107.99
Oak Valley Community Bank.	108.41
Rockies Fund, Inc. (The)	109.89
Athanor Group, Inc.	110.00
Pardee Resources Company	110.53
Anderson-Tully Company	110.80
Simi Valley Bank	111.09
Workforce Systems Corp.	111.79
Community Service Communications, Inc.	112.27
Petaluma, Bank of.	112.32
American River Holdings.	112.69
Central Steel and Wire Company	112.88
InterCounty Bancshares, Inc.	113.16
Redlands Centennial Bank	113.64
Reinhold Industries Inc.	113.64
Bay Commercial Services	114.29
Home-Stake Royalty Corporation (The)	114.48
Home-Stake Oil & Gas Company (The)	114.48
Luzerne National Bank Corporation	114.63
Snow Summit Ski Corporation	114.85
Du Art Film Laboratories, Inc.	115.21
Ash Grove Cement Company.	115.60
Slade's Ferry Bancorp.	115.87
Network Data Processing Corporation	116.46
Pennsylvania State Bank	116.70
Merchants of Shenandoah Ban-Corp	117.19
Ojai Oil Company.	117.39
Central Sierra Bank.	117.43
Verdugo Banking Company.	118.73
Mechanics Bank (The)	119.21
County Bank Corp	119.47
Sportsman's Guide, Inc. (The)	120.48
Farmer Bros. Co.	121.19
Western Sierra Bancorp.	121.26
ZEVEX International, Inc.	121.46
Preformed Line Products Company	123.58
Chemung Financial Corporation	123.71
Delhi Bank Corp	124.25
Colony Bankcorp, Inc.	124.58
Radio Frequency Company, Inc.	124.69
Cardinal Bancorp, Inc.	125.16

IBT Bancorp, Inc.	125.24
Tehama Bank	125.27
Monarch Cement Company (The)	125.32
Carco Electronics	125.88
Columbia Financial Corporation	125.98
Adrian Steel Company	126.21
Lafayette Bancorporation	126.21
Case, Pomeroy & Company, Inc.	127.86
East Carolina Bank (The)	129.11
First Citizens Bancorporation of South Carolina	129.30
Mauch Chunk Trust Company	129.66
Heritage Bank of Commerce	129.70
Davey Tree Expert Company (The)	129.89
Citizens Bancorp, Inc.	130.56
Hosoi Garden Mortuary, Inc.	131.58
Maui Land & Pineapple Company, Inc.	131.62
Stein Industries, Inc.	132.01
DNB Financial Corporation	132.20
Oak Tree Medical Systems ,Inc.	132.45
Harford National Bank	134.58
Minster State Bank	135.14
Ellensburg Telephone Company	135.37
Peninsula Bank of Commerce	136.50
Plumas Bank	136.61
Six Rivers National Bank	137.39
Factory Point Bancorp, Inc.	137.42
Exchange Bank	138.46
Four Oaks Bank & Trust Company	140.02
BSM Bancorp	140.11
Blue Ridge Real Estate Company	140.63
Amboy Bancorporation	141.01
Sonoma Valley Bank	141.51
Rhinelander Telecommunications, Inc.	141.69
Decker Manufacturing Corporation	142.56
Kohler Co.	143.78
Indians, Inc.	144.76
Ledyard National Bank	145.61
Scripps Bank	145.65
Cuban Electric Company	145.83
Limco Del Mar, Ltd.	145.99
Leslie Building Products, Inc.	148.02
O.A.K. Financial Corporation	148.43

151 - 200 %

American Industrial Loan Association	150.78
Humboldt Bancorp	151.19
Drovers Bancshares Corporation	153.02
Keller Manufacturing Company, Inc.	154.47
Northern Empire Bancshares	155.45
B.B. Walker Company	155.64
Carc, Inc.	156.25
Iron and Glass Bancorp, Inc.	156.67
Alaska Power & Telephone Company	158.21
North Valley Bancorp	160.18
Ogden Telephone Company	161.85
Bar Harbor Bankshares	163.27
Scioto Downs, Inc.	163.33
AFA Protective Systems, Inc.	164.21
Borel Bank and Trust Company	165.59
Lexcom Communications, Inc.	166.83
Call Now, Inc.	166.96
Birmingham Utilities, Inc.	167.65

First Real Estate Investment Trust of New Jersey	167.84
Marin, Bank of	170.65
Kish Bancorp, Inc.	171.46
Butte Community Bank	171.78
FCFT, Inc.	172.06
Chromaline Corporation	172.62
Benchmark Bankshares, Inc.	174.07
Computer Services, Inc.	175.05
Audio Communications Network, Inc.	176.28
Calcasieu Real Estate & Oil Co., Inc.	176.28
Kerman State Bank	178.06
York Water Company (The)	178.66
Fisher Companies Inc.	179.38
First Morris Bank	180.65
Shenandoah Telecommunications Company	183.09
Siuslaw Valley Bank	185.19
Century Realty Trust	185.34
Cable Link, Inc.	189.87
Fremont Corporation	191.03
Publix Super Markets, Inc.	191.58
California Orchard Company	192.19
Corning Natural Gas Corporation	192.65
United Security Bank, National Association	193.83
Buck Hill Falls Company	194.35
Tidewater, Bank of	195.29
First Guaranty Bank	196.60
Erie Family Life Insurance Company	197.79
VRB Bancorp	199.12
Investment Properties Associates	199.27
AMCOR Capital Corporation	200.00

Over 200 %

Roseville Communications Company	203.54
Keweenaw Land Association, Limited	204.55
North State Telephone Company	205.42
Bison Instruments, Inc.	207.10
Woodbury Telephone Company (The)	208.78
Goodheart-Willcox Company, Inc. (The)	209.03
Kentucky River Coal Corporation	213.79
Cloverleaf Kennel Club	216.67
Benjamin Moore & Co.	217.14
Hytek Microsystems, Inc.	217.39
SLH Corporation	217.39
Warwick Valley Telephone Co.	219.60
Fiduciary Trust Company International	227.47
CVF Corp.	227.49
Fall River Gas Company	228.87
A.D. Makepeace Company	228.96
Nebraska, First National of	241.62
Coal Creek Mining and Manufacturing Company	241.67
Mexco Energy Corporation	251.40
Pekin Life Insurance Company	252.53
ExperTelligence, Inc.	270.83
Portland Brewing Company	272.73
Health International, Inc.	277.78
Ravens Metal Products, Inc.	282.49
Connectivity Technologies Inc.	285.47
Rand McNally	295.36
New Ulm Telecom, Inc.	295.98
CT Communications, Inc.	297.23
Eyemakers, Inc.	297.62
Dynamic Associates, Inc.	298.17

North American Scientific, Inc..	300.00
EMC Corporation.	303.78
Avoca, Incorporated.	316.09
Kahiki Foods, Inc.	317.07
Seven J Stock Farm, Inc.	324.07
Meteor Industries, Inc.	326.45
Shopsmith, Inc..	348.53
Market Guide, Inc.	348.84
RF Industries, LTD	384.62
Thanksgiving Coffee Company, Inc.	390.63
Mendocino Brewing Company, Inc.	403.43
Biochem International Inc.	412.71
Aztec Land and Cattle Company, Limited	417.48
Fifty Associates.	418.41
Beaver Coal Company, Limited	433.14
Colorado Gaming & Entertainment Co.	447.37
Pinnacle Data Systems, Inc.	465.36
DHB Capital Group Inc.	467.86
Profit Financial Corporation	476.36
New York and Harlem Railroad Company	477.83
Planet Entertainment Corporation	493.83
Naturade, Inc..	504.76
Sims-Agricultural Products Company	535.71
Cowles Media Company	537.28
Original Sixteen to One Mine, Inc..	559.70
Holobeam, Inc..	561.80
PortaCom Wireless, Inc.	582.46
Florafax International, Inc.	607.69
Cable-Sat Systems, Inc..	612.50
Medjet Inc.	619.13
Geo Petroleum, Inc..	634.92
North Pittsburgh Systems, Inc.	638.59
Portsmouth Square, Inc.	656.93
Waste Recovery, Inc.	664.52
Genetic Vectors, Inc.	665.02
Blue Fish Clothing, Inc..	670.73
Pro Tech Communications, Inc.	673.08
Tremont Advisors, Inc..	707.55
Gaming Venture Corp., U.S.A..	712.50
Golden Cycle Gold Corporation	719.18
Lasermedics, Inc..	733.75
Nova Technologies, Inc.	769.23
Ragar Corp..	775.86
Clinicor, Inc.	784.31
Addvantage Media Group, Inc..	824.53
Meritage Hospitality Group Inc.	873.02
Power Test Investors Limited Partnership	961.54
Tidelands Royalty Trust "B"	990.57
Salient Systems, Inc..	1,007.46
HomeCapital Investment Corporation	1,082.09
Continental Health Affiliates, Inc..	1,250.00
Advantage Marketing Systems, Inc..	1,279.07
North Carolina Railroad Company.	1,292.23
Ammonia Hold, Inc..	1,405.00
Strategia Corporation.	1,436.17
Asha Corporation.	1,458.33
Watson Land Company	1,477.27
DeltaPoint, Inc..	1,488.10
Information Analysis Incorporated.	1,494.85
Magicworks Entertainment Incorporated	1,578.95
Cimetrix Incorporated	1,585.37
Conectisys Corporation	1,612.90
Market America, Inc..	1,651.61

D.H. Marketing & Consulting, Inc.	1,697.53
Pamet Systems, Inc.	1,746.67
American Tire Corporation	1,748.57
Nevada Manhattan Mining Incorporated.	2,062.79
NeuroCorp., Ltd..	2,152.78
T/F Purifiner, Inc.	2,194.44
Continental Investment Corporation	2,361.11
Al-Zar, Ltd..	2,410.98
U.S. Plastic Lumber Corporation	2,566.67
Spring Street Brewing Company, Inc.	2,750.00
Superior Supplements, Inc..	3,243.24
Personal Computer Products, Inc..	3,333.33
Westmoreland Coal Company	3,333.33
Annie's Homegrown, Inc.	3,750.00
Main Street Athletic Clubs, Inc..	4,285.71
Alden Lee Company, Inc.	4,444.44
Quigley Corporation (The).	7,207.69
VASCO Corp..	8,587.50

Based on the years presented

Over 25 %	
Food Extrusion, Inc.	811.26
Profit Financial Corporation	376.63
Level Best Golf, Inc.	371.05
Lasermedics, Inc.	368.84
Market America, Inc.	218.72
Quigley Corporation (The)	210.74
Addvantage Media Group, Inc.	162.45
Oak Tree Medical Systems ,Inc.	86.41
Clinicor, Inc.	81.06
Advantage Marketing Systems, Inc.	78.96
Portland Brewing Company	76.34
Batterymarch Trust (The)	76.16
SGI International	73.70
Fremont Corporation	51.39
North American Scientific, Inc.	50.32
DHB Capital Group Inc.	48.44
Tremont Advisors, Inc.	47.92
Continental Resources, Inc.	47.38
RF Industries, LTD	44.17
Workforce Systems Corp.	44.09
Strategia Corporation	43.10
Long Island Commercial Bank	41.63
Belle Isle Net Profits Units	41.46
Sterling Sugars, Inc.	41.43
Annie's Homegrown, Inc.	39.89
Avoca, Incorporated.	39.13
Indians, Inc.	38.57
Health International, Inc.	37.67
OPT-Sciences Corporation	36.32
Cimetrix Incorporated	36.04
Limco Del Mar, Ltd.	35.29
Savers Life Insurance Company	35.27
Hytek Microsystems, Inc.	34.87
E*Capital Corporation	34.63
Home-Stake Oil & Gas Company (The)	34.01
Market Guide, Inc.	33.93
Ledyard National Bank	33.73
Mexco Energy Corporation	33.23
Best, Inc., Frank E.	32.91
Biochem International Inc.	31.58
Best Universal Lock Co.	31.44
Stein Industries, Inc.	31.33
New Orleans Cold Storage and Warehouse Company Ltd	31.22
Blue Fish Clothing, Inc.	30.60
Oak Valley Community Bank	29.94
Central Coal & Coke Corporation	29.69
Ammonia Hold, Inc.	28.86
Humboldt Bancorp	28.50
American River Holdings	27.62
Petaluma, Bank of	27.49
Components Specialties, Inc.	26.96
Cherokee Equity Corporation	26.85
Reserve Petroleum Company (The)	26.80
Reuter Manufacturing, Inc.	26.60
Audio Communications Network, Inc.	26.40
Ravens Metal Products, Inc.	26.28
St. Louis Steel Casting Inc.	25.35
Auric Corporation	25.31

25 - 10 %	
Marin, Bank of	24.56
Waste Recovery, Inc.	24.47
DeltaPoint, Inc.	24.26
Meteor Industries, Inc.	24.17
Butte Community Bank	24.17
Verdugo Banking Company	23.93
Mortgage Oil Company	23.88
ZEVEX International, Inc.	23.37
Sportsman's Guide, Inc. (The)	23.10
Rockies Fund, Inc. (The)	22.65
Holobeam, Inc.	22.38
Scripps Bank	22.26
American Industrial Loan Association	22.21
Western Sierra Bancorp	22.14
Northern Empire Bancshares	21.22
Chromaline Corporation	21.05
Sims-Agricultural Products Company	20.85
Six Rivers National Bank	20.84
Pamet Systems, Inc.	20.81
Westbrook-Thompson Agency	20.57
Hammett (J.L.) Co.	20.35
Horizon Telcom, Inc.	20.01
Magicworks Entertainment Incorporated	19.99
Adrian Steel Company	19.98
InterUnion Financial Corporation	19.14
Beaver Coal Company, Limited	19.06
Tehama Bank	18.90
Tower Properties Company	18.66
Preformed Line Products Company	18.58
Luzerne National Bank Corporation	18.56
Network Data Processing Corporation	18.37
Torrington Water Company (The)	18.29
Pinnacle Data Systems, Inc.	18.26
VASCO Corp.	18.19
Athanor Group, Inc.	18.09
Hydraulic Press Brick Company	17.20
Reo Plastics, Inc.	17.13
Pennsylvania State Bank	17.09
Century Realty Trust	16.98
Main Street Athletic Clubs, Inc.	16.97
CT Communications, Inc.	16.88
Simi Valley Bank	16.65
Technology 80 Inc.	16.44
Four Oaks Bank & Trust Company	16.25
Chequemate International, Inc.	16.24
Fisher Companies Inc.	15.98
Americold Corporation	15.88
Southern Scottish Inns, Inc.	15.85
Sonoma Valley Bank	15.72
Rhinelander Telecommunications, Inc.	15.53
Merchants' National Properties, Inc.	15.52
Nebraska, First National of	15.49
Keller Manufacturing Company, Inc.	15.42
Lexington Precision Corporation	15.28
Sterling Chemicals Holdings, Inc.	15.07
Tidewater, Bank of	14.72
Morris Run Coal Mining Company	14.55
Western Lime Corporation	14.28
Keweenaw Land Association, Limited	14.22
Lanxide Corporation	14.12
Pacific Northwest Development Corporation	14.11

United Security Bank, National Association	14.02
Temco Service Industries, Inc.	13.98
Bison Instruments, Inc.	13.97
Radio Frequency Company, Inc.	13.86
Cowles Media Company	13.82
VRB Bancorp	13.70
Shenandoah Telecommunications Company	13.64
Redlands Centennial Bank	13.61
Burke-Parsons-Bowlby Corporation	13.42
IBT Bancorp, Inc.	13.40
Home-Stake Royalty Corporation (The)	13.35
Florafax International, Inc.	13.28
Bismarck Hotel Company	12.96
EMC Corporation	12.56
Wilton Bank (The)	12.56
Mod-U-Kraf Homes, Inc.	12.43
Chambersburg Engineering Company	12.36
Minster State Bank	12.36
Latshaw Enterprises, Inc.	12.25
RWC, Inc.	12.06
Publix Super Markets, Inc.	11.69
BFC Financial Corporation	11.55
Bryan Steam Corporation	11.46
Blue Diamond Coal Company	11.43
Nichols (J.C.) Company	11.30
Lab-Volt Systems, Inc.	11.30
North Valley Bancorp	11.28
Alaska Power & Telephone Company	11.21
First Real Estate Investment Trust of New Jersey	11.20
Queen City Investments, Inc.	11.20
Northfield Precision Instrument Corporation	11.11
Siuslaw Valley Bank	11.09
Warwick Valley Telephone Co.	11.08
Randall Bearings, Inc.	11.01
North Pittsburgh Systems, Inc.	10.98
North State Telephone Company	10.78
TNR Technical, Inc.	10.66
Bay Commercial Services	10.60
O.A.K. Financial Corporation	10.47
Exolon-ESK Company	10.45
Cable Link, Inc.	10.37
Talbot Bank of Easton, Maryland (The)	10.34
Rochester & Pittsburgh Coal Company	10.29
Benchmark Bankshares, Inc.	10.21
Pioneer Metals, Inc.	10.18
Peninsula Bank of Commerce	10.14
Case, Pomeroy & Company, Inc.	10.13
Du Art Film Laboratories, Inc.	10.01

10 - 0 %

Charter National Bancorp, Inc.	9.99
Ash Grove Cement Company	9.95
Naturade, Inc.	9.93
Monarch Cement Company (The)	9.92
Northern Lehigh Bancorp, Inc.	9.89
Lexcom Communications, Inc.	9.87
Birmingham Utilities, Inc.	9.80
Sadlier, Inc., William H.	9.79
Ocean National Corporation	9.78
Akron, Bank of	9.77
North Coast Bank	9.77
AMCOR Capital Corporation	9.71

Naylor Pipe Company	9.62
InterCounty Bancshares, Inc.	9.44
Robroy Industries, Inc.	9.41
Pennichuck Corporation	9.33
Gloucester Bank & Trust Company	9.27
DNB Financial Corporation	9.27
Hilliard Corporation (The)	9.17
Borel Bank and Trust Company	9.12
American Mart Corporation	9.12
Slade's Ferry Bancorp	9.05
Plumas Bank	8.93
Columbia Water Company	8.89
Kerman State Bank	8.77
Ellensburg Telephone Company	8.69
California-Michigan Land and Water Company	8.59
New Ulm Telecom, Inc.	8.59
Burke & Herbert Bank & Trust Company	8.59
Kish Bancorp, Inc.	8.54
Broughton Foods Company	8.51
Erie Family Life Insurance Company	8.49
Phil-Good Products Incorporated	8.44
Wichita National Life Insurance Company	8.38
East Carolina Bank (The)	8.25
Michigan Rivet Corporation	7.96
Portsmouth Square, Inc.	7.80
Hollywood, The Bank of	7.76
Drovers Bancshares Corporation	7.76
First Star Bancorp, Inc.	7.75
Woodbury Telephone Company (The)	7.66
Burnham Corporation	7.64
Factory Point Bancorp, Inc.	7.60
Kohler Co.	7.59
Arthur Treacher's, Inc.	7.59
Cardinal Bancorp, Inc.	7.54
Mercom, Inc.	7.54
First Citizens Bancorporation of South Carolina	7.50
Leslie Building Products, Inc.	7.49
Bar Harbor Bankshares	7.48
Goodheart-Willcox Company, Inc. (The)	7.47
Rancho Vista National Bank	7.43
Frederick Trading Company	7.42
Guaranty Corporation	7.27
Delhi Bank Corp.	7.23
Lady Baltimore Foods, Inc.	7.22
Kahiki Foods, Inc.	7.12
FCFT, Inc.	7.10
Ragar Corp.	7.07
American Bio Medica Corporation	7.04
Valley Water Systems, Inc.	7.03
Colony Bankcorp, Inc.	6.99
Pekin Life Insurance Company	6.95
Harford National Bank	6.95
Harriet & Henderson Yarns, Inc.	6.92
Davey Tree Expert Company (The)	6.91
Benjamin Moore & Co.	6.84
BSM Bancorp	6.84
First Guaranty Bank	6.78
Columbian Rope Company	6.76
Hanover Foods Corporation	6.73
American Public Life Insurance Company	6.64
County Bank Corp.	6.63
Amelco Corporation	6.62
Investors Financial Corporation	6.42

Sea Pines Associates, Inc.	6.40
Community Independent Bank, Inc.	6.39
Chemung Financial Corporation	6.36
Detroit Legal News Company	6.35
UTZ Engineering, Inc.	6.32
Adirondack Trust Company (The)	6.31
Union Bancorp of Evansville, Inc.	6.29
West Virginia-American Water Company	6.22
Meritage Hospitality Group Inc.	6.20
Transnational Industries, Inc.	6.20
W.T.B. Financial Corporation	6.20
Citizens National Bancorp, Inc.	6.13
Colorado Gaming & Entertainment Co.	6.12
Lancaster National Bank (The)	6.05
Conbraco Industries, Inc.	6.05
Bulova Corporation	6.04
Columbia Financial Corporation	5.92
Bozzuto's Inc.	5.86
Amboy Bancorporation	5.72
Pocono Hotels Corporation	5.71
National Properties Corporation	5.70
Iron and Glass Bancorp, Inc.	5.65
Central Steel and Wire Company	5.62
Pro Tech Communications, Inc.	5.60
Muncy Bank Financial, Inc.	5.56
Finch, Pruyn & Company, Incorporated	5.50
Roseville Communications Company	5.39
Smith Investment Company	5.36
Farmer Bros. Co.	5.29
Universal Metals & Machinery, Inc.	5.23
Wailuku Agribusiness Co., Inc.	5.22
Adams (R.P.) Company, Inc.	5.12
Kentucky River Coal Corporation	4.88
Lafayette Bancorporation	4.75
Mauch Chunk Trust Company	4.73
Honat Bancorp, Inc.	4.71
Citizens Bancorp, Inc.	4.67
Hayward Industries, Inc.	4.60
York Water Company (The)	4.59
Blue Ridge Real Estate Company	4.50
Irex Corporation	4.50
Pontiac Bancorp, Inc.	4.49
Pardee Resources Company	4.40
First of Michigan Capital Corporation	4.39
Mendocino Brewing Company, Inc.	4.35
Homasote Company	4.33
Life Insurance Company of Alabama	4.29
Logan Clay Products Company	4.27
York Corrugating Co.	4.27
EvergreenBank	4.09
Hershey Creamery Company	3.98
Barnstable Holding Co., Inc.	3.83
Hamburg Industries, Inc.	3.64
PSB Holding Corp.	3.56
Bresler & Reiner, Inc.	3.52
Decker Manufacturing Corporation	3.40
Zions Cooperative Mercantile Institution	3.33
Mills Music Trust	3.33
Reynolds, Smith and Hills, Inc.	3.32
Central Sierra Bank	3.08
Fall River Gas Company	3.02
Boswell (J.G.) Company	2.91

Elk Associates Funding Corporation	2.86
Garden City Company	2.84
Dayton and Michigan Railroad Company	2.84
Acap Corporation	2.82
Mt. Carmel Public Utility Co.	2.81
Houlihan's Restaurant Group, Inc.	2.77
Connohio, Inc.	2.77
AFA Protective Systems, Inc.	2.76
Biddeford and Saco Water Company	2.75
Viskon-Aire Corporation	2.74
Louisville Bedding Company	2.64
Chamber of Commerce Building Corporation	2.61
Connecticut River Bancorp, Inc.	2.50
Corning Natural Gas Corporation	2.46
Pay-O-Matic Corp.	2.39
Buck Hill Falls Company	2.36
Merchants of Shenandoah Ban-Corp	2.34
LAACO, Ltd.	2.32
Mt. Bachelor, Inc.	2.32
Park-Lexington Company, Inc.	2.31
Anderson-Tully Company	2.24
Mechanics Bank (The)	2.22
Anchorage, The First National Bank of	2.21
Yosemite Bank	2.12
CMP Industries, Inc.	2.05
Henry County Plywood Corporation	1.98
Carc, Inc.	1.98
Ogden Telephone Company	1.97
Kentucky Investors, Inc.	1.86
Exchange Bank	1.86
First Morris Bank	1.77
Computer Services, Inc.	1.75
Herkimer Trust Corporation, Inc.	1.75
Investors Heritage Life Insurance Company	1.70
Central Financial Corporation	1.68
Fifty Associates	1.47
Wisconsin Fuel & Light Company	1.45
Maui Land & Pineapple Company, Inc.	1.30
Old Fashion Foods, Inc.	1.27
Finance Company of Pennsylvania	1.17
Hawaii National Bancshares, Inc.	1.11
Old Forge Bank	1.11
United Vanguard Homes, Inc.	1.09
Turbotville National Bancorp, Inc.	1.07
Capital Properties, Inc.	1.02
King Kullen Grocery Co., Inc.	1.02
Dover Investments Corporation	0.96
North Coast Life Insurance Co.	0.92
Seven J Stock Farm, Inc.	0.91
Tork, Inc.	0.82
Eyemakers, Inc.	0.78
Danbury Industrial Corporation	0.77
Bruno's, Inc.	0.75
Watson Land Company	0.68
Wundies Industries, Inc.	0.59
Valley Fair Corporation (The)	0.57
Crowley Maritime Corporation	0.57
California Orchard Company	0.42
Mutual Savings Life Insurance Company	0.23
National Stock Yards Company	0.22
MidCity Financial Corporation	0.17
Walker International Industries, Inc.	0.14

0 - (10) %

Cass County Iron Company	-0.27
Snow Summit Ski Corporation	-0.31
Hamlin Bank and Trust Company	-0.39
Standard Electronics, Inc.	-0.45
Penn Fuel Gas, Inc.	-0.60
Scioto Downs, Inc.	-0.70
Indiana Natural Gas Corporation	-0.75
Thanksgiving Coffee Company, Inc.	-0.86
Fair Grounds Corporation	-0.89
Hendrick Ranch Royalties, Inc.	-1.00
Power Test Investors Limited Partnership	-1.02
Cloverleaf Kennel Club	-1.09
Ojai Oil Company	-1.17
Chatham Corporation	-1.18
Carco Electronics	-1.40
SLH Corporation	-1.69
Salient Systems, Inc.	-1.76
Auto-Graphics, Inc.	-1.76
Boston Sand & Gravel Company	-1.89
Citizens' Electric Company	-1.91
Investment Properties Associates	-2.09
First Republic Corporation of America (The)	-2.38
Troy Mills, Inc.	-2.51
TIF Instruments, Inc.	-2.53
Christian Brothers, Inc.	-3.03
Fiduciary Trust Company International	-3.29
NCC Industries, Inc.	-3.37
Monroe Title Insurance Corporation	-3.41
Paradise, Inc.	-3.47
Peckham Industries, Inc.	-3.77
Ainslie Corporation	-3.89
Seven-Up/RC Bottling Co. of Southern Calif., Inc.	-3.98
Coal Creek Mining and Manufacturing Company	-4.43
Solid Controls, Inc.	-5.32
Carolina Mills Inc.	-5.36
Farmers & Merchants Bank of Long Beach	-5.42
Sutter Basin Corporation, Ltd.	-5.43
A.D. Makepeace Company	-5.93
Westwood Incorporated	-6.35
Westwood Group, Inc. (The)	-7.83
U.S. Plastic Lumber Corporation	-7.92
M.H. Rhodes, Inc.	-8.12
Continental Investment Corporation	-8.32
Louisiana Central Net Profits Units	-8.92
Pennsylvania Manufacturers Corporation	-9.81

Over (10) %

T/F Purifiner, Inc.	-10.20
Information Analysis Incorporated	-10.41
ENDOcare, Inc.	-10.74
First Miami Bancorp, Inc.	-11.09
Crown City Plating Co.	-11.13
Kiewit Royalty Trust	-11.28
Community Service Communications, Inc.	-12.30
B.B. Walker Company	-12.36
Chesapeake Investors, Inc.	-13.84
Tidelands Royalty Trust "B"	-14.53
Southern Webbing Mills, Inc.	-15.55
Williams Industries, Incorporated	-16.29
Personal Computer Products, Inc.	-19.43

Asha Corporation	-20.07
Allstar Inns, Inc.	-21.95
St. Lawrence Seaway Corporation (The)	-22.47
New York and Harlem Railroad Company	-23.06
Original Sixteen to One Mine, Inc.	-24.49
Westar Financial Services Incorporated	-30.13
NeuroCorp., Ltd.	-31.97
Alydaar Software Corporation	-34.19
Polyplastex United, Inc.	-35.68
American Financial Enterprises, Inc.	-36.21
Westmoreland Coal Company	-40.99
Geo Petroleum, Inc.	-52.52
Citizens Growth Properties	-60.75

Based on the years presented

Over 25 %	
Exolon-ESK Company	486.42
Continental Resources, Inc.	444.41
Market America, Inc.	409.90
Guaranty Corporation	246.91
Elk Associates Funding Corporation	136.97
Ainslie Corporation	120.34
Components Specialties, Inc.	110.55
Health International, Inc.	106.06
Batterymarch Trust (The)	101.83
Radio Frequency Company, Inc.	95.12
Chromaline Corporation	87.72
Hydraulic Press Brick Company	87.10
Western Sierra Bancorp	84.47
AMCOR Capital Corporation	84.39
Naturade, Inc.	81.71
Long Island Commercial Bank	80.70
Simi Valley Bank	77.70
Indians, Inc.	76.39
Home-Stake Royalty Corporation (The)	71.75
Ash Grove Cement Company	71.31
Columbian Rope Company	70.62
Detroit Legal News Company	69.65
Tremont Advisors, Inc.	67.11
North American Scientific, Inc.	67.11
Verdugo Banking Company	66.03
Sterling Sugars, Inc.	64.32
Monarch Cement Company (The)	63.08
Northfield Precision Instrument Corporation	60.78
New Orleans Cold Storage and Warehouse Company Ltd	58.93
Paradise, Inc.	55.98
Audio Communications Network, Inc.	55.36
Limco Del Mar, Ltd.	55.02
Root Company, The A.I.	54.12
Reserve Petroleum Company (The)	51.72
Talbot Bank of Easton, Maryland (The)	51.32
Six Rivers National Bank	50.00
Blue Diamond Coal Company	49.77
DNB Financial Corporation	49.13
Luzerne National Bank Corporation	49.10
Redlands Centennial Bank	47.53
Gloucester Bank & Trust Company	47.26
Bresler & Reiner, Inc.	47.20
Mortgage Oil Company	45.84
Birmingham Utilities, Inc.	45.77
Tower Properties Company	44.78
Auric Corporation	44.50
RF Industries, LTD	44.22
Fremont Corporation	43.75
Biochem International Inc.	43.07
National Stock Yards Company	41.86
Belle Isle Net Profits Units	41.36
Bulova Corporation	41.19
Wilton Bank (The)	40.76
Athanor Group, Inc.	40.43
First Morris Bank	40.15
Central Steel and Wire Company	39.97
Snow Summit Ski Corporation	39.49
Bar Harbor Bankshares	38.44
Peninsula Bank of Commerce	38.38

Keller Manufacturing Company, Inc.	38.29
Preformed Line Products Company	37.93
Columbia Water Company	37.46
Bay Commercial Services	36.49
Central Financial Corporation	36.15
St. Louis Steel Casting Inc.	35.20
Sterling Chemicals Holdings, Inc.	35.04
Best Universal Lock Co.	34.95
Avoca, Incorporated	34.42
Burke-Parsons-Bowlby Corporation	34.26
Phil-Good Products Incorporated	34.20
Sonoma Valley Bank	34.09
Connecticut River Bancorp, Inc.	32.93
Southern Scottish Inns, Inc.	32.24
Petaluma, Bank of.	32.11
Best, Inc., Frank E.	31.92
Smith Investment Company	31.86
Capital Properties, Inc.	31.79
Scripps Bank	30.71
Stein Industries, Inc.	29.93
Humboldt Bancorp	29.44
Fisher Companies Inc.	28.42
Auto-Graphics, Inc.	28.06
Ocean National Corporation	26.91
North State Telephone Company	26.84
Woodbury Telephone Company (The)	26.61
Burke & Herbert Bank & Trust Company	26.40
Pennsylvania State Bank	25.99
Oak Valley Community Bank	25.34

25 - 10 %	
Irex Corporation	24.23
Borel Bank and Trust Company	24.09
Northern Lehigh Bancorp, Inc.	23.86
Warwick Valley Telephone Co.	22.92
Westbrook-Thompson Agency	22.89
Beaver Coal Company, Limited	22.34
United Security Bank, National Association	21.94
Louisville Bedding Company	21.81
Du Art Film Laboratories, Inc.	21.71
Charter National Bancorp, Inc.	21.46
Factory Point Bancorp, Inc.	20.88
Slade's Ferry Bancorp	20.62
Central Coal & Coke Corporation	20.41
Houlihan's Restaurant Group, Inc.	20.12
Rockies Fund, Inc. (The)	19.82
Marin, Bank of	19.52
County Bank Corp	19.25
Fifty Associates	18.75
Tidewater, Bank of	18.67
IBT Bancorp, Inc.	18.48
Four Oaks Bank & Trust Company	18.38
Lexcom Communications, Inc.	18.32
Ledyard National Bank	18.26
American River Holdings	18.21
Minster State Bank	18.16
BSM Bancorp	17.97
King Kullen Grocery Co., Inc.	17.88
Northern Empire Bancshares	17.63
Crowley Maritime Corporation	17.61
Cowles Media Company	17.32
Lancaster National Bank (The)	17.19

Butte Community Bank.	16.83
Davey Tree Expert Company (The)	16.71
Rochester & Pittsburgh Coal Company.	16.65
VRB Bancorp.	16.62
Publix Super Markets, Inc.	16.45
Latshaw Enterprises, Inc.	16.37
Investors Financial Corporation	15.94
Hollywood, The Bank of	15.87
Merchants' National Properties, Inc.	15.24
InterCounty Bancshares, Inc.	15.20
Sadlier, Inc., William H.	14.89
Columbia Financial Corporation	14.53
Amboy Bancorporation	14.44
Wundies Industries, Inc.	14.16
Penn Fuel Gas, Inc.	14.11
East Carolina Bank (The).	13.97
First Citizens Bancorporation of South Carolina	13.84
Cardinal Bancorp, Inc.	13.26
FCFT, Inc..	12.85
Case, Pomeroy & Company, Inc.	12.83
PSB Holding Corp	12.82
Pennichuck Corporation	12.82
Siuslaw Valley Bank	12.78
Adirondack Trust Company (The)	12.53
Citizens National Bancorp, Inc..	12.27
Cherokee Equity Corporation.	12.07
Merchants of Shenandoah Ban-Corp	11.59
Ojai Oil Company.	11.48
Rand McNally.	11.31
Benchmark Bankshares, Inc.	11.17
National Properties Corporation	11.04
Union Bancorp of Evansville, Inc.	11.03
Kish Bancorp, Inc.	11.01
Pioneer Metals, Inc..	10.49
California-Michigan Land and Water Company	10.38
Honat Bancorp, Inc..	10.37
North Valley Bancorp.	10.29
Hunter Manufacturing Corp.	10.06
Reynolds, Smith and Hills, Inc..	10.06
Ellensburg Telephone Company	10.02
Delhi Bank Corp	10.00

10 - 0 %

Queen City Investments, Inc.	9.78
Plumas Bank.	9.72
Corning Natural Gas Corporation.	9.63
CT Communications, Inc.	9.47
First Guaranty Bank.	9.47
Goodheart-Willcox Company, Inc. (The)	9.33
Adrian Steel Company	9.15
Technology 80 Inc.	9.14
O.A.K. Financial Corporation.	9.10
Harford National Bank	9.05
Community Service Communications, Inc.	9.00
Lafayette Bancorporation	8.91
Sims-Agricultural Products Company.	8.74
Citizens Bancorp, Inc..	8.70
Western Lime Corporation	8.66
Hamburg Industries, Inc.	8.58
North Pittsburgh Systems, Inc.	8.54

Mechanics Bank (The)	8.47
Benjamin Moore & Co..	8.46
Muncy Bank Financial, Inc..	8.40
Anderson-Tully Company.	8.11
Hilliard Corporation (The)	8.03
Kentucky River Coal Corporation.	7.85
Reo Plastics, Inc.	7.85
Mauch Chunk Trust Company	7.85
Drovers Bancshares Corporation	7.31
Farmer Bros. Co.	7.22
Akron, Bank of	7.12
Old Forge Bank	6.57
Portsmouth Square, Inc..	6.48
Fiduciary Trust Company International	6.47
West Virginia-American Water Company.	6.43
Power Test Investors Limited Partnership.	6.27
Wisconsin Fuel & Light Company	6.23
Burnham Corporation	6.18
Indiana Natural Gas Corporation	6.17
American Industrial Loan Association	5.96
Barnstable Holding Co., Inc.	5.79
Decker Manufacturing Corporation.	5.78
Tehama Bank	5.67
Hamlin Bank and Trust Company.	5.66
Finch, Pruyn & Company, Incorporated.	5.43
Watson Land Company	5.42
York Corrugating Co.	5.38
Computer Services, Inc.	5.27
First Real Estate Investment Trust of New Jersey.	5.17
Monroe Title Insurance Corporation	5.04
Central Sierra Bank	5.02
Dayton and Michigan Railroad Company.	4.96
Tork, Inc..	4.81
New Ulm Telecom, Inc.	4.44
Pekin Life Insurance Company	4.34
Kerman State Bank	3.73
EMC Corporation	3.53
Turbotville National Bancorp, Inc.	3.47
Mills Music Trust	3.27
Carc, Inc.	3.15
Shenandoah Telecommunications Company	2.92
Carolina Mills Inc..	2.82
Bryan Steam Corporation	2.63
First Star Bancorp, Inc.	2.59
Community Independent Bank, Inc..	2.46
Mt. Bachelor, Inc.	2.46
MidCity Financial Corporation	2.24
Rhinelander Telecommunications, Inc.	2.12
Alaska Power & Telephone Company.	1.90
Citizens' Electric Company	1.82
Iron and Glass Bancorp, Inc.	1.60
UTZ Engineering, Inc..	1.56
Exchange Bank	1.54
TNR Technical, Inc..	1.32
Chemung Financial Corporation	1.03
Garden City Company.	0.97
York Water Company (The).	0.56
Pontiac Bancorp, Inc.	0.56
Erie Family Life Insurance Company.	0.18
Nebraska, First National of	0.07

0 - (10) %	
W.T.B. Financial Corporation	-1.47
Farmers & Merchants Bank of Long Beach	-1.59
Cloverleaf Kennel Club	-1.89
Roseville Communications Company	-2.27
Anchorage, The First National Bank of	-2.38
Network Data Processing Corporation	-2.56
Conbraco Industries, Inc.	-3.05
Park-Lexington Company, Inc.	-3.09
Kentucky Investors, Inc.	-3.11
Addvantage Media Group, Inc.	-3.23
Hendrick Ranch Royalties, Inc.	-3.42
Investment Properties Associates	-3.93
Biddeford and Saco Water Company	-4.32
Sportsman's Guide, Inc. (The)	-5.08
Yosemite Bank	-5.27
Hershey Creamery Company	-5.46
LAACO, Ltd.	-5.59
Hayward Industries, Inc.	-6.40
Keweenaw Land Association, Limited	-6.60
Cass County Iron Company	-7.16
Robroy Industries, Inc.	-7.38
Amelco Corporation	-8.04
Life Insurance Company of Alabama	-8.45
CMP Industries, Inc.	-8.83
Louisiana Central Net Profits Units	-8.92
Market Guide, Inc.	-9.14

Over (10) %	
Lady Baltimore Foods, Inc.	-10.20
Temco Service Industries, Inc.	-10.69
California Orchard Company	-10.94
Wichita National Life Insurance Company	-11.05
Valley Water Systems, Inc.	-11.05
Investors Heritage Life Insurance Company	-11.18
Kiewit Royalty Trust	-11.34
ZEVEX International, Inc.	-11.45
AFA Protective Systems, Inc.	-12.62
Main Street Athletic Clubs, Inc.	-12.64
Coal Creek Mining and Manufacturing Company	-13.64
Williams Industries, Incorporated	-14.81
Tidelands Royalty Trust "B"	-15.02
Fall River Gas Company	-15.37
Chesapeake Investors, Inc.	-16.65
Zions Cooperative Mercantile Institution	-16.83
First of Michigan Capital Corporation	-17.14
Hawaii National Bancshares, Inc.	-17.64
Solid Controls, Inc.	-17.79
Viskon-Aire Corporation	-20.29
Savers Life Insurance Company	-20.38
Seven J Stock Farm, Inc.	-20.63
Homasote Company	-21.62
Lab-Volt Systems, Inc.	-24.44
American Public Life Insurance Company	-24.67
First Miami Bancorp, Inc.	-25.32
Herkimer Trust Corporation, Inc.	-26.98
Bozzuto's Inc.	-27.14
Pay-O-Matic Corp.	-27.74
Danbury Industrial Corporation	-28.08

American Financial Enterprises, Inc.	-30.06
Blue Ridge Real Estate Company	-30.66
Mod-U-Kraf Homes, Inc.	-30.66
Mutual Savings Life Insurance Company	-31.18
A.D. Makepeace Company	-32.92
Stonecutter Mills Corporation	-33.17
Ravens Metal Products, Inc.	-42.64
Acap Corporation	-44.30
Troy Mills, Inc.	-46.32
TIF Instruments, Inc.	-55.58
Cable Link, Inc.	-56.32
Hanover Foods Corporation	-58.62
Waste Recovery, Inc.	-59.18
Valley Fair Corporation (The)	-79.77
Pinnacle Data Systems, Inc.	-82.76
Eyemakers, Inc.	-91.49

This page intentionally left blank.

Value	

Growth

Income

Speculative

Alaska Power & Telephone Company . . . . http://www.olympus.net/apt/
Amboy Bancorporation. . . . . http://www.amboybank.com
Annie's Homegrown, Inc.. . . . . http://www.annies.com/~annies
Auto-Graphics, Inc.. . . . . http://www.auto-graphics.com
Cable Link, Inc. . . . . http://www.cable-link.com
Cable-Sat Systems, Inc.. . . . . http://www.compressent.com
Chambersburg Engineering Company . . . . http://www.ceco-beche.com
Charter National Bancorp, Inc.. . . . . http://www.charternational.com
Chromaline Corporation . . . . http://www.chromaline.com
Cimetrix Incorporated . . . . http://www.cimetrix.com
Computer Services, Inc.. . . . . http://www.csiweb.com
D.H. Marketing & Consulting, Inc.. . . . . http://www.is.ab.ca/canni/dhmc.html
DNB Financial Corporation http://www.dnb4you.com
Detroit Legal News Company . . . . http://www.legalnews.com
Dynamic Associates, Inc. . . . . http://www.dyas.com
EvergreenBank . . . . http://www.evbank.com
Eyemakers, Inc. . . . . http://www.eyemakers.com
FCFT, Inc. . . . . http://www.fcbinc.com
First Citizens Bancorporation of South Carolina . . . . http://www.fcbsc.com
Fisher Companies Inc.. . . . . http://www.fishprop.com
Hammett (J.L.) Co. . . . . http://www.hammett.com
Information Analysis Incorporated . . . . http://www.infoa.com
Keweenaw Land Association, Limited . . . . http://www.keweenaw.com
Lab-Volt Systems, Inc.. . . . . http://www.labvolt.com
Lafayette Bancorporation . . . . http://www.lbtbank.com
Ledyard National Bank . . . . http://www.ledyardbank.com
Logan Clay Products Company. . . . . http//www.loganclaypipe.com
Market Guide, Inc.. . . . . http://www.marketguide.com
Maui Land & Pineapple Company, Inc.. . . . . http://www.mauiland.com
Mt. Bachelor, Inc.. . . . . http://www.mtbachelor.com
North State Telephone Company . . . . http://Northstate.net
Petaluma, Bank of . . . . http://www.BofP.com
Quigley Corporation (The) . . . . http://www.quigleyco.com
Rand McNally . . . . http://www.randmcnally.com
SGI International . . . . http://www.sgiinternational.com
Sims-Agricultural Products Company. . . . . http://www.simsag.com
Six Rivers National Bank . . . . http://www.sixrivers.com
Startech Environmental Corporation. . . . . http://www.startech.net
Talbot Bank of Easton, Maryland (The) . . . . http://www.talbot-bank.com
VASCO Corp.. . . . . http://www.vasco.com
Zap Power Systems . . . . http://zapbikes.com

Notes